Hoover's Handbook of

World Business 2015

Hoover's Handbook of World Business 2015 is intended to provide readers with accurate and authoritative information about the enterprises covered in it. Hoover's researched all companies and organizations profiled, and in many cases contacted them directly so that companies represented could provide information. The information contained herein is as accurate as we could reasonably make it. In many cases we have relied on third-party material that we believe to be trustworthy, but were unable to independently verify. We do not warrant that the book is absolutely accurate or without error. Readers should not rely on any information contained herein in instances where such reliance might cause financial loss. The publisher, the editors, and their data suppliers specifically disclaim all warranties, including the implied warranties of merchantability and fitness for a specific purpose. This book is sold with the understanding that neither the publisher, the editors, nor any content contributors are engaged in providing investment, financial, accounting, legal, or other professional advice.

The financial data (Historical Financials sections) in this book are from a variety of sources. Mergent Inc., provided selected data for the Historical Financials sections of publicly traded companies. For private companies and for historical information on public companies prior to their becoming public, we obtained information directly from the companies or from trade sources deemed to be reliable. Hoover's, Inc., is solely responsible for the presentation of all data.

Many of the names of products and services mentioned in this book are the trademarks or service marks of the companies manufacturing or selling them and are subject to protection under US law. Space has not permitted us to indicate which names are subject to such protection, and readers are advised to consult with the owners of such marks regarding their use. Hoover's is a trademark of Hoover's, Inc.

10 9 8 7 6 5 4 3 2 1

Publishers Cataloging-in-Publication Data
Hoover's Handbook of World Business 2015

Includes indexes.

ISBN 978-1-63053-406-6

ISSN 1055-7199

1. Business enterprises — Directories. 2. Corporations — Directories.

HF3010 338.7

U.S. AND WORLD BOOK SALES

Mergent Inc.

580 Kingsley Park Drive
Fort Mill, SC
29715
Phone: 800-342-5647
e-mail: orders@mergent.com
Web: www.mergentbusinesspress.com

Mergent Inc.

CEO: Jonathan Worrall

Executive Managing Director: John Pedernales

Executive Vice President of Sales: Fred Jenkins

Managing Director of Relationship Management: Chris Henry

Managing Director of Print Products: Thomas Wecera

Production Research Assistant: Erin Keane

MERGENT CUSTOMER SERVICE

Support and Fulfillment Manager: Melanie Horvat

ABOUT MERGENT, INC.

Mergent, Inc. is a leading provider of business and financial data on global publicly listed companies. Based in the U.S, the company maintains a strong global presence, with offices in New York, Charlotte, San Diego, London, Tokyo and Melbourne.

Founded in 1900, Mergent operates one of the longest continuously collected databases of: descriptive and fundamental information on domestic and international companies; pricing and terms and conditions data on fixed income and equity securities; and corporate action data. In addition, Mergent's Indxis subsidiary develops and licenses equity and fixed income investment products based on its proprietary investment methodologies. Our licensed products have over $9 billion in assets under management and are offered by major investment management firms. The Indxis calculation platform is the chosen technology for some of the world's largest index companies. Its index calculation and pricing distribution protocols are used to administer index rules and distribute real-time pricing data.

Abbreviations

AB – Aktiebolag (Swedish)*

ADR – American Depositary Receipts

AG – Aktiengesellschaft (German)*

AFL-CIO – American Federation of Labor and Congress of Industrial Organizations

AMEX – American Stock Exchange

A/S – Aktieselskab (Danish)*

ASA – Allmenne Aksjeselskaper (Norwegian)*

ATM – asynchronous transfer mode; automated teller machine

CAD/CAM – computer-aided design/computer-aided manufacturing

CASE – computer-aided software engineering

CD-ROM – compact disc – read-only memory

CEO – chief executive officer

CFO – chief financial officer

CMOS – complementary metal-oxide semiconductor

COMECON – Council for Mutual Economic Assistance

COO – chief operating officer

DAT – digital audio tape

DOD – Department of Defense

DOE – Department of Energy

DOT – Department of Transportation

DRAM – dynamic random-access memory

DVD – digital versatile disc/digital video disc

EC – European Community

EPA – Environmental Protection Agency

EPS – earnings per share

EU – European Union

EVP – executive vice president

FCC – Federal Communications Commission

FDA – Food and Drug Administration

FDIC – Federal Deposit Insurance Corporation

FTC – Federal Trade Commission

GATT – General Agreement on Tariffs and Trade

GmbH – Gesellschaft mit beschränkter Haftung (German)*

GNP – gross national product

HDTV – high-definition television

HMO – health maintenance organization

HR – human resources

HTML – hypertext markup language

ICC – Interstate Commerce Commission

IMF – International Monetary Fund

IPO – initial public offering

IRS – Internal Revenue Service

KGaA – Kommanditgesellschaft auf Aktien (German)*

LAN – local-area network

LBO – leveraged buyout

LNG – liquefied natural gas

LP – limited partnership

Ltd. – Limited

MFN – Most Favored Nation

MITI – Ministry of International Trade and Industry (Japan)

NAFTA – North American Free Trade Agreement

Nasdaq – National Association of Securities Dealers Automated Quotations

NATO – North Atlantic Treaty Organization

NV – Naamlose Vennootschap (Dutch)*

NYSE – New York Stock Exchange

OAO – open joint stock company (Russian)

OAS – Organization of American States

OECD – Organization for Economic Cooperation and Development

OEM – original equipment manufacturer

OOO – limited liability company (Russian)

OPEC – Organization of Petroleum Exporting Countries

OS – operating system

OTC – over-the-counter

P/E – price-to-earnings ratio

PLC – public limited company (UK)*

RAM – random-access memory

R&D – research and development

RISC – reduced instruction set computer

ROA – return on assets

ROI – return on investment

SA – Société Anonyme (French)*; Sociedad(e) Anónima (Spanish and Portuguese)*

SA de CV – Sociedad Anónima de Capital Variable (Spanish)*

SEC – Securities and Exchange Commission

SEVP – senior executive vice president

SIC – Standard Industrial Classification

SpA – Società per Azioni (Italian)*

SPARC – scalable processor architecture

SVP – senior vice president

VAR – value-added reseller

VAT – value-added tax

VC – venture capitalist

VP – vice president

WAN – wide-area network

WWW – World Wide Web

ZAO – closed joint stock company (Russian)

---

* These abbreviations are used in companies' names to convey that the companies are limited liability enterprises; the meanings are usually the equivalent of *corporation* or *incorporated*.

Contents

List of Lists

HOOVER'S RANKINGS

Companies Profiled

Companies Profiled (continued)

About Hoover's Handbook of World Business 2015

This edition of *Hoover's Handbook of World Business* is focused on its mission of providing you with premier coverage of the global business scene. Featuring 300 of the world's most influential companies based outside of the United States, this book is one of the most complete sources of in-depth information on large, non-US-based business enterprises available anywhere.

Hoover's Handbook of World Business is one of our four-title series of handbooks that covers, literally, the world of business. The series is available as an indexed set, and also includes *Hoover's Handbook of American Business*, *Hoover's Handbook of Private Companies*, and *Hoover's Handbook of Emerging Companies*. This series brings you information on the biggest, fastest-growing, and most influential enterprises in the world.

HOOVER'S ONLINE FOR BUSINESS NEEDS

In addition to Hoover's widely used MasterList and Handbooks series, comprehensive coverage of more than 40,000 business enterprises is available in electronic format on our Web site at www.hoovers.com. Our goal is to provide our customers the fastest path to business with insight and actionable information about companies, industries, and key decision makers, along with the powerful tools to find and connect to the right people to get business done. Hoover's has partnered with other prestigious business information and service providers to bring you all the right business information, services, and links in one place.

We welcome the recognition we have received as the premier provider of high-quality company information — online, electronically, and in print — and continue to look for ways to make our products more available and more useful to you.

We believe that anyone who buys from, sells to, invests in, lends to, competes with, interviews with, or works for a company should know all there is to know about that enterprise. Taken together, this book and the other Hoover's products and resources represent the most complete source of basic corporate information readily available to the general public.

HOW TO USE THIS BOOK

This book has four sections:

1. "Using Hoover's Handbooks" describes the contents of our profiles and explains the ways in which we gather and compile our data.

2. "A List-Lover's Compendium" contains lists of the largest, fastest-growing, and most valuable companies of global importance.

3. The company profiles section makes up the largest and most important part of the book — 300 profiles of major business enterprises, arranged alphabetically.

4. Three indexes complete the book. The first sorts companies by industry groups, the second by headquarters location. The third index is a list of all the executives found in the Executives section of each company profile.

Using Hoover's Handbooks

SELECTION OF THE COMPANIES PROFILED

The 300 profiles in this book include a variety of international enterprises, ranging from some of the largest publicly traded companies in the world — Daimler AG, for example — to Malaysia's largest and oldest conglomerate, Sime Darby Berhad. It also includes many private businesses, such as Bertelsmann AG and LEGO, as well as a selection of government-owned entities, such as Mexico's Petróleos Mexicanos. The companies selected represent a cross-section of the largest, most influential, and most interesting companies based outside the United States.

In selecting these companies, we followed several basic criteria. We started with the global giants, including Toyota and Royal Dutch Shell, and then looked at companies with substantial activity in the US, such as Vivendi and Diageo. We also included companies that dominate their industries (e.g., AB Electrolux, the world's #1 producer of household appliances), as well as representative companies from around the world (an Indian conglomerate, Tata; two firms from Finland, Nokia and Stora Enso Oyj; and two companies from Russia, OAO Gazprom and OAO LUKOIL). Companies that weren't necessarily global powerhouses but that had a high profile with consumers (e.g., IKEA) or had interesting stories (Virgin Group) were included. Finally, because of their truly global reach, we added the Big Four accounting firms (even though they are headquartered or co-headquartered in the US).

ORGANIZATION

The profiles are presented in alphabetical order. You will find the commonly used name of the enterprise at the beginning of the profile; the full, legal name is found in the Locations section. For some companies, primarily Japanese, the commonly translated English name differs from the actual legal name of the company, so both are provided. (The legal name of Nippon Steel Corporation is Shin Nippon Seitetsu Kabushiki Kaisha.) If a company name starts with a person's first name (e.g., George Weston Limited), it is alphabetized under the first name. We've also tried to alphabetize companies where you would expect to find them — for example, Deutsche Lufthansa is in the L's and Grupo Televisa can be found under T.

The annual financial information contained in the profiles is current through fiscal year-ends occurring as late as June 2014. We have included certain nonfinancial developments, such as officer changes, through September 2014.

OVERVIEW

In the first section of the profile, we have tried to give a thumbnail description of the company and what it does. The description will usually include information on the company's strategy, reputation, and ownership. We recommend that you read this section first.

HISTORY

This extended section, which is present for most companies, reflects our belief that every enterprise is the sum of its history and that you have to know where you came from in order to know where you are going. While some companies have limited historical awareness, we think the vast majority of the enterprises in this book have colorful backgrounds. We have tried to focus on the people who made the enterprises what they are today. We have found these histories to be full of twists and ironies; they make fascinating reading.

EXECUTIVES

Here we list the names of the people who run the company, insofar as space allows. We have shown age and pay information where available, although most non-US companies are not required to report the level of detail revealed in the US.

Although companies are free to structure their management titles any way they please, most modern corporations follow standard practices. The ultimate power in any corporation lies with the shareholders, who elect a board of directors, usually including officers or "insiders," as well as individuals from outside the company. The chief officer, the person on whose desk the buck stops, is usually called the chief executive officer (CEO) in the US. In other countries, practices vary widely. In the UK, traditionally, the Managing Director performs the functions of the CEO without the title, although the use of the term

CEO is on the rise there. In Germany it is customary to have two boards of directors: a managing board populated by the top executives of the company and a higher-level supervisory board consisting of outsiders.

As corporate management has become more complex, it is common for the CEO to have a "right-hand person" who oversees the day-to-day operations of the company, allowing the CEO plenty of time to focus on strategy and long-term issues. This right-hand person is usually designated the chief operating officer (COO) and is often the president of the company. In other cases one person is both chairman and president.

We have tried to list each company's most important officers, including the chief financial officer (CFO) and the chief legal officer. For companies with US operations, we have included the names of the US CEO, CFO, and top human resources executive, where available.

The people named in the Executives section are indexed at the back of the book.

The Executives section also includes the name of the company's auditing (accounting) firm, where available.

LOCATIONS

Here we include the company's full legal name and its headquarters, street address, telephone and fax numbers, and Web site, as available. We also list the same information for the US office for each company, if one exists. Telephone numbers of foreign offices are shown using the standardized conventions of international dialing. The back of the book includes an index of companies by head-quarters location.

In some cases we have also included information on the geographic distribution of the company's business, including sales and profit data. Note that these profit numbers, like those in the Products/Operations section below, are usually operating or pretax profits rather than net profits. Operating profits are generally those before financing costs (interest income and payments) and before taxes, which are considered costs attributable to the whole company rather than to one division or part of the world. For this reason the net income figures (in the Historical Financials section) are usually much lower, since they are after interest and taxes. Pretax profits are after interest but before taxes.

PRODUCTS/OPERATIONS

This section lists as many of the company's products, services, brand names, divisions, subsidiaries, and joint ventures as we could fit. We have tried to include all its major lines and all familiar brand names. The nature of this section varies by company and the amount of information available. If the company publishes sales and profit information by type of business, we have included it (in US dollars).

COMPETITORS

In this section we have listed enterprises that compete with the profiled company. This feature is included as a quick way to locate similar companies and compare them. Because of the difficulty in identifying companies that only compete in foreign markets, the list of competitors is still weighted to large international companies with a strong US presence.

HISTORICAL FINANCIALS

Here we have tried to present as much data about each enterprise's financial performance as we could compile in the allocated space. Financial data for all companies is presented in US dollars, using the appropriate exchange rate at fiscal year-end.

While the information presented varies somewhat from industry to industry, it is less complete in the case of private companies that do not release data (although we have always tried to provide annual sales and employment). The following information is generally present.

A five-year table, with relevant annualized compound growth rates, covers:

- Sales — fiscal year sales (year-end assets for most financial companies)
- Net income — fiscal year net income (before accounting changes)
- Net profit margin — fiscal year net income as a percent of sales (as a percent of assets for most financial firms)
- Employees — fiscal year-end or average number of employees
- Stock price — the fiscal year close
- P/E — high and low price/earnings ratio
- Earnings per share — fiscal year earnings per share (EPS)
- Dividends per share — fiscal year dividends per share

The information on the number of employees is intended to aid the reader interested in knowing whether a company has a long-term trend of increasing or decreasing employment. As far as we know, we are the only company that publishes this information in print format.

The numbers on the left in each row of the Historical Financials section give the month and the year in which the company's fiscal year actually ends. Thus, a company with a September 30, 2010, year-end is shown as 9/10.

In addition, we have provided in graph form a stock price history for companies that trade on the major US exchanges. The graphs, covering up to five years, show the range of trading between the high and the low price, as well as the closing price for each fiscal year. For public companies that trade on the OTC or Pink Sheets or that do not trade on US exchanges, we graph net income. Generally, for private companies, we have graphed net income, or, if that is unavailable, sales.

Key year-end statistics in this section generally show the financial strength of the enterprise, including:

- Debt ratio (long-term debt as a percent of shareholders' equity)
- Return on equity (net income divided by the average of beginning and ending common shareholders' equity)
- Cash and cash equivalents
- Current ratio (ratio of current assets to current liabilities)
- Total long-term debt (including capital lease obligations)
- Number of shares of common stock outstanding
- Dividend yield (fiscal year dividends per share divided by the fiscal year-end closing stock price)
- Dividend payout (fiscal year dividends divided by fiscal year EPS)
- Market value at fiscal year-end (fiscal year-end closing stock price multiplied by fiscal year-end number of shares outstanding)
- Fiscal year sales for financial institutions.

Per share data has been adjusted for stock splits. The data for public companies with sponsored American Depositary Receipts has been provided to us by Morningstar, Inc. Other public company information was compiled by Hoover's, which takes full responsibility for the content of this section.

In the case of private companies that do not publicly disclose financial information, we usually did not have access to such standardized data. We have gathered estimates of sales and other statistics from numerous sources.

Hoover's Handbook of

World Business

A List-Lover's Compendium

The 100 Largest Companies by Sales in Hoover's Handbook of World Business 2015

Rank	Company	Sales ($ bil)
1	Wal-Mart Stores, Inc.	$476,294
2	China Petroleum & Chemical C	$475,778
3	Royal Dutch Shell Plc	$459,599
4	Exxon Mobil Corp.	$438,255
5	BP plc	$383,102
6	PetroChina Co Ltd	$373,004
7	Oil and Natural Gas Corp. Lt	$309,278
8	Volkswagen A.G. (Germany, Fe	$271,227
9	Toyota Motor Corp	$248,906
10	Total S.A.	$236,324
11	Glencore PLC	$232,694
12	Chevron Corporation	$228,848
13	Samsung Electronics Co., Ltd	$217,462
14	Apple Inc	$182,795
15	Berkshire Hathaway Inc.	$182,150
16	Phillips 66	$174,809
17	AXA S.A.	$172,220
18	E.ON SE	$169,067
19	Daimler AG	$162,430
20	Gazprom OAO	$159,919
21	ENI S.p.A.	$159,817
22	General Motors Co.	$155,929
23	Industrial and Commercial Ba	$151,472
24	General Electric Co	$146,045
25	Ford Motor Co. (DE)	$144,077
26	Rosneft Oil Co OJSC (Moscow)	$142,824
27	Petroleo Brasileiro S.A.	$141,462
28	Oil Co Lukoil	$141,452
29	Allianz Elementar Lebensversi	$139,623
30	CVS Health Corp	$139,367
31	Societe Generale	$138,629
32	Allianz SE	$138,377
33	Valero Energy Corp.	$138,074
34	McKesson Corp.	$137,609
35	Hon Hai Precision Industry Co	$132,534
36	UnitedHealth Group Inc	$130,474
37	AT&T Inc	$128,752
38	China Construction Bank Corp	$127,366
39	BNP Paribas (France)	$126,947
40	Fannie Mae	$125,696
41	GDF SUEZ	$122,942
42	Verizon Communications Inc	$120,550
43	JX Holdings, Inc.	$120,249
44	AmerisourceBergen Corp.	$119,569
45	Fiat Chrysler Automobiles NV	$119,258
46	Agricultural Bank of China	$117,194
47	Assicurazioni Generali S.p.A	$115,047
48	Honda Motor Co., Ltd.	$114,731
49	Costco Wholesale Corp	$112,640
50	Hewlett-Packard Co	$111,454
51	Enel Societa Per Azioni	$110,875
52	Bank of China Ltd	$107,452
53	SK Holdings Co Ltd	$106,288
54	JPMorgan Chase & Co	$106,283
55	Tesco PLC	$105,932
56	Nippon Telegraph & Telephone	$105,844
57	Carrefour S.A.	$105,561
58	Statoil ASA	$104,899
59	Bayer Motoren WK	$104,712
60	Bayerische Motoren Werke AG	$104,712
61	Banco Santander SA	$104,391
62	Express Scripts Holding Co	$104,099
63	China Mobile Limited	$104,094
64	Electricite de France	$104,073
65	Nestle S.A.	$103,667
66	BASF SE	$101,841
67	Bank of America Corp.	$101,697
68	Nissan Motor Co., Ltd.	$101,556
69	Marathon Petroleum Corp.	$100,254
70	HSBC Holdings Plc	$99,854
71	International Business Machi	$99,751
72	Credit Agricole SA	$98,724
73	Kroger Co.	$98,375
74	Noble Group Ltd	$97,878
75	China Railway Construction C	$96,928
76	Petroliam Nasional Berhad (Ma	$96,864
77	ING Groep N.V.	$95,252
78	SAIC Motor Corp Ltd	$93,462
79	Hitachi, Ltd.	$93,163
80	Citigroup Inc	$92,543
81	Cardinal Health, Inc.	$91,084
82	Boeing Co.	$90,762
83	Federal Reserve System	$90,540
84	Siemens AG (Germany)	$90,538
85	Archer Daniels Midland Co.	$89,804
86	China Railway Group Ltd	$89,264
87	Amazon.com Inc.	$88,988
88	Munich Re Group	$88,627
89	Wells Fargo & Co.	$88,069
90	Lloyds Banking Group Plc	$87,909
91	Microsoft Corporation	$86,833
92	PTT Public Co Ltd.	$86,832
93	Prudential Plc	$86,797
94	Procter & Gamble Co	$83,062
95	Hyundai Motor Co., Ltd.	$83,020
96	Indian Oil Corp., Ltd. (Indi	$83,008
97	Deutsche Telekom AG	$82,786
98	Airbus Group NV	$81,580
99	Freddie Mac	$81,221
100	Philip Morris International	$80,029

SOURCE: HOOVER'S, INC., DATABASE, OCTOBER 2014

The 100 Most Profitable Companies in Hoover's Handbook of World Business 2015

Rank	Company	Net Income ($ bil)
1	Vodafone Group Plc	$98,647
2	Fannie Mae	$83,963
3	Trinidad Drilling Ltd	$66,726
4	Freddie Mac	$48,668
5	Oil and Natural Gas Corp. Lt	$44,615
6	Industrial and Commercial Ba	$43,385
7	Apple Inc	$39,510
8	China Construction Bank Corp	$35,458
9	Gazprom OAO	$34,664
10	Exxon Mobil Corp.	$32,580
11	Samsung Electronics Co., Ltd	$28,357
12	Agricultural Bank of China	$27,472
13	Bank of China Ltd	$25,919
14	BP plc	$23,451
15	Microsoft Corporation	$22,074
16	Pfizer Inc	$22,003
17	Wells Fargo & Co.	$21,878
18	Chevron Corporation	$21,423
19	PetroChina Co Ltd	$21,408
20	China Mobile Limited	$20,101
21	Berkshire Hathaway Inc.	$19,476
22	AT&T Inc	$18,249
23	JPMorgan Chase & Co	$17,923
24	Toyota Motor Corp	$17,663
25	Rosneft Oil Co OJSC (Moscow)	$16,583
26	Petroliam Nasional Berhad (Ma	$16,519
27	International Business Machi	$16,483
28	Royal Dutch Shell Plc	$16,371
29	HSBC Holdings Plc	$16,204
30	Wal-Mart Stores, Inc.	$16,022
31	Google Inc	$14,444
32	Anheuser-Busch Inbev SA	$14,394
33	BHP Billiton Plc	$13,832
34	BHP Billiton Ltd.	$13,832
35	Johnson & Johnson	$13,831
36	Citigroup Inc	$13,673
37	Alecta pensionsforsakring, om	$13,526
38	General Electric Co	$13,057
39	Volkswagen A.G. (Germany, Fe	$12,481
40	Intel Corp	$11,704
41	Procter & Gamble Co	$11,643
42	Total S.A.	$11,620
43	Verizon Communications Inc	$11,497
44	Bank of America Corp.	$11,431
45	Nestle S.A.	$11,239
46	Petroleo Brasileiro S.A.	$11,094
47	Sberbank Russia	$11,069
48	Oracle Corp.	$10,955
49	China Petroleum & Chemical C	$10,924
50	Bank of Communications Co.,	$10,290
51	Novartis AG Basel	$10,210
52	Mitsubishi UFJ Financial Gro	$9,837
53	Roche Holding Ltd.	$9,434
54	Daimler AG	$9,420
55	Cnooc Ltd.	$9,326
56	ConocoPhillips	$9,156
57	American International Group	$9,085
58	GlaxoSmithKline Plc	$8,983
59	Norges Bank (Norway)	$8,798
60	Liberty Media Corp (DE)	$8,780
61	Coca-Cola Co (The)	$8,584
62	Philip Morris International	$8,576
63	China Merchants Bank Co Ltd	$8,547
64	Allianz Elementar Lebensversi	$8,255
65	Allianz SE	$8,255
66	Hyundai Motor Co., Ltd.	$8,122
67	Commonwealth Bank of Austral	$8,110
68	Sumitomo Mitsui Financial Gr	$8,093
69	Goldman Sachs Group, Inc.	$8,040
70	Qualcomm, Inc.	$7,967
71	Royal Bank of Canada	$7,963
72	Cisco Systems, Inc.	$7,853
73	Oil Co Lukoil	$7,832
74	Surgutneftegas OAO	$7,805
75	Disney (Walt) Co. (The)	$7,501
76	China Shenhua Energy Co., Lt	$7,446
77	Bayer Motoren WK	$7,316
78	Bayerische Motoren Werke AG	$7,316
79	ENI S.p.A.	$7,104
80	Investor AB	$7,045
81	China Minsheng Banking Corp	$6,984
82	Itau Unibanco Holding S.A.	$6,953
83	Toronto Dominion Bank	$6,822
84	Comcast Corp	$6,816
85	Industrial Bank Co., Ltd.	$6,807
86	Ecopetrol SA	$6,793
87	Siemens AG (Germany)	$6,764
88	Saudi Basic Industries Corp -	$6,740
89	BASF SE	$6,666
90	Unilever N.V.	$6,666
91	Unilever Plc (United Kingdom	$6,666
92	BNP Paribas (France)	$6,652
93	Westpac Banking Corp	$6,589
94	Statoil ASA	$6,566
95	Pepsico Inc.	$6,513
96	China Citic Bank Corp Ltd	$6,471
97	British American Tobacco Plc	$6,452
98	Australia and New Zealand Ba	$6,336
99	Telefonica, S.A.	$6,323
100	Deutsche Bundesbank	$6,321

SOURCE: HOOVER'S, INC., DATABASE, OCTOBER 2014

The 100 Largest Employers in
Hoover's Handbook of World Business 2015

Rank	Company	Employees
1	Roto Smeets NV	3291762
2	Wal-Mart Stores, Inc.	2200000
3	Tesco PLC	902312
4	G4S Plc	629135
5	Randstad Holding N.V.	595730
6	Volkswagen A.G. (Germany, Fe	572800
7	Kelly Services, Inc.	548100
8	PetroChina Co Ltd	544083
9	Yum! Brands, Inc.	537000
10	ISS A/S (Denmark)	533544
11	Compass Group PLC (United Ki	514718
12	Agricultural Bank of China	513750
13	Deutsche Post AG	480006
14	Deutsche Post RG	480006
15	Gazprom OAO	459500
16	Industrial and Commercial Ba	441902
17	McDonald's Corp	440000
18	International Business Machi	431212
19	Sodexo	419317
20	Pou Chen Corp	416515
21	Yue Yuen Industrial (Holding	413000
22	P.T. Lippo Land Development (	410095
23	United Parcel Service Inc	395000
24	Jardine Matheson Holdings Ltd	390000
25	Kroger Co.	375000
26	Hitachi, Ltd.	369116
27	China Petroleum & Chemical C	368953
28	China Construction Bank Corp	368410
29	Target Corp	366000
30	Home Depot Inc	365000
31	Carrefour S.A.	364795
32	Bunge Ltd.	350000
33	Deutscher Sparkassen-und Giro	349500
34	Siemens AG (Germany)	343000
35	Nippon Telegraph & Telephone	340211
36	Toyota Motor Corp	338875
37	Rallye S.A. Neuilly-Sur-Sein	333722
38	Nestle S.A.	333000
39	Casino Guichard Perrachon S.	329355
40	Deutsche Bahn AG	307589
41	General Electric Co	307000
42	China Telecom Corp Ltd	306545
43	Bank of China Ltd	305675
44	Accenture plc	305000
45	Hewlett-Packard Co	302000
46	CVS Health Corp	297800
47	Telefonica, S.A.	291027
48	China Railway Group Ltd	289547
49	China Unicom (Hong Kong) Ltd	283596
50	Bosch (Robert) GmbH (Germany	281381
51	Metro AG	278594
52	Securitas AB	275769
53	Daimler AG	274616
54	Panasonic Corp	271789
55	Pepsico Inc.	271000
56	Aramark	269500
57	Wells Fargo & Co.	264900
58	HSBC Holdings Plc	263000
59	Lowe's Companies Inc	262000
60	Hutchison Whampoa Ltd.	260000
61	Mondi Plc	252000
62	JPMorgan Chase & Co	251196
63	Citigroup Inc	251000
64	Sears Holdings Corp	249000
65	China Railway Construction C	246736
66	Societe Nationale des Chemins	244570
67	AT&T Inc	243000
68	Bank of America Corp.	242000
69	ArcelorMittal SA	232353
70	Fiat Chrysler Automobiles NV	229053
71	Deutsche Telekom AG	228596
72	Wal-Mart de Mexico S.A.B. de	226289
73	Sumitomo Electric Industries	225484
74	Robert Half International In	225000
75	Koninklijke Ahold NV (Nether	222000
76	China Resources Enterprise, L	217000
77	General Motors Co.	216000
78	HCA Holdings Inc	215000
79	Rewe-Zentral AG (Germany, Fed	214584
80	Jardine Cycle & Carriage Ltd	214000
81	United Technologies Corp.	211500
82	Fomento Economico Mexicano,	207657
83	Darden Restaurants, Inc. (Un	206489
84	Ping An Insurance (Group) Co	203366
85	Veolia Environnement	202800
86	Toshiba Corp	200260
87	Honda Motor Co., Ltd.	198561
88	Woolworths Ltd.	198000
89	P.T. Astra International TBK	197434
90	China Mobile Limited	197030
91	Peugeot S.A.	196885
92	Costco Wholesale Corp	195000
93	Canon, Inc.	194151
94	Yamato Holdings Co., Ltd.	193146
95	TJX Companies, Inc.	191000
96	Starbucks Corp.	191000
97	Vinci SA	190704
98	Ford Motor Co. (DE)	187000
99	Banco Santander SA	186373
100	Compagnie de Saint-Gobain	185364

SOURCE: HOOVER'S, INC., DATABASE, OCTOBER 2014

Hoover's Handbook of

World Business

The Companies

77 Bank, Ltd. (The) (Japan)

Unlike 77 Sunset Strip 77 Bank's name doesn't denote its address but its order in the history of Japanese banking. 77 Bank was founded in 1878 as the 77th national bank in Japan. Operating more than 140 branches in the northern area of Japan's largest island Honshu 77 Bank provides the usual banking services of savings and lending as well some other operations such as temporary employment property appraisal and credit-document custody. 77 Bank also provides financial-related services that include leasing credit investigation computer-based contract services and a credit card.

EXECUTIVES

President and Director, Hiroshi Kamata
Deputy President and Director, Teruhiko Ujiie
Senior Managing Director and Board Member, Yoshiaki Nagayama
Managing Director and Board Member, Reiichi Sato
Managing Director and Board Member, Kimitsugu Nagao
Managing Director and Board Member, Masayuki Yamada
Managing Director and Board Member, Mitsutaka Kambe
President and Director, Hiroshi Kamata
Senior Managing Director and Board Member, Yoshiaki Nagayama
Managing Director and Board Member, Reiichi Sato
Managing Director and Board Member, Kimitsugu Nagao
Managing Director and Board Member, Mitsutaka Kambe
Auditors: DeloitteToucheTohmatsu

LOCATIONS

HQ: 77 Bank, Ltd. (The) (Japan)
3-3-20 Chuo, Aoba-ku, Sendai, Miyagi 980-8777
Phone: (81) 22 267 1111
Web: www.77bank.co.jp

COMPETITORS

Fukuoka Financial Group	Ito-Yokado
Gunma Bank	Japan Post
	Sumitomo Mitsui

HISTORICAL FINANCIALS

Company Type: Public

Income Statement

FYE: March 31

	ASSETS ($ mil.)	NET INCOME ($ mil.)	INCOME AS % OF ASSETS	EMPLOYEES
03/14	82,418	145	0.2%	3,002
03/13	87,798	132	0.2%	3,038
03/12	92,853	130	0.1%	3,128
03/11	75,086	(367)	—	3,149
03/10	63,237	124	0.2%	3,062
Annual Growth	6.8%	4.0%	—	(0.5%)

2014 Year-End Financials

Return on assets: 0.1%	Dividends
Return on equity: 4.0%	Yield: —
Long-term debt ($ mil.): —	Payout: —
No. of shares (mil.): 374	Market value ($ mil.): —
Sales ($ mil): 1,058	

A.P. Møller - Mærsk A/S

	STOCK PRICE ($) FY Close	P/E High/Low	PER SHARE ($) Earnings	Dividends	Book Value
03/14	0.00	— —	0.39	0.00	10.28
03/13	0.00	— —	0.35	0.00	10.45
03/12	5.15	— —	0.35	0.00	10.37
Annual Growth	—	— —	2.8%	—	(0.2%)

Oceangoing containers mean big money for A.P. Møller - Mærsk. Operating in about 130 countries the conglomerate specializes in global container shipping and related services led by Maersk Line which transports cargo via a fleet of more than 500 containerships Damco which provides freight forwarding and supply chain management services and APM Terminals a major container terminal operator. Other activities include marine transportation of crude oil and natural gas (Maersk Tankers) oil and gas exploration and production (Maersk Oil and Gas) and marine towing and salvage (Svitzer). It also owns one of Denmark's largest retail chain store operators Dansk Supermarked.

In line with a recovering global economy and as a result of cost-saving measures that it began undertaking in 2008 the company achieved its best profit so far in 2010 after a loss in 2009. It made a DKK 28.2 billion ($5 billion) profit in 2010 compared to a loss of DKK 5.5 billion ($1 billion) in the prior year. Most of its business units contributed to the overall profit including its container shipping oil and gas terminal drilling and retail operations. The main factors were increased container rates and volumes reduced costs per unit and increased oil prices. Only those in its tanker and offshore business segment including Maersk Tankers Maersk FPSO and Maersk LNG recorded losses for the year.

Moving forward the company's main goal is to expand business and maintain high profitability within two primary industries —shipping and oil and gas. Within the shipping industry container shipping and terminal activities are its key priorities for investment. Investments in Maersk Tankers Damco and Svitzer will be driven by market opportunities. It is pushing Maersk Line to gain market share by sharpening its customer focus and improving its fleet. It has committed at least $3.8 billion to buy 20 of the world's largest most energy-efficient container vessels known as Triple-E. They are expected to be delivered between 2013 and 2015. Meanwhile APM Terminals aims to be the leading global port operator and a significant contributor to the group's cash flows and earnings. It is divesting certain non-core port terminals and entering into agreements to establish port terminals in such emerging markets as Brazil and Liberia.

In the oil and gas industry Maersk Oil and Maersk Drilling (including Maersk Supply Service) are marked as the group's main priorities for investment. Maersk Oil is trying to stabilize production by 2014 and thereafter gradually grow to reach a stable production rate of 400000 barrels of oil equivalent per day. As fields in the North Sea mature Maersk Oil is investing in promising oil fields in Brazil and the Gulf of Mexico. It also obtained several licenses in Greenland Norway and the UK. Maersk Drilling aims to be one of the leading drilling contractors within deep water and ultra harsh environments having already committed

about $3.8 billion to the construction of four deepwater drillships and two ultra harsh jack-up rigs.

Founded by Peter Mærsk Møller and his son Arnold Peter Møller A.P. Møller - Mærsk styles the company and family name as "Mærsk" but uses "Maersk" for the names of most of its subsidiaries. A.P. Møller - Mærsk's main shareholder is The A.P. Møller and Chastine Mc-Kinney Møller Foundation which was established by company founder A.P. Møller in 1953.

HISTORY

Arnold Peter Møller and his father sea captain Peter Mærsk Møller founded Aktieselskabet Dampskibsselskabet Svendborg (Steamship Company Svendborg) in 1904 in Svendborg Denmark. Their first ship a second-hand steamer bore on its funnel a white seven-pointed star on a blue background which had been on Peter's first ship. Later known as the Maersk star the logo adorned all subsequent ships of the company as well as ships of a second company formed eight years later — Dampskibsselskabet af 1912 Aktieselskab (Steamship Company of 1912). At that point six ships were in the Maersk fleet.

In 1917 the company began building its own ships after establishing the Odense Steel Shipyard. It launched regular liner service between the US and the Far East in 1928 calling the operation the Maersk Line. With the addition of its first tankers that year Maersk owned 35 ships.

Mærsk Mc-Kinney Møller A.P.'s son became a partner in the company in 1940. That year with Germany occupying Denmark he fled to the US with his bride on one of the last ships out. Refusing to take orders from the Nazis A.P. transferred control of the company to the US where the 26-year-old Mærsk had established operations. Most of the Maersk fleet flew under British or US flags during the war which took the life of 148 Maersk seamen and claimed 25 ships. Mærsk Mc-Kinney Møller returned to Denmark in 1947.

A.P. Møller formed the Maersk Company in 1951 in London as a shipbroker; it became one of the world's largest shipowners. The early 1960s saw A.P. Møller diversifying as it moved into oil and gas exploration and production in Denmark in 1962 and established supermarket chain Dansk Supermarked in 1964. A.P. died the next year having run the company for more than 60 years. Prior to his death he had created three foundations to hold most of the company's shares. His son Mærsk took command of A.P. Møller and the Maersk fleet which contained 88 ships. Under his leadership the company expanded even further and became more international; his business savvy became apparent when he sold some of the company's tanker fleet in the 1970s just prior to prices going down.

In 1970 A.P. Møller established domestic carrier Maersk Air. A.P. Møller began seeing its first oil production in the North Sea in 1972. The next year the company acquired its first container vessel the "Svendborg Maersk".

Maersk Container Industri was formed in 1991 to produce intermodal containers. That year Maersk and rival Sea-Land entered into a transpacific vessel-sharing agreement which was expanded into a global alliance in 1995. In 1999 just months after buying South Africa's Safmarine Container Lines Maersk bought Sea-Land's international liner services and 18 terminals. The Maersk Line and Sea-Land operations were merged to form Maersk Sealand.

In 2000 A.P. Møller planned to extend its Bilka grocery chain into southern Sweden. That year Maersk Sealand decided to shift its transshipment hub in Singapore to a Malaysian port. In 2001 Maersk Air and Scandinavian Airlines System (SAS) were together fined $45 million by the European Commission for infringing on the EC's competition rules by entering into a secret deal to monopolize certain air routes in Scandinavia. As a result Maersk Air's chairman and managing director stepped down and were replaced.

A.P. Møller which through the years had continued to operate through two separately listed companies — Aktieselskabet Dampskibsselskabet Svendborg and Dampskibsselskabet af 1912 Aktieselskab —reorganized in 2003 and wound up with a single publicly traded company –A.P. Møller - Mæsk A/S –at its head.

A.P. Møller - Mæsk purchased the majority of Kerr-McGee's North Sea oil assets in late 2005. Also that year the passenger transportation business of Maersk Air was sold to an Icelandic investment group.

Maersk Line was launched as a brand in 2006 as a result of the combined operations of Maersk Sealand and Royal P&O Nedlloyd which was acquired by A.P. Møller - Mæsk in 2005. Consolidating the businesses proved to be more difficult than expected however. The container shipping operations lost money in 2006 before posting a small profit in 2007. That year CEO Jess Søderberg stepped down two years ahead of schedule and Nils Smedegaard Andersen CEO of brewer Carlsberg and a director of A.P. Møller - Mæsk replaced him. In addition Maersk Line's management structure was simplified.

Throughout 2008 the company worked on cutting costs and in September 2009 the company combined its Maersk Logistics and Damco divisions keeping the Damco name.

EXECUTIVES

Chairman, Michael P. Rasmussen, age 60
Founder, Arnold Moller
Senior Vice President, Carsten Plougmann
Director, Sir John R. H. Bond, age 72
Vice Chairman, Poul J. Svanholm, age 79
Director, Jan Leschly, age 73
Director, Jan T?pholm, age 67
Director, Lars E. Kann-Rasmussen, age 74
Vice Chairman, Ane M?rsk Mc-Kinney Uggla, age 65
Director, Leise M?rsk Mc-Kinney M?ller, age 72
Director, Niels Jacobsen, age 57
Director, Cecilie M. Hansen, age 37
Director, Lars Pallesen, age 66
Director, John Axel Poulsen, age 67
Auditors: GrantThornton

LOCATIONS

HQ: A.P. Møller - Maersk A/S
Esplanaden 50, Copenhagen K DK-1098
Phone: (45) 33 63 33 63
Web: www.maersk.com

Sales

	% of total
Denmark	20
US	12
UK	9
Qatar	9
Other	50
Total	**100**

PRODUCTS/OPERATIONS

Sales

	% of total
Shipping	
Container	45
Tankers offshore & other	10
Retail	18
Oil &	18
Terminal	7
Other	2
Total	**100**

Selected Business Areas

Container shipping & related
  Damco (freight forwarding and supply chain management services)
  Maersk Container Industry (manufacturing of dry and reefer containers)
  Maersk Line (global container shipping)
  MCC Transport (intra-Asia container shipping)
  Safmarine (Africa Middle East and Indian subcontinent container shipping)
Oil and gas activities
  Maersk Oil (oil and gas exploration and production)
Retail & other
  Dansk Supermarked (owner of several chains of supermarkets department stores and discount markets)
  Svitzer (specialized marine services including towing salvage and emergency response)
Tankers offshore & related
  Maersk Drilling (offshore drilling activities and operation of land rigs through 50% ownership in Egyptian Drilling Company)
  Maersk FPSOs (floating oil and gas production units)
  Maersk LNG (liquefied natural gas transportation)
  Maersk Supply Service (anchor handling and platform supply vessels)
  Maersk Tankers (tanker shipping of crude oil oil products and gas)
Technology
  Maersk Fluid Technology
  Maersk Maritime Technology
Terminal activities
  APM Terminals (port operations inland transportation and container repair)

COMPETITORS

BP	ICA AB
CMA CGM	John Swire & Sons
COSCO Group	Kawasaki Kisen
China Shipping	Mediterranean Shipping
Coop Danmark	Company
DP World	Mitsui O.S.K. Lines
Evergreen Marine	NYK Line
Frontline	Neptune Orient
Hanjin Shipping	Orient Overseas
Hapag-Lloyd	PSA International
Hess Corporation	SSA Marine
Hutchison Port	Singamas
Holdings	Statoil
Hyundai Merchant	
Marine	

HISTORICAL FINANCIALS

Company Type: Public

Income Statement

FYE: December 31

	REVENUE ($ mil.)	NET INCOME ($ mil.)	NET PROFIT MARGIN	EMPLOYEES
12/13	49,136	3,577	7.3%	88,909
12/12	60,432	3,829	6.3%	121,105
12/11	56,114	2,642	4.7%	117,080
12/10	56,630	4,750	8.4%	108,110
12/09	50,333	(1,360)	—	115,386
Annual Growth	(0.6%)	—	—	(6.3%)

2013 Year-End Financials

Debt ratio: 3.9%
Return on equity: 9.1%
Cash ($ mil.): 3,255
Current ratio: 1.36
Long-term debt ($ mil.): 12,689

No. of shares (mil.): 4
Dividends
  Yield: 2.5%
  Payout: 0.0%
Market value ($ mil.): 96

	STOCK PRICE ($) FY Close	P/E High/Low		PER SHARE ($) Earnings	Dividends	Book Value
12/13	21.99	0	0	818.90	0.28	
9,107.38						
12/12	15.45	0	0	438.32	0.01	
4,223.77						
Annual Growth	42.3%	—	—	16.9%	148.5%	21.2%

Aabar Petroleum Investments Co P.J.S.C.

LOCATIONS

HQ: Aabar Petroleum Investments Co P.J.S.C.
P.O. Box 7528, Abu Dhabi
Phone:

HISTORICAL FINANCIALS

Company Type: Public

Income Statement

FYE: December 31

	REVENUE ($ mil.)	NET INCOME ($ mil.)	NET PROFIT MARGIN	EMPLOYEES
12/13	52,834	1,917	3.6%	20,078
12/12	51,902	1,511	2.9%	19,835
Annual Growth	1.8%	26.8%	—	1.2%

2013 Year-End Financials

Debt ratio: 48.9%
Return on equity: 13.2%
Cash ($ mil.): 6,818
Current ratio: 1.37
Long-term debt ($ mil.): 26,116

No. of shares (mil.): 3
Dividends
  Yield: —
  Payout: —
Market value ($ mil.): —

	STOCK PRICE ($) FY Close	P/E High/Low		PER SHARE ($) Earnings	Dividends	Book Value
12/13	0.00	—	—	548.00	0.00	
4,360.24						
12/12	0.00	—	—	432.00	0.00	
3,937.29						
/0.00	—		—	(0.00)	0.00	(0.00)
Annual Growth	—	—	—	—	—	—

Aareal Bank AG

Aareal Bank is engaged internationally in a variety of property-related banking and financial services for the public and private sectors. The company's business is organized into two primary segments. Structured property financing (its most profitable business) specializes in financing large-scale retail hotel and logistics industry properties. The consulting/services segment offers IT products that help users manage residential and commercial properties. Aareal Bank operates in more than 30 countries in Europe North America and the Asia/Pacific region. In fiscal 2014 the financial institution boosted its core business by acquiring Germany's Corealcredit Bank AG for Â342 million.

EXECUTIVES

Chairman Management Board, Wolf Schumacher, age 52, $659,650 total compensation
Member Management Board, Thomas Ortmanns, $395,790 total compensation
Member Management Board, Dirk Grosse
Head of Treasury, Dermot Hardy
Member Management Board, Thomas Ortmanns
Auditors:
PricewaterhouseCoopersAGWirtschaftsprufungsgesellschaft

LOCATIONS

HQ: Aareal Bank AG
Paulinenstrasse 15, Wiesbaden D-65189
Phone: (49) 611 348 3009   **Fax:** (49) 611 348 2637
Web: www.aareal-bank.com

COMPETITORS

AWD	Landesbank Berlin
BayernLB	UBS
Commerzbank	UniCredit Bank AG
Deutsche Bank	Wustenrot &
HSBC	Wurttembergische

HISTORICAL FINANCIALS

Company Type: Public

Income Statement   FYE: December 31

	ASSETS ($ mil.)	NET INCOME ($ mil.)	INCOME AS % OF ASSETS	EMPLOYEES
12/13	59,173	161	0.3%	2,375
12/12	60,279	138	0.2%	2,289
12/11	54,084	147	0.3%	2,353
12/10	55,163	101	0.2%	2,407
12/09	57,001	70	0.1%	2,315
Annual Growth	0.9%	22.9%	—	0.6%

2013 Year-End Financials

Return on assets: 0.2%	Dividends
Return on equity: 5.4%	Yield: —
Long-term debt ($ mil.): —	Payout: —
No. of shares (mil.): 59	Market value ($ mil.): 2,239
Sales ($ mil): 1,435	

	STOCK PRICE ($) FY Close	P/E High/Low		PER SHARE ($) Earnings	Dividends	Book Value
12/13	37.40	36	19	2.68	0.00	50.78
12/12	21.08	26	14	2.31	0.00	46.44
12/11	17.50	31	14	2.73	0.00	41.62
12/10	20.25	23	15	2.38	0.00	54.53
12/09	20.45	43	7	1.64	0.00	61.79
Annual Growth	16.3%	—	—	13.1%	—	(4.8%)

ABB Ltd

You could be forgiven for thinking that ABB is short for "A Bunch of Businesses" —though that bunch has evolved over some 130 years. ABB engineers power and automation technologies for a broad base of utility industrial and commercial customers. Its lines run from robots to light switches. Power products include transmission and distribution components as well as turnkey substation systems. Automation technologies are used to monitor and control equipment and processes in industrial plants and utilities. The company has established a presence in about 100 countries with its core businesses concentrated in power and automation markets.

Geographic Reach

ABB's operations extend to around 100 countries. A large portion of the company's production and development facilities reside in Canada China Finland Germany India Italy Norway Sweden Switzerland and the US.

Europe accounted for 36% of its total sales in 2012; the Americas and Asia each generated 27% while Africa and the Middle East brought in 10%.

Operations

ABB operates through five segments: Power Products Power Systems Discrete Automation and Motion Low Voltage Products and Process Automation. The Power Products and Power Systems segments are driven primarily by the capital expenditures of electrical utilities.

The Automation Products Process Automation and Low Voltage Products segments are impacted by the health of several industries including automotive consumer products metals and minerals paper and pulp and pharmaceuticals. A global presence and competitive cost base however have helped to buffer ABB's exposure to regional recessions and slow economies.

Major subsidiaries owned by ABB include ABB Inc. ABB Limited Baldor Electric Company Thomas & Betts Ventyx Tropos Networks ABB AG ABB Ltda. Power-One and ABB Contracting.

Sales and Marketing

ABB sells its products through direct sales and external channel partners like wholesalers distributors system integrators EPCs and OEMs.

Financial Performance

ABB generated $39.3 billion in revenues for 2012 a historic milestone for the company; this represented a 3% increase from the $37.8 billion it earned in 2011. The spike in revenues was mainly due to a solid order level as well as the favorable impact of its 2012 Thomas & Betts acquisition.

While ABB has enjoyed three straight years of revenue growth its profits slipped by 15% from $3.2 billion in 2011 to $2.7 billion in 2012 due to an increase in the cost of sales. This was the result of an unfavorable business mix coupled with higher prices involved with restructuring its segments.

Strategy

As the global economy moves away from the recession ABB has been making some milestone acquisitions to boost its product offerings operations and geographic reach. In mid-2013 it purchased Power-One a major provider of solar inverters technology used to convert the sun's energy into electricity. ABB made the $1 billion deal to boost its renewable energy business and expand its solar product portfolio.

In 2012 ABB bought Thomas & Betts (T&B) for about $3.9 billion. T&B sells electrical connectors HVAC equipment and transmission towers. The acquisition significantly added to ABB's North American presence giving it access to T&B's network of more than 6000 distributor locations and wholesalers throughout the continent. Shortly after that transaction was made ABB snapped up Tropos Networks a California firm that makes wireless technologies and products for distribution area communication networks. The acquisition broadened ABB's communications systems portfolio and enabled it to better cater to North American clients in the power transportation and mining sectors.

In 2011 ABB acquired the Trasfor Group which advanced its portfolio of specialty dry-type transformers used in drives railway rolling stock offshore wind power and other renewable energy applications. Months earlier ABB swallowed up Baldor Electric for $3.1 billion. Baldor Electric a US industrial motors business strengthened ABB's energy efficient offerings most notably in North America.

Other completed acquisitions that year include ABB's takeover of Mincom an Australia-based software and services company with clients ranging from mining companies (Rio Tinto and Anglo American) to big manufacturing companies (Boeing and Caterpillar). Not only did the deal bring an estimated $200 million in revenues but it also expanded ABB's software capabilities.

HISTORY

Asea Brown Boveri (ABB) was formed in 1988 when two giants ASEA AB of Sweden and BBC Brown Boveri of Switzerland combined their electrical engineering and equipment businesses. Percy Barnevik head of ASEA became CEO.

ASEA was born in Stockholm in 1883 when Ludwig Fredholm founded Electriska Aktiebolaget to manufacture an electric dynamo created by engineer Jonas Wenstrom. In 1890 the company merged with Wenstrom's brother's firm to form Allmanna Svenska Electriska Aktiebolaget (ASEA) a pioneer in industrial electrification. Early in the 1900s ASEA began its first railway electrification project. By the 1920s it was providing locomotives and other equipment to Sweden's national railway and by the next decade ASEA was one of Sweden's largest electric equipment manufacturers. In 1962 it bought 20% of appliance maker Electrolux. ASEA created the nuclear power venture ASEA-ATOM with the Swedish government in 1968 and bought full control in 1982.

BBC Brown Boveri was formed in 1891 as the Brown Boveri and Company partnership between Charles Brown and Walter Boveri in Baden Switzerland. It made power generation equipment and produced the first steam turbines in Europe in 1900. BBC entered Germany (1893) France (1894) and Italy (1903) and diversified into nuclear power equipment after WWII.

By 1988 BBC the bigger company had a West German network that ASEA the more profitable company coveted. Both had US joint ventures. In an unusual merger ASEA (which became ABB AB) and BBC (later ABB AG) continued as separate entities sharing equal ownership of ABB. Barnevik crafted a unique decentralized management structure under which national subsidiaries were closely linked to their local customers and labor forces. In six years ABB took over more than 150 companies worldwide.

An ABB-led consortium built one of the world's largest hydroelectric plants in Iran in 1992 and in 1995 ABB merged its transportation segment into Adtranz (a joint venture with Daimler-Benz) to form the world's #1 maker of trains.

Tragedy struck in 1996. Robert Donovan CEO of ABB's US subsidiary died in a plane crash along with Commerce Secretary Ron Brown and other executives on a trade mission. Donovan's death hastened the US unit's restructuring.

In 1997 Barnevik gave up the title of CEO remaining as chairman and was succeeded by Goran Lindahl an engineer who worked his way up the ranks at ASEA. (Barnevik remained chairman until 2001.) After 1997 profits dipped drastically Lindahl scrapped Barnevik's vaunted regional matrix structure in favor of one organized by product areas under a strong central management. Though the Asian financial crisis slowed orders ABB still pulled in large contracts including one to build the world's largest cracker plant in Texas in 1998.

In 1999 ABB acquired Elsag Bailey a Dutch maker of industrial control systems for about $1.5 billion and sold its 50% stake in Adtranz to DaimlerChrysler for about $472 million. ABB and France's ALSTOM combined their power generation businesses to form the world's largest power plant equipment maker. That year ABB AB and ABB AG were at last united under a single stock through holding company ABB Ltd.

ABB scaled back its power plant-related activities in 2000. The company sold its nuclear power business to BNFL for $485 million and its 50% stake in ABB Alstom Power to ALSTOM for $1.2 billion. (Areva acquired ALSTOM's transmission and distribution business in 2004.) In 2001 Lindahl resigned and Jorgen Centerman head of the company's automation business replaced him.

Centerman promptly reorganized ABB's industrial operations into four segments based on customer type and two based on product type.

Also in 2001 ABB acquired French company Entrelec a supplier of industrial automation and control products. With economic slowdowns occurring in the company's key markets ABB announced plans in 2001 to cut 12000 jobs over 18 months. Later that year amid rising numbers of asbestos claims against US subsidiary Combustion Engineering ABB took a $470 million fourth-quarter charge to cover asbestos liabilities. The claims charged asbestos exposures stemming from products supplied before the mid-1970s by Combustion Engineering which ABB acquired in 1990.

In 2002 ABB found itself embroiled in controversy after revealing not only a record loss but also payments of large pensions to former chairman Barnevik and former chief executive Lindahl. The former executives agreed that year to return a part (about $82 million) of their pension payouts to ABB. That year the company which faced $4.4 billion in debts after industry slumps affected its sales of power systems and equipment industrial automation and controls sold part of its financial services unit to GE Commercial Finance for $2.3 billion.

The day after the company sold its structured finances unit ABB's chief executive Jorgen Centerman resigned and was replaced by the chairman Jorgen Dormann. That year ABB sold its metering business to Germany-based Ruhrgas for $244 million.

In 2003 as part of its settlement with asbestos plaintiffs ABB placed Combustion Engineering into bankruptcy. Later that same year the company announced that it would sell its Sirius International reinsurance business to the Bermuda-based White Mountains; the deal was completed in 2004 for about $425 million. ABB also sold its upstream oil gas and petrochemicals unit to Candover Partners 3i and J.P. Morgan Partners for $925 million in 2004. (To clear the way for the sale ABB also agreed to pay US regulators $16 million in fines to settle bribery cases at US-based ABB Vetco Gray and Scotland-based ABB Vetco UK. The subsidiaries —part of the petroleum business that was sold —allegedly paid off government officials in Angola Kazakhstan and Nigeria in order to win oil contracts between 1998 and 2003.)

Sulzer CEO Fred Kindle succeeded Dormann as ABB's CEO in 2005. (Dormann remained chairman until his retirement in 2007.) The company made a number of small dispositions in 2005 including its Japanese control valves business its foundry business and several cable and power line businesses.

ABB ended years of litigation —and a major corporate headache —when it reached a settlement on an asbestos liability case related to US subsidiary Combustion Engineering in 2006. As part of the settlement ABB committed more than $1.4 billion to pay settled claims.

After consolidating its remaining businesses into the two areas power technologies and automation technologies ABB restructured its operations into five divisions in 2006: Power Products Power Systems Automation Products Process Automation and Robotics. It took further steps to streamline operations and position itself for growth for example by moving its main robotics operation from Detroit to Shanghai.

In 2006 ABB voluntarily disclosed to the US Department of Justice and the SEC that the company made payments in the Middle East that might have violated anti-bribery laws. The following year ABB disclosed similar suspect payments at subsidiaries in Asia Europe and South America.

Kindle left ABB in 2008 due to what the company called "irreconcilable differences" concerning the leadership of the company; former GE Healthcare CEO Joe Hogan became CEO of ABB later that year.

In 2008 the company dug deeper into its investment purse spending $653 million to complete 12 deals. Most notably ABB purchased Kuhlman Electric a US-based transformer manufacturer from The Carlyle Group for $513 million including assumed debt. Kuhlman Electric was integrated into ABB's Power Products division in North America and deepens ABB's geographic footprint and product offerings in the industrial and electric utility sectors.

ABB's bunch of businesses has been peeled back too. Several divestitures were completed in 2008 and 2007; ABB exited its 50% interest in South Africa's ABB Powertech Transformers to Powertech owned by the Altron Group for $11 million. In 2007 ABB sold subsidiary ABB Lummus Global to Chicago Bridge & Iron Co. for some $870 million in cash as well as its Building Systems business in Germany and power plant interests in India and Morocco to Abu Dhabi National Oil. Power Lines businesses in Brazil and Mexico were also put on the sale block for $20 million.

ABB plowed in $209 million in 2009 adding eight new operations. Among them the company acquired the assets of Sinai Engineering a designer and provider of services for electrical generation and transmission systems planning as well as construction management. The transaction completed through its US ABB Inc. expanded ABB's presence in western Canada. On the other side of the world ABB picked up South Africa's Westingcorp (Pty) Ltd. The move ramped up ABB's line of power capacitors (machines that add to a system's power quality and energy efficiency) and opened the door to local and global electric utilities and mining markets.

ABB in mid-2010 acquired K-TEK a maker of level detection technology used in the oil and gas industry as well as water and other industries. Its instrumentation and sensing technologies which number more than 350000 installations enhanced ABB's slate of measurement products part of its Process Automation division. The deal garnered K-TEK's facilities in the US the Netherlands China India and South Africa.

ABB picked up US software provider Insert Key Solutions in late 2010. Its combination with the earlier acquisition of Ventyx (valued at approximately $1 billion) from Vista Equity Partners created a comprehensive portfolio of software for managing asset-intensive businesses engaged in the utility energy and communications industries. Ventyx and Insert Key Solutions joined ABB's network management business.

EXECUTIVES

Chief Executive Officer; Member of the Executive Committee, Joseph M. (Joe) Hogan, age 57, $1,798,924 total compensation
Region Manager Central Europe, Peter Smits, age 62, $788,357 total compensation
Head of Marketing and Customer Solutions, Greg Scheu, age 53
Head of Global Markets, Frank Duggan, age 55
Head of Power Products Division, Bernhard Jucker, age 60, $754,215 total compensation
Head of Power Systems Division, Brice Koch, age 50
Head of Human Resources, Gary Steel, age 61, $619,854 total compensation
EVP and CFO, Eric Elzvik, age 54
Corporate Communications, Thomas Schmidt
Group SVP and Head Investor Relations, Michel Gerber, age 46
Region Manager North America, Enrique Santacana

CEO, Ulrich Spiesshofer, age 50, $775,921 total compensation
Head of Process Automation Division, Veli-Matti Reinikkala, age 57, $532,046 total compensation
General Counsel, Diane de Saint Victor, age 59, $647,952 total compensation
Executive Committee Member Power Systems Division, Peter Leupp, age 63, $770,005 total compensation
Chairman, Hubertus von Grunberg, age 72
Corporate Communications, Wolfram Eberhardt
Region Manager Northern Europe, Sten Jakobsson, age 65
Region Manager South America, Sergio Gomes
Region Manager North Asia, Claudio Facchin
Region Manager South Asia, BoonKiat Sim
CFO, Michel Demare
Head of Low Voltage Products Division, Tarak Mehta, age 48
Group SVP and Chief Counsel Corporate and Finance, Richard A. Brown
CTO, Prith Banerjee
Head of Discrete Automation and Motion Division, Pekka Tiitinen, age 48
Director, Michael Treschow, age 71
Director, Michel de Rosen, age 63
Director, Jacob Wallenberg, age 59
Director, Roger Agnelli, age 55
Director, Ying Yeh, age 66
Director, Hans Ulrich Marki, age 67
Director, Louis R. Hughes, age 65
Director, Bernd W. Voss, age 74
Non-Executive Member of the Board of Directors, Hans Maerki
Auditors: Ernst&YoungLtd.

LOCATIONS

HQ: ABB Ltd
Affolternstrasse 44, Zurich CH-8050
Phone: (41) 43 317 7111   **Fax:** (41) 43 317 7992
Web: www.abb.com

Sales

	$ mil.	% of total
Europe	14,073	36
Americas	10,699	27
Total	**39,336**	**100**

PRODUCTS/OPERATIONS

Sales

	$ mil.	% of total
Power Products	10,717	25
Process Automation	8,156	19
Low Voltage Products	6,638	16
Total	**39,336**	**100**

Selected Mergers and Acquisitions

FY2013
   Power-One Inc. ($1 billion; Camarillo California; maker of solar inverters)
FY2012
   Thomas & Betts Corporation ($3.9 billion; Memphis Tennessee; electrical connectors HVAC equipment and transmission towers)
   Tropos Networks Inc. (Silicon Valley California; wireless technologies and products for distribution area communication networks)
FY2011
   Trasfor Group (Switzerland; specialty dry-type transformers)
   Baldor Electric ($3.1 billion; Fort Smith Arkansas; industrial motors)

Selected Products

Automation Products
   Breakers
   Control products
   DIN-rail components
   Drives
   Enclosures
   Generators
   Instrumentation

Low-voltage switchgear
Motors
Power electronics systems
Switches
Wiring accessories
Electrical Products
  Boxes and covers (Bowers Commander Steel City)
  Cable ties (Catamount Ty-Fast Ty-Rap)
  Connectors (Blackburn Color-Keyed)
  Lighting (Carlon Red Dot Lumacell)
  Wire management systems (Carlon T&B)
HVAC
  Evaporative cooling and energy recovery equipment
    (International Energy Saver)
  Heaters (EK Campbell Reznor)
  Heating mechanical and refrigeration supplies (T&B)
Power Products
  Circuit breakers for all current and voltage levels
  High- and medium-voltage switchgear and apparatus
  Power and distribution transformers
  Sensors
Power Systems
  Power plant automation and electrification solutions
  Transmission and distribution systems
Process Automation
  Automation products and solutions
  Controls
  Industry-specific application knowledge and services
  Plant optimization
Robotics
  Industrial robots
  Industrial software products
  Robot contollers and software
Steel Structures
  Power connectors and accessories (Elastimold)
  Steel poles (Meyer)
  Transmission towers (Lehigh)

COMPETITORS

ALSTOM	Invensys
AREVA	KUKA
Baldor Electric	Kawasaki Heavy
Bharat Heavy	Industries
Electricals	Larsen & Toubro
Cisco Systems	Legrand
Cooper Industries	Metso
Crompton Greaves	Mitsubishi Heavy
Danaher	Industries
Durr	Nokia
Eaton	Rittal Corp.
Emerson Electric	Rockwell Automation
Endress + Hauser	SPX
Ericsson	Schneider Electric
FANUC	Siemens AG
GE	Toshiba
Hitachi	Voith
Honeywell	WEG Industrias
International	Yaskawa Electric
Hyosung	Yokogawa Electric
Hyundai Corporation	

HISTORICAL FINANCIALS
Company Type: Public

Income Statement   FYE: December 31

	REVENUE ($ mil.)	NET INCOME ($ mil.)	NET PROFIT MARGIN	EMPLOYEES
12/13	41,848	2,787	6.7%	147,700
12/12	39,336	2,704	6.9%	146,100
12/11	37,990	3,168	8.3%	133,600
12/10	31,589	2,561	8.1%	116,500
12/09	31,795	2,901	9.1%	116,100
Annual Growth	7.1%	(1.0%)	—	6.2%

2013 Year-End Financials

Debt ratio: 16.6%	No. of shares (mil.): —
Return on equity: 15.6%	Dividends
Cash ($ mil.): 6,485	Yield: 2.6%
Current ratio: 1.58	Payout: 58.1%
Long-term debt ($ mil.): 7,570	Market value ($ mil.): —

	STOCK PRICE ($) FY Close	P/E High/Low		PER SHARE ($) Earnings	Dividends	Book Value
12/13	26.56	21	17	1.21	0.70	8.14
12/12	20.79	19	13	1.18	0.69	7.36
12/11	18.83	20	12	1.38	0.67	6.89
12/10	22.45	20	14	1.12	0.47	6.52
12/09	19.10	17	9	1.27	0.43	6.02
Annual Growth	8.6%	—	—	(1.2%)	12.8%	7.8%

Abbey National Treasury Services PLC (United Kingdom)

LOCATIONS

HQ: Abbey National Treasury Services PLC (United Kingdom)
2 Triton Square, Regent's Place, London NW1 3AN
Phone: (44) 870 607 6000   **Fax:** (44) 20 7224 5306
Web: www.ants.co.uk

HISTORICAL FINANCIALS
Company Type: Public

Income Statement   FYE: December 31

	ASSETS ($ mil.)	NET INCOME ($ mil.)	INCOME AS % OF ASSETS	EMPLOYEES
12/13	345,929	271	0.1%	764
12/12	351,245	425	0.1%	717
12/11	340,444	531	0.2%	817
12/10	393,221	714	0.2%	679
12/09	458,091	612	0.1%	560
Annual Growth	(6.8%)	(18.4%)	—	8.1%

2013 Year-End Financials

Return on assets: 0.0%	Dividends
Return on equity: 4.7%	Yield: —
Long-term debt ($ mil.): —	Payout: —
No. of shares (mil.): —	Market value ($ mil.): —
Sales ($ mil): 5,304	

Accenture plc

For Accenture the accent is on helping businesses improve their performance. The world's largest consulting firm Accenture offers a well-balanced portfolio of management consulting technology and business process outsourcing (BPO) services to some of the top companies and government organizations in the world. Corporate clients span a broad spectrum of industries —from retail to communications —and include more than three-quarters of the FORTUNE 500. Clients use Accenture's services to enter new markets increase revenue in existing markets improve operational performance and deliver new products to market. Accenture is domiciled in Dublin but headquartered in New York.
Geographic Reach

Accenture serves clients in more than 200 cities spanning 120 countries. The majority of its revenue is balanced between the Americas and Europe Middle East and Africa (EMEA). The US is its largest individual market generating about one-third of total revenue. The remainder is made in the Asia/Pacific region.
Operations

Accenture's business is divided into five operating groups: Communications Media & Technology; Financial Services; Health & Public Service; Products; and Resources. Although revenue generated by these operating groups is well dispersed Products is the company's largest segment serving mainly consumer-oriented industries including automotive consumer goods life sciences retail transportation and travel services.

Accenture has a global network of innovation centers in the US Australia China Japan Singapore India France and South Africa.
Financial Performance

As the global economy has improved and the demand for its consulting and outsourcing services has increased Accenture recognized a 9% spike in revenue ($27.4 billion to $29.7 billion) and a 12 % rise in profits ($2.3 billion to $2.6 billion) from 2011 to 2012.

The recent growth was attributed to double digit growth across all its five operating groups. Accenture has also benefited from its growth strategy that is focused on further differentiating its products and services in the marketplace and improving its competitiveness. It has also been helped from a positive increase in the local currency.
Strategy

Accenture's strategy is focused on deepening and differentiating its industry and technology capabilities from competitors. It is doing so in part by investing in analytics cloud computing insight-driven health interactive and digital marketing mobility and smart grid. Acquisitions joint ventures and alliances are key means through which Accenture enhances and adds to its offerings. One such partnership is a five-year research collaboration with MIT announced in early 2013 to develop advanced analytics specifically how to harness the challenges of big data and develop new approaches to improve the science of decision-making. In late 2012 Accenture and GE Aviation formed a joint venture company called Taleris to provide global airlines and cargo carriers with intelligent operations services to improve efficiency.

From a geographic standpoint the company is focusing expansion efforts on certain emerging markets in particular such as Brazil China India Mexico Russia South Africa South Korea Turkey and certain countries in Southeast Asia and the Middle East.
Mergers and Acquisitions

To help its clients more effectively measure and monitor the progress of their change programs Accenture in 2013 acquired ChangeTrack Research an Australia-based provider of analytics-based tools and services for change management usage. The acquisition complemented Accenture's suite of tools and capabilities to help its clients achieve the goals of their most significant organizational transformations.

Adding to its footprint in Asia/Pacific Accenture acquired in 2012 Singapore-based Newspage Pte Ltd a provider of distributor management and mobility software that helps consumer goods companies improve their operations sales performance and data visibility.

Earlier in 2012 the company expanded its operations through the purchase of Octagon Research Solutions a provider of clinical and regulatory information management solutions and software for the pharmaceutical industry. The deal gives Accenture a means to provide clinical and regulatory services to pharmaceutical companies.

HISTORY

Accenture traces its history back to the storied accounting firm of Arthur Andersen & Co. Founded by Northwestern University professor and accounting legend Arthur Andersen in 1913 the firm's expanding scope of operations led it into forensic accounting and advising clients on financial reporting processes forming the basis for a management consulting arm. Arthur Andersen led the firm until his death in 1947. His successor Leonard Spacek split off the consulting operations as a separate unit in 1954.

The consulting business grew quickly during the 1970s and 1980s thanks in part to an orgy of US corporate re-engineering. By 1988 consulting accounted for 40% of Andersen's sales. Chafing at sharing profits with the auditors (who faced growing price pressures and a rising tide of legal action due to the accounting irregularities of their clients) the consultants sought more power within the firm. The result was a 1989 restructuring that established Andersen Worldwide (later Andersen) as the parent of two independent units Arthur Andersen and Andersen Consulting (AC). The growing revenue imbalance between the operations remained unresolved however and a year later Arthur Andersen poured gas on the flames by establishing its own business consultancy.

Meanwhile AC continued to expand during the 1990s by forming practices focused on manufacturing finance and government. It addressed the shift from mainframes to PCs by forming alliances with technology heavyweights Hewlett-Packard Sun Microsystems and Microsoft. In 1996 AC teamed up with Internet service provider BBN (acquired by GTE in 1997) to form ServiceNet a joint venture to develop Internet commerce and other systems.

The Andersen family feud took a turn for the worse in 1997 with the retirement of CEO Lawrence Weinbach. A deadlocked vote for a new leader led the board to appoint accounting partner Robert Grafton as CEO angering the consulting partners. Later that year AC asked the International Chamber of Commerce to negotiate a breakup of Andersen Worldwide. George Shaheen to whom many attributed the heightened tensions between the units resigned as CEO of AC in 1999 and was replaced by Joe Forehand.

While the separation dispute dragged on the consulting business grew and diversified amid increasing consolidation in the industry. In 1999 the company moved into e-commerce venture funding with the formation of Andersen Consulting Ventures and in 2000 it inked partnership deals with Microsoft (Microsoft system implementation services) Sun Microsystems (for B2B Internet office supply sales) and BT (Internet-based human resources services).

That year an international arbitrator finally approved AC's separation from its parent ruling that the consultancy must change its name and pay Andersen Worldwide $1 billion (far less than the $15 billion demanded by the accounting partners). Renamed Accenture the company went public in 2001. While the new name (a made-up word) might have struck some as a marketing challenge having an identity distinct from that of its former parent proved to be a stroke of luck for Accenture. Andersen broke apart in 2002 after becoming embroiled in the accounting scandals of energy giant Enron.

In 2004 Accenture successfully bid on a $10 billion 10-year contract to create a system to identify visitors and immigrants coming into the country. Dubbed US-VISIT (United States Visitor and Immigrant Status Indicator Technology) the system was to be employed by the Department of Homeland Security to prevent terrorists from entering the US. However Accenture's bid nearly ran afoul of congressional critics who tried to pass spending amendments barring firms headquartered outside the US from winning security-related business.

Forehand stepped down as CEO of Accenture in 2004 and was replaced by company veteran William Green. Forehand remained chairman until he retired in 2006 when Green was named to that post as well.

Accenture acquired Capgemini's North American health practice in 2005 for $175 million in order to strengthen its offerings to hospitals and health care systems. In 2006 the firm expanded its outsourcing operations by buying NaviSys a leading provider of software for the life insurance industry along with key assets of Kansas-based accountant Savista.

In mid-2008 Accenture swallowed up ATAN an industrial and automation services provider based in Brazil that caters to the mining energy and utilities sectors. It also obtained SOPIA a Tokyo-based consulting firm specializing in Oracle systems integration. During that year Accenture added to its transportation and travel services operations (located within its Products Division) when it bought AddVal Technology. AddVal provided software and technology used for freight order management and the deal enhanced Accenture's ability to integrate and simplify its clients' freight management services capabilities.

In late 2009 Accenture looked to solidify its position in a vital market when it obtained the Symbian professional services unit of Nokia. The unit offers engineering and support services for the Symbian operating system one of the world's most widely used operating systems for smart phones. The acquired operations provided a broad range of embedded software services for mobile devices and were rebranded Accenture Embedded Mobility Services.

Accenture obtained RiskControl a consulting firm based in Brazil in early 2010. Also that year Accenture bought Beijing Genesis Interactive Technology Company an embedded software firm providing mobile software outsourcing services to companies in China. The acquisitions furthered Accenture's penetration into the cutting-edge smart phone support services market.

Focusing on beefing up its Financial Services segment in 2011 Accenture acquired Duck Creek Technologies a provider of software and tools catering to the insurance and health care sectors. At the time of the transaction Duck Creek served about 60 clients throughout North America and the UK.

At the beginning of 2011 Pierre Nanterme the former head of the company's financial services operations was promoted to become the company's newest CEO. Green remains with Accenture as chairman.

EXECUTIVES

Senior Managing Director Strategic Initiatives; CEO Accenture Interactive, R. Timothy S. (Tim) Breene, age 64, $1,583,681 total compensation
Group Chief Executive - Financial Services, Richard A. Lumb, age 53
International Chairman, Karl-Heinz Floether, age 62, $1,237,338 total compensation
Chairman, William D. (Bill) Green, age 60, $1,237,500 total compensation
Group Chief Executive-Technology, Kevin M. Campbell, age 53, $1,122,529 total compensation
International Chairman Strategic Countries, Diego Visconti, $1,995,154 total compensation

Chief Financial Officer, Pamela J. (Pam) Craig, age 57, $1,175,265 total compensation
Director Public Relations, Fred J. Hawrysh
Principal Accounting Officer and Controller, Anthony G. (Tony) Coughlan, age 57
Chief Marketing and Communications Officer, Roxanne Taylor
Group Chief Executive - Health & Public Service, Stephen J. (Steve) Rohleder, age 57, $1,175,265 total compensation
Chief Geographic Strategy & Operations Officer, David C. Thomlinson
Managing Director North America, Jorge L. Benitez, age 54
Senior Director Investor Relations, David Straube
Group Chief Executive-Technology, Martin I. (Marty) Cole, age 58
Group Chief Executive-North America, Robert N. (Bob) Frerichs, age 62, $1,102,577 total compensation
Chief Human Resources Officer, Jill B. Smart
Chief Leadership Officer, Adrian J. Lajtha, age 57
CTO and Managing Director Technology, Donald J. (Don) Rippert
Executive Director Office of the CEO, Lori L. Lovelace
Chairman and Chief Executive Officer, Pierre Nanterme, age 55
Chief Financial Officer, David P. Rowland, age 53
Group Chief Executive Products, Gianfranco Casati, age 55
Managing Director US Federal Business, Lisa M. Mascolo, age 54
Group Chief Executive Management Consulting, Alexander (Sander) van 't Noordende, age 51
Managing Director Security Services, Alastair MacWillson
Managing Director Management Consulting North America, Walt Shill
Chief Accounting Officer; Corporate Controller, Richard P. Clark
Global Managing Director Retail Practice, Janet L. Hoffman
Country Managing Director Singapore; Managing Director Customer Relationship Management, Lay Lim Teo
Global Managing Director Electronics and High-Tech Group, Jean-Laurent Poitou
Managing Director Strategy Management Consulting Group, Mark Spelman
Chief Operating Officer, Johan G. (Jo) Deblaere, age 52
Group Chief Executive - Business Process Outsourcing, Michael J. (Mike) Salvino
Chief Strategy Officer, Shawn Collinson, age 53
Country Managing Director Brazil, Roger Ingold
Chairman Greater China, Gong Li
Chairman and Geography Managing Director India, Harsh Manglik
Country Managing Director Spain, Vicente Moreno
General Counsel Secretary and Chief Compliance Officer, Julie S. Sweet, age 48
Chief Performance Officer, Jeffrey (Jeff) Osborne
Global Managing Director Research and Development and Alliances, Gavin Michael
Head Legal UK and Ireland, Patrick B. F. Rowe
Senior Manager Corporate Communications, Ben J. Geschwind
Group COO Management Consulting, Sylvie Ouziel
Executive Director Business Applications, Kenneth (Ken) Corless
Executive Director Global Infrastructure, Vidya S. (Vid) Byanna
CIO, Frank B. Modruson
Senior Director IT Business Operations, Robert E. (Bob) Kress
Group Chief Executive Resources, Jean-Marc Ollagnier, age 53
Managing Director United Kingdom, Oliver (Olly) Benzecry, age 52

Group Chief Executive-Management Consulting, Alexander M. (Sander) van't Noordende

Group Chief Executive - Management Consulting Growth Platform, Alexander Noordende

Lead Independent Director, Mark Stuart

Group Chief Executive - Communications Media & Technology, Robert E. (Bob) Sell

President ASM Research, Jim Traficant

Director, Charles H. Giancarlo, age 56

Director, Dina Dublon, age 61

Director, Nobuyuki Idei, age 77

Lead Director, Sir Mark Moody-Stuart, age 73

Director, Robert I. (Bob) Lipp, age 76

Director, Dennis F. Hightower, age 71

Director, Wulf von Schimmelmann, age 68

Director, Blythe J. McGarvie, age 58

Director, Marjorie (Marge) Magner, age 64

Director, William L. (Bill) Kimsey, age 72

Chairman & CEO, Pierre Nanterme, age 54

Independent Director, Gilles Pelisson

Auditors: KPMGLLP

LOCATIONS

HQ: Accenture plc
1 Grand Canal Square, Grand Canal Harbour, Dublin 2
Phone: (353) 1 646 2000
Web: www.accenture.com

Sales

	% of total
Americas	45
Asia/Pacific	15

PRODUCTS/OPERATIONS

Sales

	% of total
Products	23
Financial services	22
Health & public service	15

Sales

Consulting	56
Total	**100**

Selected Mergers and Acquisitions

FY2013
ChangeTrack Research Pty Ltd (Sydney Australia; analytics-based tools and services)
FY2012
Octagon Research Solutions Inc. (clinical and regulatory information management services and software)
FY2011
Duck Creek Technologies (software and tools for insurance and health care)
CAS Computer Anwendungs- und Systemberatung (CRM and mobility software)
FY2010
Beijing Genesis Interactive Technology Co. (embedded software services)
Knowledge Rules (provider of business solutions utilizing BPM software)
Acceria (technology and consulting business services)
CadenceQuest (customer data and analytics)
Risk Control (risk management)

Selected Practice Areas

Communications and high technology
 Communications
 Electronics and high technology
 Media and entertainment
Products
 Automotive
 Consumer goods and services
 Health and life sciences
 Industrial equipment
 Retail
 Transportation and travel services
Financial services
 Banking
 Capital markets
 Insurance
Resources
 Chemicals

Energy
Natural resources
Utilities
Government

Selected Services

Business consulting
 Customer relationship management
 Finance and performance management
 Human performance
 Strategy
 Supply chain management
Outsourcing
 Application outsourcing
 Business process outsourcing (BPO)
  Customer contact
  Finance and accounting
  Human resources
  Learning
  Procurement
 Infrastructure outsourcing
Systems integration and technology
 Enterprise architecture
 Information management
 Infrastructure consulting
 Intellectual property
 Research and development

COMPETITORS

Bain & Company	Computer Sciences
Booz Allen	Corp.
Boston Consulting	Deloitte Consulting
Capgemini	HP Enterprise Services
Capgemini North	IBM
America	McKinsey & Company
Charteris	Unisys

HISTORICAL FINANCIALS

Company Type: Public

Income Statement

FYE: August 31

	REVENUE ($ mil.)	NET INCOME ($ mil.)	NET PROFIT MARGIN	EMPLOYEES
08/14	31,874	2,941	9.2%	305,000
08/13	30,394	3,281	10.8%	275,000
08/12	29,777	2,553	8.6%	257,000
08/11	27,352	2,277	8.3%	236,000
08/10	23,094	1,780	7.7%	204,000
Annual Growth	**8.4%**	**13.4%**	**—**	**10.6%**

2014 Year-End Financials

Debt ratio: 0.1%
Return on equity: 55.0%
Cash ($ mil.): 4,921
Current ratio: 1.46
Long-term debt ($ mil.): 26

No. of shares (mil.): 656
Dividends
 Yield: 0.0%
 Payout: 41.1%
Market value ($ mil.): 53,220

	STOCK PRICE ($) FY Close	P/E High/Low	PER SHARE ($) Earnings	Dividends	Book Value
08/14	81.06	18 15	4.52	1.86	8.73
08/13	72.25	16 12	4.93	1.62	7.44
08/12	61.60	17 13	3.84	1.35	6.13
08/11	53.59	18 10	3.40	0.90	5.62
08/10	36.60	16 12	2.66	1.13	4.11
Annual Growth	**22.0%**	**— —**	**14.2%**	**13.4%**	**20.7%**

ACE, Ltd.

This ACE aims to provide a full house of insurance services. Through subsidiaries ACE Limited sells property/casualty insurance life insurance and reinsurance through subsidiaries around the globe. It primarily provides property/casualty in-

surance to commercial and personal customers. Policies offered include general liability homeowners auto accident workers' compensation and specialty crop and marine coverage. The company's ACE Tempest Re businesses provide reinsurance to property/casualty insurers in North America and Europe. ACE's life insurance and life reinsurance operations are focused in the US and other select markets. Products are primarily marketed through independent brokers.

Geographic Reach

The North American insurance segment which includes property/casualty subsidiaries ACE USA ACE Bermuda and ACE Canada is ACE's largest business segment accounting for about 40% of revenue. The company's ACE International and ACE Global Markets property/casualty insurance units reach into the rest of the world while its smaller ACE Life insurance division primarily operates in emerging markets in Asia Europe and the Americas.

With its operating subsidiaries located in more than 50 countries ACE serves customers in more than 170 nations.

ACE moved its place of incorporation home from the Caymans to Switzerland in 2008. It kept executive offices in Bermuda and New York.

Strategy

ACE regularly looks to expand its product offerings and geographical presence through acquisitions and organic measures. For instance the firm launched a new property/casualty division catering to high-net-worth individuals in 2008.

To expand in high-growth geographic markets it established new offices in Turkey and Panama in 2009 and 2008. Then in early 2012 the company opened a representative office in Kiev that will allow it to directly engage in the Ukraine insurance market.

Mergers and Acquisitions

In recent years ACE has focused its geographic expansion on smaller acquisitions in emerging global marketplaces. In 2011 ACE entered two new markets for life insurance in North Asia after acquiring New York Life's life insurance operations in Hong Kong and Korea for about $425 million.

In 2012 ACE acquired Indonesian general insurance firm Asuransi Jaya Proteksi for some $130 million. It closed its purchase of Mexican surety insurer Fianzas Monterrey from New York Life for $285 million in 2013 as well as its purchase of another Mexican insurance firm ABA Seguros from Ally Financial for $865 million.

ACE broadened its specialty holdings through the 2010 acquisition of the 80% of Rain and Hail Insurance Service which it did not already own for $1.1 billion in cash. Through the deal ACE secured one of the largest crop insurers in North America. Continuing this trend in 2011 ACE acquired another agribusiness insurer Penn Miller Holding for $107 million.

Past purchases include the $2.6 billion acquisition of Combined Insurance Company of America in 2008 from insurance broker Aon Corporation. The purchase expanded the company's worldwide accident supplemental health and life underwriting business specifically for small businesses and middle-income individuals. A lull in acquisitions carried ACE through 2009 due to economic conditions.

EXECUTIVES

Division President ACE Westchester, Bruce L. Kessler

Chief Investment Officer ACE Group, Timothy A. Boroughs

Chairman and Chief Executive Officer, Evan G. Greenberg, age 59, $1,200,000 total compensation

Chief Financial Officer, Philip V. Bancroft, age 54, $670,000 total compensation

Chief Accounting Officer ACE Group, Paul B. Medini, age 56

Chairman Insurance - North America, John Lupica

Chief Risk Officer and Chief Actuary ACE Limited, Sean Ringsted

President ACE Life, Russell G. Bundschuh

Chief Communications Officer ACE Group, Patrick F. McGovern

Division President ACE Bermuda, Rees Fletcher

General Counsel, Robert F. (Bob) Cusumano, age 57, $515,000 total compensation

Division President ACE Tempest Re USA, James E. Wixtead

Vice Chairman and Chief Operating Officer ACE Limited Chairman ACE Overseas General, John W. Keogh, age 49, $675,000 total compensation

Division President Global Personal Lines and Small Commercial Insurance and COO Overseas General Insurance, Juan C. Andrade, age 45

Regional President ACE Latin America, Jorge Luis Cazar

Division President Accident, Edward Levin

Treasurer ACE Group, Ken Koreyva

Division President ACE Tempest Re Canada, Constantin (Tino) Petalas

President Combined Insurance, Brad Bennett

Chief Administration Officer, Samantha Froud

CEO ACE Private Risk Services, Robert Courtemanche

Regional President ACE Asia Pacific, Damien Sullivan

Chief Auditor ACE Group, Julie Schaekel

CIO ACE Group, Kevin Shearan

Managing Director ACE Tempest Re International, Steve Roberts

Regional President, David Robinson

COO Continental Europe, Jeff Moghrabi

Country President France, Nadia Cote

Chief Actuary, Stephen Wilson

President - Australia & New Zealand, Giles Ward

President ACE Argentina, Fernando Mendez

President ACE Chile, Juan Merchan

President ACE Puerto Rico, Judith Hernandez

Vice President General Manager, Carl Nagle

Director, Leo F. Mullin, age 71

Director, Robert M. Hernandez, age 69

Director, Michael G. (Mike) Atieh, age 61

Director, Robert Ripp, age 72

Director, Michael P. Connors, age 57

Director, Peter Menikoff, age 73

Director, Thomas J. (Tom) Neff, age 76

Director, John A. (Jack) Krol, age 76

Director, Bruce L. Crockett, age 69

Director, Eugene B. Shanks Jr.

Director, Olivier Steimer, age 58

Vice Chairman ACE Limited and ACE Group Holdings; CEO Insurance North America; Chairman and CEO USA; Chairman Westchester; Chairman and President ACE INA Holdings, Brian E. Dowd, age 50

Vice Chairman ACE Limited and ACE Group Holdings; Chairman Insurance Overseas General, John W. Keogh, age 48

Director, Mary A. Cirillo-Goldberg, age 65

Director, Theodore E. (Ted) Shasta, age 62

Auditors: PricewaterhouseCoopersLLP

LOCATIONS

HQ: ACE, Ltd.
Baerengasse 32, Zurich CH-8001
Phone: (41) 43 456 76 00
Web: www.acegroup.com

PRODUCTS/OPERATIONS

Premiums

	% of total
Insurance - North	42
Insurance - overseas	39
Life	11
Global	8
Total	**100**

COMPETITORS

AEGON	Humana
AIG	ING
AXA	Liberty Mutual
Aetna	Loews
Allianz	MetLife
Allstate	Munich Re America
American Financial Group	Munich Re Group
	Old Republic
Berkshire Hathaway	Swiss Re
CNA Surety	The Hartford
Chubb Corp	Travelers Companies
Fairfax Financial Holdings	W. R. Berkley
	White Mountains
General Re	Insurance Group
Hannover Re	XL Group plc

HISTORICAL FINANCIALS

Company Type: Public

Income Statement   FYE: December 31

	ASSETS ($ mil.)	NET INCOME ($ mil.)	INCOME AS % OF ASSETS	EMPLOYEES
12/13	94,510	3,758	4.0%	20,000
12/12	92,545	2,706	2.9%	17,000
12/11	87,505	1,585	1.8%	16,500
12/10	83,355	3,108	3.7%	16,000
12/09	77,980	2,549	3.3%	15,000
Annual Growth	4.9%	10.2%	—	7.5%

2013 Year-End Financials

Return on assets: 4.0%	Dividends
Return on equity: 13.3%	Yield: 1.9%
Long-term debt ($ mil.): —	Payout: 19.5%
No. of shares (mil.): 339	Market value ($ mil.): 35,179
Sales ($ mil): 19,261	

	STOCK PRICE ($) FY Close	P/E High/Low		Earnings	PER SHARE ($) Dividends	Book Value
12/13	103.53	9	7	10.92	2.00	84.83
12/12	79.80	10	9	7.89	2.41	80.90
12/11	70.12	16	13	4.65	1.38	72.76
12/10	62.25	7	5	9.11	1.30	68.59
12/09	50.40	7	4	7.55	1.46	58.44
Annual Growth	19.7%	—	—	9.7%	8.2%	9.8%

ACS Actividades de Construccion y Servicios, S.A.

Turning the rains (and the wind) on the plains of Spain into electricity provides the current for growth at ACS Actividades de Construccion y Servicios one of Spain's largest construction and infrastructure groups. ACS Group operates in five primary business areas: construction concessions environment industrial services and energy. The company's activities include civil engineering installation and maintenance for energy facilities transport services and highway management. ACS has grown by investing in such firms as former construction rival Dragados and Germany-based infrastructure giant HOCHTIEF. The group is active in more than 50 countries mainly in Europe and Latin America.

The group's largest and fastest-growing arm is its industrial services and energy segment which provides applied engineering construction and maintenance for the energy and communications sectors. ACS has invested in the segment's growth including making investments in renewable energies. The group develops such projects as wind farms and solar energy plants as well as traditional power stations and toll systems.

Another key arm for ACS is its construction segment which is engaged in civil commercial and residential building. Typical construction projects include roads railways parking garages sports facilities and hospitals. ACS focuses on public-private partnership arrangements for jobs such as public protection housing developments. The segment expanded with its 2009 acquisition of US builder Pulice Construction for $114 million. The deal added a Phoenix-based civil work specialist and a prime contractor for the Arizona Department of Transportation.

Through units including Urbaser and Dragados ACS' environmental segment provides facility management waste management and port and logistics chain services. It offers services for facilities including health care centers hotels office buildings schools and courthouses. In 2011 ACS sold its stake in interior cleaning services unit Clece to private equity firms for Â608 million (some $865 million); the capital should help ACS develop its core businesses.

ACS's concessions unit develops designs builds and maintains infrastructure projects primarily in Europe and North America. Holdings include a minority stake in Abertis one of the largest infrastructure companies in Europe and a stake in energy company IBERDROLA. Through Dragados ACS took an approximately two-thirds stake in Polish building firm Pol-Aqua in 2009.

Also that year ACS sold its controlling stake in electric utility Union Fenosa to pay down debts incurred through its investments in HOCHTIEF and IBERDROLA (which it had originally planned to merge with Union Fenosa). In 2010 the company made a successful hostile takeover bid to increase its stake in HOCHTIEF from about 30% to more than 50% –it ultimately wants to buy the firm outright –to better take advantage of the German company's geographic reach and to cut costs. ACS is focusing its energy business on IBERDROLA.

The global recession hurt construction firms as projects dried up or customers struggled to keep up with payments. ACS was no exception and it began looking for other noncore assets to sell. In one such deal it sold port operator Dragados Servicios Portuarios y Logisticos to a group of investors for some Â720 million (approximately $952 million) in 2010.

HISTORY

In war-torn Europe in 1942 the Spanish construction company Obras y Construcciones Industriales (Ocisa) was born. The company soon began a 50-year association with Spain's hydroelectric industry marked by the completion of the dam and reservoir project Presa de Bachimana in 1950. The company built nine more dam and reservoir projects in Spain (including Presa de la Llosa completed in 1997).

As the demand for public works projects decreased and competition increased Spanish constructors began working abroad especially in Latin America where Ocisa was contracted in 1975 to create an irrigation tunnel in Venezuela's Andes.

A six-year economic expansion measured by the success of Spain's "Big Seven" construction companies including #5 Ocisa reached its end in 1992 when the Spanish government the country's biggest builder was forced to cut spending on infrastructure. This triggered consolidation in Spain's construction industry including Ocisa's 1993 acquisition of Construcciones Padros in which Ocisa held a 25% stake. Adopting the new name OCP Construcciones it also absorbed the assets of its installation and assembly subsidiary Compania de la Distribucion de Electricidad (Grupo Cobra).

The slowdown in public works projects continued and companies sought additional pooling of resources and diversification of activities at home and abroad. In 1996 OCP bought a 40% stake in the state-owned construction firm Auxini increased to 100% a year later. Also in 1997 the OCP group led by its president Florentino Perez acquired Gines Navarro Construcciones controlled (79%) by the powerful investment group led by brothers Carlos and Juan March. The two companies combined to create Spain's third-largest construction group Actividades de Construcciones y Servicios or Grupo ACS.

Perez became chairman of the new group and promised to make it Spain's most profitable public construction company through further diversification international contracts and selective investment in real estate. Grupo March which now controlled about 37% of ACS joined with OCP shareholders including former VP Juan Torres and the Roa family to offer a portion of their shares on the market yet retained 50% of the new company among themselves. A public offering of shares in ACS was completed that year following a 4-for-1 share split.

ACS began restructuring placing its construction activities including Auxini under its subsidiary Puertos y Obras. In 1998 ACS was first listed on the IBEX-35 index of top Spanish companies.

With the construction industry continuing to consolidate Grupo ACS benefited from a boom in construction work in Spain led by liberalization of the energy markets and continued international growth especially in Latin America.

ACS further diversified into transportation in 1999 with the purchase of Continental Auto a Spanish passenger coach company and an increased stake in its subsidiary Transportes Alsina. It also placed a bid for Enatcar Spain's state-owned transportation company. The next year the group joined Finnish telecommunications firm Sonera and France's Vivendi to form a consortium to operate under one of Spain's third-generation wireless phone licenses. ACS and Sonera agreed in 2001 to form a new venture to explore additional markets in Europe and the US for 3G wireless operations.

In 2002 ACS took a major step toward expanding further by acquiring the 24% controlling stake in rival Dragados from Banco Santander Central Hispano. The next year Dragados accepted a bid by ACS for another 10% of its shares and the two companies merged operations. By combining the operations of Dragados with its own ACS built itself into one of Spain's largest construction companies.

The company acquired a 50% stake in Brazilian port authority Terminal de Santa Catarina for E25.5 million in 2006. ACS has invested further in international port terminals particularly in Brazil and India.

EXECUTIVES

Vice Chairman, Pablo Vallbona Vadell
Chairman and CEO ACS Actividades de Construccion y Servicios, Florentino Perez Rodriguez, age 65

General Manager Iridium, Francisco Fernandez Lafuente
Chairman and CEO Services Communications and Energy; Chairman and CEO of Cobra and Chairman of Etra and Imesapi, Eugenio Llorente Gomez
Finance Manager, Jose Zornoza Soto
Executive Vice Chairman, Antonio Garcia Ferrer, age 67
Subsidiary Companies Manager Dragados, Octavio del Real Sanchez
Secretary, Jose Luis del Valle Perez
Corporate General Manager ACS Actividades de Construccion y Servicios, Angel Manuel Garcia Altozano
General Manager, Jose Luis Lopez Molinillo
Director Investments and Management Control, Christina Aldamiz-Echevarria Gonzalez de Durana
CEO Vias y Contrucciones SA, Gonzalo Gomez-Zamalloa Baraibar
Chairman and CEO Construction Environment & Logistics and Concesisons; Chairman and CEO Dragados, Marcelino Fernandez Verdes
Secretary General of Construction Environment & Logistics and Concesisons, Luis Nogueira Miguelsanz
Executive Assistant Environment and Logistics, Antonio Alfonzo Sanchez
General Manager Dragados, Ignacio Segura Surinach
Civil Works Manager Dragados, Ricardo Martin de Bustamante
Building Manager Dragados, Juan Perez Luis Garcia-Gelabert Perez
Contracting Manager Dragados, Maximiliano Navascues Redondo
Technical Services Manager Dragados, Alfonso Costa Cuadrench
Chairman Vias y Construcciones, Manuel Perez Beato
Civil Works Manager Vias y Construcciones, Manuel Alvarez Mu?oz
Building Manager Vias y Construcciones, Ignacio Legorburu Escobar
General Manager Tecsa, Jose Maria Aguirre Fernandez
CEO Seis, Botteghelz Canga Botteghelz
General Manager Seis, Pablo Quiros Gracian
General Manager Drace Medio Ambiente, Fernando Garcia Arribas
General Manager FPS, Juan Mata Arbide
CEO Geocisa, Alejandro Canga Botteghelz
Chairman and CEO Urbaser, Javier Polanco Gomez-Lavin
General Manager Urbaser, Jose Maria Lopez-Pi?ol
Chairman and CEO Clece, Cristobal Valderas Alvarado
Chairman and CEO Iridium, Manuel Garcia Buey
General Manager Iridium, Victor Revuelta Garcia
General Manager Services Communications and Energy, Jose Alfonso Nebrera Garcia
Secretary General ACS Services Communications and Energy, Jose Romero de Avila Gonzalez-Albo
CEO Semi and Maessa, Daniel Vega Baladron
General Manager Cymi and Masa, Vicente Prados Tejada
General Manager Large Contract Dragados Industrial, Pablo Garcia Arenal
CEO Initec Intecsa and Makiber, Raul Llamazares de la Puente
General Manager Dragados Offshore Dragados Industrial, Pedro Ascorbe Trian
Chairman Sice Technology and Systems Dragados Industrial, Juan Enrique Ruiz Gonzalez
Vice Chairman, Pablo Vallbona Vadell
Chairman and CEO ACS Actividades de Construccion y Servicios, Florentino Perez Rodriguez, age 65
Executive Vice Chairman, Antonio Garcia Ferrer, age 67
Director, Juan March de la Lastra

Director, Jose Maria Aguirre Gonzalez
Director, Agustin Bateucas Torrego
Director, Jose Alvaro Cuervo Garcia
Director, Manuel Delgado Solis
Director, Javier Echenique Landiribar
Director, Sabina Flaxa Thienemann
Director, Jaon-David Grima i Terre
Director, Jose Maria Loizaga Viguri
Director, Pedro Lopez Jimenez
Director, Santos Marinze-Conde Gutierrez-Barquin
Director, Javier Nonzon de Caceres
Director, Miquel Roca i Junyent
Director, Julio Sacristan Fidalgo
Director, Francisco Servando Verdu Pons
Auditors: DeloitteSL

LOCATIONS

HQ: ACS Actividades de Construccion y Servicios, S.A. Avda. Pio XII, 102, Madrid 28036
Phone: (34) 91 343 9200   **Fax:** (34) 91 343 9456
Web: www.grupoacs.com

PRODUCTS/OPERATIONS

Sales

	% of total
Industrial	43
Construction	39
Environment	17
Concessions	1
Total	**100**

Selected Subsidiaries

Concessions
  Concesiones Viarias Chile S.A. (infrastructures)
  Iridium Concesiones de Infraestructuras S.A.
Construction
  Acainsa S.A. (real estate development)
  Ave Lalin
  Consorcio Tecdra S.A.
  Constructora Norte Sur S.A. (48% Chile)
  Desaladora Barcelona (28%)
  Guadarrama Iv (33%)
  Inmobiliaria Alabega S.A. (real estate development)
  Isla Verde Ute (35%)
  Soterram. Basurto Ute Tecsa-Necso (50%)
  Terminal Aeropuerto (70%)
Environment
  Consenur S.A. (management and treatment of hospital waste)
  Empordanesa de Neteja S.A. (urban solid waste management and street cleaning)
  Mapide S.A. (interior cleaning)
  Publimedia Sistemas Publicitarios S.L. (advertising services)
  RetraOil S.L. (treatment of oils and marpoles)
  Servicios Generales de Jaen S.A. (75% water)
  Somasur S.A. (intermediary company Morocco)
  Urbaser de Mejico S.A. (collection of urban solid waste and street cleaning)
  Urbaser Valencia C.A. (collection of urban solid waste and street cleaning)
  Ute Ecoparc V (20% USW treatment)
  Vertederos de Residuos S.A. (84% VERTRESA collection of urban solid waste and street cleaning)
Industrial Services
  ACS industrial Services LLC (energy production US)
  Actividades de Servicios e Instalaciones Cobra S.A. (auxiliary energy and communications distribution Guatemala)
  Andasol 1 S.A. (energy production)
  API Movilidad S.A. (road maintenance)
  BTOB Construccion Ventures S.L. (administrative management)
  Central Termica de Mejillones S.A. (engineering supply and construction Chile)
  Cobra Ingenieria de Montajes S.A. (installations and assembly)
  Cobra Peru S.A. (auxiliary energy and communications distribution)
  Coinsal Instalaciones y Servicios S.A. de C.V. (installations and assembly El Salvador)
  Cymi Holding S.A. (securities holding company Brazil)
  Dragados Gulf Construction Ltd. (Saudi Arabia)
  Emurtel S.A. (50% electrical installations)
  Enq S.L. (electrical installations)

Etra Catalu?a S.A. (electrical installations)
Extresol-1 S.L. (energy production)
Gerovitae La Guancha S.A. (senior social and health
   center operations)
Humiclima Est S.A. (air conditioning)
Incro S.A. (50% engineering)
Infraest. Energeticas Medioambi. Extreme?as S.L.
   (services)
Instalaciones y Servicios Codeven C.A. (air
   conditioning)
Mantenimiento y Montajes Industriales S.A. (industrial
   maintenance and assemblies)
Mexsemi S.A. de C.V. (99.7% assemblies Mexico)
Opade Organizac. y Promoc de Actividades Deportivas
   S.A. (athletic activities organization and promotion)
Parque Eolico Marmellar S.L. (70% energy
   production)
Portumasa S.A. (manufacture and sale of electical
   equipment Portugal)
Semi Maroc S.A. (99.7% assemblies)
Serveis Catalans Serveica S.A. (electrical installations)
SICE LLC. (design construction installation and
   maintenance of traffic and trade)
Sistemas Radiantes F. Moyano S.A.
   (telecommunications)
Tecnotel de Canarias S.A. (air conditioning)
Ute C.T. Andasol 1 (80% fossil fuel plant)
Venezolana de Limpiezas Indust. C.A. (83% VENELIN
   Venezuela)
Services
   Valdemingomez 2000 S.A. (34% Valdemingomez
      degasification)

COMPETITORS

Abengoa	Ferrovial
Acciona	Grupo San Jose
Aker Solutions	Hyundai Engineering
Andrade Gutierrez	and Construction
Balfour Beatty	Impregilo
Bechtel	Kellogg Brown &
Bilfinger Berger	Root UK
Black & Veatch	OHL
Brisa	Odebrecht
Cintra	Skanska
DP World	TECNOCOM
FCC Barcelona	VINCI

HISTORICAL FINANCIALS

Company Type: Public

Income Statement

FYE: December 31

	REVENUE ($ mil.)	NET INCOME ($ mil.)	NET PROFIT MARGIN	EMPLOYEES
12/13	53,626	965	1.8%	164,750
12/12	51,173	(2,539)	—	164,342
12/11	37,520	1,244	3.3%	164,923
12/10	21,110	1,756	8.3%	138,542
12/09	23,248	2,811	12.1%	142,085
Annual Growth	23.2%	(23.4%)	—	3.8%

2013 Year-End Financials

Debt ratio: 37.3%
Return on equity: 23.6%
Cash ($ mil.): 5,189
Current ratio: 1.11
Long-term debt ($ mil.): 9,922

No. of shares (mil.): 314
Dividends
   Yield: —
   Payout: —
Market value ($ mil.): —

AEGON N.V.

Not only has AEGON expanded across Europe it has also spread Transamerica. The Dutch life insurance giant is using its expertise in acquisition (US rival Transamerica was its largest catch) and consolidation to build a transnational collection of financial service businesses serving 40 million customers worldwide. Its subsidiaries operate primarily in the US the Netherlands and the UK offering personal and commercial life insurance pensions and annuities and accident and supplemental health insurance as well as retirement and savings advice and management services. AEGON also has insurance operations in 15 other countries in the Americas Europe and Asia as well as banking operations in the Netherlands.

The company has established a strong growth pattern for existing and new international markets largely through strategic acquisitions though its pace has slowed some due to economic downturns in 2008 and 2009. AEGON which derives about 60% of its revenues from life insurance premiums is focused on organic expansion in the high-growth regions of Asia central and eastern Europe and Latin America. To consolidate its market position in Spain AEGON in mid-2013 inked an exclusive 25-year strategic partnership with Banco Santander SA. As part of the agreement AEGON acquired a 51% stake in the joint venture which consists of a life insurance company and a non-life insurance company. The venture distributes life and general insurance products through Banco Santander's SA branch network while AEGON Spain provides back-office services.

In the Asia/Pacific region AEGON is broadening its operations partially through its Beijing-based insurance joint venture with the Chinese National Offshore Oil Corporation (CNOOC). It also formed a mutual fund joint venture with China-based Industrial Securities Co. in 2008 and it has an annuities partnership with Sony Life in Japan that began operations in 2009.

European expansion efforts include AEGON's 2009 buyout of former partner Banca Transilvania's shares in BT AEGON the Romanian pension business set up by the two companies the previous year. Acquisitions in other regions include the 2009 purchase of a 50% stake in Brazilian life insurance firm Mongeral SA. AEGON has also been focusing on broadening its global distribution channels which include independent agents brokers direct response workplace marketing banks and other financial institutions.

The company began scaling back on growth efforts in 2008 due to global economic conditions announcing plans to focus on high-growth and high-return investments in the emerging geographic markets. Later in 2008 as global financial conditions worsened AEGON secured a Â3 billion ($3.8 billion) capital infusion from the Dutch government to help it ward off economic woes. (This was fully repaid in 2011.) The funding was part of the Dutch government's bailout package designed to keep a group of banks and insurers from falling victim to the downturn in the global credit and equity markets.

To further ward off the impact of a slowing economy (and pay off its loan from the Dutch government) the company has initiated cost-containment and risk-reduction measures. It has been working to cut costs in its established market operations by reorganizing its Dutch US and UK divisions; it also restructured some global management responsibilities. In 2009 the company sold its Taiwanese life business for $84 million to Zhongwie Company. Also in 2009 it sold its Dutch real estate brokerage business and in early 2010 AEGON sold its funeral insurance business in the Netherlands.

The company announced additional restructuring measures to further streamline its operations in 2010. To reduce costs and risk exposures AEGON made plans to sharpen its focus on life pension and asset management operations and as such began seeking a buyer for Transamerica Reinsurance its US-based global life reinsurance business. The company sold Transamerica Re to French reinsurance firm SCOR for some $900 million in 2011. The sale included all of the life reinsurance operations although AEGON retained the annuity guarantee business. Further reorganization that year included cutting 300 positions in the Netherlands with associated costs of about $80 million which are expected to be accounted for before year-end. The company expects to achieve most of its cost savings in 2012.

In 2011 AEGON repurchased Â750 million in securities held by the Dutch state and completed the final repayment of the government bailout funds. Overall the company spent Â4.1 billion to repay the original Â3 billion loan including premium and interest payments. AEGON was the first company to repay the Dutch government funds issued through the 2008 bailout program. Although repayment frees AEGON to resume its acquisition activities the firm plans to continue its focus on organic growth efforts especially in Asia.

For several years AEGON has been restructuring its UK division around its core retirement and workplace savings units. In 2011 the company sold off its closed UK-based Guardian life and pensions business to private equity group Cinven for GBP275 million in cash. The sale provided proceeds for the company to recapitalize its Scottish Equitable business.

Independent trust Association AEGON (or Vereniging AEGON) controls about 33% of the company. Association AEGON is charged with safeguarding the interests of AEGON's shareholders and helped facilitate its bailout by issuing shares to the Dutch government.

HISTORY

AEGON traces its roots to 1844 when former civil servant and funeral society agent J. Oosterhoff founded Algemeene Friesche a burial society for low-income workers. The next year a similar organization Groot-Noordhollandsche was founded. These companies later became insurers and expanded nationwide. Meanwhile Olveh a civil servants' aid group was founded in 1877. The three companies merged in 1968 to form mutual insurer AGO.

AEGON's other operations came from different traditions. Vennootschap Nederland was founded in 1858 as a tontine (essentially a death pool with the survivors taking the pot) by Count A. Langrand-Dumonceau an ex-French Foreign Legionnaire from Belgium. In 1913 the company merged with Eerste Nederlandsche whose accident and health division had been previously spun off as Nieuwe Eerste Nederlandsche.

A year after Vennootschap was founded C. F. W. Wiggers van Kerchem founded a similar scheme Nillmij in the Dutch East Indies. The government promoted Nillmij to colonial civil servants and military people and for a while the company enjoyed a monopoly in the colony. Nillmij's Indonesian operations were nationalized after independence in 1957 but its Dutch subsidiaries continued to operate. All insurers were hit by fast-growing postwar government social programs. As a result industry consolidation came early to the Netherlands. In 1969 Eerste Nederlandsche Nieuwe Eerste Nederlandsche and Nillmij merged to form Ennia.

AGO demutualized in 1978 and became AGO Holding N.V. which was owned by Vereniging AGO. Meanwhile the shrinking Dutch insurance market forced companies to look overseas. AGO moved into the US in 1979 by buying Life Investors; by 1982 half of its sales came from outside the Netherlands. Ennia meanwhile expanded in Europe (it entered Spain in 1980) and the US (buying Arkansas-based National Old Line Insurance in 1981).

AGO and Ennia merged in 1983 to form AEGON. Vereniging AGO became Vereniging AEGON and received a 49% stake in the combined entity. (This stake was later reduced.) The company made more purchases at home and abroad and spent much of the rest of the decade assimilating operations.

AEGON's US units accounted for about 40% of sales in the mid-1980s and the firm increased that figure with acquisitions. In 1986 it bought Baltimore-based Monumental Corp. (life and health insurance) and expanded the company's US penetration.

This left AEGON underrepresented in Europe as deregulation paved the way for economic union and social service cutbacks spurred opportunities in private financial planning in the region. So in the 1990s AEGON began buying European companies including Regency Life (UK 1991) and Allami Biztosito (Hungary 1992). It formed an alliance with Mexico's Grupo Financiero Banamex in 1994. This reduced its reliance on US sales. It continued buying specialty operations in the US particularly asset management lines.

In 1997 AEGON began to concentrate on life insurance and financial services and shed its other operations. It bought the insurance business of Providian (now part of Washington Mutual) and sold noncore lines such as auto coverage. The next year it sold FGH Bank (mortgages) to Germany's Bayerische Vereinsbank (now Bayerische Hypotheken und Vereinsbank) and in 1999 sold auto insurer Worldwide Insurance.

That year AEGON expanded further in the US with the $9.7 billion purchase of Transamerica and bought the life and pensions businesses of the UK's Guardian Royal Exchange. In 2000 the company sold Labouchere N.V. a Dutch banking subsidiary to Dexia. Also in 2000 AEGON acquired UK-based third-party administrator HS Administrative Services.

Following the Transamerica acquisition the company divested several assets to focus on life insurance and pensions. In 2003 and 2004 diverse parts of Transamerica Finance (including its real estate tax unit and trailer leasing business) were sold to various companies including First American GE Commercial Finance and a joint venture held by Goldman Sachs and Cerberus Capital Management.

In 2005 the company sold off its German subsidiary AEGON Lebensversicherngs-AG operating as MoneyMaxx to Deutscher Ring. In 2006 it acquired a 49% stake in Mexican insurer Seguros Argos.

To expand in central and eastern Europe the company acquired pension fund management company PTE Ergo Hestia in Poland in 2007 as well as Dutch employee benefit and life insurance company OPTAS. To expand in Asia AEGON formed an annuities partnership with Sony Life in Japan in 2007. Also in 2007 AEGON USA purchased two Merrill Lynch insurance units and insurance services firm Clark Consulting.

In 2008 the company expanded in Europe by purchasing Turkish life and retirement services provider Ankara Emeklilik Hungarian pension fund UNIQA and Polish pension fund PTE Skarbiec-Emerytura as well as stakes in two similar Spanish firms.

AEGON slowed its acquisition efforts that year due to economic difficulties and began to control costs by restructuring and shedding some assets. In 2008 AEGON decided to discontinue an Indian life insurance and asset management joint venture with Ranbaxy.

EXECUTIVES

CEO AEGON The Netherlands and Member Management Board, Marco Keim, age 53
Chairman of the Executive Board and CEO, Alexander R. (Alex) Wynaendts, age 53, $1,251,311 total compensation
Global Head Sustainability, Marc A. van Weede
Member Management Board; CEO Americas, Mark W. Mullin, age 52
Senior Vice President, Greg Tucker
Member of the Executive Board and Management Board; Chief Financial Officer, Jan Nooitgedagt, age 61
CFO AEGON UK, Clare Bousfield
Member of the Management Board; Chief Executive Officer - Aegon UK, Adrian Grace
Member Supervisory Board, Irving W. Bailey II, age 72
Member of the Supervisory Board, Leo M. van Wijk, age 68
Member of the Supervisory Board, Antony Burgmans, age 67
Member of the Supervisory Board, Kornelis J. (Kees) Storm, age 72
Member of the Supervisory Board, Ben van der Veer, age 62
Member of the Supervisory Board, Dirk P. M. Verbeek, age 62
Member of the Supervisory Board, Shemaya Levy, age 68
Member of the Supervisory Board, Karla M.H. Peijs, age 70
Auditors: Ernst&YoungAccountants

LOCATIONS

HQ: AEGON N.V.
 Aegonplein 50, P.O. Box 85, The Hague 2501 CB
Phone: (31) 70 344 83 34
Web: www.aegon.com

Sales

	% of total
The	43
UK	31
The	19
Other	7
Total	**100**

PRODUCTS/OPERATIONS

Premiums

	% of total
Life insurance	87
General insurance	3

Selected Subsidiaries and Affiliates

The Americas
 AEGON USA LLC Cedar Rapids Iowa (US)
 Transamerica Advisors Life Insurance Company Little Rock Arkansas (US)
 Transamerica Advisors Life Insurance Company of New York New York New York (US)
 Monumental Life Insurance Company Cedar Rapids Iowa (US)
 Stonebridge Casualty Insurance Company Columbus Ohio (US)
 Stonebridge Life Insurance Company Rutland Vermont (US)
 Transamerica Financial Life Insurance Company Inc. Purchase New York (US)
 Transamerica Life Insurance Company Cedar Rapids Iowa (US)
 Western Reserve Life Assurance Co. of Ohio Columbus Ohio (US)
 Transamerica Life Canada Toronto Ontario (Canada)
The Netherlands
 AEGON Bank NV Utrecht
 AEGON Levensverzekering NV The Hague
 AEGON Schadeverzekering NV The Hague
 OPTAS Pensioenen NV Rotterdam
The UK
 Scottish Equitable plc Edinburgh
 Origen Financial Services Ltd. London

Positive Solutions (Financial Services) Ltd. Newcastle
Other regions
 AEGON Espa?a S.A. Madrid Spain (99.98%)
 AEGON Magyarorszag Altalanos Biztosito Zrt. Budapest Hungary
 AEGON Towarzystwo Ubezpiecze na ycie Spoka Akcyjna. Warsaw Poland
 AEGON Asset Management Company Mumbai India (75%)

Selected Joint Ventures

AEGON Sony Life Insurance Cy (50%) life insurance Tokyo
AEGON-CNOOC Life Insurance Company Ltd (50%) life insurance Shanghai
AMVEST Vastgoed BV (50%) property management and development; Utrecht Netherlands
CAN Vida y Pensiones Sociedad Anonima de Seguros (50%) life insurance and pension; Pamplona Spain
Caixa Terrassa Vida y Pensiones Sociedad Anonima de Seguros (50%) life and accident insurance and pension; Terrassa Spain

COMPETITORS

AIG
AXA
Allianz
Allstate
American General
Ameriprise
Aviva
Aviva Life Insurance India
BMO Financial Group
Canada Life
Delta Lloyd
Desjardins Financial Security
E-L Financial
Eureko
FMR
Fidelity & Guaranty Life
Franklin Templeton
Generali Deutschland
ING
Industrial Alliance Insurance and Financial Servic
Jackson National Life
John Hancock Financial Services
Legal & General Group
Lincoln Financial Group
Lloyds Banking Group
Manulife Financial
MassMutual
MetLife
Munich Re Group
Mutual of Omaha
Nationwide
New York Life
Old Mutual
OppenheimerFunds
Power Corporation of Canada
Primerica
Principal Financial
Prudential
Prudential plc
Putnam
RBC Insurance
Rabobank
SNS REAAL
Standard Life
Sun Life
Swiss Life
Symetra
T. Rowe Price
The Hartford
The Vanguard Group
Western & Southern Financial
Zurich Insurance Group

HISTORICAL FINANCIALS

Company Type: Public

Income Statement
FYE: December 31

	ASSETS ($ mil.)	NET INCOME ($ mil.)	INCOME AS % OF ASSETS	EMPLOYEES
12/13	487,013	1,346	0.3%	26,981
12/12	482,493	2,017	0.4%	26,850
12/11	446,987	1,124	0.3%	29,270
12/10	444,745	2,354	0.5%	27,474
12/09	430,203	293	0.1%	28,382
Annual Growth	3.1%	46.3%	—	(1.3%)

2013 Year-End Financials

Return on assets: 0.2%
Return on equity: 3.5%
Long-term debt ($ mil.): —
No. of shares (mil.): 2,090
Sales ($ mil.): 58,515

Dividends
Yield: 3.0%
Payout: 44.9%
Market value ($ mil.): 19,815

	STOCK PRICE ($) FY Close	P/E High/Low		PER SHARE ($) Earnings	Dividends	Book Value
12/13	9.48	50	29	0.50	0.29	16.52
12/12	6.44	17	10	0.88	0.23	20.11
12/11	4.02	—	—	(0.08)	0.00	17.69
12/10	6.13	17	10	1.11	0.00	18.36
12/09	6.41	—	—	(0.23)	0.00	15.93
Annual Growth	10.3%			—	—	0.9%

Aeon Co. Ltd. (Japan)

Japanese giant AEON CO. has enough retail ventures to last for eons. The holding company has about 180 subsidiaries and 25 affiliated companies. It runs the Aeon and Jusco chains of general merchandise stores and Japan's #1 supermarket chain with 1300 stores under the MaxValu and other banners as well as 3500-plus MINISTOP convenience stores. AEON also operates specialty chains including The Body Shop and Laura Ashley stores in Japan. It has a joint venture in Japan with Sports Authority and also operates HapYcom a leading drugstore chain in Japan. Other operations include shopping center development and financial services. Facing slow growth at home AEON is expanding in China and other Asian economies.

To that end AEON's China-based subsidiary and its MaxValu supermarket chain in 2012 formed a joint venture to operate supermarkets in China.

Sales across the vast AEON group inched up less than 1% in fiscal 2011 (ends February) vs. the previous year. Sales in Japan rose 4% while sales in the rest of Asia fell.

AEON has adopted a holding company structure in a bid to increase its responsiveness to changing (mostly negative) retail trends in Japan where it rings up about 95% of its total sales. A prolonged economic slump aging and shrinking population and weakness in the supermarket and department store sectors have the Japanese retailer looking abroad for future growth. Important Asian markets for AEON include China Hong Kong Malaysia South Korea and Thailand. The company beat a hasty retreat from North America with the sale of its majority stake in ladies apparel chain The Talbots in 2010 to better focus on its retail and financial service operations in Asia.

To grow in China AEON established a subsidiary in Shenzhen and greatly increased its investment there. At the end of fiscal 2011 (ends February)

AEON had about 80 stores in China including specialty and general merchandise stores and supermarkets. Also AEON operates two mall-style shopping centers located in Beijing and in Huizhou northeast of Shenzhen. The malls are populated by specialty shops including AEON-owned banners such as Jusco and The Body Shop.

To adapt to changing demographics in its home country AEON is focusing on the "senior market" by developing products especially for seniors and developing senior-friendly floor plans and stores as well as services. The company's My Basket chain of more than 220 small-size urban supermarkets was developed specifically to serve Japan's aging and increasingly urban population. In early 2012 the retailer spun off its My Basket division into a wholly-owned subsidiary with the aim of tripling its store count in the Tokyo metro area by the end of fiscal 2013.

Among Japanese retailers AEON is one of the most proactive in preparing to defend its business from foreign competitors including the world's #1 retailer Wal-Mart and Britain's Tesco. To compete it has cut prices and distribution costs adopted western sales techniques and has acquired smaller retailers. The company is upgrading its computer systems to rival those of US giant Wal-Mart. Also AEON beat out Wal-Mart to buy eight hypermarkets in Japan operated by France's Carrefour which abandoned the Japanese market. In mid-2012 AEON agreed to acquired a 50% stake in Tesco Japan a subsidiary of UK's largest retailer Tesco plc for just 1 yen. Tesco Japan operates about 120 small Tesco and Tsurukame supermarkets in and around Tokyo. AEON is expected to acquire the remainder of Tesco Japan in the future.

EXECUTIVES

President, Motoya Okada, age 63
Chairman, Naoki Hayashi
EVP, Noriyuki Murakami
VP, Atsunobu Agata
SEVP, Yoshiki Mori
VP; President AEON Mall, Soichi Okazaki
EVP, Hiroshi Yokoo
EVP, Jerry Black
EVP, Shouhei Murai
EVP, Masaaki Toyoshima
VP; CEO ASEAN, Nagahisa Oyama
VP; CEO China, Haruyoshi Tsuji
President and Director, Motoya Okada, age 61
VP and Director, Naoki Hayashi
Director, Masaharu Ikuta
Director, Hideki Kurashige
VP and Director, Yoshiki Mori
Director, Masami Ishizaka
Director, Takejiro Sueyoshi
Director, Keiichi Tadaki
President, Motoya Okada, age 63
Chairman, Naoki Hayashi
EVP, Noriyuki Murakami
VP, Atsunobu Agata
SEVP, Yoshiki Mori
VP; President AEON Mall, Soichi Okazaki
EVP, Hiroshi Yokoo
EVP, Jerry Black
EVP, Shouhei Murai
EVP, Masaaki Toyoshima
VP; CEO ASEAN, Nagahisa Oyama
VP; CEO China, Haruyoshi Tsuji
President and Director, Motoya Okada, age 61
VP and Director, Naoki Hayashi
Director, Masaharu Ikuta
Director, Hideki Kurashige
VP and Director, Yoshiki Mori
Director, Masami Ishizaka
Director, Takejiro Sueyoshi
Director, Keiichi Tadaki
Auditors: DeloitteToucheTohmatsu

LOCATIONS

HQ: Aeon Co. Ltd. (Japan)
1-5-1 Nakase, Mihama-ku, Chiba 261-8515
Phone: (81) 43 212 6042   **Fax:** (81) 43 212 6849
Web: www.aeon.info

Sales

	% of total
Japan	95
Asia & other	5
Total	100

PRODUCTS/OPERATIONS

Sales

	% of total
General merchandise & other	69
Service & other	19
Specialty store	9
Shopping center	3
Total	100

Selected Store Names

Abilities Jusco (CDs DVDs and books)
Asbee (shoe stores)
Blue Grass (apparel for teenage girls)
Claire's Nippon (women's clothing)
Cox (family casual clothing)
HapYcom (drugstores)
Home Wide Corp. (home centers)
JUSCO (apparel food and household item superstores)
JUS-Photo (film developing)
Laura Ashley Japan (clothing and home furnishings)
Maxvalu (supermarkets)
Mega Sports (Sports Authority stores)
MINISTOP (convenience stores)
MYCAL Corporation (supermarkets)
My Basket (small-scale supermarkets)
Nustep (family footwear stores)
Petcity (pets & pet supplies)
Sports Authority (sporting goods)

COMPETITORS

A.S. Watson	Ito-Yokado
A.S. Watson	METRO AG
Carrefour	METRO AG
Carrefour	Rakuten
Costco Wholesale	Rakuten
Costco Wholesale	Seiyu
Dairy Farm International	Seiyu
Dairy Farm International	Seven & i
	Seven & i
Fast Retailing	Takashimaya
Fast Retailing	Takashimaya
Heiwado	Tesco
Heiwado	Tesco
Isetan Mitsukoshi	The Gap
Isetan Mitsukoshi	The Gap
Ito-Yokado	Uny
	Uny

HISTORICAL FINANCIALS

Company Type: Public

Income Statement
FYE: February 28

	REVENUE ($ mil.)	NET INCOME ($ mil.)	NET PROFIT MARGIN	EMPLOYEES
02/14	62,775	447	0.7%	109,523
02/13	61,696	810	1.3%	91,646
02/12	64,736	830	1.3%	81,483
02/11	62,252	729	1.2%	74,465
02/10	56,874	350	0.6%	76,520
Annual Growth	2.5%	6.3%	—	9.4%

2014 Year-End Financials

Debt ratio: 0.2%
Return on equity: 4.2%
Cash ($ mil.): 6,419
Current ratio: 0.99
Long-term debt ($ mil.): 10,137

No. of shares (mil.): 845
Dividends
Yield: 2.0%
Payout: —
Market value ($ mil.): 10,269

STOCK PRICE ($)		P/E	PER SHARE ($)		
	FY Close	High/Low	Earnings	Dividends	Book Value
02/14	12.14	— —	0.49	0.25	19.55
02/13	11.27	— —	0.95	0.43	19.86
02/12	12.66	— —	0.95	0.26	20.72
02/11	12.54	— —	0.83	0.21	19.47
02/10	10.21	— —	0.44	0.00	16.83
Annual Growth	4.4%	— —	2.8%	—	3.8%

Ageas NV

LOCATIONS

HQ: Ageas NV
Archimedeslaan 6, Utrecht 3584 BA
Phone: (31) 30 25 25 304   **Fax:** (31) 30 25 25 310
Web: www.ageas.com

HISTORICAL FINANCIALS

Company Type: Public

Income Statement

FYE: December 31

	ASSETS ($ mil.)	NET INCOME ($ mil.)	INCOME AS % OF ASSETS	EMPLOYEES
12/13	131,802	784	0.6%	13,071
12/12	127,999	979	0.8%	13,335
12/11	117,189	(747)	—	12,557
12/10	132,721	298	0.2%	11,707
12/09	134,323	1,717	1.3%	10,374
Annual Growth	(0.5%)	(17.8%)	—	5.9%

2013 Year-End Financials

Return on assets: 0.5%
Return on equity: 6.1%
Long-term debt ($ mil.): —
No. of shares (mil.): 226
Sales ($ mil): 19,288

Dividends
  Yield: 5.9%
  Payout: 136.1%
Market value ($ mil.): 9,694

STOCK PRICE ($)		P/E	PER SHARE ($)		
	FY Close	High/Low	Earnings	Dividends	Book Value
12/13	42.81	33 22	3.43	2.55	51.83
12/12	30.25	17 1	4.13	0.00	56.35
12/11	1.52	— —	(2.97)	0.00	41.71
12/10	2.25	9 4	1.20	0.00	42.73
12/09	3.89	2 0	6.91	0.00	48.60
Annual Growth	82.1%	— —	(16.1%)	—	1.6%

Agricultural Bank of China

LOCATIONS

HQ: Agricultural Bank of China
No. 69, Jianguomen Nei Avenue, Dongcheng District, Beijing 100005
Phone: (86) 10 85109619   **Fax:** (86) 10 85108557
Web: www.abchina.com

HISTORICAL FINANCIALS

Company Type: Public

Income Statement

FYE: December 31

	ASSETS ($ mil.)	NET INCOME ($ mil.)	INCOME AS % OF ASSETS	EMPLOYEES
12/13	2,405,410	27,472	1.1%	513,750
12/12	2,124,449	23,273	1.1%	501,762
12/11	1,855,232	19,370	1.0%	490,121
12/10	1,568,269	14,393	0.9%	485,800
12/09	1,300,906	9,518	0.7%	480,098
Annual Growth	16.6%	30.3%	—	1.7%

2013 Year-End Financials

Return on assets: 1.2%
Return on equity: 20.8%
Long-term debt ($ mil.): —
No. of shares (mil.): —
Sales ($ mil): 117,193

Dividends
  Yield: 0.0%
  Payout: 16.6%
Market value ($ mil.): —

STOCK PRICE ($)		P/E	PER SHARE ($)		
	FY Close	High/Low	Earnings	Dividends	Book Value
12/13	12.33	1 1	0.08	0.01	0.43
12/12	12.60	1 1	0.07	0.01	0.37
12/11	10.63	1 0	0.06	0.00	0.32
Annual Growth	7.7%	— —	8.7%	35.7%	7.8%

Air France-KLM

Air France and KLM represent years of French and Dutch airline tradition but Air France-KLM represents a first: a holding company made up of two national airlines. Together Air France-KLM is the second-largest airline in Europe after Deutsche Lufthansa and one of the largest in the world. Through its operating units the company serves more than 250 destinations in about 125 countries with a fleet of some 590 aircraft. Air France and KLM operate independently from hubs in Paris and Amsterdam but have coordinated their operations both as sister companies and as members of the SkyTeam alliance which also includes Alitalia Delta Air Lines and Korean Air Lines.

Anticipating further uncertainty in the world economy Air France-KLM announced a three-year plan in January 2012 to strengthen profitability that comprises decreased capacity growth debt reduction to E4.5 billion ($5.9 billion) and cost cutting measures that include a freeze on pay increases at Air France and wage moderation at KLM as well as the continuation of a hiring freeze begun in September 2011. To boost demand for seats the company will decrease its fleet by cutting more than E1 billion ($1.3 billion) from its budget for expansion.

With the goal of increasing productivity by 20% Air France is consolidating its European operations into three units. One of them tasked with serving smaller cities will include Brit Air Regional and Airlinair. The second will be focused on leisure operations and will include discount line Transavia which annually carries more than 5 million passengers on low-cost medium-haul flights to several vacation spots. As a third division Air France's short-haul brand will add no-frills service.

Though the company is prepared for a challenging economic climate year-over-year revenue grew 13% in fiscal 2011. The company's cargo segment 12% of revenue was profitable that year while the more significant passenger segment 77% of revenue broke even. Maintenance representing 5% of revenue was reported to have contributed to operating income.

The company's fuel bill increased 21% between 2010 and 2011 a setback that was further exacerbated by the appreciation of the dollar relative to the euro. However the company has been hopeful that its hedging strategy will have a positive effect on its fuel expenses. Fuel hedging is when airlines lock in a pre-determined price for future jet fuel purchases.

In addition to rising fuel prices the company has been challenged by competition from low-cost carriers particularly from airlines based in the Middle East. To meet those challenges Air France-KLM has been working to expand its SkyTeam alliance to Brazil and Asia especially India. It has also been working to create joint ventures similar to one already in place with Delta Air Lines and Alitalia with Chinese airlines.

In addition to its SkyTeam alliance Air France-KLM operates a trans-Atlantic joint venture with Delta and Alitalia that offers more than 260 flights on about 145 aircraft. The company plans to use this partnership to develop more service for Asia Latin America and Africa. Another area of focus for the joint venture is Florida which since 2011 has been served by more than a dozen new flights.

And supplementing its low-cost Transavia operations Air France-KLM formed a partnership with British economy carrier Flybe to provide about 45 flights between France and the UK.

The company's Paris and Amsterdam hubs are connected by what Air France-KLM calls the Paris-Amsterdam Hubway which is served by more than 10 daily flights between the two nodes. Each of the two hubs has its own geographical emphasis and they complement each other to create a broader service area. For instance KLM is focused more on East Africa while Air France provides more service for West Africa. A third hub Lyon-Saint Exupery connects regional centers in France with the rest of Europe.

The French government owns about 16% of the combined company; employees own about 10%. Air France-KLM's board includes six directors representing employees.

EXECUTIVES

President and Chief Executive Offi cer of KLM, Peter F. Hartman, age 65
Chief Operating Officer, Alain Bassil, age 58
EVP Marketing Revenue Management and Network; Chief Commercial Officer Air France, Bruno Matheu, age 51
Executive Vice President French Sales Air France-KLM, Christian Boireau, age 64
Chairman and CEO, Jean-Cyril Spinetta, age 71, $990,375 total compensation
CFO Air France-KLM Group and Director Air France, Philippe Calavia, age 66
EVP International & the Netherlands; Managing Director KLM, Erik Varwijk, age 52
Executive Vice-President Engineering and Maintenance, Franck Terner
Executive Vice-President Corporate Secretary, Jacques Pape
Executive Vice-President Commercial Sales and Marketing, Patrick Alexandre
Executive Vice-President Commercial Marketing, Pieter Bootsma
Director, Pierre Richard, age 73
Auditors: KPMGS.A.

LOCATIONS

HQ: Air France-KLM
2, rue Robert Esnault-Pelterie, Paris 75007
Phone: (33) 1 41 56 78 00   **Fax:** (33) 1 41 56 56 00
Web: www.airfranceklm-finance.com

Sales

	% of total
Europe	30
Americas	27
Asia	20
Africa/Middle	16
Caribbean/Indian	7
Total	**100**

PRODUCTS/OPERATIONS

Sales

	% of total
Passenger	77
Cargo	12
Maintenance	5
Other	6
Total	**100**

COMPETITORS

Aer Lingus	Ryanair
Air Berlin	SAS
American Airlines	SNCF
Group	United Continental
Austrian Airlines	Virgin Atlantic
Brussels Airlines	Airways
IAG	easyJet
Lufthansa	

HISTORICAL FINANCIALS

Company Type: Public

Income Statement

FYE: December 31

	REVENUE ($ mil.)	NET INCOME ($ mil.)	NET PROFIT MARGIN	EMPLOYEES
12/13	35,148	(2,515)	—	95,961
12/12	33,806	(1,571)	—	100,744
12/11*	24,672	(571)	—	102,277
03/11	33,607	872	2.6%	102,012
03/10	28,316	(2,102)	—	104,721
Annual Growth	**5.6%**	—		**(2.2%)**

*Fiscal year change

2013 Year-End Financials

Debt ratio: 59.0%
Return on equity: (-50.9%)
Cash ($ mil.): 5,071
Current ratio: 0.73
Long-term debt ($ mil.): 11,834

No. of shares (mil.): 296
Dividends
Yield: —
Payout: —
Market value ($ mil.): 3,100

	STOCK PRICE ($) FY Close	P/E High/Low		Earnings	PER SHARE ($) Dividends	Book Value
12/13	10.47	—	—	(8.49)	0.00	10.43
12/12	9.67	—	—	(5.31)	0.00	21.92
12/11*	5.16	—	—	(1.94)	0.00	26.52
03/11	16.80	19	9	2.42	0.00	32.97
03/10	15.65	—	—	(7.15)	0.00	24.56
Annual Growth	**(9.6%)**	—	—	—	—	—
(19.3%)						

*Fiscal year change

Airbus Group NV

Airbus Group (formerly European Aeronautic Defence and Space Company EADS) succeeds in commercial and military aerospace and related services. Considered Europe's largest supplier it rivals Boeing in the competitive skies. The company's largest segment is Airbus; its commercial division ranks among the top two makers of large commercial aircraft (seats 100-plus passengers) while its military division manufactures transport tankers and mission aircraft. Other segments include Eurocopter civil/military helicopters (holds a 33% world market share); Astrium's satellites and launcher systems; and Cassidian's defense and security business that makes combat aircraft missile systems radar defense electronics and unmanned aerial systems (UAS).

In September 2012 Airbus Group announced it was considering a merger with UK-based BAE Systems a global provider of sensors flight controls and aircraft. However the proposed $45 billion merger —which would have created the largest global aerospace and defense player on the planet both in total sales and market value —was called off weeks later after it failed to pass European governmental and regulatory hurdles.

As a giant European industrial exporter Airbus Group operates between a euro/dollar exchange rate rock (pounded by fluctuating market demand) and a global economic hard place. Among its solutions Airbus Group adeptly hedges currency pitting the dollar against the euro as well as offsets the cost of US-built content (structures engines and avionics) —typically 35% to 45% of its jets —by paying in euros. Concurrently Airbus Group aims for more aggressive Airbus sales by ramping up production and tapping promising emerging markets such as Brazil China and India. Airbus Group also manages to correct the revenue ups and downs experienced in its Airbus commercial ventures with those of its other businesses thereby mitigating cyclical market downturns.

The company's strategy has reported some success; sales (in euros) increased almost 7% in 2010 over 2009 and its net income gained an altitude of Â553 million (about $733 million) from a tailspin loss of Â763 million (more than $1 billion) — with all segments posting a rise. Additionally Airbus Group's orders increased more than 80% during 2010. After suffering a stall-out due to the global economic recession industry passenger travel revved up in 2010 more than 8% while freight increased in excess of 20%; the world aircraft fleet is expected to double in 20 years.

Preparing to capitalize on demand Airbus Group hammered out its Vision 2020 goals under which it pursues the world's #1 position in air and space platforms systems and services. Services are targeted to achieve a 25% share of the business in less than 10 years. To this end Airbus Group has been scouting deals in the services sector. In August 2011 it agreed to purchase Vizada a global satellite-based mobile communication services provider from French private-equity Apax France. The whopping Â673 million ($969 million) deal bolsters Airbus Group's subsidiary Astrium a top contractor of space-technology wares in Europe and furthers opportunities beyond Europe with maritime aerospace as well as land media and other commercial customers. Hard on its heels Airbus Group took over more than 98% of Canada-based Vector Aerospace for C$625 million (about $341 million). Vector joins Eurocopter as a stand-alone business adding a multi-platform aviation repair and overhaul business.

Meanwhile Airbus Group is moving toward a better balance between its commercial and defense segments intending to source as much as 40% of its content outside Europe. The company continues to create global industrial partnerships beyond Europe's perimeters especially in Asia (including Korea and Vietnam) the Middle East (especially Saudi Arabia) and the Americas. Airbus Group formed a joint venture with India-based Larsen & Toubro (L&T; considered India's largest engineering/construction company by revenue) in early 2011. EADS will hold a minority share of 26% while L&T holds the rest. The India-based JV will manufacture electronics equipment for the defense and security industry.

In addition to growing its geographic markets Airbus Group is also boosting its technology offerings. It began test flights in 2010 for its hybrid X3 helicopter. In partnership with Northrop Grumman Airbus Group's Cassidian segment conducted maiden flights for its Euro Hawk UAS. As the demand for cyber security and cyber warfare (the protection of computer systems and data from interference) grows Cassidian seized the opportunity to acquire UK-based Regency IT in 2010 to boost its capabilities in this sector. Additionally the company developed an all-electric Cri-Cri aerobatic plane in partnership with Aero Composites Saintonge. It also backs the development of biofuels to power aircraft achieving the world's first flight of an aircraft running on pure biofuel made from algae.

Airbus Group comprises four business segments. Airbus the largest represents almost two-thirds of sales. Its A320 family includes single-aisle aircraft; staggering sales worldwide make this the top selling commercial jetliner. Airbus A330/A340 twin-aisle jets include tankers that cater to markets wanting a plane that can lift more passengers and cargo and go farther. The twin-deck A380 XWB seats ore than 500 passengers and is expected to rival Boeing's Dreamliner.

Cassidian defense & security division which leads Airbus Group's armed forces and civil security operations is the company's second largest unit after Airbus. Its activities range broadly from producing the Eurofighter (combat aircraft) to missile systems defense communication systems and electronics. Its MBDA subsidiary (owned along with BAE Systems and Finmeccanica) is recognized as the world's largest missile company. In 2012 Cassidian acquired 75% of Carl Zeiss Optronics from Carl Zeiss AG. Carl Zeiss Optronics makes optronic optic and precision-engineered products with a focus that includes border-surveillance systems vehicle sensors and submarine periscopes. In late 2011 Cassidian acquired the French company SurveyCopter maker of unmanned aerial vehicles (UAV). Partnered with Cassidian since 2003 SurveyCopter expertise is in robotic and autopilot vehicles for hostile environment utilization. The acquisition will boost Cassidian's plans to launch a new industrial line of tactical UAVs and VTOL UAVs for military and private export markets.

Eurocopter commands more than one-third of the civil and public/private helicopter fleet. Eurocopter operations experienced a market downturn in 2009 for smaller commercial helicopters; the company responded by implementing its SHAPE restructuring program which included cutting costs reducing inventories and boosting technology to help the civil helicopter business weather the crisis. Eurocopter and its Helibras affiliate began construction on a new Brazil-based rotary-wing center scheduled for a production launch in 2012. Helibras will manufacture assemble and service EC725 helicopters for use by the Brazilian armed forces.

The Astrium space group supplies satellites launchers and space services to Europe's institutional and military space programs. Astrium has driven the design and development of high-profile projects such as Galileo the European satellite navigation system and the International Space Station's Columbus space laboratory and unmanned Automated Transfer Vehicle (ATV).

Daimler AG owns about 22.5% of Airbus Group. SOGEPA (a French state holding company) and France-based Lagardere SCA together own approximately 22.5%. Spain owns 5%.

HISTORY

The growth of the European Aeronautic Defence and Space Company —EADS —is overshadowed by the long history of its components and by the obstacles overcome to cement the deal: The French and the Germans historically aren't overly fond of each other so how did it come to pass that Germany's DaimlerChrysler Aerospace AG (DASA) and France's Aerospatiale Matra put aside their differences to band together with Spain's Construcciones Aeronouticas SA (CASA)?

The US aerospace sector in the 1990s saw many companies consolidate scrambling to make their way in the post-Cold War era. Boeing the largest aerospace company in the world got that way by acquiring a number of operations including Rockwell International's aerospace and defense operations (1995) and most importantly McDonnell Douglas in a $16 billion deal (1997). In the same era defense giant Lockheed merged with Martin Marietta (1995) and acquired Loral (1997). These US companies had it relatively easy —they all paid taxes to Uncle Sam but acquisition deals in Europe were stymied by concerns over national security and privatization because much of Europe's defense industry was government-owned.

Spurred into action by their US rivals DASA and British Aerospace (now BAE SYSTEMS) — partners in Airbus —began merger talks in 1997. Fearful of being left out in the cold France's government-owned Aerospatiale —another Airbus partner —began talks to merge with Matra a French defense company controlled by Lagardere. Weeks after the Aerospatiale-Matra deal was announced in 1998 the chairman of DASA's parent company Jorgen Schrempp met with Lagardere's CEO Jean-Luc Lagardere and proposed a three-way deal. It never occurred and in 1999 the BAE SYSTEMS and DASA deal fell through as well.

Later that year Schrempp and Lagardere met again and laid the groundwork for a merger between DASA and Aerospatiale Matra. Less than three weeks after the Aerospatiale-Matra merger was completed Lagardere found itself pitching the DASA/Aerospatiale Matra merger idea to a stunned French government (which still held a 48% stake in Aerospatiale Matra). Marathon negotiations ensued. Late in the year Spain's Construcciones Aeronouticas SA (CASA) agreed to become part of EADS.

In 2000 EADS went public and Airbus announced that it would abandon its consortium structure in favor of incorporation. The next year EADS began pushing for a consolidation of army and naval equipment manufacturing among EU countries similar to the aerospace consolidation that created EADS. For Airbus the long-sought switch from consortium to corporation finally occurred in July 2001 when Airbus S.A.S. was incorporated.

EADS bought out BAE SYSTEMS' 25% share in their Astrium joint venture in 2003. In October 2004 EADS agreed to acquire US defense electronics maker Racal Instruments as part of its plan to increase defense sales in the US. Rumors surfaced the next month that EADS was discussing a merger deal with French defense company Thales.

In December 2004 EADS and BAE SYSTEMS gave Airbus the green-light to build the super-jumbo twin-deck A380 a plane that competes directly with Boeing's upcoming 787 Dreamliner. A few months later in early 2005 EADS was given preferred bidder status for the UK's Royal Air Force aerial refueling tanker contract. The program was valued at approximately $25 billion.

Claiming victory at last in 2006 Airbus beat Boeing on deliveries (434 vs. 398) but Boeing racked up a record 1004 plane orders while Airbus notched only 790. Moreover EADS' shares took a pounding in 2006 on Airbus' announcement that deliveries of the A380 would be delayed by six or seven months due to manufacturing glitches. A group of EADS shareholders cried foul and filed suit when it was revealed that co-CEO Noel Forgeard and five other EADS directors exercised stock options weeks before an internal investigation into the delays was launched. Two weeks later Forgeard fell on his sword and resigned. Louis Gallois former chairman of Societe Nationale des Chemins de Fer Francais (SNCF) France's state railway company was named to replace him. The same fate befell Airbus boss Gustav Humbert who was replaced by Christian Streiff a former executive at French building materials concern Compagnie de Saint-Gobain.

The production logjams at Airbus also prompted some of the company's airline customers to seek compensation in lieu of taking their business elsewhere (Boeing). EADS forecast that the production delays at Airbus would be a $2.5 billion drain on profits over four years. In the wake of the additional delivery delays Airbus CEO Christian Streiff was sent packing after only three months on the job. EADS Co-CEO Louis Gallois was named as his replacement.

In 2006 Daimler announced plans to gradually reduce its stake in EADS from about 30% to half that amount. Later that year EADS acquired Sofrelog of France (a maker of maritime monitoring systems). Russian bank Vneshtorgbank (100% controlled by the Russian government) also purchased a 5% stake in EADS for about $1.17 billion. The stake did not entitle Vneshtorgbank to a board seat but the move was expected to strengthen cooperation between EADS and the re-emerging Russian aerospace industry.

After long negotiations EADS shifted in 2007 to a new management structure aimed at cutting down on the damaging political bickering between its German and French management and shareholder factions. Politicians like German Chancellor Angela Merkel and French President Nicolas Sarkozy touted the compromise as a success. Others namely labor forces were more skeptical —calling the latest management shake-up just another round of musical chairs that leaves the power struggles between Paris and Munich largely unresolved.

EADS continued to expand into emerging markets especially regions including Asia the Middle East and North and South America. Deliveries included the company's (long-delayed) A380 model launched with Singapore Airlines in late 2008. Adding to Airbus's standing the all-new A350-XWB (made for the most part of lighter-weight composite materials) sliced into about two-thirds of jet demand in the Middle East. It also forged alliances and won contracts in Brazil China Japan and North America.

Airbus launched a cost-cutting initiative in 2008 that slashed some 10000 jobs. Dubbed Power8 the plan marched out cost-saving measures that aimed to reduce development cycles by two years and boost overall productivity by 20%. Central to Power8 was the spinoff of some of Airbus's man-ufacturing facilities to new partners. Partner funding of planes like the A350-XWB (spurred by assurances of subcontract work) plus plant sales risked an ongoing row between Airbus and unions as well as factory owners —stakeholders who feared plant divestitures and more job cuts. That year EADS captured its first big US military contract when Airbus North America was given the opportunity to make US Army light utility helicopters.

The company was awarded a contract to replace outdated KC-135 refueling tankers in conjunction with Northrop Grumman for the US Air Force —an upset protested by rival bidder Boeing. Soon after the Government Accountability Office (GAO) announced its findings of flaws in the bidding process. EADS and Northrop Grumman dropped out of the bidding in early 2010 with EADS vowing not to submit a proposal unless it was assured that it had a fair chance to win. By late summer — after US president Obama assured French president Nicolas Sarkozy that the Pentagon tanker bidding process would be fair —EADS announced that it would consider once again to enter into the bidding war. The contract to build the US tanker valued at approximately $35 billion went to Boeing in early 2011.

EXECUTIVES

Chief Strategy and Marketing Officer, Marwan Lahoud, age 48

Chairman North America, Ralph D. Crosby Jr., age 66

CEO and Director, Louis Gallois, age 70

CEO EADS Astrium, Francois Auque, age 58

President and CEO Airbus, Thomas (Tom) Enders, age 55

CEO North America, Sean C. O'Keefe, age 58

CTO, Jean J. Botti, age 57

President and CEO Eurocopter, Lutz Bertling, age 52

Chief Compliance Officer, Pedro Montoya, age 50

Head Corporate Communications, Pierre Bayle

Head Corporate Media Relations, Alexander Reinhardt

International Media Relations, Rod Stone

Head Airbus Military, Domingo Ure?a-Raso, age 56

Corporate Communications Spain, Jaime Perez-Guerra

SVP Latin America Strategy and Marketing, Anne Tauby

Head Investor Relations, Nathalie Errard

CFO, Harald Wilhelm

Chairman of EADS, Arnaud Lagard+?re

Chief Executive Officer - Cassidian; Member of the Executive Committee, Bernhard Bernhard Gerwert Gerwert

Head of Airbus Military; Chairman of EADS CASA; Member of the Executive Committee, Domingo Domingo Urena-Raso Urena-Raso

Chief Executive Officer - Airbus; Member of the Executive Committee, Fabrice Fabrice Bregier Bregier

Chief Operating Officer - Airbus; Member of the Executive Committee, Gunter Gunter Butschek Butschek

Chief Executive Officer - EADS North America ; Member of the Executive Committee, Sean Sean OKeefe OKeefe

Chief Human Resources Officer of EADS and Airbus; Member of the Executive Committee, Thierry Thierry Baril Baril

Non-Executive Chairman of the Board, Arnaud Arnaud Lagardere Lagardere

Director, Arnaud Lagardere, age 53

Director, Dominique D'Hinnin, age 53

Director, Lakshmi N. Mittal, age 63

Director, Michel Pebereau, age 71

CEO and Director, Louis Gallois, age 70

Director, Sir John Parker, age 70

Director, Juan Manuel Eguiagaray Ucelay, age 67
Director, Hermann-Josef Lamberti, age 57
Director, Rolf Bartke, age 67
Director, Wilfried Porth, age 55
Independent Director, Michel Michel Pebereau
Pebereau
Auditors: KPMGAccountantsN.V.

LOCATIONS

HQ: Airbus Group NV
Mendelweg 30, Leiden 2333 CS
Phone:
Web: www.airbus-group.com

Sales

	% of total
Europe	47
Asia/Pacific	25
Middle	13
North	8
Other	7
Total	**100**

PRODUCTS/OPERATIONS

Sales

	% of total
Airbus	64
Cassidian	13
Astrium	11
Eurocopter	10
Other	2
Total	**100**

Selected Operations and Interests

Business aircraft (JV with Dassault Aviation 46%)
Commercial airplanes (Airbus)
  A320 (single-aisle aircraft)
  A330/A340
  A350 XWB (extra wide body)
Helicopters (Eurocopter SAS)
  EC135 (light twin engine)
  EC175 (multi-role)
  EC225 (Super Puma)
  EC725
  E225/ED725 (twin engine)
  NH90 (medium-weight multi-role)
  Tiger (medium-weight
Satellites (Astrium)
  Ariane 5 (heavy-lift satellite)
  Automated Transfer Vehicle (ATV)
  Eurostar 3000 (telecommunications satellite)
Security combat and missile systems (Cassidian)
  Cassidian Professional Mobile Radio (PMR)
  Eurofighter (aka " Typhoon")combat aircraft (JV with
    Dassault Aviation 46%)
  MBDA missile systems (JV with BAE systems and
    Finmeccanica)
  Radars
  Unmanned Aerial Systems (UAS; partnered with
    Northrop Grumman
Other businesses
  ATR (50- to 74-seat turboprop aircraft; JV with Alenia
    Aeronautica)
  EADS North America
  EADS UK

COMPETITORS

AgustaWestland	GenCorp
BAE SYSTEMS	Lockheed Martin
BAE Systems Inc.	Northrop Grumman
Boeing	Orbital Sciences
Bombardier	RUAG Holding
E' Prime Aerospace	Raytheon
Embraer	Textron

HISTORICAL FINANCIALS

Company Type: Public

Income Statement

FYE: December 31

	REVENUE ($ mil.)	NET INCOME ($ mil.)	NET PROFIT MARGIN	EMPLOYEES
12/13	81,579	2,016	2.5%	144,061
12/12	74,443	1,618	2.2%	140,405
12/11	63,544	1,336	2.1%	133,115
12/10	61,233	740	1.2%	121,691
12/09	61,688	(1,099)	—	119,506
Annual Growth	**7.2%**	**—**	**—**	**4.8%**

2013 Year-End Financials

Debt ratio: 8.2%	No. of shares (mil.): 780
Return on equity: 13.6%	Dividends
Cash ($ mil.): 10,690	Yield: 0.0%
Current ratio: 0.97	Payout: 10.8%
Long-term debt ($ mil.): 5,446	Market value ($ mil.): 14,943

	STOCK PRICE ($) FY Close	P/E High/Low	PER SHARE ($) Earnings	Dividends	Book Value
12/13	19.15	69 17	2.53	0.27	19.43
12/12	39.71	48 34	1.98	0.18	16.69
12/11	31.40	53 32	1.64	0.12	14.05
12/10	23.45	74 43	0.91	0.00	14.59
12/09	19.90	— —	(1.35)	0.11	18.72
Annual Growth	**(1.0%)**	**— —**	**—**	**25.0%**	**0.9%**

Aisin Seiki Co., Ltd.

Nothing stops Aisin Seiki from making its line of brake systems and powertrain components for cars. Aisin's main automotive business offers automotive-related products such as transmissions brakes and engine and car navigation systems. Its Life and Energy business offers items for more comfortable living with products that range from heating and cooling systems to toilets with jet sprays; well-care items include electric wheelchairs and reclining beds. The company has around 160 consolidated subsidiaries and companies worldwide. Separate business segments include Aisin AW Group Aisin Seiki Group Advics Group and Aisin Takaoka Group.

Operations

Aisin Seiki operates through nearly 160 subsidiaries that are spread throughout four main segments. Aisin AW Group is its largest segment (39% of total sales in 2012) and makes automatic transmissions and car navigation systems. Aisin Seiki Group (36%) sells its automotive parts as well as its life and energy products. Advics Group is responsible for making brake components (15%) while Aisin Takaoka Group (5%) manufacturers the cart-iron parts for engines and brakes.

Financial Performance

Aisin Seiki saw its revenues increase by almost 3% from 2011 to 2012 but its net income decreased by roughly 20%. The slight jump in net sales was attributed to a 6% spike in sales from its Aisin AW Group segment. All other segments recorded a decrease in sales. The company's net income declined mainly due to a decrease in gross profits and an increase in selling general and administrative expenses.

Strategy

Aisin Seiki is looking to diversify its customer mix by expanding production overseas to achieve a 50% ratio by 2015. Its Advics segment in 2012

established production and sales companies in Haryana State North India and Karnataka State South India to produce brake parts that meet market demand and promote local procurement. To penetrate the most populous market in the word Advics also established a production company in Guangdong China that year.

Aisin Seiki continues to make automotive components and systems but it also focuses on increasing sales of main products such as transmissions car navigation systems and power sliding doors. The company's business segments have worked autonomously in the past; however Aisin Seiki is working to combine and link its individual businesses thus strengthening and maximizing the potential of the products and technologies that are cultivated by each company.

HISTORY

Aisin Seiki traces its roots to 1943 when Tokai Hikoki was founded to produce airplane engines for the Japanese war effort. After the war the company switched to manufacturing sewing machines and auto parts. Aisin Seiki took its present name in 1965 after Tokai Hikoki merged with Shinkawa Kogyo.

The company's operations were limited to Japan until 1969 when it signed a technical agreement with a German company regarding steering gears. International expansion continued as Aisin Seiki formed Aisin USA (to import aftermarket parts for imported cars) in 1970 Aisin Europe in 1971 and Aisin (UK) and Aisin (Australia) Pty. in 1972. Other operations sprung up in Mexico (1973) Brazil (1974) Singapore (1977) and Germany (1978). In the late 1980s the company worked at expanding the sale of body components such as sunroofs and seats.

Although Aisin Seiki USA had been formed to import parts for imported cars by 1990 the unit imported more parts for domestic cars than it did for imports. In 1996 Aisin Seiki set up Tangshan Aisin Gear a joint venture with Tangshan Gear Works to produce manual transmissions in China. The next year the company's Kariya plant which produced brake and clutch parts used in many Toyotas burned down. The disruption forced Toyota — which accounted for about 80% of the Kariya plant's sales —to temporarily shut down its 20 Japanese auto plants. Also in 1997 Aisin Seiki formed Aisin GM Allison Co. a joint venture with General Motors to produce automatic transmissions in Japan and the Pacific Rim region. Aisin GM Allison was dissolved in 2007 as GM geared up to sell Allison Transmission.

In 1998 the company formed Aisin Europe Manufacturing in the UK its first manufacturing facility in Europe. Also that year it began work on subsidiary Aisin A W Co. to supply engine parts for the Toyota facility in West Virginia. Despite increasing sales Aisin Seiki announced in 2000 that it would post a loss due to a charge for retirement benefits.

EXECUTIVES

Auditor, Minoru Hayashi, age 71
Chairman, Kanshiro Toyoda, age 72
Vice Chairman, Yasuhito Yamauchi, age 70
Senior Managing Director and Director, Toshikazu Nagura
Managing Officer, Kenji Tsujimura
President and Director, Fumio Fujimori
EVP and Director, Shunichi Nakamura
Senior Managing Director and Director, Takashi Morita
Senior Managing Director and Director, Naofumi Fujie
Managing Officer, Takashi Enomoto

Managing Officer, Masayasu Saito
Managing Officer, Kazumi Usami
Senior Managing Director and Director, Makoto Mitsuya
Senior Managing Director and Director, Toshiyuki Mizushima
Managing Officer, Yoshiaki Kato
Managing Officer, Hitoshi Okabe
Senior Managing Director and Director, Yutaka Miyamoto
Auditor, Toshihiro Gonda
Auditor, Shoichiro Toyoda
Auditor, Ryo Kobayashi
Managing Officer, Yoshihiko Kanada
Managing Officer, Seiichi Takahashi
Managing Officer, Shinsuke Yagi
Managing Officer, Masayasu Sugiura
Managing Officer, Susumu Takase
Managing Officer, Ryuji Nakamura
Managing Officer, Naoki Katsurayama
Managing Officer, Masanobu Ishikawa
Managing Officer, Naoshi Ichino
Managing Officer, Takahisa Hirose
Vice Chairman, Yasuhito Yamauchi, age 70
Director, Toshiyuki Ishikawa
EVP and Director, Norio Oku, age 67
Senior Managing Director and Director, Toshikazu Nagura
President and Director, Fumio Fujimori
Director, Takeshi Kawata
EVP and Director, Shunichi Nakamura
Director, Tsuneo Uchimoto
Senior Managing Director and Director, Shinichiro Yamamura
Senior Managing Director and Director, Takashi Morita
Senior Managing Director and Director, Naofumi Fujie
Senior Managing Director and Director, Shizuo Shimanuki
Senior Managing Director and Director, Makoto Mitsuya
Senior Managing Director and Director, Toshiyuki Mizushima
Director, Masahiro Suo
EVP and Director, Masuji Arai
Director, Tsutomu Ishikawa
Senior Managing Director and Director, Yutaka Miyamoto
Auditors: ChuoAoyamaAuditCorporation

LOCATIONS

HQ: Aisin Seiki Co., Ltd.
2-1 Asahi-machi, Kariya, Aichi 448-8650
Phone: (81) 566 24 8265
Web: www.aisin.co.jp

PRODUCTS/OPERATIONS

Sales

	% of total
Aisin AW	39
Aisin Seiki	36
Advics	15
Aisin Takaoka	5
Other	5
Total	**100**

Sales by Products

	% of total
Drivetrain	45
Brake &	20
Body-related	16
Engine-related	10
Information-related	5
Life energy &	4
Total	**100**

Selected Products

Automotive

Drivetrain products (transmission and clutch systems)
Brake and chassis products (drum brakes master cylinders air suspension systems)
Body products (door frames and locks sunroofs power seats)
Engine products (water pumps pistons exhaust manifolds)
Information and other products (navigation systems Intelligent Parking Assist)
Aftermarket products
Energy System
  GHP
  Cogeneration system
  Cryopump
  Cryocooler
  Peltier modules
Life and Amenity
  Bed furniture and fabric (ASLEEP)
  Housing equipment
  House remodeling service (Livelan)
  Home-use sewing machine
  Embroidery machine
  Facility consulting service (CONTRACT)
  Business consulting service (TSS)
  Audio equipment

COMPETITORS

APM Automotive	Magna International
BorgWarner	Meritor
Calsonic Kansei	Mitsubishi Electric
DENSO	Modine Manufacturing
DURA Automotive	Panasonic Corp
Dana Holding	Robert Bosch
Delphi Automotive	Sumitomo Electric
Systems	TRW Automotive
Eaton	Tenneco
Faurecia	Torotrak
Haldex	Valeo
Hitachi America	Visteon
Lear Corp	ZF Friedrichshafen

HISTORICAL FINANCIALS

Company Type: Public

Income Statement

FYE: March 31

	REVENUE ($ mil.)	NET INCOME ($ mil.)	NET PROFIT MARGIN	EMPLOYEES
03/14	27,341	872	3.2%	89,531
03/13	26,888	823	3.1%	83,378
03/12	28,089	676	2.4%	78,212
03/11	27,261	841	3.1%	74,671
03/10	21,994	177	0.8%	73,213
Annual Growth	**5.6%**	**48.9%**	**—**	**5.2%**

2014 Year-End Financials

Debt ratio: 0.1%
Return on equity: 9.7%
Cash ($ mil.): 2,542
Current ratio: 1.50
Long-term debt ($ mil.): 2,964
No. of shares (mil.): 282
Dividends
  Yield: 2.4%
  Payout: —
Market value ($ mil.): 10,217

	STOCK PRICE ($) FY Close	P/E High/Low	Earnings	PER SHARE ($) Dividends	Book Value
03/14	36.21	— —	3.09	0.87	45.62
03/13	30.60	— —	2.92	0.00	42.85
03/12	36.71	— —	2.40	0.00	41.94
03/11	24.25	— —	2.99	0.00	39.39
03/10	24.25	— —	0.63	0.00	33.19
Annual Growth	**10.5%**	**— —**	**48.7%**	**—**	**8.3%**

AKBANK

The vaults at Akbank have enough room for Turkish lira and the euro. The bank provides banking services in Turkey through more than 985 branches about 4100 ATMs and more than 340000 point-of-sale terminals. Internationally Akbank operates branches in Germany and in Malta; it also has subsidiary banks in the Netherlands and in Dubai. Akbank which is Turkey's second-largest publicly traded bank after Is Bankasi also provides private bank and international trade finance services. Subsidiaries provide non-banking financial capital-market and investment services. The Sabanci family and its companies control 55% of Akbank.

LOCATIONS

HQ: AKBANK
Sabanci Center 4, Istanbul, Levent 34330
Phone: (90) 212 385 55 55   **Fax:** (90) 212 269 73 83
Web: www.akbank.com

PRODUCTS/OPERATIONS

HISTORICAL FINANCIALS

Company Type: Public

Income Statement

FYE: December 31

	ASSETS ($ mil.)	NET INCOME ($ mil.)	INCOME AS % OF ASSETS	EMPLOYEES
12/13	90,778	1,509	1.7%	16,473
12/12	90,693	1,721	1.9%	16,515
12/11	73,777	1,370	1.9%	15,548
12/10	77,517	1,948	2.5%	15,550
12/09	68,356	1,825	2.7%	14,936
Annual Growth	**7.3%**	**(4.6%)**	**—**	**2.5%**

2013 Year-End Financials

Return on assets: 1.8%
Return on equity: 14.2%
Long-term debt ($ mil.): —
No. of shares (mil.): —
Sales ($ mil): 6,836
Dividends
  Yield: 1.8%
  Payout: 803.7%
Market value ($ mil.): —

	STOCK PRICE ($) FY Close	P/E High/Low	Earnings	PER SHARE ($) Dividends	Book Value
12/13	6.25	376153	0.00	0.12	0.03
12/12	10.05	408225	0.00	0.09	0.03
12/11	6.28	611265	0.00	0.05	0.02
12/10	11.25	845486	0.00	0.18	0.03
12/09	12.84	668134	0.01	0.11	0.03
Annual Growth	**(16.5%)**	**— —**	**(11.1%)**	**0.8%**	**(5.0%)**

Alecta pensionsforsakring, omsesidigt (Sweden)

LOCATIONS

HQ: Alecta pensionsforsakring, omsesidigt (Sweden)
Regeringsgatan 107, Stockholm SE-103 73
Phone: (46) 8 441 60 00   **Fax:** (46) 8 441 62 90
Web: www.alecta.se

HISTORICAL FINANCIALS

Company Type: Public

Income Statement

FYE: December 31

	ASSETS ($ mil.)	NET INCOME ($ mil.)	INCOME AS % OF ASSETS	EMPLOYEES
12/13	95,447	13,525	14.2%	424
12/12	85,837	10,446	12.2%	426
12/11	72,503	(13,343)	—	445
12/10	75,552	4,876	6.5%	459
12/09	66,096	12,758	19.3%	560
Annual Growth	9.6%	1.5%	—	(6.7%)

2013 Year-End Financials

Return on assets: 14.8%	Dividends
Return on equity: 41.8%	Yield: —
Long-term debt ($ mil.): —	Payout: —
No. of shares (mil.): —	Market value ($ mil.): —
Sales ($ mil): 12,521	

Alimentation-Couche Tard, Inc.

Alimentation Couche-Tard sells fuel for you and your car on both sides of the US-Canada border. It's the second-largest convenience store operator in North America and the leader in Canada with some 6000 outlets: Couche-Tard in Quebec; Mac's in central and western Canada; and more than 4600-plus Circle K shops in more than 40 US states and a dozen countries. (It bought the Circle K chain in the US from ConocoPhillips in 2003.) Most of its sales are rung up in the US. Alimentation Couche-Tard French for "food for those who go to bed late" sells gas at more than three-quarters of its stores. The fast-growing chain is known for expanding at home and abroad through splashy acquisitions.

Operations

In Couche-Tard's global operations Statoil Couche-Tard Mac's and Circle K are its key brands. Fuel makes up a majority of sales in every geographic region but merchandise helps even out fuel volatility and delivers generally better profit margins.

Geographic Reach

Couche-Tard operates and licenses a total of about 13100 global locations with more than 6000 convenience stores in North America. The company divides the US market into nine geographic business units with the largest retail presence in the Great Lakes region and Arizona. Its European operations include about 2260 stores concentrated in Scandinavia and the Baltics with a growing presence in Poland. In Asia it licenses the Circle K brand to operators of more than 4600 stores in a dozen mostly Asian countries.

Financial Performance

Sales at Couche-Tard's convenience stores in fiscal 2014 (ends April) climbed to $38 billion an increase of 7% over the prior year due to higher sales driven by recovering economic conditions and new store acquisitions. Net earnings rose about 42% from $573 million to $812 million due to higher revenue and some non-recurring costs in 2013 that made 2014's books look good by comparison. Without the one-time events net earnings still would have grown 23% due to contributions from acquisitions higher fuel margins in Europe and Canada and growth in same-store merchandise sales. Cash from operations rose 23% from $1161 to $1429 based on the higher net earnings one-off events in 2013 and a better exchange rate for foreign currency.

Strategy

Acquisitions are a big part of Couche-Tard's growth strategy. Its purchase of The Pantry Inc. is the latest is the latest in a long chain of acquisitions that includes the 2012 purchase of Statoil its largest ever and the purchase of Circle K nearly a decade ago. The Circle K acquisition established the Canadian firm as a major player in the US market while Statoil moved it into Europe. The fragmented US convenience store market and trend by major oil companies to cast off their retail operations has afforded Couche-Tard (and rival 7-Eleven) ample opportunity to acquire small independently-operated chains and occasionally a big fish. With about 70% of its sales (even more in the US) coming from gas Couche-Tard is vulnerable to fluctuations in motor fuel prices. To protect itself from such volatility the retailer is focused on developing its in-store merchandise sales (especially fresh foods) which return higher margins and are less volatile.

Mergers and Acquisitions

Overall in fiscal 2014 the company acquired about 166 stores and built only 25. The big news came at the end of the calendar year with Couche-Tard said it would pay $860 million for The Pantry Inc. with more than 1500 Kangaroo Express stores in 13 US states; locations are concentrated in the southeast part of the country.

The $2.6-billion purchase of Statoil Fuel & Retail ASA with about 2300 locations in northern Europe mainly in Scandinavia closed in June 2012. Statoil is a Norway-based road transport fuel retailer and operates a network of retail stores across Scandinavia Poland the Baltic States and Russia. Statoil owns and operates a dozen key terminals as well as 38 depots in eight countries and a fleet of about 400 road tankers.

EXECUTIVES

VP Operations Western Canada, Kim J. Trowbridge
President CEO and Director, Alain Bouchard, $915,855 total compensation
Chairman, Richard Fortin, age 64, $413,033 total compensation
EVP and Director, Real Plourde, $454,900 total compensation
VP Administration and Director, Jacques D'Amours
COO, Brian P. Hannasch, $286,000 total compensation
VP Development, Butch Seber
VP Operations Eastern Canada, Michel Bernard
VP Operations Central Canada, Jean-Luc Meunier
VP Administration U.S., Robert G. Campau
VP Operations Arizona Region, Geoffrey C. (Geoff) Haxel
Senior Director Franchise Operations USA Mexico and Asia, Rick Hamlin
VP Operations U.S. Midwest Region, Darrell Davis
VP Operations U.S. Great Lakes Region, Paul Rodriguez
VP Operations Florida and Gulf Coast Region, Mike Struble
VP Operations U.S. West Coast Region, Tim Tourek
VP Operations Gulf, Jason Broussard
VP Operations U.S. Southeast Region, Matt McCure
VP and CFO, Raymond Pare
VP Operations U.S. Southwest Region, Lou Valdes
VP Purchasing and Supply Chain, Alain Brisebois
Vice-President Administration, Jacques DAmours
Vice-President and Chief financial Officer, Raymond Pare
Vice-President Operations Quebec East and Atlantic Canada, Pierre Peters
Vice-President Operations quebec West Canada, Michel Doucet
Vice President, Dennis Tewell
Vice-President Operations u.s, Bruce Landini
Vice-President oPERATIONS u.s, Bill Bartolomeo
President European Operations, Jacob Schram
President Fuel Americas & Operations, Jean Bernier
Director, Jean Turmel
President CEO and Director, Alain Bouchard
EVP and Director, Real Plourde
VP Administration and Director, Jacques D'Amours
Director, Roger Desrosiers
Director, Jean A. Elie
Director, Roger Longpre
Director, Jean-Pierre Sauriol
Director, Melanie Kau
Auditors: RaymondChabotGrantThornton

LOCATIONS

HQ: Alimentation-Couche Tard, Inc.
4204 Boulevard Industriel, Laval, Quebec H7L 0E3
Phone: 450 662-3272   **Fax:** 450 662-6633
Web: www.couche-tard.com

Sales

	$ mil.	% of total
US	18,081	79
Canada	4,915	21
Total	**22,997**	**100**

201Sales

	$ mil.	% of total
Gasoline	13,673	76
Merchandise & services	4,408	24
Total	**18,081**	**100**

2012 Canada Sales

	$ mil.	% of total
Gasoline	2,724	55
Merchandise & services	2,190	45
Total	**4,915**	**100**

2012 Stores

	No.
US	
Great Lakes	693
Arizona	639
West	543
Midwest	501
Florida	399
Southwest	385
Gulf	354
Southeast	331
Canada	
Quebec	551
Quebec East &	352
Central	747
West	308
Total	**5,803**

PRODUCTS/OPERATIONS

Sales

	$ mil.	% of total
Gasoline	16,398	71
Merchandise & services	6,598	29
Total	**22,997**	**100**

Selected Proprietary Brands

Beverages
  Froster (frozen)
  Sloche (flavored)
  Sunshine Joe (coffee)
Sandwiches
  Handfull
  La Maisonnee

COMPETITORS

7-Eleven	Publix
Casey' s General Stores	QuikTrip
Chevron	Racetrac Petroleum
Cumberland Farms	Royal Dutch Shell
Exxon Mobil	Sheetz
Gate Petroleum	Shell Oil
Kroger	Sobeys
Kum & Go	The Pantry
Loblaw	TravelCenters of
Marathon Oil	America
Pilot Flying J	

HISTORICAL FINANCIALS

Company Type: Public

Income Statement
FYE: April 27

	REVENUE ($ mil.)	NET INCOME ($ mil.)	NET PROFIT MARGIN	EMPLOYEES
04/14	37,956	811	2.1%	78,000
04/13	35,543	572	1.6%	78,500
04/12	22,997	457	2.0%	60,000
04/11	18,550	369	2.0%	53,000
04/10	16,439	302	1.8%	53,000
Annual Growth	**23.3%**	**27.9%**	**—**	**10.1%**

2014 Year-End Financials

Debt ratio: 24.7%
Return on equity: 22.6%
Cash ($ mil.): 511
Current ratio: 1.21
Long-term debt ($ mil.): 2,586

No. of shares (mil.): 565
Dividends
  Yield: 0.0%
  Payout: 7.9%
Market value ($ mil.): 15,475

	STOCK PRICE ($) FY Close	P/E High/Low		PER SHARE ($) Earnings	Dividends	Book Value
04/14	27.35	59	19	1.43	0.11	7.00
04/13	58.57	57	37	1.02	0.10	5.72
04/12	42.55	50	31	0.83	0.09	4.05
04/11	26.60	41	26	0.65	0.06	3.59
04/10	18.33	37	20	0.53	0.05	2.93
Annual Growth	**10.5%**	**—**	**—**	**28.0%**	**25.6%**	**24.3%**

Allianz Elementar Lebensversicherungs-AG (Austria)

LOCATIONS

HQ: Allianz Elementar Lebensversicherungs-AG
  (Austria)
  Hietzinger Kai 101-105, Vienna A-1130
Phone: (43) 1 87807 0   **Fax:** (43) 1 87807 77000
Web: www.allianz.at

HISTORICAL FINANCIALS

Company Type: Public

Income Statement
FYE: December 31

	ASSETS ($ mil.)	NET INCOME ($ mil.)	INCOME AS % OF ASSETS	EMPLOYEES
12/13	979,588	8,254	0.8%	147,627
12/12	915,315	6,894	0.8%	144,094
12/04	3,970	0	—	51
12/03	3,511	0	—	48
Annual Growth	**75.6%**	**—**	**—**	**123.3%**

2013 Year-End Financials

Return on assets: 0.8%
Return on equity: 11.9%
Long-term debt ($ mil.): —
No. of shares (mil.): 453
Sales ($ mil): 139,623

Dividends
  Yield: —
  Payout: —
Market value ($ mil.): —

	STOCK PRICE ($) FY Close	P/E High/Low	Earnings	PER SHARE ($) Dividends	Book Value
12/13	0.00	— —	17.97	0.00	151.97
Annual Growth	**—**	**— —**	**—**	**—**	**—**

Allianz SE

One of the world's biggest insurers Allianz SE offers a range of insurance products and services —including life health and property/casualty coverage for individuals and businesses —through more than 1000 subsidiaries ventures and affiliates operating all over the globe (though its key markets are France Germany Italy and the US). The company serves some 78 million customers. In addition to selling insurance Allianz provides retail and institutional asset management services through Allianz Global Investors private equity investment through Allianz Capital Partners and banking services through Allianz Bank.

Geographic Reach

Allianz operates in more than 70 countries with most of its operations in Europe. It also operates in the Asia/Pacific region and the Americas.

Operations

On the insurance front Allianz gets about half of its revenues from its life and health division which operates and serves under the Allianz brand and serves individual and group accounts. The property/casualty operations account for 45% of revenues. Allianz offers specialty property/casualty and marine insurance under the Allianz Global Corporate and Specialty brand. The unit has offices in more than a dozen locations and is one of the world's largest providers of marine insurance.

Though it has restructured to focus on core insurance and asset management offerings Allianz still has banking operations in Germany and other global regions.

Sales and Marketing

Allianz markets its products through independent agents and brokers dedicated agents bank representatives and direct marketing channels. It has about 150000 sales force associates 1200 distribution partners and about 2000 agencies in its worldwide network.

Financials

Allianz reported a 3% increase in revenues to some E106 billion in 2012 due to higher earnings in the property/casualty and asset management segments slightly offset by a decline in the life and health segment. Net income nearly doubled to E5.5 billion due to growth in operational performance and improved investment returns.

Strategy

Allianz is focused on achieving sustainable growth in its property/casualty life and health and asset management operations. It also seeks to achieve operational synergies among its businesses through shared technology investments capital allocations and best practice sharing. The company's investment strategy is conservative with the goal of providing stable returns.

While the US and Europe are Allianz's largest markets the company is pursuing growth in emerging markets as well. It has established significant operations in select Asian countries and it is expanding its presence in Central and Eastern Europe and the Asia/Pacific region. Targeted markets include China India and Russia.

Ownership

Allianz is part of a web of interlocking German corporate ownership. It holds a stake in reinsurance giant Munich Re which in turn has a small stake in Allianz. Munich Re is also the company's principal external reinsurer though Allianz itself reinsures a significant amount of its insurance companies' risk. Allianz also serves as a reinsurer for third parties.

HISTORY

Carl Thieme founded Allianz in Germany in 1890. That year the company took part in the creation of the Calamity Association of Accident Insurance Companies a consortium of German Austrian Swiss and Russian firms to insure international commerce.

By 1898 Thieme had established offices in the UK Switzerland and the Netherlands. His successor Paul von der Nahmer expanded Allianz into the Balkans France Italy Scandinavia and the US. After a hiatus during WWI Allianz returned to foreign markets.

In WWII Allianz insured Auschwitz Dachau and other death camps. Company documents show Allianz wasn't worried about risk at the SS troop-guarded camps. After the German defeat the victors seized Allianz's foreign holdings except for a stake in Spain's Plus Ultra. In the 1950s Allianz repurchased confiscated holdings in Italian and Austrian companies.

Allianz saturated the German market and began a full-scale international drive in the late 1950s and 1960s. It became Europe's largest insurer through a series of acquisitions beginning in 1973. Allianz formed Los Angeles-based Allianz Insurance in 1977.

In 1981 Allianz launched a takeover (which turned hostile) of the UK's Eagle Star insurance company. After a 1983 bidding joust with Britain's

B.A.T Industries (now part of Zurich Financial Services) Allianz withdrew.

The firm consoled itself by shopping. In 1984 it won control of Riunione Adriatica di Sicurta (Ras) Italy's second-largest insurance company. Two years later the firm bought Cornhill (now Allianz Insurance plc) on its third try. As the Iron Curtain crumbled Allianz in 1989 acquired 49% of Hungaria Biztosito. Its "drang nach Osten" continued the next year after national reunification when it gained control of Deutsche Versicherungs AG East Germany's insurance monopoly. Allianz that year became the first German insurer licensed in Japan; it also bought the US's Fireman's Fund Insurance.

Natural disasters led to large claims and set the company back in 1992 the first time in 20 years it lost money from its German operations. Allianz restructured operations that year; profits surged in 1993 mostly from international business.

Allianz expanded in Mexico in 1995 forming a life and health insurance joint venture with Grupo Financiero BanCrecer (now owned by Grupo Financiero Banorte). The company set up an asset management arm in Hong Kong in 1996 with an eye to further Asian expansion getting a license in China the next year. In 1997 after Holocaust survivors sued Allianz and other insurers for failing to pay on life policies after WWII Allianz agreed to participate in a repayment fund.

In 1998 Allianz bought control of Assurances Generales de France; it was the white knight that prevented Assicurazioni Generali from taking the company. In 1999 Allianz said it would restructure some of its insurance operations including spinning off its marine and aviation lines to better compete in the multinational market. That year US subsidiary Allianz Life bought Life USA Holding. In 2000 Allianz bought 70% of PIMCO Advisors Holdings to strengthen its asset management operations. That year the company continued its push into Asia buying a 12% stake in Hana Bank of South Korea and planning to boost its ownership of Malaysia British Assurance Life. Also in 2000 Allianz acquired Dutch insurer Zwolsche Algemeene.

Allianz remained acquisitive in 2001 buying US investment manager Nicholas-Applegate and taking a majority stake in ROSNO one of Russia's largest insurers. Also that year it bought a nearly 96% stake in German banking giant Dresdner and acquired the remainder the following year.

Allianz paid out claims of some $1.3 billion relating to the terrorist attacks on the World Trade Center. The company set up a terrorism insurance unit offering coverage primarily for companies within the European Union.

After a year of record losses (primarily due to investment losses and Dresdner's struggles) former CEO Henning Schulte-Noelle stepped down and assumed the chair post in 2003. Allianz's stock lost more than 75% of its value in 2002.

Getting out of the red Allianz rebounded some in 2003 thanks to the upturn in the stock markets and the streamlining of its operations (the company reduced its employee total by some 8000 people). Allianz also raised some $5 billion to improve its capital base.

The company sold most of its Canadian property/casualty operations to ING Canada in 2004.

The company transitioned to a Societas Europaea a joint stock company that is ruled by European Union standards in 2006 and changed its name from Allianz AG to Allianz SE.

Also in 2006 Allianz consolidated its worldwide specialty property/casualty and marine insurance operations (including the Allianz Global Risks and Allianz Marine & Aviation units) under the Allianz Global Corporate & Specialty brand.

In 2008 Allianz invested $2.5 billion in ailing US insurer Hartford Financial Services giving Allianz

an option to own about 20% of Hartford. (Hartford repurchased the debt in 2012.)

To focus on its insurance operations the company sold its Dresdner Bank subsidiary one of Germany's largest banks offering both retail and investment banking to Commerzbank in a $14.4 billion cash and stock transaction in early 2009.

EXECUTIVES

Chairman of the Management Board; Chief Executive Officer, Michael Diekmann, age 60, $1,623,840 total compensation
Member Management Board Insurance German Speaking Countries and Allianz Banking and Director Labor Relations, Gerhard Rupprecht, age 66, $1,030,330 total compensation
Vice Chairman, Gerhard Cromme, age 71
Member Management Board Global Insurance Lines & Anglo Markets, Clement B. Booth, age 60, $927,640 total compensation
Chairman, Henning Schulte-Noelle, age 72
Member Management Board Asset Management Worldwide, Jay Ralph, age 54
Member Management Board Insurance USA, Gary C. Bhojwani
Member Management Board Insurance German-Speaking Countries, Werner Zedelius, age 57, $1,030,330 total compensation
Member Management Board Insurance Europe I + II Africa South America P/C Sustainability Program, Enrico T. Cucchiani, age 64, $927,640 total compensation
Chairman Australia, John S. Curtis, age 64
Vice Chairman, Rolf Zimmermann, age 62
Chief Risk Officer, Thomas C. Wilson, age 53
Member of the Management Board; Chief Operating Officer, Christof Mascher, age 54, $279,698 total compensation
CIO Allianz SE and Allianz Managed Operations and Services (AMOS), Ralf Schneider, age 51
Member of the Management Board; Insurance Western & Southern Europe, Dieter Wemmer
Member of the Management Board; Insurance Iberia & Latin America ; Legal & Compliance; M&A, Helga Jung
Member of the Management Board with responsibility for Insurance Growth Markets, Manuel Bauer
Member of the Management Board; Chief Financial Officer, Maximilian Zimmerer
Member of the Management Board; Controlling; Reporting; Risk; IR, Oliver Baete
Board Member, Igor Landau, age 70
Board Member, Peter D. Sutherland, age 68
Vice Chairman, Gerhard Cromme, age 71
Board Member, Jorg Reinbrecht, age 57
Board Member, Godfrey R. (Geoff) Hayward, age 55
Vice Chairman, Rolf Zimmermann, age 62
Board Member, Peter Kossubek, age 61
Member of the Supervisory Board; Employee Representative, Franz Heiss
Member of the Supervisory Board, Renate Koecher
Auditors: KPMGDeutscheTreuhand-GesellschaftAG

LOCATIONS

HQ: Allianz SE
Koeniginstrasse 28, Munich D-80802
Phone: (49) 89 38 00 0   **Fax:** (49) 89 38 00 3425
Web: www.allianz.com

PRODUCTS/OPERATIONS

Sales

	% of total
Life & health insurance	49
Asset management	6
Corporate & other	1
Total	**100**

Selected Operations and Brands
Allianz
Allianz Global Corporate and Specialty
Allianz Global Investors
Allianz Worldwide Care
Euler Hermes
PIMCO

COMPETITORS

AEGON	Munich Re Group
AXA	New York Life
Allstate	Nippon Life Insurance
Aviva	Old Mutual
Berkshire Hathaway	Prudential
CNP Assurances	Prudential plc
Citigroup	RSA Insurance
ERGO	State Farm
Generali	Swiss Re
Generali Deutschland	Talanx
Groupama	The Hartford
ING	Victoria Versicherung
Legal & General Group	Zurich Insurance Group
MetLife	ageas SA/NV

HISTORICAL FINANCIALS
Company Type: Public

Income Statement
FYE: December 31

	ASSETS ($ mil.)	NET INCOME ($ mil.)	INCOME AS % OF ASSETS	EMPLOYEES
12/13	979,588	8,254	0.8%	147,627
12/12	915,544	6,813	0.7%	144,094
12/11	829,713	3,291	0.4%	141,938
12/10	836,409	6,762	0.8%	151,338
12/09	841,357	6,190	0.7%	153,203
Annual Growth	3.9%	7.5%	—	(0.9%)

2013 Year-End Financials

Return on assets: 0.8%   Dividends
Return on equity: 11.5%   Yield: 2.4%
Long-term debt ($ mil.): —   Payout: —
No. of shares (mil.): 453   Market value ($ mil.): 8,226
Sales ($ mil): 138,377

	STOCK PRICE ($) FY Close	P/E High/Low		PER SHARE ($) Earnings	Dividends	Book Value
12/13	18.13	3	2	17.97	0.44	151.97
12/12	13.82	2	1	14.95	0.43	155.76
12/11	9.47	5	2	7.09	0.00	128.40
12/10	11.87	2	1	14.88	0.38	131.87
12/09	12.45	3	1	13.69	1.02	128.24
Annual Growth	9.9%	—	—	7.0%	(19.2%)	4.3%

Allied Irish Banks Plc

Allied Irish Banks (AIB) one of Ireland's largest banks and private employers is looking beyond the Emerald Isle for its proverbial pot o' gold. The company offers retail and commercial accounts and loans life insurance financing leasing pension and trust services through a network of 200 branches 74 EBS Limited offices 10 business centers and 755 ATMs. The company's capital markets division offers commercial treasury services corporate finance and investment banking services. In the US AIB specializes in financial services for the not-for-profit sector.

Operations

Over the years AIB has reorganized into a more simplified structure in which its divisions were integrated and its AIB and First Trust operations were more closely aligned. To attract additional customers the bank also introduced mobile banking services to its offerings.

HISTORY

Allied Irish Banks was formed in 1966 by the "trinity" of Provincial Bank (founded 1825) The Royal Bank (founded 1836) and Munster and Leinster (founded 1885 but with origins back to the late 1600s). Both AIB and its then-larger rival Bank of Ireland had to consolidate in order to compete with North American banks entering Ireland. From its start AIB sought to expand overseas and by 1968 it had an alliance with Canada's Toronto-Dominion Bank.

In the 1970s AIB expanded its branch network to England and Scotland. The 1980s saw AIB boost its presence in the US market (it had already debuted AIB branches) with the acquisition of First Maryland Bancorp.

The Irish Parliament's Finance Act of 1986 instituted a withholding tax known as the Deposit Interest Retention Tax (DIRT) for Irish residents. Consequently (with a wink and a nod) AIB and other banks let customers create bogus non-resident accounts to avoid paying DIRT. An investigation indicated that at one point AIB's branch in Tralee had 14700 non-resident accounts on its rolls –more than half the local population. After tax authorities began probing many of the accounts in question were reclassified as "resident" and customers had to pay the taxes on them. In 1991 AIB was reprimanded but neither the bank nor its customers have paid the remaining $100 million tax bill.

Tom Mulcahy who integrated AIB's treasury investment and international banking activities became chief executive in 1994. Mulcahy a respected leader envisioned AIB as an international Ireland-based bank.

In 1995 AIB bought UK-based investment fund manager John Govett from London Pacific Group (now Berkeley Technology Limited). Mulcahy moved AIB the same year into Eastern Europe with a stake in Poland-based Wielkopolski Bank Kredytowy (or WBK).

AIB was busy in 1999. It gained a toehold in Asia by entering a cross-marketing agreement with Singapore's Keppet TatLee bank a survivor of the region's financial crisis. Liberalized Singapore banking laws allowed AIB the right to buy one-quarter of the bank by 2001. AIB also bought an 80% stake of Bank Zachodni in Poland in 1999.

That year AIB merged First Maryland Bancorp and its other US holdings into the renamed Allfirst Financial a sizable mid-Atlantic states bank.

To consolidate its power in Eastern Europe in 2001 AIB merged its Polish banks (Wielkopolski Bank Kredytowy and Bank Zachodni) into Bank Zachodni WBK. That year Mulcahy retired but was appointed by the Irish government to take over as chairman of troubled airline Aer Lingus.

AIB lost nearly $700 million from 1996 to 2002 apparently from bogus foreign exchange transactions made by rogue trader John Rusnak who pleaded guilty to bank fraud.

In 2003 AIB sold troubled Maryland-based bank Allfirst Financial to M&T Bank Corporation. As part of the deal AIB assumed ownership of more than 20% of M&T becoming the company's largest shareholder. Under AIB's direction Allfirst had grown into a major regional player with about 250 branches in Maryland Pennsylvania Virginia and Washington DC.

In the midst of the global financial crisis the Irish government injected Â2 billion ($2.8 billion) into AIB in exchange for a 25% share in voting rights in 2008. Ireland also provided capital for

Bank of Ireland and Irish Bank Resolution Corporation to help stabilize the plunging Irish financial system. AIB also sought capital from the private sector.

EXECUTIVES

CFO AIB Group, Bernard Byrne
Head Corporate Relations and Communications, Catherine Burke
Managing Director AIB Poland, Gerry Byrne, age 58
Managing Director AIB Bank, Robbie Henneberry, age 50
Manager Group Investor Relations, Rose O'Donovan
Managing Director Great Britan adn Northern Ireland, Nick Treble, age 54
Group Press Officer Corporate Relations and Communications, Ronan Sheridan
Deputy Chairman, Michael Somers, age 72
Chief Executive Officer, David Duffy
Senior Vice President with AIB Corporate Banking North America, Denise Magyer
Director, Robert G. (Bob) Wilmers, age 78
Director, Kieran Crowley, age 62
Director, Jennifer Winter, age 53
Director, Sean O' Driscoll, age 56
Director, Declan Collier, age 59
Director, Dick Spring, age 64
Director, Jim O'Hara, age 63
Director, Catherine Woods, age 52
Deputy Chairman, Michael Somers, age 71
Auditors: KPMG

LOCATIONS

HQ: Allied Irish Banks Plc
  Bankcentre, Ballsbridge, Dublin 4
Phone: (353) 1 6600311   **Fax:** 212 515-6710
Web: www.aibgroup.com

COMPETITORS

Bank Millennium	HSBC
Bank of America	Irish Bank Resolution
Bank of Ireland	Lloyds Banking Group
Barclays	Royal Bank of Scotland
Citigroup	Ulster Bank

HISTORICAL FINANCIALS
Company Type: Public

Income Statement
FYE: December 31

	ASSETS ($ mil.)	NET INCOME ($ mil.)	INCOME AS % OF ASSETS	EMPLOYEES
12/13	162,088	(2,198)	—	12,648
12/12	161,482	(4,806)	—	14,708
12/11	176,751	(2,990)	—	16,716
12/10	194,361	(13,694)	—	23,208
12/09	251,111	(3,476)	—	23,275
Annual Growth	(10.4%)	—	—	(14.1%)

2013 Year-End Financials
Return on assets: (-1.3%)
Return on equity: (-14.7%)
Long-term debt ($ mil.): —
No. of shares (mil.): —
Sales ($ mil): 5,133

Dividends
  Yield: —
  Payout: —
  Market value ($ mil.): —

	STOCK PRICE ($) FY Close	P/E High/Low		Earnings	PER SHARE ($) Dividends	Book Value
12/13	1.53	—	—	(0.00)	0.00	0.03
12/12	0.60	—	—	(0.01)	0.00	0.03
12/11	0.68	—	—	(0.01)	0.00	0.04
12/10	0.88	—	—	(7.55)	0.00	0.40
12/09	3.51	—	—	(3.10)	0.00	17.48
Annual Growth (18.7%) (80.0%)		—		—	—	—

Alpha Bank AE

Alpha Bank is the second-largest bank in Greece (after National Bank of Greece). It provides business and personal banking services through more than 650 branches in Greece and hundreds more in Cyprus Albania Bulgaria Romania Serbia and Ukraine as well as in New York London and Jersey in the UK Channel Islands. In addition to loans deposit accounts and credit cards the Alpha Bank group also offers retail banking asset management investment banking private banking insurance brokerage leasing and factoring. Founded in 1879 Alpha Bank has been buffeted by economic turmoil in Greece. Still it acquired Emporiki Bank S.A. from Credit Agricole in mid-2013.

LOCATIONS

HQ: Alpha Bank AE
  40 Stadiou Street, Athens GR-102 52
Phone: (30) 210 326 0000   **Fax:** (30) 210 326 5438
Web: www.alpha.gr

PRODUCTS/OPERATIONS

HISTORICAL FINANCIALS
Company Type: Public

Income Statement
FYE: December 31

	ASSETS ($ mil.)	NET INCOME ($ mil.)	INCOME AS % OF ASSETS	EMPLOYEES
12/13	101,461	4,023	4.0%	16,934
12/12	76,917	(1,431)	—	13,650
12/11	76,505	(4,928)	—	14,337
12/10	89,401	114	0.1%	14,896
12/09	100,257	503	0.5%	15,163
Annual Growth	0.3%	68.1%	—	2.8%

2013 Year-End Financials
Return on assets: 4.4%
Return on equity: 64.1%
Long-term debt ($ mil.): —
No. of shares (mil.): —
Sales ($ mil): 10,381

Dividends
  Yield: 195.3%
  Payout: 152.7%
  Market value ($ mil.): —

	STOCK PRICE ($) FY Close	P/E High/Low		Earnings	PER SHARE ($) Dividends	Book Value
12/13	0.26	3	1	0.61	0.51	1.05
12/12	0.61	—	—	(2.68)	0.00	1.88
12/11	0.23	—	—	(9.40)	0.00	4.73
12/10	1.32	419	105	0.03	0.26	14.46
12/09	4.35	18	3	0.92	0.26	20.88
Annual Growth (50.6%) (52.6%)		—	—	(10.0%)	17.9%	

Alstom

Alstom is all about speed and power. Alstom's Power segment is a world leader providing boilers turbines air quality systems generators and controls for coal gas hydroelectric and nuclear power generation. Turnkey power plant and wind farm setups are available as well as emission reduction systems. Alstom claims it has equipped 25% of the world's operating power plants. Its Transport business is a world-leading manufacturer of all things railroad-related from commuter trains and locomotives to signaling equipment to rail infrastructure. It also makes high-speed trains and provides complete turnkey railroad setup. Alstom's Grid segment mainly addresses the growing smart-grid market in the utility sector.

After seeing its revenue decrease in 2009 and 2010 Alstom enjoyed a 6% increase in its fiscal 2011 sales. Orders were also up in 2011 by 28%. Net income however was down 62% in 2011 over 2010.

Alstom operates in about 100 countries but the company has been reshifting its focus from the developed world to newly developing markets. Orders from clients in emerging countries grew from 35% of the global total in fiscal 2010 to 60% in fiscal 2011. Orders in the Brazil-Russia-India-China sector increased from 10% of the global total in fiscal 2010 to 25% in 2011. Alstom is building its BRIC operations by striking partnerships and joint-venture deals with several companies in those areas. Among them is a 50-50 venture with Shanghai Electric to make boilers. Meanwhile Alstom is correspondingly downsizing operations in Europe and North America where the company did experience some growth in 2011 but not as strong as that in emerging markets.

Alstom is also concentrating its R&D efforts on such promising technologies as turbine upgrades carbon capture and storage programs and tidal thermal and solar power in its Power segment; train control systems and VHS (very-high speed) in the Transport segment; and super grids as well as smart grids in its Grid operations. Alstom is anticipating strong growth in its new equipment service railway and transmission businesses.

Alstom had shed some business to focus on its Power and Transport segments but it has now added another major category to its operations Grid a business it has developed with the acquisition of Utility Integration Solutions and a partnership with Microsoft in the US and the acquisition of Psymetrix a smart grid services company in the UK.

Buoyed by strong orders in renewable energy technology Alstom has entered into an agreement with EDF Energies Nouvelles to develop offshore wind power. It also made an investment in Bright-Source Energy a solar company.

HISTORY

GEC Alsthom was incorporated in the Netherlands in 1989 as a 50/50 joint venture between France's Compagnie Generale d'Electricite (or GCE later Alcatel and now Alcatel-Lucent) and The General Electric Company plc (GEC later Marconi and now telent) of the UK. Merging the power and transportation subsidiary of one to the other's power-systems unit suited a consolidating energy sector.

GEC Alsthom already had railway plants in Belgium France Spain and the UK and in 1994 the company expanded into Germany by purchasing 51% of Preussag AG's Linke-Hofmann-Busch GmbH. The following year GEC Alsthom expanded

into Brazil when it bought 60% of CMW Equipamentos SA (railway signaling systems) from Odebrecht Group a Brazil-based holding company.

The formation of joint ventures and acquisitions continued throughout the 1990s. GEC Alsthom forged a joint venture with Romania-based turbogenerator maker General Turbo (1995); bought Elmac South America's largest maker of industrial electric motors from Siemens (1996); and purchased Wessex Traincare a UK rolling-stock repair firm (1998). Also in 1998 GEC Alsthom bought Cegelec (electrical contracting and industrial process control) from Alcatel. Later that year GEC Alsthom was taken public and it name changed to Alstom.

Alstom joined with ASEA Brown Boveri to form ABB Alstom Power (power generation) and sold its heavy-duty gas turbine business to General Electric (GE) in 1999. The company continued divesting non-core industrial units in 2000 by selling its diesel-engines unit to MAN. Later that year ALSTOM announced that its subsidiary Les Chantiers de l'Atlantique signed a letter of intent to build the largest cruise liner ever the Queen Mary 2 for Cunard Line.

The company bought ABB's share in ABB Alstom Power for around $1.2 billion in 2000 renaming it Alstom Power. Alstom also announced plans to open a new marine manufacturing facility in the Philadelphia Naval Yard to support US Navy and commercial vessel requirements for electrical equipment. The same year Alstom bought a 51% stake in rail equipment company Fiat Ferroviaria.

In 2001 Alcatel and Marconi sold their stakes in the company. To close out the year Alstom sold its contracting operations (electrical installation) to a management buyout group (financed by CDC Equity Capital and Charterhouse Development Capital) for about $660 million. The company launched "Restore Value" a debt reduction plan in early 2002 to be facilitated by the sale of additional shares in the company. Alstom announced the following year a plan to raise E3 billion by the end of 2004 through the sale of non-core businesses.

Alstom Power Conversion was sold in late 2005 to Barclays Private Equity in a management buyout. The business changed its name to Converteam.

In early 2006 Alstom reached an agreement with the Aker Yards unit (now STX Europe a subsidiary of South Korea-based STX Business Group) of Norwegian conglomerate Aker under which Aker Yards acquired 75% of a new company taking in the Alstom Marine business including the Chantiers de l'Atlantique shipbuilding subsidiary while Alstom retained a 25% stake in the business. Depending on financial performance Alstom agreed to sell the 25% stake to Aker Yards in 2010 for up to E125 million. Until that time Alstom had committed to investing an estimated E350 million in the marine business while four large banks extended E550 million in construction financing to the new entity. In March 2010 Alstom sold its remaining 25% stake in the Marine business.

By 2006 Alstom was largely out of crisis mode and on more secure financial footing. It was profitable and growing sales and had whittled its debt down to E1.2 billion (around $1.5 billion). Alstom was ready to resume acquisitions and to expand operations. The company signed a framework agreement with the Bouygues group that saw the construction firm acquire around one-quarter of Alstom's equity (most of it shares bought from the French government). Bouygues group became Alstom's reference shareholder and agreed to purchase a 50% stake in Alstom's hydro power business Alstom Hydro Holding. That 50/50 joint venture was formally established in late 2006.

In late 2006 Alstom sold its train renovation business in the UK to Railcare Ltd. The unit of Alstom Transport had annual sales of E60 million (about Å40 million or $79 million) and employed 430 people at two facilities. While the business was similar in nature to railroad rolling stock manufacturing Alstom no longer made rolling stock in the UK and the business wasn't as profitable as the parent company would have liked.

By early 2007 Alstom had reduced its net debt to E64 million (nearly $89 million) through positive cash flow and the release of E700 million in cash collateral related to the company's bonds. In closing out the 2007 fiscal year the company announced that it was debt-free.

As part of its goal to increase its manufacturing capabilities the company made a number of acquisitions in 2007. Alstom picked up Ecotecnia a Spanish manufacturer of wind power generation equipment and solar panels for E350 million ($471 million). It also acquired the assets of Power Systems Mfg. (PSM) a subsidiary of Calpine for $242 million in cash. PSM provides parts and upgrades for gas turbines. Alstom made PSM part of its Power Service Sector. Qingdao Sizhou Electric Power Equipment a Chinese manufacturer of boiler auxiliaries also joined the pack. Sizhou specializes in coal-fired power generation. The firm has been renamed Alstom Sizhou.

Prior to the final disposal of the last of its Marine activities in November 2008 the company divested itself of its former Transmission & Distribution sector to shift its main focus on two sectors Transport and Power.

Alstom entered into a strategic partnership with Russian rail supplier Transmashholding (TMH) in 2008 creating a joint venture to make passenger rail cars in the Tver region of Russia in response to a bid from Russian Railways.

In 2009 Alstom purchased 51% of China-based manufacturer Wuhan Boiler to gain entry into the Chinese boiler sector. China is considered the largest market for coal-fired power plant boilers and Alstom has built a new energy-efficient boiler production facility in Hubei province. The facility which will serve as an exporting base and research and development center for Asia/Pacific began production in late 2009.

Also in 2009 French state-controlled nuclear reactor manufacturer AREVA selected Alstom and Schneider Electric as top bidders for its power transmission and distribution business. Bidding losers included non-French companies Toshiba and General Electric. The French consortium Alstom-Schneider has agreed not to lay off workers and will hire AREVA employees wherever possible. French president Nicolas Sarkozy who represents the government's 93% stake in AREVA supported the decision. The deal was completed in June 2010.

In 2009 Bouygues exchanged its 50% stake in Alstom Hydro for 4.4 million Alstom shares giving Bouygues a 32% stake in Alstom.

It also teamed up with India-based Bharat Forge a metal forming company to manufacture steam turbine islands in India in 2010.

Alstom further expanded in Russia in late 2010 when it signed strategic agreements with major Russian energy companies FSK Inter RAO Mosenergo (a subsidiary of Gazprom) Rosatom Rostechnologii and RusHydro to jointly provide hydropower generation thermal power generation nuclear power generation and electricity transmission.

The company made job cuts in Switzerland from its power transmission division in 2011 amid increased competition from Asia.

EXECUTIVES

Chairman and CEO, Patrick Kron, age 60, $408,288 total compensation
Deputy CEO Power Sector, Philippe Joubert, age 60
SVP Corporate Communications, Patrick Bessy
President Power Service Sector, Walter Graenicher
Chief Financial Officer, Nicolas Tissot, age 48
EVP; President Transport, Henri Poupart-Lafarge, age 45
Director Corporate Information, Philippe Kasse
EVP; President Grid Sector, Gregoire Poux-Guillaume
Managing Director North America Alstom Transport, Guillaume Mehlman
General Counsel, Keith Carr
President of Alstom Thermal Power and Executive Vice-President of Alstom, Philippe Cochet
EVP; President Renewable Power, Jerome Pecresse
SVP Human Resources, Bruno Guillemet, age 57
Senior Vice President for Alstom ?s steam business, Andreas Lusch
Director, Klaus J. Mangold, age 69
Director, Candace K. Beinecke
Director, Jean-Martin Folz, age 67
Director, Olivier Bouygues, age 62
Director, James W. (Jim) Leng, age 67
Director, Georges Chodron de Courcel, age 64
Director, Jean-Paul Bechat, age 69
Director, Pascal Colombani, age 67
Director, Gerard Hauser, age 72
Director, Alan M. Thomson, age 67
Director, Philippe Marien, age 58
Auditors: Ernst&Young

LOCATIONS

HQ: Alstom
3, avenue Andre Malraux, Levallois-Perret 92300
Phone: (33) 1 41 49 20 00
Web: www.alstom.com

Sales by Origin

	% of total
Europe	70
North	15
Asia/Pacific	9
South & Central	4
Middle East &	2
Total	**100**

Sales by Destination

	% of total
Europe	52
North	16
Middle East &	13
Asia/Pacific	13
South & Central	6
Total	**100**

PRODUCTS/OPERATIONS

Sales

	% of total
Power	70
Transport	30
Total	**100**

Selected Products and Services

Power
  Air quality control systems
  Boilers
  Coal-fired (steam) power plants
  Control systems
  Energy recovery
  Environmental systems
  Gas-fired power plants
  Generators and turbogenerators
  Heat exchange
  Hydroelectric power plants
  Maintenance and service
  Nuclear power plants
  Product retrofitting

  Turbines
  Turnkey power plants
  Wind farms
Transport
  Communication systems
  Freight trains
  Information solutions
  Infrastructure maintenance
  Passenger trains
  Power supply
  Rolling stock services
  Station utilities
  Subsystems
  Track laying
  Trains (high speed very high speed regional commuter locomotives metros trams tram-trains)
  Turnkey systems
  Workshops and depots

COMPETITORS

ABB
Amsted Industries
Babcock & Wilcox
Bharat Heavy Electricals
Cummins
GE Energy
Global Power Equipment Services
Greenbrier Rail Services
Hitachi
Hyundai Heavy Industries
McDermott

Mitsui Engineering & Shipbuilding
Nippon Sharyo
Nordex
RailWorks
Siemens AG
Siemens Energy
Siemens Mobility
Toshiba
Trinity Industries
Vestas Wind Systems
Vossloh
Westinghouse Air Brake

HISTORICAL FINANCIALS

Company Type: Public

Income Statement

FYE: March 31

	REVENUE ($ mil.)	NET INCOME ($ mil.)	NET PROFIT MARGIN	EMPLOYEES
03/14	27,955	766	2.7%	86,125
03/13	25,994	1,028	4.0%	86,252
03/12	26,602	976	3.7%	93,998
03/11	29,767	657	2.2%	94,648
03/10	26,497	1,641	6.2%	77,740
Annual Growth	**1.3%**	**(17.3%)**	**—**	**2.6%**

2014 Year-End Financials

Debt ratio: 25.9%
Return on equity: 11.0%
Cash ($ mil.): 3,199
Current ratio: 0.93
Long-term debt ($ mil.): 6,078

No. of shares (mil.): 308
Dividends
  Yield: 4.0%
  Payout: 7.8%
Market value ($ mil.): 824

	STOCK PRICE ($) FY Close	P/E High/Low		Earnings	PER SHARE ($) Dividends	Book Value
03/14	2.67	4	3	2.46	0.11	22.54
03/13	4.03	3	2	3.39	0.16	20.85
03/12	3.84	5	2	3.28	0.17	19.61
03/11	5.90	8	5	2.22	0.15	19.62
03/10	6.50	4	3	5.64	0.29	18.77
Annual Growth	**(19.9%)**	**—**		**—(18.8%)**	**(22.1%)**	**4.7%**

Aluminum Corp of China Ltd.

LOCATIONS

HQ: Aluminum Corp of China Ltd.
No. 62, North Xizhimen Street, Haidian District, Beijing 100082
Phone: (86) 10 8229 8560   **Fax:** (86) 10 8229 8158
Web: www.chalco.com.cn

HISTORICAL FINANCIALS

Company Type: Public

Income Statement

FYE: December 31

	REVENUE ($ mil.)	NET INCOME ($ mil.)	NET PROFIT MARGIN	EMPLOYEES
12/13	27,987	161	0.6%	90,207
12/12	23,977	(1,320)	—	97,990
12/11	23,175	37	0.2%	101,259
12/10	18,355	118	0.6%	108,256
12/09	10,291	(679)	—	107,831
Annual Growth	**28.4%**	**—**	**—**	**(4.4%)**

2013 Year-End Financials

Debt ratio: 9.9%
Return on equity: 2.2%
Cash ($ mil.): 1,880
Current ratio: 0.65
Long-term debt ($ mil.): 7,647

No. of shares (mil.): —
Dividends
  Yield: —
  Payout: —
Market value ($ mil.): —

	STOCK PRICE ($) FY Close	P/E High/Low		Earnings	PER SHARE ($) Dividends	Book Value
12/13	8.70	5	3	0.01	0.00	0.54
12/12	11.91	—	—	(0.10)	0.00	0.52
12/11	10.80	31	13	0.00	0.00	0.61
12/10	22.79	13	7	0.01	0.00	0.58
12/09	27.25	—	—	(0.05)	0.15	0.55
Annual Growth	**(24.8%)**	**—**	**—**	**—**	**—**	**(0.2%)**

America Movil, S.A.B. de C.V.

America Movil offers wireless phone service from the Rio Grande to Tierra del Fuego. The company is Latin America's top mobile carrier with more than 225 million subscribers in 18 countries. In Mexico the company enjoys a 70% market share with nearly 65 million subscribers to its Telcel brand which has 260+ retail stores. Its second largest market is Brazil which serves more than 50 million subscribers through Claro. America Movil also provides fixed-line service in Central America and the Caribbean with more than 5 million lines. TracFone Wireless is America Movil's US presence. Majority owner Carlos Slim Helu combined America Movil with his fixed-line businesses Telmex in 2010 as part of a broader restructuring effort.

The $21 billion dollar deal was structured so that America Movil acquired the minority stakes in Telmex that Helu did not already own through a stock transaction with their controlling holding company Carso Global Telecom. The plan combined Helu's wired and wireless telecom interests in hopes of holding ground against increasing competition from smaller telephone companies and cable television operators like Televisa which offer bundled phone TV and Internet services. The combined wired operations of Telmex and the wireless business of America Movil provides phone TV and Internet services. As one company the merger was slated to save about $700 million in administrative costs following the delisting of Telint and Carso Global.

In the US the company operates through subsidiary TracFone which is a leading provider of prepaid wireless services. TracFone products feature a pay-as-you-go prepaid mobile phone with no annual contracts or activation fees. Its services account for more than 5% of America Movil's total revenue. The company also owns more than 71% of Telvista a call center company with locations in the US and Mexico.

America Movil's operating revenues rose more than 8% in 2010 over 2009.

In 2012 Tracfone acquired Simple Mobile which is one of the largest mobile virtual network operators for T-Mobile. The previous year America Movil paid $75 million for a license to provide Costa Rica with satellite television wireless phone and Internet service under its Claro brand. Currently the only telecom provider in the country is the government-controlled Instituto Costarricsense de Electricidad (Grupo ICE). Telefonica also plans to provide telecom services in Costa Rica.

America Movil is acquiring 100% control of Telmex by buying the 40+% of the company it doesn't already own. Telmex will be delisted from the exchanges it trades on when the acquisition is complete and it now operates as a brand that provides fixed-line service in Mexico and Columbia.

The family of Mexican billionaire Carlos Slim Helu (also the world's wealthiest person) controls more than 46% of America Movil; AT&T owns nearly one quarter of the company and operates as a competitor in some of its smaller markets.

HISTORY

The company was formed in 2000 as a result of a spinoff from Telmex which was at the time Mexico's largest local and long-distance phone service provider. In late 2006 America Movil acquired majority owner America Telecom in a move to streamline the structure of the company and to free up assets for share buybacks or dividends.

The company expanded its presence in the Caribbean region in 2007 with the acquisition of Puerto Rico Telephone from Verizon Communications and a handful of other shareholders for nearly $2 billion. The next year it bought Jamaican wireless service provider Oceanic Digital Jamaica and became licenced to provide wireless services in Panama.

Also in 2008 the company rebranded its operations in Argentina Paraguay and Uruguay to its Claro brand which America Movil now uses for all of its operations in Central America and the Caribbean. That year it bought Estesa Holding a cable TV and data services provider in Nicaragua for $48 million. The acquisition of Estesa boosted America Movil's cable television and broadband offerings and gave the company greater access to the Nicaraguan market.

EXECUTIVES

CEO and Director, Daniel Hajj Aboumrad, age 46
Director, Jaime Chico Pardo, age 63
Director, Rayford (Ray) Wilkins Jr., age 61
Director, Alejandro Soberon Kuri, age 52
Director, David Ibarra Mu?oz, age 83

Director, Carlos Bremer Gutierrez, age 52
Director, Pablo Roberto Gonzalez Guajardo, age 45
Director, Ernesto Vega Velasco, age 76
Director, Mike Viola, age 59
Auditors: ManceraS.C.

LOCATIONS

HQ: America Movil, S.A.B. de C.V.
Lago Zurich 245, Plaza Carso/Edificio Telcel, Piso 16,
Colonia Granada Ampliacion, Mexico, D.F. 11529
Phone: (52) 55 2581 4449   **Fax:** (52) 55 2581 4422
Web: www.americamovil.com

Sales

	% of total
Mexico	25
Mexico	18
Brazil	25
Columbia &	8
Southern	7
US	5
Andean	4
Caribbean	4
Central	2
Eliminations (3.3.)	
Total	**100**

PRODUCTS/OPERATIONS

Sales

	% of total
Mobile voice	44
Fixed voice	23
Mobile data voice	13
Fixed data	11
Paid	2
Other	7
Total	**100**

Selected Operations

America Movil Peru (8.3 million subscribers)
AM Wireless Uruguay (800000 subscribers)
AMX Argentina (17 million subscribers)
AMX Paraguay (500000 subscribers)
Claro Chile (3.6 million subscribers)
Claro Panama (100000 subscribers)
Codetel (Dominican Republic 4.8 million subscribers)
Comcel (Colombia 27.7 million subscribers)
Conecel (Ecuador 9.4 million subscribers)
CTE (El Salvador 800000 subscribers)
ENITEL (Nicaragua 2.2 million subscribers)
Oceanic (Jamaica 400000 subscribers)
Sercom Honduras (1.4 million subscribers)
TELPRI (Puerto Rico 1.6 million subscribers)
TracFone (US 14.4 million subscribers)
Telgua (Guatemala 1.2 million subscribers)

COMPETITORS

AT&T	Sprint Nextel
Alfa SA	TIM Participac?es
Axtel	Tele Norte Leste
Brasil Telecom	Telecom Argentina
Cable & Wireless	Telefonica
Communications	Telefonica Brasil
Iusacell	Telefonica de
Millicom	Argentina
NII Holdings	Telemig Celular
Portugal Telecom	Vivo Participac?es

HISTORICAL FINANCIALS

Company Type: Public

Income Statement

FYE: December 31

	REVENUE ($ mil.)	NET INCOME ($ mil.)	NET PROFIT MARGIN	EMPLOYEES
12/13	60,030	5,698	9.5%	173,174
12/12	59,648	7,037	11.8%	158,719
12/11	47,627	5,931	12.5%	158,694
12/10	49,032	7,350	15.0%	150,079
12/09	42,871	7,080	16.5%	53,661
Annual Growth	**8.8%**	**(5.3%)**	**—**	**34.0%**

2013 Year-End Financials

Debt ratio: 3.6%	No. of shares (mil.): —
Return on equity: 29.6%	Dividends
Cash ($ mil.): 3,678	Yield: 1.4%
Current ratio: 0.86	Payout: 2.6%
Long-term debt ($ mil.): 35,469	Market value ($ mil.): —

	STOCK PRICE ($) FY Close	P/E High/Low		PER SHARE ($) Earnings	Dividends	Book Value
12/13	23.37	0	0	0.08	0.34	0.22
12/12	23.14	0	0	0.09	0.30	0.31
12/11	22.60	0	0	0.08	0.00	0.27
12/10	57.34	0	0	0.09	0.25	0.31
12/09	46.98	0	0	0.09	0.61	(0.00)
Annual Growth	**(16.0%)**	**—**	**—**	**(3.8%)**	**(13.4%)**	**—**

AMP Ltd.

AMP is on top —down under. The company is one of Australia's largest insurance and investment management groups. Through its AMP Financial Services (AFS) division more than 2000 representatives sell the company's financial offerings which include life home vehicle travel and business insurance as well as retirement products financial planning and advice superannuation products (professionally managed retirement investment funds) and banking. AMP Capital Investors provides investment management to AFS and to other individual and institutional investors. AMP Limited also provides retail financial services under the Hillcross and Arrive Wealth Management brands.

HISTORY

AMP was conceived in Sydney in 1848 by W. S. Walsh (a clergyman) Thomas Mort (a businessman) and Thomas Holt (a wool trader) who convened with two others to discuss forming a mutual life insurance company in Australia. (Many of the UK's and US's largest mutuals were also founded about this time.) The next year Australian Mutual Provident Society was born; it opened for business with a staff of two: secretary William Perry and a small boy. In its first year the company sold only 42 policies. Luckily no one died in the first three years of operations and the company was able to build up some reserves. The company grew slowly over the next decade appointing just two agents — in Auckland New Zealand and Hobart Australia.

Sales took off with the 1860 appointment of the company's first full-time agent Benjamin Short who had the novel idea of actively recruiting customers and actually "selling" policies. The company opened an office in New Zealand in 1871; it opened a branch in the UK in 1908.

In the next few decades the company helped build the Australian economy through investment of its reserves. It funded industry and infrastructure including farming communities as part of the South Australian Land Development Scheme. The company grew free of foreign competition protected by regulations severely restricting the activities of foreign companies in the banking and financial industries in Australia. In 1958 the company formed AMP Fire and General Insurance (changed to AMP General in 1990).

In 1988 AMP moved abroad with the acquisition of London Life Assurance. The following year it made history with its acquisition of funds management group Pearl Assurance then the largest takeover of a British financial firm by a foreign company.

The company founded AMP Asset Management in 1991 to manage its overseas assets. In 1995 the company expanded its international presence through a joint venture with the financial services arm of UK-based Virgin Group. The company also began offering mortgage and banking products in Australia through a new unit Priority One.

After a careful inquiry in 1996 AMP's board recommended demutualization; policyholders approved in 1997 and the conversion was completed the next year with the company taking the name AMP Limited. Trading got off to a rocky start however as the company imposed an unusual pricing mechanism by which the official initial stock price was linked to pricing activity over the first five days of trading. This was done to protect individual policyholders from typical opening-day stock gyrations but institutional investors were unable to value their investments for several days (a technical breach of accounting rules).

AMP bought Citibank's New Zealand retail banking business and UK fund manager Henderson in 1998. The next year AMP battled to buy general insurer GIO Australia Holdings picking up 57% after resistance to its original low-ball offer; it also bought UK mutual insurer National Provident Institution (NPI).

The company streamlined all of its investment-management operations into a single unit in 1999 and expanded Asian operations with offices in Beijing and Tokyo. In 2000 the problems arising from the GIO takeover resulted in a board shakeup; chairman Ian Burgess resigned.

Local rival Suncorp-Metway bought AMP's domestic general insurance unit in 2001 and Churchill Insurance (a subsidiary of Credit Suisse) acquired its similar operations in the UK that year.

AMP split off its UK-based operations as HHG at the end of 2003 (retaining a 10% share). HHG eventually changed its name to Henderson Group plc in 2005. AMP sold its shares in Henderson later that year.

EXECUTIVES

General Manager Public Affairs, Matthew Percival, $303,597 total compensation

Managing Director and CEO, Craig Dunn, age 50, $725,000 total compensation

Managing Director AMP Financial Services, Craig Meller, age 51

Managing Director AMP Capital Investors, Stephen Dunne, $427,221 total compensation

General Manager Human Resources, Fiona Wardlaw

Chairman, Peter Mason, age 67

Chief Information Officer, Lee Barnett

Chief Financial Officer, Colin Storrie, age 46

General Manager Group Strategy, Jonathan Deane

General Counsel, Brian Salter

Director, Richard H. (Rick) Allert, age 69

Managing Director and CEO, Craig Dunn, age 50

Director, John Palmer, age 66

Director, Paul A. Fegan, age 53

Director, Nora L. Scheinkestel, age 53

Director, Catherine Brenner, age 42

Director, Brian Clark, age 65

Director, Peter Shergold, age 67

Auditors: Ernst&Young

LOCATIONS

HQ: AMP Ltd.
33 Alfred Street, Sydney, New South Wales 2000
Phone: (61) 2 9257 5000   **Fax:** (61) 2 9257 7178
Web: www.amp.com.au

PRODUCTS/OPERATIONS

Sales

	% of total
Investment	75
Fee	12
Life insurance premiums & related	10
Other	3
Total	**100**

COMPETITORS

AXA Asia Pacific	National Australia
Australia and New	Bank
Zealand Banking	QBE
Aviva	RSA Insurance
Commonwealth Bank of	St. Andrew' s Australia
Australia	Suncorp-Metway
Macquarie Group	ageas SA/NV

HISTORICAL FINANCIALS

Company Type: Public

Income Statement
FYE: December 31

	ASSETS ($ mil.)	NET INCOME ($ mil.)	INCOME AS % OF ASSETS	EMPLOYEES
12/13	119,111	600	0.5%	5,700
12/12	123,395	731	0.6%	5,829
12/11	112,176	699	0.6%	6,000
12/10	90,783	788	0.9%	3,700
12/09	80,789	664	0.8%	3,500
Annual Growth	10.2%	(2.5%)	—	13.0%

2013 Year-End Financials

Return on assets: 0.5%	Dividends
Return on equity: 8.6%	Yield: 6.2%
Long-term debt ($ mil.): —	Payout: 371.8%
No. of shares (mil.): —	Market value ($ mil.): —
Sales ($ mil): 17,982	

	STOCK PRICE ($) FY Close	P/E High/Low	PER SHARE ($) Earnings	Dividends	Book Value
12/13	15.82	93 52	0.20	0.24	2.47
Annual Growth	—	— —	—	—	—

Anglo American Plc (United Kingdom)

Anglo American's name might be a little misleading —it has never been American. The UK-based company owns significant stakes in global producers of platinum (75% of Anglo Platinum) and diamonds (85% of De Beers S.A.). In addition Anglo American has interests in ferrous and base metals and industrial minerals. It ranks among the world's largest iron ore producers and is also a leading copper producer. Anglo is one of the world's largest coal miners and exporters of metallurgical coal a key raw material in steel production. It also produces thermal coal used to generate electricity. The founding Oppenheimer family no longer controls Anglo American.

Anglo American has been growing by strategic investments in long-life low-cost assets. It also has been increasing its organic growth by delivering projects ahead of or on schedule. For the past five years the company has been slimming down its operations setting strict targets and investing in strategic growth opportunities. It does not look to

investments on the basis of short-term drivers but makes its decisions based on long-term investments that will be sound for the next decade or beyond. The company tries to look beyond current market volatility while making its investments.

It 2009 Anglo decided to continue investing in four major projects: Kolomela iron ore mine in South Africa Barro Alto (nickel) and Minas-Rio (iron ore) mines in Brazil and Los Bronces copper mine in Chile. By 2011 all but the Minas-Rio iron ore project had started production on or ahead of schedule. A discovery of caves at the Minas-Rio iron ore project caused a delay in the work schedule because of a need for specialized assessment.

In 2011 Anglo delivered a strong performance which was boosted by higher prices. The company achieved a record group operating profit that year of $11.1 billion up 14% from the prior year and driven in part by solid performances by its Kumba Iron Ore Metallurgical Coal and Thermal Coal divisions. However the company's net income dipped slightly from that in 2010 when the company posted larger gains on divestments.

Anglo also made acquisitions in 2011 that significantly increased its growth. Perhaps its most historic purchase in recent years was its agreement in late 2011 to acquire the Oppenheimer family's 40% stake in giant diamond company De Beers for $5.1 billion. The interest of the Oppenheimers —who had been in the diamond industry for more than a century —increased Anglo American's 45% stake to 85%. The government of Botswana holds the remaining 15%.

In addition to giving it majority control of the mining company Anglo American believes the acquisition will provide it with De Beers' expertise in administrative functions such as financial management supply chain and technical operations. The acquisition comes after a new 10-year sales agreement with the mining company's partner the government of Botswana. De Beers and Russia's AL-ROSA account for about half of the world's diamond production.

The company also stirred up controversy in 2011 by selling nearly 25% of its stake in Anglo American Sur copper mining subsidiary in Chile to Japan's Mitsubishi Corporation for $5.4 billion. The deal angered Chilean mining and government officials because Codelco Chile's state-owned resources company and the world's largest copper company wanted to exercise its option to buy a 49% stake in the company. Chile acted quickly to obtain a court injunction to block Anglo from selling any more of its shares of Anglo American Sur. Although in 2012 a Chilean court rejected a bid by Codelco to have 49% of the dividends from Anglo American Sur frozen and held in escrow the dispute may drag on for years.

Anglo American and Lafarge SA agreed in 2011 to form a joint venture valued at $2.8 billion to combine their cement aggregates ready-mixed concrete asphalt and contracting businesses in the UK (Tarmac UK and Lafarge UK). The joint operations are expected to save a total of about $96 million a year through increased efficiency and improved logistics. The venture is designed to take advantage of an anticipated economic recovery. The UK's Competition Commission however ruled in 2012 that both Anglo and Lafarge would have to divest several operations including Lafarge's Hope cement plant in northern England —one of the largest in the UK.

The company also significantly expanded its metallurgical coal interests in 2011 with the acquisition of Peace River Coal Limited Partnership which holds exploration leases in British Columbia. Peace River Coal holds approximately 1 billion metric tons of high-quality coking coal.

In 2012 the company completed the final step of its $1.4 billion divestment of the Scaw Metals

Group by selling Scaw South Africa an integrated steel maker to an investment consortium led by the Industrial Development Corporation of South Africa. The sale follows Anglo's disposal of Scaw's Moly-Cop and AltaSteel businesses to OneSteel in 2010.

HISTORY

In 1905 the Oppenheimers a German family with a major interest in the Premier Diamond Mining Company of South Africa began buying some of the region's richest gold-bearing land. The family formed Anglo American Corporation of South Africa in 1917 to raise money from J. P. Morgan and other US investors. The name was chosen to disguise the company's German background during WWI.

Under Ernest Oppenheimer the company bought diamond fields in German Southwest Africa (now Namibia) in 1920 breaking the De Beers hegemony in diamond production. Oppenheimer's 1928 negotiations with Hans Merensky the person credited with the discovery of South Africa's "platinum arc" led to Anglo American's interest in platinum.

The diamond monopoly resurfaced in 1929 when Anglo American won control of De Beers formed by Cecil Rhodes in 1888 with the help of England's powerful Rothschild family.

Anglo American and De Beers had become the largest gold producers in South Africa by the 1950s. They were also major world producers of coal uranium and copper. In the 1960s and 1970s Anglo American expanded through mergers and cross holdings in industrial and financial companies. It set up Luxembourg-based Minorco to own holdings outside South Africa and help the company avoid sanctions placed on firms doing business in the apartheid country.

Minorco sold its interest in Consolidated Gold Fields in 1989 and in 1990 it bought Freeport-McMoRan Gold Company (US). In 1993 Minorco bought Anglo American's and De Beers' South American European and Australian operations as part of a swap that put all of Anglo American's non-African assets except diamonds in Minorco's hands. Some analysts claimed the company had moved the assets to protect them from possible nationalization by the new black-controlled South African government. The company spun off insurer African Life to a group of black investors in 1994.

Anglo American bought a stake in UK-based conglomerate Lonrho (now Lonmin) in 1996. In 1997 Anglo American made mining acquisitions in Zambia Colombia and Tanzania and began reorganizing its gold and diamond operations. In 1998 the company's First National and Southern Life financial units merged with Rand Merchant Bank's Momentum Life Assurers to form FirstRand. (Anglo American has divested most of its interest in FirstRand.)

The company moved to the UK in 1999 and began trading on the London Stock Exchange in an effort to reach international investors. When it was based in South Africa Anglo American was unable to send its money overseas (the result of boycotts connected to that country's apartheid policies) so it bulked up on South African interests. Anglo American has evolved such that it can depend on product and geographic diversity to weather global economic turmoil. South African operations now make up less than half of the company's total sales and its base metals and platinum units each account for about a quarter of sales.

In 2000 the company bought UK building materials company Tarmac plc and later sold Tarmac America to Greece-based Titan Cement for $636

million. That year De Beers paid $590 million for Anglovaal Mining's stake in De Beers' flagship Venetia diamond mine and $900 million for Royal Dutch Shell's Australian coal mining business. On the disposal side Anglo American sold its 68% stake in LTA and its 14% stake in Li & Fung a Hong Kong trading company. Harry Oppenheimer died that year at the age of 92.

In a surprising move in early 2001 Anglo American announced that it had formed a consortium with Central Holding (the Oppenheimer family) and Debswana Diamond to acquire De Beers. In February De Beers agreed to be acquired in a deal worth about $17.6 billion. The deal —giving Anglo American and Central Holding 45% each and Debswana a 10% stake —was completed in June 2001.

In 2002 Anglo American and Japan-based conglomerate Mitsui pooled their Australian coal resources; Anglo American owns 51% of the joint venture. The company also completed a $1.3 billion deal that year for Chilean copper assets (two mines and a smelter) formerly owned by Exxon Mobil. In 2003 the company eyed the red hot iron ore market when it acquired a controlling stake in South Africa-based iron producer Kumba Resources.

Anglo American sold its 20% stake in Gold Fields to Norilsk Nickel in 2004 and reduced its stake in AngloGold Ashanti to 42% from its former 51% in 2006 then to below 20% the following year and finally entirely in 2009. In divesting its gold interests Anglo American seemed to capitulate to demands from the investor community and the idea that the gold industry is sufficiently different from the rest of the mining industry as to necessitate separate management.

The company set up new units in 2009 along product and geographical lines. The new divisions consisted of platinum (South Africa) copper (Chile) nickel (Brazil) metallurgical coal (Australia) thermal coal (South Africa) Kumba Iron Ore (of which Anglo American owned 65% South Africa) and Iron Ore Brazil. The change capped off several years of reorganization and divestment.

In 2009 the board of Anglo American rejected an offer to merge with rival Xstrata (renamed Glencore in 2014). Although Xstrata called the bid a "merger of equals" based on similar capitalization sizes Anglo American's board was not convinced of the benefits of the $68 billion all stock deal. Although Anglo American used to have a majority stake in AngloGold Ashanti it divested its remaining shares in 2009.

In 2010 Anglo American through its subsidiary Anglo Zinc completed the divestment of its zinc assets to Vedanta Resources subsidiary Sterlite Industries in a $1.3 billion deal. That year the company also sold Tarmac's aggregates businesses in France Germany Poland and the Czech Republic as well as its French and Belgian concrete products operations for $483 million.

Nicky Oppenheimer grandson of the founder retired from the board in 2011.

EXECUTIVES

Group Director Human Resources and Communications, Mervyn Walker, age 54
Chairman, Sir John Parker, age 71
CEO Anglo Platinum, Neville F. Nicolau, age 54
Managing Director Tarmac, Karim Hajjar
Group Head Safety and Sustainable Development, Dorian Emmett, age 61
Executive Director Anglo American South Africa, Godfrey G. Gomwe, age 57
CEO Copper, John MacKenzie, age 45
Group Director Non-Core Assets, Duncan Wanblad, age 46
CEO Thermal Coal, Norman B. Mbazima, age 56

Group Head Corporate Communications and Branding, Anik Michaud
CEO Kumba Iron Ore, Chris Griffith, age 49
Group Director Mining and Technology, Brian Beamish, age 57
Group Director Business Performance and Projects, David Weston, age 55
Media Relations, James Wyatt-Tilby
Media Relations South Africa, Pranill Ramchander
Head Investor Relations South Africa, Anna Mulholland
CEO Anglo Nickel, Walter De Simoni, age 58
CEO Metallurgical Coal, Seamus French, age 51
CEO Iron Ore Brazil, Stephan Weber, age 52
Group Director Strategy and Business Development, Peter Whitcutt, age 48
Manager Internal and External Reporting, Hermien Botes
Chief Medical Officer, Brian Brink
Manager International Social and Community Development, Jonathan Samuel
Chief Financial Officer, Mark Gelmon
Chief Executive Officer; Director, Robin Forshaw
CEO and Board Member, Cynthia B. Carroll, age 56
Board Member, Jack E. Thompson, age 65
Board Member, Nicholas F. (Nicky) Oppenheimer, age 69
Board Member, Sir Chung-Kong (C.K.) Chow, age 62
Director Finance and Board Member, Rene Medori, age 56
Board Member, Sir Philip Hampton, age 61
Board Member, David Challen, age 71
Board Member, Tshmano Mohau Frederick (Fred) Phaswana, age 69
Board Member, Peter Woicke, age 71
Board Member, Ray O'Rourke, age 67
Director, Phuthuma F. Nhleko, age 54
Board Member, Mamphela Ramphele, age 67
Independent Director, Alaudin Sachedina
Independent Director, Richard Simpson
Auditors: DeloitteLLP

LOCATIONS

HQ: Anglo American Plc (United Kingdom)
20 Carlton House Terrace, London SW1Y 5AN
Phone: (44) 20 7968 8888   **Fax:** (44) 20 7968 8500
Web: www.angloamerican.com

PRODUCTS/OPERATIONS

Sales

	% of total
Iron ore &	22
Platinum	20
Copper	14
Metallurgical	12
Thermal	10
Diamonds	9
Nickel	1
Other mining &	12
Total	**100**

Selected Subsidiaries

Platinum
  Anglo Platinum Corporation Limited (75% South Africa)
Base Metals
Anglo American Sur (75% copper mines Chile)
  Empresa Minera de Mantos Blancos SA (copper Chile)
  Minera Loma de Niquel CA (91% nickel Venezuela)
  Minera Quellaveco SA (80% copper Peru)
  Minera Sur Andes Limitada (copper Chile)
Coal
Anglo Coal (South Africa)
  Anglo Coal (Callide) Pty Limited (Australia)
Ferrous Metals and Industries
  Kumba Resources Limited (65%; coal iron ore heavy minerals; South Africa)
Industrial Minerals
  Copebras Limitada (phosphate products Brazil)
Diamonds
  De Beers S.A. (45%)

BHP Billiton
Freeport-McMoRan
Glencore Xstrata
Impala Platinum
Norilsk Nickel
Pe?oles

Rio Tinto Limited
Teck
Vale
Vedanta Resources
Xstrata

HISTORICAL FINANCIALS

Company Type: Public

Income Statement

FYE: December 31

	REVENUE ($ mil.)	NET INCOME ($ mil.)	NET PROFIT MARGIN	EMPLOYEES
12/13	29,342	(961)	—	98,000
12/12	28,680	(1,470)	—	106,000
12/11	30,580	6,169	20.2%	100,000
12/10	27,960	6,544	23.4%	100,000
12/09	20,858	2,425	11.6%	107,000
Annual Growth	8.9%	—	—	(2.2%)

2013 Year-End Financials

Debt ratio: 25.0%
Return on equity: (-2.7%)
Cash ($ mil.): 7,704
Current ratio: 1.93
Long-term debt ($ mil.): 15,740

No. of shares (mil.): 1,394
Dividends
  Yield: 3.5%
  Payout: —
Market value ($ mil.): 15,182

	STOCK PRICE ($) FY Close	P/E High/Low		PER SHARE ($) Earnings	Dividends	Book Value
12/13	10.89	—	—	(0.75)	0.39	22.72
12/12	15.61	—	—	(1.17)	0.35	27.04
12/11	18.15	5	3	4.89	0.30	29.54
12/10	26.11	5	3	5.18	0.11	25.94
12/09	21.68	11	3	1.98	0.20	19.84
Annual Growth	(15.8%)	—	—	—	17.8%	3.4%

Anheuser-Busch Inbev SA

Anheuser-Busch InBev (AB InBev) knows how to say "beer" in a lot of languages. The company operates more than 140 breweries across six geographic regions worldwide. It boasts a product list of 200-plus brands including global best-sellers Budweiser (brewed by Anheuser Busch) Stella Artois and Beck's. The Belgian brewer holds a slew of regional beers including Leffe and Hoegaarden as well as local favorites Michelob Skol and Brahma. AB InBev controls Mexico's largest brewer Grupo Modelo which produces Corona Extra Modelo Especial and Pacifico. AB InBev isn't just for grown ups - it also makes and distributes soft drinks mostly in Latin America. All told it operates in some 20 countries worldwide.

Operations

In addition to its beverage production AB InBev has nearly 40 global facilities making everything from malt syrup to hop pellets to labels bottles and cans. It also has hop farms in Germany and the US.

Non-beer operations include an exclusive license to bottle and distribute PepsiCo products (Pepsi 7UP and Gatorade) in Brazil through its Ambev subsidiary. The unit also handles PepsiCo products in other parts of Latin America and has a exclusive deal to distribute Monster Energy drinks in Brazil. Soft drinks account for about 10% of AB InBev revenue.

Geographic Reach

The company brews beer and soda at plants spread across its six geographic zones. Latin America North and Asia Pacific have the highest number of factories with about 35 each. Latin America South and North America come in next with around 20 each. Western Europe the original home of the InBev part of AB InBev has about 15 and the Central and Eastern Europe region has around 10. Most of the facilities produce beer but nearly 20 produce both beer and soda and about a dozen (mostly in Latin America) make only soda.

North America original home of the AB part of AB InBev accounts for the majority of sales for the company.

Sales and Marketing

The company distributes it products globally according to local regulations and agreements. Generally it pursues direct distribution where possible and indirect distribution elsewhere. When using indirect distribution it strives to secure exclusive agreements. In regions where AB InBev has no direct affiliates it often licenses local brewers to produce its key brands.

Though the company has a long list of brands its employs a "focus brands" marketing strategy wherein its concentrates money people and attention on the brands that account for about 70% of its beer sales by volume. Those include its three global brands Budweiser Beck's and Stella Artois; what it calls multi-country brands (Leffe and Hoegaarden); and its "local champions" including Bud Light Jupiler Sibirskaya Korona Skol Harbin and Quilmes.

Financial Performance

AB InBev saw a modest 7% increase in revenue (adjusted to account for acquisitions and disposals) mainly due to price increases in North and South America as well as increased sales volume in Asia. Acquisitions and disposals also positively impacted nearly all the company's expenses resulting in a modest $9 million profit for 2012.

Strategy

In both developed and developing markets which each account for about half the company's sales AB InBev focuses its efforts on it core brands while developing regional favorites as well. It uses large events and social media to stay connected with its customers and introduce new products to bring in new customers.

The company also keeps costs in check through strict financial discipline and improving manufacturing efficiencies.

In 2013 the company expects to invest in new capacity projects in China Brazil and Argentina to meet future demand expectations in these growing markets.

Mergers and Acquisitions

In 2013 AB InBev acquired almost all of Mexico's largest beer company Grupo Modelo (it had already owned 50%) for some $20 billion. Owner of the ubiquitous south of the US border brands Corona Extra Modelo Especial and Pacifico Modelo will help expand AB InBev's annual revenues to around $47 billion with operations in 24 countries. The deal allows AB InBev further exposure in emerging markets like Mexico an economy that grew by 4.6% in the first quarter of 2012. Part of the arrangement include selling Grupo Modelo's US business to rival brewer Constellation Brands for about $5 billion.

HISTORY

Monks at the Leffe Abbey in Belgium were brewing beer as early as 1240 and surviving records from 1366 mention Belgium's Den Horen brewery. Belgian master brewer Sebastien Artois (best known for his Stella Artois lager) took over Den Horen in 1717. In 1853 the Piedboeuf family founded a brewery at Liege and established the Jupiler lager. Albert Van Damme assumed management of that brewery in 1920.

Over the years the Artois and Piedboeuf families took over or established operations both in and outside Belgium. Direct descendants (the clans de Spoelberch Van Damme and de Mevius) of the two families were still managing the companies in 1987 when they decided the key to survival in the fragmented European beer market was to merge.

Artois-Piedboeuf-Interbrew acquired the Hoegaarden brewery in Belgium in 1989. The company changed its name to Interbrew three years later acquired another Belgian brewery (Belle-Vue) and bought stakes in breweries in Bulgaria Croatia and Hungary. In 1995 Dommelsche Bierbrouwerij bought Allied Breweries Nederland an Allied Domecq subsidiary and Interbrew acquired the Oranjeboom breweries in the Netherlands.

The company purchased John Labatt Ltd. for $2 billion in 1995. As a result of the deal Interbrew gained control of Latrobe Brewing (Rolling Rock beer US) 22% of Mexico's FEMSA Cerveza (increased to 30% in 1998) the Toronto Argonauts football team 90% of the Toronto Blue Jays (it sold an 80% stake in the baseball team to cable firm Rogers Communications in 2000) and various broadcast properties.

Interbrew sold many noncore assets including Lehigh Valley Dairies (US) and John Labatt Retail (pubs UK) in 1996. Also that year the company established joint ventures in the Dominican Republic and the US (to import Mexican beers through FEMSA).

In 1998 Interbrew paid $250 million for 50% of the Doosan Group's Oriental Brewery South Korea's second-largest brewer and bought a majority stake in Russian brewer Rosar. The next year Interbrew combined its Russian operations with Sun Brewing forming Russian brewer Sun-Interbrew. It then bought Korea's Jinro-Coors Brewery for about $378 million. Hugo Powell was later named CEO of Interbrew.

Interbrew bought Britain's third-largest brewer Whitbread Beer Company in 2000 for $590 million. Having gained a foothold in the UK market the company then bought Bass Brewers from Bass PLC in 2000 for more than $3 billion. Interbrew went public on the Euronext (Brussels) exchange in 2000.

In 2001 Baron Paul De Keersmaeker retired as chairman and was replaced by Pierre Jean Everaert. That year the company took an 80% stake in Germany's tenth-largest brewer Diebels. Interbrew also sold Carling which controls about 18% of the UK beer market to Coors for $1.7 billion after being ordered to remedy unfair competition advantages related to the Bass Brewers purchase.

John Brock former COO of Cadbury Schweppes became CEO of Interbrew in 2003. That year it sold a minority stake of its Namibian Breweries in southern Africa to Diageo and Heineken.

In 2004 Interbrew purchased a 70% stake in Chinese brewer Zhejiang Shiliang which gave Interbrew nearly a 50% market share in China's Zhejiang province.

InBev was created through a 2005 merger of Interbrew and AmBev. The merger resulted in a series of transactions between Interbrew subsidiary Labatt and Mexico's FEMSA. By creating InBev Interbrew gave up interest in distributing FEMSA beer brands in the US. In return Interbrew retained full control of the US division of Labatt. InBev merged Labatt U.S.A. with what was Beck's North America to create its US operations.

Exiting the Slovenian market InBev sold its stake in Pivovarna Union to Pivovarna Lasko in 2005. That year it also acquired Russian premium brewer Tinkoff and sold its stake in soft-drink company Bremer Erfrischungsgetranke to Coca-Cola. It sold its minority stake in Spanish brewer Damm as well. At year-end Carlos Brito formerly zone president for the company's North American operations succeeded John Brock as CEO of InBev.

Saying it intended to concentrate on import brands in the US market in 2006 the company sold subsidiary InBev USA's domestic beer brand Rolling Rock to Anheuser-Busch for $82 million. Later in the year InBev and A-B struck an additional deal for A-B to serve as the exclusive distributor for some of its European brands such as Beck's Bass and Stella Artois. In addition it paid some $1 billion to increase its stake in Quinsa an Argentine brewer to 90% from 57% that year.

EXECUTIVES

Chairman, Kornelis J. (Kees) Storm, age 72
Chief People and Technology Officer, Claudio Garcia, age 46
Chief Executive Officer, Carlos Brito, age 54, $1,279,044 total compensation
CFO, Felipe Dutra, age 49
Chief Supply Officer, Sabine Chalmers, age 50
Chief Sales Officer, Bernardo Pinto Paiva, age 45
Chief Supply Officer, Claudio Braz Ferro, age 46
Chief Procurement Officer, Tony Milikin
Zone President Asia Pacific, Michel Dimitrios Doukeris, age 37
Chief Marketing Officer, Miguel Patricio
Zone President Central and Eastern Europe, Stuart MacFarlane
President Asia Pacific, Ricardo Tadeu
Chief Supply Officer, Claudio Ferro
Director, Stefan Descheemaeker, age 54
Director, Kornelis J. (Kees) Storm, age 71
Director, August A. Busch IV, age 49
Director, Jorge Paulo Lemann, age 75
Director, Jean-Luc Dehaene, age 71
Director, Gregoire de Spoelberch, age 46
Director, Marcel H. Telles, age 64
Director, Roberto Moses Thompson Motta, age 56
Director, Carlos A. Sicupira, age 67
Director, Alexandre Van Damme, age 50
Director, Mark Winkelman, age 69
Director, Comte Arnoud de Pret, age 69
Auditors:
PricewaterhouseCoopersBedrijfsrevisorenBCVBA

LOCATIONS

HQ: Anheuser-Busch Inbev SA
Brouwerijplein 1, Leuven 3000
Phone: (32) 16 27 6111 **Fax:** (32) 16 50 6111
Web: www.ab-inbev.com

Sales

	$ mil.	% of total
North America	16,028	40
Latin America		
North	11,455	29
South	3,023	8
Europe		
Western	3,625	9
Central & Eastern	1,668	4
Asia/Pacific	2,690	7
Global Export & Holding Companies	1,270	3
Total	**39,758**	**100**

PRODUCTS/OPERATIONS

Selected Brands
Global brands
  Becks
  Budweiser
  Stella Artois
Multi-country brands
  Hoegaarden
  Leffe
Local brands

Asia Pacific
  Harbin
  Sedrin
Central & Eastern Europe
  Chernigivske
  Klinskoye
  Sibirskaya Korona
Latin America
  Antarctica
  Bohemia
  Brahma
  Quilmes
  Skol
North America
  Bud Light
  Bud Light Lime
  Bud Light Lime Lime-A-Rita
  Bud Light Platinum
  Corona
  Labatt
  Michelob ULTRA
  Modelo Especial
  Natural Light
  Pacifico
Western Europe
  Jupiler
  Hasseroder
  Lowenbrau
  Spaten

Selected Subsidiaries and Affiliates
Anheuser-Busch Companies Inc. (US)
Bass Beers Worldwide Limited (UK)
Brasserie de L' Abbaye De Leffe S.A. (98% Belgium)
Brasserie de Luxembourg Mousel - Diekirch (96% Luxembourg)
Brauerei Beck GmbH & Co. KG (Germany)
Brauerei Diebels GmbH & Co. KG (Germany)
Brouwerij Van Hoegaarden N.V. (Belgium)
Cerveceria y Malteria Quilmes Saica y G (62% Argentina)
Cobrew N.V. (Belgium)
Companhia de Bebidas Das Americas - AmBev (62% Brazil)
Grupo Modelo S.A.B. de C.V. (95% Mexico)
Haake-Beck Brauerei GmbH & Co. KG (Germany)
Harbin Brewing Company Limited (China)
InBev Baisha (Hunan) Brewery Co. Ltd. (China)
InBev Double Deer Group Co. Ltd. (55% China)
Interbrew International B.V. (The Netherlands)
Labatt Brewing Company Limited (62% Canada)
Nanjing InBev Jinling Brewery Co. Ltd. (China)
PJSC Sun InBev Ukraine (99% Ukraine)
Spaten - Franziskaner - Brau GmbH (Germany)

COMPETITORS

Anchor Brewers	Fraser & Neave
Asahi Breweries	Grolsch
Asia Pacific Breweries	Heineken
Bavaria S.A.	Holsten-Brauerei
Beijing Enterprises	Kirin Holdings Company
Big Rock Brewery	Lion
Boston Beer	Molson Coors
Carlsberg	Pyramid Breweries
Central European	Radeberger Gruppe
Distribution	SABMiller
Coca-Cola	San Miguel Corporation
Coca-Cola FEMSA	Sapporo
Constellation Brands	Suntory Holdings
Craft Brew Alliance	Thai Beverage
Cuauhtemoc Moctezuma	Tsingtao
Diageo	UB Group
FEMSA	Yuengling & Son

HISTORICAL FINANCIALS
Company Type: Public

Income Statement
FYE: December 31

	REVENUE ($ mil.)	NET INCOME ($ mil.)	NET PROFIT MARGIN	EMPLOYEES
12/13	43,195	14,394	33.3%	154,587
12/12	39,758	7,243	18.2%	117,632
12/11	39,046	5,855	15.0%	116,278
12/10	36,297	4,026	11.1%	114,313
12/09	36,758	4,613	12.5%	116,489
Annual Growth	**4.1%**	**32.9%**	**—**	**7.3%**

2013 Year-End Financials
Debt ratio: 34.6%
Return on equity: 31.4%
Cash ($ mil.): 9,839
Current ratio: 0.73
Long-term debt ($ mil.): 41,274
No. of shares (mil.): 1,606
Dividends
  Yield: 2.8%
  Payout: 34.7%
Market value ($ mil.): 170,999

	STOCK PRICE ($) FY Close	P/E High/Low		PER SHARE ($) Earnings	Dividends	Book Value
12/13	106.46	12	9	8.72	3.03	31.36
12/12	87.41	20	13	4.45	1.56	25.68
12/11	60.99	17	14	3.63	1.18	23.46
12/10	57.09	25	18	2.50	0.49	22.13
12/09	52.03	18	13	2.90	0.00	19.06
Annual Growth	**19.6%**	**—**	**—**	**31.7%**	**—**	**13.3%**

ArcelorMittal SA

Few metal makers have the mettle of Arcelor-Mittal. The company is easily the largest steel-making entity in the world producing more than 90 million metric tons of crude steel annually about 6% of the world steel output. Operating in more than 60 countries ArcelorMittal manufactures the full range of steel products: slabs and coil coated steel and tinplate wire rod and rebar and billets and blooms as well as all manner of electrical steel products. It also has 20 mining operations and is one of the world's largest iron ore producers. In 2011 it produced 54 million metric tons of iron ore and 8 million metric tons of metallurgical coal. CEO and founder Lakshmi Mittal controls about 41% of ArcelorMittal.

Geographic Reach

ArcelorMittal operates through subsidiaries in Europe Africa Asia and the Americas (including ArcelorMittal Brasil). It's the largest producer of steel in North and South America and Africa the second-largest steel producer in the Commonwealth of Independent States region and has a growing presence in Asia including investments in China. It is also the largest steel producer in the European Union.

In addition many of ArcelorMittal's units have access to developing markets that are expected to experience significant future growth in steel consumption such as Central and Eastern Europe South America India Africa and Russia. Overall about 48% of its steel is produced in Europe 36% in the Americas and 16% in other countries such as Kazakhstan South Africa and Ukraine.

Sales and Marketing

ArcelorMittal produces a wide variety of products across all steel-consuming industries including the automotive appliance engineering construction energy and machinery markets. The company sells its products in local markets and through a centralized marketing organization in more than 170 countries. Its strategy depends on maintaining its size and scale in the global steel market vertical integration of its operations producing a diverse portfolio of products and continuously improving its quality.

Strategy

ArcelorMittal became a conglomerate through acquisitions and strategic partnerships. In 2013 it formed a joint venture with Nippon Steel & Sumitomo Metal to buy ThyssenKrupp Steel USA from ThyssenKrupp for $1.5 billion. The deal (completed in 2014) is expected to deliver $60 million in annual savings.

To focus on its core businesses and pay down debt in 2013 the company sold 15% of its ArcelorMittal Mines Canada subsidiary to Chinese and Korean steelmakers for $1.1 billion. The prior year it sold New Jersey-based Skyline Steel a North American steel foundation and piling products distributor and specialty steel plate and bar producer Astralloy to US-based Nucor for $605 million.

In 2011 the company spun off its stainless and specialty steels steel operations into Aperam which immediately became the world's sixth-largest stainless steel producer. ArcelorMittal made the decision in 2010 to spin off its stainless steel units in Europe and Brazil after determining that they were underperforming and would better thrive as a separate business.

Mergers and Acquisitions

In 2012 ArcelorMittal expanded its presence in China by increasing its stake in a joint venture with Valin Group known as Valin ArcelorMittal Automotive (VAMA) from 33% to 49%. VAMA is trying to enhance its position in China as a supplier of high-strength steels and products for the automotive market. The joint venture scheduled to become operational in 2014 will increase its planned capacity from 1.2 million tons to 1.5 million tons.

After spinning its wheels in an escalating bidding war in 2011 ArcelorMittal joined rival Nunavut Iron Ore in making a joint acquisition of Canada-based Baffinland Iron Mines for $594 million. Both companies sought access to Baffinland's Mary River Project an undeveloped deposit of iron ore on sparsely populated North Baffin Island located inside the Arctic Circle as a source of raw materials. The venture faces stiff challenges including building an infrastructure around the mine's formidable location and shipping the ore out to Europe and other production sites.

Also that year the company bought a 40% stake in G Steel Public Company greatly expanding its presence in Asia. G Steel produces about 2.5 million ton of steel annually at its two slab-rolling plants in Thailand. The deal was part of ArcelorMittal's strategy of establishing a presence in emerging markets with with the potential for future growth.

HISTORY

ArcelorMittal is the product of decades of steelmaking by India's Mittal family. In 1967 patriarch Mohan Mittal unsuccessfully tried to open a steel mill in Egypt. He and his four younger brothers then set up a steel company in India but squabbles pushed Mohan to chart his own course eventually giving rise to an empire that flourished under the Ispat name. Mohan's son Lakshmi began working part-time at the family steel mill while in school; he started full-time at 21 after graduating in 1971.

Mohan set up an operation in Indonesia in 1975 (Ispat Indo) and put Lakshmi in charge. The next year fueled by ambitions and held back by government regulations in India Lakshmi formed Ispat International in Jakarta Indonesia to focus on expansion through acquisitions. He spent the next

decade strengthening the Indonesian operations and perfecting the minimill process using direct-reduced iron (DRI).

Ispat took advantage of the recessionary late 1980s and early 1990s by making a string of acquisitions. In 1988 it took over the management of Trinidad and Tobago's state steel companies (bought in 1994; renamed Caribbean Ispat).

In 1992 Ispat bought Mexico's third-largest (albeit bankrupt) steel and DRI producer. Two years later it acquired Canada's Sidbec-Dosco steelmaker. Also that year Lakshmi took exclusive control of international operations leaving his brothers Pramod and Vinod to control the Indian divisions.

The mid-1990s brought more acquisitions: In 1995 Ispat bought Germany's Hamburger Stahlwerks and a mill in Kazakhstan. The next year it purchased Ireland's only steelmaker Irish Steel. Lakshmi moved to London in 1996 and purchased a home on Bishops Avenue known as "millionaire's row." (Saudi Arabia's King Fahd was a neighbor.)

In 1997 the company bought the long-product (wire rod) division of Germany's Thyssen AG (renamed Ispat Stahlwerk Ruhrort and Ispat Walzdraht Hochfeld). It also completed a $776 million IPO.

Ispat acquired Chicago-based Inland Steel in 1998 (and renamed it Ispat Inland) including the steel-finishing operations of I/N Tek (60% Inland-owned joint venture with Nippon Steel) and I/N Kote (50% Inland-owned joint venture with NSC).

In 1999 Ispat formed a joint venture with Mexican steelmaker Grupo Imsa to make flat-rolled steel to sell throughout most of the Americas. It also paid $96 million for France-based Usinor's Unimetal Trefileurope and Societe Metallurgique de Revigny subsidiaries which specialize in carbon long products. That year Ispat Inland became the target of a US federal criminal grand jury investigation and a related civil lawsuit for allegedly defrauding the Louisiana Highway Department. (The case was settled for $30 million with the cost split between Ispat Inland and Contech Construction Products Inc. of Ohio.)

In 2000 the company responded to a downturn in the steel industry by starting a Web-based joint venture with Commerce One to connect buyers and sellers in the worldwide metals market. It also offered to buy VSZ Slovakia's #1 steelworks but was outbid by U.S. Steel.

After struggling with heavy debt high labor and energy costs new environmental regulations and EU steel quotas in 2001 Ispat closed down its subsidiary Irish Ispat which accounted for about 2% of the parent company's steel production.

In 2002 the company's 51%-owned pipe making subsidiary Productura Mexicana de Tuberia sold almost all of its production assets.

The present ArcelorMittal was forged in 2004 when Ispat International (of which the Mittal family owned 70%) purchased LNM Holdings (wholly owned by the Mittals) for $13 billion. In 2006 the former Mittal Steel agreed to buy rival Arcelor for about $34 billion to create ArcelorMittal.

Mittal Steel had established its hold on the world steel market through its 2005 purchase of the US-based International Steel Group (ISG) for $4.5 billion. The purchase made the company the largest steel producer (ahead of U.S. Steel and Nucor) in the US a market that had long been a targeted area for expansion for CEO Mittal. Once the deal closed the company combined ISG's operations with those of subsidiary Ispat Inland to form a single North American entity Mittal Steel USA (now ArcelorMittal USA).

Also in 2005 Mittal Steel acquired a 93% stake in Ukrainian state-run steel company KryvorizhStal with the winning $4.84 billion bid in an auction held by the Ukrainian government. The price was

high but Mittal was anxious to gain a stronger foothold in the region –and to keep its rivals away from KryvorizhStal. (This fact incidentally went a long way to convincing Mittal it needed to combine with Arcelor; the competition for acquisitions was driving prices dramatically upward.)

The company also began to broaden its portfolio outside the steel industry dipping its toe into the energy business. In mid-2005 Mittal formed two joint ventures with India's government-controlled Oil & Natural Gas Corporation: one to buy stakes in foreign oil and gas projects the other involved in oil and gas trading and shipping. The ventures began to look for business in places like Indonesia Kazakhstan Angola and Trinidad and Tobago.

After consolidating his family's various steel interests in the early part of this decade Mittal began work on the steel industry as a whole and was soon the world's largest steel producer.

By 2006 Mittal Steel no longer was content to be merely the world's largest steel producer; it wanted to dominate the market. The company announced an offer to the shareholders of Arcelor then the industry's #2 player to buy that company and in the process create the world's first 100-million-ton steel producer. Arcelor and seemingly half the governments of Western Europe initially fought the attempt.

Mittal improved its proposed price however and Arcelor's board finally approved the offer when Mittal also made ownership/corporate governance concessions. The combined company is 43% owned by the Mittal family. After a few months of a transitional management team arrangement Lakshmi Mittal took over as CEO of the combined company toward the end of 2006.

In 2009 ArcelorMittal completed its acquisition of the laser-welding steel activities of Noble International a leader in the niche industry. It also acquired Mexican steel producer Sicarsta for nearly $1.5 billion an acquisition that combined with its Lazaro Cardenas created Mexico's largest steel company.

In 2011 the company spun off its stainless and specialty steels steel operations into Aperam which immediately became the world's sixth-largest stainless steel producer. ArcelorMittal made the decision in 2010 to spin off its stainless steel units in Europe and Brazil after determining that they were underperforming and would better thrive as a separate business.

EXECUTIVES

executive Vice-President of ArcelorMittal visited ArcelorMittal Ostrava, Gerhard Renz, age 66

EVP Finance, Bhikam C. Agarwal, age 62

Chairman and CEO, Lakshmi N. Mittal, age 63

SEVP Asia Africa Commonwealth of Independent States (excluding China and India); Distribution Solutions; Tubular Products and Corporate Responsibility, Gonzalo Urquijo, age 51

SEVP Long Carbon Worldwide, Michel Wurth, age 60

EVP; Chief Executive Stainless, Bernard Fontana, age 52

CFO, Aditya Mittal, age 37

President and CEO ArcelorMittal Mines Canada, Serge Miller

SEVP; Head Mining, Peter G. J. Kukielski, age 57

VP; CEO Long Carbon Europe, Augustine Kochuparampil

EVP and Head Marketing and Commercial Coordination, Michael B. Pfitzner, age 64

EVP; CEO India and China, Vijay K. Bhatnagar, age 68

EVP; CEO ArcelorMittal USA, Michael G. (Mike) Rippey, age 57

EVP; CEO ArcelorMittal Mining, Bill Scotting, age 56

EVP; CEO Flat Americas; CTO, Louis (Lou) Schorsch, age 65
Member Group Management Board Shared Services, Davinder K. Chugh, age 57
Member Group Management Board Corporate Finance Mergers and Acquisitions and Business Development including India (chapter 1) and Risk Management, Sudhir Maheshwari, age 50
Secretary, Henk Scheffer
Corporate Communications, Nicola Davidson
Media Contact North America, Bill Steers
VP ArcelorMittal North American Investor Relations, Thomas A. (Tom) McCue
CFO Stainless Steel, Julien Onillon, age 43
Member Group Management Board Technology and Projects Asia and Africa, Christophe Cornier, age 61
EVP; CEO Distribution Solutions, Philippe Darmayan, age 61
EVP and CTO, Pierre Gugliermina, age 62
EVP; CEO Flat Carbon Europe, Robrecht Himpe, age 56
EVP; CEO Africa and Commonwealth of Independent States (CIS), Arnaud Poupart-Lafarge, age 48
Secretary Group Management Board, Sujogya Dash
Head Media Relations, Giles Read
Corporate Media Contact, Arne Langner
Corporate Media Contact, Jean Lasar
Corporate Media Contact, Lynn Robbroeckx
Media Contact Spain, Ignacio Agreda
Director Investor Relations, Daniel Fairclough
CEO ArcelorMittal Kryviy Rih, Rinat Starkov
EVP and Head Human Resources, Willie Smit
VP; CEO Long Carbon Central and South America, Augusto Augusto Espeschit de Almeida Almeida
VP; CEO Flat Carbon South America, Benjamin Baptista
VP; CEO ArcelorMittal Mexico, Bill Bill Chisholm Chisholm
Vice President Chief Marketing Officer, Brian Aranha
Independent Member of Board of Directors, Bruno Bruno Lafont Lafont
VP; CEO - Flat Carbon Europe Business Division North, Geert Van Poelvoorde
Vice President Global research and development, Gregory Ludkovsky
Independent Member of Board of Directors, Guillaume Guillaume de Luxembourg Luxembourg
VP; CEO Flat Carbon Europe Business Division Southwest, Jean-Luc Maurange
Executive Vice President Long Carbon Americas, Jefferson Paula
Member of Management Committee and Vice President; CEO; ArcelorMittal Dofasco; Hamilton, Juergen Juergen Schachler Schachler
Member of Management Committee and Vice President; Mining Operations, Kleber Kleber Silva Silva
Member of Management Committee; Vice President; Chief Technology Officer, Marc Marc Vereecke Vereecke
VP; CEO ArcelorMittal South Africa, Nku Nymebezi-Heita
VP; CEO Long Carbon North America, PS (Venkat) Venkataramanan
Executive Vice President; Head of Mining Projects and Exploration; Member of the Management Committee, Philippus Philippus du Toit Toit
VP; CEO Flat Carbon Europe Business Division East; CEO ArcelorMittal Poland, Sanjay Sanjay Samaddar Samaddar
Vice President Chief Commercial Officer, Simon Wandke
Vice President and Head of Americas Iron Ore Operations, Steven Steven Wood Wood

VP and Director of Security; Health; Assets Safety; Environment and Mining Sustainability, Suresh Suresh Rajapakse Rajapakse
VP; CEO Distribution Solutions, Alain Le Grix
Executive Vice President, Henri Blaffart
Board Member, Lewis B. (Lew) Kaden, age 71
Board Member, Narayanan Vaghul, age 77
Board Member, Wilbur L. Ross Jr., age 76
Board Member, Vanisha Mittal Bhatia, age 33
Board Member, Antoine Spillmann, age 50
Board Member, Prince Guillaume de Luxembourg, age 50
Board Member, Suzanne P. Nimocks
Board Member, Jeannot Krecke, age 62
Non Independent Member of Board of Directors, Jeannot Jeannot Krecke Krecke
Independent Director, Tye Tye Burt Burt
Non Independent Member of Board of Directors, Vanisha Vanisha Mittal Bhatia Bhatia
Auditors: DeloitteS.A.

LOCATIONS

HQ: ArcelorMittal SA
19, Avenue de la Liberte, Luxembourg L-2930
Phone: (352) 4792 2484   Fax: (352) 4792 89 3937
Web: www.arcelormittal.com

Sales

	$ mil.	% of total
Europe	37,446	48
Asia & Africa	12,564	16

PRODUCTS/OPERATIONS

Sales

	$ mil.	% of total
Flat Carbon Products		
Americas	19,301	21
Steel Solutions & Services	15,744	17
Total	**78,025**	**100**

Segments and Selected Products
Flat Carbon Europe
Coated products
Coil
Cold-rolled
Hot-rolled
Plate
Slab
Tin plate
Flat Carbon Americas
Coated products
Steel
Plate
Coil
Cold-rolled
Hot-rolled
Slabs
Long Carbon Americas & Europe
Billets
Blooms
Rebar
Sections
Wire rod
Asia Africa & Comonwealth of Independent States
Flat products
Long products
Pipes
Tubes
ArcelorMittal Steel Solutions & Services (in-house trading and distribution arm)

COMPETITORS

AK Steel Holding Corporation
BHP Billiton
Baosteel
BlueScope Steel
China Steel
Essar Group
Evraz
Gerdau
JFE Holdings
Mechel OAO
Nippon Steel & Sumitomo Metal Corporation
Nucor
POSCO
Severstal
Shougang Corp.
Tata Steel
Tenaris
Ternium
ThyssenKrupp Steel
United States Steel

HISTORICAL FINANCIALS

Company Type: Public

Income Statement

FYE: December 31

	REVENUE ($ mil.)	NET INCOME ($ mil.)	NET PROFIT MARGIN	EMPLOYEES
12/13	79,440	(2,545)	—	232,353
12/12	84,213	(3,726)	—	273,811
12/11	93,973	2,263	2.4%	260,523
12/10	78,025	2,916	3.7%	273,811
12/09	65,110	118	0.2%	281,703
Annual Growth	5.1%	—	—	(4.7%)

2013 Year-End Financials

Debt ratio: 19.8%
Return on equity: (-5.0%)
Cash ($ mil.): 6,072
Current ratio: 1.35
Long-term debt ($ mil.): 18,219
No. of shares (mil.): 1,653
Dividends
Yield: 2.7%
Payout: —
Market value ($ mil.): 29,500

	STOCK PRICE ($) FY Close	P/E High/Low	Earnings	PER SHARE ($) Dividends	Book Value
12/13	17.84	— —	(1.46)	0.49	30.11
12/12	17.47	— —	(2.41)	0.64	33.39
12/11	18.19	26 10	1.19	0.64	36.60
12/10	38.13	25 14	1.72	0.64	40.31
12/09	45.75	585214	0.08	0.64	40.44
Annual Growth	(21.0%)	— —	—	(6.4%)	(7.1%)

Asea Brown Boveri AG (Austria)

LOCATIONS

HQ: Asea Brown Boveri AG (Austria)
P.O. Box 8131, Zurich CH-8050
Phone: (41) 43 317 71 11   Fax: (41) 43 317 79 58
Web: www.abb.com

HISTORICAL FINANCIALS

Company Type: Public

Income Statement

FYE: December 31

	REVENUE ($ mil.)	NET INCOME ($ mil.)	NET PROFIT MARGIN	EMPLOYEES
12/13	41,848	2,787	6.7%	147,700
12/12	39,336	2,704	6.9%	0
12/11	37,990	3,168	8.3%	0
12/94	230	0	0.0%	1,609
12/93	216	1	0.8%	0
Annual Growth	30.1%	44.9%	—	—

2013 Year-End Financials

Debt ratio: 16.6%
Return on equity: 15.6%
Cash ($ mil.): 6,021
Current ratio: 1.58
Long-term debt ($ mil.): 7,570

No. of shares (mil.): —
Dividends
Yield: —
Payout: 57.3%
Market value ($ mil.): —

Assicurazioni Generali S.p.A.

Italy's largest insurance company (and one of the largest in Europe) Assicurazioni Generali writes insurance for risks as varied as pensions and car insurance. Present in more than 60 countries Generali's core businesses are involved in both personal and commercial insurance (including life accident health motor fire marine/aviation and reinsurance); the rest concentrate on other financial services and real estate. Generali is noted for being a leading insurer of satellite and space missions which it has been covering since 1964. In more earthbound realms the company targets individuals and small to midsized businesses and has been in business since 1831.

Generali operates through more than 500 companies throughout the world. Life insurance makes up the lion's share of its business with products that include savings and protection policies health business and supplementary pension policies. More than two-thirds of its written premiums are generated through its life insurance segment. Its non-life segment centers on retail markets.

Although Generali promotes its financial services operations including Banca Generali and BSI such services as wealth management and bank insurance products only account for about 10% of its revenues.

Italy Germany and France are Generali's largest markets with Austria and Spain significantly adding to sales. Its Italian property/casualty subsidiary Alleanza Toro holds a good chunk of Generali's domestic operations serving more than 3 million customers; it offers products under the Alleanza and Toro brands.

Generali's results in 2011 were affected by broadspread economic instabilities in the euro-zone. Its life insurance results suffered impairment losses on Greek government bonds and its non-life markets were impacted by adverse trading conditions. Revenues for the year fell almost 13% to $104.9 billion down from the $120.3 billion achieved in 2010. Net income sank 44% to $1.5 billion down from $2.7 billion. Written premiums also dropped by 6%. At year end the company had more than $600 billion worth of assets and a $36.5 billion property portfolio. The company is looking to grow its operating results by 10% in 2012.

Generali's strategy for growth is based entering new market segments and countries. With its place firmly cemented in Western Europe it is looking to expand its presence in Eastern Europe Latin America and Asia through joint ventures and acquisitions. To that end Generali has targeted the fast-growing life insurance market of Vietnam and launched its Generali Vietnam Life Insurance Company subsidiary in 2011. Its BSI private banking division also received license to provide banking and investment services in Hong Kong that year.

Other strategic initiatives include improving its overall operating efficiencies including centralizing its IT operations into a single data center; optimiz-

ing its distribution networks and the developing proprietary networks; delivering innovative products; and diversifying its distribution methods. To reach younger customers it is particularly vested in providing direct channels via mobile applications and the web. The company leads in direct-to-consumers telephone and online channels in Italy Germany and France where it offers both life and property/casualty products.

The company's largest shareholder is Mediobanca with 13% of the its shares. Other institutional shareholders collectively own 55% of the company and retail shareholders own almost 32%.

HISTORY

Assicurazioni Generali was founded as Assicurazioni Generali Austro-Italiche in 1831 by a group of merchants led by Giuseppe Morpurgo in the Austro-Hungarian port of Trieste. Formed to provide insurance to the city's bustling trade industry the company offered life marine fire flood and shipping coverage. That year Morpurgo established what he intended to be Generali's headquarters in Venice. (While the company maintained offices in both cities Trieste ultimately won out.)

By 1835 Generali had opened 25 offices in Central and Western Europe; it had also expelled Morpurgo. The firm moved into Africa and Asia in the 1880s. In 1900 Generali began selling injury and theft insurance. In 1907 Generali's Prague office provided the young experimental writer Franz Kafka his first job. (He found it disagreeable and quit after a few months.)

During WWI the firm's Venice office pledged allegiance to Italy while the office in Trieste (still part of Austria-Hungary) stayed loyal to the Hapsburgs. After the war Trieste was absorbed by the new Italian republic. Under Edgardo Morpurgo Generali expanded further in the 1920s managing 30 subsidiaries and operating in 17 countries. As fascist Italy aligned itself with Germany in the 1930s adoption of anti-Semitic laws caused Morpurgo and a number of other high-ranking Jewish employees to flee the country. In 1938 Generali moved its headquarters to Rome (but moved them back to Trieste after war's end).

The firm maintained steady business both before and during Nazi occupation in WWII; in 1945 however the Soviets seized all Italian properties in Eastern Europe including 14 Generali subsidiaries. In 1950 Generali invaded the US market offering shipping and fire insurance and reinsurance. Generali established a cooperative agreement with Aetna Life and Casualty (now Aetna Inc.) in 1966 further cementing its US connections.

In 1988 Generali tried to acquire French insurer Compagnie du Midi. Foreshadowing Generali's later dealings with Istituto Nazionale delle Assicurazioni (INA) Midi escaped Generali's grasp through a merger with AXA. As the Iron Curtain frayed in 1989 Generali formed AB Generali Budapest through a joint venture with a Hungarian insurer. In 1990 the firm opened an office in Tokyo through an agreement with Taisho Marine and Fire Insurance (which became Mitsui Marine & Fire Insurance and is now Mitsui Sumitomo Insurance). By 1993 Generali had become Italy's largest insurer.

In 1997 the firm was accused along with other major European insurers of not paying on policies of Holocaust victims. (It moved to settle claims in 1999.)

The company focused on the German and Swiss markets in 1998 acquiring controlling interests in insurer AMB Aachener und Muncher (now AMB Generali) and in Banca della Svizzera Italiana. Also that year Generali and Commerzbank established an alliance that gave the companies more access to each other's markets.

In 1999 Generali succeeded in a hostile takeover of INA its largest domestic competitor. The move pre-empted INA's proposed merger with San Paolo IMI which would have knocked Generali to second place among the country's insurers.

Avoiding violation of the EU's antitrust laws in connection with the INA acquisition the company sold four subsidiaries (including Italian insurers Aurora and Navale) in 2000.

In 2002 Generali rolled together three Italian securities investments firms —Altinia Ina Sim and Prime Consult Sim —into Banca Generali.

The insurer entrenched itself in Germany by acquiring a controlling interest in one of the country's largest insurers AMB Generali (formerly Aachener und Muncher) and establishing an alliance with Commerzbank in 2006. In Spain the company boosted its presence with its 2009 acquisition of local insurers Estrella Seguros and Vitalicio Seguros. Generali also acquired the remaining shares of its majority-owned Italian life insurance firm Alleanza Assicurazioni in 2009 and then merged Alleanza with its Italian property/casualty subsidiary Toro Assicurazioni into a new company named Alleanza Toro.

Some of the company's acquisitions in Eastern Europe have drawn questions from its own board members. More specifically a joint venture struck in 2008 with Czech insurer PPF Group drew in Italy's market regulators. Citing differences with the company's strategy Cesare Geronzi resigned as chairman in 2011.

EXECUTIVES

Managing Director, Sergio Balbinot, age 54
Financial Reporting, Massimo Romano, age 55
Vice Chairman, Vincent Bollore, age 62
Vice Chairman, Francesco G. Caltagirone, age 71
Vice Chairman, Alberto N. Nagel, age 49
Assistant General Manager Mergers & Acquisitions, Amerigo Borrini
Assistant General Manager Group Communication, Mauro Giusto, age 54
Deputy General Manager Human Resources & Organization, Lodovico Floriani
Real Estate, Giancarlo Scotti
Assistant General Manager Group Control Strategic Planning and Tax, Stefano Meroi, age 49
General Manager and CFO, Raffaele Agrusti, age 57
Deputy General Manager Insurance Operations, Valter Trevisani, age 52
Head Research and Development, Lorenzo Savorelli, age 55
Assistant General Manager Technical Insurance Area and International and European Union Relations, Franco Urlini, age 54
Group Compliance, Antonio Cangeri
Head Group Internal Audit, Alessandro Busetti
Assistant General Manager Group Legal and Corporate Affairs, Oliviero E. Pessi
Chief Risk Officer, Stefano Ferri
Chief Information Technology Officer, Massimo Paltrinieri
Head Investor Relations, Salvatore Colotti
Chief Investment Officer, Philippe Setbon
Chairman, Eugenio Colucci
Chairman, Gabriele Galateri
Controller, Generali S.p.A
CEO, Mario Greco
Managing Director, Sergio Balbinot, age 54
Board Member, Paolo Scaroni, age 68
Vice Chairman, Vincent Bollore, age 62
Group CEO and Managing Director, Giovanni Perissinotto, age 59
Vice Chairman, Francesco G. Caltagirone, age 71
Board Member, Lorenzo Pellicioli, age 63
Board Member, Diego Della Valle, age 61
Board Member, Alessandro (Att) Pedersoli, age 85
Vice Chairman, Alberto N. Nagel, age 49

Board Member, Reinfried Pohl, age 86
Board Member, Petr Kellner, age 50
Chairman, Gabriele Galateri
Auditors: PricewaterhouseCoopersSpA

LOCATIONS

HQ: Assicurazioni Generali S.p.A.
Piazza Duca degli Abruzzi 2, P.O. Box 538, Trieste
34132
Phone: (39) 40 6711   **Fax:** (39) 40 671 600
Web: www.generali.com

Written Premiums by Location

	% of total
Europe	
Italy	29
Germany	24
France	19
Austria	4
Spain	4
Switzerland	2
Other	10
Other	8
Total	**100**

PRODUCTS/OPERATIONS

Revenues

	% of total
Life	59
Property/casualty	31
Financial	10
Total	**100**

Written Premiums

	% of total
Life	67
Non-life	33
Total	**100**

Mergers Acquisitions Divestitur

2011
Sale of stake in Afore Banorte Generali (Mexican pension business operations
Sale of 51% stake in B-Source S.A. (Swiss banking services)

2010
Participation in Intesa Vita sold

2009
Merger of Alleanza Assicurazioni in Assicurazioni Generali and creation of Alleanza Toro
Agreement for the purchase of 30% stake in Guotai AMC (asset manager China)

2008
Generali PPF Holding acquires majority stakes in Ardaf e Rai (insurance companies Romania)
Joint venture with Czech Group PPF and incorporation of Generali PPF Holding (Generali owns a 51 stake)

2007
BSI acquires Banca del Gottardo (bank Switzerlan
Nuova Tirrena sold to Groupama

2006
Purchase of Toro Assicurazioni (65.5% insurance Italy)
Purchase of majority stake in Orel-G (insurance Bulgaria)
Purchase of majority stake in Garant Auto e Garant Life (insurance companies Ukraine)
Purchase of majority stake in Delta Osiguranje (insurance Serbia)
Purchase of Libertas Osiguranje (insurance Croatia)
BSI acquires Banca Unione di Credito (credit union bank Switzerland
Squeeze out of minorities shareholders of Generali Schweiz Holding (Switzerland
Squeeze out of minorities shareholders of Generali Holding Vienna (Austria)
Partial squeeze out of minorities shareholders of AMB Generali Holding (Germany)

COMPETITORS

AIG	FonSai
AXA	ING
Allianz	Milano Assicurazioni
Assurances Generales	Swiss Re
de France	Unipol
Camfin	Zurich Insurance Group
ERGO	ageas SA/NV
Eureko	

HISTORICAL FINANCIALS

Company Type: Public

Income Statement

FYE: December 31

	ASSETS ($ mil.)	NET INCOME ($ mil.)	INCOME AS % OF ASSETS	EMPLOYEES
12/13	619,057	2,636	0.4%	77,185
12/12	582,241	118	0.0%	79,454
12/11	547,204	1,107	0.2%	81,997
12/10	565,381	2,277	0.4%	85,368
12/09	610,537	1,885	0.3%	85,322
Annual Growth	**0.3%**	**8.7%**	**—**	**(2.5%)**

2013 Year-End Financials

Return on assets: 0.4%
Return on equity: 9.6%
Long-term debt ($ mil.): —
No. of shares (mil.): 1,556
Sales ($ mil): 115,046

Dividends
  Yield: —
  Payout: —
Market value ($ mil.): 36,337

	STOCK PRICE ($) FY Close	P/E High/Low	PER SHARE ($) Earnings	Dividends	Book Value
12/13	23.34	36 23	1.71	0.00	17.49
12/12	17.00	486299	0.08	0.00	16.79
12/11	14.74	81 43	0.72	0.00	12.87
12/10	19.10	42 29	1.47	0.00	15.04
12/09	25.96	66 28	1.34	0.00	15.41
Annual Growth	**(2.6%)**	**—**	**6.2%**	**—**	**3.2%**

AUDI AG Vormals Audi-NSU Auto Union AG

LOCATIONS

HQ: AUDI AG Vormals Audi-NSU Auto Union AG
I/FF-12, P.O. Box 10 04 57, Ingolstadt 85045
Phone: (49) 841 89 0   **Fax:** (49) 841 89 325 24
Web: www.audi.com

HISTORICAL FINANCIALS

Company Type: Public

Income Statement

FYE: December 31

	REVENUE ($ mil.)	NET INCOME ($ mil.)	NET PROFIT MARGIN	EMPLOYEES
12/13	68,671	5,453	7.9%	71,781
12/12	64,282	5,646	8.8%	67,231
12/11	57,036	5,676	10.0%	62,806
12/10	47,433	3,461	7.3%	59,513
12/09	42,986	1,872	4.4%	58,011
Annual Growth	**12.4%**	**30.6%**	**—**	**5.5%**

2013 Year-End Financials

Debt ratio: 16.3%
Return on equity: 23.9%
Cash ($ mil.): 18,354
Current ratio: 1.54
Long-term debt ($ mil.): 525

No. of shares (mil.): 43
Dividends
  Yield: —
  Payout: —
Market value ($ mil.): 38,270

	STOCK PRICE ($) FY Close	P/E High/Low	Earnings	PER SHARE ($) Dividends	Book Value
12/13	890.00	18 14	126.84	0.00	584.95
12/12	702.39	14 10	131.30	0.00	452.77
12/11	741.00	18 11	132.01	0.00	382.14
12/10	899.00	28 26	80.48	0.00	347.73
12/09	705.00	51 26	43.55	0.00	342.42
Annual Growth	**6.0%**	**—**	**30.6%**	**—**	**14.3%**

Australia and New Zealand Banking Group Ltd

Australia and New Zealand Banking Group (ANZ) one of Australia's Big Four banks and one of New Zealand's top banks offers commercial and retail banking and financial services from about 1400 branches and offices primarily in Australia and New Zealand but also across the Asia/Pacific region. Offerings include standard deposit and lending services credit cards wealth management agribusiness finance and insurance and foreign exchange services for other financial institutions. Altogether the group serves 8 million customers in more than 30 countries including China Germany India the UK and the US. ANZ traces its roots to the 1835 founding of Bank of Australasia.

ANZ which generates about 95% of its revenues in Australia and New Zealand is focused on expansion in the Asia/Pacific region where it has opened new branches and acquired existing operations. In 2009 it bought the businesses of Royal Bank of Scotland (which had been selling noncore operations) in six Asian countries (Hong Kong Indonesia Philippines Singapore Taiwan and Vietnam) for $550 million. ANZ typically teams with other firms to enter new markets or accelerate growth; the bank has taken minority stakes or formed partnerships with among others Metrobank (Philippines) Bank of Tianjin (China) Sacombank (Vietnam) Panin Bank (Indonesia) and AmBank Group (Malaysia).

To further its strategy of becoming a superregional bank ANZ entered an agreement with wheat marketer AWB Limited allowing the bank to exclusively market its offerings to AWB's 100000 customers. In 2010 the company acquired the loan and deposit books of Landmark Financial Services a division of AWB's Landmark rural arm. Landmark Financial Services provides services to some 10000 agribusiness customers.

In a bid to catch up with its rivals in domestic fund management the company formed OnePath (formerly ING Australia) a wealth management joint venture with Dutch financial services giant ING Groep. The division offers investment retirement insurance and superannuation products. In late 2009 ANZ bought out ING's 51% stake in the venture and rebranded it OnePath. OnePath has about A$54 billion in funds under management.

HISTORY

Captain Cook claimed Australia for the crown in 1770. By 1800 convicts and free immigrants had built a thriving wool trade with the mother country but the land needed financial infrastructure. In 1835 the Bank of Australasia was founded and two years later Union Bank of Australia both backed by London investors. In 1838 the Union Bank moved into New Zealand.

Economic depression during the 1840s helped both the Bank of Australasia and the Union Bank pick off some of their competitors. In 1852 English Scottish and Australia Bank was founded. A gold rush revived the economy and led to several decades of growth during which much of the banks' profits were returned to London.

In 1951 Australasia and Union banks merged to form ANZ. For the next 20-some years Australia's banks developed a large branch network. ANZ formed a savings bank subsidiary Australia and New Zealand Savings Bank in 1955. For the next 15 years the combined bank made sporadic overtures to English Scottish and Australia Bank and in 1970 the marriage finally took place. ANZ became the third-largest bank in Australia.

The company moved its headquarters from London to Australia in 1976. Merger mania hit Australia in the early 1980s as the industry geared up for foreign competition after an open-door policy was instituted. ANZ began building operations inside and outside the country. It bought UK-based Grindlays Bank Group and its offices in 40 countries.

During the 1980s and 1990s ANZ built up its holdings overseas and broadened its offerings into insurance leasing asset management and securities often through acquisitions while trimming a variety of operating companies it had accumulated. In 1995 alone it sold about 75 companies.

Although ANZ still derived about 75% of sales from its home markets its foreign exposure brought pain when the Asian currency crisis spread to Russia and South America in 1998. ANZ realigned its business and liquidated noncore Asian operations. As part of this effort in 1999 the company sold its retail brokerage operations to Citigroup's Salomon Smith Barney and bought a stake in E*Trade's Australian operations.

Also in 1999 ANZ reaffirmed its commitment to Asia. The company's Indonesian subsidiary PT ANZ Panin Bank bought the credit card operations of PT Bank Papan Sejahtera from the Indonesian Bank Restructuring Agency.

ANZ sold its Grindlays subsidiaries in 2000 to Standard Chartered in order to simplify operations.

In 2003 ANZ bought the National Bank of New Zealand from Lloyds Banking Group. Although the Reserve Bank of New Zealand initially required that the two banks remain separate legal entities it eventually permitted them to merge with caveats. The new subsidiary known as ANZ National Bank must see itself as a New Zealand company first and foremost and it must establish facilities that will allow it to operate as a stand alone in the event any of its foreign service providers including its Australian owner fails to deliver.

A year later ANZ sold the majority of its London-headquartered project finance business to Standard Chartered for about $1.5 billion. The business operated in four regions: the UK the US the Middle East and South Asia (especially India).

ANZ then expanded in the Pacific region buying Bank of Hawaii's operations in Papua New Guinea Vanuatu and Fiji. ANZ started selling mutual funds in India but abandoned those plans for a pan-Asian Internet bank it developed with Oversea-Chinese Banking Corporation of Singapore.

EXECUTIVES

CEO and Director, Michael R. P. Smith, age 58
Chairman, John P. Morschel, age 72

Deputy CEO, Graham K. Hodges, $872,700 total compensation
Chief Executive Officer, Philip (Phil) Chronican, age 58
CEO Global Wealth and Private, Joyce A. Phillips
Group Managing Director Human Resources, Susie Babani
CEO ANZ New Zealand, David Hisco
Chief Risk Officer, Nigel Williams
CIO, Anne Weatherston
General Manager Regional Commercial Banking, Tania Motton
CFO, Shayne Elliott
General Manager America and Head of Relationship Banking America, Doug Stolberg
Executive Director Head of Transaction Banking, William Evans
COO, Alistair Currie
Director, Ian J. Macfarlane, age 67
Director, Gregory J. Clark, age 70
CEO and Director, Michael R. P. Smith, age 58
Director, Alison M. Watkins, age 50
Director, David E. Meiklejohn, age 72
Director, Hsien Yang Lee
Auditors: KPMG

LOCATIONS

HQ: Australia and New Zealand Banking Group Ltd
Level 9, 833 Collins Street, Docklands, Melbourne, Victoria 3008
Phone: (61) 3 9273 5555 **Fax:** (61) 3 8542 5252
Web: www.anz.com

Sales

	% of total
Australia	75
New	19
Asia/Pacific Europe and	6
Total	**100**

PRODUCTS/OPERATIONS

Sales

	% of total
Retail	41
Institutional	35
Commercial	19
Wealth	3
Partnerships	2
Total	**100**

COMPETITORS

AMP Limited	HSBC
Bank Central Asia	Macquarie Group
Bank Danamon Indonesia	National Australia
Bank Mandiri	Bank
Bank Rakyat	Sumitomo Trust and
Bank of East Asia	Banking
Commonwealth Bank of	Suncorp-Metway
Australia	Westpac Banking
HBOS Australia	

HISTORICAL FINANCIALS

Company Type: Public

Income Statement

FYE: September 30

	ASSETS ($ mil.)	NET INCOME ($ mil.)	INCOME AS % OF ASSETS	EMPLOYEES
09/14	672,786	6,335	0.9%	50,328
09/13	654,877	5,842	0.9%	47,512
09/12	670,134	5,907	0.9%	45,900
09/11	577,526	5,202	0.9%	50,439
09/10	514,775	4,357	0.8%	46,917
Annual Growth	**6.9%**	**9.8%**	**—**	**1.8%**

2014 Year-End Financials

Return on assets: 0.9%	Dividends
Return on equity: 15.3%	Yield: 5.8%
Long-term debt ($ mil.): —	Payout: 57.2%
No. of shares (mil.): —	Market value ($ mil.): —
Sales ($ mil): 31,555	

	STOCK PRICE ($) FY Close	P/E High/Low		PER SHARE ($) Earnings	Dividends	Book Value
09/14	27.07	10	7	2.24	1.57	15.63
09/13	28.59	14	9	2.09	1.47	15.56
09/12	25.69	13	8	2.15	1.49	15.90
09/11	18.58	14	8	1.93	1.39	14.08
09/10	22.94	12	7	1.69	0.91	12.95
Annual Growth	**4.2%**	**—**	**—**	**7.3%**	**14.6%**	**4.8%**

Aviva Plc (United Kingdom)

In the consolidating European insurance industry Aviva is a lively player. As the top insurance provider in the UK and a leading insurance firm worldwide Aviva offers both life and general insurance. Its long-term savings segment focuses on life insurance pensions unit trusts and other products while its general insurance segment includes the stuff which is called "non-life" or "property/casualty" elsewhere: home auto accident and fire coverage. Its Aviva Investors arm provides asset management globally. In the UK it also offers private medical insurance through employers. All of the company's businesses operate under the Aviva banner.

Geographic Reach

Aviva operates in about 20 countries. In addition to the UK which accounts for about a third of sales primary markets include Canada France Ireland Italy and Spain. The company also has operations in emerging markets such as China India Poland Turkey and Singapore.

Operations

Aviva's long-term insurance segment includes life insurance pensions annuities bonds savings and other investment and protection products and accounts for about three-fourths of annual revenues. General insurance offerings include personal and commercial property/casualty coverage as well as health plans and account for nearly a quarter of sales.

Sales and Marketing

Aviva distributes its products through many channels —including direct sales forces independent brokers partners and bank representatives —tailored to each market where it operates. The firm spent about Â22 million ($36 million) on marketing efforts during 2012.

Financial Performance

Revenue has fluctuated for Aviva in recent years due to economic conditions and restructuring measures. In 2012 the company achieved 21% revenue growth (to some Â47 billion or $75 billion) due to higher investment income levels. Increased revenue was especially seen in core markets including France Italy and Spain as well as certain emerging markets.

The company reported a net loss of Â3 billion ($5 billion) in 2012 however due to changes in investment contract provisions and unallocated investment surplus charges.

Strategy

Through restructuring measures in recent years Aviva has refocused on producing attractive financial returns in its narrowed business markets reducing capital volatility to build financial strength and improving revenue growth and profits.

After taking a big hit in 2008 due to investment losses tied to the global recession Aviva has downsized its operations in subsequent years to try to repair the damage including the sale of noncore international operations. To further focus on priority markets where it has a strong presence in 2012 Aviva sold its Czech Hungarian and Romanian life insurance and pension operations to MetLife for an undisclosed price. It has also steadily reduced its stake in Netherlands-based Delta Lloyd lowering its interest to some 20% in 2012.

The company agreed to sell its Aviva USA division which includes life insurance and annuity operations to Athene Holding for some $1.8 billion in 2012. The sale includes related asset management operations; Aviva will retain certain third-party asset management operations in the US held by its Aviva Investors unit. In addition Aviva agreed to sell operations in Russia Malaysia and Sri Lanka that year.

To further simplify its business the company has combined the operations of a number of businesses especially in Europe to simplify its product range and shorten the time to launch new products. The company has also simplified its branding messages across its operations. Its global operations now operate as Aviva.

HISTORY

When insurers hiked premiums after the 1861 Great Tooley Street Fire of London merchants formed Commercial Union Fire Insurance (CU). It opened offices throughout the UK and in foreign ports and soon added life (1862) and marine (1863) coverage.

Over the next 20 years CU's foreign business thrived. The firm had offices across the US by the 1880s. In the 1890s CU entered Australia India and Southeast Asia. Foreign business eventually accounted for some 75% of CU's sales.

CU went shopping in the 20th century adding accident insurer Palatine Insurance Co. of Manchester in 1900 and rescuing two companies ruined by San Francisco's 1906 earthquake and fire. CU recovered from the Depression with the help of a booming auto insurance market and spent most of the 1930s and WWII consolidating operations to cut costs.

Profits suffered in the 1950s as CU faced increased competition in the US. To boost sales it merged with both multiline rival North British and Mercantile and life insurer Northern and Employers Assurance in the early 1960s. While US business continued to lag in the 1970s the company's European business grew.

From 1982 to 1996 CU cut its operations in the US entered new markets (Poland 1992; South Africa and Vietnam 1996) and sold its New Zealand subsidiaries (1995). As competition in the UK increased the company in 1997 reorganized and merged with General Accident in 1998.

General Accident & Employers Liability Assurance Association (GA) was formed in 1885 in Perth Scotland to sell workers' compensation insurance. Within a few years GA had branches in London and Scotland. It diversified into insurance for train accidents (1887) autos (1896) and fire (1899); in 1906 its name changed to General Accident Fire and Life Assurance.

GA expanded into Australia Europe and Africa at the turn of the century. After WWI the company's auto insurance grew along with car ownership. During the 1930s the company entered the US auto insurance market. WWII put a stop to GA's growth.

The company expanded after the war forming Pennsylvania General Fire Insurance Association (1963) and acquiring the UK's Yorkshire Insurance Co. (1967). By the 1980s about one-third of its sales came from the US.

After 1986 GA acquired some 500 real estate brokerage agencies to cross-sell its home and life insurance. To increase presence in Asia and the Pacific the company in 1988 acquired NZI Corp. a New Zealand banking and insurance company whose failing operations cost GA millions. At the same time new US government regulations and a series of damaging storms hammered the company.

In response GA cut costs posting a profit by 1993. As the industry consolidated the company bought nonstandard auto insurer Sabre (1995) life insurer Provident Mutual (1996) and General Insurance Group Ltd. in Canada (1997). Unable to compete on its own GA merged with Commercial Union to form CGU in 1998.

After the merger CGU added personal pension plans and entered alliances to sell insurance in Italy and India. Merger costs and exceptional losses for 1998 hit operating profits hard. In 1999 CGU upped its stake in French bank Societe Generale to about 7% to help it fend off a hostile takeover attempt by Banque Nationale de Paris (now BNP Paribas).

In 2000 CGU merged with rival Norwich Union to form CGNU and made plans to exit the Canadian life and the US general insurance businesses. In 2001 CGNU sold its US property/casualty operations to White Mountains Insurance.

In an attempt to strengthen its brand name the company changed its name to Aviva in 2002. Following the name change the company merged and rebranded many of its subsidiaries. Aviva also made changes to its Asian operations in 2004 selling its general insurance business in Asia to Mitsui Sumitomo Insurance.

Back home Aviva acquired UK-based automotive service company RAC in 2005 (sold to The Carlyle Group in 2011) to gain access to its auto insurance and loan businesses. To get to the meaty middle Aviva stripped off RAC's non-core businesses including its fleet services which it sold to VT Group in 2006. At around the same time the company also divested its 50% ownership in Lex Vehicle Leasing to HBOS (which later merged with Lloyds TSB to become Lloyds Banking Group).

Looking to Asia for operational strategies Aviva moved more of its back-office operations to India and Sri Lanka but then reversed the trend in 2008 when it sold the business process outsourcing units to WNS.

Having entered Russia in March 2006 Aviva gained an 8% share of the Russian market by 2011 through a major push including the purchase of the Russian pension fund operations of ING in 2009. In 2010 the company re-entered the Singaporean insurance market after a five-year absence by offering direct online car insurance.

As part of an effort to focus on the Aviva brand the company changed the long-time UK brand name of Norwich Union to Aviva UK in 2009. It also changed brand names in Ireland and Poland in 2010.

The company expand its US investment management operations through the Â83 million ($128 million) purchase of River Road Asset Management in 2010.

The company sold its Aviva Australia insurance and wealth management operations business to National Australia Bank in 2009 for $825 million. To loosen up a bit more cash Aviva then spun off about 40% of its Netherlands-based Delta Lloyd subsidiary in an initial public offering. It hoped to raise around $1.2 billion Euros but actually got $995 million. In 2011 the company reduced its stake in its Netherlands-based Delta Lloyd subsidiary to 43%. Aviva also exited its partnership in the United Arab Emirates that year.

Aviva also sold its UK roadside assistance and insurance unit RAC to The Carlyle Group for Â1 billion (about $1.6 billion) in 2011 to focus on its insurance and savings businesses.

EXECUTIVES

Interim Executive Deputy Chairman, John McFarlane, age 67
Executive Director Developed Markets, Trevor J. Matthews, age 62
Chairman, Lord Colin M. Sharman, age 71, $969,309 total compensation
Director Corporate Affairs Aviva Investors, Paul Lockstone
Head Group Media Relations, Andrew Reid
CEO Aviva USA, Christopher J. (Chris) Littlefield, age 46
CEO of Aviva, Andrew Moss, age 56, $1,846,577 total compensation
Global Business Development Director Aviva Investors, Erich Gerth, age 51
CEO Aviva France, Jean-Pierre Menanteau, age 50
Director Corporate Affairs United Kingdom, Hayley Stimpson
Head Group Media Relations, Sue Winston
CEO Higher Growth Markets, Simon Machell, age 51
Marketing Director UK Business, Gary Price
Group Director Human Resources, John Ainley, age 57
COO, Cathryn Riley
Director Investor Relations, Charles Barrows, age 50
CEO UK General Insurance, David McMillan
Head Investor Relations, Jessie Burrows
Chief Executive; Aviva Europe; Executive Director, Igal Mayer, age 53
Regional Development and Strategy Director Aviva Asia, Anupam Sahay
Chief Risk Officer, Robin Spencer, age 44
Chief Executive - Aviva Investors, Alain Dromer, age 59
EVP and COO Operations and Technology Aviva Canada, Robert Merizzi
CEO Investors North America, Greg Boal
Director Global Investment Solutions, Richard Field
Chief Marketing and Communications Officer, Amanda Mackenzie, age 50
Chief Executive; Aviva North America, Richard Hoskins
Director Human Resources Aviva Investors, Nigel Clemson
EVP Claims and Procurement Aviva Canada, Jim Haskins
Head Consultant Relationship Management Aviva Investors, Jonathan May
Manager Investor Relations, Susie Yeoh
Company Secretary, Graham Jones
Chief Risk Officer North America, Dan Guilbert
Head Advertising and Media UK Life, Sue Helmont
CEO Aviva UK & Ireland General Insurance, Maurice Tulloch
Chief Actuary Aviva USA, John D. Currier Jr.
Director Group Communications, Nigel Prideaux
Deputy Director Strategy France, Pierre-Emmanuel Lefebvre, age 35
Secretary Executive Committee, Stanislas Belot, age 37
Deputy CFO and Chief Capital Officer, Tim Harris
Managing Director of Aviva NDB Insurance, Shah Rouf
Head Investor Relations, Jonathan Price
Director Corporate Risk Solutions, Dipak Warren

Director Corporate Affairs Europe, Jon Bunn
Chief Executive Officer; Aviva UK & Ireland Life,
  David Barral
CEO France, Philippe Maso
Head of Investor Relations, David Elliot
Director of Investor Relations, Sophie Garrett
Senior Manager, Anna Cardell
General Manager marketing and bancassurance,
  Amal Perera
Chief Accounting Officer, David Rogers
Chief Risk Officer, John Hodgson
finance Director, John Lister
Vice President of corporate affairs, Sally Turney
Head of Investor Relations, Shaheen Iqbal
Business Development Director, Simon Warsop
Vice President of Claims, Wayne Ross
Group General Counsel; Company Secretary,
  Kirstine Cooper
Director, Michael J. (Mike) Hawker, age 54
Interim Executive Deputy Chairman, John
  McFarlane, age 67
Executive Director Developed Markets, Trevor J.
  Matthews, age 62
Director, Russell F. Walls, age 70
CEO of Aviva, Andrew Moss, age 56
Director, Richard K. Goeltz, age 71
Director, Scott Wheway, age 46
Director, Euleen Y. K. Goh, age 58
Director, Mary Francis, age 66
CFO and Director, Patrick C. (Pat) Regan, age 46
Non-Executive Independent Director, Gay Evans
Non-Executive Independent Director, Glyn Barker
Auditors: Ernst&YoungLLP

LOCATIONS

HQ: Aviva Plc (United Kingdom)
  St. Helen' s, 1 Undershaft, London EC3P 3DQ
Phone: (44) 20 7662 8934
Web: www.aviva.com

Revenues

	% of total
UK & Ireland	46
France	30
High growth markets	5
Total	**100**

PRODUCTS/OPERATIONS

Revenues

	% of total
Long-term (life)	76
General insurance &	23
Fund	1
Total	**100**

COMPETITORS

AEGON	Legal & General
AXA	Group
Ageas Insurance	Lloyds Banking Group
International	Prudential plc
Allianz	QBE
Bank of Ireland	RSA Insurance
Canada Life	Royal Bank of Scotland
Friends Provident	Standard Life
Generali	Zurich Insurance Group
ING	

HISTORICAL FINANCIALS
Company Type: Public

Income Statement
FYE: December 31

	ASSETS ($ mil.)	NET INCOME ($ mil.)	INCOME AS % OF ASSETS	EMPLOYEES
12/13	460,864	3,318	0.7%	27,718
12/12	508,848	(5,186)	—	33,122
12/11	482,575	347	0.1%	36,562
12/10	574,642	2,271	0.4%	45,142
12/09	573,964	1,757	0.3%	46,327
Annual Growth	**(5.3%)**	**17.2%**	**—**	**(12.1%)**

2013 Year-End Financials

Return on assets: 0.6%
Return on equity: 20.7%
Long-term debt ($ mil.): —
No. of shares (mil.): —
Sales ($ mil): 57,255

Dividends
  Yield: 2.9%
  Payout: 108.4%
Market value ($ mil.): —

	STOCK PRICE ($) FY Close	P/E High/Low	PER SHARE ($) Earnings	Dividends	Book Value
12/13	15.15	62 35	1.07	0.45	5.35
12/12	12.41	— —	(1.82)	0.82	5.35
12/11	9.25	682353	0.09	2.06	7.35
12/10	12.41	70 39	0.77	0.73	7.70
12/09	13.07	105 83	0.61	0.00	6.76
Annual Growth	**3.8%**	**— —**	**14.9%**	**—**	**(5.7%)**

AXA Banque Europe SA

LOCATIONS

HQ: AXA Banque Europe SA
  25 Boulevard du souverain, Brussels B-1170
Phone: (32) 3 678 61 11
Web: www.axabank.eu

HISTORICAL FINANCIALS
Company Type: Public

Income Statement
FYE: December 31

	ASSETS ($ mil.)	NET INCOME ($ mil.)	INCOME AS % OF ASSETS	EMPLOYEES
12/13	50,781	(16)	—	0
12/12	51,689	(30)	—	0
12/11	54,114	(191)	—	0
12/10	41,994	16	0.0%	0
12/09	37,881	(14)	—	0
Annual Growth	**7.6%**	**—**	**—**	**—**

2013 Year-End Financials

Return on assets: (-0.0%)
Return on equity: (-1.5%)
Long-term debt ($ mil.): —
No. of shares (mil.): 395
Sales ($ mil): 3,449

Dividends
  Yield: —
  Payout: —
Market value ($ mil.): —

AXA S.A.

The insurance world revolves around this AXA. The company which started as a sleepy collection of mutual insurance companies is today one of the world's largest insurers and a financial management powerhouse. In addition to its strong presence in France AXA owns US-based AXA Financial which controls life insurance firm AXA Equitable and investment manager AllianceBernstein. The company also has major subsidiaries in the UK (AXA UK) Germany (AXA Konzern) Japan (AXA Life) and Belgium (AXA Belgium). The AXA companies offer life insurance personal and commercial property and casualty insurance financial services and asset management services. AXA has about Â1 trillion (or $1.45 trillion) in assets under management.

Geographic Reach

Rather than trying to run a cross-border organization AXA instead buys and builds up businesses in each country rebranding them under the AXA name. The company serves more than 100 million customers in 60 countries primarily in Europe North America and Asia as well as in Africa Latin America and the Middle East. The central and eastern European market is the largest geographic segment accounting for about 30% of annual sales.

Operations

AXA's operations are divided into five segments with the largest business division –life and savings –accounting for about 60% of annual revenues. Life and savings products include savings retirement life insurance and health insurance offerings for groups and individuals; the division serves some 40 million customers in 30 countries around the globe. AXA's property/casualty segment accounting for about 30% of sales offers commercial and personal auto homeowners property and liability insurance primarily in Europe the Middle East and Latin America.

Meanwhile the asset management (investment fund management) international insurance (corporate solutions assurance offerings) and banking (retail banking savings and mortgage loans in Europe) segments together account for the remainder of revenues. The asset management business while small compared to AXA's two larger segments has a sizable presence in the investment market with assets under management of more than Â1000 billion.

Sales and Marketing

AXA markets its products through independent agents and brokers as well as through direct and salaried sales forces. It also has distribution partnerships with entities including banks car dealerships and other retail locations.

AXA sells its products both to individuals and to corporate groups. Its commercial property/casualty unit primarily targets small to midsized companies. The asset management business targets institutional investors (including AXA's insurance subsidiaries) and individuals.

Financial Performance

AXA reported revenues of some Â86 billion ($132 billion) in 2011 a decrease of about 19% from 2010 sales. A majority of the decline is due to the divestiture of operations in certain regions. However gains on asset sales caused AXA's net income to rise 46% to $4.5 billion.

Other factors impacting revenues included decreased insurance sales in regions including Latin America the Mediterranean Belgium France Japan and Central and Eastern Europe which was offset by growth in the US Switzerland Hong Kong and other Asian markets.

Strategy

AXA invests in a diverse spread of business to reduce risk and volatility across its operations and it focuses on building a solid business foundation and distribution network in each respective market where it operates.

To focus on core operations (life and savings property/casualty and asset management) as well as to free up capital and allow for expansion in emerging markets AXA is conducting some divestitures. For instance in 2013 the company sold the older books of life insurance policies issued by its MONY Life subsidiaries to Protective Life for some $1.1 billion to reduce its exposure to the underperforming North America market. AXA plans to focus on growth in the US in select markets where it has experienced momentum.

In addition in late 2011 the company sold its Canadian arm to Intact Financial for about $2.6 billion. Also in 2011 AXA exited its Australian and New Zealand joint venture operations through a complex transaction with Australian insurer AMP. (However AXA also expanded its Asian operations through the AMP deal.)

Mergers and Acquisitions

The transaction with AMP was one of the company's largest deals conducted in recent years. Through the transaction AXA took full control of the Asian operations of former majority-owned subsidiary AXA Asia Pacific (AXA APH) in 2011 for some A$9.8 billion ($9.4 billion) gaining full control of subsidiaries joint ventures and partnerships in China Hong Kong India Indonesia Malaysia the Philippines Singapore and Thailand. Former joint-venture partner AMP took full control of AXA APH's operations in Australia and New Zealand for some A$3.5 billion ($3.4 billion).

AXA further expanded its insurance operations in emerging markets in 2012 when it acquired the Asian (mainly Hong Kong and Singapore) and Latin American (Mexico) property/casualty operations of HSBC. The purchase also expanded AXA's bancassurance operations (where insurance is sold at partnering retail banks) in the regions.

Ownership

Mutuelles AXA (two mutuals) controls AXA through a more than 20% stake. In 2010 AXA voluntarily delisted its stock from the NYSE to focus on its larger-volume listing on the Euronext Paris exchange.

HISTORY

AXA dates to the 1817 formation of regional fire insurer Compagnie d'Assurances Mutuelles contre l'incendie in Rouen France (northwest of Paris). In 1881 France's first mutual life insurer was founded: Mutuelle Vie.

In 1946 these two operations and the younger Anciennes Mutuelles Accidents (founded 1922) were brought together by Sahut d'Izarn (general manager of Compagnie d'Assurances) as the Groupe Ancienne Mutuelle. Later members included Ancienne Mutuelle de Calvados (1946) Ancienne Mutuelle of Orleans (1950) Mutualite Generale (1953) and Participation (1954).

A long-term thinker d'Izarn named not only his successor Lucien Aubert but also Aubert's successor: Claude Bebear a 23-year-old friend of d'Izarn's son. Never having held a job Bebear found the whole thing amusing and decided to try it.

Groupe Ancienne Mutuelle prospered during the 1960s thanks to d'Izarn's disciplined management but his technophobia kept the company from entering the computer age.

D'Izarn died in 1972. Aubert capitulated to worker demands during a series of strikes in the early 1970s; Bebear ended a 1974 strike by threatening to use force against an employee sit-in then ousted Aubert. Bebear spent the rest of the 1970s upgrading the firm's technology. During this period the company became known as Mutuelles Unies.

Bebear then began building the firm through a series of spectacular acquisitions. In 1982 Mutuelles Unies gained control of crisis-ridden stock insurer Drouot. Two years later the company's name became AXA (which has no meaning and was chosen because it is pronounced the same in most Western languages). When another old-line insurer Providence went on the market AXA went after it. Providence's management was entertaining another offer when AXA bought tiny inactive Bayas Tudjus which held the right to a seat on the Providence board. Bebear capitalized on small stockholders' dissatisfaction to spark a bidding war and used a new issue of Drouot stock in 1986 to buy Providence —France's first hostile takeover.

AXA bought lackluster US firm Equitable (later named AXA Financial) in 1991 infusing $1 billion into the firm in return for the right to own up to 50% of its stock upon demutualization in 1992. AXA moved into Asia with the purchase of Australia's National Mutual in 1995.

Bebear consolidated the operations into a global organization. In 1996 AXA bought the ailing Union des Assurances de Paris which had done poorly since its 1994 privatization. It bought the 52% of Belgian insurer Royale Belge SA it didn't already own as well as Belgian savings bank Anhyp in 1998.

Bebear raised hackles when he supported the Societe Generale-Paribas bank merger then supported BNP's hostile takeover attempt of both (which garnered only Paribas). In 1999 AXA bought Guardian Royal Exchange then sold the life and pensions business to Dutch insurer AEGON; Bebear announced his retirement in 1999. In 2000 he stepped down from the management board but took over as chairman of the supervisory board. Henri de Castries was placed in the top executive position as chairman of the management board.

That year AXA took control of Japan's Nippon Dantai Life Insurance. It also bought the remaining shares of AXA Financial and the 44% of AXA UK (formerly Sun Life and Provincial Holdings) it didn't already own. The next year AXA unloaded its debt-heavy subsidiary Banque Worms to Deutsche Bank.

In an attempt to strengthen its US retail insurance and annuity business AXA through subsidiary AXA Financial bought MONY Group for some $1.5 billion in 2004. The deal was opposed by some of MONY's shareholders but it ultimately gained approval. On the down side AXA discontinued its slumping US-based reinsurance operations (AXA Corporate Solutions Reinsurance and AXA Corporate Solutions Life Reinsurance).

Also in 2004 the company exited its operations in Uruguay thus exiting the South American market and sold its Dutch brokerage and health insurance subsidiaries and its German mortgage lending business.

AXA made a major coup in the insurance industry when it acquired the Winterthur Group from Credit Suisse Group for Â7.9 billion ($11 billion) in 2006. Winterthur added subsidiaries in 17 countries with 13 million customers and especially strengthened AXA's European operations. The primary Swiss Winterthur division was renamed AXA Versicherungen. AXA also sold the assets of AXA Re that year.

In 2007 AXA sold noncore Dutch subsidiaries AXA Netherlands Winterthur Netherlands and DBV Netherlands. To expand its insurance operations in emerging markets AXA acquired South Korean car insurance provider Kyobo Auto (now Kyobo AXA General Insurance). In addition it formed a partnership with BNP Paribas to provide property/casualty insurance in the Ukraine.

That year the company's property fund division AXA Investment Managers announced plans to invest more than $15 billion in Asian real estate by 2013. In addition AXA established the AXA Research Fund in 2008 to invest $500 million in social science research institutions over five years.

After a long career at the center of AXA's operations Bebear retired as chairman of the supervisory board in 2008 but retained the title of honorary chairman of the company.

AXA bought out its Turkish joint venture partner pension fund Oyak for $525 million in 2008 to take full control of AXA Holding A.S. (formerly AXA Oyak) a provider of life and other insurance products in the fast-growing Turkish market. Later that year the company purchased #3 Mexican life insurance company ING Seguros (now AXA Seguros) for $1.5 billion from ING Groep. AXA also made an investment in the Russian property/casualty market.

To further expand in emerging markets by targeting the high-growth regions of Central and Eastern Europe in 2010 AXA entered the Romanian life insurance market with the buy of Omniasig Life. The deal followed AXA's buy of minority interests in Omniasig's Hungarian Czech and Polish subsidiaries from the European Bank for Reconstruction and Development in late 2009.

To focus on core operations in 2010 the company sold parts of its UK life insurance business (including traditional life and pension corporate pension and annuity operations) to acquisition vehicle Resolution Ltd. for Â3.3 billion ($4.1 million). Resolution added the acquired operations to another insurance firm Friends Provident picked up in 2009; the former AXA operations are now known as Friends Life. The asset sale allowed AXA UK to focus its life operations on high-growth wealth management services including its specialist pension and direct protection businesses. AXA UK also retained its property/casualty health insurance and investment management operations.

AXA also simplified its management organization to reduce complexities and create a nimble leadership team to face future customer needs and economic challenges. In 2010 the company streamlined its governance structure by combining its supervisory board and its management board into a single board of directors led by Henri de Castries as chairman and CEO; Castries had previously been chairman of the management board.

AXA took full control of the Asian operations of former majority-owned subsidiary AXA Asia Pacific (AXA APH in which it previously owned a 54% stake) in 2011 to strengthen its operations in the fast-paced region. The firm completed a deal with Australian insurer AMP through which AMP acquired all of AXA APH for some A$13.3 billion ($12.8 billion); AMP then sold the Asian operations to AXA for some A$9.8 billion ($9.4 billion) while retaining AXA APH's operations in Australia and New Zealand. The deal was agreed upon in late 2010 after a year-long bidding war for control of AXA APH between AMP and rival National Australia Bank (NAB).

Also in 2011 it sold its roughly 16% stake in Taikang Life (China's fourth-largest life insurer) to a group of shareholders for $1.2 billion to meet regulatory conditions for the AXA APH asset acquisition. (AXA gained a stronger position in another joint venture in China with Industrial and Commercial Bank of China through the AXA APH deal.)

EXECUTIVES

Chairman and CEO, Henri de Castries, age 60, $662,600 total compensation
Deputy CEO and Board Member, Denis Duverne, age 61, $569,836 total compensation
Vice Chairman, Norbert Dentressangle, age 60
CEO AXA UK, Paul J. Evans, age 49
CEO AXA Asia Pacific Holdings Australia, Andrew (Andy) Penn, age 51
CEO Northern Central and Eastern Europe, Jacques de Vaucleroy, age 54

CEO France, Nicolas Moreau, age 49, $580,835 total compensation

President and CEO AXA Financial and AXA Equitable, Mark Pearson, age 56

Vice Chairman Asia Pacific, John R. Dacey, $365,532 total compensation

General Counsel and Head of Human Resources, George Stansfield

CEO AXA Japan, Jean-Louis Laurent Josi, age 45

Member of the Executive Committee; Group Chief Operating Officer, Veronique Weill

CEO Mediterranean-Latin America Region (MedLA), Jean-Laurent Granier

Investor Marketing and Events, Laurence Letty

CEO Northern Central and Eastern Europe, Alfred Bouckaert

Chairman and CEO AllianceBernstein, Peter S. Kraus

SVP and Head Investor Relations, Mattieu Rouot

Financial Analyst France, Thomas Hude

Vice President, Yadl Gabel

Member of the Executive Committee; Chief Executive Officer of AXA Konzern AG, Thomas Buberl

Board Member, Jean-Martin Folz, age 67

Board Member, Michel Pebereau, age 71

Deputy CEO and Board Member, Denis Duverne, age 61

Vice Chairman, Norbert Dentressangle, age 60

Board Member, Jacques de Chateauvieux, age 64

Board Member, Anthony J. Hamilton, age 73

Board Member, Dominique Reiniche, age 58

Board Member, Giuseppe Mussari, age 52

Board Member, Wendy Cooper, age 64

Board Member, Francois Martineau, age 64

Board Member, Ramon de Oliveira, age 60

Board Member, Isabelle Kocher, age 48

Board Member, Suet-Fern Lee, age 56

Auditors: PricewaterhouseCoopersAudit

LOCATIONS

HQ: AXA S.A.
25, avenue Matignon, Paris 75008
Phone: (33) 1 40 75 57 00
Web: www.axa.com

Sales

	% of total
Central & Eastern	31
France	24
Mediterranean & Latin	15
US	12
Asia/Pacific	10
UK &	5
Direct	3
Total	**100**

PRODUCTS/OPERATIONS

Sales

	% of total
Life &	60
Property/casualty	31
Asset	4
International	4
Banking &	1
Total	**100**

Selected Brands and Divisions

Africa
  AXA Holding Maroc
Asia-Pacific
  AXA China
  AXA Japan
  AXA Financial Services (Singapore)
  Kyobo AXA General Insurance
Asset Management
  AXA Investment Managers (US)
  AllianceBernstein (US)
Europe
  AXA Bank (Germany)
  AXA Bank Europe (Belgium)

AXA Banque (France)
AXA Czech Republic Insurance
AXA Czech Republic Pension Funds
AXA France Assurance
AXA Holdings Belgium
AXA Holdings Ireland
AXA Hungary
AXA Insurance
AXA Italia
AXA Konzern (Germany)
AXA Lebensversicherung (Germany)
AXA Life
AXA Life Europe
AXA Luxembourg
AXA Mediterranean
AXA MPS Vita
AXA MPS Danni
AXA Poland Pension Funds
AXA Poland
AXA Portugal Companhia de Seguros
AXA Portugal Companhia de Seguros de Vida
AXA Turkey
AXA UK
AXA Versicherung (Germany)
Seguro Directo
International Insurance
  AXA Assistance
  AXA Corporate Solutions Assurance
  AXA Corporate Solutions Life Reinsurance Company
  Colisee
North America
  AXA Financial (US)
  AXA Seguros (Mexico)

COMPETITORS

ACE Limited	JPMorgan Chase
AEGON	Legal & General
AIG	Group
Ageas Insurance	Merrill Lynch
International	MetLife
Allianz	Munich Re Group
Allstate	Nationwide
Aviva	New York Life
BNP Paribas	Nippon Life Insurance
Bank of America	Prudential
Berkshire Hathaway	Prudential plc
CIGNA	State Farm
CNP Assurances	Sumitomo Life
Citigroup	Talanx
Dai-ichi Life	The Hartford
Eureko	Travelers Companies
Generali	Zurich Insurance Group
ING	

HISTORICAL FINANCIALS

Company Type: Public

Income Statement

FYE: December 31

	ASSETS ($ mil.)	NET INCOME ($ mil.)	INCOME AS % OF ASSETS	EMPLOYEES
12/13	1,042,385	6,170	0.6%	93,146
12/12	1,004,154	5,472	0.5%	94,364
12/11	944,329	5,592	0.6%	96,999
12/10	979,224	3,679	0.4%	102,957
12/09	1,020,286	5,194	0.5%	103,432
Annual Growth	0.5%	4.4%	—	(2.6%)

2013 Year-End Financials

Return on assets: 0.5%
Return on equity: 8.4%
Long-term debt ($ mil.): —
No. of shares (mil.): —
Sales ($ mil): 172,219

Dividends
  Yield: 3.3%
  Payout: 41.1%
Market value ($ mil.): —

	STOCK PRICE ($) FY Close	P/E High/Low		PER SHARE ($) Earnings	Dividends	Book Value
12/13	27.89	30	17	2.41	0.93	30.18
12/12	18.22	19	10	2.16	0.89	29.61
12/11	12.86	25	11	2.26	0.89	26.85
12/10	16.65	45	21	1.45	1.25	28.98
12/09	23.68	42	9	2.18	1.10	29.42
Annual Growth	4.2%	—	—	2.6%	(4.2%)	0.6%

BAE Systems Plc

BAE Systems helped win the Battle of Britain in 1940 with its Spitfire and Mosquito fighters; today it is a leading military contractor and major foreign player in the US defense market. BAE's main operating groups —electronic systems cyber & intelligence and platforms & services —provide products and services that include electro-optical sensors flight controls commercial and financial security ship repair and modernization and aircraft. BAE's fighter aircraft include the Hawk Tornado and the next-generation Eurofighter Typhoon. North America is BAE's biggest market with the US Department of Defense (DoD) its largest single customer.

Financial Analysis

Struggling with declining budgets in customer markets the company weathered a year-over-year 2011 sales decline of 14%.

By segment platforms & services (UK) fell 4%. Operations in this segment which accounts for about 32% of revenue include UK-based air and maritime activities as well as such shared services as the Advanced Technology Center. Platforms & services (US) plummeted about 31%. This segment which represents about 27% of revenue is made up of the US-headquartered land & armaments business and operates additionally in the UK Sweden and South Africa.

Platforms & services (international) which operates in Australia India Oman and Saudi Arabia was down 12%. The segment accounting for 20% of revenue was busy with the first Saudi Typhoon squadron becoming operational and the launch of the first Royal Australian Navy Landing Helicopter Dock hull. Electronics systems —representing 14% of revenue —decreased about 11%. This segment's operations include electronic warfare systems military and commercial digital engine and flight controls and hybrid electric drive systems. Cyber & intelligence's 2011 year-over-year revenue rose 16%. The segment accounting for 7% of revenue handles cyber government and commercial security operations.

Strategy

Amid sharp reductions in defense spending in both of the company's biggest markets the US and UK BAE Systems has launched a strategy that besides focusing on electronics and cyber & intelligence includes developing more export business to support its platforms segments and expanding its operations internationally.

Also to further its focus on core businesses BAE Systems has disposed of several units in 2011 including Swiss-Photonics and BAE Systems' remaining share in Saab AB as well as its business in regional aircraft asset management and its US-based composites structures and California-based advanced ceramics units. In 2012 the company sold its safety products business.

Also in 2011 BAE Systems settled a tough legal situation agreeing to pay a fine of up to $79 million after reaching a civil settlement with the US Department of State for alleged violations of US defense export control regulations. The company's US subsidiary BAE Systems Inc. was not involved in the matter.

Mergers & Acquisitions

As a segment targeted for additional growth cyber & intelligence has expanded recently with some major acquisitions. In 2011 BAE Systems acquired the intelligence service businesses of L-1 Identity Solutions as well as ETI A/S a Danish cyber and intelligence company and Norkom Group which provides anti-money laundering services. In other business the segment enjoyed a boost in commercial sales for its Detica unit and invested in the UK Security Operations Center.

Company Background

In September 2012 BAE Systems agreed to merge with Airbus. However the proposed $45 billion —which would have created the largest global aerospace and defense player on the planet both in total sales and market value —was called off weeks later after it failed to pass European governmental and regulatory hurdles.

HISTORY

Post-Wright brothers and pre-WWII a host of aviation companies sprang up to serve the British Empire —too many to survive after the war when the empire contracted. Parliament took steps in 1960 to save the industry by merging companies to form larger stronger entities —Hawker-Siddeley Aviation and British Aircraft Corporation (BAC).

Hawker-Siddeley made up of aircraft and missiles divisions was created by combining A.V. Roe Gloster Aircraft Hawker Aircraft Armstrong Whitworth and Folland Aircraft. It attained fame in the 1960s for developing the Harrier "jump jet."

BAC was formed from the merger of Bristol Aeroplane English Electric and Vicker-Armstrong. In 1962 it joined France's Aerospatiale to build the supersonic Concorde and became a partner in ventures to develop the Tornado and Jaguar fighters. The cost of these ventures plus the commercial failure of the Concorde was more than the company could bear. Realizing British aviation was again in trouble the British government nationalized BAC and Hawker-Siddeley in 1976 and merged them in 1977 with Scottish Aviation to form British Aerospace (BAe).

BAe joined the Airbus consortium in 1979. A partial privatization of the company began in 1981 when the government sold 52% to the public (the remaining stake sold in 1985). Also in 1981 BAe announced a joint venture with Comsat General and announced that it would be the prime contractor for L-SAT-1 the European Space Agency's telecommunications satellite. Later in the decade BAe bought Steinheil Optronik (optical equipment) and Ballast Nedam Groep (civil and marine engineering).

BAe formed Ballast Nedam Construction in 1990. It also began to restructure its troubled regional aircraft division in 1992 by laying off thousands of workers and closing a major plant. It divested its corporate jet business to Raytheon and won a $7.5 billion contract from Saudi Arabia for Tornado jets in 1993. BAe sold its satellite business in 1994. Matra BAe Dynamics the world's third largest maker of tactical missiles was formed in a 1996 merger between BAe and Lagardere subsidiary Matra Hachette. BAe joined Lockheed Martin in a competition to build fighter jets for the UK and the US.

BAe's emphasis on large jetliners led to the 1998 breakup of Aero International its two-year-old regional aircraft joint venture with Aerospatiale

(France) and Alenia (Italy). Shortly thereafter BAe spent $454 million for a 35% stake in Swedish military jet maker Saab. Also in 1998 BAe bought Siemens' UK- and Australia-based defense electronics operations. In 1999 BAe acquired the electronic systems defense unit of Marconi Electronic Systems (MES) for $12.7 billion (including US-based Tracor). The company changed its corporate identity to BAE SYSTEMS to remove the British influence from its name.

The UK government agreed to loan BAE about $836 million in 2000 to support the Airbus A3XX superjumbo airliner project. The same year BAE acquired Lockheed Martin's control systems unit for about $510 million. The prime contractor for the UK's new Type 45 destroyer BAE was named to build two of the first three Type 45s. Late in the year BAE spent about $1.7 billion for a group of Lockheed Martin's defense electronics businesses including its Sanders airborne electronics unit. BAE sold its power and controls business (actuation equipment and starter motors) to Cobham.

Early in 2001 the company sold its 54% stake in BAE SYSTEMS CANADA (now known as CMC Electronics) to Oncap a Toronto-based investment fund as part of a $398 million management buy-out of the affiliate. The same year the Airbus Industrie consortium finally became Airbus S.A.S. a corporation. In late 2001 BAE announced that it would phase out its regional aircraft business.

The following year (2002) BAE sold its defensive-countermeasures business to Esterline Technologies. Just a year later it took a 29% stake in Alvis maker of the Challenger main battle tank. In 2004 General Dynamics made a 280 pence a share bid for Alvis; BAE topped that offer in early June with a bid of 320 pence a share (about $650 million) and a deal was struck. BAE then combined Alvis with its RO Defence group to form a new business unit Land Systems. Prior to the Alvis deal BAE was reportedly in merger talks with US contractors (including General Dynamics).

BAE was selected as the prime contractor for the UK's next two aircraft carriers in 2003. In 2004 however the Ministry of Defence took away that designation and brought in Thales to work on the carrier project. The controversy was ratcheted up another notch in 2005 when Halliburton subsidiary Kellogg Brown & Root (now KBR an independent company) was brought in as the physical integrator of the project. A spending review by the UK's Ministry of Defence in 2006 however put any final decisions about Britain's future carrier plans on hold until mid-2007 when yet another deal was worked out. The new carrier plan combined the shipbuilding operations of BAE with those of VT Group —Britain's only remaining shipbuilding concerns.

The joint venture known as BVT Surface Fleet provided the Royal Navy with two new aircraft carriers in a contract valued at £3.8 billion (about $7.6 billion). The deal aimed not only to secure the jobs at the UK's last remaining shipbuilders during the life of the carrier contract but also to create a single UK-based shipbuilding concern that safeguarded jobs in the long term as VT and BAE's shipbuilding operations would no longer compete with each other for bringing big contracts to the UK. VT owned 45% of BVT and BAE owned the majority. VT had the option of selling its stake in BVT for a guaranteed minimum of £380 million (about $535 million) and it took that option in 2009 in order to focus on its growing support services business.

It was revealed in early 2005 that BAE was seeking buyers for its aerostructures business which made airframe components for such customers as Airbus Boeing Cessna and Raytheon. Around this time BAE reduced its stake in Saab from 35% to 22%. Also in 2005 BAE acquired —

through its North American subsidiary —US-based United Defense Industries (UDI) in a deal worth about $4.2 billion as part of its push to get more US defense contracts. As part of the company's BAE Systems Land & Armaments business UDI made armored vehicles (including the Bradley Fighting Vehicle) landing craft and weapons systems. Upon closing the UDI deal BAE SYSTEMS North America changed its name to BAE Systems Inc.

The sale of the company's Airbus stake to Airbus for £2.75 billion (about $3.3 billion) in 2006 was effected in order to focus on its defense businesses —primarily in the US. Selling its Airbus stake helped fund expansion in the US defense sector. That year BAE sold its aerostructures business which made Avro jet aircraft to Spirit AeroSystems. With the closure of its commercial aerospace unit and the sale of its stake in Airbus BAE essentially became a military contractor.

In 2007 BAE made its first move toward a major US defense acquisition since the completion of the EADS deal when it bought Armor Holdings for about $4.5 billion. The deal positioned it as a more powerful competitor in the tactical military vehicle sector; a fact that gained significance as the US military fleet of HUMVEEs aged driving demand for a next-generation replacement which turned out to be the Mine Resistant Ambush Protect (MRAP) vehicle. Prior to the acquisition Armor won a Marine Corps contract to build over 1000 MRAPs which was in addition to the more than 440 MRAPs that BAE already had contracts to build. The combined contracts were worth about $730 million.

The company had a good year in 2008. It acquired three companies. US-based MTC Technologies was purchased for $375 million; it brought technical and professional services used especially in equipment integration and modernization for the US military and intelligence agency sectors. It was incorporated into the company's EI&S group. To target the national security market Detica was acquired for £543 million (almost $960 million plus the assumption of net debt) in the fall. Supporting the company's Program & Support business Detica provides business and technology consultancy with expertise in security and threat intelligence. Investing down under BAE SYSTEMS paid about $650 million for Tenix Defence a leading Australian defense contractor. That year Ian King (former COO) was appointed CEO after Mike Turner (CEO since 2002) retired after serving 42 years at BAE.

BAE SYSTEMS met with some turbulence in early 2010 when it lost out on a follow-up contract with the DoD; the deal had previously generated a whopping $2 billion in annual sales for the company. Instead the DoD awarded the contract to make medium tactical vehicles to Oshkosh Corporation.

EXECUTIVES

Board Member; President and CEO BAE Systems Inc., Linda P. Hudson, age 64
Group General Counsel, Philip Bramwell
Group Managing Director Programmes and Support, Nigel Whitehead
Director Group HR, Alastair Imrie
EVP Product Sectors, Tom Arseneault
SVP Strategy and Planning BAE Systems Inc., Douglas E. (Doug) Belair
Director Group Strategy, Andrew Davies
Director Group Communications, Charlotte Lambkin
EVP Service Sectors, Lawrence B. (Larry) Prior III, age 58
Director Group Strategy, Kevin Taylor
EVP Service Sectors, David A. (Dave) Herr

SVP Information Management and CIO BAE
Systems Inc., D. Michael Bennett
SVP Corporate Communications BAE Systems
Inc., John Suttle
CEO and Board Member, Ian King, age 58,
$1,230,205 total compensation
Director Group Business Development, Alan
Garwood, age 59
Group Managing Director International, Guy
Griffiths
Secretary, David Parkes
SVP Human Resources BAE Systems Inc., Curt
Grey
Director Group Media Relations, John Neilson
Head Financial Public Relations, Lindsay Walls
Manager Media Relations Land Systems, Mike
Sweeney
Head of Communications BAE Systems Australia,
Simon Latimer
Manager Media Relations Global Tectical Systems
Land Systems South Africa, Natasha Pheiffer
VP Internal Audit BAE Systems Inc., Michelle
Lamberton
SVP Finance BAE Systems Inc., Brad Jacobs
Group Finance Director, Peter Lynas
Non-Executive Independent Chairman of the
Board, Keith Edelman
Senior Independent Non-Executive Director,
William Tuffy
Chairman, Dick Oliver
Board Member; President and CEO BAE Systems
Inc., Linda P. Hudson, age 64
Board Member, Nicholas C. (Nick) Rose, age 55
Board Member, Michael Hartnall, age 72
Board Member, Sir Peter J. Mason, age 68
Board Member, Carl G. Symon, age 67
CEO and Board Member, Ian King, age 58
Board Member, Paul Anderson
Group Finance Director, Peter Lynas
Non-Independent Non-Executive Director, John
Chillcott
Non-Independent Non-Executive Director, Simon
Peters
Auditors: KPMGAuditPlc

LOCATIONS

HQ: BAE Systems Plc
6 Carlton Gardens, London SW1Y 5 AD
Phone: (44) 1252 373232
Web: www.baesystems.com

Sales

	% of total
US	41
Europe	
UK	21
Rest of Middle East	15
Saudi	13
Rest of Middle Asia/Pacific	
Australia	6
Rest of Africa & Central & South	2
Canada	2
Total	**100**

PRODUCTS/OPERATIONS

Sales

	% of total
Platforms services	
Platforms & services	32
Platforms & services	27
Platforms & services	20
Electronic	14
Cyber &	7
Total	**100**

Sales

	% of total
Long-term	53

Sale of	26
Provision of	21
Royalty	
Total	**100**

Selected Products and Services

Air
  Avionics
  Combat aircraft
  Commercial aircraft
  Controls (flight and engine)
  Jet trainers
  Maintenance repair and upgrades
  Missiles and counter measures
  Reconnaissance aircraft
  Unmanned aerial vehicle (UAV)
Homeland Security
  Border and coastal surveillance
Information Technology
Intelligence Security & Resilience
Land
  Artillery
  Combat and tactical vehicles
  Munitions
  Radar
  Unmanned systems
Sea
  Amphibious and auxiliary ships
  Naval guns
  Submarines
  Underwater systems
  Warships
Systems Integration & Electronics
  C4ISR (Command Control Communications
    Computers Intelligence Surveillance
    Reconnaissance)
  Communications
  Electronic warfare & countermeasures
  Imaging systems
  Intelligence systems
  Navigation systems
  Sensor systems
Technology and Innovation
Through-Life Support

COMPETITORS

Astronautics	Horstman Defence
Boeing	Systems
Bombardier	ITT Corp.
DRS Technologies	L-3 Communications
EADS	Lockheed Martin
Fabbrica D' Armi Pietro	Meggitt-USA
Beretta	Navistar International
Finmeccanica	Northrop Grumman
GenCorp	RUAG Holding
General Dynamics	Rockwell Collins
Goodrich Corp.	Sotera Defense
High Performance	Thales
Technologies	Ultra Electronics
Honeywell	United Technologies
International	

HISTORICAL FINANCIALS

Company Type: Public

Income Statement

FYE: December 31

	REVENUE ($ mil.)	NET INCOME ($ mil.)	NET PROFIT MARGIN	EMPLOYEES
12/13	27,869	277	1.0%	78,000
12/12	26,789	1,721	6.4%	81,000
12/11	27,452	1,915	7.0%	87,000
12/10	32,756	1,633	5.0%	92,000
12/09	32,997	(108)	—	98,000
Annual Growth	**(4.1%)**	**—**		**(5.5%)**

2013 Year-End Financials

Debt ratio: 24.5%	No. of shares (mil.): —
Return on equity: 4.7%	Dividends
Cash ($ mil.): 3,672	Yield: 4.0%
Current ratio: 0.73	Payout: 3,593.7%
Long-term debt ($ mil.): 4,171	Market value ($ mil.): —

STOCK PRICE ($) FY Close	P/E High/Low	PER SHARE ($) Earnings	Dividends	Book Value
12/13	29.29	1543993	0.09	1.20	1.74
12/12	22.28	186126	0.53	1.15	1.84
12/11	17.66	155102	0.57	2.81	2.02
12/10	20.85	201132	0.47	0.95	2.43
12/09	23.18	—	(0.03)	0.95	2.13
Annual Growth	**6.0%**	**—**	**—**	**5.9%**	**(4.9%)**

Baloise Holding AG

Founded in 1863 as a fire insurance company Baloise-Holding today is a general insurer that sells such standardized products as group and individual life policies and accident property and auto insurance to small firms and individuals. The company is one of the leading insurers in Switzerland operating primarily there and in Germany; together the countries account for about 80% of its sales. Through subsidiaries it also operates in six other nearby countries including Croatia and Serbia. Baloise also provides banking pension plans and other financial services through its Baloise Bank SoBa. The company uses its own sales force as well as partner distributors and independent brokers to sell its wares.

Baloise has been growing adding Croatia Liechtenstein and Serbia to the fold in 2007. Company strategy includes strengthening its brand to gain new customers and expanding regionally with "culturally compatibility" in mind. Its brands include Baloise Basler Deutcher Ring and Osiguranje Zagreb.

At the end of 2008 a challenging year for businesses worldwide Baloise declared a 50% drop in profits and that its stock lost about 30% of its value (beating the 35% lost by the Swiss Market Index on average). Believing its fundamentals are strong the company has been buying back shares and it paid shareholders their usual dividend.

In 2009 the company agreed to acquire the Luxembourg non-life insurance operations of Fortis Insurance for Ä23 million ($34 million). The purchase strenthens its property/casualty operations in the Luxembourg market.

HISTORY

In 1863 15 business leaders in Basel Switzerland formed the Baloise Fire Insurance Company. This was followed in 1864 by the formation of the Baloise transportation and life insurance companies.

Baloise-Holding was created in 1962 as a holding company for the previously independent insurance entities. In 1971 it merged all of its non-life companies into the Baloise Insurance Group.

Under its then-new chairman and president Rolf Schauble Baloise-Holding began in 1993 to reorganize its operations as it implemented a new corporate strategy. Key components of the strategy included a focus on the company's core European markets and a pattern of discarding less-profitable businesses. In 1998 Baloise-Holding sold off its US operations.

Strengthening its position as a full-fledged financial services company in 2000 Baloise acquired Swiss bank Solothurner (now Baloise Bank SoBa).

The same year it purchased Belgian bank HBK-Spaarbank Belgian insurer Amazon Insurance N.V. and Swiss regional bank Solothurner Bank SoBa.

However in 2004 the company's Belgian unit Mercator sold its banking unit to ING.

The company acquired life insurer MONEY-MAXX Lebensversicherung AG from the Dutch Aegon Group in 2005.

EXECUTIVES

Head of Deutscher Ring Germany, Wolfgang Fauter, age 63

Head of Baloise Assurances Luxembourg, Andre Bredimus

Head of Baloise Bank SoBa, Alois Muller

Vice Chairman, Georg F. Krayer, age 71

Head Asset Management, Martin Wenk, age 57

Head of Corporate Development, Thomas Wodrich

Group CEO, Martin Strobel, age 48

Head of Information Systems and Logistics, Rene Guttinger

Head Finance, German Egloff, age 56

Head of Accounting/Controlling, Urs Bienz

Head of Basler Securitas Germany, Frank Grund

Head of Baloise Asset Management, Reto Diezi

Head of Real Estate/Mortgages, Urs Degen

Head of Baloise Fund Invest, Robert Antonietti

Head Corporate Center, Thomas Sieber

Head of Compliance, Peter Kalberer

Head of Runoff, Bruno Rappo

Chairman, Andreas Burckhardt, age 63

Head of Financial Management, Stefan Nolker

Corporate Human Resources, Markus Jordi, age 53

Head of Investment Strategy and Investment Controlling, Bernhard Casar

Member of the Corporate Executive Committee; Head of Division International, Jan Meulder

Member of Corporate Executive Committee; Head of Corporate Division Switzerland, Michael Mueller

Director, Werner Kummer, age 67

Director, Hansjorg Frei, age 72

Vice Chairman, Georg F. Krayer, age 71

Director, Gertrud Hohler, age 72

Director, Arend Oetker, age 73

Director, Christoph Albrecht, age 74

Director, Klaus Jenny, age 70

Director, Eveline Saupper, age 56

Non-Executive Independent Director, Michael Becker

Non-Executive Independent Director, Thomas Pleines

Non-Executive Independent Director, Andreas Beerli

Non-Executive Independent Director, Georges-Antoine Boccard

Non-Executive Independent Director, Hans Frei

Auditors: PricewaterhouseCoopersAG

LOCATIONS

HQ: Baloise Holding AG
Aeschengraben 21, Basel CH-4002
Phone: (41) 58 285 85 85   **Fax:** (41) 58 285 70 70
Web: www.baloise.com

PRODUCTS/OPERATIONS

Sales

	% of total
Life	59
Other	41
Total	**100**

Selected Subsidiaries

Austria
  Basler Versicherungen (insurance and pension products for private and business clients)
Belgium
  Mercator Verzekeringen (personal and property insurance for individuals and small to mid-sized businesses)
Croatia

Osiguranje Zagreb (personal and property insurance for individuals and small to mid-sized businesses)
Germany
  Basler Versicherungen (personal and property insurance for individuals small and mid-sized enterprises and selected industrial clients)
  Deutscher Ring (insurance and pension products for individuals)
Luxembourg
  Baloise Assurances (life personal and property insurance for private and business clients)
Serbia
  Basler Osiguranja (personal and property insurance for individuals and small to mid-sized businesses)
Switzerland
  Baloise Bank SoBa (banking products and services)
  Basler Versicherungen (insurance and pension products for individuals and small to mid-sized enterprises)

COMPETITORS

AEGON	Helvetia Group
AIG	ING
AXA	Itausa
AXA Versicherungen	Munich Re Group
Allianz	Prudential plc
Eureko	Swiss Life
Hannover Re	Zurich Insurance Group

HISTORICAL FINANCIALS

Company Type: Public

Income Statement

FYE: December 31

	ASSETS ($ mil.)	NET INCOME ($ mil.)	INCOME AS % OF ASSETS	EMPLOYEES
12/13	84,952	1,019	1.2%	8,613
12/12	80,208	958	1.2%	8,795
12/11	73,412	129	0.2%	9,141
12/10	69,878	929	1.3%	8,797
12/09	65,332	810	1.2%	9,400
Annual Growth	**6.8%**	**5.9%**	**—**	**(2.2%)**

2013 Year-End Financials

Return on assets: 1.2%
Return on equity: 18.7%
Long-term debt ($ mil.): —
No. of shares (mil.): 46
Sales ($ mil): 10,860

Dividends
  Yield: 0.0%
  Payout: 3.1%
Market value ($ mil.): 583

	STOCK PRICE ($) FY Close	P/E High/Low		PER SHARE ($) Earnings	Dividends	Book Value
12/13	12.42	2	1	10.53	0.33	116.02
12/12	7.89	1	1	9.91	0.34	112.25
12/11	9.71	11	9	1.37	0.37	87.76
12/10	9.15	1	1	9.50	0.25	92.83
12/09	10.25	1	1	8.32	0.20	87.80
Annual Growth	**4.9%**		**—**	**6.1%**	**13.1%**	**7.2%**

Banca Popolare di Milano

Founded in 1865 Banca Popolare di Milano (also known as Pop Milano) is a cooperative bank with some 700 branches in Italy concentrated in and around Milan and in northern and central portions of the country. It also operates an online bank (Webank) and commercial banks Banca Popolare di Mantova and Banca Akros. In addition to standard retail services such as deposit accounts credit cards and loans the company offers corporate and investment banking insurance and wealth management. Banca Popolare di Milano has grown by acquiring other banks. Currently it serves about 1.4 million customers primarily private small- and medium-sized businesses.

EXECUTIVES

President of the Management Board, Andrea C. Bonomi

Chief Lending Officer, Paolo Testi

Chief Commercial Officer, Iacopo De Francisco

Chief Operating Officer, Giovanni Sordello

Risk Management Manager, Raffaele Barteselli

Chairman of the Supervisory Board, Piero Giarda

Director, Rocco Corigliano

Director, Jean-Jacques Tamburini, age 66

Director, Giuseppe Coppini

Director, Enrico Airaghi

Director, Luca Caniato

Director, Emilio Castelnuovo

Director, Enrico Corali

Director, Eugenio Crosta

Director, Roberto Fusilli

Director, Piero Lonardi

Director, Maria Martellini

Director, Michele Motterlini

Director, Gianfranco Pittatore

Director, Marcello Priori

Director, Graziano Tarantini, age 53

Director, Valerio Tavormina

Auditors: PricewaterhouseCoopersSpA

LOCATIONS

HQ: Banca Popolare di Milano
Piazza F. Meda 4, Milan I-20121
Phone: (39) 02 77001   **Fax:** (39) 02 7700 2993
Web: www.gruppobpm.it

2012 Branch Locations

	No.
Lombardia	475
Piemonte	103
Lazio	80
Puglia	41
Emilia	35
Other	35
Total	**769**

COMPETITORS

Banco Popolare	Monte dei Paschi di
Deutsche Bank (Italy)	Siena
Intesa Sanpaolo	UniCredit
Mediobanca	

HISTORICAL FINANCIALS

Company Type: Public

Income Statement

FYE: December 31

	ASSETS ($ mil.)	NET INCOME ($ mil.)	INCOME AS % OF ASSETS	EMPLOYEES
12/13	67,946	40	0.1%	7,846
12/12	69,164	(566)	—	8,312
12/11	67,170	(794)	—	8,467
12/08	62,968	105	0.2%	8,786
12/07	64,200	476	0.7%	8,378
Annual Growth	**0.9%**	**(33.6%)**	**—**	**(1.1%)**

2013 Year-End Financials

Return on assets: 0.0%
Return on equity: 0.7%
Long-term debt ($ mil.): —
No. of shares (mil.): —
Sales ($ mil): 3,255

Dividends
  Yield: —
  Payout: —
Market value ($ mil.): —

	STOCK PRICE ($) FY Close	P/E High/Low	PER SHARE ($) Earnings	Dividends	Book Value
12/13	3.80	794717	0.01	0.00	1.55
12/12	2.79	—	(0.18)	0.00	1.64
Annual Growth	36.2%	—	—	—	(1.0%)

Banco Bilbao Vizcaya Argentaria SA (BBVA)

It's not Cortez revisited but Banco Bilbao Vizcaya Argentaria (BBVA) —one of Spain's top banks —is conquering the New World. Although much of its business activity is in Spain (more than half of its loans) the company also operates in about 10 Latin American countries through subsidiaries including BBVA Bancomer in Mexico; Banco Bilbao Vizcaya Argentaria Chile; and BBVA Banco Frances in Argentina. With some 7400 offices in 30 countries the bank offers retail corporate and institutional banking; investment banking; asset management; insurance; and securities brokerage. BBVA also operates in other European countries and is expanding in China as well as in the US where it owns Compass Bank.

The company is focused on five geographic areas: Spain Mexico South America the US and Eurasia (which includes BBVA's Portugese and Turkish operations).

As one of Spain's largest banks (along with Santander) BBVA has been struggling with the world-wide financial downturn and the sovereign debt crisis. Unemployment in the country remains above 20% and the gross domestic product has been shrinking. More than a quarter of the bank's real estate loans are non-performing loans which has led to lower revenues. Another key market Mexico has seen some bright spots (mortgage activities have begun to rebound there) but is also still vulnerable to the troubled economic climate. Goodwill impairment in the US contributed to a loss in the market in 2011. That year BBVA's revenues grew 11% to $47.2 billion but net income fell 41% to $3.9 billion. A decrease in net interest income (due to an upturn in interest rates in the Eurozone) a decline in asset values slower customer activities and a reduction of earnings from portfolio sales all served to drag down the company's earnings.

As part of a larger restructuring of banks in Spain the company acquired Unnim Banc which had been taken over by the Bank of Spain for a symbolic Â1 in 2012. BBVA also assumed 20% of Unnim's real estate losses amounting to some Â300 million. The acquisition gives the bank more than 600 branches in Catalonia which has been a target market for BBVA. The deal also made BBVA Spain's largest bank by assets.

The company has worked to expand internationally to help diversify operations beyond its home market. BBVA has targeted Asia as a growth market forming an alliance with China's CITIC Group. In accordance the company owns a 30% stake in CITIC International Financial Holdings and a 15% stake in China Citic Bank.

BBVA is expanding in other markets too. In 2011 it acquired Credit Uruguay Banco from Credit Agricole to become one of Uruguay's largest financial institutions. The company also bought a 25% stake in Turkish bank Garanti which it jointly manages with Turkish conglomerate Dogus Group.

To better focus on its expansion in the US BBVA is selling its Puerto Rican operations to OFG Bancorp for $500 million. The sale represents less than 1% of BBVA's total assets. BBVA plans to sell other operations in Latin America including the Provida Bancomer and Horizonte Peru pension management companies.

HISTORY

Banco Bilbao Vizcaya Argentaria (BBVA) is the progeny of the 2000 merger of Banco Bilbao Vizcaya (BBV) and Argentaria Caja Postal y Banco Hipotecario. BBV formed when Banco de Bilbao and Banco de Vizcaya merged in 1988 while Argentaria Caja Postal y Banco Hipotecario coalesced from the 1991 merger of six government-owned banks.

In 1857 a group of Basque businessmen banded together to offer loans and other banking services to businesses. The bank —eventually Banco de Bilbao —helped fund the region's industrialization. Its first foray beyond the Basque region was Paris not Madrid in 1902. It later entered London Madrid and other major European cities.

Franco's rise to power and the isolation of WWII deterred industrial growth. In protectionist Spain Bilbao bought 16 banks between 1941 and 1943 and formed a unit to focus on US and Latin American partnerships.

In the 1960s Bilbao reorganized and formed a unit focused on industrial growth. It rolled with the punches as banking rules continued to change in the 1970s and 1980s. The bank expanded consumer services began issuing credit cards (1971) and bought banks that couldn't cope with changing regulations.

To compete in financially deregulated Europe Spain's overpopulated banking industry began to consolidate in the early 1990s. After #3 Bilbao failed to take over #2 Banco Espanol de Credito it merged with regional rival Banco de Vizcaya.

Formed in 1901 by Basque merchants Banco de Vizcaya expanded through purchases and had some 200 branches by 1935 including offices in Europe's leading cities. During the post-WWII bust it bought weaker banks and invested in Spain's industrial complex.

In the 1960s and 1970s Vizcaya added industrial banking insurance personal investment management and leasing. The bank refocused on international growth opening branches in London Mexico City New York and other cities. It entered consumer banking and became another participant in the branch race; by 1980 Vizcaya had some 900 offices. Looking to be a strong player in deregulated Europe the bank merged with Bilbao in 1988; together the two banks had nearly 3400 branches.

The merger almost unraveled after Vizcaya chair Pedro Toledo (set to lead the new bank with Bilbao chair Jose Angel Sanchez Asiain) died in 1989. The two banks fought over Toledo's replacement until the Bank of Spain suggested in 1990 Bilbao executive Emilio Ybarra y Churruca become the only chair.

Until 1992 government regulations and strong unions prevented BBV from cutting some 5000 jobs and 600 branches. After Europe's 1992 deregulation the company targeted Latin America buying banks in Mexico and Peru (1995); Argentina Colombia and Venezuela (1996); and Brazil and Chile (1997). The merger of rivals Banco Santander and Banco Central Hispanoamericano in 1999 prompted BBV to merge with Argentaria in 2000.

After the merger BBVA teamed with top Spanish telecom Telefonica to develop online banking services. The duo announced plans to merge BBVA's Uno-e online bank with First-e one of Europe's first Internet-only banks. The merger which would have created the largest Internet bank in the world collapsed as the dotcom crisis began and online banks experienced losses.

Also in 2000 BBVA bought 30% of Grupo Financiero Bancomer Mexico's #2 bank and merged it into its existing Mexican bank Grupo Financiero BBV-Probursa; the resulting Grupo Financiero BBVA-Bancomer is the country's largest bank. The bank completed the renaming of its subsidiaries to reflect their position as BBVA subsidiaries in 2002.

In 2004 BBVA bought the 40% of Mexico's BBVA Bancomer that it did not already own. To finance about half of the approximately $4 billion bid the company issued 195 million new shares.

The next year BBVA tried to buy the rest of Italian bank Banca Nazionale del Lavoro (BNL) (it already owned 15%). However Italian regulatory bodies nixed the deal and BNP Paribas bought BNL. BBVA later sold its stake in the Italian bank.

To break into the US market BBVA purchased Texas banks Laredo National Bancshares for $850 million in 2005 Texas Regional Bancshares for more than $2 billion in 2006 and State National Bancshares for $480 million in 2007. BBVA's strategy in the US was centered around capturing more of the lucrative business transacted between the US and Mexico and to access the exploding Spanish-speaking market in the states. BBVA expanded its US operations again when it bought Compass Bank in 2007.

Adding on to its US operations BBVA acquired the failed Guaranty Financial Group in 2009. The deal which was facilitated by the FDIC fit in with BBVA's strategy of expanding in the Sunbelt especially Texas. BBVA merged its previously acquired State National Bancshares Laredo National Bancshares and Texas Regional Bancshares into Compass.

EXECUTIVES

Head Legal Tax Audit and Compliance, Eduardo Arbizu Lostao
Head Risk, Manuel Castro
Head Brand and Communication, Gregorio Panadero Illera, age 45
Head South America, Vicente Rodero Rodero
Head Strategy and Development, Carlos Torres Vila
Secretary, Domingo Armengol Calvo
Director Investor Relations, Pedro Barahona
Head Human Resources and Services, Juan Ignacio Apoita Gordo
Chief Executive Officer; Executive Director, Angel Fernandez
General Secretary, Domingo Armengol
Head of Chairmans Office, Fernando Gutierrez
Director of Human Resources and Services, Juan Gordo
Chief Risk Officer, Manuel Aladro
Chief Financial Officer, Manuel Cid
Director of Innovation and Technology, Ramon Valls
Director, Jose Maldonado Ramos, age 61
Director, Ramon Bustamante y de la Mora, age 65
Director, Juan Carlos Alvarez Mezquiriz, age 55
Director, Ignacio Ferrero Jordi, age 69
Director, Enrique Medina Fernandez, age 71
Director, Jose Antonio Fernandez Rivero, age 64
Director, Carlos Loring Martinez de Irujo, age 67
Director, Susana Rodriguez Vidarte, age 58
Director, Tomas Alfaro Drake, age 62
Director, Rafael Bermejo Blanco, age 74
Director, Juan Pi Llorens, age 64
Independent Director, Belen Lopez
Independent Director, Carlos Irujo
Independent Director, Enrique Fernandez

Independent Director, Ignacio Jordi
Independent Director, Jose Rivero
Independent Director, Jose Garcia-Suelto
Independent Director, Juan Llorens
Independent Director, Ramon Mora
Independent Director, Susana Vidarte
Independent Director, Tomas Drake
Auditors: DeloitteSL

LOCATIONS

HQ: Banco Bilbao Vizcaya Argentaria SA (BBVA)
Plaza de San Nicolas, 4, Bilbao, Viscaya 48005
Phone: (34) 91 537 7000   **Fax:** (34) 91 537 6766
Web: www.bbva.com

Sales

	% of total
Mexico	34
Spain	26
Eurasia	20
South	20
Total	**100**

PRODUCTS/OPERATIONS

Sales

	% of total
Interest	61
Fees &	14
Net gains on financial assets &	3
Dividends	1
Other	21
Total	**100**

Selected Subsidiaries and Affiliates

BBVA Banco Frances (Argentina)
BBVA Bancomer S.A. DE C.V. (Mexico 99.9%)
BBVA Chile
BBVA Colombia (95%)
BBVA Compass (US)
BBVA Dinero Express S.A.U. (financial services)
BBVA Luxinvest S.A. (Luxembourg)
BBVA Patrimonios Gestora SGIIC S.A. (private bank)
BBVA Portugal
BBVA Puerto Rico
BBVA Seguros S.A. DE Seguros Y Reaseguros (insurance 99.9%)
CITIC International Financial Holdings Limited (Hong Kong 30%)
Seguros Bancomer S.A. DE C.V. (Mexico)
Uno-e Bank S.A. (online services)

Selected Acquisitions

2012
Unnim Banc S.A. (E1; Spain; savings bank)
2011
Turkiye Garanti Bankasi A.S. (E4.4 billion; Turkey; bank; 25%)
Credit Uruguay Banco (E78 million; Uruguay; bank)

COMPETITORS

ABN AMRO Group	Banorte
BNP Paribas	Barclays
Banamex	Credit Suisse
Banco Comercial	DEPFA BANK
Portugues	Deutsche Bank
Banco Galicia	Espirito Santo
Banco Popular Espa?ol	Grupo Santander
Banco de la Nacion	HSBC
Argentina	JPMorgan Chase
Banco do Brasil	Santander Rio
Bankinter	Societe Generale

HISTORICAL FINANCIALS

Company Type: Public

Income Statement

FYE: December 31

	ASSETS ($ mil.)	NET INCOME ($ mil.)	INCOME AS % OF ASSETS	EMPLOYEES
12/13	802,051	3,067	0.4%	109,305
12/12	840,632	2,209	0.3%	115,852
12/11	773,080	3,885	0.5%	110,645
12/10	739,769	6,164	0.8%	104,755
12/09	770,798	6,064	0.8%	104,416
Annual Growth	**1.0%**	**(15.7%)**	**—**	**1.2%**

2013 Year-End Financials

Return on assets: 0.3%	Dividends
Return on equity: 5.3%	Yield: 4.4%
Long-term debt ($ mil.): —	Payout: 185.5%
No. of shares (mil.): —	Market value ($ mil.): —
Sales ($ mil): 48,338	

	STOCK PRICE ($) FY Close	P/E High/Low	PER SHARE ($) Earnings	Dividends	Book Value
12/13	12.39	60 37	0.54	0.55	10.12
12/12	9.42	53 27	0.42	0.53	10.05
12/11	8.57	39 20	0.83	1.10	10.16
12/10	10.17	32 12	1.53	0.94	10.84
12/09	18.04	40 10	1.54	0.39	11.26
Annual Growth	**(9.0%)**	**—**	**(23.2%)**	**9.4%**	**(2.6%)**

Banco BPI SA (Portugal)

Banco BPI is well aware of the color of Portuguese money. The bank is engaged in a wide range of investment banking and commercial banking activities. Investment-related services offered by the bank include corporate finance equities treasury and bonds asset management private banking and venture capital. Its commercial business includes banking for individuals companies and institutions and the usual array of lending leasing and mortgaging and credit services. Banco BPI serves about 1.5 million customers through some 700 branches across Portugal as well as about 35 investment centers and various other operations. The company has insurance partnerships in Portugal with Allianz and Cosec.

In 2009 the Portugese government made an offer to buy Companhia de Seguro de Creditos or Cosec a provider of credit and bond insurance services. Banco BPI joinly owns Cosec with France's Euler Hermes.

EXECUTIVES

Chairman, Artur Santos Silva, age 73
Deputy Chairman and Chairman Executive Committee, Fernando Ulrich, age 62
Deputy Chairman, Antonio Domingues, age 58
Executive Committee Member Corporate Banking Network Institutional Banking and State Business Sector Project Finance Credit risk Corporate Marketing Office for Angola Madrid Branch and Building Finance, Maria Celeste Hagatong, age 62
Executive Committee Member Investment Banking Private Equity Investor Relations Risk Analysis and Control Division and Financial and Economic Studies, Manuel Ferreira de Silva, age 57

Executive Committee Member Individuals and Small Businesses Loans to Individuals and Small Businesses Emigration and External Promoters, Pedro Barreto, age 48
Deputy Chairman, Carlos da Camara Pestana
Deputy Chairman and Chairman Executive Committee, Fernando Ulrich, age 62
Deputy Chairman, Carlos da Camara Pestana
Auditors: Deloitte&AssociadosSROCSA

LOCATIONS

HQ: Banco BPI SA (Portugal)
Rua Tenente Valadim 284, 3 piso, Porto 4100-476
Phone: (351) 22 607 3337   **Fax:** (351) 22 607 4738
Web: www.bpi.pt

COMPETITORS

Banco Comercial	Espirito Santo
Portugues	Espirito Santo
Banco Espirito Santo	Investment Bank
Caixa Geral de	
Depositos	

HISTORICAL FINANCIALS

Company Type: Public

Income Statement

FYE: December 31

	ASSETS ($ mil.)	NET INCOME ($ mil.)	INCOME AS % OF ASSETS	EMPLOYEES
12/13	58,786	92	0.2%	8,864
12/12	58,738	328	0.6%	8,821
12/11	55,561	(368)	—	9,292
12/10	61,109	247	0.4%	9,494
12/09	68,353	252	0.4%	9,437
Annual Growth	**(3.7%)**	**(22.3%)**	**—**	**(1.6%)**

2013 Year-End Financials

Return on assets: 0.1%	Dividends
Return on equity: 3.6%	Yield: —
Long-term debt ($ mil.): —	Payout: —
No. of shares (mil.): 1,383	Market value ($ mil.): —
Sales ($ mil): 2,870	

Banco Comercial Portugues, S.A.

With its home country's history of exploration it's no surprise that Banco Comercial Portugues (BCP) is charting a successful course through the world's financial markets. BCP offers a multitude of financial services for business and consumer customers under the Millennium bcp brand. It provides asset management through Millennium bcp fundos de investimento private banking through Millennium Banque Privee and vehicle management through Millennium bcp renting. BCP also offers health insurance in Portugal through Medis. In addition to about 1510 branches the bank has on its home turf it also has operations in Africa Asia Europe (primarily Poland and Greece) and North America.

Geographic Reach

The company operates almost 775 branches in Portugal as well as roughly 680 branches internationally.

Company Background

Banco Comercial Portugues (BCP) was formed in 1985 by a group of Portugal's leading industrialists; it was the first private commercial bank to open after civil unrest brought socialism to the country.

LOCATIONS

HQ: Banco Comercial Portugues, S.A.
Praca D. Joao I, 28, Porto 4000-295
Phone: (351) 21 321 1081   **Fax:** (351) 21 321 1079
Web: www.millenniumbcp.pt

PRODUCTS/OPERATIONS

HISTORICAL FINANCIALS

Company Type: Public

Income Statement

	ASSETS ($ mil.)	NET INCOME ($ mil.)	INCOME AS % OF ASSETS	EMPLOYEES
12/13	112,902	(1,019)	—	18,873
12/12	118,287	(1,606)	—	21,297
12/11	120,914	(1,097)	—	21,470
12/10	133,850	403	0.3%	21,774
12/09	137,647	324	0.2%	21,796
Annual Growth	(4.8%)	—		(3.5%)

FYE: December 31

2013 Year-End Financials

Return on assets: (-0.8%)   Dividends
Return on equity: (-24.8%)   Yield: —
Long-term debt ($ mil.): —   Payout: —
No. of shares (mil.): —   Market value ($ mil.): —
Sales ($ mil): 5,168

	STOCK PRICE ($) FY Close	P/E High/Low		PER SHARE ($) Earnings	Dividends	Book Value
12/13	1.00	—	—	(0.06)	0.00	0.18
Annual Growth	—		—	—	—	—

Banco De Sabadell SA

Banco de Sabadell (also known as BancoSabadell) is one of the top banking groups in Spain offering corporate commercial and private banking through more than 2000 branches. The company operates under five banking brands: SabadellAtlantico and Banco Herrero for business banking; Solbank which specializes in providing banking services for tourists and the tourism industry; ActivoBank for online banking; and BancoUrquijo for private banking. BancoSabadell also offers bancassurance products asset management and securities brokerage. The company has a presence in about 20 countries. It is looking across the Atlantic for growth especially in Florida as well as in Mexico.

BancoSabadell acquired Miami-based Mellon United National Bank (which it rebranded Sabadell United Bank) and its 15 branches from The Bank of New York Mellon in 2010. The following year it acquired the assets and branches of the failed Lydian Private Bank further adding to its operations in the region. In 2007 the company acquired TransAtlantic Bank and BBVA's private banking business also both based in Miami.

Closer to home BancoSabadell acquired smaller rival Banco Guipuzcoano in 2010. The following year it acquired savings bank Caja de Ahorros del Mediterraneo (CAM) which had been seized by the government for a symbolic E1. That deal brought some 5 million additional customers to the bank

increased its assets by around 75% and upped its branch numbers by more than 900. CAM (now SabadellCAM) will be integrated into BancoSabadell's operations over time.

In 2008 company sold a 50% stake in its insurance operations to Zurich Financial Services which is managing the business.

EXECUTIVES

Deputy General Manager, Blanca Corominas
Deputy General Director, Carlos Santamans
Deputy General Manager, Cirus Cabot
Deputy General Manager, Enric Masachs
Deputy General Manager, Federico Castillo
Deputy General Director, Fernando Munoz
Deputy General Manager, Ignacio Casellas
Chief Executive Officer; Executive Director, Jaime Romojaro
Deputy General Manager, Jaime Vallverdu
Deputy General Director, Jaume Balsells
Third Vice Chairman of the Board; Independent Director, Javier Landiribar
Deputy General Manager, Javier Hernandez
Deputy General Manager, Joan Sierra
Deputy General Manager, Jose Puig
General Controller; Director, Jose Rodriguez
Second Vice Chairman of the Board, Jose Bosch
Executive Chairman of the Board, Jose Creus
Deputy General Manager, Juan Alonso
Deputy General Manager, Luis Vall
Non-Member Secretary of the Board, Miguel Junyent
General Director, Miquel Guell
Deputy General Manager, Pablo Moreno
Deputy General Manager, Pedro Sologaistua
Deputy General Manager, Rafael Nauffal
Deputy General Director, Ramon Reina
Deputy General Manager, Salvador Terradas
Chief Financial Officer; General Director, Tomas Muina
Deputy General Manager, Ramon Pol
Independent Director, Francesc Selvas
Independent Director, Hector Moreno
Independent Director, Joan Andreu
Independent Director, Joaquin Corachan
Second Vice Chairman of the Board, Jose Bosch
Independent Director, Jose Sufrategui
Independent Director, Maria Lloveras
Independent Director, Sol Comadran
Auditors: PricewaterhouseCoopersAuditoresS.L.

LOCATIONS

HQ: Banco De Sabadell SA
Plaza de Sant Roc, 20, Barcelona, Sabadell 08201
Phone: (34) 93 902 323 555   **Fax:** (34) 93 935 916 062
Web: www.bancsabadell.com

COMPETITORS

BBVA	Banco de Valencia
Banco Pastor	Grupo Santander
Banco Popular Espa?ol	

HISTORICAL FINANCIALS

Company Type: Public

Income Statement

	ASSETS ($ mil.)	NET INCOME ($ mil.)	INCOME AS % OF ASSETS	EMPLOYEES
12/13	225,015	28	0.0%	16,427
12/12	212,927	18	0.0%	14,291
12/11	129,910	5	0.0%	10,675
12/10	129,954	3	0.0%	10,777
12/09	119,312	5	0.0%	9,466
Annual Growth	17.2%	51.4%	—	14.8%

FYE: December 31

2013 Year-End Financials

Return on assets: 0.0%   Dividends
Return on equity: 0.2%   Yield: 0.0%
Long-term debt ($ mil.): —   Payout: 669.8%
No. of shares (mil.): —   Market value ($ mil.): —
Sales ($ mil): 10,541

	STOCK PRICE ($) FY Close	P/E High/Low		PER SHARE ($) Earnings	Dividends	Book Value
12/13	5.03	266	92	0.10	0.65	3.55
12/12	5.77	437	226	0.04	1.27	3.88
12/11	8.68	100	73	0.19	0.41	5.43
12/10	7.90	68	37	0.37	0.29	5.73
12/09	13.95	68	45	0.57	0.58	6.06
Annual Growth	(22.5%)	—	—	(35.7%)	2.5%	(12.5%)

Banco do Brasil S.A.

LOCATIONS

HQ: Banco do Brasil S.A.
SBS Q.1, BL C, Lote 32, ED. Sede III, 5 Andar, Asa Sul, Brasilia, DF 70073-901
Phone: (55) 61 3310 3752   **Fax:** (55) 61 3310 3735
Web: www.bb.com.br

PRODUCTS/OPERATIONS

Sales

	% of total
Interest	
Loans &	48
Securities	22
Other	6
Noninterest	
Banking	8
Insurance pension plan &	3
Other	13
Total	**100**

Selected Subsidiaries

Ativos S.A. (debt collection)
BB Administradora de Cart?es de Credito S.A.
BB Banco Popular do Brasil S.A.
BB Corretora de Seguros e Administradora de Bens S.A. (broker)
BB Gest?o de Recursos-Distribuidora de Titulos e Valores Mobilarios S.A. (asset management)
BB Leasing Company Ltd.
BB Securities Ltd.
BV Participac?es S.A. (50% holding company)
Banco do Brasil - AG. Viena
Banco Nossa Caixa S.A.
Besc Distribuidora de Titulos e Valores Mobilarios S.A. (99.6% asset management)
Brasilcap Capitalizac?oes S.A. (49.9% capitalization)
Brasilsaude Companhia de Seguros (49.9% health insurance)
Cia. de Seguros Alianca do Brasil (insurance)
Kepler Weber S.A. (18% industry)

HISTORICAL FINANCIALS

Company Type: Public

Income Statement

FYE: December 31

	ASSETS ($ mil.)	NET INCOME ($ mil.)	INCOME AS % OF ASSETS	EMPLOYEES
12/13	491,985	4,418	0.9%	0
12/12	555,632	5,500	1.0%	0
12/11	518,403	6,799	1.3%	113,810
12/10	483,626	6,804	1.4%	109,026
12/09	402,735	7,705	1.9%	103,971
Annual Growth	5.1%	(13.0%)	—	—

2013 Year-End Financials

Return on assets: 0.9%
Return on equity: 14.6%
Long-term debt ($ mil.): —
No. of shares (mil.): —
Sales ($ mil): 54,450

Dividends
Yield: 10.0%
Payout: 12.9%
Market value ($ mil.): —

	STOCK PRICE ($) FY Close	P/E High/Low	PER SHARE ($) Earnings	Dividends	Book Value
12/13	10.38	1 0	1.56	1.05	(0.00)
12/12	12.67	1 1	1.92	0.65	(0.00)
12/11	12.60	1 1	2.37	0.30	11.70
12/10	19.50	2 1	2.49	0.90	11.44
12/09	18.00	1 1	2.98	0.08	9.02
Annual Growth	(12.9%)	— —	(15.0%)	90.7%	

HISTORICAL FINANCIALS

Company Type: Public

Income Statement

FYE: December 31

	ASSETS ($ mil.)	NET INCOME ($ mil.)	INCOME AS % OF ASSETS	EMPLOYEES
12/13	110,975	(712)	—	10,216
12/12	110,308	126	0.1%	9,944
12/11	103,783	(140)	—	9,863
12/10	111,962	683	0.6%	9,858
12/09	118,554	752	0.6%	9,359
Annual Growth	(1.6%)	—	—	2.2%

2013 Year-End Financials

Return on assets: (-0.6%)
Return on equity: (-7.7%)
Long-term debt ($ mil.): —
No. of shares (mil.): —
Sales ($ mil): 6,536

Dividends
Yield: —
Payout: —
Market value ($ mil.): —

	STOCK PRICE ($) FY Close	P/E High/Low	PER SHARE ($) Earnings	Dividends	Book Value
12/13	1.46	— —	(0.18)	0.00	2.14
12/12	1.24	575 22	0.04	0.39	2.32
12/11	1.71	— —	(0.05)	0.21	4.96
12/10	3.73	34 14	0.55	0.25	7.96
12/09	6.65	39 13	0.71	1.79	8.23
Annual Growth	(31.5%) (28.6%)	— —	—	—	—

Banco Espirito Santo S.A.

EXECUTIVES

Vice-Chairman and CEO, Ricardo Espirito Santo Salgado, age 70
Chairman, Alberto Alves de Oliveira Pinto, age 82
Vice-Chairman, Bruno Bernard Marie Joseph de Laage de Meux
Vice-Chairman and CEO, Ricardo Espirito Santo Salgado, age 70
Vice-Chairman, Bruno Bernard Marie Joseph de Laage de Meux
Auditors: KPMG

LOCATIONS

HQ: Banco Espirito Santo S.A.
 Avenida da Liberdade, no. 195, Lisbon 1250-142
Phone: (351) 21 359 7390   **Fax:** (351) 21 359 7309
Web: www.bes.pt

2012 Branches

	No.
Portugal	666
Angola	41
Libya	33
Spain	26
Cape	2
Other	7
Total	**775**

COMPETITORS

BNP Paribas
Banco BPI
Banco Comercial
 Portugues
Caixa Geral de
 Depositos
Citigroup
Grupo Santander

Banco Popular Espanol, S.A.

Banco Popular Espanol certainly lives up to its middle name. One of Spain's top banks (after giants Banco Santander and BBVA) Banco Popular offers commercial and retail banking services through more than 2200 branches. It operates mainly at home where it specializes in commercial loans to small and midsized businesses. Non-banking offerings include mutual funds asset management life insurance factoring and securities brokerage. Banco Popular also owns Banco Popular Portugal and mortgage bank Banco Popular Hipotecario and it owns a 60% stake in private bank Popular Banca Privada. (Dexia owns the rest.) The bank also sells property/casualty coverage by German insurer Allianz.

Operations

Banco Popular operates in four segments: commercial banking asset and insurance management real estate and institutional and market.

Geographic Reach

Banco Popular is headquartered in Madrid with 2100 branches across Spain and another 200 abroad (in Portugal and the US).

Financial Performance

Revenue rose 3% in 2012 for Banco Popular as interest and other loan-related income rose along with the company's collections and mediation services. However the bank reported a net loss compared to a net income the year before as it took massive writedowns of Â9.6 billion to meet regulatory requirements. On the flip side cash flow actually rose by nearly Â2 billion as cash from financing activities saved the day.

While the world watched Spain and the EU prop up Spanish banks amid the global recession in

---

2012 Banco Popular reasserted its independence and took no aid.

Strategy

Banco Popular strives for growth through organic means. It does this by marketing its loans and accounts to individuals and businesses while managing its risks. To keep risks low and allow it to decline the state aid that kept many Spanish banks functioning the bank sold nearly Â200 million in assets including real estate a technology company and its point-of-sale terminal business.

HISTORY

Things got rolling in 1926 for Banco Popular Espanol then known as Banco Popular de los Previsores del Porvenir. Formed to provide "all the types of operations ... proper to credit companies" the bank endured the Spanish Civil War and WWII before adopting its present name in 1947.

Banco Popular grew rapidly in the 1960s as Spain's economy stabilized and banks grappled with a decree that they separate their commercial and investment operations. In 1962 Banco Popular implemented merchant banking services through Banco Europeo de Negocios or Eurobanco (Banco Popular acquired the rest of it in 1974.) Like most of its peers Banco Popular sidestepped the restrictive banking laws by launching specialized companies. In 1964 it joined forces with Heller Overseas (now a Fuji Bank subsidiary) to form Heller Factoring Espanola in 1964; it created investment fund manager Sogeval in 1965 and leasing company Iberleasing in 1966.

Banking restrictions also led to Banco Popular's 1967 creation of five "Popularinsa" regional banking companies: Banco de Andalucia Banco de Castilla Banco de Credito Balear Banco de Galicia and Banco de Vasconia. By the late 1970s legal changes allowed Banco Popular and the regional banks to act as one. In 1987 the "Popularinsa" banks were made subsidiaries. Two years later Javier Valls was tapped to join his elder brother Luis in the bank's chairmanship.

In 1991 the bank stuck a tentative toe in the international water forming Banco Popular Comercial in France. But while its peers scrambled furiously to become cross-border players the company's growth plan remained focused on domestic retail and commercial banking. Such dedication did not go unrewarded: Banco Popular has consistently been ranked as one of the world's most profitable banks.

To build on its products and services the bank allied with US-based Bankers Trust (now part of Deutsche Bank) in 1994 to offer investment services to its top-end customers in Spain. In 1996 it joined French credit company Cofinoga to issue private-label credit cards and on-the-spot credit in Spain; through agreements with foreign banks Banco Popular also moved into Canada Southeast Asia and Latin America that year.

German-based insurer Allianz bought into the bank in 1998 (its stake is now less than 10%). In 1999 the bank moved to cut costs by consolidating its fund management and private banking services. Banco Popular started Internet-based Bancopopular-e.com in 2000. Luis Valls resigned in 2004. Angel Ron then became co-chairman with Javier Valls who resigned in 2006 and left Ron as the sole chair. Luis Valls died in 2006.

The company sold Banco Popular France to Credit Mutuel in 2008.

EXECUTIVES

Regional Manager Murcia, Antonio Perez
Director, Jose M. Lucia Aguire
Vice Chairman and CEO, Roberto Higuera
Director, Helena Irene Revoredo Delvecchio

Secretary and Director, Francisco Aparicio
Director, Jose M. Mas Millet, age 59
Director, Americo Ferreira de Amorim
Director, Luis Montuenga
Director, Eric Gancedo
Vice Chairman, Luis Herrando
Director, Manuel Morillo
Director, Miguel Nigorra
Director, Nicolas Osuna
Director, Jose R. Rodriguez
Director, Vincente Santana
Director, Miguel A. de Solis
Director, Vicente Tardio
Director, Casimiro Molins
Auditors: PricewaterhouseCoopersAuditoresS.L.

LOCATIONS

HQ: Banco Popular Espanol, S.A.
Velazquez 34, Madrid 28001
Phone: (34) 91 520 70 00   **Fax:** (34) 91 577 92 08
Web: www.bancopopular.es

Sales

	% of total
Spain	94
Portugal	6
Total	**100**

PRODUCTS/OPERATIONS

Sales

	% of total
Interest	82
Fees &	13
Net exchange	1
Investments	1
Other	3
Total	**100**

COMPETITORS

BBVA	Bankinter
Banco Espa?ol de	Barclays
Credito	Espirito Santo
Banco Pastor	Grupo Santander
Banco de Sabadell	La Caixa

HISTORICAL FINANCIALS

Company Type: Public

Income Statement   FYE: December 31

	ASSETS ($ mil.)	NET INCOME ($ mil.)	INCOME AS % OF ASSETS	EMPLOYEES
12/13	203,552	447	0.2%	16,027
12/12	207,748	(3,243)	—	16,501
12/11	169,346	620	0.4%	14,062
12/10	174,175	789	0.5%	14,252
12/09	186,251	1,103	0.6%	14,431
Annual Growth	2.2%	(20.2%)	—	2.7%

2013 Year-End Financials

Return on assets: 0.2%	Dividends
Return on equity: 3.0%	Yield: —
Long-term debt ($ mil.): —	Payout: —
No. of shares (mil.): 1,904	Market value ($ mil.): —
Sales ($ mil): 8,891	

Banco Santander Chile

LOCATIONS

HQ: Banco Santander Chile
Bandera 140, 19th Floor, Santiago
Phone: (11) 562 320 2000
Web: www.santander.cl

HISTORICAL FINANCIALS

Company Type: Public

Income Statement   FYE: December 31

	ASSETS ($ mil.)	NET INCOME ($ mil.)	INCOME AS % OF ASSETS	EMPLOYEES
12/13	51,602	841	1.6%	11,516
12/12	51,524	741	1.4%	11,713
12/11	47,440	772	1.6%	11,566
12/10	47,189	1,019	2.2%	11,001
12/09	40,951	850	2.1%	11,118
Annual Growth	5.9%	(0.3%)	—	0.9%

2013 Year-End Financials

Return on assets: 1.7%	Dividends
Return on equity: 19.6%	Yield: 3.4%
Long-term debt ($ mil.): —	Payout: 0.0%
No. of shares (mil.): —	Market value ($ mil.): —
Sales ($ mil): 3,919	

	STOCK PRICE ($) FY Close	P/E High/Low		PER SHARE ($) Earnings	Dividends	Book Value
12/13	23.57	0	0	0.00	0.81	0.02
12/12	28.49	0	0	0.00	0.89	0.02
12/11	75.70	0	0	0.00	0.00	0.02
12/10	93.47	0	0	0.01	0.80	0.02
12/09	64.78	0	0	0.00	0.61	0.02
Annual Growth	(22.3%)	—	—	(0.3%)	7.1%	8.0%

Banco Santander SA

What started a contender in the running of the banks in Spain Banco Santander has expanded over the years to become one of the largest banks in the world. Beyond Spain it offers retail banking and consumer finance in Portugal the UK and other parts of Europe as well as the US. Subsidiaries such as Banco Santander Chile Banco Santander (Brasil) Santander Rio in Argentina and Grupo Financiero Santander make it a top banking group in Latin America which accounts for about 40% of the group's revenues. Other units offer asset management private banking corporate and investment banking and insurance. All told the company has some 100 million customers and 14800 locations in more than 40 countries.

Over the years Santander has expanded to become more geographically diverse —a key strategy for the company as it looks to reduce risk. The bank's strategy revolves around making acquisitions and boosting deposits in growth nations; it generates more than half of its profits in emerging markets. Santander has taken advantage of the economic downturn to snap up businesses and asset portfolios at bargain prices.

One target market for growth is Latin America where profits have been growing; the company hopes to further strengthen its presence in the re-

gion. In 2010 Santander took full control of its Mexico unit by acquiring Bank of America's 25% stake in Grupo Financiero Santander for Â2 billion ($2.5 billion) as well as the rest of Puerto Rican unit Santander BanCorp it didn't already own. It then acquired GE Capital's $2 billion consumer mortgage business in Mexico for $162 million plus the assumption of debt. The company has also been opening new branches in the region. While the financial downturn and the European sovereign debt crisis has been rough for Spain and Portugal Mexico holds promise for growth. Hoping to cash in on some of that growth Banco Santander spun off nearly 25% of Grupo Financiero Santander in a public offering worth more than $4 billion.

Banco Santander also made a big move into Eastern Europe. In 2011 it paid Â4 billion (nearly $6 billion) for Poland's Bank Zachodni. The acquisition may signal more acquisitions for Santander in neighboring East European countries.

In addition to Latin America and Europe Banco Santander is making its move in the US. The company's American holdings include Northeast regional bank Santander Holdings USA (formerly Sovereign Bancorp). In 2010 Santander bought a Â2.5 billion ($3 billion) auto loan portfolio from Citigroup.

Banco Santander also operates Santander UK the result of the 2010 merger of Abbey National Bradford & Bingley and the former Alliance & Leicester (all of which were acquired by Santander). Santander's acquisitions in the UK helped bump up profits from the region in 2009 and 2010 but in 2011 profits slipped as a result of remediation charges related to mis-sold payment protection insurance. In 2010 Santander announced plans to buy some 315 Royal Bank of Scotland branches in the UK for about Â2 billion ($3 billion) further expanding its presence there. That deal which has been delayed includes a wealth management business with some 84000 clients.

Santander also has started making inroads in China. The bank is seeking to acquire a 20% stake in Bank of Beijing Consumer Finance Company for CNY 306 million ($49.8 million). Previously in 2011 it established a rural bank joint venture with China Construction Bank. It is among several other foreign banks that are extending their presence to rural China where few people have access to financial services.

On the other hand Santander has been selling some assets in order to shore up its balance sheet and meet new capital reserve requirements. In 2011 the company announced plans to sell a 35% stake in its American automotive financing unit for more than $1 billion. It then sold a minority stake in Banco Santander Chile to further increase its core capital ratio. Santander also sold its Columbian unit to CorpBanca of Chile for $1.2 billion.

Despite the group's diverse operations the troubled debt market in Europe and the slowly recovering global economy have taken their toll on Santander. Although acquisitions helped Santander's revenues grow 25% in 2011 profits fell some 36% that year largely as a result of the slowdown in Spain and Portugal. The bank has never needed a bailout though and achieved its minimum capital requirements months early in 2011. Santander believes that as the economy continues to improve it is well-positioned around the world to grow even further.

The Botin family has led Grupo Santander since its founding in 1857. Emilio Botin Sanz de Sautuola y Garcia de los Rios Spain's richest man (depending on whom you ask) has been chairman since 1986.

HISTORY

In 1857 a group of Basque businessmen had formed Banco Santander to finance Latin American trade. The emergence of Cantabria as a leading province after WWI helped the bank expand first regionally and then nationally.

The Botin family has been closely identified with the bank for decades. Emilio Botin served first as a board member and then for a few years as chairman before his death in 1923. The post was held by his son Emilio Botin-Sanz de Sautuola from 1950 to 1986 when "his" son Emilio Botin Sanz de Sautuola y Garcia de los Rios (known as Don Emilio) took over.

Spanish banks were spared the worst of the Great Depression (thanks to their isolation and the country's shunning the gold standard) but Spain's civil war was draining. In the early 1940s Santander expanded into Madrid and other major Spanish cities and merged with a few rivals. In the 1950s and 1960s as interest rates were controlled and mergers halted banks competed by building branch networks and investing overseas particularly in Latin America. In 1965 Santander joined with Bank of America to form Bankinter (it divested most of its stake by the mid-1990s).

Tight economic controls were relaxed in the 1970s after Franco's death. Despite global recession Santander continued to invest in Latin America through the mid-1980s.

In the late 1980s Santander prepared to compete in a deregulated Spain and Europe forming alliances with Royal Bank of Scotland Kemper (now part of Zurich Financial Services) and Metropolitan Life Insurance. In 1989 the bank jump-started competition by introducing Spain's first high-interest account.

Santander focused on home in the 1990s. Spurned by Banco Hispano Americano (BHA) Santander acquired a 60% stake in the ailing Banco Espanol de Credito (Banesto) which became wholly owned in 1998. The bank took a hit when Latin America plunged into an economic crisis that year. With profit margins falling the bank merged with BCH in 1999.

BCH was formed by the 1991 merger of Banco Central and BHA. BHA had been established in 1900 by investors in Latin America; Central had been founded in 1919. The mixed banks offered both commercial and investment banking; they funded industrialization and investment in Latin America and became two of Spain's largest banks before the civil war.

After the war BHA sold its Latin American assets when the currency dried up while Central used mergers and acquisitions to expand across Spain. Isolated from WWII by Franco the two banks used their dual strategies to fund overseas investment and domestic-branch growth.

After Franco's death the banks faced increased competition at home and abroad. Central bought BHA in 1991 to remain competitive as Spain entered the European Economic Community (now the EU) in 1992.

Following the merger BCH trimmed 20% of its branches fired some 10000 employees and sold unprofitable holdings. Focused on Latin America the bank took small stakes in small banks. Losing its edge BCH merged with Santander in 1999.

In 2000 the newly merged BSCH focused on expanding in Europe and Latin America. Among its European moves was its alliance with Societe Generale to buy investment-fund management firms particularly in the US. In Latin America the bank bought Brazil's Banco Meridional Banco do Estado de S o Paulo (Banespa) and Grupo Financiero Serfin Mexico's #3 bank. Critics questioned the $5 billion price tag BSCH paid for Banespa charging that the formerly state-run bank was overvalued in

2001. Executive in-fighting saw ex-Santander chairman Emilio Botin triumph over ex-BCH chairman Jose Maria Amusategui for control of BSCH's helm. Soon after the bank started doing business as simply Santander Central Hispano. The following year the bank sold off its shares of Germany's Commerzbank and France's Societe Generale.

In one of Europe's largest cross-border bank mergers ever Santander paid more than Â12 billion ($15 billion) for British bank Abbey National in 2004. It solidified its UK operations through the approximately Â1.25 billion ($2.6 billion) purchase of Alliance & Leicester. Abbey then acquired the retail deposit business of Bradford & Bingley after it was nationalized in 2008.

Another acquisition helped Santander grow in South America. In 2007 the company along with Royal Bank of Scotland and Fortis acquired the Netherlands-based ABN AMRO (the international retail banking giant with more than 4350 branches) for around Â71 billion ($87 billion). As part of the bid Banco Santander took ABN AMRO's Brazilian operations doubling its market share in Brazil. Also a part of the ABN AMRO deal Santander became the largest non-government-owned bank in Uruguay.

In 2009 the Venezuelan government took over Banco Santander subsidiary Banco de Venezuela the third-largest bank in the country. The government paid some Â755 million ($1 billion) to nationalize the bank.

Also that year Santander acquired the approximately three-quarters of Sovereign it didn't already own. Santander then purchased a more than Â3 billion ($4 billion) US car loan portfolio and a loan servicing platform from HSBC.

EXECUTIVES

Chairman, Emilio Botin Sanz de Sautuola y Garcia de los Rios, age 79
Second Vice Chairman, Matias Rodriguez Inciarte, age 66
EVP Strategy and Asia, Juan Rodriguez Inciarte, age 61
EVP Global Wholesale Banking, Jose Garcia Cantera, age 48
EVP Risk, Javier Peralta de las Heras, age 64
Third Vice Chairman, Guillermo de la Dehesa Romero, age 73
First Vice Chairman, Fernando de Asua Alvarez, age 82
Executive Vice President Finance and Investor Relations, Jose Antonio Alvarez Alvarez, age 54
EVP Global Private Banking and Asset Management, Javier Marin, age 48
EVP Human Resources, Jose Luis Gomez Alciturri, age 65
EVP Santander Totta, Nuno Amado, age 55
Chief Executive Officer, Javier Marin Romano, age 48
Second Vice Chairman, Matias Rodriguez Inciarte, age 66
Director, Luis Alberto Salazar-Simpson, age 73
EVP Strategy and Asia, Juan Rodriguez Inciarte, age 61
Director, Antonio Escamez Torres, age 62
EVP America and Director, Francisco Luzon Lopez, age 65
Second Vice Chairman and CEO, Alfredo Saenz Abad, age 70
Director, Lord Terence (Terry) Burns, age 70
CEO Santander UK; Director, Ana P. Botin, age 53
Fourth Vice Chairman, Manuel Soto Serrano, age 73
Third Vice Chairman, Guillermo de la Dehesa Romero, age 73
First Vice Chairman, Fernando de Asua Alvarez, age 82
Director, Antonio Basagoiti Garcia-Tu?on, age 71
Director, Javier Botin, age 37

Director, Rodrigo Echenique Gordillo, age 67
Director, Abel Matutes Juan, age 72
Director, Angel Jado Becerro de Bengoa, age 68
Director, Isabel Tocino Biscarolasaga, age 63
Director, Vittorio Corbo Lioi, age 70

LOCATIONS

HQ: Banco Santander SA
28660 Boadilla del Monte, Madrid
Phone: (34) 91 259 6514   **Fax:** (34) 91 254 1038
Web: www.gruposantander.com

PRODUCTS/OPERATIONS

Sales

	% of total
Interest	67
Fees &	14
Income from insurance & reinsurance contracts	7
Net gains on financial assets &	3
Other	9
Total	**100**

COMPETITORS

BBVA	Citigroup
Banco Comercial	Deutsche Bank
Portugues	Espirito Santo
Banco Popular Espa?ol	HSBC
Banco do Brasil	JPMorgan Chase
Bank of America	

HISTORICAL FINANCIALS

Company Type: Public

Income Statement

FYE: December 31

	ASSETS ($ mil.)	NET INCOME ($ mil.)	INCOME AS % OF ASSETS	EMPLOYEES
12/13	1,535,938	6,016	0.4%	186,373
12/12	1,673,432	2,906	0.2%	188,779
12/11	1,618,788	6,921	0.4%	187,233
12/10	1,629,469	10,949	0.7%	172,909
12/09	1,599,794	12,882	0.8%	169,460
Annual Growth	(1.0%)	(17.3%)	—	2.4%

2013 Year-End Financials

Return on assets: 0.3%	Dividends
Return on equity: 6.0%	Yield: 6.9%
Long-term debt ($ mil.): —	Payout: 151.2%
No. of shares (mil.): —	Market value ($ mil.): —
Sales ($ mil) 104,390	

	STOCK PRICE ($) FY Close	P/E High/Low	PER SHARE ($) Earnings	Dividends	Book Value
12/13	9.07	44 28	0.55	0.63	8.57
12/12	8.17	67 34	0.29	0.64	9.53
12/11	7.52	40 19	0.78	0.79	11.09
12/10	10.65	36 15	1.25	0.64	12.05
12/09	16.44	37 8	1.50	1.07	12.02
Annual Growth (8.1%)	(13.8%)	—	(22.1%)	(12.4%)	

Bangkok Bank Public Co., Ltd. (Thailand)

Bangkok Bank wants to protect the baht you've got. One of the largest commercial banks in Thailand Bangkok Bank provides a variety of banking services to individual and commercial clients including checking and savings accounts loans Internet banking and treasury and investment banking services. It operates about 1200 branches serving 16 million customers throughout Thailand about a dozen other Southeast Asian countries the UK and the US. The bank was founded in 1944 in response to the difficulty Thai businessmen encountered in receiving credit facilities from foreign banks; it has since had a hand in developing its homeland's industry and agriculture.

EXECUTIVES

President and Director, Chartsiri Sophonpanich, age 54
EVP Conglomerate 2, Yaowadee Nakhata
EVP Human Resources, Ruchanee Nopmuang
EVP Technology, Kajornvut Tayanukorn
EVP and Manager Japan Desk, Hitoshi Ozawa
Vice President, Ian Guy Gillard
EVP and Manager Multinational II, Bussakorn Pao-In
Vice President, Amphorn Purinthawarakun
Vice President; Company Secretary, Aphichat Romyarup
Vice President, Ayut Kritsanamara
Vice President of Finance Management, Bunsong Bunyasaranan
Vice President, Chaiyong Rattanacharoensiri
VP of Large Business Enterprises; Mgng.Dir. of Large Business Enterprises of Siam City Bank; Dir., Charnsak Fueangfu
Chairman of the Board, Chatri Sophonphanit, age 79
Vice President, Chirana O-sotsin
Vice President, Chitwatthana Charuwatthanachai
Vice President, Chok Ranong
Vice President, Khanit Si
Vice President, Kirati Laisathit
Vice President of International Banking Group, Korbsak Phutrakun
Chairman of the Executive Board; Director, Kosit Panpiemrat
Vice President, Krisorn Bharami-uaychai
Vice President, Kunthida Siwayathorn
Vice President of Regional Business Expansion; International Banking Group, Lin Kung
Vice President, Mali Sintraphannathorn
Vice President, Manusiri Karnchana
Vice President, Narin Ophamurathawong
Vice President, Natthaphorn Luengsuwan
Vice President, Niraman Laisathit
Vice President, Panit Tunwatthanachit
Vice President, Parnsak Pruksakit
Vice President, Phakorn Wanaptikun
Vice President, Phornnit Tunwatthanachit
Vice President of Audit and Control, Phornthep Kitsanayothin
Vice President, Piyada Sucharitkun
Vice President, Piyaphan Thananithi
Vice President, Pratsani Ui-yamaphan
Vice President, Ratchada Thiratharathorn
Vice President of Foreign Exchange Trading Department, Sa-ard Thirarotchanawong
Vice President of Human Resources, Saowani Siriphat
Vice President, Shairit Anuchitworawong
Vice President, Shuphorn Chantharawichai
Vice President, Siridet Ueang-udomsin
Vice President of Loan Recovery and Legal, Songkhram Sakunphram
Vice President of Credit Management, Suraphong Winyawong
Vice President of Special Credit; Executive Director; Director, Suwan Thaensathit
Vice President, Than Siriphokhi
Vice President, Thanit Sirichot
Vice President, Tharisa Thanyasiri
Vice President, Thawat Triwannakun

Assistant President ; Director, Thawilap Ritthaphirom
Vice President of Credit Management and Credit Acceptance, Thawisak Thanatsrang
Vice President, Thongchai A-nanthothai
Vice President of Correspondence Banking, Wanlapha Klinpathum
Vice President, Wirasak Sutanthawibun
Vice Chairman of the Executive Board; Director, Decha Tulanan
Senior Vice President of Technology, Suthira Sriphaibun
Vice President, Sutthirat Phashirat
President and Director, Chartsiri Sophonpanich, age 54
Vice Chairman, Staporn Kavitanon, age 71
Director, Piti Sithi-Amnuai, age 78
Member Board of Executive Directors, Amorn Chandarasomboon, age 81
Director, Charn Sophonpanich, age 70
Vice Chairman Board of Executive Directors, Deja Tulananda, age 76
SEVP and Director, Prasong Uthaisangchai, age 65
SEVP and Director, Suvarn Thansathit, age 67
Director, Phornthep Phornprapha, age 65
Director, Gasinee Witoonchart, age 64
Director, Adm. Prachet Siridej, age 76
Director, Kovit Poshyananda, age 76
Member Board of Executive Directors, Singh Tangtatswas, age 69
Director, Kanung Luchai, age 88
Director, Prince Mongkolchaleam Yugala, age 75
Chairman Board of Executive Directors, Kosit Panpiemras, age 69
Independent Director, Kesini Withunchat
Independent Director, Khanueng Ruechai
Chairman of the Executive Board; Director, Kosit Panpiemrat
Independent Director, Kowit Posayanon
Independent Director, Mongkhonchaloem Yukhon
Independent Director, Prachet Siridet
Auditors: DeloitteToucheTohmatsuJaiyos

LOCATIONS

HQ: Bangkok Bank Public Co., Ltd. (Thailand)
   333 Silom Road, Bangkok 10500
Phone: (66) 0 2231 4333   **Fax:** 212 422-0728
Web: www.bangkokbank.com

PRODUCTS/OPERATIONS

Sales

	% of total
Interest	
Loans	61
Investments	11
Interbank & money market	5
Noninterest	
Fees & service	17
Gain on	4
Gain on disposal of	1
Other	1
Total	**100**

COMPETITORS

Bank of Ayudhya	Siam Commercial
CIMB Group	Standard Chartered
DBS Group Holdings	TMB Bank
KASIKORNBANK	Thanachart Capital
Krung Thai	United Overseas Bank

HISTORICAL FINANCIALS
Company Type: Public

Income Statement
FYE: December 31

	ASSETS ($ mil.)	NET INCOME ($ mil.)	INCOME AS % OF ASSETS	EMPLOYEES
12/13	79,311	1,096	1.4%	24,096
12/12	79,046	1,079	1.4%	22,934
12/11	66,949	868	1.3%	21,503
12/10	64,913	818	1.3%	21,229
12/09	53,187	617	1.2%	20,735
Annual Growth	10.5%	15.5%	—	3.8%

2013 Year-End Financials

Return on assets: 1.4%
Return on equity: 12.6%
Long-term debt ($ mil.): —
No. of shares (mil.): 1,908
Sales ($ mil): 4,372
Dividends
 Yield: —
 Payout: —
Market value ($ mil.): 14,145

	STOCK PRICE ($) FY Close	P/E High/Low		PER SHARE ($) Earnings	Dividends	Book Value
12/13	7.41	0	0	0.57	0.00	4.74
12/12	5.39	0	0	0.57	0.00	4.68
12/11	4.42	0	0	0.46	0.00	4.06
12/10	4.31	0	0	0.43	0.00	4.02
12/09	3.75	0	0	0.32	0.00	3.03
Annual Growth	18.6%	—	—	15.5%	—	11.8%

Bank fur Arbeit und Wirtschaft AG (Austria)

Putting your money in BAWAG beats hiding your money in a mattress. As one of the largest banks in Austria BAWAG P.S.K. (for short) operates a network of more than 150 BAWAG branches and some 1300 P.S.K. post office outlets around the country. It focuses on small and mid-sized business and retail customers. The BAWAG P.S.K. Group includes more than 50 companies in Austria and abroad. Among its Austrian bank subsidiaries are easybank and – VKB. The company also has banking units in Malta Slovenia Hungary and Libya. BAWAG P.S.K. is owned by Cerberus Capital Management.

Bank for Arbeit und Wirtschaft AG (BEWAG merged with its subsidiary company – sterreichische Postsparkasse (Austrian Postal Savings Bank or P.S.K.) in 2005. Although the company still includes its longer title it is more commonly known by its shorter name BAWAG P.S.K.

The Austrian Federation of Trade Unions in 2006 decided to put BAWAG P.S.K. on the block as it faced controversy. Mired in the Refco financial scandal the bank was hit with a US class action lawsuit by Refco creditors seeking to recoup their money. BAWAG P.S.K. acknowledged playing a role in the failure of Refco and agreed to a $675 million settlement (to Refco creditors and investors) to avoid prosecution by the US government. In a government-brokered deal several banks pledged capital to the beleaguered bank. BAWAG P.S.K.'s management and board were overhauled and a consortium led by Cerberus acquired the company at the end of that year.

BAWAG P.S.K. began refocusing on its core Austrian banking business. It sold piano-maker Bosendorfer to Yamaha in 2007 and unloaded its

43%-stake in broadcasting company ATV Privat-TV Services the following year.

In 2008 the bank sold its Slovakia bank ISTROBANKA to KBC and got rid of its Czech subsidiary. In 2009 BAWAG shed its Irish subsidiary and liquidated BAWAG Capital Advisors in efforts to streamline its business.

Although BAWAG has been stepping away from its international operations the bank is again looking to expand abroad through acquisitions in western and eastern Europe.

LOCATIONS

HQ: Bank fur Arbeit und Wirtschaft AG (Austria)
Georg-Coch-Platz 2, Vienna 1018
Phone: (43) 5 99 05 0
Web: www.bawagpsk.com

HISTORICAL FINANCIALS

Company Type: Public

Income Statement

FYE: December 31

	ASSETS ($ mil.)	NET INCOME ($ mil.)	INCOME AS % OF ASSETS	EMPLOYEES
12/13	50,115	315	0.6%	3,695
12/12	54,389	141	0.3%	4,003
12/11	53,131	158	0.3%	4,038
12/10	51,602	163	0.3%	4,812
12/09	59,387	(31)	—	4,954
Annual Growth	(4.2%)	—	—	(7.1%)

2013 Year-End Financials

Return on assets: 0.5%
Return on equity: 9.4%
Long-term debt ($ mil.): —
No. of shares (mil.): 250
Sales ($ mil): 2,259
Dividends
Yield: —
Payout: —
Market value ($ mil.): —

Bank Hapoalim B.M. (Israel)

The largest bank in Israel Bank Hapoalim caters to individual commercial and corporate clients at home and abroad. Within Israel the Bank Hapoalim Group has more than 270 full-service branches and business centers. Another 30 express branches are in the works. Overseas it has about 45 branches correspondent offices and financial subsidiaries in Asia Australia Europe Latin America and North America; its international focus is on private banking and the corporate sector. Bank Hapoalim provides investment banking services including the underwriting of and investment in companies; it also provides trust services to individuals and businesses.

Bank Hapoalim was founded in 1921. Shari Arison Israel's wealthiest person is the controlling shareholder.

The bank has undergone major shakeups in its leadership since Arison took control of the bank in 2007. Dan Dankner also came on board as chairman that year. In March 2009 Zvi Ziv resigned as CEO after clashing with Dankner; deputy CEO Zion Keinan was picked to replace him. Bank of Israel (the nation's central bank) then wrangled with Arison over Hapoalim's performance and leadership threatening to remove Dankner if significant changes weren't made. Dankner seemed

to get the message and resigned in 2009. Yair Seroussi replaced him.

The company planned to acquire control of Ukraine bank OJSC Ukraininan Innovation Bank (Ukrinbank) but was blocked by Bank of Israel. As a result Bank Hapoalim has suspended its planned growth in Eastern Europe. However it is examining opportunities in other regions to add to such investments as Bank Pozitif in Turkey and DKB in Kazakhstan. Other international businesses include Hapoalim Switzerland The PAM Group and Bank Hapoalim (Cayman). Hapoalim Securities U.S.A. offers securities trading for customers in Israel and abroad.

EXECUTIVES

Member of the Management Board; Chief Financial Officer, Ran Oz, age 46
Chairman, Yair Seroussi, age 59
Head Information Technology, Zvi Naggan
Chief Legal Advisor, Ilan Mazur
Head Client Asset Management, Hanna Pri-Zan
Head International Banking, Orit Lerer
Head Global Treasury, Anat (Moti) Levin
Chief Accountant, Ofer Levy
Head Human Resources Logistics and Procurement, Efrat Yavetz
Chief Risk Officer, Dan Koller
Head Retail Banking, Lilach Asher-Topilsky
Head Corporate Banking, Shimon Gal
Vice President, Micha Shimoni
Chief Risk Officer, Tzahi Cohen
Deputy Chief Executive Officer; Head of Strategy; Member of the Management Board, Ari Pinto
Secretary, Yoram Weisberg
Director, Dan (Danny) Dankner, age 49
External Director, Yosef Yarom
Director, Irit Izakson
Director, Nira Dror
Director, Pnina Dvorin
Director, Moshe Koren
Director, Prof Yair E. Orgler, age 74
Director, Efrat Peled
Director, Nir Zichlinskey
Director, Oded Sarig
Director, Leslie Littner
Director, Mali Baron, age 67
Director, Iris Dror
Director, Ronen Israel
Director, Imri Tov
External Director, Amnon Deek
External Director, Dafna Schwartz
Auditors: SomekhChaikin

LOCATIONS

HQ: Bank Hapoalim B.M. (Israel)
50 Rothschild Blvd., Tel-Aviv 66883
Phone: (972) 3 567 3333   **Fax:** (972) 3 560 7028
Web: www.bankhapoalim.com

Sales

	% of total
Israel	87
Europe	8
North	5
Total	**100**

COMPETITORS

Bank Leumi le-Israel
First International
 Bank of Israel
Israel Discount Bank
Mizrahi Tefahot
UBS

HISTORICAL FINANCIALS

Company Type: Public

Income Statement

FYE: December 31

	ASSETS ($ mil.)	NET INCOME ($ mil.)	INCOME AS % OF ASSETS	EMPLOYEES
12/13	109,581	743	0.7%	12,891
12/12	100,980	682	0.7%	13,484
12/11	93,300	718	0.8%	13,408
12/10	90,552	628	0.7%	13,605
12/09	81,934	348	0.4%	13,821
Annual Growth	7.5%	20.9%	—	(1.7%)

2013 Year-End Financials

Return on assets: 0.6%
Return on equity: 9.2%
Long-term debt ($ mil.): —
No. of shares (mil.): 1,320
Sales ($ mil): 5,386
Dividends
Yield: 0.0%
Payout: —
Market value ($ mil.): 37,029

	STOCK PRICE ($) FY Close	P/E High/Low		PER SHARE ($) Earnings	Dividends	Book Value
12/13	28.04	1	0	1.12	0.02	6.34
12/12	21.82	0	0	1.03	0.00	5.44
12/11	16.05	1	1	0.54	0.02	4.71
12/10	26.50	1	1	0.47	0.00	4.92
12/09	19.60	1	0	0.26	0.00	4.13
Annual Growth	9.4%	—	—	43.9%	—	11.3%

Bank Leumi Le-Israel B.M.

Bank Leumi le-Israel looms large as one of Israel's largest financial institutions. The company whose name translates as National Bank of Israel offers retail banking (for consumers and small businesses) commercial banking (middle-market businesses) corporate banking (large companies) and private banking (wealthy clients) through deposits mortgages and other loans credit cards trust services and investments. It has about 235 branches in Israel and more than 80 locations (including branches agencies and representative offices) in some 20 countries including the US. Subsidiary Leumi Partners provides corporate investment banking services and makes direct investments in nonbanking businesses.

Other subsidiaries include The Arab Israel Bank Leumi Mortgage Bank and retail and private banking units in the UK Switzerland Luxembourg and Romania. In 2011 Bank Leumi bought Geneva-based private bank Banque Safdie from the Safdie family. It plans to merge the firm with Bank Leumi Switzerland. In a restructuring move that will cut costs Bank Leumi plans to absorb Leumi Mortgage Bank in 2012. The company will then provide mortgage services through a newly created mortgage division.

After the Israeli parliament passed a number of capital market reform laws in 2005 Bank Leumi was compelled to sell its mutual fund and investment portfolio management operations. It has since focused on providing investment and pension counseling to its clients.

The Israeli government owns more than 10% of Bank Leumi but has been selling off its stake in the company and intends to eventually divest its entire holding.

HISTORY

At the beginning of the 20th century a group of prominent Jewish men led by Austrian Zionist Theodor Herzl founded the Jewish Colonial Trust (which would later become known as Otzar Hitsyashvut Hayehudim or OHH). An advocate of the Jewish settlement of Palestine the trust recognized the need for a financial institution to promote colonization in the region which was then part of the Ottoman Empire. In 1902 it established the Anglo-Palestine Company the forerunner of Bank Leumi le-Israel. A year later the London-based company opened its first Palestinian office in Jaffa (now Tel Aviv).

As WWI began the company had half a dozen branches. The outbreak of hostilities between Great Britain and the Ottoman Empire forced the London-based bank to close its offices but it continued to operate from the Spanish Consulate in Jerusalem. By the mid-1920s the company was known as the Anglo-Palestine Bank and was playing a significant role in the development of local agriculture.

During the following decade Palestine saw an influx of refugees from Nazism in Europe. The bank assisted in transferring assets to Palestine and anchored the area's economy through WWII. When Israel gained independence in 1948 the Anglo-Palestine Bank became the nation's fiscal agency and printed monetary notes for the new government. It began to focus its efforts on international operations and in 1950 opened its first US office in New York City. But even though it was the national bank of the newly formed Israeli state the bank was still based in London. In 1951 a company named leumi Le'Israel was founded in Tel Aviv and assumed control of the bank which took the name Bank Leumi le-Israel (National Bank of Israel) in 1954. Also that year the government formed the Bank of Israel and Bank Leumi resumed its commercial banking activities.

Bank Leumi maintained its status as Israel's leading bank until the 1980s when triple-digit inflation hit the country. The bottom fell out in 1983 when investors pulled out of the stock market fearing devaluation of the shekel. As they had done for several years Bank Leumi and Israel's other major banking groups reacted by taking out massive loans to buy their own stock and shield against losses in share price. The artificially inflated bank stocks crashed and thousands of individual investors lost their savings. The Israeli government intervened paying some $7 billion to bail out the banks. Though the state now held most of Bank Leumi's stock the OHH maintained voting rights.

In 1986 following a government inquiry into the stock scandal chairman Ernst Japhet and the company's board were forced to resign prompting more contention. On their way out Japhet and his officers received millions of dollars in severance pay and monthly pensions. The ramifications of what became known as "Leumigate" resulted in the company's next two chairmen also being ousted over the next two years. Rival Bank Hapoalim wrested the mantle of Israel's #1 bank from Bank Leumi in 1987.

The government sold off 10% of its interest in the firm to a unit of Deutsche Bank in 1993 and in 1995 mandated that banks sell their nonfinancial holdings. That year Galia Maor became CEO as the first woman head of an Israeli bank and Eitan Raff became chairman (he announced his retirement in 2010).

Controversy continued however. In 1997 Bank Leumi sold a majority stake in Migdal Insurance to Assicurazioni Generali which amplified questions regarding the buyer's handling of life insurance policies of Jewish Holocaust victims. The inquiry spread to Bank Leumi which released information about dormant accounts the next year but nonetheless faced government scrutiny and lawsuits from descendants of Holocaust victims.

In 2006 an Israeli law established a company to collect restitution for property deemed abandoned by Holocaust victims who had made bank deposits and bought real estate and bank shares in Israel in anticipation of the establishment of a Jewish homeland in Palestine. After years of wrangling The Company for Restitution of Holocaust Victims Assets in mid-2009 filed suit against Bank Leumi considered to be the holder of the most Jewish Holocaust assets; the lawsuit asked for NIS 300 million ($75 million) in restitution for more than 3500 victims. Denying any financial culpability the bank later that year offered NIS 20 million ($5 million). In 2010 it agreed to arbitration.

EXECUTIVES

Chairman, David Brodet, age 70
Deputy CEO and Head of Banking, Baruch Lederman
Deputy CEO and Head Operations and Information Systems, Itzhak Malach
President and CEO, Rakefet Russak-Aminoach, $876,253 total compensation
EVP and Head Economics and Finance, Ron M. Fainaro, age 46
Deputy CEO and Head Capital Markets, Prof Daniel Tsiddon
First EVP Chief Accounting Officer and Head of Accounting, Menachem Schwartz
EVP and Head Banking, Tamar Yassur
EVP and Head Structured Finance and Real Estate, Yoel Mintz
First EVP and Head Commercial Banking, Gideon Altman
First EVP and Head Corporate, Yaacov (Kobi) Haber
First EVP, Dan Cohen
Head of the Office of the Chief Executive Officer and the Strategy Department, Avner Mendelson
Vice President and Chief Executive Officer of Bank Leumi USA, Itzhak Aboulafia
Co-Chief Executive Officer, Ron Ron Fainaro Fainaro
EVP and Head Internal Audit, Sasson Mordechay
Head of Credit Dept., Shahar Malkiel
Vice President and Deputy Head of Operations; Administration & Systems Abroad, Shlomo Pergament
Bank and Group Secretary, Yael Rudnicki
EVP and Head Risk Management, Hedva Ber
EVP and Head Capital Markets, Itai Ben-Zeev
EVP and Head Accounting, Shlomo Goldfarb
EVP, Nomi Sandhaus
EVP and Head Operations and Information Systems, Dan Yerushalmi
Director, Doron Cohen
Director, Zvi Koren, age 72
Director, Yaacov Goldman, age 57
Director, Moshe Vidman
Director, Prof Israel Gilead
Director, Rami Avraham Guzman
Director, Jacob Mashaal
Director, Nurit Segal
Director, Moshe Dovrat
Director, Zipora Gal Yam
Director, Prof Arieh Gans
Director, Prof Efraim Sadka
Director, Reuven Adler
Director, Amos Sapir
Director, David Avner
Director, Prof Gabriela Shalev
External Director, Gabriella Shilo
External Director, Haim Samet
Director, Miryam (Miri) Katz
Director, Avraham (Rami) Guzman
Director, Prof Yedidia (Zvi) Stern
Director, Yehuda Drori
Director, Yoav Nardi
External Director, Zipora Samet
Auditors: SomekhChaikin

LOCATIONS

HQ: Bank Leumi Le-Israel B.M.
34 Yehuda Halevi Street, Tel-Aviv 65546
Phone: (972) 3 514 8111   **Fax:** (972) 3 566 1872
Web: www.bankleumi.com

COMPETITORS

Bank Hapoalim	HSBC
Bank of America	Israel Discount Bank
Citigroup	Mizrahi Tefahot
First International	Standard Chartered
Bank of Israel	UniCredit

HISTORICAL FINANCIALS

Company Type: Public

Income Statement

FYE: December 31

	ASSETS ($ mil.)	NET INCOME ($ mil.)	INCOME AS % OF ASSETS	EMPLOYEES
12/13	107,885	561	0.5%	13,004
12/12	100,919	249	0.2%	13,407
12/11	95,697	494	0.5%	13,633
12/10	92,610	671	0.7%	13,490
12/09	85,168	533	0.6%	13,342
Annual Growth	6.1%	1.3%	—	(0.6%)

2013 Year-End Financials

Return on assets: 0.5%
Return on equity: 7.5%
Long-term debt ($ mil.): —
No. of shares (mil.): 1,473
Sales ($ mil): 5,086
Dividends
Yield: —
Payout: —
Market value ($ mil.): 5,747

	STOCK PRICE ($) FY Close	P/E High/Low		PER SHARE ($) Earnings	Dividends	Book Value
12/13	3.90	0	0	0.38	0.00	5.17
12/12	3.45	0	0	0.17	0.00	4.54
12/11	3.05	0	0	0.33	0.00	4.15
12/10	5.10	0	0	0.45	0.00	4.53
12/09	3.35	0	0	0.36	0.00	3.93
Annual Growth	3.9%	—	—	1.2%	—	7.1%

Bank of Canada (Ottawa)

Whether you say "bank" or "banque" the Bank of Canada is the country's central bank. It is responsible for setting monetary policy (by setting interest rates) issuing and safeguarding currency from counterfeiting managing the Canadian banking system and managing funds for the government and other clients. The Bank of Canada works through six regional offices including one in New York City. A governor senior deputy governor 12 outside directors and the Deputy Minister of Finance oversee the bank which averages a $1.8 billion profit annually. The funds are contributed to the government. The Bank of Canada was formed in 1934 as a private entity; it became part of the government four years later.

Perhaps not wanting to mimic its southern neighbor's fluctuating interest rates the Bank of

Canada has eight set dates throughout the year when it announces whether or not it will adjust interest rates.

Despite a worldwide financial crisis Canada's banks had all but regained their pre-recession (2007) status by 2009 without a penny of government help. No Canadian bank has failed since 1991 in part because of sound policies by Bank of Canada.

Bank directors are appointed by the Minister of Finance for a three-year term. Appointees are subject to approval by Canada's Cabinet the Governor in Council.

LOCATIONS

HQ: Bank of Canada (Ottawa)
234 Wellington Street, Ottawa, Ontario K1A 0G9
Phone: 613 782-8111   **Fax:** 613 782-7713
Web: www.bankofcanada.ca

PRODUCTS/OPERATIONS

HISTORICAL FINANCIALS

Company Type: Public

Income Statement

FYE: December 31

	ASSETS ($ mil.)	NET INCOME ($ mil.)	INCOME AS % OF ASSETS	EMPLOYEES
12/13	85,867	946	1.1%	1,252
12/12	78,231	1,105	1.4%	1,239
12/11	62,981	1,229	2.0%	1,228
12/10	61,346	1,164	1.9%	1,305
12/09	68,060	1,281	1.9%	1,311
Annual Growth	6.0%	(7.3%)		(1.1%)

2013 Year-End Financials

Return on assets: 1.1%
Return on equity: 230.2%
Long-term debt ($ mil.): —
No. of shares (mil.): 0
Sales ($ mil): 1,673

Dividends
Yield: —
Payout: —
Market value ($ mil.): —

Bank of China Ltd

The Bank of China (BOC) has its sights set on global conquest —of the financial kind. One of the largest banks in the world's most populous country BOC is a financial giant. It has more than 10000 domestic branches as well as foreign offices in about 30 countries. Commercial banking (including corporate and retail banking and treasury operations) accounts for about 90% of its revenues. BOC International provides investment banking services in China the UK the US and Singapore. BOC Group Insurance sells general and life insurance products in China. The group provides aircraft leasing through BOC Aviation. China's government owns about 70% of BOC one of the nation's four state-owned commercial banks.

Despite the sluggish economic climate around the world BOC's operating income and profits both grew by 19% in 2011. Additionally its assets grew by 13% to RMB 11.8 trillion ($1.9 trillion). The solid performance was credited to an increase in both interest and noninterest earnings and the bank's relatively low portfolio of bad loans decreased even further that year. Loan demand remains healthy and the bank expects to grow its domestic lending by more than 10% in 2012.

It could be argued that BOC's goal of becoming a premier multinational banking group was achieved in late 2011 when the company was named to the list of Global Systematically Important Financial Institutions (firms that are considered too big to fail). It was China's only company to be named to the list. BOC's strategic development plan for further growth includes efforts to streamline its structure expand internationally (it was the first major Chinese bank to offer RMB products in the US) and invest in its technology and branch network. In 2011 BOC divested some of its riskier holdings in bonds issued by Ireland Italy Greece Portugal and Spain.

HISTORY

The Bank of China (BOC) has always had strong ties to the government of China. Established as a central bank in 1912 right after the establishment of the Provisional Government of the Republic of China BOC became a government-chartered international exchange bank in 1928. Their first overseas branch was opened in London in 1929 leading to a global network of 34 overseas branches over the next two decades.

After WWII the bank specialized in foreign exchange supporting foreign trade and the development of China's national economy. Between 1984 and 2001 BOC issued bonds in the international capital market 27 times. In 1993 when China initiated reform in its foreign exchange system BOC played a key role in the unification of exchange rates foreign exchange purchases and sales and the incorporation of foreign-funded enterprises into the foreign exchange sales system.

In 1994 BOC began to transform from a specialized bank to a wider-based state-owned commercial bank by issuing its first BOC Hong Kong dollar notes and then Macao pataca notes. The issue of both notes helped stabilize their respective markets.

BOC International Holdings a wholly owned subsidiary of BOC specializing in investment banking was incorporated in Hong Kong in 1998. Three years later the group restructured its Hong Kong operations by merging 10 of its member banks into Bank of China (Hong Kong) Limited a locally registered bank that successfully listed on the Hong Kong Stock Exchange in July 2003.

The bank was not free of scandal. A 2002 probe into BOC's New York branch by the US Office of the Comptroller of the Currency revealed that preferential treatment was given to certain customers who had personal relationships with some members of the bank's previous management. Regulators from the US and China fined BOC $20 million for "unsafe and unsound" business practices.

In 2005 the Royal Bank of Scotland (RBS) formed a consortium that bought a 10% stake in BOC. In exchange BOC agreed to distribute the Scottish bank's credit cards and other products. RBS sold its stake in 2009 and the banks ended their partnership agreement.

BOC went public in 2006. Its IPO was estimated to be the world's largest in six years. Foreign banks and investors scrambled for a piece of the action; Saudi investor Prince Alwaleed bin Talal invested $2 billion in the bank. The successful IPO was fraught with symbolism for the banking industry in China which had been struggling. China had had to bail out two of the country's top banks BOC and China Construction Bank three times within six years. And for decades money in China's state banks had been used to support failing state companies leaving the banks with a mountain of bad loans.

To increase its non-interest income BOC acquired Singapore Aircraft Leasing (since renamed BOC Aviation) for $965 million in late 2006. The

BOC Aviation portfolio includes more than 75 aircraft in about 20 countries.

BOC announced plans in 2008 to acquire 20% of French private bank La Compagnie Financiere Edmond de Rothschild but dropped those plans in 2009 after failing to get approval from Chinese regulators.

In early 2009 BOC faced selloffs by major investors as several subprime-battered financial institutions lined up to divest their stakes in the bank. UBS sold its entire 1% stake and Bank of America dumped its 3% share. Royal Bank of Scotland also sold its 4% stake in BOC. The two banks then cut their strategic partnership ties.

EXECUTIVES

EVP and Executive Director, Li Zaohang, age 58
EVP, Wang Yongli, age 49
Vice Chairman and President, Li Lihui, age 61
Secretary to the Board of Directors, Zhang Bingxun, age 64
Chairman of the Board, Gang Xiao
Vice Chairman of the Board; Head of Bank, Lihui Li
Chief Credit Risk Officer, Weijian Zhan
Chief Auditor, Yanfen Liu
Secretary of the Board, Yaosheng Fan
Director, Alberto Togni, age 76
EVP and Executive Director, Li Zaohang, age 58
Director, Anthony F. Neoh, age 67
EVP and Executive Director, Zhou Zaiqun, age 60
Vice Chairman and President, Li Lihui, age 61
Director, Hong Zhihua, age 59
Director, Huang Haibo, age 59
Director, Cai Haoyi, age 59
Director, Huang Shizhong, age 51
Director, Huang Danhan, age 64
Independent Non-Executive Director, Danhan Huang
Independent Non-Executive Director, Guoliang Dai
Non-Executive Director, Haoyi Cai
Non-Executive Director, Lina Liu
Independent Non-Executive Director, Nout Wellink
Non-Executive Director, Qi Zhang
Independent Non-Executive Director, Shizhong Huang
Independent Non-Executive Director, Wenyao Zhou
Non-Executive Director, Xiangdong Zhang
Non-Executive Director, Yansong Jiang
Auditors: PricewaterhouseCoopers

LOCATIONS

HQ: Bank of China Ltd
No. 1 Fuxingmen Nei Dajie, Beijing 100818
Phone: (86) 10 6659 6688   **Fax:** (86) 10 6601 6871
Web: www.boc.cn

PRODUCTS/OPERATIONS

Sales

	% of total
Interest	
Loans &	57
Securities & financial	11
Other	11
Noninterest	
Fees &	14
Net trading	2
Other	5
Total	**100**

Selected Subsidiaries

Bank of China Group Insurance Company Limited
BOC Aviation Private Limited
BOC Hong Kong (Group) Limited
Bank of China Group Investment Limited
Chiyu Banking Corporation Limited (commercial banking 47%)

Nanyang Commercial Bank Limited (commercial banking 66%)
Tai Fung Bank Limited (commercial banking 50.3%)

COMPETITORS

Agricultural Bank of China
Bank of East Asia
CITIC International Financial
Cathay Financial Holding
China Construction Bank
China Development Bank
China Merchants Bank
China Minsheng Banking
Chuo Mitsui Trust
HSBC
Hang Seng Bank
Industrial and Commercial Bank of China
Shanghai Pudong Development Bank

HISTORICAL FINANCIALS

Company Type: Public

Income Statement

FYE: December 31

	ASSETS ($ mil.)	NET INCOME ($ mil.)	INCOME AS % OF ASSETS	EMPLOYEES
12/13	2,291,797	25,919	1.1%	305,675
12/12	2,034,025	22,365	1.1%	302,016
12/11	1,879,458	19,728	1.0%	289,951
12/10	1,586,847	15,841	1.0%	279,301
12/09	1,281,772	11,836	0.9%	262,566
Annual Growth	15.6%	21.6%	—	3.9%

2013 Year-End Financials

Return on assets: 1.1%
Return on equity: 17.9%
Long-term debt ($ mil.): —
No. of shares (mil.): —
Sales ($ mil): 107,452
Dividends
Yield: 49.3%
Payout: 17.7%
Market value ($ mil.): —

	STOCK PRICE ($) FY Close	P/E High/Low		PER SHARE ($) Earnings	Dividends	Book Value
12/13	11.56	1	0	0.09	0.03	0.55
12/12	11.36	1	0	0.08	0.02	0.47
12/11	9.15	1	0	0.07	0.01	0.41
12/10	13.08	1	1	0.06	0.02	0.35
12/09	13.46	1	1	0.05	0.01	0.30
Annual Growth	(3.7%)	—	—	17.5%	34.1%	16.4%

Bank of Communications Co., Ltd.

Bank of Communications (BoCom) is one of the largest commercial banks in China based on total assets. The company offers services in corporate banking personal banking and treasury operations. Its offerings include personal savings accounts personal loans corporate loans trade financing wealth management e-banking and credit card services. BoCom boasts 30 provincial branches and a network of more than 2600 outlets in some 180 cities —including overseas branches in New York Tokyo and Singapore and representative offices in London and Frankfurt. The bank is also one of China's oldest. HSBC Holdings holds close to a 20% interest in BoCom.

Geographic Reach

BoCom has a dozen overseas institutions that consist of branches located in Hong Kong New York Tokyo Singapore Seoul Frankfurt Macau Ho Chi Minh City Sydney and San Francisco. It also operates a representative office in Taipei and Bank of Communications (UK) Co. Ltd.

Operations

The bank organizes its operations into four segments. Its personal banking unit focuses on personal savings bank cards personal lending payment and settlement investment services insurance services and wealth management. BoComm's corporate banking segment comprises cash management supply chain financing investment banking financial institution banking and asset custody services. The company's international banking unit consists of foreign exchange wealth management document settlement remittance and bill services trade finance and offshore banking. BoComm's fourth segment e-banking provides personal online banking enterprise online banking telephone banking and self-help banking.

Strategy

The company has continued to expand its offerings by venturing into new lines of business. With its purchase of an 85% stake in Hubei International Trust and Investment Corporation BoComm entered the trust industry. Soon after it began to also cater to the insurance industry with the launch of BoCommLife Insurance a joint venture with the Commonwealth Bank of Australia. BoCom is among the nation's first commercial banks allowed to tap into the insurance industry.

EXECUTIVES

Vice Chairman and President, Ximing Niu, age 58
EVP and CFO, Yu Yali, age 57
EVP and CIO, Hou Weidong, age 55
EVP, Dicky Peter Yip, age 67
Chief Risk Officer, Yang Dongping, age 57
General Manager and Chief Accountant, Teng Tieqi
Director, Hu Huating
Director, Wong (Peter) Tung Shun
Director, Gu Mingchao
Director, Lei Jun
Director, Li (Eric) Ka-cheung

LOCATIONS

HQ: Bank of Communications Co., Ltd.
No. 188 Yincheng Zhong Road, Pudong New District, Shanghai 200120
Phone: (86) 21 58766688   **Fax:** (86) 21 58798398
Web: www.bankcomm.com

PRODUCTS/OPERATIONS

Selected Services

Personal Banking
    Personal Savings in Local and Foreign Currencies
    Bank Card
    Personal Lending
    Wealth Management
Corporate Banking
    Deposit Services
    Financing Services
    Settlement Services
    Wealth Management
    Financial Institutional Banking Services
International Banking
    ForexWealth Management
    Document Settlement
    Remittance and bill services
    Trade finance
    Offshore Banking
E-Banking
    Telephone Bank
    Personal Online Banking
    Corporate Online Banking

COMPETITORS

Bank of China
Bank of China (Hong Kong)
Bank of East Asia
China Construction Bank
China Development Bank
China Merchants Bank
China Minsheng Banking
Chong Hing Bank
Hang Seng Bank
Industrial and Commercial Bank of China
Public Financial Holdings
Shanghai Pudong Development Bank

HISTORICAL FINANCIALS

Company Type: Public

Income Statement

FYE: December 31

	ASSETS ($ mil.)	NET INCOME ($ mil.)	INCOME AS % OF ASSETS	EMPLOYEES
12/13	984,645	10,290	1.0%	99,919
12/12	845,872	9,363	1.1%	96,259
12/11	732,584	8,060	1.1%	90,149
12/10	599,489	5,922	1.0%	85,290
12/09	484,642	4,410	0.9%	79,122
Annual Growth	19.4%	23.6%		6.0%

2013 Year-End Financials

Return on assets: 1.1%
Return on equity: 15.5%
Long-term debt ($ mil.): —
No. of shares (mil.): —
Sales ($ mil): 49,082
Dividends
Yield: 0.0%
Payout: 16.0%
Market value ($ mil.): —

	STOCK PRICE ($) FY Close	P/E High/Low		PER SHARE ($) Earnings	Dividends	Book Value
12/13	19.15	1	1	0.14	0.02	0.93
12/12	17.99	1	0	0.14	0.01	0.82
12/11	19.15	1	1	0.13	0.00	0.70
12/10	25.00	1	1	0.10	0.05	0.55
Annual Growth	(8.5%)	—	—	8.4%	(17.0%)	14.3%

Bank of East Asia Ltd.

Bank of East Asia provides retail and commercial banking services in Hong Kong and mainland China. Its offerings include deposit accounts consumer loans mortgages business loans credit cards private banking and investment management. Bank of East Asia has some 130 locations in Hong Kong and more than 60 in mainland China; internationally it has about 30 offices in the British Virgin Islands Malaysia Singapore the UK and Vietnam. The bank's subsidiaries include online securities and futures brokerage provider East Asia Securities Blue Cross (Asia-Pacific) Insurance and Tricor which performs outsourced business services.

Like many of its peers Bank of East Asia is seeking new revenue lines by branching into related industries. In 2009 it arranged to buy a minority stake in fund house Golden Eagle Asset Management allowing it to enter China's growing fund market. Bank of East Asia also launched a trust business in that country.

With an increased focus on Hong Kong and China the bank is also streamlining elsewhere. It sold a majority stake of its Canadian network (a half-dozen branches) to Industrial and Commercial Bank of China (ICBC) in 2010 and arranged to sell its US operations to that company the following year.

EXECUTIVES

Chairman and CEO, David K. P. Li, age 76
General Manager Personal Banking Division, Hon shing Tong
General Manager China Division, Raymond H. K. Yu
Director, Richard T. K. Li, age 46
Director, Isidro Faine Casas, age 72
Director, Allan C. Y. Wong, age 63
Director, Shau-Kee Lee, age 84
Director, Thomas P. K. Kwok, age 60
Deputy Chief Executive and Executive Director, Joseph Y. W. Pang, age 63
Director, Winston Yau-lai Lo, age 73
Director, William W. H. Doo, age 70
Director, Aubrey K. S. Li, age 63
Director, Fook-wo Li, age 97
Director, Chung-hin Wong, age 81
Director, Prof Arthur K. C. Li, age 69
Director, William M. W. Mong, age 85
Director, Kay peng Khoo, age 76
Director, Man-kou Tan, age 77
Director, Kenneth C. M. Lo, age 72
Director, Eric F. C. Li, age 85
Director, Stephen Charles K. S. Li, age 55
Director, Khoon ean Kuok, age 59
Independent Non-Executive Director, Kin Cheung
Auditors: KPMG

LOCATIONS

HQ: Bank of East Asia Ltd.
10 Des Voeux Road Central,
Phone: (852) 3608 3608   **Fax:** (852) 3608 6000
Web: www.hkbea.com

COMPETITORS

Bank of China (Hong Kong)	Dah Sing Banking
Bank of Communications	Dah Sing Financial Holdings Limited
CITIC International Financial	Hang Seng Bank
China Development Bank	Public Financical Holdings
China Minsheng Banking	Shanghai Pudong Development Bank
Chong Hing Bank	

HISTORICAL FINANCIALS

Company Type: Public

Income Statement

FYE: December 31

	ASSETS ($ mil.)	NET INCOME ($ mil.)	INCOME AS % OF ASSETS	EMPLOYEES
12/13	97,236	852	0.9%	12,698
12/12	89,285	781	0.9%	12,441
12/11	78,707	561	0.7%	12,238
12/10	68,728	543	0.8%	11,412
12/09	55,978	330	0.6%	10,540
Annual Growth	14.8%	26.7%	—	4.8%

2013 Year-End Financials

Return on assets: 0.9%	Dividends
Return on equity: 10.9%	Yield: 0.0%
Long-term debt ($ mil.): —	Payout: 0.5%
No. of shares (mil.): —	Market value ($ mil.): —
Sales ($ mil): 4,177	

	STOCK PRICE ($) FY Close	P/E High/Low		PER SHARE ($) Earnings	Dividends	Book Value
12/13	4.14	0	0	0.36	0.00	3.59
12/12	3.86	0	0	0.35	0.00	3.31
12/11	3.70	0	0	0.25	0.00	2.95
12/10	4.15	0	0	0.25	0.00	2.79
12/09	3.92	0	0	0.18	0.00	2.45
Annual Growth	1.4%	—	—	19.6%	36.5%	10.0%

Bank of Ireland (Ireland)

The one-time unofficial bank of the Irish state that traces its history to 1783 Bank of Ireland is now a full-blown financial services provider for consumers and businesses operating about 250 retail branches in Ireland and approximately 50 more in Northern Ireland. The bank offers traditional services such as deposits loans mortgages and life insurance. It provides similar services in the UK through some 11500 post office locations. Bank of Ireland also offers corporate finance and capital markets services in the US and Europe. The group's segments include Retail Ireland Bank of Ireland Life Retail UK and Corporate and Treasury.

Financial Performance

Still feeling the effects of the 2008 global financial crisis's blow to Ireland's economy Bank of Ireland reported a fifth straight year of reductions in revenue in 2012 (a 22% decline) which was attributed to lower interest income and fees. With the exception of 2011 the bank's net income has also been on a downward trajectory since 2008; in 2012 it reported a $2.4 billion dip into the red a decline driven by lower revenue and exacerbated by a minimal decline in expenses. The bank has been cutting back expenses including its operations and personnel costs but high regulatory costs and unfavorable current exchange rates offset its expense reductions. Strong capital and reductions in its leveraged debts were bright spots in the bank's finances in 2012.

Strategy

After its 2008 government bailout the Bank of Ireland was forced to sell off assets in order to strengthen its balance sheet. Among the divisions it sold was Bank of Ireland Asset Management which went to State Street Corporation. Other divestitures included Bank of Ireland Securities (formerly the largest Irish-owned asset administration provider) to Northern Trust the US business of its Foreign Currency Exchange subsidiary to Wells Fargo and asset-based lender Burdale Financial also to Wells Fargo.

Other divisions may be put up for sale further giving the bank a boost in capital. The bank is focused on reducing its operating expenses and debt levels.

Company Background

The Irish banking system was hit particularly hard by the global financial crisis in 2008 and a number of companies (including Bank of Ireland) required government bailouts. In mid-2011 Ireland's Central Bank Governor Patrick Honohan stated that his nation's banks had returned to financial soundness.

In late 2009 the government established the National Asset Management Agency or NAMA in re-

sponse to the nation's fiscal troubles. NAMA is a "bad bank" charged with buying toxic property loans from Irish banks in exchange for government bonds; it was designed to help get bad loans off the banks' books while providing liquidity and credit to the nation. In 2011 Bank of Ireland completed its final asset transfers to NAMA. By then Ireland's banks and the global outlook looked healthier but the sovereign debt crisis threw Europe into turbulence that shook up both consumer and business confidence. This time though all eyes were turned toward other weakened nations such as Greece Spain and Portugal.

HISTORY

Bank of Ireland opened for business in Dublin in 1783 at Mary's Abbey. The bank had Â600000 19 employees and a desire to offer more consistent service than the unstable private banks traders and merchants active at the time.

In 1784 Bank of Ireland began to print notes. As the government's unofficial banker it received all funds owed to the Irish treasury and administered all loans to and from the state.

By 1790 the bank's original building at Mary's Abbey had expanded into four. The bank's growth continued to outpace its premises. In 1803 the bank acquired Parliament House in College Green; after five years of remodeling the building was opened to the public. (It remained the bank's headquarters until the 1960s.)

Over time the bank ventured out of Dublin to open branch offices. Expansion began in 1825 with the establishment of seven branches; by 1883 the number had risen to 58 and by 1920 there were 75.

In 1926 the bank bought National Land Bank and renamed it National City Bank. More acquisitions followed —Hibernian Bank in 1958 and National Bank in 1965.

Much like its counterparts in the US the company was impacted by declining real estate values and higher unemployment rates in its home country. In 2008 the Irish government injected Â2 billion ($2.8 billion) into the bank in exchange for a 25% voting stake. Ireland also provided capital for Allied Irish Banks and Irish Bank Resolution to help stabilize the nation's financial system which plunged amid the global financial crisis and its own financial slump.

As part of the bailout the bank was compelled to sell off parts of itself. Bank of Ireland divested two units Iridian Asset Management and Guggenheim Alternative Investment Management in 2009. Other sales followed.

EXECUTIVES

Chief Executive Corporate and Treasury Division, Michael Torpey, age 56
CEO UK Division, Des Crowley, age 54, $409,895 total compensation
Group Communications, Dan Loughrey
Deputy Governor, Patrick H. O'Sullivan, age 65
Director, Kent Atkinson, age 69
Head of Non Core Division, Denis Donovan, age 60, $410,660 total compensation
Group CEO and Director, Richie Boucher, age 55, $346,834 total compensation
Group Treasury, Sean Crowe
Branch Network Ireland, Tim O'Neill
Group Payments, Vincent Brennan
Group Customer Operations, Joe Larkin
Business Banking Ireland and UK, Mark Cunningham
Global Markets, Austin Jennings
Group CFO, Andrew Keating
Consumer Banking Ireland and UK, Stephen Mason

Bank of Ireland UK, David McGowan
Corporate Banking, Tom Hayes
Post Office Financial and Travel Services, Patrick Waldron
Wealth Management, Mick Sweeney
Governor, Patrick J. Molloy, age 75
Divisional HR Capital Markets and Group Functions, Amy Burke
Group Investor Relations, Tony Joyce
Divisional HR Group Manufacturing, Marlene Shanley
HR Retail Ireland and UK, Neville Bourke
Chief Credit and Market Risk Officer, Vincent Mulvey, age 53
Chief Governance Risk Officer, Peter Morris
CEO Retail Ireland, Liam McLoughlin, age 51
Group Services, Orla Cunningham
Secretary, Helen Nolan
Group Regulatory and Operational Risk, John Murphy
Chief Customer and Operating Officer, Nick Fahy
Group Growth and Development, Donal Collins
Group IT, Larry Kiernan
Risk Strategy Analysis and Reporting, Declan Murray
Divisional Finance Retail Ireland and UK, Niall O?Shea
Head Group Manufacturing, Senan Murphy
Head of Group HR, Julie Sharp
COO, Kay Hanneffy
Credit and Market Risk Capital Markets, Tom McGivney
Retail Credit Ireland and UK, Tom Fee
Head of Acquisition Finance Germany, Ralph Betz
Governor, Archie Kane
Executive Vice President, Joe Connolly
Director, Patrick T. Kennedy, age 45
Deputy Governor, Patrick H. O'Sullivan, age 65
Director, Kent Atkinson, age 69
Director, Jerome J. Kennedy, age 65
Director, Paul M. Haran, age 56
Group CEO and Director, Richie Boucher, age 55
Director, Joe Walsh
Director, Tom Considine
Director, Pat Butler
Director, Patrick Mulvihill
Auditors: PricewaterhouseCoopers

LOCATIONS

HQ: Bank of Ireland (Ireland)
40 Mespil Road, Dublin 4
Phone:
Web: www.bankofireland.com

COMPETITORS

AIB	National Irish Bank
Barclays	Nationwide Building
HSBC	Society
Irish Bank Resolution	Northern Bank
Lloyds Banking Group	Ulster Bank
NatWest	permanent tsb

HISTORICAL FINANCIALS

Company Type: Public

Income Statement FYE: December 31

	ASSETS ($ mil.)	NET INCOME ($ mil.)	INCOME AS % OF ASSETS	EMPLOYEES
12/13	181,917	(670)	—	23,086
12/12	195,263	(2,404)	—	12,016
12/11	200,329	58	0.0%	13,234
12/10	224,141	(821)	—	14,235
12/09	260,895	(2,103)	—	14,647
Annual Growth	(8.6%)	—	—	12.0%

2013 Year-End Financials

Return on assets: (-0.3%)
Return on equity: (-5.9%)
Long-term debt ($ mil.): —
No. of shares (mil.): —
Sales ($ mil.) 8,454

Dividends
Yield: —
Payout: —
Market value ($ mil.) —

	STOCK PRICE ($) FY Close	P/E High/Low	Earnings	PER SHARE ($) Dividends	Book Value
12/13	14.41	— —	(0.03)	0.00	0.34
12/12	6.50	— —	(0.09)	0.00	0.38
12/11	4.24	— —	(0.01)	0.00	0.44
12/10	2.65	— —	(0.29)	0.00	1.87
12/09	7.66	— —	(2.43)	0.00	9.59
Annual Growth 17.1% (56.8%)		—	—	—	—

Bank of Kyoto, Ltd. (Japan)

For financial services in Kyoto proper protocol might involve a visit to The Bank of Kyoto. The regional bank serves Kyoto and neighboring prefectures through some 165 branch offices. The bank serves businesses particularly small and medium-sized local companies as well as individual consumers. In addition to traditional deposit banking and lending The Bank of Kyoto and its subsidiaries offer credit cards leasing stock brokerage and business consulting services. The bank has worked to expand its operations beyond its home base and has opened branches to the north in the Kinki Region. Founded in 1941 the bank has about $81 billion in assets and ranks as Kyoto Prefecture's largest retail bank.

Geographic Reach
The Bank of Kyoto operates 110 branches in Kyoto Prefecture 28 in Osaka Prefecture a dozen in Shiga eight in Hyogo and seven branches in Nara.

Strategy
The Bank of Kyoto is aggressively opening branches to expand its reach beyond Kyoto Prefecture. Since opening its first branch at Kusatsu in Shiga Prefecture in 2000 the bank has opened branches in five neighboring prefectures (Kyoto Osaka Shiga Nara and Hyogo).

EXECUTIVES

Chairman, Yasuo Kashihara
President and Director, Hideo Takasaki
Senior Managing Director, Issei Daido
Managing Director, Hisayoshi Nakamura
Managing Director, Yoshio Nishi
Managing Director, Katsuyuki Toyobe
Managing Director, Masayuki Kobayashi
Managing Director, Junji Inoguchi
Managing Director, Nobuhiro Doi
Managing Executive Officer, Hiroshi Okuno
Managing Executive Officer, Yojiro Nagayasu
Managing Executive Officer, Yuji Kitayama
President and Director, Hideo Takasaki
Senior Managing Director, Issei Daido
Managing Director, Hisayoshi Nakamura
Managing Director, Yoshio Nishi
Managing Director, Katsuyuki Toyobe
Managing Director, Masayuki Kobayashi
Managing Director, Junji Inoguchi

Managing Director, Nobuhiro Doi
Auditors: DeloitteToucheTohmatsu

LOCATIONS

HQ: Bank of Kyoto, Ltd. (Japan)
700 Yakushimae-cho, Karasuma-dori Matsubara-Agaru, Shimogyo-ku, Kyoto 600-8652
Phone: (81) 75 361 2211   **Fax:** (81) 75 343 1276
Web: www.kyotobank.co.jp

COMPETITORS

Mitsubishi UFJ	Sumitomo Mitsui
Financial Group	Sumitomo Trust and
Mizuho Financial	Banking
Resona	

HISTORICAL FINANCIALS

Company Type: Public

Income Statement FYE: March 31

	ASSETS ($ mil.)	NET INCOME ($ mil.)	INCOME AS % OF ASSETS	EMPLOYEES
03/14	76,476	162	0.2%	3,566
03/13	81,057	186	0.2%	3,570
03/12	89,714	189	0.2%	3,545
03/11	87,986	221	0.3%	3,485
03/10	76,174	167	0.2%	3,393
Annual Growth	0.1%	(0.8%)	—	1.3%

2014 Year-End Financials

Return on assets: 0.2%
Return on equity: 3.3%
Long-term debt ($ mil.): —
No. of shares (mil.): 377
Sales ($ mil): 1,025

Dividends
Yield: —
Payout: —
Market value ($ mil.): —

	STOCK PRICE ($) FY Close	P/E High/Low	Earnings	PER SHARE ($) Dividends	Book Value
03/14	0.00	— —	0.43	0.00	13.99
03/13	0.00	— —	0.46	0.00	13.02
03/12	8.56	— —	0.47	0.00	13.84
Annual Growth	—	— —	(2.2%)	—	0.3%

Bank of Montreal

LOCATIONS

HQ: Bank of Montreal
129 rue Saint-Jacques, Montreal, Quebec H2Y 1L6
Phone: 416 867-6785   **Fax:** 416 867-6793
Web: www.bmo.com

PRODUCTS/OPERATIONS

Sales

	% of total
Interest	
Loans	48
Securities	14
Deposits with	1
Noninterest	
Securities commissions &	7
Deposit & payment service	5
Securitization	5
Lending	3
Mutual fund	4
Trading	3
Underwriting & advisory	3
Other	7
Total	**100**

HISTORICAL FINANCIALS

Company Type: Public

Income Statement

FYE: October 31

	ASSETS ($ mil.)	NET INCOME ($ mil.)	INCOME AS % OF ASSETS	EMPLOYEES
10/14	526,078	3,822	0.7%	0
10/13	513,702	3,999	0.8%	45,500
10/12	526,880	4,126	0.8%	46,000
10/11	502,570	3,053	0.6%	47,000
10/10	404,083	2,758	0.7%	37,947
Annual Growth	6.8%	8.5%	—	—

2014 Year-End Financials

Return on assets: 0.7%
Return on equity: 13.2%
Long-term debt ($ mil.): —
No. of shares (mil.): 649
Sales ($ mil): 19,033

Dividends
Yield: 4.2%
Payout: 51.8%
Market value ($ mil.): 47,121

	STOCK PRICE ($) FY Close	P/E High/Low		PER SHARE ($) Earnings	Dividends	Book Value
10/14	72.60	10	8	5.73	2.79	47.25
10/13	69.70	10	8	5.99	2.88	45.14
10/12	59.12	10	8	6.17	2.83	44.16
10/11	59.17	14	10	4.86	2.88	41.41
10/10	59.25	13	9	4.66	3.44	37.92
Annual Growth	5.2%	—	—	5.3%	(5.1%)	5.7%

Bank of Nova Scotia
Halifax

The last place to look for The Bank of Nova Scotia's headquarters is in Nova Scotia. Although the company (aka Scotiabank) was founded in that province in 1832 it moved to Toronto in 1900. One of Canada's Big Five banks (along with Royal Bank of Canada TD Bank Bank of Montreal and CIBC) Scotiabank provides retail corporate and investment banking services around the world. In addition to about 1000 domestic branches Scotiabank has approximately 1700 offices in more than 50 other countries mainly in the Caribbean and Central and South America. Services include deposit accounts loans insurance brokerage asset management mutual funds and trust services.

While its domestic competitors have been expanding in the US Scotiabank has been focused mainly on making inroads in the Caribbean Latin America and Asia. The bank plans growth in Mexico the Caribbean and South America in addition to its home market. As it looks outward for growth Scotiabank has benefitted from a strong Canadian dollar bolstered by the nation's natural resources sector. The company reported record net income for fiscal 2010.

In 2012 the company rebranded its Scotia Capital Scotia Waterous and ScotiaMocotta investment banking units as Scotiabank in an effort to solidify its brand. The firms became part of Scotiabank's Global Banking and Markets division which offers such services as securities underwriting and mergers and acquisitions advice to corporate clients.

Later that year Scotiabank acquired US-based Howard Weil a boutique investment bank focused on the energy sector. The company built its investment banking practice in South America through

the 2010 acquisitions of Dresdner Bank Brazil from Germany's Commerzbank and Royal Bank of Scotland's wholesale banking operations in Colombia.

Domestically Scotiabank wants to be the dominant money manager. As part of its strategy it announced a consolidated wealth management arm in 2009: Scotia Asset Management which includes ScotiaFunds ScotiaMcLeod and Scotia Cassels Investment Counsel. The year before Scotiabank acquired a large minority stake of fund manager CI Financial from Sun Life Financial. In a similar move the company acquired Dundee Corporation's stake in DundeeWealth for some $2.3 billion in 2011. The acquisition gave Scotiabank control of another one of Canada's largest wealth managers.

In 2012 Scotiabank agreed to buy ING Bank of Canada from Dutch group ING for C$3.1 billion. ING Bank of Canada operating as ING Direct primarily serves its clients via the Internet and has marketed itself as an alternative to big banks. Scotiabank plans to continue to run ING Direct as a standalone bank. (ING Groep has been selling off parts of its business as it tries to gain capital strength.)

The company also expanded its wealth management segment with the 2010 acquisition of the money management operations of BNP Paribas in the Bahamas the Cayman Islands and Panama and an agreement to purchase The WaterStreet Group which caters to ultra-high-net-worth clients. Scotiabank is also growing its wealth management business by offering new investment products.

Increasing its focus on insurance as well Scotiabank in 2009 rebranded its ScotiaLife Financial business which offers credit travel life and health coverage. It has also built up its online brokerage capabilities acquiring TradeFreedom Securities in 2007 and E*TRADE Canada from E*TRADE in 2008. Other areas of focus for Scotiabank include mobile banking and global foreign exchange.

Beyond Canada the company owns interests in banks in Chile (Scotiabank Chile formerly Banco del Desarrollo) Mexico (Scotiabank Inverlat) and Central America (Scotiabank El Salvador and Groupo BNS de Costa Rica). In 2010 Scotiabank bought Royal Bank of Scotland's Chilean business and its wholesale banking operations in Colombia making it the only Canadian-owned institution with a presence in the latter country. More expansion in the Caribbean was achieved when Scotiabank acquired R&G Financial's troubled R-G Premier Bank of Puerto Rico. The transaction which was assisted by the FDIC added nearly 30 branches to Scotiabank's network on the island.

Scotiabank expanded in Peru one of South America's fastest-growing economies with its 2006 acquisition of some 80% of Banco Wiese Sudameris (now Scotiabank Peru) from Italian banking group Banca Intesa (now Intesa Sanpaolo) which held on to the rest. It also holds an interest in Peru-based pension-fund manager AFP ProFuturo. Scotiabank entered Uruguay for the first time in 2010 by buying controlling stakes in private bank Nuevo Banco Comercial and consumer lender Pronto. Further expanding in Latin America during 2011 the company acquired wholesale bank Dresdner Bank Brasil (now Scotiabank Brasil) and a majority stake in Colombia-based retail bank Banco Colpatria. In 2012 it announced plans to buy a majority of Colfondos a Colombian pension fund firm with more than $9 billion in assets under management.

Building its position in the Asia-Pacific region Scotiabank in 2009 increased its stake in Thailand's Thanachart Bank to 49% the Thai limit for foreign ownership. The next year Thanachart acquired Siam City Bank making it Thailand's fifth-largest bank. Scotiabank also upped its stake in China's Xi'an City Commercial Bank to almost

15% and arranged to acquire nearly 20% of the state-run Chinese institution Bank of Guangzhou.

EXECUTIVES

Chairman, John T. Mayberry, age 70
Group Head Global Corporate and Investment Banking and Co-Chief Executive Officer Scotia Capital, Stephen D. (Steve) McDonald
Group Head and Chief Risk Officer, Robert H. (Rob) Pitfield
President CEO and Director, Richard E. (Rick) Waugh, $1,000,000 total compensation
Group Head Global Human Resources and Communications, Sylvia D. Chrominska
Vice Chairman Chief Operating Officer, Sarabjit S. (Sabi) Marwah
Executive Vice President General Counsel Secretary, Deborah M. Alexander
Executive Vice President, Alberta G. Cefis
Group Head Global Wealth Management, Christopher J. (Chris) Hodgson
President, Brian J. Porter, $450,000 total compensation
Group Head International Banking, Dieter W. Jentsch
EVP Enterprise Effectiveness, Luc A. Vanneste, $400,000 total compensation
Executive Vice President and Chief Administration Officer Global Banking and Markets, Anne Marie O'Donovan
Group Head Global Capital Markets and Co-Chief Executive Officer Scotia Capital, Michael (Mike) Durland
EVP Latin America, Wendy G. Hannam
Executive Vice President Information Technology and Solutions, Kimberlee B. (Kim) McKenzie
Executive Vice President Chief Financial Officer, Sean McGuckin
Executive Vice President Global Wealth Management, Barbara F. (Barb) Mason
EVP Retail Products and Services Canadian Banking, Robin S. Hibberd
Group Head Canadian Banking, Anatol von Hahn
EVP and Chief Credit Officer, Stephen P. Hart
Executive Vice President Treasurer, Jeffrey C. (Jeff) Heath
EVP and President and CEO Grupo Financiero Scotiabank Mexico, Troy Wright
Executive Vice President Chief Administrative Officer, Marianne Hasold-Schilter
Executive Vice President; Chief Administration Officer - Scotia Capital, Anne ODonovan
Executive Vice President - Mexico; President & Chief Executive Officer - BNS Mexico, Nicole Polignac
EVP Global Human Resources, Sue Graham Parker
EVP Retail Distribution Canadian Banking, James McPhedran
Executive Vice President Global Human Resources, Sue Parker
Director, Barbara S. Thomas, age 63
Director, Ronald A. (Ron) Brenneman, age 67
Director, Paul D. Sobey, age 55
President CEO and Director, Richard E. (Rick) Waugh
Vice Chairman and COO, Sarabjit S. (Sabi) Marwah
Director, Thomas C. (Tom) O'Neill, age 67
Director, John C. Kerr, age 68
Director, C. J. Chen, age 66
Director, N. Ashleigh Everett, age 56
Director, Allan C. Shaw, age 69
Director, Michael J. L. Kirby, age 71
Director, Alexis E. Rovzar de la Torre, age 62
Director, Indira V. Samarasekera, age 60
Director, David A. Dodge
Auditors: KPMGLLP

LOCATIONS

HQ: Bank of Nova Scotia Halifax
Bank of Nova Scotia Building, 1709 Hollis Street,
Halifax, Nova Scotia B3J 1W1
Phone: 416 866-6161   **Fax:** 416 866-7767
Web: www.scotiabank.com

PRODUCTS/OPERATIONS

Sales

	% of total
Interest	
Loans	51
Securities	18
Other	2
Noninterest	
Trading	4
Deposit & payment	4
Credit	4
Investment management brokerage & trust	3
Mutual	2
Underwriting fees & other	2
Card	2
Other	8
Total	**100**

Selected Canadian Subsidiaries

BNS Capital Trust
BNS Investment Inc.
   Montreal Trust Company of Canada
   Scotia Merchant Capital Corporation
Dundee Bank of Canada
Maple Trust Company
National Trustco Inc.
   The Bank of Nova Scotia Trust Company
   National Trust Company
RoyNat Inc.
Scotia Capital Inc.
   1548489 Ontario Limited
      Scotia iTrade Corp.
Scotia Asset Management L.P.
Scotia Capital Inc.
Scotia Dealer Advantage Inc.
Scotia Insurance Agency Inc.
Scotia Life Insurance Company
Scotia Mortgage Corporation
Scotia Securities Inc.
Scotiabank Capital Trust
Scotiabank Subordinated Notes Trust.
Scotiabank Tier 1 Trust

Selected International Subsidiaries

The Bank of Nova Scotia Berhad (Malaysia)
The Bank of Nova Scotia International Limited
   (Bahamas)
   The Bank of Nova Scotia Asia Limited (Singapore)
   The Bank of Nova Scotia Trust Company (Bahamas)
   Ltd.
      Scotiabank & Trust (Cayman) Ltd. (Cayman Islands)
BNS (Colombia) Holdings Limited
Grupo BNS de Costa Rica S.A.
Scotia Insurance (Barbados) Limited
Scotiabank (Bahamas) Limited
Scotiabank (British Virgin Islands) Limited
Scotiabank Caribbean Treasury Limited (Bahamas)
Scotiabank (Hong Kong) Limited
Scotiabank (Ireland) Limited
Scotia Group Jamaica Limited (72%)
   The Bank of Nova Scotia Jamaica Limited
   Scotia DBG Investments Limited (77% Jamaica)
Grupo Financiero Scotiabank Inverlat S.A. de C.V. (97%
   Mexico)
Nova Scotia Inversiones Limitada (Chile)
   Scotiabank Chile S.A.
Scotia Capital (USA) Inc.
Scotia Holdings (US) Inc.
   The Bank of Nova Scotia Trust Company of New York
   Scotiabanc Inc. (US)
Scotia International Limited (Bahamas)
   Scotiabank Anguilla Limited
Scotiabank de Puerto Rico
Scotiabank El Salvador S.A.
Scotiabank Europe plc (UK)
Scotiabank Peru S.A.A.
Scotiabank Trinidad and Tobago Limited

COMPETITORS

BMO Financial Group	HSBC Bank Canada
Banamex	JPMorgan Chase
Banco Santander Chile	National Bank of
Bank of America	Canada
Bicsa Panama	RBC Financial Group
CIBC	TD Bank
Citigroup	

HISTORICAL FINANCIALS

Company Type: Public

Income Statement

FYE: October 31

	ASSETS ($ mil.)	NET INCOME ($ mil.)	INCOME AS % OF ASSETS	EMPLOYEES
10/14	720,015	6,180	0.9%	86,932
10/13	711,122	5,932	0.8%	83,000
10/12	669,863	6,039	0.9%	81,497
10/11	577,548	4,978	0.9%	75,362
10/10	516,989	3,963	0.8%	70,772
Annual Growth	**8.6%**	**11.7%**	**—**	**5.3%**

2014 Year-End Financials

Return on assets: 0.8%
Return on equity: 14.9%
Long-term debt ($ mil.): —
No. of shares (mil.): 1,216
Sales ($ mil): 27,864
Dividends
   Yield: 4.1%
   Payout: 47.6%
Market value ($ mil.): 74,576

	STOCK PRICE ($) FY Close	P/E High/Low		PER SHARE ($) Earnings	Dividends	Book Value
10/14	61.30	10	8	5.06	2.35	35.19
10/13	60.77	11	9	4.92	2.34	35.32
10/12	54.38	11	8	5.23	2.18	33.56
10/11	52.61	14	10	4.64	2.06	30.20
10/10	53.51	14	10	3.84	1.92	26.01
Annual Growth	**3.5%**	**—**	**—**	**7.1%**	**5.2%**	**7.8%**

Bank of Yokohama, Ltd.

The Bank of Yokohama serves its native Kanagawa prefecture and southern portions of neighboring Tokyo. It offers standard retail services the likes of deposits housing loans credit cards securities brokerage and investment products and advice. The bank also provides small and medium-sized commercial financing including venture capital investment and boasts units that offer leasing and factoring. The Bank of Yokohama which was formed in 1920 and had total assets of 13 billion Yen in 2014 operates more than 610 Japanese branches plus representative offices in Bangkok Hong Kong London New York and Shanghai. Through a joint venture it shares branches with Hamagin Tokai Tokyo Securities.

EXECUTIVES

Deputy President and Representative Director, Chiyuki Okubo
Chairman, Tadashi Ogawa, age 71
Managing Executive Officer and Director, Seiichi Yoneda
Managing Executive Officer and Director, Atsushi Mochizuki
Managing Executive Officer, Shunji Komatsu
President and Representative Director, Tatsumaro Terazawa
Managing Executive Officer and Representative Director, Kengo Takano

Managing Executive Officer and Director, Susumu Koshida
Managing Executive Officer, Shizumi Maesako
Managing Executive Officer, Yoshiyuki Hiranuma
Deputy President and Representative Director, Chiyuki Okubo
Representative Director, Masaki Itoh
Managing Executive Officer and Director, Seiichi Yoneda
Managing Executive Officer and Director, Atsushi Mochizuki
Managing Executive Officer and Director, Takashi Noguchi
President and Representative Director, Tatsumaro Terazawa
Managing Executive Officer and Representative Director, Kengo Takano
Auditors: DeloitteToucheTohmatsu

LOCATIONS

HQ: Bank of Yokohama, Ltd.
3-1-1 Minatomirai, Nishi-ku, Yokohama, Kanagawa 220-8611
Phone: (81) 45 225 1111   **Fax:** (81) 45 225 1160
Web: www.boy.co.jp

COMPETITORS

Mitsubishi UFJ	Sumitomo Mitsui
Financial Group	Suruga Bank
Mizuho Financial	Tokyo Star Bank
Norinchukin Bank	

HISTORICAL FINANCIALS

Company Type: Public

Income Statement

FYE: March 31

	ASSETS ($ mil.)	NET INCOME ($ mil.)	INCOME AS % OF ASSETS	EMPLOYEES
03/14	134,006	587	0.4%	4,780
03/13	143,144	588	0.4%	4,751
03/12	156,066	624	0.4%	4,752
03/11	151,202	568	0.4%	4,768
03/10	128,301	331	0.3%	4,784
Annual Growth	**1.1%**	**15.4%**	**—**	**(0.0%)**

2014 Year-End Financials

Return on assets: 0.4%
Return on equity: 7.1%
Long-term debt ($ mil.): —
No. of shares (mil.): 1,281
Sales ($ mil): 2,889
Dividends
   Yield: 2.2%
   Payout: 104.0%
Market value ($ mil.): 25,496

	STOCK PRICE ($) FY Close	P/E High/Low		PER SHARE ($) Earnings	Dividends	Book Value
03/14	19.90	—	—	0.45	0.45	6.97
03/13	23.18	—	—	0.44	0.00	7.27
03/12	19.90	—	—	0.46	0.00	7.54
03/11	47.80	—	—	0.42	0.46	6.99
03/10	48.75	—	—	0.24	0.43	6.00
Annual Growth	**(20.1%)**	**—**	**—**	**16.8%**	**1.1%**	**3.8%**

Bankinter, S.A.

Founded in 1965 as a joint venture between what is now Grupo Santander and Bank of America Bankinter is among the top six banks in Spain. The company offers a variety of consumer and business banking services through about 360 branch locations agents telephone services mobile banking and the Internet. A pioneer in Internet stock trading Bankinter conducts more than half of its transactions online. It serves corporations individuals and small enterprises. Bankinter provides mutual and pension funds mortgages leasing and securities brokerage focusing on convenient low-cost delivery and customer service. Investment firm Cartival S.A. owns about 23% of Bankinter.

Although Bankinter has about 360 branches in Spain more than half of its transactions are conducted on the Internet. The bank has pioneered technologies to make its online services more accessible including making Web pages compatible with software used by the visually impaired.

The bank is making a strong push to court the small and medium enterprise (SME) segment of the market. In recent years Bankinter launched dozens of new service centers catering to SMEs. The bank also continues to open other private banking and business management branches in fast-growing towns throughout the country.

Bankinter announced in 2009 it will buy the 50% of auto insurer Linea Directa Aseguradora it already does not own from Royal Bank of Scotland. The proposed shift follows a change in control at Royal Bank which was taken over by the government in 2008.

France's Credit Agricole owns about 20% of Bankinter. Through investment firm Cartival former Bankinter chairman Jaime Botin controls more than 15% of the bank's stock. The Botin family leads Grupo Santander which includes Spain's largest bank.

HISTORY

In 1962 Franco tried to end mixed banks in Spain with a decree that prevented banks from taking part in both commercial and investment operations. The banks circumvented this through cosmetic compliance spending the next decade nominally spinning off operations. In 1965 Banco Santander (now Grupo Santander) and Bank of America created Banco Intercontinental Espanol (Bankinter) in Madrid to specialize in industrial banking.

From 1970 to 1985 Bankinter evolved into a retail bank; it introduced credit cards personal loans and other services and offered financing to larger corporations. Bankinter was not consumed by the great branch race that defined banking-industry competition in Franco-era Spain; the bank had only 150 branches by 1985.

The bank became independent as both Bank of America (in 1987) and Santander (1994) reduced their stock holdings. Bankinter began diversifying its operations opening branches and gaining more clients. Bankinter's successful 1987 introduction of a high-interest special deposit account was dulled when other banks followed suit slowing growth. The bank took its current name in 1990 and in 1991 introduced some of Spain's first mutual funds. Within a recession-hammered economy Bankinter worked to cut costs through the introduction of telephone banking (1992) and other innovative conveniences.

Attracted by the low-cost liquidity of private banking Bankinter entered that segment in 1995. It took a step in the "allfinanz" direction that year creating an auto and home insurance alliance with Royal Bank of Scotland subsidiary Direct Line; the UK bank already had insurance ventures with Bankinter sibling Santander. Two years later Bankinter began BKNet Spain's first online stock-trading service.

In 1998 the bank opened a Mexican office to explore the possibility of transferring its high-tech operations into that country. As the financial industry's global consolidation continued the bank in 1999 said it was seeking a foreign ally possibly one

that could help expand Bankinter's online technology.

The bank found willing partners later that year inking deals to form an Internet bank in Spain with a joint venture of US Web portal Lycos (now part of Terra Networks) and German media giant Bertelsmann as well as another Internet bank with Portugal's Banco Espirito Santo.

Although Bankinter recorded 2004 as a particularly profitable year with income up nearly 25% it also suffered the death of a deputy manager Jose Garcia in the March 11 terrorist attacks against Madrid.

In 2007 the bank sold 50% of its life insurance division to Spanish insurer Mapfre. The sale boosted Bankinter's capital.

In 2008 Credit Agricole increased its ownership in the bank to about 20%. It became the bank's largest shareholder edging out former chairman Jaime Botin.

EXECUTIVES

Chairman, Pedro Guerrero Guerrero
CEO, Maria Dolores Dancausa
Director, Jose Ramon Arce Gomez
Director, John de Zuleta Greenebaum
Director, Fabiola Arredondo de Vara
Director, Marcelino Botin-Sanz de Sautola y Naveda
Director, Fernando Masaveu Herrero
Auditors: PricewaterhouseCoopersAuditoresS.L.

LOCATIONS

HQ: Bankinter, S.A.
Paseo de la Castellana, 29, Madrid 28046
Phone: (34) 91 339 75 00   **Fax:** (34) 91 339 83 23
Web: www.bankinter.es

PRODUCTS/OPERATIONS

Selected Subsidiaries
Aircraft S.A.
Bankinter Consultoria Asesoramiento y Atencion
  Telefonica S.A.
Bankinter Gestion de Seguros S.A.
Bankinter International B.V. (Netherlands)
Bankinter Seguros de Vida S.A.
Gesbankinter S.A.
Hispamarket S.A.
Intergestora S.A.
Intergestora Nuevas Tecnologias S.C.R. S.A.
Intermobiliaria S.A.

COMPETITORS

AEGON	Banco de Sabadell
BBVA	Deutsche Bank
Banco Espa?ol de	Espirito Santo
Credito	Grupo Santander
Banco Guipuzcoano	La Caixa
Banco Popular Espa?ol	

HISTORICAL FINANCIALS
Company Type: Public

Income Statement
FYE: December 31

	ASSETS ($ mil.)	NET INCOME ($ mil.)	INCOME AS % OF ASSETS	EMPLOYEES
12/13	75,907	296	0.4%	3,820
12/12	76,665	164	0.2%	3,853
12/11	76,949	234	0.3%	3,904
12/10	72,475	201	0.3%	4,740
12/09	78,464	366	0.5%	4,694
Annual Growth	(0.8%)	(5.2%)	—	(5.0%)

2013 Year-End Financials

Return on assets: 0.3%
Return on equity: 6.4%
Long-term debt ($ mil.): —
No. of shares (mil.): 895
Sales ($ mil): 3,742

Dividends
Yield: 1.2%
Payout: 48.5%
Market value ($ mil.): 5,821

	STOCK PRICE ($) FY Close	P/E High/Low	PER SHARE ($) Earnings	Dividends	Book Value
12/13	6.50	58 21	0.37	0.08	5.23
12/12	4.35	52 18	0.30	0.14	7.55
12/11	6.01	39 21	0.45	0.24	8.37
12/10	5.30	65 27	0.43	0.26	7.29
12/09	11.10	48 26	0.82	1.42	7.86
Annual Growth (9.7%)	(12.5%)	—	(18.0%)	(51.2%)	

Banque et Caisse d'Epargne de l'Etat, (Luxembourg)

LOCATIONS

HQ: Banque et Caisse d' Epargne de l' Etat,
  (Luxembourg)
1, Place de Metz, Luxembourg L- 2954
Phone: (352) 4015 1   **Fax:** (352) 4015 2099
Web: www.bcee.lu

HISTORICAL FINANCIALS
Company Type: Public

Income Statement
FYE: December 31

	ASSETS ($ mil.)	NET INCOME ($ mil.)	INCOME AS % OF ASSETS	EMPLOYEES
12/13	56,052	328	0.6%	1,803
12/12	53,372	299	0.6%	1,804
12/11	51,403	162	0.3%	1,804
12/10	50,771	289	0.6%	1,811
12/09	54,225	320	0.6%	1,799
Annual Growth	0.8%	0.6%	—	0.1%

2013 Year-End Financials

Return on assets: 0.5%
Return on equity: 6.7%
Long-term debt ($ mil.): —
No. of shares (mil.): —
Sales ($ mil): 873

Dividends
Yield: —
Payout: —
Market value ($ mil.): —

Banque Nationale de Belgique (National Bank of Belgium)

No prizes for guessing the role of the Nationale Bank van Belgiq. NBB is indeed the national central bank for Belgium and a member of the European System of Central Banks (ESCB). Founded in 1850 the institution performs a variety of functions aimed at maintaining stability and liquidity for Belgium's banks and financial markets including arranging fund transfers between banks overseeing settlement activities for securities markets and issuing banknotes and coins. The bank's chief executive known as its governor is appointed by the Belgian monarch. NBB is also known by its names in French (Banque nationale de Belgique) English (National Bank of Belgium) and German (Belgische Nationalbank).

The bank carries out various other functions within Belgium's financial system. As the nation's lender of last resort NBB is also able to provide emergency funds when times of exceptional financial crisis. It did as much in 2008 with the cross-national bailout of Fortis. NBB has also printed currency notes (and distributed coins struck by Belgium's Royal Mint) since 1851.

Auditors: Ernst&YoungReviseursd'EntreprisesSCC

LOCATIONS

HQ: Banque Nationale de Belgique (National Bank of Belgium)
Boulevard de Berlaimont 14, Brussels BE-1000
Phone: (32) 2 221 21 11 **Fax:** (32) 2 221 31 00
Web: www.nbb.be

COMPETITORS

Bank of England	Federal Reserve
Deutsche Bundesbank	Swiss National Bank

HISTORICAL FINANCIALS

Company Type: Public

Income Statement

	ASSETS ($ mil.)	NET INCOME ($ mil.)	INCOME AS % OF ASSETS	EMPLOYEES
12/13	107,110	1,303	1.2%	2,301
12/12	144,660	1,762	1.2%	2,103
12/11	165,193	1,162	0.7%	2,101
12/10	99,973	1,113	1.1%	2,065
12/09	146,160	2,754	1.9%	2,095
Annual Growth	(7.5%)	(17.1%)	—	2.4%

	STOCK PRICE ($) FY Close	P/E High/Low	PER SHARE ($) Earnings	Dividends	Book Value
12/13	3,857.57 19,257.07	— —	(0.00)	0.00	
12/12	2,975.00 18,613.61	— —	(0.00)	0.00	
12/11	2,600.00 16,122.66	— —	(0.00)	0.00	
12/10	4,900.00 15,756.78	— —	(0.00)	0.00	
12/09	4,800.00 16,507.98	— —	(0.00)	0.00	
Annual Growth	(5.3%)	— —	—	—	3.9%

Baoshan Iron & Steel Co Ltd

Blast furnaces and steel mills nsk

EXECUTIVES

Chairman, Wenbo He

LOCATIONS

HQ: Baoshan Iron & Steel Co Ltd
Baosteel Command Center, No. 885, Fujin Road,
Baoshan District, Shanghai 201900
Phone: (86) 21 26647000 **Fax:** (86) 21 26646999
Web: www.baosteel.com/plc/

PRODUCTS/OPERATIONS

HISTORICAL FINANCIALS

Company Type: Public

Income Statement

FYE: December 31

	REVENUE ($ mil.)	NET INCOME ($ mil.)	NET PROFIT MARGIN	EMPLOYEES
12/13	31,389	961	3.1%	0
12/12	30,719	1,666	5.4%	32,598
12/11	35,405	1,169	3.3%	41,919
12/10	30,707	1,955	6.4%	42,308
12/09	21,752	851	3.9%	42,318
Annual Growth	9.6%		3.1%	—	—

2013 Year-End Financials

Debt ratio: 3.1%	No. of shares (mil.): —
Return on equity: 5.2%	Dividends
Cash ($ mil.): 2,127	Yield: —
Current ratio: 0.82	Payout: —
Long-term debt ($ mil.): 1,355	Market value ($ mil.): —

Barclays Africa Group Ltd

Can Absa help with your banking needs in Africa? Absa-lutely! Serving nearly 12 million consumers small businesses and commercial clients the company's Absa Bank is one of the largest retail banks and mortgage lenders in South Africa with about 700 branches and 9000 ATMs most of them in that country. The bank and other subsidiaries offer deposits loans credit cards insurance investments financial planning brokerage wealth management and investment banking services. British bank Barclays owns about 55% of Absa Group making it one of South Africa's largest foreign investors since apartheid ended in 1994.

Beyond South Africa Absa Group owns some 80% of Barclays Bank Mozambique and a majority of National Bank of Commerce in Tanzania. The company which also has representative offices in Namibia and Nigeria is taking steps to broaden its presence in its existing markets and the surrounding region. It acquired Global Alliance Seguros a Mozambique-based life and property/casualty insurer in 2011. Absa Group launched an insurance unit in Botswana that year as well.

In 2008 Absa Group acquired controlling interests in Meeg Bank and Woolworths Holdings' financial services operations further strengthening its presence in South Africa. The moves came after Absa Group canceled plans to buy Barclays' retail operations in Zimbabwe Zambia Kenya Botswana Ghana Tanzania the Seychelles and Mauritius. Additional acquisitions are expected.

The traditionally consumer-focused company is also making efforts to attract more commercial clients. During 2010 it established a corporate bank and invested in a transactional banking platform for commercial clients. Meanwhile the company is not ignoring consumers however as it retooled its retail franchise to focus more on value rather than volume. Absa Group has also used technology to simplify processes streamline customer service and improve access to banking.

Maria Ramos was named CEO of Absa Group in 2009 after former chief executive Steve Booysen retired after 20 years with the company.

EXECUTIVES

Deputy Group Chief Executive and Director, Louis L. von Zeuner, age 51
CEO Bancassurance, Willie T. Lategan, age 45
Executive Director Marketing and Communications, Happy Ntshingila, age 53
Group Chief Executive and Director, Maria Ramos, age 55
Finance Director and Board Member, David W. P. Hodnett, age 44
COO, N. Alfie Naidoo, age 46
Chief Executive Absa Capital, Stephen van Coller, age 48
Chief Executive Absa Africa, John Gachora
Director, Trevor S. Munday, age 64
Director, Robert Le Blanc, age 57
Deputy Group Chief Executive and Director, Louis L. von Zeuner, age 51
Director, Antony Jenkins
Director, Shauket A. Fakie, age 61
Director, Yolanda Z. Cuba, age 36
Director, Garth Griffin, age 64
Director, Eduardo C. Mondlane Jr., age 56
Director, Brand S.G. Pretorius, age 65
Director, Johan B. Willemse, age 58
Finance Director and Board Member, David W. P. Hodnett, age 44
Auditors: PricewaterhouseCoopersInc.

LOCATIONS

HQ: Barclays Africa Group Ltd
7th Floor, Absa Towers West, 15 Troye Street,
Johannesburg 2001
Phone: (27) 11 350 4000
Web: www.barclaysafrica.com

PRODUCTS/OPERATIONS

Sales

	% of total
Interest & similar	68
Net fee & commission	21
Net insurance premium	6
Gains from banking & trading	3
Other	2
Total	**100**

COMPETITORS

FirstRand	Standard Bank Group
Nedcor	Standard Chartered
Sanlam	

HISTORICAL FINANCIALS

Company Type: Public

Income Statement

FYE: December 31

	ASSETS ($ mil.)	NET INCOME ($ mil.)	INCOME AS % OF ASSETS	EMPLOYEES
12/13	91,102	1,137	1.2%	46,320
12/12	94,899	985	1.0%	0
12/11	97,146	1,194	1.2%	39,659
12/10	107,841	1,221	1.1%	43,239
12/09	96,981	924	1.0%	36,150
Annual Growth	(1.6%)	5.3%	—	6.4%

Return on assets: 1.3%
Return on equity: 16.6%
Long-term debt ($ mil.): —
No. of shares (mil.): 847
Sales ($ mil.): 9,065

Dividends
Yield: 9.6%
Payout: 1.7%
Market value ($ mil.): 21,606

	STOCK PRICE ($) FY Close	P/E High/Low		PER SHARE ($) Earnings	Dividends	Book Value
12/13	25.50	0	0	1.34	2.45	8.66
12/12	38.98	0	0	1.37	1.61	10.95
12/11	34.85	0	0	1.66	0.03	10.73
12/10	42.00	0	0	1.70	1.16	11.82
12/09	34.85	0	0	1.30	0.02	9.54
Annual Growth	(7.5%)	—	—	0.8%	245.1%	(2.4%)

Barclays Bank Plc

Barclays Bank is the flagship subsidiary of global financial group Barclays PLC. The bank is primarily active in the UK where it has some 1700 branches but also has significant retail and commercial operations in Europe Africa (it owns more than half of South African bank Absa Group) the Middle East and the US. Barclays Bank offers standard retail services such as deposit accounts and lending including Woolwich-brand mortgages. The bank also provides commercial money transfer services insurance products the Barclaycard line of credit cards and financial advisory services. Barclays Bank traces its roots to the late 17th century.

Barclays Bank has been building up its portfolio of global credit card accounts especially as other financial groups sell off noncore units during the economic recovery. In 2010 the company acquired the Italian credit card accounts of Citigroup in a deal that included some 197000 card accounts and approximately E234 million ($320 million) worth of assets. It previously bought Goldfish the struggling UK credit card unit of Discover Financial Services for some Â46 million ($70 million). In 2011 Barclays acquired Egg UK's credit card portfolio which added more than 1 million accounts; it has agreed to buy more Citibank card accounts.

The bank has also been offloading some of its own holdings as part of an overall corporate restructuring. In 2010 Barclays sold its US subprime loan servicing business HomEq Servicing to Ocwen Financial. It also announced plans to abandon retail banking in certain international markets and instead focus on wholesale and commercial banking. In 2011 it shuttered its Indonesian retail unit Bank Akita which it had acquired only two years before. The company also sold its Russian retail and commercial operations to a group of investors citing difficulties competing in the market. Barclays will instead focus on its investment banking activities in the region.

In 2010 Barclays acquired Standard Life Bank from Standard Life for Â226 million ($369 million). The deal added Standard Life's savings and mortgage books to the Barclays fold. Also as part of the deal Barclays and Standard Life entered into a partnership whereby Barclays markets pension products to its clients.

Despite challenges in the economy especially in regards to Europe's debt problems Barclays Bank's revenues grew 8% in 2011. Its Africa business performed relatively strongly with credit impairments improving as did Barclaycard thanks to the portfolio acquisitions which delivered profits. That year the bank closed nearly 150 European branches (largely located in Spain) the costs of which contributed to a 5% decline in net income.

EXECUTIVES

President Barclays PLC, Robert E. (Bob) Diamond Jr., age 62
Chairman, Sir David A. Walker, age 70
Chairman, Marcus Agius, age 67
Chief Operations and Technology Officer, Shaygan Kheradpir, age 53
CEO Barclaycard, Valerie (Val) Soranno-Keating
Chief Executive Americas, Hugh E. (Skip) McGee III
Chief Executive Barclays Wealth, Thomas L. (Tom) Kalaris
Group General Counsel, Mark Harding
Co-Chief Executive Corporate and Investment Banking, Thomas (Tom) King
CEO Retail and Business Banking, Ashok Vaswani
Co-Chief Executive Corporate and Investment Banking, Jerry del Missier
Chief Risk Officer, Robert Le Blanc, age 57
Director Human Resources, Cathy Turner
Group Chief Executive, Antony Jenkins
Group Finance Director and Board Member, Christopher (Chris) Lucas, age 53
Chief Executive Absa Group and Barclays Africa, Maria Ramos, age 55
Co-Chief Executive of Corporate and Investment Banking, Eric Bommensath
Co-Chief Executive Corporate and Investment Banking, Rich Ricci
Director Media Relations, Giles Croot
Head of Compliance and Government and Regulatory Relations, Sir Hector Sants
Group Financial Controller and Acting Chief Financial Officer, Peter Estlin
Group Finance Director, Tushar Morzaria
Group Chief Executive and Board Member, Robert E. (Bob) Diamond Jr., age 61
Director, Sir John M. Sunderland, age 68
Director, Fulvio Conti, age 66
Director, Sir Michael D. V. (Mike) Rake, age 66
Director, Alison J. Carnwath, age 61
Director, Reuben Jeffery III
Group Finance Director and Board Member, Christopher (Chris) Lucas, age 53
Director, David Booth, age 59
Director, Simon J. Fraser
Director, Dambisa Moyo, age 45
Auditors: PricewaterhouseCoopersLLP

LOCATIONS

HQ: Barclays Bank Plc
1 Churchill Place, London E14 5HP
Phone: (44) 20 7116 1000
Web: www.barclays.com

PRODUCTS/OPERATIONS

2011 Assets

	% of total
Cash &	7
Trading portfolio	10
Financial assets designated at fair	2
Derivative financial	34
Loans &	31
Reverse purchase agreements & similar	10
Available for sale financial	4
Goodwill &	2
Total	**100**

Sales

	% of total
Interest	48
Fees &	24
Net trading	18
Net investment	5
Net insurance premiums &	5
Total	**100**

COMPETITORS

Citibank
Credit Suisse
Deutsche Bank
HSBC
ING

Lloyds Banking Group
Nationwide Building Society
Royal Bank of Scotland
Standard Chartered

HISTORICAL FINANCIALS

Income Statement   FYE: December 31

	ASSETS ($ mil.)	NET INCOME ($ mil.)	INCOME AS % OF ASSETS	EMPLOYEES
12/13	2,169,572	1,591	0.1%	139,600
12/12	2,402,885	(1,165)	—	139,200
12/11	2,415,227	5,586	0.2%	149,700
12/10	2,313,492	6,477	0.3%	151,300
12/09	2,233,641	16,184	0.7%	153,800
Annual Growth	(0.7%)	(44.0%)		(2.4%)

2013 Year-End Financials

Return on assets: 0.0%
Return on equity: 1.5%
Long-term debt ($ mil.): —
No. of shares (mil.): —
Sales ($ mil): 60,895

Dividends
Yield: —
Payout: —
Market value ($ mil.): —

	STOCK PRICE ($) FY Close	P/E High/Low		PER SHARE ($) Earnings	Dividends	Book Value
12/13	42.55	—	—	(0.00)	0.00	43.04
12/12	31.81	—	—	(0.00)	0.00	41.31
12/11	35.53	—	—	(0.00)	0.00	40.95
12/10	37.61	—	—	(0.00)	0.00	39.23
12/09	34.07	—	—	(0.00)	0.00	38.67
Annual Growth	5.7%	—	—	—	—	2.7%

Barclays PLC

Raising the bar for global finance Barclays owns one of Europe's largest banks a top market-making investment bank the top UK credit card and an international wealth management firm. Its flagship Barclays Bank has some 1700 branches in the UK as well as operations throughout Europe Africa the Middle East and the US. Its Barclaycard arm has more than 20 million credit cards and provides consumer lending and payment processing services primarily in Europe. Barclays Capital is one of the largest investment banks in the world (thanks largely to its acquisition of the North American operations of Lehman Brothers). Altogether Barclays serves more than 48 million customers in more than 50 countries.

Barclays' largest segment is the investment banking business Barclays Capital which represents nearly 40% of the group's income. Its second-largest segment UK Retail and Business Banking provides consumer and commercial banking Woolwich-branded mortgages insurance and money transmission services. Other segments include Barclaycard Europe Retail and Business Banking (active in France Spain Italy and Portugal) Africa Retail and Business Banking (including South African bank Absa). In addition to Barclays Capital the corporate and investment banking operations include Barclays Corporate Barclays Wealth and Investment Management (which oversees Barclays' 20% stake in BlackRock). There has been speculation that Barclays may regroup in a major way (a la Citigroup or RBS) in order to split off its riskier assets.

To weather the global economic crisis Barclays has already sold some businesses cut costs through branch closures and workforce reductions and restructured its credit market exposures. In early 2015 Barclays sold its Spanish retail and corporate banking operations to CaixaBank as it works on a major restructuring and shrinks some of its struggling European divisions. The company sold its African custody and securities business to Standard Chartered in 2010 and Barclays Capital wound down its Barclays Venture arm. The investment bank also sold Barclays Private Equity now Equistone Partners to that unit's management in an effort to raise more capital. Additionally Barclays has categorized its holding in BlackRock as available-for-sale after writing down the value of the stake in mid-2011.

To offset some of its exposure to the UK economy Barclays has been expanding its international business mostly in the US and in emerging markets. In 2011 the group sold its Russian retail business to focus on investment banking in that market. (Barclays found it difficult to compete in Russia where the majority of assets are held by state-owned banks.)

To boost its retail and commercial banking operations the company has sought opportunistic acquisitions as other financial groups sell off noncore units at discounted rates. In one such deal it bought Standard Life Bank from Scottish insurer Standard Life which exited the banking business for Å226 million ($368.5 million) in 2010. The price was a significant discount from Standard Life Bank's net asset value. Barclays has been in talks to buy other businesses in similar transactions.

Barclays has also expanded its Barclaycard operations. Its 2008 acquisition of the money-losing Goldfish credit card operations from Discover Financial Services added some 1.7 million accounts and the follow-up purchases of Citibank's Portuguese and Italian credit card units added another 600000 accounts. In 2011 the company acquired the approximately 1.2 million UK card accounts held by Egg Banking at a discount. Continuing to build the card business the company bought some 60000 MBNA Europe Bank UK small business accounts from Bank of America. Barclays has also been an innovator with its money transfer operations introducing contactless cards and mobile phone person-to-person transfers.

With the help of the corporate shuffling the company's revenues grew by some 6% in 2011. Among the star performers that year were the UK Retail and Business Banking Barclaycard Africa Retail and Business Banking and Barclays Wealth segments which all saw double-digit growth in profits. Also in 2011 Barclay's European retail banking business returned to profitability after losing money the previous year. The tough economic climate though especially related to concerns over European sovereign debt brought down earnings in the investment bank's operations (which in turn proved a drag on overall performance). However Barclays believes it is on strong footing in terms of capital funding and liquidity.

More troubles hit Barclays in mid-2012 though as the company admitted to manipulating the London Interbank Offered Rate (LIBOR) a benchmark for daily global short-term interest rates. The bank repeatedly manipulated the LIBOR in order to make its funding position look stronger than it actually was; the rigging also helped the bank make money on credit derivatives. Chairman Martin Agius and CEO Bob Diamond both resigned as a result of the developments and the company paid US and UK regulators some Å290 million ($453 million) in settlement fines. Shortly after the LIBOR scandal the UK's Serious Fraud Office launched an inquiry into payments Barclays made to sovereign investor Qatar Holding in 2008. That same year investment fund Qatar Investment Authority became the bank's largest shareholder with a 5% stake. Investigations for both the bid-rigging and bribery allegations continue.

HISTORY

Barclays first spread its wings in 1736 when James Barclay united his family's goldsmithing and banking businesses. As other family members joined the London enterprise it became known as Barclays Bevan & Tritton (1782).

Banking first became regulated in the 19th century. To ward off takeovers 20 banks combined with Barclays in 1896. The new firm Barclay & Co. began preying on other banks. Within 20 years it bought 17 including the Colonial Bank chartered in 1836 to serve the West Indies and British Guiana (now Guyana). The company renamed Barclays Bank Ltd. in 1917 weathered the Depression as the UK's #2 bank.

Barclays began expanding again after WWII and by the late 1950s it had become the UK's top bank. It had a computer network by 1959 and in 1966 it introduced the Barclaycard in conjunction with Bank of America's BankAmericard (now Visa).

In 1968 the UK's Monopolies Commission barred Barclays' merger with two other big London banks but had no objections to a two-way merger so Barclays bought competitor Martins.

Barclays moved into the US consumer finance market in 1980 when it bought American Credit 138 former Beneficial Finance offices and Bankers Trust's branch network.

During the 1980s London banks faced competition from invading overseas banks local building societies and other financial firms. Banking reform in 1984 led to formation of a holding company for Barclays Bank PLC.

To prepare for British financial deregulation in 1986 Barclays formed Barclays de Zoete Wedd (BZW) by merging its merchant bank with two other London financial firms. Faced with sagging profits Barclays sold its California bank in 1988 and its US consumer finance business in 1989.

In 1990 Barclays bought private German bank Merck Finck & Co. and Paris bank L'Europeenne de Banque. The company countered 1992's bad-loan-induced losses by accelerating a cost-cutting program begun in 1989. To appease stockholders chairman and CEO Andrew Buxton (a descendant of one of the bank's founding families) gave up his CEO title hiring Martin Taylor (previously CEO of textile firm Courtaulds) for the post.

The company sold its Australian retail banking business in 1994 then began trimming other operations including French corporate banking and US mortgage operations. However it bought the Wells Fargo Nikko Investment Company to boost Asian operations.

Barclays' piecemeal sale of BZW signaled its failure to become a global investment banking powerhouse. In 1997 it sold BZW's European investment banking business to Credit Suisse First Boston retaining the fixed-income and foreign exchange business. (Credit Suisse bought Barclays' Asian investment banking operations in 1998.)

Losses in Russia and a $250 million bailout of US hedge fund Long-Term Capital Management hit Barclays Capital in 1998. Taylor resigned that year in part because of his radical plans for the bank. Sir Peter Middleton stepped in as acting CEO; Barclays later tapped Canadian banker Matthew Barrett for the post. (Middleton also became chairman upon Buxton's retirement.)

Barclays in 1999 started a move toward online banking at the expense of traditional branches.

The company announced free lifetime Internet access for new bank customers.

In 2000 the bank ruffled feathers when it announced the closure of about 170 mostly rural UK branches. Also in 2000 the company sold its Dial auto leasing unit to ABN AMRO and bought Woolwich plc. The following year Barclay's closed its own life insurance division opting instead to sell the life insurance and pension products of London-based Legal & General Group.

In 2004 chief executive Barrett was named Barclays' chairman succeeding Peter Middleton who became chairman of Centre for Effective Dispute Resolution (CEDR) and later chancellor of the University of Sheffield.

After exiting the South African market in 1987 over apartheid concerns Barclays returned in a big way in 2005 buying a majority stake (about 57%) in the Absa Group one of the country's largest retail banks. The deal also represented the largest-ever direct foreign investment there. The next year Barclays sold its South African businesses including corporate international retail and commercial operations to Absa.

The company entered the US credit card market when it bought Juniper Financial (now Barclays Bank Delaware) from Canadian Imperial Bank of Commerce (CIBC) in 2004. In a previous hook-up with CIBC Barclays merged its Caribbean banking business with CIBC's to create an 85-branch regional bank FirstCaribbean International Bank with each company owning 44%; Barclays sold its stake to CIBC in 2006.

In 2005 the bank sold its vendor finance businesses in the UK and Germany to CIT Group. Barclays said that the sale will allow it to focus on its commercial leasing business.

The bank moved to assimilate its Woolwich acquisition in 2006 when it closed 200 branches and consolidated Woolwich branches into existing Barclays locations. It retained the Woolwich mortgage brand but switched account holders to Barclays accounts.

The company and HSBC formed a joint venture that manages their cash handling operations in the UK. Named Vaultex the joint venture acquired Loomis Cash Management in 2007.

Marcus Agius succeeded the retiring Matthew Barrett as chairman in 2007.

Although the company withdrew its bid for Dutch banking giant ABN AMRO (narrowly escaping that troubled deal) in 2008 it bought Russian bank Expobank from Petropavlovsk Finance. Expobank was one of the largest ATM networks in Russia and part of the booming consumer banking industry there. Also that year Barclays sold noncore business Barclays Life and its portfolio of some 760000 life and pension policies to Swiss Re for Å753 million ($1.5 billion).

The group chose not to participate in the UK's bank bailouts as the global financial crisis intensified in late 2008 but pursued its own capital-raising plan. Through the deal sovereign investment fund Qatar Investment Authority became the bank's largest shareholder with a 5% stake.

In 2009 it shut down US-based subprime mortgage lender EquiFirst which it had purchased from Regions Financial before it fell victim to the mortgage bust.

Later that year it sold a majority of Barclays Global Investors to American money manager BlackRock for Å9.5 billion ($15 billion). In exchange it gained a 20% stake in the new BlackRock with some $3 trillion under management for institutional clients around the world. The deal provided the bank with much-needed cash and cleared the way for a commercial partnership with BlackRock.

Another major transaction was the Å1 billion ($1.8 billion) acquisition of Lehman Brothers'

North American operations a deal which made Barclays Capital one of the world's largest investment banks.

EXECUTIVES

Chairman, Sir David A. Walker, age 74
Chief Operations and Technology Officer, Shaygan Kheradpir, age 53
Deputy Chairman, Sir Michael D. V. (Mike) Rake, age 66
CEO Barclaycard, Valerie (Val) Soranno-Keating
Chief Executive Americas, Hugh E. (Skip) McGee III
Chief Executive Barclays Wealth Management and Executive Chairman of Barclays in the Americas, Thomas L. (Tom) Kalaris
Secretary, Lawrence Dickinson
Interim Chief Operations and Technology Officer, Darryl West
Head Corporate Communications and Media Relations New York, Michael O'Looney
Group General Counsel, Mark Harding
Co-Chief Executive Corporate and Investment Banking, Thomas (Tom) King
CEO Retail and Business Banking, Ashok Vaswani
President Barclays Capital and Co-CEO Corporate and Investment Banking, Jerry del Missier
Group Chief Risk Officer, Robert Le Blanc, age 56
Director Human Resources, Cathy Turner
Group Chief Executive and Director, Antony Jenkins
Group Finance Director and Director, Christopher (Chris) Lucas, age 53, $1,273,639 total compensation
Group Treasurer, Jon Stone
CEO Absa Group and Barclays Africa, Maria Ramos, age 55
CEO Barclays Commercial Bank, Eduardo Eguren
CEO Global Retail and Commercial Banking Emerging Markets, Vinit Chandra
Head Legal Operations, Cate Campany
Managing Director Egypt and North Africa, Khalid Elgibaly
Director Payment Innovations Barclaycard, Dan Salmons
Director Digital Banking UK, Sean Gilchrist
Managing Director Barclays Business, Steve Cooper
Co-Chief Executive Corporate and Investment Banking, Eric Bommensath
Managing Director and Head Business Strategy and Platforms Barclays Wealth Americas, Paul Morton
Head Global Research and Investment; Head Barclays Wealth Americas, Mitch Cox
CEO Corporate and Investment Banking, Rich Ricci
Head Debit Cards UK Retail Banking, Brian Cunnington
Finance Director, Tushar Morzaria
Director, Sir John M. Sunderland, age 68
Director, R. Leigh Clifford, age 65
Director, Fulvio Conti, age 67
Deputy Chairman, Sir Michael D. V. (Mike) Rake, age 66
Director, Alison J. Carnwath, age 60
Director, Sir Andrew Likierman, age 70
Group Chief Executive and Director, Antony Jenkins
Director, Reuben Jeffery III
Group Finance Director and Director, Christopher (Chris) Lucas, age 53
Director, David Booth, age 59
Director, Simon J. Fraser
Director, Dambisa Moyo, age 45
Auditors: PricewaterhouseCoopersLLP

LOCATIONS

HQ: Barclays PLC
    1 Churchill Place, London E14 5HP
Phone: (44) 20 7116 1000
Web: www.barclays.com

Sales

	% of total
UK	42
Americas	21
Africa & Middle	17
Europe	15
Asia	5
Total	**100**

PRODUCTS/OPERATIONS

Sales by Segment

	% of total
Barclays	36
UK Retail & Business	16
Barclaycard	14
Africa Retail & Business	13
Barclays	10
Barclays	6
Europe Retail & Business	5
Investment	
Total	**100**

COMPETITORS

AXA UK	Lloyds Banking Group
Bank of New York	Mitsubishi UFJ
Mellon	Financial Group
CIBC	Mizuho Financial
Citigroup	RBC Financial Group
Deutsche Bank	Royal Bank of Scotland
Grupo Santander	Standard Chartered
HSBC	The Vanguard Group
Invesco	UBS
JPMorgan Chase	

HISTORICAL FINANCIALS

Company Type: Public

Income Statement

FYE: December 31

	ASSETS ($ mil.)	NET INCOME ($ mil.)	INCOME AS % OF ASSETS	EMPLOYEES
12/13	2,168,625	892	0.0%	140,300
12/12	2,402,198	(1,677)	—	143,700
12/11	2,415,420	4,645	0.2%	141,100
12/10	2,312,882	5,533	0.2%	147,500
12/09	2,233,286	15,212	0.7%	144,200
Annual Growth	(0.7%)	(50.8%)	—	(0.7%)

2013 Year-End Financials

Return on assets: 0.0%
Return on equity: 0.9%
Long-term debt ($ mil.): —
No. of shares (mil.): —
Sales ($ mil): 60,952
Dividends
  Yield: 2.1%
  Payout: 1,659.1%
Market value ($ mil.): —

	STOCK PRICE ($) FY Close	P/E High/Low		PER SHARE ($) Earnings	Dividends	Book Value
12/13	18.13	1395	1120	0.06	0.40	5.68
12/12	17.32	—	—	(0.14)	0.38	7.06
12/11	10.99	215	81	0.37	0.89	7.04
12/10	16.52	187	119	0.44	0.27	6.48
12/09	17.60	79	8	1.32	0.07	6.71
Annual Growth	0.7%	—	—	(53.6%)	56.8%	(4.1%)

BASF SE

The world is BASF's ester. BASF is the world's largest chemical company ahead of Dow and DuPont. It has more than 370 manufacturing facilities and does business worldwide through six business segments: plastics (polymers and polyurethanes) performance products (including dispersions and pigments adhesives and sealants personal care and pharma additives paper chemicals and lubricant additives) chemicals (plasticizers and solvents) oil and gas exploration and production (through subsidiary Wintershall AG) functional solutions (catalysts coatings and construction chemicals) and agricultural products (fungicides herbicides insecticides). BASF has divested most of its fertilizer operations.

BASF uses what it calls Verbund strategy throughout its facilities –plants are both customers and suppliers of each other. While the company still gets more than half its sales from Europe it continues to expand overseas particularly in Asia. It saw early on that the chemicals market in Asia would be the equal of that in Europe and wanted a healthy piece of the action. With a new unit based in the US it has begun positioning itself to become a leading supplier of battery materials for automotive battery applications –including cathode materials used to produce advanced lithium-ion batteries for electric vehicles.

In 2011 several events affected the growth of the company including the nuclear diaster in Japan Germany's decision to exit nuclear energy the suspension of crude oil in Libya and the debt crisis in Europe. Weak demand and an increase in the cost of raw materals also plagued BASF's two top divisions plastics and chemicals.

However BASF managed to surpass the record levels it set in 2010 in sales and earnings. After cutting costs and raising prices the company posted $98.7 billion in sales in 2011 up nearly 17% over the previous year as well as a net income of $8.3 billion up nearly 38%. But most of the increase was due to the sale of its 10% stake in K+S AG which began its exit from the fertilizer business. By 2012 BASF had sold most of its fertilizer operations including production plants in Antwerp Belgium and its share of the PEC-Rhin joint venture in France to Russia's EuroChem in a deal worth about $1.1 billion.

The company initiated several projects in 2011 including the startup of the first leg of the Nord Stream offshore gas pipeline that will eventually extend from Russia to Germany. Wintershall is involved in constructing the Nord Stream and South Stream gas pipelines to connect gas from Russia to Europe.

It also strengthened its presence in Asia that year by beginning the second expansion of its petrochemical site in Nanjing China with 50-50 joint venture partner Sinopec. And it founded BASF Hock Mining Chemical (China) Company with JiNing Hock Mining & Engineering Equipment Company. BASF holds a 75% stake in BASF Hock which makes cavity-filling products for the coal mining industry.

Much of the company's expansion has targeted the US market as well. In early 2012 the company halted its cultivation and development of genetically modified (GM) plants in Europe. Heavy resistance from European consumers farmers and politicians resulted in the company moving its plant science division from Limburgerhof Germany to Raleigh North Carolina. Some of its products for the European market included its Amflora starch potato for industrial use developed to be resistant to blight disease.

That year the company also strengthened its global crop protection operations by buying US-based Becker Underwood for $1.02 billion. The Iowa-based company provides biological seed treatment worldwide from 10 production sites. The BASF Crop Protection division plans to create Functional Crop Care a global business unit that will merge existing R&D and marketing activities in seed treatment crop protection and plant health with those of Becker Underwood.

BASF has also been collaborating with US-based Monsanto in the research and development of crops that have higher yields and better resistance to disease. For its GM products BASF focuses on markets in the Americas and Asia. It has not completely closed the door on Europe; it is still seeking authorizations to sell its potato products there.

In early 2012 BASF began a new global business unit Battery Materials to integrate its battery materials activities within an operating unit of New Jersey-based subsidiary BASF Catalysts. In moves to become a global leader in the supply of battery materials the company has made a series of acquisitions and licensing agreements to broaden its coverage of technology materials and components to serve cell and battery manufacturers worldwide. It has been licensed by the Argonne National Laboratory in Illinois to commercialize some of its advanced cathode materials used in hybrid and full-electric vehicles.

Adding to its battery operations again in 2012 BASF acquired Cleveland-based Novolyte Technologies from private equity group Arsenal Capital Partners for an undisclosed price. Novolyte manufactures electrolyte formulations for lithium-ion batteries and other specialty chemicals. It operates sites in the US and China. BASF will continue Novolyte's joint venture with Korean company Foosung which produces lithium hexafluorophosphate a high-purity specialty salt used in producing lithium-iron battery electrolytes. The electrolytes are key components in lithium-ion batteries for the automotive consumer and industrial markets.

To expand its leadership position in polyurethane systems the company acquired US-based ITWC in 2012. ITWC manufactures cast elastomer polyurethane systems and polyester polyols in facilities in Iowa and California. The acquisition extends BASF's North American polyurethanes operations. Cast elastomers known for their abrasion resistance are used in several applications including industrial tires recreational wheels transportation gears and pulleys and sealants and adhesives.

The company's venture capital unit also poured $18.2 million into US-based renewable specialty chemicals company Allylix in 2012. Allylix owns a technology platform for developing terpenes and other chemicals for flavor and fragrance food ingredients cosmetics and other markets.

To expand its Nutrition and Health division in 2012 BASF acquired Equatec a UK-based supplier of omega-3 fatty acids for the pharmaceutical industry for an undisclosed price. Equatec which has a production site on the Isle of Lewis in Scotland will become part of BASF's Pharma Ingredients and Services unit.

BASF acquired inge watertechnologies a Germany-based provider of ultrafiltration membrane technology used to treat drinking water process water wastewater and seawater in 2011. The deal improves BASF's position in the water treatment industry and fits within its growth strategy for its chemicals and membrane filtration business.

After shelving previous efforts to exit the business in 2011 BASF formed a styrenics joint venture with INEOS called Styrolution. The venture produces styrene monomers polystyrene acrylonitrile butadiene styrene styrene-butadiene block copolymers and other styrene-based copolymers and copolymer blends. Styrolution is projected to have annual sales of $6.6 billion.

HISTORY

Originally named Badische Anilin & Soda-Fabrik BASF AG was founded in Mannheim Germany by jeweler Frederick Englehorn in 1861. Unable to find enough land for expansion in Mannheim BASF moved to nearby Ludwigshafen in 1865. The company was a pioneer in coal tar dyes and it developed a synthetic indigo in 1897. Its synthetic dyes rapidly replaced more expensive organic dyes.

BASF scientist Fritz Haber synthesized ammonia in 1909 giving BASF access to the market for nitrogenous fertilizer (1913). Haber received a Nobel Prize in 1918 but was later charged with war crimes for his work with poison gases. Managed by Carl Bosch another Nobel Prize winner BASF joined the I.G. Farben cartel with Bayer Hoechst and others in 1925 to create a German chemical colossus. Within the cartel BASF developed polystyrene PVC and magnetic tape. Part of the Nazi war machine I.G. Farben made synthetic rubber and used labor from the Auschwitz concentration camp during WWII.

After the war I.G. Farben was dismantled. BASF regained its independence in 1952 and rebuilt its war-ravaged factories. Strong postwar domestic demand for basic chemicals aided its recovery and in 1958 BASF launched a US joint venture with Dow Chemical. (BASF bought out Dow's half in 1978.) The company moved into petrochemicals and became a leading manufacturer of plastic and synthetic fiber.

In the US the company purchased Wyandotte Chemicals (1969) Chemetron (1979) and Inmont (1985) among others. To expand its natural gas business in Europe in 1991 the company signed deals with Russia's Gazprom and France's Elf Aquitaine. BASF bought Mobil's polystyrene-resin business and gained almost 10% of the US market.

BASF bought Imperial Chemical's polypropylene business in 1994 and became Europe's second-largest producer of the plastic. The next year the company paid $1.4 billion for the pharmaceutical arm of UK retailer Boots.

In 1997 BASF formed a joint venture with PetroFina (now TOTAL); in 2001 the venture opened the world's largest liquid steam cracker in Port Arthur Texas.

BASF made seven major acquisitions in 1998 including the complexing business of Ciba Specialty Chemicals. It also made six divestitures which included its European buildings-paints operations sold to Nobel N.V.

In 1999 the US fined the company $225 million for its part in a worldwide vitamin price-fixing cartel (in 2001 the European Commission fined it another $260 million bringing the total expected cost of fines out-of-court settlements and legal expenses to about $800 million). BASF also faced a class-action suit as a result of the scheme. That year the company moved into oil and gas exploration in Russia through a partnership agreement with Russia's Gazprom. BASF also merged its textile operations into Bayer and Hoechst's DyStar joint venture forming a $1 billion company that is a world-leading dye maker.

BASF completed its acquisition of Rohm and Haas' industrial coatings business in 2000 and bought the Cyanamid division (herbicides fungicides and pesticides) of American Home Products (now Wyeth). That year BASF expanded its superabsorbents business by paying $656 million for US-based Amcol International's Chemdal International unit.

Rather than attempt to compete in the rapidly consolidating pharmaceutical industry in 2001 BASF sold its midsized Knoll Pharmaceutical unit to Abbott Laboratories for about $6.9 billion. It also announced that it was closing 10 plants and cutting about 4000 jobs (4% of its workforce).

BASF sold its fibers unit in 2003 to focus on core chemical operations which it added to throughout the next few years. For example it bought a portion of Bayer's agchem businesses for $1.3 billion when European antitrust regulators mandated the Bayer divestment following its acquisition of Aventis CropScience. BASF also acquired Honeywell Specialty Materials' engineering plastics business in exchange for its fibers division. BASF's acquisition later that year of MSA's Callery Chemical Division strengthened BASF's line of inorganics which it planned to focus on providing to the pharmaceutical industry. Other acquisitions included Ticona's nylon 66 business and Sunoco's plasticizers unit.

That year also brought chairman Jorgen Hambrecht's announcement that the company would push forward with a restructuring of its North American business. The focus of the plan was to save more than $250 million over the next three years. Included among the steps were job cuts of approximately 1000 and the relocation of its North American headquarters (though remaining in New Jersey) in late 2004. (The move to smaller facilities was enabled by the sale of Knoll Pharmaceuticals in 2001 which reduced operations at the home base.)

BASF sold Basell its petrochemical JV with Shell in 2005. The two companies had announced in 2004 that they planned to exit the polyolefins business with the sale of Basell. The deal was finalized late the next year. Investment group Access Industries came in with the winning bid of about $5.7 billion. That company's name was changed to LyondellBasell after its 2007 acquisition of Lyondell Chemical Company.

The company opened two Verbund sites in Asia —one in Nanjing China and the other in Kuantan Malaysia. The Chinese site delivered its first product in early 2005 and began operating fully in the middle of that year. It's the centerpiece and primary operation of BASF-YPC a joint venture with Sinopec that was formed in 2000. BASF's goal is to achieve 70% of its sales in the region from local production by 2015; that figure hovered at about 60% in 2008.

The company also legally changed its name from BASF Aktiengesellschaft to BASF SE in 2008. The move made formal BASF's transition to a European company as opposed to one organized in Germany.

In 2009 BASF spent about $4 billion to acquire Swiss chemicals giant Ciba. Following a review phase of Ciba's operations and their fit within the structure of BASF the company began integrating Ciba into its performance products segment; this entailed the sale or closure of almost half of Ciba's 55 manufacturing facilities and the loss of about 3700 of its employees. As part of that strategy BASF SE sold the Regulatory and Safety Testing businesses of Ciba's Expert Services unit to London-based Intertek Group in 2010.

Also in 2010 BASF acquired specialty chemicals company Cognis GmbH in a $3.8 billion deal. Cognis gave BASF a boost in entering several high-margin business lines such as personal care and cosmetics.

EXECUTIVES

Deputy Chairman Supervisory Board, Michael Diekmann, age 60

President Performance Polymers, Wolfgang Hapke, age 59

Member Executive Board Crop Protection Coatings and Specialty Chemicals Research Division BASF Plant Science South America Regional Division, Stefan Marcinowski, age 62

Chairman Supervisory Board, Eggert Voscherau, age 71

Member Executive Board and CFO, Hans-Ulrich Engel, age 56

Chairman Executive Board, Kurt W. Bock, age 57

Member Executive Board Inorganics Petrochemicals Intermediates Chemicals Research and Engineering and BASF Future Business, Andreas Kreimeyer, age 60

SVP Investor Relations, Magdalena Moll

President Competence Center Specialty Chemicals Research, Harald Lauke, age 55

Head Corporate Media Relations, Michael Grabicki

President Market and Business Development Asia Pacific Hong Kong, Albert Heuser, age 59

President Polyurethanes, Wayne T. Smith

President South America, Alfred Hackenberger, age 63

President Care Chemicals Division, Gabriel Tanbourgi, age 59

Member Executive Board, Harald Schwager, age 55

President Performance Chemicals, Hans W. Reiners

Member Executive Board, Michael Heinz, age 50

Member Executive Board and and Industrial Relations Director, Margret Suckale, age 58

Deputy Chairman Supervisory Board, Robert Oswald, age 59

President Dispersions and Pigments, Markus Kramer

SVP Communications and Government Relations BASF Group, Elisabeth Schick, age 49

President Health and Safety Division, Ulrich von Deessen

President BASF Plant Science, Peter Eckes

President Asia Pacific, Saori Dubourg, age 43

Head of Research Chemicals, Friedrich Seitz, age 59

Vice Chairman Executive Board, Martin Brudermuller, age 53

President Paper Chemicals, Uwe Liebelt, age 48

VP Corporate Communications, Stefanie Wettberg

President Paper Chemicals, Fred Baumgartner

Independent Chairman of the Board, Vincenzo Pontolillo

President of the BASF Crop Protection division, Markus Heldt

Senior Vice President for Latin America, Eduardo Leduc

Deputy Chairman Supervisory Board, Michael Diekmann, age 60

Member Supervisory Board, Stephen K. Green, age 65

Member Supervisory Board, Max D. Kley, age 74

Member Supervisory Board, Michael Vassiliadis, age 50

Deputy Chairman Supervisory Board, Robert Oswald, age 59

Member Supervisory Board, Ralf-Gerd Bastian, age 58

Member Supervisory Board, Wolfgang Daniel, age 57

Member Supervisory Board, Prof Francois Diederich, age 60

Member Supervisory Board, Ralf Sikorski, age 53

Member Supervisory Board, Franz Fehrenbach

Member Supervisory Board, Denise Schellemans

Non-Executive Independent Director, Chiara Ruggieri

Non-Executive Director, Cosma Gelsomino

Non-Executive Independent Director, Lorenzo Idda

Auditors: KPMGDeutscheTreuhand-GesellschaftAG

LOCATIONS

HQ: BASF SE
Carl-Bosch-Strasse 38, Ludwigshafen D-67056
Phone: (49) 621 60 0 **Fax:** (49) 621 602525
Web: www.basf.com

Sales by Region

	% of total
Europe	
Other countries	17
Asia/Pacific	18
Total	**100**

PRODUCTS/OPERATIONS

Sales

	% of total
Performance Products	21
Chemicals	18
Oil & Gas	16
Plastics	15
Agricultural Solutions	6
Total	**100**

Selected Products

Oil and Gas
  Crude oil and natural gas exploration
  Natural gas distribution and trading
Chemicals
  Inorganics
  Ammonia
  Formaldehyde
  Melamine
  Sulfuric acid
  Urea
  Intermediates
  Performance chemicals
  Water-based resins
  Petrochemicals
  Feedstocks
  Industrial gases
  Plasticizers
  Specialty chemicals
Plastics
  Engineering plastics
  Foams
  Polyamides and intermediates
  Polyurethanes
  Styrenics
Functional Solutions
  Catalysts
  Battery materials
  Chemical catalysts
  Coatings
    Automotive coatings
    Decorative paints
    Industrial coatings
    Pigments
  Construction chemicals
Performance Products
  Automotive fluids
  Care chemicals
  Paper chemicals
  Pharma ingredients
  Textile chemicals
Agricultural Solutions
  Crop protection
  Fungicides
  Herbicides
  Insecticides

COMPETITORS

3M	Evonik Degussa
Air Products	Exxon Mobil
Akzo Nobel	FMC
Albemarle	Formosa Plastics
Ashland Inc.	Henkel
BP	LANXESS
Bayer AG	LG Group
Cargill	Monsanto Company
DSM	Royal Dutch Shell
Dow Chemical	SABIC
DuPont	TOTAL
Eastman Chemical	Taminco

HISTORICAL FINANCIALS

Company Type: Public

Income Statement

FYE: December 31

	REVENUE ($ mil.)	NET INCOME ($ mil.)	NET PROFIT MARGIN	EMPLOYEES
12/13	101,841	6,666	6.5%	112,206
12/12	103,768	6,430	6.2%	113,262
12/11	95,064	8,003	8.4%	111,141
12/10	85,485	6,098	7.1%	109,140
12/09	73,026	2,031	2.8%	104,779
Annual Growth	**8.7%**	**34.6%**		**1.7%**

2013 Year-End Financials

Debt ratio: 6.9%
Return on equity: 18.7%
Cash ($ mil.): 2,498
Current ratio: 1.84
Long-term debt ($ mil.): —
No. of shares (mil.): 918
Dividends
  Yield: 2.2%
  Payout: —
Market value ($ mil.): 99,003

	STOCK PRICE ($) FY Close	P/E High/Low		PER SHARE ($) Earnings	Dividends	Book Value
12/13	107.79	39	29	7.26	2.47	40.64
12/12	95.00	32	20	7.00	2.41	35.27
12/11	69.73	29	15	8.70	0.00	33.99
12/10	79.96	31	16	6.64	1.62	31.19
12/09	62.10	89	30	2.22	1.89	27.41
Annual Growth	**14.8%**	—	—	**34.5%**	**6.9%**	**10.3%**

Bayer AG

You could get a headache trying to name all of Bayer's products. The company which created aspirin in 1897 makes pharmaceuticals OTC drugs and animal health care products through Bayer HealthCare plastics and high-performance specialty materials via Bayer MaterialScience and crop protection and home garden care items through Bayer CropScience. Aside from Bayer Aspirin the company's best-known consumer brands include Aleve Alka-Seltzer and One-A-Day vitamins. Its top selling pharmaceuticals include multiple sclerosis treatment Betaseron and birth control pill YAZ. Also known as Bayer Group the firm has some 300 operating subsidiaries worldwide; it operates in the US through Bayer Corporation.

Geographic Reach

The majority of Bayer's sales come from European countries (roughly 40% of revenues) and North America (about 25% of sales) and most of the company's core manufacturing facilities are in Germany and the US.

Sales and Marketing

Bayer markets over 5000 products through a global sales and distribution network. Offerings from its largest division the HealthCare segment are distributed primarily through wholesalers and pharmacy chains while CropScience products are sold through wholesalers and regional distributors.

Strategy

Bayer is growing all three of its core businesses by enhancing its strong positions in key markets as well as by expanding into emerging geographic areas and investing in innovative technologies. Within its HealthCare division which accounts for just about half of its annual sales the company's growth strategy includes making targeted acquisitions entering into licensing and development deals with other pharmaceutical companies and performing in-house research and development. To counteract the effect of weakened sales in Europe and North America the HealthCare Pharmaceuticals segment is working to expand drug marketing efforts in China Brazil Mexico Russia and other high-growth markets.

As revenue from the company's healthcare business has grown it has made moves to focus its efforts there. To that end in 2014 Bayer announced it would spin off Bayer MaterialScience in an IPO.

Mergers and Acquisitions

Acquisitions in the health arena include the company's 2014 purchase of Merck's consumer care business which brought well-known brands including Claritin MiraLAX Coppertone and Dr. Scholl's under the Bayer umbrella. The company paid about $14.2 billion for the deal and moved into second place globally among OTC companies between a Novartis- GlaxoSmithKline joint venture and Johnson & Johnson.

HISTORY

Friedrich Bayer founded Bayer in Germany in 1863 to make synthetic dyes. Research led to such discoveries as Antinonin (synthetic pesticide 1892) aspirin (1897) and synthetic rubber (1915).

Under Carl Duisberg Bayer allegedly made the first poison gas used by Germany in WWI. During the war the US seized Bayer's US operations and trademark rights and sold them to Sterling Drug.

In 1925 Bayer BASF Hoechst and other German chemical concerns merged to form I.G. Farben Trust. Their photography businesses combined as Agfa also joined the trust. Between wars Bayer developed polyurethanes and the first sulfa drug Prontosil (1935).

During WWII the trust took over chemical plants of Nazi-occupied countries used slave labor and helped make Zyklon B gas used to kill people at Auschwitz. At war's end Bayer lost its 50% of Winthrop Laboratories (US) and Bayer of Canada (to Sterling Drug). The 1945 Potsdam Agreement called for the breakup of I.G. Farben and Bayer AG emerged in 1951 as an independent company with many of its original operations including Agfa.

After rebuilding in West Germany Bayer AG and Monsanto formed a joint venture (Mobay 1954); Bayer AG later bought Monsanto's share (1967). In the 1960s the company offered more dyes plastics and polyurethanes and added factories worldwide. Agfa merged with Gevaert (photography Belgium) in 1964; Bayer AG retained 60%. Over the next 25 years it acquired Miles Labs (Alka-Seltzer US 1978) the rest of Agfa-Gevaert (1981) Compugraphic (electronic imaging US 1989) and Nova's Polysar (rubber Canada 1990).

Bayer AG integrated its US holdings under the name Miles in 1992 (renamed Bayer Corporation in 1995). The next year it introduced its first genetically engineered product Kogenate hemophilia treatment. It regained US rights to the Bayer brand and logo in 1994 by paying SmithKline Beecham $1 billion for the North American business of Sterling Winthrop.

Bayer AG formed a joint venture with Swiss rival Roche Holding in 1996 to market over-the-counter Roche drugs in the US. In 1997 Bayer Baxter International Rhone-Poulenc Rorer and Green Cross agreed to a $670 million settlement over blood products that infected thousands of hemophiliacs with HIV during the 1980s.

In 1998 the company sold the food-ingredients arm of its Haarmann & Reimer unit to Tate & Lyle. Bayer bought US-based Chiron's diagnostics operations for $1.1 billion created a North American joint venture with Crompton & Knowles' seed-treatment unit and formed a research alliance with Millennium Pharmaceuticals. The firm spun off all but 30% of its photographic and electronic pre-

press business as Agfa-Gevaert (it plans to sell its remaining stake to Goldman Sachs).

Bayer Hoechst and BASF merged their textile activities in 1999 to form the world's largest dye-making company. The next year Bayer boosted its polyurethane business by paying $2.5 billion for US-based Lyondell Chemical's polyols unit. The company also formed a joint venture with Exelixis Pharmaceuticals to develop gene-based insecticides and announced it would develop an anti-impotence drug to rival Pfizer's Viagra (which drug launched in 2003 as Levitra).

In 2001 Bayer agreed to invest as much as $874 million on two drug-development deals with US genomics company CuraGen (Bayer will take a 7% stake).

The company's summer was marred by the one-two punch of sharply lower profits and the recall of Baycol (known as Lipobay in Europe) its popular cholesterol-lowering drug that has been linked to more than 100 deaths worldwide. Days after the recall Bayer announced that it would consider a pharmaceuticals deal in which its drug unit was the junior partner (possible partners included Merck & Co. Novartis Roche Eli Lilly Aventis and Sanofi-Synthelabo —the last two of which now form Sanofi-Aventis). Bayer announced in September 2001 that it was separating its health care and agrochemical operations from the chemicals and polymers businesses (in December it announced that it would do the same thing with the two units resulting in four independent operating units) but that it was keeping its pharmaceuticals business. Bayer did indicate an interest in forming a majority-owned joint venture preferably with a European partner for the pharmaceutical unit. The company finally decided against that move in late 2003 after failing to make a deal advantageous enough.

In a bid to bolster its agrochemical business Bayer acquired Aventis CropScience in 2002 for about $5 billion plus $2 billion in debt. The company was combined with Bayer Crop Protection to form Bayer CropScience.

That change precipitated a series of restructurings and realignments of Bayer's divisions. The company condensed seven units to four so that its health care agrochemical chemical and polymer operations would be able to operate with greater autonomy from one another. The successive restructurings were meant to pave the way for the sale of individual operations —such as its household insecticide business which Bayer sold to S.C. Johnson & Son in October 2002. In mid-2003 the company along with partner GlaxoSmithKline launched Levitra its rival to Pfizer's $1 billion-earning Viagra.

Late in 2003 Bayer announced that it planned to separate the chemicals business (combined with parts of Bayer MaterialScience) and spin it off to Bayer shareholders. The separation of its former chemicals subgroup was completed in 2005 when Bayer spun off the unit as a publicly traded company called LANXESS. Afterward Bayer began to concentrate on three core businesses: HealthCare CropScience and MaterialScience.

The company's OTC drugs unit got much larger in 2005 when Bayer bought Roche's consumer health unit for nearly $3 billion. The deal created one of the world's top three non-prescription drugs companies combining Bayer's aspirin Alka-Seltzer and Midol brands with Roche's Aleve pain relievers among others.

In 2006 Bayer acquired Schering AG for about $20 billion after a hostile bidding war with Merck. Bayer purchased Schering to strengthen its presence in the specialty pharmaceuticals business especially women's health. Schering AG was merged with Bayer's existing prescription drug business to create Bayer Schering Pharma AG (which was re-

named Bayer Pharma AGand began operating as Bayer HealthCare Pharmaceuticals in 2011).

The Consumer Care unit acquired the Citracal line of calcium supplements in 2007 from Mission Pharmacal and it purchased OTC cough and cold remedies from Topsun Science and Technology for $170 million to increase the group's standing in China in 2008. It also picked up the OTC business of Sagmel which it added to its Eastern European operations for some $410 million. The moves catapulted the company into the top five in the region.

Also in 2008 the HealthCare division grew again through equipment firm MEDRAD's acquisition of medical device maker Possis Medical for $360 million and Bayer HealthCare Pharmaceutical's purchase of biotech development firm DIREVO for $300 million. In the US Bayer netted itself two prescription dermatology product lines from SkinMedica (Desonate for dermatitis and NeoBenz for acne). The CropScience unit purchased Agro-Green's crop protection business that year as well.

In 2009 the company got a new CEO when Marijn Dekkers formerly head of Thermo Fisher Scientific was appointed to lead Bayer.

The MaterialScience division opened two new manufacturing plants for polyurethane ingredients in China in 2009 and 2010 while the CropScience division expanded its German and US production facilities in 2010. The unit also picked up US-based biotech company Athenix for which it paid about $365 million in 2009.

The MaterialScience unit also grew through the purchase of Artificial Muscle a California-based maker of electroactive polymers for consumer electronic applications in 2010.

EXECUTIVES

Chairman Board of Management, Marijn E. Dekkers, age 57

Chairman Supervisory Board, Manfred Schneider, age 76

Member Management Board Innovation Technology and Environment and Asia/Pacific, Wolfgang Plischke, age 63, $659,411 total compensation

Member Board of Management Bayer CropScience, Achim Noack, age 55

CEO Bayer CropScience, Sandra E. Peterson, age 56

Member Management Board Strategy and Human Resources and Americas Africa and Middle East, Richard Pott, age 61, $659,411 total compensation

President and CEO Bayer Corporation and Bayer MaterialScience LLC, Gregory S. (Greg) Babe, age 57

Deputy Chairman Supervisory Board, Thomas de Win, age 56

CEO Bayer MaterialScience, Patrick W. Thomas, age 57

CFO and Member Board of Management, Werner Baumann, age 52

COO CropScience, Lykele van der Broek, age 61

Head Investor Relations, Alexander Rosar

Manager Law Patents and Insurance, Roland Hartwig, age 60

Executive Committee Member Bayer HealthCare; Head Pharmaceuticals Division, Andreas Fibig, age 52

Chairman Bayer Business Services, Daniel Hartert

Head Communications, Michael Schade

Head Corporate Policy and Media Relations, Michael Preuss

Head Media Relations, Gunter Forneck

CEO Bayer HealthCare, Jorg Reinhardt, age 58

Managing Director Bayer Technology Services, Dirk Van Meirvenne, age 51

Head Public Policy/Environment, Dirk Frenzel

Member Supervisory Board, Clemens A. H. Borsig, age 65

Member Supervisory Board, Paul Achleitner, age 58

Member Supervisory Board, Ekkehard D. Schulz, age 73
Member Supervisory Board, Jurgen Weber, age 72
Member Supervisory Board, Klaus Sturany, age 68
Member Supervisory Board, Klaus Kleinfeld, age 56
Member Supervisory Board, Helmut Panke, age 68
Member Supervisory Board, Hubertus Schmoldt, age 70
Member Supervisory Board, Ernst-Ludwig Winnacker, age 73
Member Supervisory Board, Prof Hans-Olaf Henkel, age 74
Member Supervisory Board, Petra Kronen, age 50
Deputy Chairman Supervisory Board, Thomas de Win, age 56
Member Supervisory Board, Thomas Fischer, age 59
Member Supervisory Board, Willy Beuman, age 57
Member Supervisory Board, Reiner Hoffman, age 58
Member Supervisory Board, Peter Hausmann, age 61
Member Supervisory Board, Oliver Zuhlke, age 45
Member Supervisory Board, Andre Aich, age 44
Member Supervisory Board, Roswitha Su?elbeck, age 59
Auditors: PricewaterhouseCoopersAG

LOCATIONS

HQ: Bayer AG
Kaiser-Wilhelm Allee, Leverkusen D-51368
Phone: (49) 214 30 1   **Fax:** (49) 214 30 71985
Web: www.bayer.com

Sales

	% of total
Europe	39
Asia/Pacific	21
Total	**100**

PRODUCTS/OPERATIONS

Sales

	% of total
Health Care	
Consumer Health	17
CropScience	
Environmental Science Bioscience	4
Total	**100**

Selected Operations and Products

HealthCare
  Animal health products
  Diabetes care products
  Consumer care products (over-the-counter drugs)
  Pharmaceuticals
MaterialScience
  Coatings
  Colorants
  Plastics
  Polyurethanes
CropScience
  BioScience (biotechnology and seeds)
  Crop protection (insecticides and herbicides)
  Environmental science (lawn care and non-agricultural pesticides)

Selected Brands

HealthCare
Adalat (cardiovascular medication)
Advantage (animal health)
Aleve/Flanax (analgesic)
Alka-Seltzer (analgesic and antacid)
Aspirin (analgesic)
Aspirin Cardio (cardiovascular)
Avalox/Avelox (antibiotic)
Bepanthen/Bepanthol (skin care treatment)
Betaferon/Betaseron (multiple sclerosis medication)
Baytril (animal health infections)
Breeze/Contour (diabetes care glucose meters)
Canesten (antifungal)
Cipro/Ciprobay (antibiotic)
Glucobay (diabetes treatment)
Iopamiron (diagnostic imaging)
Kogenate (hematology/cardiology)
Levitra (impotence drug)

Magnevist (diagnostic imaging)
Mirena (contraceptive)
Nexavar (oncology)
One-A-Day (vitamins)
Supradyn (multivitamin)
Ultravist (diagnostic imaging)
Yasmin/Yasminelle/YAZ (contraceptive)
MaterialScience
  Baydur/Bayflex/Bayblend (polyurethane)
  Desmodur/Desmophen (isocyanates polyesters and polyols for polyurethanes)
  Makrolon (polycarbonate resin)
CropScience
  Betanal (herbicides)
  Confidor/Gaucho/Admire/Merit (insecticides/seed treatment)
  Decis (insecticides)
  Flint/Stratego/Sphere/Nativo (fungicides)
  Folicur/Raxil (fungicides/seed treatment)
  Poncho (seed treatment)
  Proline (fungicides)
  Puma (herbicides)

COMPETITORS

3M	GE Healthcare
Abbott Labs	GlaxoSmithKline
Actavis Inc.	Johnson & Johnson
Akzo Nobel	Merck
AstraZeneca	Merck KGaA
BASF SE	Mitsubishi Chemical
Baxter International	Holdings
Boehringer Ingelheim	Monsanto Company
Boston Scientific	Novartis
Bristol-Myers Squibb	Pfizer
Celanese	Ranbaxy Laboratories
DSM	Rhodia
Dow Chemical	Roche Holding
DuPont	Sanofi
Eastman Chemical	Syngenta
Eli Lilly	Teva
Evonik Degussa	

HISTORICAL FINANCIALS

Company Type: Public

Income Statement

FYE: December 31

	REVENUE ($ mil.)	NET INCOME ($ mil.)	NET PROFIT MARGIN	EMPLOYEES
12/13	55,285	4,390	7.9%	113,200
12/12	52,405	3,223	6.2%	110,500
12/11	47,247	3,194	6.8%	111,800
12/10	46,960	1,741	3.7%	111,400
12/09	44,899	1,957	4.4%	108,400
Annual Growth	5.3%	22.4%	—	1.1%

2013 Year-End Financials

Debt ratio: 9.2%
Return on equity: 16.2%
Cash ($ mil.): 2,288
Current ratio: 1.36
Long-term debt ($ mil.): —
No. of shares (mil.): 826
Dividends
  Yield: 1.2%
  Payout: 39.3%
Market value ($ mil.): 117,427

	STOCK PRICE ($) FY Close	P/E High/Low		PER SHARE ($) Earnings	Dividends	Book Value
12/13	142.00	70	44	5.31	1.80	34.49
12/12	95.92	57	33	3.90	1.56	29.44
12/11	63.80	55	29	3.87	3.06	30.05
12/10	73.36	99	56	2.10	1.34	30.48
12/09	79.80	103	47	2.45	1.37	32.92
Annual Growth	15.5%	—	—	21.4%	7.1%	1.2%

Bayer Motoren WK

LOCATIONS

HQ: Bayer Motoren WK
Petuelring 130, Munchen 80788
Phone: (49) 89 382 25387
Web: www.bmwgroup.com

HISTORICAL FINANCIALS

Company Type: Public

Income Statement

FYE: December 31

	REVENUE ($ mil.)	NET INCOME ($ mil.)	NET PROFIT MARGIN	EMPLOYEES
12/13	104,711	7,315	7.0%	110,351
12/12	101,289	6,702	6.6%	105,876
Annual Growth	3.4%	9.2%	—	4.2%

2013 Year-End Financials

Debt ratio: —
Return on equity: 16.1%
Cash ($ mil.): 10,551
Current ratio: 1.04
Long-term debt ($ mil.): —
No. of shares (mil.): 602
Dividends
  Yield: —
  Payout: —
Market value ($ mil.): —

	STOCK PRICE ($) FY Close	P/E High/Low	PER SHARE ($) Earnings	Dividends	Book Value
12/13	0.00	—	11.15	0.00	81.08
12/12	0.00	—	10.21	0.00	66.78
/0.00	—	(0.00)	0.00	(0.00)	
Annual Growth					

Bayerische Landesbank (Germany)

Bayerische Landesbank (BayernLB) acts as the principal bank to the state of Bavaria and as the central clearing house for the 75 Bavarian sparkassen (savings banks). Also serving corporations national and local governments financial institutions and real estate firms the bank offers a variety of services including financing security underwriting and trading and risk management. It provides retail and private banking services for individuals through its Internet bank Deutsche Kreditbank which also targets infrastructure customers in eastern Europe. BayernLB is recovering after losing billions in the global economic crisis.

Gerd Hausler was named BayernLB's CEO in 2010. He succeeded Stefan Ermisch who served on an interim basis for four months following the resignation of Michael Kemmer. Hausler was most recently a manager and board member of financial investment firm RHJ International.

Michael Kemmer resigned after the company announced it would write off its investment in Austria's Hypo Alpe-Adria-Bank which was nationalized in late 2009 to prevent collapse. BayernLB had acquired a majority stake in the bank in 2007 as part of an ill-timed international expansion of its retail banking operations.

To regain a stable footing the bank has restructured to cut operating costs and sold risk assets and noncore units. It is also refocusing on its core financing operations in Bavarian and other German markets especially for midsized companies and large corporations. In 2010 it sold its 75%-owned Landesbank Saar subsidiary which operates in the German state of Saarland and in France. That year BayenLB also ended merger talks with WestLB another central bank in recovery. The combined entity would've become Germany's third-largest bank. However BayenLB's management didn't find that deal presented good enough advantages.

BayernLB is jointly owned by the state of Bavaria (94%) and the Association of Bavarian Savings Banks.

HISTORY

Bayerische Landesbank Girozentrale (the Bavarian regional bank clearinghouse) was formed by the government in 1972 from the merger of Bayerische Landesbodenkreditanstalt (the state authority for funding projects in Bavaria formed 1884) and Bayerische Gemeindebank (Girozentrale) – fentliche Bankanstalt (the central institution for local public authorities established 1914).

Amid the oil crisis of the 1970s the bank known as BayernLB joined with Commerzbank Dresdner Bank and other West German banks in a consortium to buy from Deutsche Bank a 25% stake in Daimler-Benz; then-Chancellor Helmut Schmidt wished to keep the automaker out of Iranian hands.

BayernLB began expanding outside Germany in the late 1970s; it opened an office in New York City by 1981. Three years later the bank joined with Westdeutsche Landesbank Commerzbank Deutsche Bank and Dresdner Bank to create the venture capital firm Deutsche Wagnisfinanzierung.

During the mid-1980s talk of merging West Germany's fragmented system of 11 Landesbanken and savings banks (a byproduct of post-WWII banking reforms) led BayernLB and Landesbank Stuttgart to consider merging to form a southern Landesbank. However by 1989 the bank had rallied against plans by the centralized Deutscher Sparkassen- und Giroverband to consolidate the operations of the various Landesbanken. That year it held indecisive merger talks with Landesbank Rheinland-Palatine.

Later the bank eschewed mergers and began looking eastward. In 1991 it acquired Czech bank Interbanka. BayernLB first sought out the Hungarian privatization authority in 1992 and by 1994 BayernLB purchased a one-quarter stake in the then-privatizing Hungarian Foreign Trade Bank (MKB; 75%-owned by 1999). The bank also looked to Asia opening an offshore banking branch in Malaysia in 1995. The bank gained assets closer to home by taking a 31% stake in the Austrian Bank for Arbeit und Wirtschaft (Bawag; increased to nearly half by 1999).

BayernLB opened another offshore branch in Thailand in 1996 but two years later began to see negative consequences to its expansion in the East when the Asian currency crisis hit walloping the bank's normally stellar credit rating.

In 2000 the European Commission said it would take action against the German government over the role of the Landesbanken claiming a breach of antitrust laws. The legal threat laid the groundwork for strategic cooperation —and even talks of a merger —between BayernLB and Landesbank Hessen-Thoringen. Bavaria's government also pressured BayernLB raiding the bank in search of evidence related to alleged embezzlement in Singapore.

In 2001 BayernLB after much European Union antitrust scrutiny announced a partial privatization plan. The next year BayernLB changed its legal name from Bayerische Landesbank Girozentrale to simply Bayerische Landesbank.

When the global economy fell into crisis in 2008 BayernLB was the first German bank to take money from the country's bailout program. It received E4.5 billion ($6.9 billion) from the German government's E80 billion rescue fund and raised another E1 billion from two state-backed shareholders. The bank which has branches in Asia North America and other parts of Europe to complement its offices in Germany restructured in order to focus on its core European markets and cut approximately 30% of its workforce.

EXECUTIVES

CEO, Gerd Hausler, age 63
COO and CFO, Stephan Winkelmeier, age 46
Member Board of Management Head Corporate & Mittelstand, Michael Bucker, age 52
Chief Risk Officer, Marcus Kramer, age 50
Deputy CEO, Edgar Zoller, age 57
Member Management Board Markets, Nils Niermann, age 45
Chairman, Michael Schneider
Deputy Chairman, Walter Strohmaier
Auditors: KPMGDeutscheTreuhand-GesellschaftAG

LOCATIONS

HQ: Bayerische Landesbank (Germany)
Brienner Strasse 18, Munich D-80333
Phone: (49) 89 21 71 01   **Fax:** (49) 89 21 71 2 35 79
Web: www.bayernlb.de

PRODUCTS/OPERATIONS

Selected Subsidiaries

Banque LBLux S.A. (Luxembourg)
BayTech Venture Capital Beratungs GmbH
Bayern Consult Unternehmensberatung GmbH
Bayernimmo KG
BayernLB Private Equity
BayernInvest Luxembourg S.A.
Deutsche Kreditbank AG
MKB Bank Zrt (Hungary)

COMPETITORS

Aareal Bank	Landesbank Berlin
Commerzbank	UniCredit Bank AG
DZ BANK	WGZ BANK
Deutsche Bank	WestLB
Deutsche Postbank	Wustenrot &
KfW	Wurttembergische
Landesbank	
Baden-Wurttemberg	

HISTORICAL FINANCIALS

Company Type: Public

Income Statement

FYE: December 31

	ASSETS ($ mil.)	NET INCOME ($ mil.)	INCOME AS % OF ASSETS	EMPLOYEES
12/13	351,894	165	0.0%	8,568
12/12	378,046	1,004	0.3%	9,932
12/11	399,862	134	0.0%	10,893
12/10	423,399	849	0.2%	10,853
12/09	488,090	(3,772)	—	11,821
Annual Growth	(7.9%)	—	—	(7.7%)

2013 Year-End Financials

Return on assets: 0.0%
Return on equity: 0.8%
Long-term debt ($ mil.): —
No. of shares (mil.): —
Sales ($ mil): 12,674
Dividends
  Yield: —
  Payout: —
  Market value ($ mil.): —

Bayerische Motoren Werke AG

Bayerische Motoren Werke better known as BMW is among the top 10 automakers in the world. It manufactures premium brand cars and off-road vehicles under the BMW MINI and Rolls-Royce names as well as motorcycles under the BMW and Husqvarna names. Spare parts and accessories are also offered. Its vehicles and products are sold worldwide through company branches independent dealers subsidiaries and importers. BMW's financial services segment offers car leasing and credit financing for both retail and corporate fleet customers; dealer financing; insurance; and deposit banking.

Geographic Reach

BMW operates in more than 150 countries. It generates about half of its revenue in Europe while the remainder is well dispersed among the Americas (mainly the US) China and other parts of the world.

Operations

To support global markets BMW has 17 production facilities in Austria Germany the UK the US China and South Africa. It also has about 10 R&D centers in Austria Germany the US Japan and China. Some assembly is undertaken with external partners in emerging markets including India Malaysia Thailand and Russia.

Sales and Marketing

The company has a global sales network that spans more than 140 countries. BMW and MINI brand products are sold in Germany through the company's own branches and independent authorized dealers. Sales outside of Germany are carried out mainly by subsidiaries and in certain markets by independent importers. Rolls-Royce brand vehicles are sold in the US by a subsidiary and elsewhere by dealers. At year end 2012 BMW's car sales network was made up of 3300 BMW 1550 MINI and 110 Rolls-Royce dealerships worldwide.

Financial Performance

Fiscal 2012 was the most successful year in BMW's history in terms of financial performance as the company posted strong growth in sales volumes revenues and earnings for the year. The number of BMW MINI and Rolls-Royce vehicles delivered to customers was up about 11% over fiscal 2011 (itself previously a record year) and all three brands set new records thanks in part to increased demand for passenger vehicles in Asia and the Americas. Group revenues in 2012 grew by about 12% while group profit rose by some 4% despite greater investments in green and other technologies and higher personnel costs. Growth in its motorcycle and financial services segments also contributed to positive sales performance. BMW spent 2011 and 2010 getting the company back on track following the global economic crisis in 2008 and 2009.

Strategy

BMW is in the midst of what it call its Number ONE strategy an initiative begun in 2007 that continues today to boost profitability and enable expansion of its global production and sales networks. From 2007 to 2012 the company expanded from 23 production facilities to 29. More recent manufacturing plants have been opened in China through its BMW Brilliance joint venture with Brilliance China Automotive. BMW's goal is to sell more than two million BMW MINI and Rolls-Royce vehicles by 2016 —up from the 1.85 million cars it sold in fiscal 2012.

From an environmental perspective BMW's strategy is to invest in and develop technologies that support making its vehicle fleet more fuel efficient and reducing carbon dioxide emissions by 25% between 2008 and 2020. To this end it is increasing R&D expenditures in part to support continued development of a new fuel efficient engine family called Efficient Dynamics and improvement of a hybrid technology called ActiveHybrid. New vehicle models like the pure electric BMWi family are expected to launch in late 2013.

Additionally BMW looks for opportunities to partner with companies that are pushing developments in sustainable mobility. In early 2013 for instance BMW signed an agreement with one of the top automakers in the world Toyota to collaborate on fuel cells and lightweight construction technologies. BMW and Toyota also conduct joint research on lithium-air batteries the next generation of lithium-ion technology.

In other areas of its business BMW is dealing with contracting motorcycle markets worldwide and is therefore changing strategic course. In early 2013 it announced plans to sell its Husqvarna motorcycle business to Austrian company Pierer Industrie AG in order to focus in the future exclusively on the BMW motorcycle brand.

Ownership

Stefan Quandt and sister Susanne Klatten children of the late Herbert Quandt and both members of BMW's supervisory board together hold about a 28% stake in the company. Their mother Johanna Quandt also holds a certain share of voting rights. They are part of one of Germany's richest family dynasties.

HISTORY

BMW's logo speaks to its origin: a propeller in blue and white the colors of Bavaria. In 1913 Karl Rapp opened an aircraft-engine design shop near Munich. He named it Bayerische Motoren Werke (BMW) in 1917. The end of WWI brought German aircraft production to a halt and BMW shifted to making railway brakes until the 1930s. BMW debuted its first motorcycle the R32 in 1923 and the company began making automobiles in 1928 after buying small-car company Fahrzeugwerke Eisenach.

In 1933 BMW launched a line of larger cars. The company built aircraft engines for Hitler's Luftwaffe in the 1930s and stopped all auto and motorcycle production in 1941. BMW chief Josef Popp resisted and was ousted. Under the Nazis the company operated in occupied countries built rockets and developed the world's first production jet engine.

With its factories dismantled after WWII BMW survived by making kitchen and garden equipment. In 1948 it introduced a one-cylinder motorcycle which sold well as cheap transportation in postwar Germany. BMW autos in the 1950s were large and expensive and sold poorly. When motorcycle sales dropped the company escaped demise in the mid-1950s by launching the Isetta a seven-foot three-wheeled "bubble car."

Herbert Quandt saved the enterprise in 1959 by buying control for $1 million. Quandt's BMW focused on sports sedans and released the first of the "New Range" of BMWs in 1961. Success of the niche enabled BMW to buy automaker Hans Glas in 1966.

In the 1970s BMW's European exports soared and the company set up a distribution subsidiary in the US. The company also produced larger cars that put BMW on par with Mercedes-Benz.

Rapid export growth in the US Asia and Australia continued in the 1980s but Japanese bikes and poor demand hurt motorcycle sales. The launch of the company's luxury vehicles in 1986

heated up the BMW-Mercedes rivalry. US sales peaked that year and fell 45% by 1991. However in 1992 BMW outsold Mercedes in Europe for the first time and became the first European carmaker to operate a US plant since Volkswagen pulled out in 1988.

BMW teamed with the UK's Rolls-Royce aerospace firm in 1990 to make jet engines for planes that included executive business-travel jets such as the Gulfstream V.

The company bought UK carmaker Rover from British Aerospace and Honda in 1994 and introduced a cheaper vehicle the four-wheel-drive Discovery. It launched Highlander Land Rover in 1996 to meet a growing demand for 4x4 utility vehicles.

BMW offered to buy the luxury Rolls-Royce auto unit (including the Bentley) from UK-based Vickers in 1998 but lost out when Volkswagen (VW) countered with a higher offer. The company fared better however when aircraft engine maker Rolls-Royce sold the Rolls-Royce auto brand name and logo to BMW for $66 million. (VW got to use the name until 2003.) Also in 1998 BMW along with other German companies was hit by a class-action lawsuit brought by Holocaust survivors seeking compensation for their work as slave laborers during WWII. (BMW participated in a settlement agreement late the following year.)

In mid-1998 BMW began cutting jobs at its money-losing Rover unit. As Rover's plants continued their downward trend in 1999 BMW's board forced out chairman Bernd Pischetsrieder who spearheaded the Rover acquisition in 1994. The UK later pledged to help pay for renovations at Rover's Longbridge plant to save about 14000 jobs and prevent it from moving operations to Hungary.

The company in 2000 sold its Land Rover SUV operations to Ford in a deal worth about $2.7 billion. Also that year BMW handed over its Rover Cars operations and MG brand to the Phoenix Consortium a UK-based group led by former Rover CEO John Towers.

In 2001 BMW launched its MINI brand in the UK; other European markets soon followed. BMW brought the MINI Cooper to US shores in 2002. The following year BMW took control of the Rolls-Royce brand from Volkswagen and began making Rolls-Royce Phantoms in Goodwood in the south of England.

Despite selling the operations of Rover in 2000 BMW still retained the rights to the brand. In 2006 BMW agreed to sell the Rover brand to an unidentified buyer at an undisclosed price although Dow Jones Newswires reported the buyer was Shanghai Automotive Industry Corp. and the price was nearly $21 million. That deal however was derailed a month later when Ford Motor said it would exercise its right of first refusal agreement with BMW and take control of the brand for about $11 million.

Like its automotive OEM brethren BMW's activities were negatively impacted by the global recession. In 2009 and 2008 it saw consumer spending dip; more than 10% fewer BMW MINI and Rolls-Royce cars were sold than in 2008. BMW's automotive segment suffered an operating loss. Although international motorcycle demand eroded by about one-third BMW fared relatively better with volumes slumping by 14% from 2008. BMW's financial services operation edged up slightly despite weak new used and leased business as well as bad debt accounts. Year-over-year group sales tumbled about 5% in 2009 and earnings by more than 35%. BMW managed to generate a positive cash flow from operating activities albeit lower than 2008's level.

As a result of the economic crash BMW shifted direction in several areas. It trimmed vehicle production by more than 10% to align with lower demand reduced its workforce and cut back on R&D by some 8% and capital investments by 20%.

Even with the realignment and reductions BMW remained true to its green initiatives having rolled out 49 models in 2009 that meet the EU5 emissions standard. Its BMW 330d with BluePerformance technology was hailed as the first car on the market to comply with the EU6 emission standard effective in 2014. In 2009 BMW added numerous new car models including the MINI E which was launched on a trial basis giving BMW experience in delivering lithium-ion technology. Rolls-Royce got the Ghost a coupe version of the Phantom. The company made way for an inorganic sand core technology; the light alloy foundry method applies mineral binders that tout virtually no smell or emissions along with lower maintenance expenses and stronger yield.

As the company began recovering from the economic crisis BMW's joint venture with SGL Group gained momentum in 2010. SGL Automotive began investing $100 million to open a carbon fiber manufacturing plant in Washington's Moses Lake with production of lightweight carbon fiber reinforced plastics (CFRP) dedicated to BMW's Megacity Vehicle line. BMW announced in late 2010 that it would invested approximately Â530 million (more than $750 million) to launch the new Megacity Vehicle in 2013. Simultaneously BMW is working with SB Limotive a JV between Bosch and Samsung SDI to source the battery cells that will power the Megacity. The new facility and supply agreement are a strategic step in BMW's move to commercialize manufacture of CFRPs for future cars.

EXECUTIVES

Deputy Chairman Supervisory Board, Manfred Schoch, $148,852 total compensation

Chairman Supervisory Board, Joachim Milberg, age 71, $223,278 total compensation

Deputy Chairman Supervisory Board, Karl-Ludwig Kley, age 63

Deputy Chairman Supervisory Board, Stefan Quandt, $148,852 total compensation

Chairman Management Board, Norbert Reithofer, age 59, $1,183,980 total compensation

Member Management Board Sales and Marketing, Ian Robertson, age 57, $591,990 total compensation

Head Development ?Small Classes? Product Line and Member Supervisory Board, Anton Ruf, $71,538 total compensation

Member Management Board Production, Harald Kruger, age 50, $591,990 total compensation

Member Management Board Finance, Friedrich Eichiner, age 60, $591,990 total compensation

Member Management Board Purchasing and Supplier Network, Klaus Draeger, age 59, $581,876 total compensation

Member Management Board Production, Frank-Peter Arndt, age 58, $580,492 total compensation

Deputy Chairman Supervisory Board, Stefan Schmid, $161,909 total compensation

Member Management Board Development, Herbert Diess, age 57, $618,198 total compensation

General Counsel, Dieter Dieter Loechelt Loechelt

Member of the Management Board; Head of Human Resources; Industrial Relations Director, Harald Harald Krueger Krueger

Member Supervisory Board, Wolfgang Mayrhuber, age 67

Member Supervisory Board, Robert W. (Bob) Lane, age 64

Deputy Chairman Supervisory Board, Manfred Schoch

Deputy Chairman Supervisory Board, Karl-Ludwig Kley, age 63

Deputy Chairman Supervisory Board, Stefan Quandt

Member Supervisory Board, Franz M. Haniel

Member Supervisory Board, Susanne Klatten, age 51

Member Supervisory Board, Willibald Low

Member Supervisory Board, Werner Zierer

Member Supervisory Board, Bertin Eichler, age 62

Member Supervisory Board, Prof Renate Kocher, age 61

Head Development ?Small Classes? Product Line and Member Supervisory Board, Anton Ruf

Member Supervisory Board, Franz Oberlander

Deputy Chairman Supervisory Board, Stefan Schmid

Member Supervisory Board, Maria Schmidt

Member Supervisory Board, Reinhard Huttl

Member Supervisory Board, Horst Lischka

Member of the Supervisory Board; Employee Representative, Franz Franz Oberlaender Oberlaender

Member of the Supervisory Board, Henning Henning Kagermann Kagermann

Member of the Supervisory Board; Employee Representative, Juergen Juergen Wechsler Wechsler

Member of the Supervisory Board, Reinhard Reinhard Huettl Huettl

Member of the Supervisory Board, Renate Renate Koecher Koecher

Member of the Supervisory Board; Employee Representative, Willibald Willibald Loew Loew

Auditors: KPMGAGWirtschaftsprufungsgesellschaft

LOCATIONS

HQ: Bayerische Motoren Werke AG
Petuelring 130, Munich 80788
Phone: (49) 89 3 82 0   **Fax:** (49) 89 3895 5858
Web: www.bmwgroup.com

Sales

	% of total
Europe	
Germany	16
Rest of	30
Americas	
US	17
Rest of	4
Asia	
China	19
Other	14
Total	**100**

PRODUCTS/OPERATIONS

Sales

	% of total
Automobiles	77
Financial	21
Motorcycles	2
Total	**100**

Selected Products

Automobiles
BMW
    1 Series3-door5-doorConvertibleCoupe
    3 SeriesConvertibleCoupeSedanTouring
    5 SeriesGran TurismoSedanTouring
    6 SeriesConvertibleCoupeGran Coupe
    7 SeriesSedan
    X3 X5 X6 sports utility vehicles
    M ModelsM3 ConvertibleM3 CoupeM3 SedanM6 ConvertibleM6 Coupe
    Z4CoupeRoadster
MINI
    John Cooper Works (Hardtop Convertible Clubman)
    MINI Cooper
    MINI Cooper Clubman
    MINI Cooper Convertible
    MINI Cooper S
    MINI Cooper S Clubman
    MINI Cooper S Convertible
Rolls-Royce
    Ghost
    Phantom
    Phantom Coupe
Motorcycles
    BMW
    Husqvarna

COMPETITORS

Chrysler	Mitsubishi Motors
Daimler	Nissan
Ducati	Porsche
Fiat	Renault
Ford Motor	Saab Automobile
General Motors	Suzuki Motor
Harley-Davidson	Toyota
Honda	Ultra Motorcycle
Kawasaki Heavy Industries	Volkswagen
	Yamaha
Mazda	Yamaha Motor

HISTORICAL FINANCIALS

Company Type: Public

Income Statement

FYE: December 31

	REVENUE ($ mil.)	NET INCOME ($ mil.)	NET PROFIT MARGIN	EMPLOYEES
12/13	104,711	7,315	7.0%	110,351
12/12	101,289	6,716	6.6%	105,876
12/11	89,016	6,313	7.1%	100,306
12/10	80,940	4,306	5.3%	95,453
12/09	73,009	293	0.4%	96,230
Annual Growth	**9.4%**	**123.4%**	**—**	**3.5%**

2013 Year-End Financials

Debt ratio: 69.9%
Return on equity: 16.1%
Cash ($ mil.): 10,551
Current ratio: 1.04
Long-term debt ($ mil.): 54,312

No. of shares (mil.): 602
Dividends
  Yield: 1.8%
  Payout: 11.8%
Market value ($ mil.): 23,737

	STOCK PRICE ($) FY Close	P/E High/Low		PER SHARE ($) Earnings	Dividends	Book Value
12/13	39.43	9	6	11.15	0.74	81.08
12/12	32.60	7	5	10.24	0.67	66.33
12/11	22.23	9	5	9.64	0.76	58.09
12/10	26.09	10	5	6.57	0.08	51.30
12/09	15.19	126	45	0.45	0.09	47.63
Annual Growth	**26.9%**		**—**	**—123.5%**	**69.4%**	**14.2%**

Bharat Petroleum Corp Ltd. (India)

Although it carries the ancient Sanskrit name for India (Bharat) Bharat Petroleum Corporation Limited (BPCL) is a modern refining and distribution company. It vies with Hindustan Petroleum for the #2 slot behind Indian Oil. The company's refineries —in Mumbai Kochi and Numaligarh (62%-owned) —collectively process more than 24 million metric tons of crude oil per year. BPCL sells engine oils and gasolines liquefied petroleum gas (LPG) and kerosene. It has10000 gas stations a national network of kerosene dealers and more than 2450 LPG distributors. The company operates 50 LPG bottling plants and serves more than 30 million LPG customers across India.

With an eye to expanding BPCL's global hydrocarbon supply and lowering production costs BPCL's exploration and production unit Bharat PetroResources partners with major oil companies to develop oil and gas fields in India and abroad. In fiscal 2011 Bharat PetroResources reported five oil and gas discoveries in Brazil Indonesia and Mozambique.

BPCL is also modernizing and expanding its Indian refineries to handle increased demand. In fiscal 2011 it teamed up with Bharat Oman Refineries to develop a 6 million metric-ton-per-year refinery in Madya Pradesh to support BPCL's activities in the central and northern part of India. It also launched an expansion of its Kochi refinery to expand that plant's capacity from 7.5 million metric tons per year to 9.5 million metric tons per year.

It is also expanding its gas station network to meet growing domestic demand adding 600 retail outlets in fiscal 2011 with another 700 projected to be added in fiscal 2012. Depending on future growth BPCL may add up to 2500 gas stations by 2017.

Higher oil prices increased production and the expansion of its retail network helped to lift BPCL's revenues in fiscal 2011. Increased costs related to crude oil for resale and raw materials meant that net income was essentially flat for the year.

The Indian government owns 55% of the firm although it is considering eventually selling this stake as part of industrywide deregulation.

EXECUTIVES

Executive Director Corporate Finance, S. Varadarajan

General Manager Projects Kochi Refinery, K. N. Ravindran

Executive Director Kochi Refinery, E. Nandakumar

Chairman and Managing Director, R.K. Singh

Executive Director Gas, A.K. Bansal

General Manager International Trade, P.V. Kumar

Finance Director, S.K. Joshi

Human Resources Director, S. Mohan

General Manager Human Resources Mumbai Refinery, S. Vijayakumar

General Manager Sales Retail HQ, Sharad K. Sharma

General Manager Sales Strategy Retail HQ, V. Anand

Executive Director Refineries Finance, J. Ravichandran

Chief Vigilance Officer, I. Sasikala

Executive Director Pipelines, Anurag Deepak

Refineries Director, B.K. Datta

Executive Director Industrial and Commercial, D.M. Reddy

Executive Director Human Resources Development, Dipti Sanzgiri

Marketing Director, K.K. Gupta

Executive Director Planning, P. S. Bhargava

Executive Director International Trade, R. K. Mehra

General Manager Engineering and Advanced Services Kochi Refinery, Thomas Chacko

Executive Director Human Resources Services, S. P. Gathoo

Executive Director Engineering and Projects, S. P. Mathur

Executive Director Retail, S. Ramesh

Executive Director Audit, Sumita Bose Roy

General Manager Infrastructure and Services, A. K. Kaushik

General Manager Quality Control, Basudev Rana

General Manager Corporate Marketing, Brij Pal Singh

General Manager Lubes, George Paul

Chief Procurement Officer, Arun Singh

General Manager Logistics Retail, G. S. Wankhede

General Manager Marketing Gas, I. Srinivas Rao

General Manager Corporate Treasury, J. Dinaker

General Manager ERP - CC, K. B. Narayanan
General Manager Sales LPG HQ, K. P. Chandy
Executive Director Mumbai Refinery, K. V.
  Seshadri
General Manager Retail South, K. V. Shenoy
General Manager Operations Mumbai Refinery,
  Prasad K. Panicker
General Manager Pipeline Projects E&P, M. M.
  Chawla
General Manager Human Resources Kochi
  Refinery, M. P. Govindarajan
General Manager Urban Retailing, Monica Widhani
General Manager Engineering and Advanced
  Services Mumbai Refinery, Thomas Zachariah
General Manager Corporate Finance, P.
  Balasubramanian
General Manager Highway Retailing, P. C.
  Srivastava
Executive Director Retail East, Pallav Ghosh
General Manager Refinery Coordination, P.
  Padmanabhan
General Manager Retail North, Pramod Sharma
General Manager Finance Retail HQ, R. P. Natekar
General Manager Aviation, S. B. Bhattacharya
General Manager Legal, S. K. Agrawal
General Manager Rural Retailing and Real Estate,
  S. K. Mathur
General Manager Operations Kochi Refinery,
  Tomy Mathews
General Manager Talent Management, T. Somanath
Deputy General Manager Employee Satifaction
  Enhancement, Madhu Sagar
Deputy General Manager Brand and Public
  Relations, M. M. Somaya
Secretary, S.V. Kulkarni
General Manager Projects, P. Kumaraswamy

LOCATIONS

HQ: Bharat Petroleum Corp Ltd. (India)
Bharat Bhavan, 4 & 6 Currimbhoy Road, Ballard
Estate, Mumbai 400 001
Phone: (91) 22 2271 3000 Fax: (91) 22 2271 3688
Web: www.bharatpetroleum.in

PRODUCTS/OPERATIONS

Selected Operations
Aviation (jet fuel operations)
Exploration and production
Liquefied petroleum gas (Bharatgas cooking gas)
Lubricants (automotive and industrial lubricants)
Industrial and commercial (fuels and petrochemicals for
  industrial and commercial clients)
Refining (crude oil processing)
Retail (petrol diesel and kerosene retail outlets)

COMPETITORS

BG Group   Idemitsu Kosan
BP   Indian Oil
Bongaigaon Refinery Reliance Industries
Exxon Mobil   Royal Dutch Shell
GAIL   TOTAL
Hindustan Petroleum

HISTORICAL FINANCIALS

Company Type: Public

Income Statement
FYE: March 31

	REVENUE ($ mil.)	NET INCOME ($ mil.)	NET PROFIT MARGIN	EMPLOYEES
03/13	44,612	346	0.8%	13,213
03/12	41,698	153	0.4%	13,429
03/11	34,488	366	1.1%	13,915
03/10	29,241	383	1.3%	13,898
03/09	26,819	142	0.5%	14,016
Annual Growth	13.6%	24.9%	—	(1.5%)

2013 Year-End Financials
Debt ratio: 0.7%
Return on equity: 11.5%
Cash ($ mil.): 524
Current ratio: 0.92
Long-term debt ($ mil.): 2,339
No. of shares (mil.): 723
Dividends
  Yield: —
  Payout: —
Market value ($ mil.): —

BHP Billiton Ltd.

Two heads (or headquarters) are better than one. Aussie minerals and oil company BHP Limited acquired UK miner Billiton plc in 2001. The result: a two-headquartered dual-listed company run as a single entity with the same board of directors and management. The Melbourne side is BHP Billiton Limited the London side is BHP Billiton Plc; collectively they are known as BHP Billiton. One of the largest diversified natural resources companies it ranks among the world's top producers of iron ore and coal (thermal and metallurgical). Other products include aluminum copper manganese nickel silver uranium and potash. BHP also has crude oil and natural gas holdings. The company may spin off its diamond assets.

The company has far-flung operations. In Canada's Saskatchewan province BHP produces potash a primary raw material used to manufacture fertilizers and a top priority for the global titans of mining. In Australia it operates a coal-producing joint venture with Mitsubishi that has mining projects in Australia. Its Australian minerals businesses include not only iron ore coal and potash but also copper and uranium. Its Chilean operations include a 58% stake in the Escondida mine one of the world's largest and lowest-cost copper producers. BHP's oil and gas operations are worldwide ranging from its Shenzi deepwater oil and gas field in the Gulf of Mexico to onshore natural gas production in Pakistan.

As a result of global demand for its resources BHP Billiton turned in a good performance for 2011. Strong demand from China and other developing countries helped contribute to BHP's sharp increase in revenue that year. The company recorded net sales of $71.7 billion (up 36% from 2010) and a net income of $23.7 billion (up 86%). It also achieved record production for most of its commodities including its 11th consecutive record in iron ore.

The company has created a diversified portfolio of tier one natural resources by investing in large high-quality low-cost assets. In addition to strategic acquisitions BHP seeks organic growth through investments in major projects for its segments. In 2011 it poured about $13 billion in 11 projects to help grow several of its businesses: natural gas iron ore coal copper and diamonds. The company expected its organic growth program to exceed more than $80 billion in new development spending by 2015.

With mineral prices falling rapidly in 2012 however the company may not meet its $80 billion spending target for investments and is reviewing its expansion plans. The price of iron ore for example has declined 29% since the company announced its plans for investments in early 2011.

Recent investments in on-shore shale assets in the US are also cause for concern. In 2011 BHP acquired Chesapeake Energy Corp.'s Fayetteville shale gas holdings in Arkansas for $4.75 billion. That year it also acquired Petrohawk Energy another US-based gas producer with projects in the Eagle Ford and Haynesville shale plays for $15.1 billion. In 2012 natural gas prices began to plum-

met. Although the company defended the long-term growth outlook for the shale assets it did not rule out a possible writedown later that year for those investments.

Following the Petrohawk announcement in 2011 BHP acquired three subsidiaries of HWE Mining a company owned by Leighton Holdings for $735 million. The HWE Mining subsidiaries provide contract iron ore mining services in Western Australia to BHP and the acquisition allows the company to both own and operate the mines.

BHP may also exit the diamonds business entirely. In 2012 it sold its 51% stake in the Chidliak diamond exploration project in Canada's Baffin Island to the project operator Peregrine Diamonds giving it full ownership. The sale follows BHP's review of its diamond businesses to determine whether they fit in its strategy. The company also owns an 80% stake in Canada's EKATI diamond mine which is still under review. The company could receive less than $500 million for the sale of the mine.

HISTORY

In 1883 Charles Rasp a boundary rider for the Mt. Gipps sheep station believed valuable ore lay in the Broken Hill outcrop in New South Wales Australia. He gathered a few young speculators and The Broken Hill Proprietary Company (BHP) was incorporated in 1885. BHP immediately found a massive lode of silver lead and zinc. None of the founders knew how to run a mine so they recruited US engineers William Patton and Herman Schlapp. From the beginning labor and management clashed. The founding directors set up the head office in Melbourne far from the mine and gambled with gold sovereigns in the boardroom. But the miners worked in dangerous conditions. An 1892 labor strike was the first of BHP's bitter strikes.

In 1902 the new general manager Guillaume Delprat invented a flotation process that recovered valuable metals from iron ore waste. Delprat also foresaw a future in steel although Australia had no steel industry. BHP commissioned the Newcastle steelworks in 1915 and soon became the country's largest steel producer. BHP's 1935 purchase of Australian Iron and Steel its only competitor gave it a virtual steel monopoly while high tariffs protected it from outside competition. Its exhausted Broken Hill mine was closed that year.

In the 1960s BHP got into oil when it partnered with Esso Standard the Australian subsidiary of Standard Oil of New Jersey for offshore exploration. In 1967 the partners found oil in the Bass Strait which soon supplied 70% of Australia's petroleum. In the 1960s and 1970s BHP began expanding its iron ore manganese and coal interests. Meanwhile public opposition mounted to BHP's market power and labor practices and in 1972 the government took steps to limit BHP's power removing some subsidies and tax breaks.

The weak steel market of the 1970s and 1980s caused BHP to lay off almost a third of its steelworkers in 1983 but with government intervention BHP radically improved its steel productivity. In 1984 BHP bought Utah International's mining assets from General Electric (including Chile's rich Escondida copper mine). In 1986 corporate raider Robert Holmes a Court took a run at BHP; BHP decided to become an international mining company to prevent further raids. Its acquisitions in the late 1980s included ERG Inc. and Monsanto Oil (combined into BHP Americas) Aquila Steel and Pacific Refining in Hawaii.

A peace deal with Holmes a Court gave BHP about 37% of Foster's Brewing but in 1992 BHP took a $700 million write-down after Foster's stock declined. BHP also bought Arizona-based Magma

Copper in 1996 but plunging world copper prices forced a $420 million write-down.

With new worries over Asia's economic troubles BHP soon was struggling. In 1997 BHP sold most of its stake in Foster's and three senior executives resigned. In 1998 the company unloaded Pacific Refining which was acquired by Tesoro Petroleum for about $275 million.

As BHP's woes continued CEO John Prescott resigned; Paul Anderson was recruited from Duke Energy to succeed Prescott. In 1999 D. R. Argus took over as chairman replacing Jeremy Ellis. In a restructuring move the company sold its engineering power insurance and information technology businesses in 1999 and 2000. BHP began to sell $2 billion worth of steel operations (including its long product unit OneSteel). In 2000 the company shortened its official name to BHP Limited.

BHP acquired Billiton in 2001 forming BHP Billiton Ltd. and BHP Billiton plc. The combined BHP Billiton had sales of almost $20 billion and a market capitalization approaching $30 billion. In addition BHP paid $436 million for Dia Met Minerals which owned 29% of Canada's only producing diamond mine Ekati.

Also in 2001 BHP Billiton and Alcoa combined their North American metals distribution businesses as joint venture Integris Metals (subsequently sold and integrated into Ryerson). In order to focus on its minerals and oil and gas operations in 2002 BHP Billiton spun off its steel business as BHP Steel (now called Bluescope Steel).

In 2005 BHP Billiton acquired metals and minerals company WMC Resources which had been the subject of much takeover speculation and the target of the Swiss mining heavyweight Xstrata (since renamed Glencore). Its offer of $7.3 billion surpassed Xstrata's and was accepted and endorsed by the WMC board which had turned down the two earlier proposals by Xstrata. The addition of WMC added significantly to BHP Billiton's copper nickel and uranium operations.

In 2008 BHP Billiton Mitsubishi Alliance (BMA) spent $2.4 billion to buy the Saraji East metallurgical coal project from New Hope Corporation. Each of BMA's owners paid $1.2 billion to New Hope for the project which lies adjacent to one of BMA's coal mines.

Though the global recession of 2008-2009 certainly pushed the company's fortunes down BHP Billiton experienced eyebrow-raising growth thanks in part to generally high commodity prices and the emerging Asian economies. China for example represented 20% of the company's total sales in 2007 doubling its share from just three years prior. The continent as a whole accounted for more than half of sales.

Due to the strong demand BHP Billiton increased production of iron ore coking coal and manganese. The shifting nature of the market though changed the company's highest-grossing segments. In 2009 high coal prices helped that business immensely while conversely the Base Metals business of copper lead zinc and precious metals mining suffered from low prices driving down the unit's revenues. On the petroleum side the company continued to acquire oil and gas exploration leases in the Gulf of Mexico.

Two failed deals by BHP Billiton occurred in 2010: a $39 billion takeover of Potash Corporation of Saskatchewan and a proposed joint venture with Rio Tinto Ltd. BHP Billiton's offer for Potash Corporation was first rejected by that company's board as inadequate and then by Canadian regulators who ruled the offer to be anticompetitive. After a $150 billion bid to buy Rio Tinto fell through due to the global economic meltdown the companies proposed a joint iron ore venture in Western Australia which also failed because of opposition from European regulatory authorities.

In 2010 BHP Billiton acquired Athabasca Potash Inc. (API) for about $320 million. API's projects are located in Saskatchewan close to BHP Billiton's own potash operations.

EXECUTIVES

Chairman, Jacques A. (Jac) Nasser, age 65
Group Executive and Chief Executive Ferrous and Coal, Marcus P. Randolph, age 58
Chief Executive Officer; Executive Director, Marius Kloppers, age 52, $1,677,070 total compensation
Group Executive and Chief People Officer, Karen J. Wood, age 58, $854,514 total compensation
Group Executive and Chief Executive Non-Ferrous, Andrew Mackenzie
Investor Relations Americas, Scott Espenshade
Group Company Secretary, Jane F. McAloon, age 50
President Iron Ore, Ian R. Ashby
CFO BHP Billiton Petroleum, David Powell
Group Executive and Chief Executive Petroleum, J. Michael (Mike) Yeager, age 62
Group Executive and Chief Commercial Officer, Alberto Calderon, age 55
Group Executive and CFO, Graham Kerr
Investor Relations United Kingdom and South Africa, Andre Liebenberg
Media Relations United Kingdom South Africa and Americas, Ruban Yogarajah
Group Executive and Chief Marketing Officer, Mike Henry
VP Human Resources BHP Billiton Petroleum, David J. Nelson
Investor Relations Australia, Brendan Harris
Investor Relations Australia, Leng Lau
Media Relations Australia, Kelly Quirke
Media Relations Australia, Fiona Martin
Investor Relations Contact Officer, James Agar
Deputy Company Secretary, Nicola Evans
President - Aluminium; Manganese and Nickel, Daniel Malchuk
President Copper, Peter BeavenBAcc
Director, Wayne W. Murdy, age 70
Director, Sir John G. S. Buchanan, age 70
Director, John M. Schubert, age 71
Director, Alan L. Boeckmann, age 66
Director, Keith C. Rumble, age 60
CEO and Director, Marius Kloppers, age 51
Director, Malcolm W. Broomhead, age 62
Director, Carolyn Hewson, age 59
Director, David A. Crawford, age 70
Group Company Secretary and Director, Jane F. McAloon, age 49
Director, Carlos Cordeiro, age 58
Director, Baroness Shriti Vadera
Independent Non-Executive Director, Lindsay Maxsted
Independent Non-Executive Director, Pat Davies
Auditors: KPMGAuditPlc

LOCATIONS

HQ: BHP Billiton Ltd.
BHP Billiton Centre, 171 Collins Street, Melbourne, Victoria 3000
Phone: (61) 3 9609 3333   **Fax:** (61) 3 9609 3015
Web: www.bhpbilliton.com

Sales

	$ mil.	% of total
Asia		
China	20,261	28
Japan	9,002	13
Other countries	15,805	22
Europe (including UK)	9,413	13
North America	6,167	9
Australia	5,487	8
South America	2,592	4
Southern Africa	1,548	2
Other regions	1,464	2
Total	**71,739**	**100**

PRODUCTS/OPERATIONS

Sales

	$ mil.	% of total
Iron ore	20,412	28
Base metals	14,152	20
Coal		
Energy coal	5,507	8
Petroleum	10,737	15
Stainless steel materials	3,861	5
Diamonds & specialty products	1,517	2
Total	**71,739**	**100**

Selected Divisions

Coal
  Metallurgical
  Energy
Iron ore
Petroleum
  Crude oil
  Ethane
  LPG
  Natural gas
Base metals
  Copper
  Gold
  Lead
  Silver
  Zinc
Aluminum
  Alumina
  Aluminum
  Bauxite
Manganese
Stainless steel materials
  Cobalt
  Ferrochrome
  Nickel
Diamonds and specialty products
  Diamonds
  Potash
  Titanium minerals

COMPETITORS

Alcoa
Anglo American
ArcelorMittal
BP
Chevron
Chinalco
Codelco
ConocoPhillips
Exxon Mobil
Fortescue Metals
Freeport-McMoRan
Koch Industries Inc.
Kumba Iron Ore
Marathon Oil
Newmont Mining
Nippon Steel & Sumitomo Metal Corporation
Norsk Hydro ASA
Repsol
Rio Tinto Limited
Royal Dutch Shell
TOTAL
Tata Europe
Teck
Vale
Xstrata

HISTORICAL FINANCIALS

Company Type: Public

Income Statement

FYE: June 30

	REVENUE ($ mil.)	NET INCOME ($ mil.)	NET PROFIT MARGIN	EMPLOYEES
06/14	67,206	13,832	20.6%	47,044
06/13	65,968	10,876	16.5%	49,496
06/12	72,226	15,417	21.3%	46,370
06/11	71,739	23,648	33.0%	40,757
06/10	52,798	12,722	24.1%	39,570
Annual Growth	**6.2%**	**2.1%**	**—**	**4.4%**

2014 Year-End Financials

Debt ratio: 22.8%
Return on equity: 18.4%
Cash ($ mil.): 8,803
Current ratio: 1.23
Long-term debt ($ mil.): 30,327

No. of shares (mil.): —
Dividends
  Yield: 3.4%
  Payout: 91.0%
Market value ($ mil.): —

	STOCK PRICE ($) FY Close	P/E High/Low		PER SHARE ($) Earnings	Dividends	Book Value
06/14	68.45	28	22	2.59	2.36	14.87
06/13	57.66	39	28	2.04	2.28	13.28
06/12	65.30	33	21	2.88	2.20	12.38
06/11	94.63	24	14	4.27	1.82	10.66
06/10	61.99	36	22	2.28	1.66	8.72
Annual Growth	2.5%	—	—	3.3%	9.2%	14.3%

BHP Billiton Plc

BHP Billiton Plc is one half of a dual-listed mining giant. It is headquartered in London; the other part of the company BHP Billiton Limited is based in Australia. Although they maintain separate listings the companies are managed as a single entity and have the same management team and board of directors. One of the largest diversified natural resources companies it ranks among the world's top producers of iron ore and coal (thermal and metallurgical). Other products include aluminum copper manganese nickel silver uranium and potash. BHP also has significant crude oil and natural gas holdings. For more information on the company refer to Hoover's BHP Billiton Limited profile.

In mid-2005 BHP Billiton acquired the Australian metals and minerals company WMC Resources which had been the subject of much takeover speculation and the target of the Swiss mining heavyweight Xstrata (since renamed Glencore). BHP Billiton opened talks with WMC's board and made an offer for the Australian company in early 2005. The offer of $7.3 billion surpassed Xstrata's and was accepted and endorsed by the WMC board which had turned down the two earlier proposals by Xstrata.

The potential addition of WMC Resources adds significantly to BHP Billiton's copper nickel and uranium operations.

HISTORY

After starting out on its own in 1860 Billiton was subsequently bought first by Royal Dutch Shell and then by Gencor only to end up on its own once again. In 1860 a group of Dutch shareholders formed Billiton NV. The company bought the rich tin deposits of Billiton island (now part of Indonesia) for which it was named. The business grew to include tin and lead smelting in the Netherlands. Billiton NV began mining bauxite in the 1940s but WWII caused a production slowdown.

While demand for petroleum products exploded in the 1950s and 1960s in 1970 the industry nosedived. Royal Dutch Shell (formed from the merger of Royal Dutch and Shell Transport and Trading) responded by diversifying buying Billiton NV which it renamed Billiton International. Shell had gotten its start in commodities in the 1880s selling Russian oil of the Rothschilds to the Far East. Royal Dutch formed in 1890 after buying the rights to drill for oil in the Dutch East Indies. The two companies merged in 1907.

The 1970 Billiton purchase helped Royal Dutch Shell make up for the 1970s oil shortage and rationing that had resulted from OPEC's crude oil price hikes. Slow worldwide economic growth a major recession and oil and chemicals overcapacity impacted the company in the late 1970s and early 1980s.

Royal Dutch Shell sold Billiton in 1994 to Gencor which had been formed in 1980 by the merger of General Mining and Finance Corporation and Union Corporation. General Mining began mining gold in South Africa in the 1890s and Gencor continued its predecessors' metals and manufacturing operations. Gencor however spent the early 1980s focused on manufacturing because it anticipated a downturn in base metals. But the recession inflation and high interest rates stifled Gencor's success and the company became known as an unfocused conglomerate. In 1986 a newly appointed chairman separated Gencor's manufacturing and mining interests.

By 1989 Gencor had cut its staff and reorganized. That year it bought 31% of South Africa's Richards Bay aluminum smelter. Within two years Gencor had become a holding company with a primary interest in mining. In 1993 the firm unbundled its non-mining activities. With the end of apartheid in 1994 Gencor was able to expand abroad. Its purchase of Billiton catapulted its presence into 13 countries but in 1996 the metals market spiraled downward.

Billiton was spun off by Gencor in 1997. It took over all of Gencor's nonprecious metal interests including its aluminum titanium ferroalloy and coal assets. That year Billiton combined its nickel interests with QNI of Australia. Making good on its plan to buy new base metals assets Billiton entered a joint venture in 1998 to explore for lead and zinc with Ireland's Ennex. Billiton also sold its metals brokerage subsidiary to Metallgesellschaft AG (Germany).

In 1999 Billiton announced that it would invest in smaller companies with promising properties and limit its own in-house exploration operations. It entered joint ventures with PT Taraco Mining to explore for coal in Indonesia and with Comet Resources to develop the Ravensthorpe Nickel Project in Western Australia.

Billiton's offer for a 21% stake in the Gove bauxite-alumina project in Australia was bested by Alcan in 2000. The company agreed to pay Alcoa about $1.5 billion for its majority stake in the Worsley alumina refinery in Australia. With Anglo American and Glencore International (now Glencore Xstrata) it acquired a 50% stake in Colombia's Cerrejon Zona Norte coal mine for $384 million; it then bought Canadian mining company Rio Algom (copper molybdenum uranium and coal) for $1.2 billion.

In 2001 Billiton closed the purchase of Alcoa's share of the Worsley smelter. The same year Billiton agreed to be acquired by Aussie natural resources company BHP Ltd. to form a dual-listed entity —known collectively as BHP Billiton —consisting of BHP Billiton Limited (run from Melbourne) and BHP Billiton plc (run from London). The deal closed in June 2001.

EXECUTIVES

CEO, Andrew Mackenzie
CFO, Alex Vanselow, age 51, $186,846 total compensation
Chairman BHP Billiton South Africa, Xolani Mkhwanazi, age 59
CFO BHP Billiton Petroleum, David Powell
President Copper, Peter Beaven
President Manganese, Tom Schutte
CFO, Graham Kerr
President Iron Ore, Jimmy Wilson

President Stainless Steel Materials, Glenn Kellow
President and COO New Mexico Coal, Jac Fourie
President Marketing & Technology, Mike Henry
President Diamonds and Specialty Products, Tim Cutt
President Aluminium Manganese & Nickel, Daniel Malchuk
President Coal, Dean Della Valle
Chairman of the UK Trustees for the Christchurch Earthquake appeal, Ondra Bank
President Aluminium Manganese & Nickel, Daniel MalchukBE
Director, Wayne W. Murdy, age 69
Director, John G. S. Buchanan, age 69
Director, John M. Schubert, age 70
Director, Alan L. Boeckmann, age 65
Director, Keith C. Rumble, age 59
CEO and Director, Marius Kloppers, age 51
Director, Malcolm W. Broomhead, age 60
Director, Carolyn Hewson, age 58
Director, David A. Crawford, age 69
Group Company Secretary and Director, Jane F. McAloon, age 49
Director, Carlos Cordeiro, age 57
Director, Baroness Shriti Vadera
Auditors: KPMGAuditPlc

LOCATIONS

HQ: BHP Billiton Plc
Neathouse Place, Victoria, London SW1V 1BH
Phone: (44) 20 7802 4000   Fax: (44) 20 7802 4111
Web: www.bhpbilliton.com

COMPETITORS

Alcoa	Norilsk Nickel
Anglo American	Norsk Hydro ASA
BP	Rio Tinto plc
Chevron	Vale
Newmont Mining	Xstrata

HISTORICAL FINANCIALS

Company Type: Public

Income Statement

FYE: June 30

	REVENUE ($ mil.)	NET INCOME ($ mil.)	NET PROFIT MARGIN	EMPLOYEES
06/14	67,206	13,832	20.6%	47,044
06/13	65,968	10,876	16.5%	49,496
06/12	72,226	15,417	21.3%	46,370
06/11	71,739	23,648	33.0%	40,757
06/10	52,798	12,722	24.1%	39,570
Annual Growth	6.2%	2.1%	—	4.4%

2014 Year-End Financials

Debt ratio: 22.8%
Return on equity: 18.4%
Cash ($ mil.): 8,803
Current ratio: 1.23
Long-term debt ($ mil.): 30,327

No. of shares (mil.): —
Dividends
  Yield: 3.6%
  Payout: 91.0%
Market value ($ mil.): —

	STOCK PRICE ($) FY Close	P/E High/Low		PER SHARE ($) Earnings	Dividends	Book Value
06/14	65.23	26	19	2.59	2.36	14.87
06/13	51.27	35	25	2.04	2.28	13.28
06/12	57.19	28	18	2.88	2.20	12.38
06/11	78.43	20	12	4.27	1.82	10.66
06/10	51.44	31	18	2.28	1.66	8.72
Annual Growth	6.1%	—	—	3.3%	9.2%	14.3%

BNP Paribas (France)

One of Europe's largest banks BNP Paribas operates about 7150 branches in some 75 countries across Europe North America Africa and Asia. The company and its many subsidiaries specialize in retail banking corporate and investment banking and investment services. BNP Paribas operates in Italy through BNL banca commerciale. The French banking giant also owns Belgium's BNP Paribas Fortis which operates more than 1000 branches in Europe and the US. In the western US the company owns BancWest (the parent of Bank of the West and First Hawaiian Bank). BNP Paribas earns more than half of its revenue outside its home country of France.

Geographic Reach

The Paris-based bank is active in four domestic markets: Belgium France Italy and Luxembourg. Europe is the bank's largest market accounting for more than 75% of revenue. North America contributes about 10% while the Asia-Pacific and Africa region and other countries each contribute more than 5%. BNP Paribas has operations in 78 countries overall.

Operations

Retail banking with some 6800 branches spread across 40 countries accounts for more than 60% of the bank's revenue. BNP Paribas is engaged in retail banking in France Italy (Banca Nazionale del Lavoro acquired in 2006) Belgium and Luxembourg (BNP Paribas Fortis and BGL BNP Paribas) and throughout the euro zone the US and in Asia the Mediterranean Basin Africa Turkey and Central and Eastern Europe.

BNP Paribas' Investment Solutions division includes BNP Paribas Securities BNP Paribas Wealth Management and insurance firms BNP Paribas Cardif and Pinnacle Insurance (Cardif Pinnacle).

Other holdings include private bank BNP Paribas Banque Privee consumer lender Cetelem online brokerage Cortal Consors BNP Paribas Asset Management.

Financial Performance

The bank's revenue has been declining since 2010 as the lackluster economic environment in Europe depressed results. In 2013 BNP Parisbas reported revenues of Å38.8billion a decline of less than 1% versus 2012 (and 12% since 2010). Net income fell about 25% year over year to Å4.8 billion. Of the bank's three core businesses retail banking (the largest) posted a 2% decline in annual revenue while revenue from corporate and investment banking fell 11%. investment solutions saw its revenue climb 2% year over year.

Strategy

Major acquisitions in recent years have turned BNP Paribas into a leading bank in the euro zone and beyond. The company has expanded its operations into about a dozen countries since 2004.

Despite all of this growth BNP Paribas has not been immune to difficulties in the banking sector especially in Europe where banks were exposed to sovereign debt. Indeed BNP Paribas took a Å3 billion ($4.1 billion) hit after it marked down the value of its Greek debt by about 60%. It also reduced exposure to other European government debt in places such as Italy and Spain.

While retail banking has remained relatively strong BNP Paribas has seen declines in its corporate and investment banking unit due to poor market conditions and losses on sales of sovereign bond debt. As a result the bank is engaged in ongoing cost cutting and the implementation of 2014-2016 business development plan. The plan includes three fundamental programs: Simple & Efficient a reorganization and efficiency program now under way; the Asia Pacific plan intended to increase revenues at Corporate and Investment Banking and Investment Solutions; and Hello bank! aimed at developing the digital bank.

Mergers and Acquisitions

In November 2013 BNP acquired Belgium's 25% share in its local consumer-banking unit BNP Paribas Fortis for 3.25 billion euros ($4.37 billion) as the country works to cut public debt. It also acquired Poland's Bank BGZ from Rabobank Group in 2013.

Two of the French bank's most transformative acquisitions included the deal to buy Italian bank Banca Nazionale del Lavoro in 2006 and the 75% purchase of Fortis Bank (which also included a 25% stake in Fortis Insurance). Both deals boosted BNP Paribas' retail banking business across Europe. Retail banking is now responsible for more than 60% of BNP Paribas' revenues.

In addition to the Fortis and BNL acquisitions BNP Paribas looked to grow in new markets. BNP Paribas acquired Sahara Bank in Libya and a 51% stake in UkrSibbank one of Ukraine's leading banks. In 2011 BNP Paribas continued its strategy of expanding in high growth markets and acquired a majority of South Africa's Cadiz Securities. BNP Paribas also owns Banque Internationale pour le Commerce et l'Industrie which is active in six African nations and a majority of Tork Ekonomi Bankasi in Turkey. BNP Paribas has been expanding in China Egypt Israel and Russia as well.

In 2012 the comany sold the bulk of its controlling stake in real estate firm Klepierre to US mall owner Simon for some Å1.5 billion (around $2 billion) to further raise its capital levels.

HISTORY

BNP Paribas Group's predecessor Banque Nationale de Paris (BNP) is the progeny of two state banks with parallel histories; each was set up to jump-start the economy after a revolution in 1848.

For a century Paris-based Comptoir National d'Escompte de Paris (CNEP) bounced between private and public status depending on government whim. It was the #3 bank in France from the late 19th century through the 1950s.

Banque National pour le Commerce et l'Industrie (BNCI) started in Alsace a region that was part of Germany from the Franco-Prussian War until WWI. BNCI served as an economic bridge between Germany and France which had to give the bank governmental resuscitation during the Depression. By the 1960s BNCI had passed CNEP in size.

French leader Charles de Gaulle expected banking to drive post-WWII reconstruction and in 1945 CNEP and BNCI were nationalized. In 1966 France's finance minister merged them and they became BNP. That year the company started an association with Dresdner Bank of Germany under which the two still operate joint ventures primarily in Eastern Europe.

By 1993 privatization was again in vogue and BNP was cut loose by the government. It expanded outside France to ameliorate the influences of the French economy and government. Even before it was privatized BNP was involved in such politically charged actions as the bailout of OPEC money repository Banque Arabe and the extension of credit to Algeria's state oil company Sonatrach.

The privatized BNP looked overseas in the late 1990s. In 1997 alone it won the right to operate in New Zealand bought Laurentian Bank and Trust of the Bahamas took control of its joint venture with Egypt's Banque du Caire and opened a subsidiary in Brazil.

BNP bought failed Peregrine Investment's Chinese operations in 1998. That year the bank also expanded in Peru opened an office in Algeria opened a representative office in Uzbekistan set up an investment banking subsidiary in India and bought Australian stock brokerage operations from Prudential.

After a decade of globe-trotting BNP brought it on home in 1999 and set off a year of tumult in French banking. As France's other two large banks (Societe Generale and Paribas) made plans to merge BNP decided it would absorb both banks as a means to get a bigger chunk of the to-be-privatized Credit Lyonnais and to protect France from Euro-megabank penetration by creating the globe's largest bank.

Executives at Societe Generale (SG) had other ideas forming a cartel called "Action Against the BNP Raid." Meanwhile BNP tried to boost to controlling stakes its holdings in the two banks. (In Europe's cross-ownership tradition the target banks also owned part of BNP.) France's central bank tried unsuccessfully to negotiate a deal (the government supported the triumvirate merger). A war of words was played out in the media and finally shareholders had to vote on the proposals. In the end BNP won control of Paribas but not SG. As BNP prepared to integrate a reluctant Paribas into its operations regulators ordered BNP to relinquish its stake in SG. The newly merged company was dubbed BNP Paribas Group.

In 2000 BNP Paribas and Avis Group launched a fleet-management joint venture. BNP also bought 150 shopping centers from French retailer Carrefour and the 40% of merchant bank Cobepa that it didn't already own. In 2001 BNP Paribas took full control of US-based BancWest. The company bought United California Bank from UFJ Holdings (now part of Mitsubishi UFJ Financial Group) the following year.

The bank opened up a second "home market" when it bought Italy's Banca Nazionale del Lavoro (BNL) for $11 billion in 2006.

In 2008 as the world's economies struggled to stay afloat the French government agreed to inject Å10.5 billion ($14 billion) into the nation's top six banks including BNP Paribas. The government didn't receive shares in the banks it assisted; rather the capital injections were meant to help reenergize lending activities in France. A year after receiving the cash BNP Paribas announced plans to repay the government's aid.

After a couple of false starts and a seven-month saga BNP Paribas acquired control of Fortis Banque (also known as Fortis Bank) in 2009. Fortis' Dutch operations were excluded from the transaction. The deal further cemented BNP Paribas as a top European bank. Fortis Bank was nationalized in October 2008 to prevent its collapse and the takeover by BNP Paribas was delayed and revised to satisfy Fortis shareholders and other interested parties. Upon the closing of the deal BNP Paribas became the market leader in Belgium and Luxembourg. The Belgian government gained more than 10% of BNP Paribas in the transaction.

BNP Paribas complimented its 2009 acquisition of Fortis with the purchase of private bank Insinger de Beaufort.

EXECUTIVES

Head Group Risk Management, Michel Konczaty
COO, Philippe Bordenave
COO Corporate & Investment Banking and Investment Solutions, Georges Chodron de Courcel, age 64, $803,412 total compensation
Chairman, Baudouin Prot, age 63, $1,324,710 total compensation
Managing Director and Head Compliance and Internal Control Coordinator, Jean Clamon, age 62, $648,370 total compensation
CEO and Director, Jean-Laurent Bonnafe, age 53

Global Head Information Technology and Processes, Alain Marbach, age 52
CEO and General Manager BNL, Fabio Gallia, age 50
Deputy Chief Operating Officer and Head of Investment Solutions Personal Finance and International Retail Banking, Jacques d'Estais
Deputy Chief Operating Officer and Head of Corporate and Investment Banking, Alain Papiasse, age 55
COO, Francois Villeroy de Galhau, age 55
Head of Asia-Pacific Region, Eric Raynaud
Head of Human Resources, Yves Martrenchar, age 57
Senior Latin American Economist, Nader Nazmi
Human Resources Director of Real Estate, Pascal Maury
Chief Executive Officer, Jean-Laurent Bonnafe
Director, Louis Schweitzer, age 71
Director, Claude Bebear, age 78
Director, Helene Ploix, age 68
Director, Denis Kessler, age 62
CEO and Director, Jean-Laurent Bonnafe, age 52
Director, Laurence Parisot, age 54
Director, Jean-Marie Gianno, age 61
Director, Prof Jean-Francois Lepetit, age 71
Director, Daniela Weber-Rey, age 56
Director, Meglena Kuneva, age 56
Auditors: Deloitte&Associes

LOCATIONS

HQ: BNP Paribas (France)
16, boulevard des Italiens, Paris 75009
Phone: (33) 1 40 14 45 46
Web: www.bnpparibas.com

PRODUCTS/OPERATIONS

Sales by Segment

	% of total
Retail	54
Corporate and investment	27
Investment	14
Other	5
Total	**100**

COMPETITORS

ABN AMRO Group	HSBC
BBVA	JPMorgan Chase
Banco Popular Espa?ol	Natixis
Bank of America	Societe Generale
Barclays	U.S. Bancorp
Citigroup	UBS
Credit Agricole	Wells Fargo
Deutsche Bank	

HISTORICAL FINANCIALS

Company Type: Public

Income Statement

FYE: December 31

	ASSETS ($ mil.)	NET INCOME ($ mil.)	INCOME AS % OF ASSETS	EMPLOYEES
12/13	2,478,315	6,652	0.3%	184,545
12/12	2,513,902	8,637	0.3%	188,551
12/11	2,541,999	7,825	0.3%	198,423
12/10	2,674,279	10,496	0.4%	205,348
12/09	2,964,257	8,401	0.3%	201,740
Annual Growth	**(4.4%)**	**(5.7%)**	**—**	**(2.2%)**

2013 Year-End Financials

Return on assets: 0.2%
Return on equity: 5.5%
Long-term debt ($ mil.): —
No. of shares (mil.): 1,242
Sales ($ mil): 126,947
Dividends
Yield: 2.4%
Payout: 33.9%
Market value ($ mil.): 48,701

	STOCK PRICE ($) FY Close	P/E High/Low		PER SHARE ($) Earnings	Dividends	Book Value
12/13	39.20	20	12	5.07	0.97	97.06
12/12	29.21	10	5	6.79	0.75	91.38
12/11	19.65	16	6	6.22	2.72	81.80
12/10	31.95	13	6	8.46	1.87	83.57
12/09	40.16	18	5	7.49	1.64	84.52
Annual Growth	**(0.6%)**	**—**	**—**	**(9.3%)**	**(12.3%)**	**3.5%**

Boc Hong Kong Holdings Ltd

BOC Hong Kong (Holdings) is the parent of Bank of China (Hong Kong) which has about 300 branches in Hong Kong as well as on mainland China. The bank serves local businesses and consumers providing loans deposit accounts and other standard services as well as securities brokerage wealth management and project financing and syndication. It also prints currency. In addition Bank of China (Hong Kong) owns Nanyang Commercial Bank and some 70% of Chiyu Banking Corporation (both are also based in Hong Kong) as well as BOC Credit Card (International). Bank of China which is controlled by the Chinese government owns about two-thirds of BOC Hong Kong.

The company wants to diversify its revenue mix by focusing on increasing its business in wealth management insurance and corporate finance. It is looking to China for growth and has plans to expand to other parts of Asia as well.

EXECUTIVES

Vice Chairman, Changji Sun, age 71
Deputy Chief Executive, Yim Nam Lam, age 61
Company Secretary, Jason C. W. Yeung, age 59
Chairman, Xiao Gang, age 55
Vice Chairman and Chief Executive, Guangbei He, age 59
Executive Director and Deputy Chief Executive, Yingxin Gao, age 51
Chief Risk Officer, Alex Y. S. Cheung, age 52
CIO, Peter Y. K. Liu, age 62
Deputy Chief Executive, David S. H. Wong, age 62
Chief Financial Officer, Zhuo Chengwen
Senior Vice President General Manager Hong Kong & Macau, Chris Clark
Vice Chairman, Changji Sun, age 71
Vice Chairman and Chief Executive, Guangbei He, age 59
Auditors: PricewaterhouseCoopers

LOCATIONS

HQ: Boc Hong Kong Holdings Ltd
52nd Floor, Bank of China Tower, 1 Garden Road,
Phone: (852) 2846 2700   **Fax:** (852) 2810 5830
Web: www.bochk.com

COMPETITORS

AXA Asia Pacific	Citigroup
Bank of Communications	Dah Sing Financial
Bank of East Asia	Holdings Limited
CITIC International	HSBC
Financial	Hang Seng Bank
Chong Hing Bank	Standard Chartered

HISTORICAL FINANCIALS

Company Type: Public

Income Statement

FYE: December 31

	ASSETS ($ mil.)	NET INCOME ($ mil.)	INCOME AS % OF ASSETS	EMPLOYEES
12/13	263,989	2,869	1.1%	14,647
12/12	236,174	2,700	1.1%	14,638
12/11	223,804	2,630	1.2%	14,475
12/10	213,705	2,083	1.0%	13,806
12/09	156,400	1,769	1.1%	13,244
Annual Growth	**14.0%**	**12.8%**	**—**	**2.5%**

2013 Year-End Financials

Return on assets: 1.1%
Return on equity: 14.3%
Long-term debt ($ mil.): —
No. of shares (mil.): —
Sales ($ mil): 8,395
Dividends
Yield: 0.0%
Payout: 19.2%
Market value ($ mil.): —

	STOCK PRICE ($) FY Close	P/E High/Low		PER SHARE ($) Earnings	Dividends	Book Value
12/13	64.52	1	0	0.27	0.05	1.94
12/12	63.05	1	0	0.26	0.05	1.84
12/11	47.16	1	0	0.25	0.05	1.58
12/10	68.43	1	0	0.20	0.04	1.40
12/09	45.44	1	0	0.17	0.01	1.26
Annual Growth	**9.2%**	**—**	**—**	**12.8%**	**44.8%**	**11.5%**

Bosch (Robert) GmbH (Germany Fed. Rep.)

Robert Bosch has spent more than a century establishing a name for really "boss" automobile and industrial equipment as well as consumer goods and building systems. Bosch operates via 350 subsidiaries in 60 countries; its core lines include automotive systems from diesel/hybrid drive to steering starter motors and generators electronics and brakes. Subsidiary Bosch Rexroth makes electric hydraulic and pneumatic machinery for industrial use. Bosch Security makes various protection systems. Bosch also makes photovoltaic and wind-turbine components heat pumps for buildings and home appliances through Bosch-Siemens Hausgerate. Charitable foundation Robert Bosch Stiftung controls the company.

Operations

Bosch divides its business into four main categories. The company's Automotive Technology group is the world's largest independent auto parts supplier. The Industrial Technology segment includes Drive and Control Technology and Packaging Technology which supply the mechanical engineering and packaging and process engineering sectors respectively. Consumer Goods provides Power Tools and Household Appliances and the Energy and Building Technology segment offers HVAC solar energy and security systems products and services.

Geographic Reach

The company has operations in 60 countries and plies its wares globally. Sales outside its home country of Germany account for about 75% of revenue. In response to the global recession which hit the automotive industry particularly hard Bosch has been expanding in the Asia Pacific region where recession effects have been minimal or delayed.

Financial Performance

Bosch continues to reflect global economic problems on its books. It was looking for a modest 3% to 5% gain in revenue for 2012 but missed that guidance with only a 2% increase. Consolidations and disposals took a Å600 million bite out of the gains. Europe the company's largest market saw a sales drop and Asia/Pacific its number two region was a mixed bag with China and India stagnating but Southeast Asia delivering double digit growth. The region finished with an exchange rate-adjusted .6% dip in sales. South America particularly Brazil and Argentina posted a drop of about 10% (after exchange rate adjustments). North America was a bright spot with a 9% adjusted increase in sales. Improving auto sales and consumer goods movement helped the region. Bosch believes its products which contribute to increased efficiency safety and comfort saw the most gains in 2012.

Strategy

To deal with the economic woes of recent years and position itself for growth Bosch has been investing in Asia. To that end in 2012 the Bosch Automotive Aftermarket division spent about $120 million euros in a spark plug and brake pad manufacturing facility in Nanjing China. The facility which represents Bosch's largest investment anywhere will also house testing and R&D operations. The move puts Bosch in the center of fast growing Asia and positions it close to many of its automotive OEM customers.

Mergers and Acquisitions

The company announced in 2013 that it was acquiring software firm Bauer Optimierungstechnik. The company which will become part of Bosch's Energy and Building Solutions group makes software-based air conditioning and ventilation control systems.

Ownership

Bosch is unique not only in that it is large (with ties to almost every automobile enterprise in the world) but that it is heavy influenced by a charitable foundation. Robert Bosch Stiftung holds 92% of shares in the company. (More than 90% of voting rights are held by Robert Bosch Industrietreuhand an industrial trust.) The remaining shares are held by the Bosch family and other investors.

HISTORY

Self-taught electrical engineer Robert Bosch opened a Stuttgart workshop in 1886 and the following year produced the world's first alternator for a stationary engine. In 1897 his company built the first automobile alternator. Later electrical automotive product launches included spark plugs (1902) starters (1912) and regulators (1913). Bosch believed in treating employees well and shortened their workday to eight hours (extraordinary for 1906).

US operations begun in 1909 were confiscated during WWI as part of a trade embargo against Germany. Bosch survived the German depression of the 1920s introduced power tools (1928) and appliances (1933) and bought Blaupunkt (car radios 1933). Industrial and military demand for the company's products continued from the 1930s until WWII. Bosch died in 1942 and left 90% of his company to charity.

Bosch suffered severe damage in WWII and its US operations were again confiscated. It rebuilt after the war and enjoyed growing demand for its appliances and automotive products as postwar incomes increased worldwide. In 1963 Hans Merkle took the helm. Believing fuel efficiency and pollution control would be important issues in the future Bosch invested heavily to develop automo-

tive components that would raise gas mileage and lower emissions. The company made the world's first electronic fuel-injection (EFI) system in 1967. Also that year Bosch and Siemens (West Germany) formed Bosch-Siemens Hausgerate to make home appliances.

The oil crisis of the 1970s increased awareness of fuel efficiency and benefited sales of EFI systems. Buying a plant in Charleston South Carolina Bosch re-entered the US in 1974 to make fuel-injection systems. It introduced the first antilock braking system in 1978.

A 1984 strike against Bosch in Germany disrupted automobile production throughout Europe. In the late 1980s the company developed technology for multiplexing (employing one wire to replace many by using semiconductor controllers) in automobiles established it as an industry standard and licensed it to chip makers Intel (US) Philips (the Netherlands) and Motorola (US). Throughout the 1980s and into the 1990s Bosch acquired various telecommunications companies.

In 1993 Bosch's sales dropped for the first time since 1967. In response the company cut its workforce. In 1996 Bosch bought Emerson's half of joint venture S-B Power Tool Co. which makes Bosch Dremel and Skil brand tools. Further consolidating its position as a world leader in braking systems Bosch also purchased AlliedSignal's struggling light-vehicle braking unit. The company sold its private mobile radio business to Motorola in 1997 and to speed its business for mobile phones bought Dancall Telecom (a maker of mobile-phone handsets) from UK-based Amstrad.

In 1998 the company's Bosch-Siemens Hausgerate joint venture opened a plant in the US and bought Masco's Thermador unit (cooktops ovens and ranges). In 1999 Bosch sold its US-based telecom unit to a joint venture of Motorola and Cisco Systems. The next year UK-based General Electric Company (now Marconi) bought the German operations of Bosch's telecom unit.

Early in 2000 the company sold its mobile-phone business to Siemens AG. That year the company's joint venture with Siemens bought Rexroth AG (Atecs Mannesmann AG's automation and packaging technology group) for about $9.2 billion. The new division was named Bosch Rexroth AG. In 2001 Bosch bought out Siemens' stake in Bosch Rexroth and consolidated its operations as a wholly owned subsidiary.

In 2006 Robert Bosch purchased Telex Communications for $420 million. Telex is a provider of audio wireless communications and safety equipment with applications in large public places including stadiums and airports.

Bosch along with the entire automotive industry was hard hit in the global economic crisis of 2008 and 2009. Bosch struggled to stay in the public's favor by avoiding cuts in headcount as it worked to shore up net earnings which waned more than 85% in 2008 from 2007 and plunged to a loss of Å1214 ($1.6 billion) in 2009. In response Bosch shed weaker units. North American sales which declined more than 10% in 2009 from 2008 were partially offset by Bosch's hammering out a sale with Akebono Brake Industry. The Japanese manufacturer of brakes bought Bosch's North American foundation brake production. (Bosch's significant stake in Akebono gave the German auto parts maker a solid position.) The transaction included Bosch assets to manufacture corner modules drum brakes disc brakes and related parts at plants in Michigan Tennessee and South Carolina.

In late 2008 Bosch sold its "car infotainment" business branded Blaupunkt to Aurelius a German investment group. The deal comprised the trade name and portfolio of car radio hi-fi component and advanced navigation devices. Also that

same year it bought a majority stake in ersol Solar Energy (renamed Bosch Solar Energy in 2009) a German manufacturer of wafer-based mono- and polycrystalline silicon solar cells and thin-film solar modules used to generate electricity from sunlight.

LOCATIONS

HQ: Bosch (Robert) GmbH (Germany Fed. Rep.)
Postfach 10 60 50, Stuttgart D-70049
Phone: (49) 711 811 0   **Fax:** (49) 711 811 6630
Web: www.bosch.com

Sales

	% of total
Europe	57
Asia/Pacific	24
Americas	19
Total	**100**

PRODUCTS/OPERATIONS

Sales

	% of total
Automotive	59
Consumer goods & building	26
Industrial	15
Total	**100**

Selected Divisions and Products

Automotive Technology
  Car multimedia
  Chassis systems brakes
  Chassis systmes control
  Diesel systems
  Electrical drives
  Gasoline systems
  Starter motors and generators
  Steering systems
Consumer Goods and Building Technology
  Household appliances
  Power tools
  Security systems
  Thermotechnology (gas-fired hot water heating
    systems)
Industrial Technology
  Drive and control technology
  Packaging technology
  Solar energy

HISTORICAL FINANCIALS

Company Type: Public

Income Statement

FYE: December 31

	REVENUE ($ mil.)	NET INCOME ($ mil.)	NET PROFIT MARGIN	EMPLOYEES
12/13	63,423	1,508	2.4%	281,381
12/12	69,150	2,980	4.3%	305,877
12/11	66,605	2,258	3.4%	302,519
12/10	63,250	3,181	5.0%	283,507
12/09	54,992	(1,815)	—	270,687
Annual Growth	3.6%	—	—	1.0%

2013 Year-End Financials

Debt ratio: 11.2%	No. of shares (mil.): 1,200
Return on equity: 4.1%	Dividends
Cash ($ mil.): 5,230	Yield: —
Current ratio: 1.81	Payout: —
Long-term debt ($ mil.): 5,526	Market value ($ mil.): —

Bouygues S.A.

If all roads lead to Bouygues that's because the company built them. Bouygues (pronounced "bweeg") operates in three primary business areas:

construction; telecommunications; and media. Its largest segment construction is involved in road work buildings and property development and accounts for more than 75% of the group's sales. Subsidiaries include Colas (road construction and maintenance about 40% of sales) and Bouygues Construction (around 30%). Bouygues Immobilier is its property development arm with interests in commercial and residential development. The group owns 90% stake of Bouygues Telecom (France's #3 mobile phone carrier); more than 40% of TF1 (France's #1 TV channel); and 29% of ALSTOM.

Geographic Reach

Paris-based Bouygues SA's largest market is France which accounts for two-thirds of its total sales. The rest of Europe contributes about 15%. The firm is also active in North America Asia Africa the Middle East and Central and South America. Overall the group does business in more than 80 countries worldwide.

Operations

Bouygues SA is a diversified industrial group focused on two sectors: construction with Bouygues Construction (building civil works energy and services) Bouygyes Immobilier (property) and Colas (roads); and telecoms/media which includes TF1 (Television Francaise 1 SA) and Bouygues Telecom.

Subsidiary Bouygues Construction is a force in itself with several subsidiaries performing civil construction and electrical/maintenance work. The group focuses on public-private partnerships those lucrative partnerships that governments use to build roads prisons schools and other infrastructure. Bouygues has increasingly participated in sustainable development projects with investments in training research and resources.

Road builder Colas which accounts for about 40% of the group's sales provides construction and maintenance services as well as producing materials such as concrete and aggregates from its quarries and plants.

The French conglomerate also has a 29% stake in Alstom (making it the largest shareholder) which builds rail cars ships and power plants.

Financial Performance

Bouygues reported Å33.3 billion ($45.9 billion) in sales in 2013 of which about a third was rung up outside of France. The firm's net profit (before the writedown of Alstom) was Å647 million ($893.6). Taking the Å1.4 billion write-down into account Bouygues posted a loss of Å757 million ($1.04 billion). (As of the end of 2013 Bouygues owned about 29% of Alstrom the French train and turbine maker that is reported to be a takeover target of GE.) On a constant exchange basis the company's sales were flat in 2013 compared with 2012 while profits continued a downward trend accelerated by the Alstom write-down.

The group's construction and property development businesses posted sales gains in 2013 versus 2012 while revenue at Colas was flat. Other businesses including Bouygues Telecom and TF1 saw their sales decline. On a regional basis France and the European Union which together represent about 75% of the group's total revenue posted low-single-digit declines with steeper declines suffered in the Middle East and across the Americas. Africa the Asia-Pacific Region and the rest of Europe posted annual sales gains.

Strategy

To reduce its dependence on its home country and Europe the French firm is expanding in international markets especially Asia and the Middle East. Currently Bouygues Construction generates 46% of its sales outside of France while Colas generates 43% in international markets.

Bouygues Construction also is broadening its operations in electrical contracting and property

development and expects to expand its presence in Europe as well. In 2010 the group acquired the UK division of Dutch builder Heijmans for Å45 million ($59 million). Two years later the company bought Thomas Vale Group which is active in central England. Although tough economic conditions caused a cut in revenues in 2010 Bouygues has secured a number of lucrative international projects such as the Singapore Sports Hub and a rail tunnel in Hong Kong. It is also involved in its first North American projects.

Looking to grow its telecoms businss Bouygues in 2014 bid Å10.5 billion ($14.4 billion) in cash to acquire the telecoms arm of Vivendi SFR and 46% of the new company in a planned spin-off. It lost out to French cable operator Numericable. A tie-up between SFR and Bouygues would have created Europe's seventh-biggest telecoms group by sales and in France would rank ahead of market leader Orange in market share.

Company Background

Bouygues SA is controlled by the founding Bouygues family and led by billionaire Martin Bouygues.

HISTORY

With the equivalent of $1700 in borrowed money Francis Bouygues son of a Paris engineer started Entreprise Francis Bouygues in 1952 as an industrial works and construction firm in the Paris region of France. Within four years his firm had expanded into property development.

By the mid-1960s Bouygues had entered the civil engineering and public works sectors and developed regional construction units across France. In 1970 it was listed on the Paris stock exchange. Four years later the company established Bouygues Offshore to build oil platforms.

In 1978 the firm built Terminal 2 of Paris' Charles de Gaulle airport. Three years later it won the contract to construct the University of Riyadh in Saudi Arabia (then the world's largest building project at 3.2 million sq. ft.) which was completed in 1984. That year Bouygues acquired France's #3 water supply company Saur and power transmission and supply firm ETDE.

Expansion continued in 1986 with the purchase of the Screg Group which included Colas France's top highway contractor. The next year the company led a consortium to buy 50% of newly privatized network Societe Television Francaise 1 (TF1). Bouygues became the largest shareholder with a 25% stake (increased to 40% by 1999). In 1988 the company began building the Channel Tunnel (completed 1994) and moved into its new ultramodern headquarters dubbed Challenger in Saint-Quentin-en-Yvelines outside Paris.

After rumors of failing health Francis Bouygues resigned as chairman in 1989. His son Martin took over as chairman and CEO although the patriarch called France's "Emperor of Concrete" remained on the board until his death in 1993.

Despite fears that the group would suffer without its founder's leadership Bouygues continued to grow with the 1989 acquisition of a majority interest in Grands Moulins de Paris France's largest flour milling firm (sold 1998). In 1990 it purchased Swiss construction group Losinger.

The company entered the telecom industry in 1993 with a national paging network and added a mobile phone license a year later. In 1996 the group listed 40% of Bouygues Offshore's shares on the New York and Paris stock exchanges. Also that year it launched mobile phone operator Bouygues Telecom and entered a partnership with Telecom Italia.

By 1999 Bouygues Telecom had reached 2 million customers and Bouygues bought back a 20% share held by the UK's Cable and Wireless to in-

crease its stake to nearly 54%. That year Bouygues Offshore bought Norwegian engineering firm Kvaerner and the group spun off its construction sector creating Bouygues Construction.

After word circulated that Deutsche Telekom wanted to acquire the group's telecom unit Bouygues became the target of takeover rumors. Francois Pinault France's richest businessman became Bouygues' largest non-family shareholder when he increased his stake to 14% (later reduced to about 2%). Pinault's biggest rival Bernard Arnault upped his stake to more than 9% of the group fueling speculation of a battle over control of the board.

In 2001 the company pulled out of France's auction for a third-generation wireless license and remained the only European incumbent mobile carrier without a major domestic investment in 3G technology (until 2009). The next year the company agreed to buy Telecom Italia's stake in Bouygues Telecom increasing Bouygues' ownership in the mobile operator from 54% to more than 65%. In 2002 the company sold its 51% stake in oil field platform construction unit Bouygues Offshore to Italian oil services group Saipem which announced plans to bid for the remaining shares.

However talks with German utility giant E.ON over the sale of Bouygues' Saur subsidiary failed that year after E.ON decided to focus instead on its electricity and gas operations.

In 2005 Bouygues was more successful when it sought to sell Saur piecemeal. It sold several divisions of the subsidiary (Coved Saur France Saur International and Stereau) to French private equity firm PAI Partners but retained the African and Italian (Sigesa-Crea) divisions of the firm.

Bouygues bought the French government's 21% stake in ALSTOM for $2.5 billion in 2006. The deal was approved on the condition that it not try to control the company for at least three years. Bouygues did build up its holding after the acquisition though eventually holding 29% of the shares.

In 2008 property developer Bouygues Immobilier expanded with the acquisition of Urbis a French rival. That year Colas bought the Gouyer Group of companies (distribution of construction materials) in Martinique and Guadeloupe while Bouygues Telecom acquired a fixed-line network that allowed it to launch the Bbox broadband router and Internet services that include VoIP e-mail Internet access and television; the telecom unit also gained the previously denied right to offer the iPhone 3G.

EXECUTIVES

Deputy CEO and Director, Olivier Bouygues, age 63, $920,000 total compensation

EVP Information Systems and New Technologies and Director, Alain Pouyat, age 70, $920,000 total compensation

Chairman and CEO, Martin Bouygues, age 62, $920,000 total compensation

Director; Chairman and CEO TF1, Nonce Paolini, age 65

Corporate Secretary, Jean-Francois Guillemin, age 62

Director; Chairman CEO and Director Bouygues Construction, Yves Gabriel, age 64, $850,000 total compensation

SVP Human Resources and Administration, Jean-Claude Tostivin, age 67

CEO and Director Bouygues Telecom, Olivier Roussat, age 50

CFO, Philippe Marien, age 58

Press Contact, Emilie Combe

Director, Jean Peyrelevade, age 75

Director; Chairman CEO and Director Colas, Herve Le Bouc, age 61

Deputy CEO and Director, Olivier Bouygues, age 63

EVP Information Systems and New Technologies and Director, Alain Pouyat, age 70
Director, Georges Chodron de Courcel, age 64
Director; Chairman and CEO TF1, Nonce Paolini, age 65
Director; Chairman CEO and Director Bouygues Immobilier, Francois Bertiere, age 63
Director, Pierre Barberis, age 72
Director, Francis Bouygues, age 90
Director, Lucien Douroux, age 81
Director, Patrick Kron, age 61
Director, Patricia Barbizet, age 59
Director; Chairman CEO and Director Bouygues Construction, Yves Gabriel, age 64
Director, Francois-Henri Pinault, age 52
Director, Helman le Pas de Secheval, age 46
Auditors: Mazars&Guerard

LOCATIONS

HQ: Bouygues S.A.
32 avenue Hoche, Paris, Cedex 08 75378
Phone: (33) 1 44 20 10 00
Web: www.bouygues.com

Sales

	% of total
Europe	
France	69
Other	14
North	7
Asia/Pacific	5
Africa & Middle	5
Central & South	-
Total	**100**

PRODUCTS/OPERATIONS

Sales by Segment

	% of total
Construction	74
Telecoms	18
Media	8
Total	**100**

Sales

	% of total
Colas	37
Bouygues	29
Bouygues	18
TF1	8
Bouygues	8
Other	-
Total	**100**

Selected Subsidiaries and Affiliates

Construction
  Autoroute de liaison Seine-Sarthe SA (33%)
  Bouygues Batiment Ile-de-France SA (99.9%)
    Bati-Renov SA (99.3%)
  Bouygues Batiment International SA (99.9%)
    Bouygues Thai Ltd (49%)
    DTP Singapour Pte Ltd (99.9%)
    Kohler Investment SA (Luxembourg 99.9%)
  Bouygues Construction SA (99.9%)
  ETDE SA (99.9%)
    Exprimm IT (99.9%)
    Icel Maidstone Ltd (UK 99.9%)
  Quille SA (99.9%)
  Westminster Local Education Partnership Ltd (UK 80%)
Media
  Metro France Publications (15%)
  Television Francaise 1 SA (TF1 43%)
  TF1 Video (43%)
  TV Breizh (43%)
Property
  Bouygues Immobilier
  Parque Empresarial Cristalia SL
  SNC Bouygues Immobilier Entreprises Ile-de-France
Roads
  Cofiroute (16%)
  Colas Guadeloupe (97%)
  Colas Hungaria (97%)
  Colas Polska (97%)
  Colas SA (96%)

Spac (97%)
Telecommunications
  Bouygues Telecom SA (90%)

COMPETITORS

AMEC	Foster Wheeler
Alarko	GDF SUEZ
Anglian Water Group	Groupe SNEF
Atlantia	HOCHTIEF
Balfour Beatty	Hyundai Engineering
Bechtel	and Construction
Bilfinger Berger	MWH Global
Bovis Lend Lease	Orange
CANAL+	SFR
CSCEC	SUEZ Environnement
Dragados	Severn Trent
EIFFAGE	Skanska
FCC Barcelona	Technip
Fluor	VINCI

HISTORICAL FINANCIALS

Company Type: Public

Income Statement

FYE: December 31

	REVENUE ($ mil.)	NET INCOME ($ mil.)	NET PROFIT MARGIN	EMPLOYEES
12/13	46,039	(1,042)	—	128,067
12/12	44,357	834	1.9%	133,780
12/11	42,483	1,383	3.3%	130,827
12/10	41,983	1,433	3.4%	133,456
12/09	45,366	1,900	4.2%	133,971
Annual Growth	**0.4%**	**—**	**—**	**(1.1%)**

2013 Year-End Financials

Debt ratio: 32.0%
Return on equity: (-9.6%)
Cash ($ mil.): 4,914
Current ratio: 0.94
Long-term debt ($ mil.): 9,102
No. of shares (mil.): 319
Dividends
  Yield: 0.0%
  Payout: —
Market value ($ mil.): —

	STOCK PRICE ($) FY Close	P/E High/Low		PER SHARE ($) Earnings	Dividends	Book Value
12/13	0.00	—	—	(3.26)	0.75	30.86
12/12	20.00	—	—	2.64	0.73	34.87
12/11	20.00	11	3	3.96	0.89	34.35
12/10	8.49	7	4	4.04	0.72	34.54
Annual Growth	**—**			**—**	**1.3%**	**(2.8%)**

BP p.l.c.

BP is also BO (Big Oil). It is the world's #3 publicly traded integrated oil concern behind Exxon Mobil and Royal Dutch Shell. BP explores for oil and gas in 30 countries with proved reserves of 17 billion barrels of oil equivalent. It's the largest oil and gas producer in the US and a top refiner with 15 plants processing more than 2 million barrels of crude oil per day; it is also a major producer of petrochemicals. BP operates about 20000 BP Connect gas stations worldwide. The company took a major hit in 2010 when a Gulf of Mexico oil rig exploded and killed 11 workers. Millions of gallons of crude spilled into the Gulf and BP was forced to set aside $20 billion to pay for related damages in 2011 and 2012.

Company Background

The spill developed into a major political economic and public relations crisis for the company as it struggled to cap the leaking well clean up the massive spill and mollify Gulf Coast communities which saw their fishing industry decimated and their coastlines inundated by oil. To address the growing crisis in 2010 the company established an escrow account of $20 billion managed by a third party to reimburse claims from people and businesses financially damaged by the oil spill. (It settled with individual and business plaintiffs for $7.8 billion in 2012 but still faced federal state and local government charges). In a plea deal with the US government in 2012 BP plead guilty to criminal misconduct (12 felony counts) and in 2013 agreed to pay $4.5 billion in damages. The company has paid a total of about $40 billion related to the spill.

Financial Performance

Revenue was basically flat while profit plummeted 55% as the company paid off charges related to the Deepwater Horizon disaster.

Strategy

After the costly Gulf spill BP embarked on a "shrink to grow" strategy (set to run through 2014) of selling older oilfields around the world to generate cash for settlements and simplify its upstream operations. All told the company has sold about $37 billion in assets. Completed divestitures include one of the largest transactions in the Gulf of Mexico —BP's sale of a number of oil and gas fields in the deepwater Gulf of Mexico region to Plains Exploration & Production for $5.55 billion in November 2012. In July it sold assets in Canada Egypt and the Permian Basin in the US to fellow explorer Apache for about $7 billion. The deal included BP receiving a $5 billion cash advance. In 2011 BP sold its Colombian assets to Talisman Energy and Ecopetrol for $1.9 billion and properties in Venezuela and Vietnam to its Russian joint venture TNK-BP for $1.8 billion.

TNK-BP was BP's longtime drilling venture with several Russian partners. After years of feuding with those partners in 2013 BP sold that business to Russian state oil company Rosneft as part of a complex package of deals worth a whopping $55 billion. The transaction gave BP a nearly 20% stake in Rosneft and about $12.3 billion in cash allowing it to pursue offshore drilling opportunities in the Arctic Ocean and settle billions of dollars in US Gulf spill penalties. Several BP competitors Exxon Mobil Italy's Eni and Norway's Statoil already have Russian Arctic drilling deals.

On the renewables side of the business since 2006 BP has invested $7 billion (including $1.3 billion in 2009) to develop wind solar and other green energy sources.

HISTORY

The company which was formed in 1998 from the merger of British Petroleum and Amoco grew by buying Atlantic Richfield Company.

BP (formerly BP Amoco) was born on two sides of the Atlantic. In the US Amoco emerged from Standard Oil Trust organized by John D. Rockefeller in 1882. In 1886 he bought Lima (Ohio) oil a high-sulfur crude anticipating the discovery of a sulfur-removing process. Such a process was indeed patented in 1887 and in 1889 Standard organized Standard Oil of Indiana which later established such innovations as company-owned service stations and a research lab at the refinery.

Overseas British Petroleum (BP) was a twinkle in the eye of English adventurer William D'Arcy who began oil exploration of Persia in 1901. In 1908 bankrolled by Burmah Oil D'Arcy's firm was the first to strike oil in the Middle East. D'Arcy and Burmah Oil formed Anglo-Persian Oil in 1909 and the British government took a 51% stake in 1914.

Back in the US Standard was broken up into 34 independent oil companies in 1911. Standard Oil of Indiana kept its oil refining and US marketing operations. In 1925 it added a few Mexican and

Venezuelan firms including Pan American Petroleum and Transport which held half of American Oil Co. known for Amoco antiknock gasoline. It began Amoco Chemicals in 1945.

Anglo-Persian took the BP name in 1954 and bought its own Standard Oil: After making a strike in Alaska in 1969 BP swapped Alaskan reserves for a 25% interest (later upped to 55%) in Standard Oil of Ohio (SOHIO). BP also struck North Sea oil in 1970. But falling oil and copper prices in the mid-1980s and a dry hole in the Beaufort Sea hurt earnings. Under Robert Horton SOHIO sold off units. BP also bought livestock feed producer Purina Mills (1986 sold 1998) and the rest of SOHIO (1987).

Standard Oil of Indiana had its own problems including being kicked out of Iran after the Islamic revolution and causing a major oil spill off the French coast in 1978. The firm which became Amoco in 1985 bought Canada's Dome Petroleum in 1988 making it the largest private owner of North American gas reserves but the big purchase proved hard to swallow.

In 1992 Amoco hurled itself into overseas oil exploration. It was the first foreign oil company to explore the Chinese mainland. But by 1995 production was down. That year John Browne often compared to Rockefeller became BP's CEO. In 1996 BP and Mobil merged their European fuel and lubricants operations and the British government sold its remaining stake in BP.

As oil prices tumbled in 1998 BP merged with Amoco in a $52 billion deal that formed BP Amoco. The new oil major agreed the following year to buy US-based Atlantic Richfield (ARCO) in a deal that closed in 2000. BP Amoco sold ARCO's Alaskan properties to Phillips (later ConocoPhillips) for $7 billion to gain regulatory approval for the purchase.

Its stake in Siberian oil fields was nearly taken away in a controversial 1999 bankruptcy sale before BP Amoco and Russia's Tyumen Oil agreed to cooperate. In 2000 BP Amoco and Shell Oil sold their stakes in Altura Energy to Occidental Petroleum for $3.6 billion. Also that year BP Amoco bought motor-oil maker Burmah Castrol for $4.7 billion. It paid $1.5 billion for the 18% of former ARCO exploration and production unit Vastar Resources that it didn't already own.

The company adopted BP as its main worldwide brand in 2000 and it officially shortened its name the next year.

In 2001 BP agreed to swap control of its stake in German natural gas supplier Ruhrgas plus $1.6 billion in cash and $950 million in assumed debt to German utility giant E.ON for a majority interest in Veba Oel owner of Germany's largest gas station chain. Regulators moved to keep E.ON from acquiring the Ruhrgas stake but BP agreed to make up the difference in cash if necessary and the deal proceeded. The agreement allowed BP to take full ownership of Veba Oel in 2002. To recoup some of its investment BP (with E.ON's consent) sold Veba Oel's exploration and production operations to Petro-Canada.

That year BP increased it stake in Russian oil and gas producer Sidanco from 10% to 25%.

In 2003 BP sold its Boqueron field and Desarrollo Zulia Occidental assets both located in Venezuela to Europe's Perenco. In late 2005 BP sold its petrochemical unit Innovene to INEOS for a reported $9 billion.

An explosion and fire in 2005 at BP's Texas City refinery killed 15 workers and injured many more.

In 2006 the company sold its remaining producing properties on the Outer Continental Shelf of the Gulf of Mexico to Apache Corporation for $845 million. That year BP sold its 28% stake in the Shenzi field in the Gulf of Mexico to Repsol for $2.2 billion. It also acquired a $1 billion stake in Rosneft.

In 2006 the discovery of corrosion in a major oil pipeline forced BP to close down part of its Prudhoe Bay oilfield (which represents 8% of daily US crude production) for several weeks.

That year the company also announced plans to invest $3 billion to reconfigure its Whiting Refinery in Indiana to process Canadian heavy crude oil.

In 2007 the company sold its Coryton refinery in the UK to Petroplus Holdings for $1.4 billion. That year BP acquired Chevron's 31% stake in a Netherlands-based refinery and other assets for $900 million.

BP's long-term chief executive John Browne was forced to step down in 2007 over a personal scandal and was replaced by BP veteran Tony Hayward. That year the company announced a major restructuring with a focus on core divisions Exploration & Production and Refining & Marketing and a new Alternative Energy unit dedicated to solar power wind energy and carbon capture technology.

In 2007 BP agreed to pay US authorities $373.5 million in fines relating to the 2005 Texas City refinery explosion the 2006 Alaska oil spill and a propane price-fixing scandal.

In 2008 the company signed a deal with Enbridge to pipe oil sands crude from Canada to the Texas Gulf Coast. Enbridge and BP will spend up to $2 billion to expand existing pipelines and build new connections to deliver up to 250000 barrels a day to Gulf Coast refiners by 2012. In another oil sands move BP and Husky Energy teamed up that same year to create an integrated North American oil sands business through two joint ventures BP-Husky Refinery LLC operated by BP and the Sunrise Oil Sands Partnership (SOSP) operated by Husky. BP committed $2.8 billion to create SOSP.

In 2008 BP acquired 90000 net acres of natural gas assets in the Arkoma Basin Woodford Shale play in the US from Chesapeake Energy for $1.75 billion. It subsequently bought a 25% stake in that company's Fayetteville Shale assets in Arkansas for $1.9 billion.

Boosting its North Sea assets in 2010 the company agreed to buy two oil fields in the Norwegian sector from TOTAL for $991 million. That year BP acquired Devon Energy's international assets for $7 billion in a deal that among other things gave BP a foothold in the emerging major oil play off the coast of Brazil. The company also gained properties in Azerbaijan and the Gulf of Mexico. (In 2010 it agreed to sell four of these mature deepwater oil and gas fields in Gulf of Mexico to Marubeni Oil and Gas for $650 million in order to pay down debt).

The global recession and the slump in demand for oil and gas products saw BP's revenues (along with those of its industry peers) plummet in 2009. Improved market conditions in 2010 lifted revenues. However the company reported a $4.9 billion loss for 2010 as a result of the Gulf oil spill and its aftermath the cost of which was pegged at almost $41 billion.

EXECUTIVES

CEO, Robert W. (Bob) Dudley, $1,160,100 total compensation
Company Secretary, David J. Jackson, age 61
Chairman, Carl-Henric Svanberg
EVP Corporate Business Activities and Director, Byron E. Grote, age 65, $2,754,894 total compensation
Group General Counsel, Rupert Bondy, age 52
Chief Executive Refining and Marketing, Iain C. Conn, $1,377,447 total compensation
EVP Strategy and Integration, Steve Westwell, age 55

President General Manager of BP Egypt, Hesham Mekawi
Press Officer, Robert Wine
Press Officer, Sheila Williams
EVP and Chief of Staff, Dev Sanyal
Director of Group Investor Relations, Jessica Mitchell
Head of North America Investor Relations, Nick Wayth
Manager Investor Relations, Gerry Bye
Chief Executive Upstream, H. Lamar McKay
Manager Investor Relations North America, Brian Sullivan
Director of Group Media, David Nicholas
Press Officer, Toby Odone
Head of Gulf Coast Restoration Organization, Mike Utsler
EVP Corporate Business Activities, Katrina Landis
President BP Wind Energy, John Graham
EVP Safety and Operational Risk, Mark Bly
COO Strategy and Regions Upstream, Andy Hopwood
EVP Exploration, Mike Daly
EVP Safety and Operational Risk, Bob Fryar
COO Production, Bernard Looney
EVP Group Human Resources Director, Helmut Schuster
Press Officer, Mark Salt
Manager Press Office, Carolyn Copland
Manager Investor Relations, Ruban Chandran
CFO, Brian Gilvary
Director, Cynthia B. Carroll, age 57
Director, George David, age 71
CEO and Director, Robert W. (Bob) Dudley, age 57
Director, Antony Burgmans, age 67
Director, Andrew B. Shilston, age 58
Director, Sir William M. (Bill) Castell, age 66
EVP Corporate Business Activities and Director, Byron E. Grote, age 65
Director, Ian E. L. Davis, age 63
Director, Paul M. Anderson, age 68
Chief Executive Refining and Marketing, Iain C. Conn, age 51
Director, Adm. Frank L. (Skip) Bowman
Director, Phuthuma F. Nhleko, age 54
Director, Brendan Nelson, age 64
CFO and Director, Brian Gilvary
Director, Dame Ann Dowling
Auditors: Ernst&YoungLLP

LOCATIONS

HQ: BP p.l.c.
1 St. James Square, London SW1Y 4PD
Phone: (44) 20 7496 4000   **Fax:** (44) 20 7496 4570
Web: www.bp.com

Sales

	$ mil.	% of total
US	130,940	35
Other countries	244,640	65
Total	**375,580**	**100**

PRODUCTS/OPERATIONS

Sales

	$ mil.	% of total
Refining & marketing	346,491	82
Exploration & production	71,940	17
Other	1,985	1
Adjustments	(44836)	-
Total	**375,580**	**100**

Major Operations
Refining and marketing
Marketing
Refining
Supply and trading
Transportation and shipping
Exploration and production
Field developmen
Gas processing and marketing
Oil and gas exploratio

Pipelines and transporta
Gas and power
Natural gas marketing and trading
Natural gas liquids
Chemicals
Chemical intermedia
Feedstock
Performance products
Polymers
Other
Coal mining
Solar power

Selected Subsidiaries

Atlantic Richfield Co
BP America Inc. (US)
BP Amoco Chemcal Company (US)
BP Oil Australia
BP Exploration Operating Company
BP Espa?a (Spain)
BP International
BP Norge (Norway)
BP Oil New Zealand
BP Shipping
BP Southern Africa (South Africa)
Burmah Castrol
The Standard Oil Company (US)

COMPETITORS

Apache	Koch Industries Inc.
Ashland Inc.	Marathon Oil
BASF SE	Norsk Hydro ASA
BG Group	Occidental Petroleum
BHP Billiton	PEMEX
Chevron	PETROBRAS
ConocoPhillips	Petroleos de Venezuela
Dow Chemical	Repsol
DuPont	Royal Dutch Shell
Eni	Sinclair Oil
Exxon Mobil	Sunoco
Hess Corporation	TOTAL
Huntsman International	Valero Energy
Imperial Oil	

HISTORICAL FINANCIALS

Company Type: Public

Income Statement

FYE: December 31

	REVENUE ($ mil.)	NET INCOME ($ mil.)	NET PROFIT MARGIN	EMPLOYEES
12/13	383,102	23,451	6.1%	83,900
12/12	381,589	11,582	3.0%	85,700
12/11	382,333	25,700	6.7%	83,400
12/10	302,545	(3,719)	—	79,700
12/09	243,965	16,578	6.8%	80,300
Annual Growth	11.9%	9.1%		1.1%

2013 Year-End Financials

Debt ratio: 15.7%
Return on equity: 18.9%
Cash ($ mil.): 22,520
Current ratio: 1.33
Long-term debt ($ mil.): 40,811

No. of shares (mil.): —
Dividends
 Yield: 4.5%
 Payout: 98.2%
Market value ($ mil.): —

	STOCK PRICE ($) FY Close	P/E High/Low	PER SHARE ($) Earnings	Dividends	Book Value
12/13	48.61	39 32	1.23	2.19	6.94
12/12	41.64	79 60	0.60	1.98	6.19
12/11	42.74	36 26	1.34	1.68	5.87
12/10	44.17	— —	(0.20)	2.52	5.05
12/09	57.97	68 39	0.88	3.36	5.42
Annual Growth	(4.3%)	— —	8.9%	(10.1%)	6.4%

BRED Banque Populaire (France)

LOCATIONS

HQ: BRED Banque Populaire (France)
 18, quai de la Rapee, Paris, Cedex 12 75604
Phone: (33) 1 48 98 60 00
Web: www.bred.fr

HISTORICAL FINANCIALS

Company Type: Public

Income Statement

FYE: December 31

	ASSETS ($ mil.)	NET INCOME ($ mil.)	INCOME AS % OF ASSETS	EMPLOYEES
12/13	63,955	251	0.4%	3,596
12/12	60,981	237	0.4%	3,228
12/11	59,299	301	0.5%	3,286
12/10	46,889	327	0.7%	3,317
12/09	53,875	350	0.6%	3,286
Annual Growth	4.4%	(7.9%)	—	2.3%

2013 Year-End Financials

Return on assets: 0.3%
Return on equity: 6.5%
Long-term debt ($ mil.): —
No. of shares (mil.): 56
Sales ($ mil): 3,444

Dividends
 Yield: —
 Payout: —
Market value ($ mil.): —

Bridgestone Corp. (Japan)

Bridgestone is one rolling stone that gathers no moss. Vying with Michelin to be the world's largest tire maker Bridgestone makes tires for a variety of vehicle types. In addition to passenger and commercial vehicle tires the company makes tires for construction and mining vehicles agricultural machinery and aircraft. It also manufactures a range of non-tire products including consumer products like golf balls and bicycles polyurethane foam for industrial applications and adhesive film for the solar industry. Bridgestone operates some 180 manufacturing plants in 25 countries and sells its products worldwide.

In response to declining consumer demand skyrocketing rubber prices and the unpredictable global economy the company has reworked its long-term growth strategy in an effort to streamline its operations and increase revenue in targeted business areas. The strategy - implemented in 2008 - focuses on closing and restructuring operations in certain businesses to cut costs (It sold two steel cord production facilities in Italy and China to Bekaert in 2010.) and increasing production at its plants in emerging markets. (For instance it is ramping up tire production in China India and Brazil to meet growing consumer demand in the regions.) Other key aspects of its strategy include bolstering its commercial and specialty passenger tire businesses particularly its runflat and UHP (ultra-high-performance) replacement passenger tires.

In 2010 tires accounted for more than 80% of Bridgestone's revenues; about three-quarters of its sales were earned overseas. After being hit hard by the economic downturn in 2008 and 2009 the company saw its sales and profits bounce back in 2010 an improvement that it attributes to its renewed strategic direction and an uptick in the global economy.

Bridgestone is also looking to its diversified products business segment to fuel its long-term growth. It is investing in the research and development of eco-friendly products such as adhesive films for solar cells which hold promise for growth as the renewable energy sector expands. The company is also rolling out an eco-friendly tire as well the ECOPIA which it markets in China India and other countries. In addition it continues to manufacture peripheral consumer products for Japan and elsewhere such as Bridgestone-branded golf balls and clubs as well as bicycles and related accessories.

The company operates through more than 50 major subsidiaries and affiliates. In the US subsidiary Bridgestone Americas operates the Bridgestone Retail Operations and Firestone Diversified Products businesses.

HISTORY

In 1906 Shojiro Ishibashi and his brother Tokujiro assumed control of the family's clothing business. They focused on making "tabi" traditional Japanese footwear and in 1923 began working with rubber for soles. In 1931 Shojiro formed Bridgestone (Ishibashi means "stone bridge" in Japanese) to make tires and during that decade the company began producing auto tires airplane tires and golf balls. Bridgestone followed the Japanese military to occupied territories where it built plants. The company's headquarters moved to Tokyo in 1937.

Although Bridgestone lost all of its overseas factories during WWII its Japanese plants escaped damage. The company began making bicycles in 1946 and signed a technical assistance pact with Goodyear five years later enabling Bridgestone to import badly needed technology. In the 1950s and 1960s Bridgestone started making nylon tires and radials and again set up facilities overseas mostly elsewhere in Asia. The company benefited from the rapid growth in Japanese auto sales in the 1970s. Shojiro died at age 87 in 1976.

In 1983 Bridgestone bought a plant in LaVergne Tennessee from tire maker Firestone. Five years later Bridgestone topped Italian tire maker Pirelli's bid and bought the rest of Firestone for $2.6 billion valuing the tire manufacturer at a lofty 26 times its earnings. Bridgestone/Firestone (currently Bridgestone Americas Holding and soon to be Bridgestone Americas Inc.) became Bridgestone's largest subsidiary. Harvey Firestone had founded his tire business in 1900 and expanded with the auto industry in the US. In the 1920s he leased 1 million acres in Liberia for rubber plantations and established a chain of auto supply and service outlets. After WWII Firestone started making synthetic rubber and automotive components expanded overseas and acquired US tire producers Dayton Tire & Rubber and Seiberling.

At the time of Firestone's purchase General Motors (GM) dropped it as a supplier. Bridgestone/Firestone compensated for this loss in volume by selling more tires through mass-market retailers. It began selling tires to GM's Saturn Corporation in 1990.

The following year new Bridgestone/Firestone chairman Yoichiro Kaizaki moved to cut production costs alienating union workers. He became company head in 1993. During the early 1990s Bridgestone bought Colonial Rubber Works a US roofing material manufacturer and America Off The Road Company which makes tires for heavy equipment. To improve its distribution in 1992 Bridgestone renamed its 1550 North American MasterCare auto service centers "Tire Zone at Firestone" and took the unheard-of step of selling rival Michelin's tires. It expanded operations in Brazil Indonesia Mexico Thailand and the US the next year.

Bridgestone's US operations have been plagued with problems such as disputes with the United Rubber Workers (URW) union. Tensions rose in 1995 when the company hired 2300 permanent replacement workers during a plant strike. In 1996 after URW members had become part of United Steelworkers of America the two sides approved a new contract.

In 1997 Bridgestone built a South Carolina plant to help reduce Japanese imports. Although sales remained almost steady that year net profit dropped nearly 50% when a change in accounting caused the company to write off costs associated with its Firestone purchase.

Bridgestone developed a "run-flat" tire in 1998 that remains functional for up to 50 miles without air. Expanding its markets Bridgestone opened a retail outlet in Moscow in 1999 and acquired a radial tire plant in China from South Korea's Kumho Industrial Company in 2000. That year the company recalled approximately 6.5 million Firestone ATX ATX II and Wilderness AT tires after dozens of incidents where the tires came apart at road speeds. The affected tires had been used on light trucks and SUVs since 1990 many of them as original equipment on the Ford Explorer. Not long after the recall Bridgestone/Firestone chairman and CEO Masatoshi Ono retired and was replaced by John Lampe. The fallout and ensuing blame-game (improper inflation guidelines/unstable vehicle vs. faulty tires) essentially ended Bridgestone's 95-year relationship with Ford (Bridgestone still does business with Ford outside the Americas).

In 2001 Bridgestone replaced president Yoichiro Kaizaki with SVP Shigeo Watanabe. Public bickering between Ford and Bridgestone over the cause of the multiple Firestone/Ford Explorer accidents continued unabated into the spring of 2001. Finally in May Bridgestone announced that it was ending its with Ford Motor which accounted for about 2% of sales. The two companies' founders —Henry Ford and Harvey Firestone —had been friends in the early days of mass automobile production. Then in June while revealing that it would face its first loss since listing 30 years previously Bridgestone announced that it would close the Decatur Illinois plant at which many of the recalled tires were made. The plant employed about 1500 workers. Later in the year the company announced that it would recall an additional 3.5 million tires at a cost of nearly $30 million.

Near the end of 2001 Bridgestone announced it would inflate its beleaguered Bridgestone/Firestone subsidiary with $1.3 billion in cash. The company also announced the restructuring of its Bridgestone/Firestone operations. The company established Bridgestone/Firestone Americas Holding Inc. (formerly known as Bridgestone/Firestone Inc.) to serve as a holding company for Bridgestone/Firestone North American Tire LLC (North American tire manufacturing and wholesale and original equipment sales). Bridgestone/Firestone Americas Holding also came to oversee the operations of newly created BFS Retail & Commercial Operations LLC (company-owned stores in the United States and Canada) and BFS Diversified Products LLC (non-tire operations in the Americas including building products synthetic and natural rubber and textiles).

Bridgestone and Continental AG entered into an agreement in early 2002 whereby the two companies will adapt run-flat technology to conventional wheel systems (conventional systems utilize special wheels). In early 2003 the company's US subsidiary changed its name from Bridgestone/Firestone Americas Holding to Bridgestone Americas Holding. Later in the year the company was awarded a contract to supply tires for the Airbus A380 aircraft; the deal was reportedly worth $84.3 million.

In 2005 Bridgestone purchased the Indonesian rubber plantations business (Goodyear Sumatra Plantations) of Goodyear Tire & Rubber for about $62 million.

Watanabe stepped down as chairman president and CEO the next year; he was replaced by EVP Shoshi Arakawa.

In 2007 Bridgestone purchased Bandag a retread company in the US with international production facilities. In late 2008 Bridgestone formed a joint venture with Indian auto parts maker Sundaram Industries part of TVS Group. The following year the company built a plant in Thailand to produce rubber parts for retread tires. The cost of the facility was approximately Å5.2 billion.

The company also sold off operations during this period. In 2010 Bridgestone sold two steel cord production facilities for approximately $100 million to Bekaert a steel cord producer based in Belgium. The manufacturing facilities in Italy and China generated approximately 10% of Bridgestone's total production capacity. In 2009 it closed factories in New Zealand and Adelaide Australia. (Steel cords are used to reinforce tires.)

To help with brand identification in 2009 the company changed the name of many of its subsidiaries (and in some cases dropped the name Firestone altogether). Bridgestone Americas Holding became Bridgestone Americas; Bridgestone Firestone North American Tire became Bridgestone Americas Tire Operations; BFS Retail & Commercial Operations became Bridgestone Retail Operations.

EXECUTIVES

SVP, Asahiko (Duke) Nishiyama
VP Senior Officer and Director, Kazuo Kakehi
COO, Kazuhisa Nishigai
VP Senior Officer and Chief Marketing Officer, Shuichi Ishibashi
VP Senior Officer and Director; Chairman President and CEO Bridgestone Europe, Toru Tsuda
Managing Director Tire Business Operations and Chief International Tire Business, Takashi Urano
VP Senior Officer and Director, Mikio Masunaga
Corporate Officer Deputy Human Resources Representative and the Central Research Institute, Hideki Yokoyama
VP and Senior Officer, Kiyoshi Nomura
Corporate Officer Bridgestone Americas Inc. (Akron) Dispatch, Hideo (Hank) Hara, age 63
Chairman and CEO, Masaaki Tsuya
SVP, Narumi (Nick) Zaitsu
Managing Director GLC, Yasumi Kawasaki
SVP and CTO, Yoshiyuki Morimoto
VP and Officer, Satoshi Tagomori
Corporate Officer Disaster Management Safety, Yoshiharu Inoue
VP and Officer, Natsuki Fujii
Corporate Officer Contact Corporate Communications, Naomi Eto
VP and Officer, Yasuo Ryuto
Corporate Officer Quality Staff, Yoichi Sato
VP and Officer, Isaku Motohashi
VP and Officer, Fumihiro Yanaga
VP and Senior Officer, Masato Hiruma
Corporate Officer and Group CEO, Hidekazu Ishibashi
Corproate Officer Tire Business Division, Shimizu Minoru
Corporate Officer Mamoru Tooru Hiroshi Toshi, Kunitoshi Takeda
VP; Chairman Bridgestone Europe, Eduardo Minardi
Managing Executive Officer; President and CEO of Subsidiary, Franco Annunziato
VP and Senior Officer; President and CEO Bridgestone Americas, Gary Garfield
Executive Officer; Chief Director of GLC Operation Planning, Masahito Tsuji
VP and Senior Officer; CEO Bridgestone Tire Japan, Minoru Shimizu
Executive Officer; Chief Director of Production Technology Basic Development, Seiichiro Kawai
Executive Officer, Tatsuro Hamada
VP Senior Officer and CIO, Yuichiro Takenami
VP, Akihiro Eto
VP and Senior Officer, Yasushi Ota
VP and Senior Officer, Masakazu Sekiguchi
VP Senior Officer and Director, Kazuo Kakehi
VP Senior Officer and Director, Kazuhisa Nishigai
VP Senior Officer and Director; Chairman President and CEO Bridgestone Europe, Toru Tsuda
VP Senior Officer and Director, Mikio Masunaga
VP Senior Officer Chief Risk Management Officer Chief Compliance Officer and Director; Acting Chairman Americas, Masaaki Tsuya
Director, Sakie Tachibana Fukushima
Director, Takao Enkawa
Independent Director, Kimiko Murofushi
Independent Director, Sakie Tachibana-Fukushima
Independent Director, Scott Davis
Auditors: DeloitteToucheTohmatsu

LOCATIONS

HQ: Bridgestone Corp. (Japan)
3-1-1 Kyobashi, Chuo-ku, Tokyo 104-8340
Phone: (81) 3 6836 3162
Web: www.bridgestone.co.jp

Sales

	% of total
The	42
Japan	26
Europe	13
Other	19
Total	**100**

PRODUCTS/OPERATIONS

Sales

	% of total
Tires	83
Diversified	17
Total	**100**

Selected Products

Tires and tubes
  Agricultural machinery
  Aircraft
  Buses
  Cars
  Commercial vehicles
  Construction and mining vehicles
  Monorails
  Motorcycles
  Race cars
  Scooters
  Trucks
Diversified products
  Bicycles and bicycle accessories
  Chemical and industrial
    Adhesive and anti-reflective film for glass and flat-panel displays
    Conveyor belts
    Electronic paper for still image display
    High-performance films
    Hydraulic hoses
    Marine fenders
    Panel type water tank

Polyurethane foam
Rubber tracks
Seismic isolators
Single crystal wafers for semiconductor devices
Sporting goods
Golf apparel
Golf balls
Golf clubs

COMPETITORS

3M	Huffy Corporation
Acushnet	Kumho Tire
Callaway Golf	Marangoni
Continental AG	Michelin
Cooper Tire &	Pirelli
Rubber	Sime Darby
Goodyear Tire &	Sumitomo Rubber
Rubber	Trelleborg
Hankook Tire	Yokohama Rubber

HISTORICAL FINANCIALS

Company Type: Public

Income Statement

FYE: December 31

	REVENUE ($ mil.)	NET INCOME ($ mil.)	NET PROFIT MARGIN	EMPLOYEES
12/13	33,991	1,924	5.7%	145,029
12/12	35,292	1,992	5.6%	143,448
12/11	39,081	1,330	3.4%	143,124
12/10	35,181	1,216	3.5%	139,822
12/09	28,108	11	0.0%	137,135
Annual Growth	4.9%	261.4%	—	1.4%

2013 Year-End Financials

Debt ratio: 0.1%
Return on equity: 12.7%
Cash ($ mil.): 2,729
Current ratio: 1.62
Long-term debt ($ mil.): 2,693

No. of shares (mil.): 782
Dividends
Yield: 1.1%
Payout: —
Market value ($ mil.): 14,956

	STOCK PRICE ($) FY Close	P/E High/Low	PER SHARE ($) Earnings	Dividends	Book Value
12/13	19.10	— —	2.46	0.22	22.67
12/12	51.67	— —	2.54	0.70	21.05
12/11	45.00	— —	1.70	0.00	19.25
12/10	38.73	— —	1.55	0.41	18.48
12/09	35.11	— —	0.01	0.40	15.47
Annual Growth	(14.1%)		— 261.4%	(13.7%)	10.0%

BT Group Plc

Once BT Group's rivals could have fit into one of the company's signature red phone booths. Though competition has taken a toll BT still wears the crown as the UK's top telecommunications carrier. It offers local and long-distance phone service and provides Internet access and other data and IT services. BT Group operates through four divisions —corporate clients are served through its BT Global Services unit while BT Retail oversees residential and small business service. The BT Wholesale and Openreach divisions are devoted to the broadband and local network needs of other carriers. BT which claims to be the world's oldest communications company is working to adapt to the age of mobile communications.

Geographic Reach

The UK is London-based BT Group's largest market accounting for more than three-quarters of its annual sales. Key European markets for the company include Italy Germany and Spain. In North America BT serves customers from offices in 25 cities. The firm also has a presence in high-growth regions in Asia Pacific Latin America the Middle East and Africa.

Operations

BT Global Services the group's enterprise telecommunications division is its largest segment by sales accounting for nearly 40% of revenue in fiscal 2013 (ended March). It provides voice and data communications as well as managed network and IT services to corporate and public sector customers in more than 170 countries; the UK government is the company's largest client. BT Global Services also operates customer contact and data centers and offers customer relationship management and managed network security.

Consumer services offered through BT Retail accounted for 37% of the group's fiscal 2013 revenue. BT Retail serves individual and small business customers (up to 1000 employees) in the UK with fixed-line broadband mobile broadband and Wi-Fi and digital television service. While it holds well over half of the domestic market for residential fixed-line service its number of access lines continues to drop as more people switch to cell phones. (Due to regulatory laws BT is unable to offer mobile cell phone service). Its growing pay TV brand BT Vision is seen in 575000 homes up from 423000 in 2009. BT Expedite BT Ireland and BT Redcare all operate as standalone businesses under BT Retail.

BT Wholesale provides network services to more than 1000 communications service providers in the UK. It operates the only network that covers the entire country and many competitors pay to use its network to enable their own services. BT Wholesale manages the network infrastructure for Virgin Media and KCOM while O2 and Vodafone use its fixed-line network for their business customers. Contracts typically run three to five years and 40% of its customers are signed to these long-term contracts.

Openreach is the group's smallest segment. It was created in 2006 as part of a settlement with regulatory agency Ofcom to ensure that other companies have full access to BT's network. About 500 communications service providers including BT divisions rely on Openreach for network communications.

Financial Performance

BT Group's revenue declined 5% in fiscal 2013 (ended March) versus the prior year to Å18.2 billion. (Revenue and profit figures have not been adjusted for the effects of currency translation.) The decline reflected lower revenue from calls and lines difficult economic conditions in Europe and the financial sector and regulatory price reductions. The 8% drop in proceeds from calls and lines was caused by the continued migration from fixed-line calls to mobile broadband data and IP services. The decline was partially offset by a 7% annual increase in broadband and convergence revenue. Three of BT's four operating segments posted declines in fiscal 2013 with BT Global Services BT Retail and BT Wholesale down 8% 3% and 11% respectively. Broadband services unit Openreach with an 8% jump in revenue was the exception.

Net income grew 14% in fiscal 2013 versus 2012 while net cash outflow grew by Å600 million over the same period.

Strategy

BT is pursuing new business in Turkey the Middle East Africa and high-growth areas of the Asia-Pacific Region. Investments in Asia have included adding sales marketing and operational staff and investing in network resources.

Notable contract wins for BT Global Services include its selection by the International Olympic Committee to provide communications services for the 2012 Olympic Games in London; an extension agreement with Unilever to continue supplying managed services to the company's global operations; and a deal with Swiss private banker UBS to provide voice and data telecom services worldwide.

As established carriers face mounting competition in the high-speed Internet space from the likes of Virgin and TalkTalk some have sought partnerships to shore up their online businesses. In 2010 BT took over management of the broadband network of France-based rival Orange's UK business which is experiencing a declining subscriber base.

BT is a very expensive company to operate - those cables don't lay themselves. It pays billions in taxes (around Å3 billion annually) to the UK Exchequer. After being in business for more than 100 years it also spends a lot on pension payments.

Mergers and Acquisitions

In 2013 BT Group acquired the London-based technology group Tikit Group for Å64.2 million ($103 million). The move was designed to strengthen BT Retail's position as a provider of ICT services to law firms in the UK. Tikit's clients include legal and accountancy firms.

Ownership

Asset manager Invesco owns about 10% of BT Group's stock.

HISTORY

In 1879 the British Post Office (now known as Royal Mail and formerly Consignia) got the exclusive right to operate telegraph systems. When private firms tried to offer phone service the government objected arguing in court that its telegraph monopoly was imperiled. The courts agreed and the Post Office was empowered to license private phone companies collect a 10% royalty and operate its own systems.

The private National Telephone Company emerged as the leading phone outfit competing with the Post Office. When National's license expired in 1911 the Post Office took over and became the monopoly phone company. In 1936 the phone system introduced its familiar red phone booths designed for King George V's jubilee.

Under a 1981 law telecommunications were split from the Post Office and placed under the new British Telecommunications (BT). The government also allowed competitor Mercury Communications —formerly One 2 One and now known as T-Mobile (UK) —to compete. The Thatcher government soon called for BT's privatization.

After the Telecommunications Act of 1984 BT went public in one of the largest UK stock offerings in history. The act set up the regulatory Office of Telecommunications (OFTEL). The next year Cellnet BT's joint venture with Securicor launched its mobile phone network. To become a multinational concern BT bought control of Canadian phone equipment maker Mitel (1986 sold in 1992) and 20% of firm McCaw Cellular (1989 sold to AT&T in 1994).

In 1990 the British government opened the UK to more phone competition and BT responded with improvements to its network and a workforce reduction. The government sold almost all of its remaining shares in BT in 1993. The next year the company bought a 20% stake in MCI the #2 US long-distance carrier and the two formed Concert a joint venture to compete in the international arena. BT's 1996 attempt to buy Cable and Wireless failed when the company asked for more than BT was willing to pay.

In 1996 BT announced a plan to buy out MCI but as losses mounted from MCI's expansion into the US local market BT in 1997 lowered its bid and lost MCI to upstart WorldCom. In 1998 BT bought the remaining 25% stake in Concert and found a new US partner in AT&T; the two agreed in 1999 to merge most of their international operations in a $10 billion global joint venture that took the Concert name (but after repeated losses the two parent companies dismantled the venture in 2002).

Also in 1999 BT expanded in continental Europe Latin America (a 20% stake in IMPSAT) Asia (with AT&T a 30% stake in Japan Telecom) and the US where it bought systems integration firm Syntegra (USA) (formerly Control Data Systems and now part of BT Americas) and Yellow Book USA. At home BT bought out Securicor's stake in Cellnet. UK regulators also ordered the company to upgrade its UK phone network and open it to rivals by 2001.

BT bought Ireland's Esat Telecom in 2000. That year the government sold its remaining stake in BT and the company bought Telenor's stake in VIAG Interkom; early the next year the company took full ownership of the German mobile phone company. Also in early 2001 BT sold its stakes in Japan Telecom and J-Phone Communications to Vodafone which later that year bought BT's Airtel Movil (now known as Vodafone Espana) interest.

BT Group countered increasing competition and mounting debt woes through restructuring that included the 2001 spinoff of its domestic and international wireless businesses combined under the mmO2 brand (formerly BT Wireless) which included BT Cellnet a leading UK mobile phone operator. The decision left BT Group as the only top-tier European telecom firm without a wireless network.

To further its restructuring the company in 2002 sold its Yellow Pages unit Yell to two buyout firms: Hicks Muse Tate & Furst (now HM Capital Partners) and Apax Partners. And in a further effort to cut debt it sold much of its property holdings and unloaded interests in the Pacific Rim.

The company also sold a 77% stake in Brightstar its technology incubator to private equity investment firm Coller Capital and New Venture Partners in a deal valued at $77 million. BT Group held a 23% stake and remained a limited partner in a new venture (NVP Brightstar) that continued to work closely with its BT Exact unit.

In 2002 BT dismantled Concert its failed business telecom services joint venture with AT&T that combined most of the companies' international operations. The company also sold its 26% stake in France's Cegetel to Vivendi Universal. It also has unloaded other noncore assets including its 21% stake in Hong Kong wireless carrier SmarTone Telecommunications in its continuing effort to reduce debt.

In a major reorganization BT Group turned itself into a holding company. Ordered to upgrade and open its domestic networks it split its UK fixed-line network operations into separate wholesale and retail businesses.

BT Group also expanded its information communications technology (ICT) services offered to multisite corporations in the US. It signed its largest IT services deal to date valued at $3 billion over eight-and-a-half years with the Reuters Group. BT Group also acquired financial services extranet provider Radianz from Reuters for $175 million.

The company in 2005 acquired Infonet a leading provider of corporate managed voice and data network services. The company renamed BT Infonet is part of the BT Global Services unit. That year BT Group also acquired SkyNet Systems a provider of Internet protocol-based LAN systems. To expand its global professional services offerings the company made several purchases in 2006 including US-based Counterpane Internet Security a provider of managed networked security services.

BT refocused its other international holdings to concentrate on Europe. It acquired Fiat's Italian telecom subsidiary Atlanet in early 2006 and later

that year BT bought Fiat's Brazilian telecom business Telexis. It additionally acquired Indian Internet protocol communications services provider i2i Enterprise.

In 2007 the company purchased Comsat International a data communication services provider expanding its presence in Latin America. Also in 2007 BT bought the IT infrastructure division of France-based CS Communication & Systemes. Meanwhile it increased its North American presence with the acquisition of IT consulting and software provider International Network Services.

BT has responded to the growing global demand for business services with the acquisition of service providers from a range of disciplines in Europe and the US. In 2008 it bought German information technology firms Stemmer and SND from net AG to boost its presence in the region. The company also acquired UK online classified advertising specialist Ufindus which became part of BT's online directory business.

Also that year it bought US videoconferencing specialist Wire One Holdings to improve the capability and geographic reach of its conferencing unit and it picked up Silicon Valley-based integrated communications software developer Ribbit Corporation for $105 million as an addition to its existing software holdings.

EXECUTIVES

Regional Manager South West BT Regions, Michael Dunn

Head Data Centres BT Operate, David Edwards

Chief Executive and Board Member, Ian P. Livingston, age 49, $1,250,301 total compensation

Director Shared Services BT Global Services, Dave Mitchell

Regional Director BTLB Wales & West Midlands - BT Business BT Retail, Paul Evans

Chief Executive BT Wholesale, Sally Davis, age 60

Chief Procurement Officer, Neil Rogers

Country Manager BT Italia, Corrado Sciolla, age 51

Chairman, Sir Michael D. V. (Mike) Rake, age 66

CEO Openreach, Steve Robertson

Chief Executive BT Operate, Roel Louwhoff, age 50

Group Director London, Duncan Ingram

Director Client Business Development ? Managed Services BT Wholesale, Steve Edwards

Chief Executive, Gavin Patterson, age 46

President BT France, Olivier Huart, age 48

Director Group Public Policy, Dorothy Smith

CEO BT Northern Ireland and the Republic of Ireland, Graham Sutherland

Managing Director Retail Strategy, Sean M.G. Williams

CEO BT Germany, Karsten Lereuth

President Americas and Asia-Pacific, Michael Boustridge, age 51

President BT EMEA and Latin America, Luis ?lvarez

CEO BT Ireland, Chris Clark

Regional Director Yorkshire and the Humber, John Anderson

CEO Benelux, Bas Burger, age 43

Managing Director BT Consumer BT Retail, John Petter

Company Secretary, Andrew Parker, age 54

Group Finance Director and Board Member, Anthony E. A. (Tony) Chanmugam, age 60

VP European Affairs, Adrian Whitchurch

VP Global Portfolio BT Global Services, Neil Sutton

Chief Executive Officer - BT Wholesale, Nigel Stagg

Managing Director Customer Service BT Retail, Warren Buckley

Director Marketing and Brand, Suzi Williams

Regional Director ICT BT Business, John Dovey

Manager European Regulation, Henk Mannekens

Manager Public Affairs, Christine van der Steur

General Director BT Russia & CIS Countries, Richard van Wageningen

Regional Director East Midlands, Andrew Bacon

Leader Customers and Markets Venture - Strategic Research BT Innovate & Design East of England, John Seton

Chief Customer Innovation Officer BT Innovate & Design, Paul Excell

General Manager BT Openzone BT Retail, Chris Bruce

Director Service Operations BT Operate, Ashley Hannah

Regional Manager East of England BT Regions, Annette Thorpe

Head Data Network and ICT Sales (Midlands) BT Retail, Graham Wilkinson

Director Professional and Managed Services BT Engage IT BT Retail, Steve Alton

Regional Manager East Midlands BT Regions, Paul Bimson

Director Wireless Broadband BT Retail, David Hughes

General Manager London, Andrew Campling

General Manager Contact Delivery BT Retail, Julie Lowther

General Manager Digital Care BT Retail, Graeme Stoker

General Manager BT Supply Chain Operations North BT Procurement & Supply Chain, Chris Atkins

Head BT DWP Core Programmes BT Global Services, Chris Millman

Disruptive Futurist BT Global Services, Ian Neild

CEO BT South Tyneside BT Global Services, Margie Burdis

Regional Manager North East BT Regions, Simon Roberson

Director Central Government & Home Affairs BT Global Services, Mike Blackburn

Programme Director Manchester Communications Academy BT Global Services, Sue Webster

General Manager Product Development BT Innovate & Design, Steve Henderson

Head Sales Programmes and Alliance Partners-Shared Services BT Global Services, Sami Istephan

Director Retail North BT Global Services, Paul Skelt

Account Director BT Global Services, Mike Wrench

Regional Manager North West BT Regions, Peter Connor

Regional Director South East, Mike Gavin

Head PR and Communications BT Regions, Barbara Wise

Academies Project BT Global Services, Denise Westbury-Haines

Business Development Director - BT London 2012 BT Group, Jon Lane

Programme Manager Community Investment, Beth Courtier

General Manager ? CRM BT Wholesale, Stephen Hunt

Managing Director Research 21C CE & Technology Strategy BT Innovate & Design, Mike Galvin

Regional Manager South East BT Regions, Peter Cowen

Regional Director South West, Maj. Jon Reynolds

Head Business Improvement BT Global Services, Mike Buhagiar

Project Orchard BT Wholesale, Ranulf Scarborough

Senior Audit Manager, Jane Shipway

Head Commercial Management BT Retail, James Hennah

Manager Senior Client Business Development BT Retail, Liz King

Programme Manager BT Innovate & Design, Kelvin Blake

Head Learning and Development BT Operate, Mary Scarratt

Performance and Reporting Manager BT Group, Ian Wood

Service Director (BT Retail) Satellite MNS + OpenZone BT Operate, Keith Lawton

Regional Manager West Midlands BT Regions, Ian Binks

Programme Director BT Global Services, Zulfi Hussain

General Manager Market Development BT Wholesale, Peter Barnes

VP Global Services Transformation Programmes BT Innovate & Design, Jacqueline Steed

Head Marketing - GSUK Vertical Markets BT Global Services, Paul Woodman

Regional Manager Yorkshire and Humber BT Regions, Trevor Higgins

Director Wales, Ann Beynon

Regional Manager South Wales, Ceri Fitzpatrick

Director Sustainability Enablement BT Global Services, Sharanne Basham-Pyke

Managing Director Energy and Services MNC UK BT Global Services, Mark Rosson

Deputy General Manager ICT Solutions, Dai Jeremiah

Account Director BT Wholesale, Robert Milloy

Head HR COO and Public Sector BT Global Services, Mathew Davies

Director BT Scotland, Brendan Dick

General Manager Retail Custom Service Solutions BT Retail, Rosemary Calder

Head Customer Satisfaction BT Global Services, Robert Cole

Director Service Management BT Wholesale, Angus Flett

Director BT Devolved Government BT Global Services, Tom Kelly

Director Contracts Requirements BT Innovate & Design, Ed Lindsay

Director Human Resources Reward and Employee Relations BT Group, Jim McInally

Lead Consultant Devolved Government BT Global Services, Martin Southern

Senior Manager Media and Corporate Relations BT Group, Anna Steven

Director Next Generation Access Programme BT Design & Innovate, Ian Stirrat

Chief Architect, Howard Watson

Regional Business Development Director BT Global Services, Janice Hailwood

Head of strategic university research for BT, Jeff Patmore

Research Scientist, Jia-Yan Gu

Sales Manager BTB Mobility Solutions, Mark Barrow

President GB&FM and Sales & Marketing, Tom Regent

Group People Director, Clare Clare Chapman Chapman

CIO, Clive Selley

Chief Executive Officer - BT Global Services, Luis Alvarez

CEO BT Benelux, Joris van Oers

Chief Executive and Board Member, Ian P. Livingston, age 49

Independent Non-Executive Director, Phil Hodkinson, age 56

Board Member, J. Eric Daniels, age 62

Board Member; Chief Executive BT Retail, Gavin Patterson, age 46

Board Member, Rt. Hon. Patricia Hewitt, age 65

Group Finance Director and Board Member, Anthony E. A. (Tony) Chanmugam, age 60

Board Member, Tony Ball, age 58

Independent Non-Executive Director, Jasmine Jasmine Whitbread Whitbread

Non-Executive Director, Karen Karen Richardson Richardson

Independent Non-Executive Director, Nicholas Nicholas Rose Rose

Auditors: PricewaterhouseCoopersLLP

LOCATIONS

HQ: BT Group Plc
BT Centre, 81 Newgate Street, London EC1A 7AJ
Phone: (44) 20 7356 5000   Fax: (44) 20 7356 5520
Web: www.bt.com

Sales

	% of total
Europe Middle East Africa	
UK	77
Other	14
Americas	6
Asia	3
Total	**100**

PRODUCTS/OPERATIONS

Sales

	% of total
BT Global	39
BT	37
BT	14
Openreach	10
Total	**100**

Sales by Market

%	
ICT & managed networks	34
Calls & lines	26
Broadband & convergence	17
Conveyance interconnectcircuits WLR global carrier& other wholesale	8
Transit	4
Other	11
Total	**0** **100**

Selected Subsidiaries and Affiliates

Basilica Computing Limited (IT services)

British Telecommunications plc (telecommunication related services and products)

BT Americas Inc. (telecommunication related services and products US)

BT Australasia Pty Limited (telecommunication related services and products Australia)

BT Centre Nominee 2 Limited (property holding company)

BT Communications Ireland Limited (telecommunications services)

BT Conferencing Inc. (Audio video and Web conferencing services US)

BT Convergent Solutions Limited (communications related services and products)

BT ESPA?A Compa?ia de Servicios Globales de Telecomunicaciones S.A. (telecommunication related services and products Spain)

BT Fleet Limited (fleet management)

BT France SA (telecommunication related services and products)

BT Frontline Pte Ltd (communications related services and products Singapore)

BT (Germany) GmbH & Co. oHG (telecommunication related services and products)

BT Global Services Limited (international telecommunications network systems)

BT Holdings Limited (investment holding company)

BT Hong Kong Limited (telecommunication related services and products)

BT Infrastructures Critiques (IT systems and network services France)

BT INS Inc (Information telecommunication consulting and software US)

BT Italia SpA (telecommunications related services and products Italy 97%)

BT Limited (international telecommunication network systems provider)

BT Nederland NV (telecommunication related services and products The Netherlands)

BT US Investments Limited (investments holding company US)

Communications Global Network Services Limited (telecommunication related services and products Bermuda)

Communication Networking Services (UK) (telecommunication related services and products)

Infonet Services Corporation (global managed network services provider US)

Infonet USA Corporation (global managed network services provider US)

Radianz Americas Inc. (global managed network services provider US)

COMPETITORS

Accenture	THUS Ltd.
BSkyB	TalkTalk
COLT Group	Telecom Italia
Cable & Wireless	Telecom plus
Capgemini	Telefonica
Deutsche Telekom	Telenor
Easynet	TeliaSonera
IBM Global Services	Verizon Enterprise
KCOM Group	Solutions
KPN	Virgin Media
Orange	Vodafone
Orange	
Orange Business Services	

HISTORICAL FINANCIALS

Company Type: Public

Income Statement

FYE: March 31

	REVENUE ($ mil.)	NET INCOME ($ mil.)	NET PROFIT MARGIN	EMPLOYEES
03/14	30,444	3,359	11.0%	87,800
03/13	27,379	3,177	11.6%	87,900
03/12	30,280	3,208	10.6%	89,015
03/11	32,301	2,416	7.5%	92,600
03/10	31,634	1,559	4.9%	97,800
Annual Growth	(1.0%)	21.2%	—	(2.7%)

2014 Year-End Financials

Debt ratio: 65.6%
Return on equity: ***,***.*%
Cash ($ mil.): 1,157
Current ratio: 0.74
Long-term debt ($ mil.): 13,220
No. of shares (mil.): —
Dividends
Yield: 2.3%
Payout: 636.6%
Market value ($ mil.): —

	STOCK PRICE ($) FY Close	P/E High/Low	PER SHARE ($) Earnings	Dividends	Book Value
03/14	63.85	754404	0.41	1.53	(0.12)
03/13	42.03	380270	0.39	3.21	(0.05)
03/12	36.16	363245	0.39	3.00	0.25
03/11	30.08	420197	0.30	1.05	0.38
03/10	18.71	479182	0.20	0.50	(0.49)
Annual Growth	35.9%	—	—	20.2%	32.2%	—

Bunge Ltd.

Bunge's businesses stretch from the farm field to your local supermarket shelf. A leading integrated agribusiness and food company Bunge produces stores and sells agricultural products such as oilseeds and grains which it turns into vegetable oils and protein meals. Customers include animal feed poultry and aquaculture producers. The agribusiness markets vegetable oils used in the biodiesel industry. The company's edible oil products segment sells packaged oils like shortening and margarine under brands Bunge Pro Floriol and Olek. A sugar and bioenergy unit produces sugar and ethanol which are sold primarily in Brazil. Bunge also mixes and distributes crop fertilizers to farmers in South America.

Geographic Reach

Bunge has operations in Africa Asia the Caribbean Europe the Middle East North and South America. Europe is the company's largest market accounting for nearly a third of total sales. The US represents about a quarter of sales while Asia accounts for nearly a fifth.

Operations

The integrated agribusiness and food company divides its operations into four divisions. Agribusiness is the largest accounting for nearly three-quarters of the company's sales. It's primarily involved in the purchase storage transport processing and ultimately the sale of agricultural commodities in North and South America Europe and Asia. Bunge's Food and Ingredients division houses edible oils products and milling products and includes businesses that produce and sell edible oils shortenings margarines mayonnaise and milled products such as wheat flours corn-based products and rice. The Sugar and Bioenergy segment produces and sells sugar and ethanol derived from sugarcane. The firm's shrinking Fertilizer arm makes blends and distributes fertilizer products for the agricultural industry primarily in South America.

Financial Performance

Bunge's sales approached $61 billion in 2012 a 4% increase versus 2011. Agribusiness and Edible Oil Products outperformed the company's other business segments posting sales increases of 15% and 7% respectively. The company's Sugar and Bioenergy operation's sales tumbled 20% in 2012 versus the prior year while sales of milling products declined by nearly 9%. Asia Canada and the US each posted double-digit annual sales comparisons while sales in Europe rose 6%. Brazil posted a 3% gain in 2012 sales while Argentina suffered a 16% decline. Overall 2012 marked the third consecutive year of increasing sales for Bunge although the rate of growth has slowed. Indeed in 2011 sales jumped 29% versus 2010.

Net income plunged 93% in 2012 its second year of steep decline due primarily to an after-tax charge related to the impairment of the Sugar & Bioenergy segment goodwill and a loss of $342 million for results of discontinued operations.

Strategy

Diversified Bunge is building some of its businesses while retrenching in others such as fertilizer. Indeed in 2013 the company sold its Brazilian fertilizer business to Yara International ASA for $750 million in cash. Also in 2012 the firm sold its 28% stake in Soloe LLC its joint venture with DuPont formed in 2003 for $440 million. Bunge will continue to supply fertilizer to farmers as part of its grain organization activities.

Bunge intends to fuel growth by investing in projects that strengthen its leadership in grains oilseeds and food ingredients.

Mergers and Acquisitions

In line with its focus on agriculture and environmental concerns Bunge in 2012 acquired London-based Climate Change Capital Group parent to Climate Change Capital (CCC) a UK-regulated sustainable asset manager and adviser. CCC makes investments in projects companies and technologies focusing on carbon finance private equity and property. Also in 2012 Bunge's subsidiary in India acquired the edible oils and fats business of Amrit Banaspati. The purchase which included the rights to the vanaspati (cooking oil) brand GAGAN furthers Bunge's presence in the Indian consumer foods market. The deal followed Bunge's purchase (through its North American subsidiary) of a pair of margarine production facilities and their assets from The C.F. Sauer Company in mid-2011. Bunge scooped up an assortment of low saturated and trans-fat products for its North American customers which include restaurants and food processors.

In April 2012 Bunge purchased the assets of MCN BioProducts a privately-held Canadian technology company. The purchase creates opportunities for Bunge to provide protein alternatives in existing and new markets.

HISTORY

In 2003 Bunge announced it acquired the India-based edible oils and fats businesses of Hindustan Lever as well as India oilseed-crushing business Prestige Foods Limited. That year it also sold its private-label retail bottled-oil business to ACH Food.

The company also sold the bakery business of its North American subsidiary to Dawn Food Products for about $82 million. The business included Bunge North America's frozen dough mixes syrups and toppings products. These changes allowed Bunge to continue its focus on its edible-oils business. In addition the acquisition of Cereol in 2003 made Bunge the world's largest oilseed producer.

The company is expanding into Eastern Europe and Asia. As part of that effort it purchased Poland's Kama Foods in 2004. Activity in Russia includes the purchase of a grain terminal in Rostov to handle the increase in Russian exports of wheat and barley. Taking its first step into China in 2005 Bunge purchased a controlling interest in a soybean crushing and refining plant in Shandong Province.

Bunge agreed to acquire Corn Products International (renamed Ingredion) in June 2008. In November 2008 Corn Products announced its board withdrew its support for its planned takeover without citing a reason. A week later Bunge issued a statement saying that although the company still believed the takeover was a good fit that it was not in its best interests to do pursue the takeover at that time. Falling corn prices and the weak economy are believed to be the deciding factors in the cancellation of the deal. Bunge is already the #3 agribusiness company in the global marketplace (after #1 Cargill and #2 Archer Daniels Midland). The acquisition of Corn Products would have given Bunge a much stronger presence in corn as well as greater access to markets in Asia and North and South America. Bunge did add to its holdings in 2008 when it acquired the international sugar trading and marketing division of European ingredients giant Tate & Lyle.

Founded in 1818 as a grain trading company in Amsterdam Bunge was held mostly by families descended from founder Johann Bunge until it went public in 2001.

EXECUTIVES

Executive Chairman of the Board, Alberto Weisser, age 58, $1,200,000 total compensation
Managing Director Global Government and Corporate Affairs, Carl L. Hausmann, age 67
Managing Director Bunge Global Agribusiness; CEO Bunge Product Lines, Raul Padilla, age 58
CEO Bunge Europe Middle East & Africa, Jean-Louis Gourbin, age 66
Deputy Chairman, L. Patrick Lupo, age 63
Chief Financial Officer; Global Operational Excellence Officer, Andrew J. (Drew) Burke, age 59, $500,000 total compensation
CEO Bunge Asia, Christopher S. White, age 61
Managing Director Food and Ingredients, Gordon Hardie
President and Chief Executive Officer; Bunge Brazil, Pedro Pullen Parente, age 61
Chief Personnel Officer, Vicente C. Teixeira, age 62
Chief Development Officer and Managing Director Sugar and Bioenergy, D. Benedict Pearcy, age 45, $427,490 total compensation

Chief Executive Officer; Director, Soren W. Schroder, age 52
Manager External Communications, Susan Burns
CEO Bunge Argentina, Enrique Humanes
General Counsel Secretary Managing Director, Frank Jimenez
CEO Bunge EMEA, Tommy Jensen
Director, Larry G. Pillard, age 66
Director, Ernest G. Bachrach, age 61
Deputy Chairman, L. Patrick Lupo, age 63
Director, Michael H. Bulkin, age 74
Director, Jorge Born Jr., age 51
Director, Enrique H. Boilini, age 52
Director, Octavio Caraballo, age 70
Director, Francis Coppinger, age 62
Director, Bernard de La Tour d'Auvergne Lauraguais, age 69
Director, William Engels, age 54
Independent Director, Bernard Lauraguais
Independent Director, Kathleen Hyle
Independent Director, James Hackett
Auditors: Deloitte&ToucheLLP

LOCATIONS

HQ: Bunge Ltd.
50 Main Street, White Plains, NY 10606
Phone: 914 684-2800
Web: www.bunge.com

Sales

	$ mil.	% of total
Europe	19,475	32
US	15,249	25
Asia	11,160	18
Brazil	8,583	14
Argentina	3,059	5
Canada	2,322	4
Other regions	1,143	2
Total	**60,991**	**100**

PRODUCTS/OPERATIONS

Sales

	$ mil.	% of total
Agribusiness	44,561	73
Edible oil products	9,472	16
Sugar & bioenergy	4,659	8
Milling products	1,833	2
Fertilizer	466	1
Total	**60,991**	**100**

Selected Products and Services

Agribusiness
  Purchase storage transport processing and sale of agricultural commodities
    Corn
    Rapeseed (canola seed)
    Soybeans
    Sunflower seed
    Wheat
  Sugar
  Sugar cane-based ethanol
Fertilizer
  Mining and processing of phosphate ore
  Production
    Ammonia
    Ammonium nitrate
    Dicalcium phosphate
    Monoammonium phosphate
    Nitric acid
    Phosphate rock
    Phosphate-based animal feed ingredients
    Phosphoric acid
    Sulfuric acid
    Triple superphosphate
    Urea
Food and food ingredients
  Bulk oils
  Edible oils
    Rapeseed (canola oil)
    Soybean
    Sunflower
  Margarines
  Mayonnaise
  Packaged vegetable oils

Shortenings
Milling
  Brazil
    Bakery mixes
    Wheat flours
  North America
    Corn oil
    Corn-based animal feed
    Corn/soy meal
    Dry-milled cornmeal
    Flours
    Grits
    Soy-fortified cornmeal

Selected Joint Ventures

Agribusiness
  AGRI-Bunge LLC (34% AGRI Industries grain
    origination and Mississippi river terminal operation)
  Biocolza-Oleos E Farinhas de Colza S.A. (40% joint
    venture with Tagol; rapeseed oil crushing and
    biodiesel production; Portugal)
  Biodiesel Bilbao S.A. (20% with Acciona
    Biocombustibles S.A.; biofuel production; Spain)
  Bunge-Ergon Vicksburg LLC (BEV; 50% with Ergon
    Ethanol Inc.; ethanol production)
  Diester Industries International S.A.S. (DII) (DII; 40%
    with Diester Industries a subsidiary of Sofiproteol;
    biodiesel production and marketing; Germany)
  Ecofuel S.A. (50% with AGD; biodiesel production;
    Argentina)
  Southwest Iowa Renewable Energy LLC (SIRE; 26%
    with agricultural producers located in Southwest
    Iowa; ethanol production)
Fertilizer
  Bunge Maroc Phosphore S.A. (50% with Office
    Cherifien Des Phosphates (OCP); fertilizer
    production; Morocco)
Food Products
  Harinera La Espiga S.A. de C.V. (32% with Grupo Neva
    S.A. de C.V. and Cerrollera S.A. de C.V.; wheat
    milling and bakery dry mix production; Mexico)

Selected Subsidiaries

Argentina
  Fertimport S.A.
  Guide S.A.
Belgium
  Afrique Initiatives
Bulgaria
  Kaliakra A.D.
Canada
  CF Oils Investments Inc.
  Leblanc & Lafrance Inc.
  Neptune Bulk Terminals (Canada) Ltd.
China
  Bunge Sanwei Oil & Fat Co. Ltd.
  Taixing Zhenhua Oils & Fats Co. Ltd.
Cyprus
  Brea Commodities Limited
France
  Diester Industries International S.A.S.
Italy
  Escercizio Raccordi Ferroviari S.p.A.
Latvia
  Dan Store LSEZ SIA
Mexico
  Harinera La Espiga S.A. de C.V.
  Inmobiliaria A. Gil S.A.
  Inmobiliaria Gilsa S.A.
Poland
  Polska Trade Services S.p.z.o.o.
  Warsaw Mathematical Institute Sp z.o.o.
  Z.T. Kruszwica S.A.
Romania
  SC Interoil S.A.
  SC Muntenia S.A.
  SC Unirea S.A.
Russia
  LLC Bunge CIS
  OJS Kholmsky
  Rostov Grain Terminal LLC
Spain
  Biodiesel Bilbao S.L.
  Estacion de Descarga y Carga S.A. (Esdecasa)
  Huelva Belts S.L.
  Moyresa Girasol S.L.
Switzerland
  Ecoinvest Carbon S.A.
  Oleina S.A.
Ukraine
  Black Sea Industries Limited

Suntrade S.E.
Uruguay
  Agritrade S.A.
US
  Biofuels Company of America LLC
  The Crete Mills Inc.
  Delphos Terminal Company Inc.
  International Produce Inc.
  Renewable Energy Group Inc.
  Solae Holdings LLC
  Southwest Iowa Renewable Energy LLC
Venezuela
  Almacen Terminal Santana C.A.
Vietnam
  Baria Joint Stock Company of Services for Import
    Export of Agro-Forestry Products and Fertilizer

COMPETITORS

ADM	LifeLine
Ag Processing Inc.	Louis Dreyfus Group
Associated British	Mosaic Company
Foods	Potash Corp
CHS	Repsol
Cargill	Rich Products
ConAgra	Sadia
Cosan	Sudzucker
Danisco A/S	Tereos
Dawn Food Products	Unilever
General Mills	Ventura Foods
Ingredion	Wilmar

HISTORICAL FINANCIALS

Company Type: Public

Income Statement

FYE: December 31

	REVENUE ($ mil.)	NET INCOME ($ mil.)	NET PROFIT MARGIN	EMPLOYEES
12/13	61,347	306	0.5%	350,000
12/12	60,991	64	0.1%	36,000
12/11	58,743	942	1.6%	34,000
12/10	45,707	2,354	5.2%	33,021
12/09	41,926	361	0.9%	25,945
Annual Growth	10.0%	(4.0%)	—	91.6%

2013 Year-End Financials

Debt ratio: 17.3%	No. of shares (mil.): 147
Return on equity: 2.9%	Dividends
Cash ($ mil.): 742	Yield: 1.3%
Current ratio: 1.42	Payout: 75.2%
Long-term debt ($ mil.): 3,179	Market value ($ mil.): 12,136

	STOCK PRICE ($) FY Close	P/E High/Low		PER SHARE ($) Earnings	Dividends	Book Value
12/13	82.11	53	42	1.55	1.14	66.69
12/12	72.69	389	301	0.19	1.04	74.22
12/11	57.20	12	9	6.07	0.00	81.48
12/10	65.52	4	3	15.06	0.88	83.34
12/09	63.83	32	19	2.22	0.80	70.80
Annual Growth	6.5%	—	—	(8.6%)	9.3%	(1.5%)

Canadian Imperial Bank of Commerce

Canadian Imperial Bank of Commerce (CIBC) is both Canadian and imperial when it comes to growing its business. CIBC has more than 1000 domestic branches that offer a range of consumer and business financial services including deposits loans investments and insurance. It operates in two main segments: CIBC Retail Markets (con-

sumer and small business banking credit cards wealth management) and wholesale banking arm CIBC World Markets (merchant and investment banking capital markets services and research for corporate institutional and government clients). Internationally CIBC owns a majority of First-Caribbean International Bank.

CIBC also operates retail brokerage CIBC Wood Gundy and offers investment management services in Hong Kong and Singapore. Active mainly in North America CIBC World Markets has operations in Asia Australia and Europe as well. The unit has identified lending securitization foreign exchange and electronic trading as areas of possible growth.

CIBC is selling its stake in trust and custody services provider CIBC Mellon to its partner in the joint venture The Bank of New York Mellon for an undisclosed amount. The sale fits in with the company's goals of focusing on its core operations.

In 2011 CIBC bought a 41% stake in American Century Investments a US asset management company with $111 billion under management. The deal helps increase the firm's fee-based income and grows its asset management business internationally. The company is now buying the private wealth management business of MFS McLean Budden which oversees some $1.4 billion in assets for high-net-worth investors.

CIBC is looking to expand its wealth management business throughout North America. To that end in 2013 it acquired Atlanta-based Atlantic Trust from Invesco for $210 million. The purchase provides CIBC with entry into the US private wealth market where high-net-worth personal financial assets are growing 50% faster than those of the average US household and builds on the bank's recent purchase of MFS McLean Budden in Canada. Also CIBC is seeking a more substantial retail banking presence in the US like larger competitors Toronto-Dominion Bank of Montreal and Royal Bank of Canada. Though it is the smallest of Canada's Big Five banks (which also includes Scotiabank) the company is aiming to be among the top three in its home market. To that end it has been adding new products opening branches extending business hours and enhancing its technology. In 2010 it strengthened its credit card business in Canada through the acquisition of a $2 billion credit card portfolio from Citigroup. The deal made CIBC Canada's largest credit card issuer. Also thin 2010 the company acquired CIT's business credit operations in Canada to bolster its asset-based lending.

CIBC more than doubled its net income and earnings per share that year after economic conditions and losses in its structured credit business weighed on its bottom line in 2008 and 2009. The company experienced fewer loan write-offs thanks to improved performance in its credit card and personal lending portfolios.

CIBC made a move in 2011 that may signal that it is looking for acquisitions abroad as well. That year it bought more than 20% of Bermuda-based Bank of N.T. Butterfield. The acquisition may be small but it is a shift from CIBC's previous cost-cutting approach.

HISTORY

In 1858 Bank of Canada was chartered; Toronto financier William McMaster bought the charter in 1866 when investors failed to raise enough money to open it and changed the name to Canadian Bank of Commerce.

The firm opened in 1867 bought the Gore Bank of Hamilton (1870) and expanded within seven years to 24 branches in Ontario as well as Montreal and New York. Led by Edmund Walker the bank spread west of the Great Lakes with the opening of a Winnipeg Manitoba branch in 1893 and joined the Gold Rush with branches in Dawson City Yukon Territory and Skagway Alaska in 1898.

As the new century began the bank's purchases spanned the breadth of Canada from the Bank of British Columbia (1901) to Halifax Banking (1903) and the Merchants Bank of Prince Edward Island (1906). More buys followed in the 1920s; the bank's assets peaked in 1929 and then plunged during the Depression. It recovered during WWII.

In 1961 Canadian Bank of Commerce merged with Imperial Bank of Canada to become Canadian Imperial Bank of Commerce (CIBC). Imperial Bank was founded in 1875 by Henry Howland; it went west to Calgary and Edmonton and became known as "The Mining Bank." It bought Barclays Bank (Canada) in 1956.

As the energy and agriculture sectors declined in the early 1980s two of CIBC's largest borrowers Dome Petroleum and tractor maker Massey-Ferguson defaulted on their loans. Deregulation opened investment banking to CIBC which in 1988 bought a majority share of Wood Gundy one of Canada's largest investment dealers; CIBC also purchased Merrill Lynch Canada's retail brokerage business.

In 1992 CIBC added substantially to its loss reserves (resulting in an earnings drop of 98%) to cover real estate losses from developer Olympia & York and others. This launched more cost-cutting as the company reorganized by operating segments.

Deregulation allowed CIBC to begin selling insurance in 1993; the company built a collection of life credit personal property/casualty and nonmedical health companies.

In 1996 the bank formed Intria a processing and technical support subsidiary. The next year CIBC Wood Gundy became CIBC World Markets and CIBC bought securities firm Oppenheimer & Co. and added its stock underwriting and brokerage abilities to CIBC World Markets.

In 1998 increasing foreign competition prompted CIBC and Toronto-Dominion to plan a merger (as did Royal Bank of Canada and Bank of Montreal); the government halted both plans citing Canada's already highly concentrated banking industry.

Spurned the bank overhauled its operations to spark growth in the late 1990s. To cut costs it eliminated some 4000 jobs and sold its more than $1-billion real estate portfolio. It teamed with the Winn-Dixie (1999) and Safeway (2000) supermarket chains to operate electronic branches in the US. The firm scaled back its disappointing international operations and began selling its insurance units.

In 2000 CIBC created Amicus as a holding company for CIBC World Markets' retail electronic banking business. The following year the bank sold its merchant card services business to US-based Global Payments.

In 2002 the company snagged US-based Merrill Lynch's Canadian retail brokerage asset management and securities operations renaming it CIBC Asset Management Inc. That same year CIBC merged its Caribbean banking business with that of UK-based Barclays to create FirstCaribbean Bank.

The next year CIBC sold the Oppenheimer private client and asset-management divisions to Fahnestock Viner (now Oppenheimer Holdings). It sold Juniper Financial a Delaware-based credit card issuer to Barclays for some $293 million in 2004.

In 2004 and again in 2006 CIBC was sued by creditors of Internet telecommunications company Global Crossing stating that the bank had engaged in insider trading to the tune of $2 billion. Creditors demanded a return of the proceeds. CIBC de-nied the claims but in 2006 two units of the bank agreed to pay $17.4 million to investors in the ill-fated telecom.

More trouble came in 2005 when CIBC agreed to pay some $2.4 billion in an investor class-action suit to resolve claims that the company helped notorious energy trader Enron to conceal losses.

EXECUTIVES

Senior Executive Vice-President Managing Director, Richard E. Venn, age 64
SEVP and Chief Risk Officer, Tom D. Woods, age 62, $352,830 total compensation
President; Chief Executive Officer; Director, Gerald T. (Gerry) McCaughey, age 57, $849,500 total compensation
Chairman, Charles Sirois, age 59
SEVP; Group Head Wholesale International and Technology and Operations, Richard W. Nesbitt, age 59, $238,380 total compensation
Senior Executive Vice-President CIBC and Group, Victor Dodig
SEVP and Group Head Retail and Business Banking, J. David Williamson, age 54, $288,339 total compensation
Chief Financial Officer; Senior Executive Vice President, Kevin Glass
Vice Chairman and SEVP, Rt. Hon. Jim Prentice
Vice President of Legal Affairs and General Counsel, Alvaro Diaz
Vice President of Corporate Development, Andres Franco
Vice-President General Counsel, Charles Gerber
Vice President of Exploration, Christian Rios
Vice President - Legal, Corey M. Dean
Director, Gary F. Colter, age 67
Director, Ronald W. (Ron) Tysoe, age 60
President CEO and Director, Gerald T. (Gerry) McCaughey, age 57
Director, Linda S. Hasenfratz, age 46
Director, Robert J. (Bob) Steacy, age 63
Director, Dominic D'Alessandro, age 65
Director, Patrick D. Daniel, age 66
Director, Jane L. Peverett, age 55
Director, Brent S. Belzberg, age 62
Director, Leslie Rahl, age 62
Director, John P. Manley, age 63
Director, Katharine B. (Kate) Stevenson, age 51
Director, Gordon D. Giffin, age 63
Director, Nicholas D. Le Pan, age 61
Director, Luc Desjardins, age 60
Vice Chairman and SEVP, Rt. Hon. Jim Prentice
Auditors: Ernst&YoungLLP

LOCATIONS

HQ: Canadian Imperial Bank of Commerce
Commerce Court, Toronto, Ontario M5L 1A2
Phone: 416 980-2211
Web: www.cibc.com

PRODUCTS/OPERATIONS

Sales

	% of total
Interest	
Loans	49
Securities &	12
Noninterest	
Deposit & payment	5
Mutual fund	5
Foreign exchange other than	4
Securitized	4
Trading	4
Commissions on securities	3
Investment management & custodial	3
Underwriting & advisory	3
Available-for-sale securities	3
Other	5
Total	**100**

COMPETITORS

BMO Financial Group	JPMorgan Chase
Barclays	National Bank of
Caisses centrale	Canada
Desjardins	RBC Financial Group
Citigroup	Scotiabank
Goldman Sachs	TD Bank

HISTORICAL FINANCIALS

Company Type: Public

Income Statement

FYE: October 31

	ASSETS ($ mil.)	NET INCOME ($ mil.)	INCOME AS % OF ASSETS	EMPLOYEES
10/14	370,794	2,875	0.8%	44,424
10/13	380,892	3,253	0.9%	43,039
10/12	394,456	3,340	0.8%	42,595
10/11	385,287	2,878	0.7%	42,239
10/10	345,577	2,406	0.7%	42,354
Annual Growth	1.8%	4.6%	—	1.2%

2014 Year-End Financials

Return on assets: 0.7%
Return on equity: 17.4%
Long-term debt ($ mil.): —
No. of shares (mil.): 397
Sales ($ mil): 15,544

Dividends
Yield: 4.3%
Payout: 54.3%
Market value ($ mil.): 36,268

	STOCK PRICE ($) FY Close	P/E High/Low		PER SHARE ($) Earnings	Dividends	Book Value
10/14	91.35	10	8	7.02	3.62	41.91
10/13	85.15	10	8	7.87	3.71	43.71
10/12	78.58	10	8	7.87	3.61	41.81
10/11	75.45	14	9	6.74	3.52	39.92
10/10	76.60	13	9	5.76	3.42	39.47
Annual Growth	4.5%	—	—	5.1%	1.4%	1.5%

Canon, Inc.

For Canon image is everything. The company makes printers multifunction document equipment and other computer peripherals for home and office use (more than half of sales). It also remains a force in the consumer and professional photography industry making still and video digital cameras LCD projectors lenses and binoculars. Canon also operates an industrial segment featuring such diverse products as semiconductor manufacturing equipment television broadcast lenses and devices used for eye examinations. Customers in its home country of Japan generate just 20% of the company's revenues.

Most of Canon's manufacturing is done in Japan but it also has plants in countries including Brazil France Germany the Netherlands China Malaysia Taiwan Thailand Vietnam and the US. Nearly 60% of Canon's revenues are divided between Europe which has the slightly larger share and the Americas served by subsidiaries including Canon U.S.A. and Canon Canada. The company circulates its products in those regions primarily through large distributors.

Like many companies Canon fell victim to the global recession with 2009 sales falling nearly one-quarter. Although the company recuperated with a 30% gain in 2010 it still hasn't returned to the level of growth it has typically had over the past decade. The deceptive 1% increase in revenues for 2011 when looked at in US currency reaching more than $45 billion was actually a 4% dip to

Â3.6 trillion albeit by a less-dramatic drop than recession-addled 2009. Net profit of Â255 trillion (about $3.2 billion) is much closer to pre-recession levels though it's still essentially flat in domestic currency compared to 2010.

Canon-branded products are the company's primary source of revenue but it also sells equipment that is branded for its partners. Competitor Hewlett-Packard is among those customer-partners accounting for approximately 20% of sales. With the market relatively underpenetrated with color office products Canon and its competitors are pushing to shift customers away from monochrome products for growth in this segment.

While rivals such as Xerox may be digging deep into back office enterprise IT services Canon has stayed more focused on the front office. In 2011 however the company created the Canon Information and Imaging Solutions subsidiary under Canon U.S.A. to focus on the IT services market. The new company will look to cloud computing and other software and services for such areas as business process optimization security services and elements of enterprise resource planning. In 2012 Canon announced it would acquire Belgium-based document management and IT services company I.R.I.S. Group. Canon has partnered with the company for years and bought a 17% stake in it in 2009. Besides bringing in complementary products the purchase will fuel Canon's consultancy aspirations.

Perhaps still best known for its cameras Canon has seen its photographic business steadily decline as traditional camera manufacturers have started to directly compete with electronics manufacturers. However the company remains a leader in the digital camera market where it concentrates on high-end single-lens-reflex (SLR) devices which include professional video cameras used in broadcast and major motion picture production. Canon's third primary product group industry encompasses a diverse portfolio including semiconductor and LCD lithography equipment medical imaging equipment lenses micromotors and large-format printers.

Canon faces stiff competition in all of its segments all over the world. In Japan the digital camera market is particularly heated. Although the company's brand remains strong globally it faces intense rivalries with foes such as Sony Nikon and Panasonic. To increase its competitiveness Canon hopes to find ways to bring products and services to its customers via the cloud and boost its R&D activity in the US and Europe. It will also keep an eye out for acquisitions that could bring in new technologies. The company's sales efforts will focus on strengthening its group companies in developed countries and forging approaches in emerging markets according to the conditions in each region.

HISTORY

Takeshi Mitarai and a friend Saburo Uchida formed Seiki Kogaku Kenkyusho (Precision Optical Research Laboratory) in Tokyo in 1933 to make Japan's first 35mm camera. In 1935 the camera was introduced under the brand name Kwanon (after Quan Yin the Buddhist goddess of mercy) —but later renamed Canon. In response to a pre-WWII military buildup the company made X-ray machines for the Japanese.

In 1947 the company became Canon Camera Company as the brand name gained popularity. Canon opened its first overseas branch in New York in 1955. It diversified into business equipment by introducing the first 10-key electronic calculator (1964) and a plain-paper photocopier (1968) independent of Xerox's patented technology. Canon dropped "Camera Company" from its name in 1969.

The company invented the "liquid dry" copying system which used plain paper and liquid developer in 1972. It failed to produce new cameras and was surpassed by Minolta (now defunct) as Japan's top camera exporter. Sales were sluggish in the early 1970s and in 1975 Canon suspended dividends for the first time since WWII.

At that time Canon's managing director Ryuzaburo Kaku convinced Mitarai that the company's problems stemmed from indecisive leadership and weak marketing. Kaku turned Canon around unleashing the electronic AE-1 in a media blitz that in 1976 included the first-ever TV commercials for a 35mm camera. With automated features the AE-1 appealed to the clumsiest photographers. Its success catapulted Canon past Minolta as the world's #1 camera maker.

In 1979 Canon introduced the first copier to use a dry developer. As the copier market matured in the early 1980s Canon shifted to making other automated office equipment including laser printers and fax machines.

Mitarai died in 1984. Minolta the next year again displaced Canon as the world's #1 camera maker when it introduced a fully automated model. But Canon came back in 1987 with the electronic optical system (EOS) auto-focus camera which returned the company to preeminence in 1990. That year the company initiated an ink cartridge recycling program. Canon teamed up with IBM in 1992 to produce portable PCs. In 1993 Takeshi Mitarai's son Hajime who joined Canon in 1974 was named president and began expanding product development.

In 1995 Canon introduced the world's first color ferroelectric LCD designed to replace cathode ray tubes in computer and TV screens as the industry standard. When Hajime died that year cousin Fujio Mitarai a 34-year Canon employee who served as the head of Canon U.S.A. in the 1980s was named president and CEO. In 1996 the company made Canon Latin America a direct subsidiary of Canon U.S.A. with the "kyosei" idea that regionalized control would make the subsidiary more efficient.

Canon stopped making PCs in 1997. The next year the company unveiled its Hyper Photo System which combines a scanner PC server and printer to produce photo prints and expanded its copier remanufacturing operations. In 1999 after 16 years of production Canon stopped making optical memory cards. The company also opened a research and development facility in the US.

In 2000 Canon and Toshiba began working together to develop technology for flat-panel displays. Canon expanded its line of digital cameras in 2001; the company's sales in that segment almost doubled that year.

The next year the company announced that it would merge two of its office equipment subsidiaries Copyer and Canon Aptex in an effort to improve operating efficiency.

In 2004 Canon formed a joint venture with Toshiba to develop surface-conduction electron-emitter display (SED) products. Canon acquired Toshiba's stake in the company in 2007.

In 2010 Canon acquired Oce Europe's largest manufacturer of printers to solidify its position in that key geographic market. The company maintained the Oce brand following completion of the transaction operating the Dutch supplier of office machines as a division.

EXECUTIVES

Chairman President and CEO, Fujio Mitarai, age 79
EVP and CFO, Toshizo Tanaka, age 74
EVP; Group Executive Corporate Planning Development, Kunio Watanabe, age 70
Senior Managing Director; President and CEO Canon U.S.A., Yoroku (Joe) Adachi, age 67
Senior Managing Director; Chief Executive Peripheral Products Operations, Yasuo Mitsuhashi, age 65
EVP Canon USA, Seymour E. Liebman, age 65
Executive Officer Medical Equipment, Yukiaki Hashimoto
Senior Managing Director; Chief Executive Office Imaging Products Operations, Masaki Nakaoka, age 65
Senior Managing Director; Group Executive Device Technology Development, Shigeyuki Matsumoto, age 64
Group Executive Network Visual Solution Business Promotion, Masanori Yamada
President and CEO Canon Canada, Kazuto (Kevin) Ogawa
Senior Managing Director; Group Executive Production Engineering, Haruhisa Honda, age 66
Managing Director; Chief Executive Image Communication Products Operations, Masaya Maeda, age 62
President and CEO Canon France, Kenji Kobayashi
Senior Executive Officer; Group Executive Global Manufacturing, Sachio Kageyama
Group Executive Human Resources Management and Organization, Kazuto Ono
Deputy Chief Executive Peripheral Products Operations, Akio Noguchi
Group Executive Quality Management, Hiroyuki Suematsu
Director; Group Executive Digital Platform Technology Development, Yasuhiro Tani
EVP CTO and Board Member, Toshiaki Ikoma, age 73
President and CEO Canon Europe, Rokus van Iperen
Managing Director; President and CEO Canon (China), Hideki Ozawa
Deputy Chief Executive Image Communication Products Operations, Masato Okada
Senior Managing Director; Group Executive Procurement, Toshio Homma
Director; Group Executive Information and Communication Systems, Makoto Araki
Group Executive Corporate Intellectual Property and Legal, Kenichi Nagasawa
EVP Canon USA, Yuichi Ishizuka
Senior Vice President, Eliott Peck
Senior Vice President, Joseph G. Warren
Vice President General Manager Imaging Systems Group, Sam Yoshida
Chief Executive Optical Products Operations, Shigeyuki Uzawa
Chief Executive Inkjet Products Operations, Naoji Otsuka
Group Executive Public Affairs, Kazuhiko Noguchi
Group Executive Semiconductor Production Equipment Group, Hiroaki Takeishi
Group Executive R&D Project Group, Nobutoshi Mizusawa
EVP CFO and Board Member, Toshizo Tanaka, age 73
Senior Managing Director, Kunio Watanabe, age 69
Senior Managing Director; President and CEO Canon USA, Yoroku (Joe) Adachi, age 66
Senior Managing Director; Chief Executive Peripheral Products Operations, Yasuo Mitsuhashi, age 65
Managing Director; President and CEO Canon Europa, Ryoichi Bamba, age 66
Managing Director; Chief Executive Inkjet Products Operations, Katsuichi Shimizu, age 67
Managing Director, Tomonori Iwashita, age 64
Managing Director; Chief Executive Office Imaging Products Operations, Masaki Nakaoka, age 64
Senior Managing Director, Shigeyuki Matsumoto, age 64
Managing Director, Haruhisa Honda, age 66

Managing Director; Chief Executive Image Communication Products Operations, Masaya Maeda, age 62
Director; Group Executive Digital Platform Technology Development, Yasuhiro Tani
EVP CTO and Board Member, Toshiaki Ikoma, age 73
Managing Director, Masahiro Osawa, age 66
Managing Director; President and CEO Canon (China), Hideki Ozawa
Managing Director; Chief Executive L Printer Products Operations, Toshio Homma
Director; Group Executive Information and Communication Systems Headquarters, Makoto Araki
Auditors: Ernst&YoungShinNihon

LOCATIONS

HQ: Canon, Inc.
30-2, Shimomaruko 3-chome, Ohta-ku, Tokyo 146-8501
Phone: (81) 3 3758 2111
Web: www.canon.jp

Sales

	% of total
Europe	31
Americas	27
Asia and	22
Japan	20
Total	**100**

PRODUCTS/OPERATIONS

Sales

	% of total
Office	53
Consumer	36
Industrial &	11
Total	**100**

Selected Products
Office
  Copy machines
    Office
    Personal
    Full-color
  Large format inkjet printers
  Laser printers
  Office imaging software
  Office network digital multifunction devices
  Toner Cartridges
Consumer
  Broadcasting equipment
  Cameras
    SLR
    Compact Digital
    Video camcorders
  Inkjet and photo printers
  Lenses
  Liquid-crystal display projectors
Industrial and other
  Color label card printers
  Document scanners
  LCD Lithography Systems
  Medical equipment
    Digital Radiography
    Ophthalmic Equipment
  Semiconductor production equipment

COMPETITORS

ASML	Lexmark
Agfa	NEC
Barco	Nikon
CASIO COMPUTER	Oce
Citizen	Oki Electric
Eastman Kodak	Olympus
Epson	Panasonic Corp
FUJIFILM	Philips Electronics
Fujitsu	Ricoh Company
Hewlett-Packard	SANYO
Hitachi	Samsung Electronics
Hoya Corp.	Sharp Corp.
IBM	Sony
JVC KENWOOD	Toshiba
Konica Minolta	Xerox
Kyocera	

HISTORICAL FINANCIALS

Company Type: Public

Income Statement

FYE: December 31

	REVENUE ($ mil.)	NET INCOME ($ mil.)	NET PROFIT MARGIN	EMPLOYEES
12/13	35,546	2,195	6.2%	194,151
12/12	40,401	2,607	6.5%	196,968
12/11	45,969	3,212	7.0%	198,307
12/10	45,573	3,031	6.7%	197,386
12/09	34,734	1,424	4.1%	168,879
Annual Growth	0.6%	11.4%	—	3.5%

2013 Year-End Financials

Debt ratio: 0.0%
Return on equity: 8.3%
Cash ($ mil.): 7,515
Current ratio: 2.69
Long-term debt ($ mil.): 13

No. of shares (mil.): 1,137
Dividends
Yield: 4.4%
Payout: 74.0%
Market value ($ mil.): 36,384

	STOCK PRICE ($) FY Close	P/E High/Low		PER SHARE ($) Earnings	Dividends	Book Value
12/13	32.00	0	0	1.91	1.41	24.38
12/12	39.21	0	0	2.22	1.49	26.17
12/11	44.04	0	0	2.64	0.00	27.44
12/10	51.34	0	0	2.46	1.23	26.48
12/09	42.32	0	0	1.15	1.15	23.57
Annual Growth	(6.7%)	—	—	13.5%	5.3%	0.9%

Carrefour S.A.

At the junction of groceries merchandise and services you'll find Carrefour (which means "crossroads"). One of the world's largest retailers (behind Wal-Mart and Tesco) Carrefour operates more than 10600 stores under various banners including hypermarkets (Carrefour) supermarkets (Carrefour Market formerly Champion) convenience stores (City Express Proxi) and cash-and-carry outlets (Promocash) in more than 30 countries in Europe Latin America and Asia. France with some 4780 Carrefour stores is the retailer's largest market. Carrefour is struggling to reverse a decade-long sales slump at home while expanding in fast-growing emerging markets in Asia and Latin America.

Geographic Reach
France is Carrefour's largest market accounting for 47% of sales in 2013. Other countries in Europe including Belgium Italy Poland Romania and Spain contributed about a quarter of its total sales. About 18% of the group's sales are rung up in Latin America (where it has market leading positions in Argentina and Brazil) while Asia (including China) accounts for nearly 9%.

Operations
Carrefour which pioneered the hypermarket format operates about 1420 of the huge general merchandise and grocery stores on three continents accounting for the majority of its sales. It also operates more than 2900 supermarkets in 19 countries under the Carrefour market and other banners. The French retail giant also operates a growing number of more than 5600 convenience stores 90% of which are operating under franchising agreements. Its cash & carry stores mostly in France combine wholesaling and hypermarkets offering larger quantities to cater to professionals. Carrefour also sells food and nonfood items online in France Brazil Spain and other countries.

Financial Performance
Carrefour reversed a three-year slide in sales in 2013 posting sales of Â74.9 billion ($102 billion) a modest 2% gain at constant exchange rates versus 2012. Notably its sales grew organically by more than 1% in France reversing a prolonged slump at home. Indeed in France Carrefour posted its best year of organic growth since 2007 across all of its store formats with hypermarkets performing particularly well. Beyond France sales grew in by double digits in Latin America driven by strong performance in Brazil and Argentina. While sales declined by 3% overall in Europe they showed signs of improvement particularly in Spain in the second half of 2013. Sales grew more modestly in Asia driven in part by expansion in China where Carrefour opened 20 new hypermarkets over the course of the year.

Net income was essentially flat (up 0.1%) in 2013 versus 2012 while recurring operating income rose 10% over the same period.

Strategy
Under the leadership of CEO Georges Plassat (who took over in May 2012) Carrefour is in the midst of a three-year recovery plan which appears to be meeting with some success. Plassat has reduced the company's exposure to ailing euro zone countries including Greece and Spain. Carrefour in mid-2012 sold its stake in its joint venture Carrefour Marinopoulos —operator of Greece's leading supermarket chain —at a loss to its partner. It also spun off its Dia discount chain though its working to reacquire the French locations. The spinoff enables Carrefour to concentrate on restoring its weaker domestic operations. Other efforts to revive its retail business include the sale of $1.2 billion worth of assets —including its stores in Japan and Mexico —to support lower prices and attract new shoppers.

Emerging markets are the growth driver for Carrefour. Overall the multi-format retailer does business in 34 countries including North Africa and the Middle East (Lebanon Jordan and the UAE). In 2013 Carrefour opened 810 new stores including 20 in China where it is looking to newly developing urban areas. Eastern Europe is also a focus for the company which entered Georgia in fall 2012 and is continuing its expansion in Poland and Romania. While it has been busy trimming the number of hypermarkets and supermarkets it operates Carrefour is growing its convenience store and cash & carry operations which boast smaller stores that can be situated closer to customers.

Mergers and Acquisitions
In late 2014 Carrefour got the go ahead from the Competition Authority to acquire Dia France from Spain's Dia. Under the terms of the agreement Carrefour will acquire more than 800 Dia stores and be required to sell about 55. (Carrefour previously owned Dia but spun it off in 2011 when the company was listed on the Spanish stock exchange.)

In 2014 Carrefour's convenience store business acquired 128 stores from the Coop Alsace network. Also in 2014 the company bought the RAST supermarket chain of 10 stores in Poland.

HISTORY

Although its predecessor was actually a supermarket opened by Marcel Fournier and Louis Defforey in a Fournier's department store basement in Annecy France the first Carrefour supermarket was founded in 1963 at the intersection of five roads (Carrefour means "crossroads"). That year

Carrefour opened a vast store dubbed a "hypermarket" by the media in Sainte-Genevieve-des-Bois outside Paris.

The company opened additional outlets in France and moved into other countries including Belgium (1969) Switzerland (1970 —the year it went public) Italy and the UK (1972) and Spain (1973). Carrefour stepped up international expansion during the mid-1970s after French legislation limited its growth within the country.

Carrefour exported its French-style hypermarkets to the US (Philadelphia) in 1988. Scant advertising limited selection and a union strike led Carrefour to close its US operations in 1993. Carrefour opened its first hypermarket in Taiwan in 1989. The next year it formed Carma a 50-50 joint venture with Groupama to sell insurance. Carrefour paid over $1 billion for two rival chains (the bankrupt Montlaur chain and Euromarche) in 1991.

Daniel Bernard replaced Michel Bon the hard-charging expansion architect in 1992 after a 50% drop in first-half profits. A year later Carrefour partnered with Mexican retailer Gigante to open a chain of hypermarkets in Mexico. (In 1998 Carrefour bought Gigante's share of the joint venture.) In 1996 the company bought a 41% stake in rival GMB (Cora hypermarket chain) and sold its 11% stake in US warehouse retailer Costco (it now owns 20% of Costco UK). The next year Carrefour allowed 16 hypermarkets owned by Guyenne et Gascogne Coop Atlantique and Chareton to operate under the Carrefour name. It expanded into Poland in 1997 and the Czech Republic in 1998.

Its biggest acquisition (at the time) came in 1998 when Carrefour acquired French supermarket operator Comptoirs Modernes (with about 800 stores under the Stoc Comod and Marche Plus flags). Carrefour also entered the Indonesian market that year.

In August 1999 Carrefour announced a deal even bigger than the one for Comptoirs Modernes —a $16.3 billion merger with fellow French grocer Promodes which operated more than 6000 hypermarkets supermarkets convenience stores and discount stores in Europe. Paul-Auguste Halley and Leonor Duval Lemonnier founded Promodes in Normandy France in 1961. Initially a wholesale food distributor Promodes opened its first supermarket in 1962. This was followed by a cash-and-carry wholesale outlet (1964) a hypermarket (1970) and convenience stores (Shopi and 8 a Huit during the 1970s). To gain regulatory approval for the acquisition Carrefour divested its stake in the Cora chain and sold nearly 40 other stores in France and Spain. The Promodes acquisition was completed in 2000.

The company joined with US retailer Sears and software maker Oracle among others to form Internet-based supply exchange GlobalNetXchange in early 2000. Also that year Carrefour bought Belgian retailer GB (about 500 stores).

In 2001 Carrefour sold its 74%-stake in Picard Surgeles (frozen food stores). Carrefour also opened its first Japanese grocery store near Tokyo that year.

The grocer sold its 10% stake in PetSmart Inc. in a public offering in July 2002. That December Carrefour acquired the remaining 20% of the shares of Centro Comerciales Carrefour its Spanish subsidiary it didn't already own in a public tender offer.

In February 2003 Carrefour acquired two hypermarkets in Italy from Hyparlo. In October it entered the Scandinavian market through a franchise partnership and supply agreement with Norwegian grocer NorgesGruppen. Soon after Carrefour Poland acquired two hypermarkets there from troubled Dutch retailer Royal Ahold. In late 2003

Carrefour's discount chain Ed acquired 44 Treff Marche shops in France from German retailer Edeka.

The company sold its seven-hypermarket Chilean division in January 2004 to Distribucion Y Servicio. In April Carrefour opened its first Champion supermarket in Beijing. In September it entered Norway with six Meny Champion discount supermarkets in Oslo in partnership with Norway's NorgesGruppen.

In February 2005 Luc Vandevelde the former chairman of troubled British retailer Marks and Spencer succeeded Daniel Bernard as non-executive chairman of Carrefour. Bernard had been with Carrefour for 13 years. No stranger to the company Vandevelde was chief executive of Promodes when it merged with Carrefour in 1999. Concurrently ex-CFO Jose-Luis Duran was named CEO. In March Carrefour sold its 29 hypermarkets in Mexico to Grupo Comercial Chedraui for an undisclosed sum. Also in March Carrefour exited the Japanese market with the sale of its eight hypermarkets there to Japanese retail giant AEON CO. On the plus side Carrefour completed the acquisition of Chris Cash & Carry of Cyprus through its Greek subsidiary Carrefour Marinopoulos. In November the French retailer acquired full ownership of three of its Chinese hypermarket joint ventures from its local partners: Kunming Department Store Co. a unit of China's Kunming Sinobright (Group) Co.; Hunan Yiyou Commercial Trade Co.; and Xinjiang Grandscape Investment Co. Also in 2005 Carrefour swapped 15 of its hypermarkets in Slovakia and the Czech Republic for five outlets in Taiwan operated by rival Tesco exiting both countries.

Carrefour increased its ownership stake in Groupe Hyparlo in late 2005 to 49% (up from 20% in 2004).

In 2006 the company pulled out of South Korea where it held a relatively weak market position. Carrefour sold its 32 stores there to local fashion retailer E.Land for about $1.9 billion. In July Carrefour acquired 98% of the share capital and 99% of the voting rights of Hyparlo which operates stores under the Carrefour banner in France and Romania. The retailer launched its own mobile phone service Carrefour Mobile at all 218 of its hypermarkets in France in late 2006. (Rival Auchan launched a similar product earlier in the year.)

Vandevelde resigned his position in 2007 as non-executive chairman after a falling out with the controlling Halley family. In July Carrefour acquired 250 Spanish discount supermarkets trading under the PLUS banner for about $275 million. About the same time it sold a dozen hypermarkets in Portugal to Sonae the country's largest retailer for about $920 million. In October Carrefour added to its holdings in Romania with the purchase of the Artima supermarket chain there from Polish-based private equity firm Enterprise Investors for about $87 million.

In March 2008 the Halley family split its 13% stake in Carrefour into two separate holding companies —Halley Participations SAS and Comet BV —thereby ceding control of the French retail giant to Blue Capital. In May Robert Halley stepped down as chairman of the company's supervisory board and was replaced by the deputy chairman Amaury de Seze. Blue Capital which recently was granted two seats on the company's supervisory board won a third with the appointment of Bernard Arnault.

Duran stepped down in January 2009 and Lars Olofsson took over as top executive. In June the company opened its first location in Russia: a hypermarket in Moscow. A second Russian store debuted in September.

In November 2010 Carrefour sold its 42 stores in Thailand to Casino Guichard-Perrachon's Big C affiliate there for some Å868 million ($1.17 billion).

At Carrefour's annual meeting in June 2011 chairman Amaury de Seze stepped down and Olofsson added the chairman's title. Olofsson retired in May 2012 and was succeeded by Georges Plassat who joined Carrefour as COO in April 2012.

EXECUTIVES

Director Financial Communications and Investor Relations, Patrice Lambert-de Diesbach, age 57

Chairman and CEO, Georges Plassat

Group Marketing Director, Patrick Rouvillois

Group Chief Commercial Officer, Jose C. Gonzales-Hurtado, age 50

Executive Director China and Taiwan, Thierry Garnier, age 46

Vice Chairman, Sebastien Bazin, age 52

Executive Director Convenience Stores and Cash, Gerard Dorey

Chief Human Resources and Organization Officer, Jean-Christophe Deslarzes, age 50

Executive Director Group Merchandise, Eric Legros

Executive Director France, Noel Prioux, age 54

Executive Director Belgium, Gerard Lavinay

Executive Director Italy, Giuseppe Brambilla

Executive Director Group Supply Chain, Roberto Canevari, age 48

Executive Director Turkey, Guillaume de Colonges

Executive Director Poland, Jean Anthoine

Executive Director Brazil, Luiz Fazzio

Executive Director Hypermarkets France, Guillaume Vicaire

General Secretary, Pierre Alexandre Teulie

Group General Counsel, Franck Tassan

Executive Director Group Financial Control, Charles Desmartis

Executive Director Supermarkets France, Alexandre Falck

Executive Director Formats and Channels, Laurent Bendavid

Group Communications Director, Florence Baranes Cohen

Executive Director Group Strategy and Mergers & Acquisitions, Vincent Abello

Executive Director Europe (excluding France), Thomas M. Hubner, age 56

Chief Financial Officer, Pierre-Jean Sivignon

Executive Director Spain, Pascal Clouzard

Corporate Commercial Development Products & Offer Director, Dor Sela

Executive Director India, Jean-Noel Bironneau

Executive Director Argentina, Daniel Fernandez

Executive Director Taiwan, Patrick Ganaye

Executive Director Romania, Francois Melchior de Polignac

Executive Director International Partnerships, Stephane Thouin

Director, Rene Brillet, age 71

Director, Charles Edelstenne, age 77

Director, Thierry Breton, age 59

Director, Anne-Claire Taittinger, age 63

Director, Nicolas Bazire, age 57

Director, Jean-Laurent Bonnafe, age 52

Director, Amaury-Daniel de Seze, age 67

Vice Chairman, Sebastien Bazin, age 52

Director, Rene Abate, age 64

Director, Bernard Arnault

Director, Mathilde Lemoine

Auditors: KPMGAudit

LOCATIONS

HQ: Carrefour S.A.
33, avenue Emile-Zola, TSA 55 555, Boulogne-Billancourt 92649
Phone: (33) 1 41 04 26 00   **Fax:** (22) 1 41 04 26 01
Web: www.carrefour.com

Sales

	% of total
Europe	
France	43
Other	29
Latin	19
Asia	9
Total	**100**

2011 Stores

	No.
Europe	
France	4,631
Other	3,964
Latin	583
Asia	380
Partner	213
Total	**9,771**

PRODUCTS/OPERATIONS

2011 Stores

	No.
Convenience	5,170
Supermarkets	2,995
Hypermarkets	1,452
Cash &	154
Total	**9,771**

Sales

	% of total
Hypermarket	63
Supermarket	24
Other	13
Total	**100**

Selected Operations and Banners

Hypermarkets
  Carrefour
Supermarkets
  Champion
  GB
  Globi
  GS
  Marinopoulos
  Norte
  Super GB
  Super GS
  Unic
Hard discount stores
  Ed
  Minipreco
Other stores
  Cash-and-carry stores
  Docks Market
  Promocash
  Puntocash
Convenience stores
  8 a Huit
  Di per Di
  GB Express
  Marche Plus
  Proxi
  Shopi
Other Operations
Carfuel (petroleum products)
Comptoirs Modernes (supermarkets)
Costco UK (20% warehouse club)
Erteco (hard-discount stores)
Financiera Pryca (46% consumer credit Spain)
Fourcar B.V. (investments The Netherlands)
GlobalNetXchange (Internet-based supply exchange joint venture)
Ooshop (online shopping)
Prodirest (catering)
Providange (auto centers)
S2P (60% consumer credit)

COMPETITORS

AEON	Ito-Yokado
ALDI	La Rinascente
Auchan	Lianhua Supermarket
Brasileira de	Lidl
Distribuic?o	Lotteshopping
Casino Guichard	METRO AG

China Nepstar	Marui Group
Dairy Farm	Migros
International	REWE
Delhaize	Rallye
E.Leclerc	Royal Ahold
Edeka Zentrale	SHV Holdings
Eroski	Super Indo
Falabella	Tengelmann
Galeries Lafayette	Tesco
Globex Utilidades	Wal-Mart
H&M	WuMart
ITM Entreprises	Zara

HISTORICAL FINANCIALS

Company Type: Public

Income Statement

FYE: December 31

	REVENUE ($ mil.)	NET INCOME ($ mil.)	NET PROFIT MARGIN	EMPLOYEES
12/13	105,561	1,738	1.6%	364,795
12/12	103,414	1,625	1.6%	357,980
12/11	107,051	479	0.4%	371,003
12/10	122,478	579	0.5%	471,755
12/09	125,875	471	0.4%	475,976
Annual Growth	**(4.3%)**	**38.6%**	**—**	**(6.4%)**

2013 Year-End Financials

Debt ratio: 44.7%
Return on equity: 16.4%
Cash ($ mil.): 6,549
Current ratio: 0.84
Long-term debt ($ mil.): 12,824

No. of shares (mil.): 701
Dividends
  Yield: 3.5%
  Payout: 11.0%
Market value ($ mil.): 5,525

	STOCK PRICE ($) FY Close	P/E High/Low		PER SHARE ($) Earnings	Dividends	Book Value
12/13	7.88	8	5	2.51	0.28	15.40
12/12	5.15	5	3	2.39	0.90	14.38
12/11	4.48	30	12	0.72	1.93	12.71
Annual Growth	**32.6%**	**—**	**—**	**36.4%**	**(38.1%)**	**4.9%**

Casino Guichard Perrachon S.A.

You won't hit the jackpot at Casino Guichard-Perrachon but odds are you'll go home with the groceries. One of the world's leading food retailers Casino Group owns and operates more than 11700 stores including hypermarkets (mostly Geant) supermarkets (Casino and Monoprix to name a few) restaurants (Casino Cafeteria) and discount stores (Leader Price). It is the third-largest food retailer (behind Carrefour and Auchan) and the #1 convenience store operator in France (primarily Petit Casino but other banners include Franprix Vival and Spar). Most of its stores are in France but it has outlets in 8 countries in Asia and South America including Brazil Colombia Thailand and Vietnam.

After a blip in 2009 when net sales dipped by just over 1% vs. the previous year Casino's sales (in local currency) rebounded by more than 8% in 2010. Profitability improved as well (up 7.5% for the year). With emerging economies in South America and Asia outperforming France Casino's international operation outperformed its domestic one with net sales overseas increasing by more than 22% while sales at home grew by less than 2%. Indeed international sales are a rapidly-growing part of Casino's revenue stream accounting for

48% of sales in 2011 up from 34% just two years ago. Key international markets for the French firm include Brazil where it operates more than 1500 stores Colombia Thailand and Vietnam.

More than 90% of Casino's growing international business comes from the fast-growing South American and Asian markets where the company is placing its bets. Brazil and Colombia together account for more than two-thirds of the company's overseas sales. Casino owns a 43% stake in Brazil's #1 retailer Companhia Brasileira de Distribuic o (CBD) operator of the Pio de Acucar supermarket chain there. The French retailer also operates in the Indian Ocean region where it owns a majority stake in Vindemia an operator of supermarkets and hypermarkets in Asia and Africa. In Thailand Casino's Big C affiliate in late 2010 acquired about 40 stores (including 34 hypermarkets) from rival Carrefour for E868 million (about $1.17 billion). (Casino owns a 36% stake in that country's Big C Supercentre chain which is second in store count in Thailand to UK-owned Tesco Lotus.) The move doubled Big C's presence in Greater Bangkok.

At home price competition from discounters has hurt Casino and its rival Carrefour as French shoppers eschew their traditional hypermarkets and supermarkets for discount stores. In response Casino has strengthened its position in the convenience and discount store markets. Indeed convenience and discount stores are the retailer's most popular formats accounting for 60% of sales in France.

Casino shored up its balance sheet through a plan to dispose of some E1 billion ($1.3 billion) of assets by the end of 2010. The divestments included the sale of 42 superette Casino supermarket and Franprix-Leader price stores in 2008. Future divestments will include the sale of E334 million ($424 million) of soon-to-be-built real estate to Mercialys a property company spun off by Casino in 2006. Mercialys will pay for the properties in stock which will be redistributed to Casino shareholders as a dividend. Casino has been reducing its stake in Mercialys thereby raising E138 million ($182 million). It currently owns about 40% of the property company.

The company's 125-plus Geant hypermarkets (warehouse-style stores that sell groceries and other merchandise) and convenience stores together contribute more than 50% of revenues. Casino Cafeteria operates about 275 eating places in varying size and cuisines including Poncholito (Tex-Mex) and La Pastaria (Italian). Casino is also active in e-commerce (Cdiscount.com).

Casino is controlled by Euris which is controlled by Jean-Charles Naouri Casino's chairman and CEO.

HISTORY

Frenchman Geoffroy Guichard married Antonia Perrachon a grocer's daughter in 1889 in Saint-Etienne France. Three years later Geoffroy took over his father-in-law's general store (a converted "casino" or musical hall). In 1898 the company became Societe des Magasins du Casino. By 1900 when it became a joint stock company Casino had 50 stores; it opened its 100th store in 1904. That year the company introduced its first private-label product: canned sardines. In 1917 Guichard named his two sons Mario and Jean as managers.

By WWI there were about 215 branches more than 50 in Saint-Etienne. From 1919 to the early 1920s the company opened several factories to manufacture goods such as food soap and perfumes. In 1925 the elder Guichard retired leaving the day-to-day operations of Casino to his two sons. (Geoffroy died in 1940.) WWII took a heavy toll on the company: About 70 Casino stores were leveled and another 450 were damaged.

The company began opening cafeterias in 1967 and in 1976 it formed Casino USA to run them. Casino USA bought an interest in the California-based Thriftimart volume retailer in 1983 renaming the company after Thriftimart's Smart & Final warehouse stores.

Casino grew by acquiring companies across France including CEDIS (16 hypermarkets 116 supermarkets and 722 smaller stores in eastern France; 1985) and La Ruche Meridionale (18 hypermarkets and 112 supermarkets in southern France 1990). Casino bought nearly 300 hypermarkets and supermarkets from Rallye SA in 1992 giving Rallye about 30% of the company. The company opened its first hypermarket in Warsaw Poland in 1996.

Rival Promodes made a roughly $4.5 billion hostile takeover bid for Casino in 1997. Guichard family members voted against the Promodes offer instead backing a $3.9 billion friendly offer from Rallye (increasing their stake to nearly 50%). Casino also launched a massive counterattack — buying more than 600 Franprix and Leader Price supermarket stores from food manufacturer TLC Beatrice and acquiring a 21% stake in hypermarket chain Monoprix. Promodes withdrew its bid four months later.

Casino expanded internationally in the late 1990s acquiring stakes in food retailers in Argentina (Libertad) Uruguay (Disco) Colombia (Almacenes Exito SA) Brazil (Companhia Brasileira de Distribuicio) and Thailand (Big C the country's largest retailer). It also opened its first hypermarket in Taichung Taiwan.

Expansion in France included a joint venture (called Opera) formed in 1999 with retailer Cora SA to buy food and nonfood goods for the Casino and Cora stores and the acquisition of 100 convenience stores (converted to the Petit Casino banner) in southwest France from retailer Guyenne et Gascogne.

Casino acquired 100 Proxi convenience stores in southeast France in 2000 from Montagne (most became Vival franchises) and more than 400 convenience stores (Eco Service and others) from Auchan. Casino also bought 51% of French online retailer Cdiscount.com (CDs videos CD-ROMs and DVDs) and upped its ownership in several of its international supermarket operations including gaining 100% ownership of Libertad. It also increased its ownership of Monoprix to 49%.

In July 2002 Casino bought a 38% stake in Laurus NV its financially troubled Dutch rival. Laurus operates nearly 2000 supermarkets in the Netherlands Spain and Belgium. (Soon after Casino sold Laurus's unprofitable stores in Spain and Belgium.) Also in 2002 the company sold its wine division Les Chais Beaucairois to wine and spirits company Marie Brizard for $22 million.

Chief executive Pierre Bouchut unexpectedly left Casino in March 2005. Jean-Charles Naouri the company's chairman and controlling shareholder replaced him. In May Casino took joint control of Brazil's leading food retailer Companhia Brasileira de Distribuicio along with the family of Abilio Diniz. Previously Casino held a minority stake in the supermarket chain. Casino spun off some of its shopping center assets in an October IPO for part of its real estate assets in France including shopping mall properties adjacent to its hypermarket and supermarkets as well as the land under its cafeterias.

In 2006 the French supermarket operator spun off its property company Mercialys. (Following the IPO Casino holds about a 60% stake in Mercialys.) In January 2006 Casino increased its stake in Colombia's biggest retailer Exito to nearly 39%. The company in July sold its 19 hypermarkets in Poland to METRO AG its German rival for about $1.1 billion as part of its asset disposal program. In September Casino sold its 50% stake in its Tai-wanese subsidiary Far Eastern Geant to its joint venture partner Far Eastern Department Stores.

Real estate sales continued in late 2007 with the announcement that Casino plans to sell nearly $930 million in assets including 255 grocery stores in France. The retailer says it plans to use the proceeds from the sale of these "mature" assets for high-potential projects in France and abroad. In May 2007 Casino sold its 55% stake of the California-based Smart & Final warehouse grocery chain to Apollo Management for $813 million thereby exiting the US market.

Casino acquired in July 2008 about 90% of the French textile maker International Textiles Associes (or INTEXA) from members of the Broyer family. Also Casino exercised its option in 2008 to increase its share in Dutch supermarket operator Super de Boer (formerly Laurus acquired in 2002) to a majority stake. However in December 2009 Casino sold its 57% stake in Super de Boer to Dutch rival Jumbo Groep Holding for E552.5 (nearly $800 million).

In November 2009 Casino acquired the remaining shares of Leader Price and Franprix chains from the Baud family bringing its ownership stake up to 100% in both chains.

EXECUTIVES

Chairman Chief Executive Officer, Jean-Charles Naouri, age 65
Finance Director, Antoine Giscard d'Estaing
Secretary, Jacques Dumas, age 62
Director, Frederic Saint-Geours
Director, Abilio dos Santos Diniz, age 78
Director, Marc Ladreit de Lacharriere, age 73
Director, Didier Carlier, age 63
Director, Philippe Houze, age 66
Director, Gerald de Roquemaurel, age 68
Director, David de Rothschild, age 72
Director, Jean-Marie Grisard, age 71
Director, Catherine Lucet
Director, Gilles Pinoncely, age 73
Director, Rose-Marie Van Lerberghe, age 74
Director, Henri M.E.V. Giscard d'Estaing, age 58
Director, Didier Leveque
Director, Michel Savart
Auditors: CabinetDidierKling&Associes

LOCATIONS

HQ: Casino Guichard Perrachon S.A.
1, Esplanade de France, Saint-Etienne, Cedex 2 42008
Phone: (33) 4 77 45 31 31   **Fax:** (33) 4 77 45 38 38
Web: www.groupe-casino.fr/en/

2011 Stores

	No.
France	9,450
International	
Brazil	1,571
Colombia	351
Thailand	221
Indian	53
Uruguay	52
Argentina	24
Vietnam	23
Total	**11,745**

PRODUCTS/OPERATIONS

2011 Stores (France)

	No.
Hypermarkets	127
Supermarkets	1,833
Discount	608
Superettes &	6,587
Other	295
Total	**9,450**

Selected Operations

Banque du Groupe Casino (60% financial services)

Big C (36% Thailand)
Casino Enterprise (non-food operations)
Cativen (66% Venezuela)
Cdiscount.com (67% e-commerce)
Companhia Brasileira de Distribuic?o (34% Brazil)
Devoto (97% supermarkets Uruguay)
Exito Colombia SA (55% supermarkets)
Franprix (supermarkets)
Geant (hypermarkets)
Imagica (photo and digital imaging processing)
Leader Price (supermarkets)
Libertad (hypermarkets Argentina)
Vindemia (supermarkets; Madagascar Mauritius Reunion)

COMPETITORS

ALDI	ITM Entreprises
Auchan	Kingfisher
Carrefour	METRO AG
E.Leclerc	Migros
Groupe Flo	Tesco
Guyenne et Gascogne	Wal-Mart Brazil
IGA	

HISTORICAL FINANCIALS

Company Type: Public

Income Statement

FYE: December 31

	REVENUE ($ mil.)	NET INCOME ($ mil.)	NET PROFIT MARGIN	EMPLOYEES
12/13	66,971	1,171	1.7%	329,355
12/12	55,319	1,399	2.5%	316,711
12/11	44,444	734	1.7%	223,050
12/10	38,917	736	1.9%	170,248
12/09	38,545	851	2.2%	163,208
Annual Growth	14.8%	8.3%	—	19.2%

2013 Year-End Financials

Debt ratio: 37.2%
Return on equity: 11.2%
Cash ($ mil.): 7,479
Current ratio: 0.94
Long-term debt ($ mil.): 11,724

No. of shares (mil.): 113
Dividends
　Yield: 6.7%
　Payout: 13.8%
Market value ($ mil.): 2,596

	STOCK PRICE ($) FY Close	P/E High/Low		PER SHARE ($) Earnings	Dividends	Book Value
12/13	22.95	6	4	10.16	1.55	93.43
12/12	19.37	4	3	12.38	1.27	87.88
Annual Growth	18.5%	—	—	(4.8%)	5.1%	1.5%

Cathay Financial Holding Co

One of the largest financial services firms in Taiwan Cathay Financial Holding Co. owns companies involved in banking insurance brokerage and more. Its holdings include life accident and health insurer Cathay Life; property/casualty coverage provider Cathay Century; brokerage firm Cathay Securities; and Cathay United Bank which offers consumer banking services such as deposit accounts home mortgages credit cards and car loans as well as international banking and trust services. Cathay Financial Group also has units devoted to venture capital investing. All told the company has more than 700 locations and claims a customer base of more than ten million.

EXECUTIVES

Director; Chairman Cathay Insurance (China), Fa-Te Chang

Director; President Cathay Life Insurance, Ming-Ho Hsiung

Chairman Cathay Financial Holdings and Cathay Life Insurance, Hong-Tu Tsai

Vice Chairman; Chairman Cathay United Bank, Gregory K.H. Wang

President and Director, Chang-Ken Lee

CFO and First Deputy Spokesperson, Grace Chen

Director; Managing Director Cathay Life Insurance, Cheng-Ta Tsai

Director; Chairman Cathay Century Insurance, Cheng-Chiu Tsai

Director; Vice Chairman Cathay United Bank, Tsu-Pei Chen

Director; President Cathay Century Insurance, J. H. Hsu

EVP and Director; Chairman Cathay Securities Corporation, David P. Sun

EVP and Spokesperson, Alan Lee

Director; Chairman Cathay Insurance (China), Fa-Te Chang

Director; President Cathay Life Insurance, Ming-Ho Hsiung

Vice Chairman; Chairman Cathay United Bank, Gregory K.H. Wang

President and Director, Chang-Ken Lee

Director; Managing Director Cathay Life Insurance, Cheng-Ta Tsai

Director; Chairman Cathay Century Insurance, Cheng-Chiu Tsai

Director; Vice Chairman Cathay United Bank, Tsu-Pei Chen

Director; President Cathay Century Insurance, J. H. Hsu

EVP and Director; Chairman Cathay Securities Corporation, David P. Sun

Auditors: Ernst&Young

LOCATIONS

HQ: Cathay Financial Holding Co
No. 296, Sec. 4, Ren Ai Road, Da' an District, Taipei 106
Phone: (886) 2 2708 7698   **Fax:** (886) 2 2325 2488
Web: www.cathayholdings.com.tw

COMPETITORS

Bank of China	Hua Nan Financial
Chang Hwa Bank	Mega Financial
Chinatrust Financial	Shin Kong
E.Sun	SinoPac Holdings
First Financial	Taishin
Holding	Taiwan Business Bank

HISTORICAL FINANCIALS
Company Type: Public

Income Statement
FYE: December 31

	ASSETS ($ mil.)	NET INCOME ($ mil.)	INCOME AS % OF ASSETS	EMPLOYEES
12/13	203,777	966	0.5%	44,487
12/12	189,889	555	0.3%	44,678
12/11	165,140	372	0.2%	43,904
12/10	161,137	148	0.1%	42,605
12/09	134,269	338	0.3%	43,340
Annual Growth	11.0%	30.0%	—	0.7%

2013 Year-End Financials

Return on assets: 0.5%	Dividends
Return on equity: 10.9%	Yield: 0.0%
Long-term debt ($ mil.): —	Payout: 0.2%
No. of shares (mil.): —	Market value ($ mil.): —
Sales ($ mil) 13,311	

	STOCK PRICE ($) FY Close	P/E High/Low		PER SHARE ($) Earnings	Dividends	Book Value
12/13	13.41	0	0	0.08	0.00	0.79
12/12	10.00	0	0	0.05	0.00	0.78
12/11	10.60	—	—	0.03	0.00	0.66
12/10	15.49	—	—	0.01	0.00	0.70
12/09	19.92	—	—	0.03	0.00	0.62
Annual Growth	(9.4%)	—	—	28.1%	—	6.2%

Celesio AG

Celesio likes being a middleman when it comes to pharmaceuticals. The company is one of Europe's largest drug wholesalers holding market-leading positions in several of the countries it serves. Its largest wholesale markets are France Germany and the UK. In addition to more than 130 wholesale distribution branches serving 65000 pharmacies Celesio owns retail chains consisting of 2200 pharmacies in Europe including Norway Italy and the UK. Celesio which was founded in 1835 and was acquired by North American pharmaceuticals distributor McKesson in 2014 has a presence in 14 countries.

Change in Company Type

McKesson purchased Celesio in 2014 in an $8.3 billion deal to expand its operations into Europe. Through an expanded global presence McKesson aims to increase globalization in a rapidly changing health care market; the combined entity is expected to benefit from increased purchasing power technology resources supply chain efficiencies and global sourcing capabilities.

EXECUTIVES

Deputy Chairman Supervisory Board, Ihno Goldenstein

Chairman of the Management Board and CEO, Markus Pinger, age 51

Chief Financial Officer, Christian Holzherr, age 51

Head Manufacturer Solutions and Head Global Strategic Marketing and Business Innovation Unit, Michael Lonsert

Head Corporate Communications, Rainer Berghausen

Supervisory Board Member, Hanspeter Spek, age 65

Supervisory Board Member, Klaus Trutzschler, age 64

Supervisory Board Member, Jorg Lauenroth-Mago

Supervisory Board Member, W. M. Henning Rehder

Deputy Chairman Supervisory Board, Ihno Goldenstein

Supervisory Board Member, Prof Julius Michael Curtius

Supervisory Board Member, Dirk-Uwe Kerrmann

Supervisory Board Member, Ulrich Neumeister

Group Managing Director Celesio Wholesale, Wolfgang Mahr, age 55

Supervisory Board Member, Hubertus Erlen

Supervisory Board Member, Klaus Borowicz

Supervisory Board Member, Susan Naumann

Auditors: Ernst&YoungAG

LOCATIONS

HQ: Celesio AG
Neckartalstrasse 155, Stuttgart D-70376
Phone: (49) 711 50 01 00   **Fax:** (49) 711 50 01 12 60
Web: www.celesio.com

Sales

	% of total
France	29
UK	21
Germany	19
Other	31
Total	**100**

PRODUCTS/OPERATIONS

Sales

	% of total
Pharmacy solutions	82
Manufacturing solutions	3

Selected Subsidiaries

Pharmacy Solutions (wholesale distribution division)
  AAH Pharmaceuticals Ltd. (UK)
  AFM S.p.A. (Italy)
  Cahill May Roberts Group Ltd (Ireland)
  GEHE Pharma Handel GmbH (Germany)
  GEHE Pharma Praha spol. S r.o. (Czech Republic)
  Herba Chemosan Apotheker AG (Austria)
  Kemofarmacija d.d. (Slovenia Romania and Croatia)
  Laboratoria Flandria NV (Belgian)
  Norsk Medisinaldepot AS (Norway)
  OCP Repartition (France)
  OCP Portugal Produtos Farmaceuticos SA (Portugal)
  Panpharma Participacoes S.A. (54% Brazil)
  Pharma Belgium SA
  Rudolf Spiegel GmbH (Germany)
  Tjellesen Max Jenne A/S (Denmark)
Patient and Consumer Solutions (retail pharmacies division)
  Admenta Italia S.p.A.
  Apotheke DocMorris (retail franchise)
  Brocacef (45% Netherlands)
  DocMorris Kooperationen GmbH (mail order)
  Lekarny Lloyds s.r.o. (Czech Republic)
  Lloyds Pharmacy Limited (UK)
  Lloydspharma SA (Belgium)
  Unicare Pharmacy Limited (Ireland)
  Vitusapotek AS (Norway)
Manufacturer Solutions (marketing logistics and services division)
  Celesio Medco
  Evolution Homecare
  Movianto
  pharmexx

COMPETITORS

Alliance Boots	Profarma Distribuidora
Cardinal Health	Sigma Pharmaceuticals
Co-operative Group	Superdrug
Mawdsleys	UDG Healthcare
Mediq	Waymade
PHOENIX Pharma	

HISTORICAL FINANCIALS
Company Type: Public

Income Statement
FYE: December 31

	REVENUE ($ mil.)	NET INCOME ($ mil.)	NET PROFIT MARGIN	EMPLOYEES
12/13	29,472	220	0.7%	28,653
12/12	29,354	(205)	—	28,877
12/11	29,783	2	0.0%	36,670
12/10	31,154	346	1.1%	36,411
12/09	30,969	(1)	—	46,095
Annual Growth	(1.2%)	—	—	(11.2%)

2013 Year-End Financials

Debt ratio: 34.4%	No. of shares (mil.): 170
Return on equity: 7.4%	Dividends
Cash ($ mil.): 737	Yield: 0.0%
Current ratio: 1.28	Payout: 6.5%
Long-term debt ($ mil.): 1,921	Market value ($ mil.): 1,068

	STOCK PRICE ($) FY Close	P/E High/Low		PER SHARE ($) Earnings	Dividends	Book Value
12/13	6.28	13	7	1.27	0.08	17.47
12/12	3.35	—	—	(1.21)	0.04	16.75
12/11	3.11	977414		0.01	0.17	19.36
12/10	4.89	8	4	1.98	0.08	20.37
12/09	5.00	—	—	(0.00)	0.09	19.77
Annual Growth	5.9%	—	—		(0.8%)	(3.0%)

Central Bank of Ireland (Ireland)

LOCATIONS

HQ: Central Bank of Ireland (Ireland)
P.O. Box No. 559, Dame Street, Dublin 2
Phone: (353) 1 224 6278 **Fax:** (353) 1 671 6561
Web: www.centralbank.ie

HISTORICAL FINANCIALS

Company Type: Public

Income Statement

FYE: December 31

	ASSETS ($ mil.)	NET INCOME ($ mil.)	INCOME AS % OF ASSETS	EMPLOYEES
12/13	148,839	2,090	1.4%	1,384
12/12	181,213	1,894	1.0%	1,394
12/11	227,966	1,552	0.7%	1,372
12/10	273,682	1,125	0.4%	1,226
12/09	179,922	1,345	0.7%	1,044
Annual Growth	(4.6%)	11.6%	—	7.3%

Centrica Plc

Centrica is centered on integrated energy operations in the UK and North America through four major brands —British Gas Centrica Energy Centrica Storage and Direct Energy. The UK's largest gas supplier British Gas serves about 12 million homes and 1 million businesses with electricity gas and energy-related services in the UK. Through its Direct Energy unit Centrica supplies gas and power to residential customers in Canada and the US. Centrica is also engaged in gas exploration and production and storage operations. Other activities include gas and electricity production wholesale energy marketing international retail energy marketing drain cleaning services (the Dyno Group) and appliance sales.

Through Centrica Energy Centrica held proved and probable reserves of about 440 million barrels of oil equivalent in 2011. Centrica Storage handles the company's gas storage operations. Its Rough storage facility under the North Sea accounts for 70% of the UK's natural gas storage.

A major aspect of the company's strategy includes growing its core British Gas business and upstream operations (including gas supply storage and renewables) while establishing a leadership position as an integrated North American energy

business. Centrica also intends to increase its gas production by 50% —to around 75 million barrels of oil equivalent over the next three to five years — by extending its geographic reach. The company also looks to investing in power generation using offshore wind nuclear and biomass technologies to supply its customers' needs. It plans to double the profitability of its business by 2014 through targeted acquisitions both upstream and downstream.

Centrica began in 2012 a program to save Â500 million ($788 million) in costs over the next two years by identifying efficiencies. Although the company plans to continue investing for further growth it has already started cutting 2300 positions company-wide as well as implementing a pay freeze across much of the group. It set out to develop a better relationship with its customers by simplifying the purchase of gas and electricity. It also decided to make the cost of delivery more transparent by giving its customers a breakdown on their bill of the actual costs of providing the energy.

Through its aggressive acquisition strategy in North America the company has gained more than 6 million retail power and gas supply customers in less than a decade as part of its Direct Energy operations. Building on its portfolio of offerings in 2011 it acquired Illinois-based Home Warranty of America (HWA) for Â30 million ($48 million). HWA provides whole home warranty plans to more than 70000 customers through a network of 4000 contractors.

Direct Energy also made three acquisitions in 2011 for its residential energy supply business in North America: Gateway Energy Services First Choice Power and Vectren Retail. The deals part of the company's strategy of acquiring smaller suppliers and buying in deregulated markets added more than 750000 customers.

In a major move to grow its upstream business and its Norwegian operations Centrica completed a Â936 million ($1.5 billion) deal in 2012 to acquire Norwegian assets from Statoil and ConocoPhillips. Combined the new assets will increase the company's reserves by almost 40% and its production by more than 30%. The acquisition includes proved and probable reserves of 117 million barrels of oil equivalent and production of 34000 barrels of oil evalent per day. The buy also makes Centrica one of Norway's fastest growing companies with a third of its gas and oil production originating from that region. The company's upstream operations also have a presence in Trinidad and the Netherlands.

In spite of the growth of Centrica's gas assets the company decided to raise its gas and electricity prices by 17% in late 2011 to cover the rising wholesale commodity prices in the first half of the year. Mild weather that year led to a decline per household averaging 21% less in gas and 4% less in electricity consumption. With lower residential demand customer bills were 4% lower on average in 2011. Consumer complaints over higher prices for heating homes in the UK led to protests at the offices of utility companies and at town halls early in 2012.

The company's upstream businesses in the UK produced higher profits in 2011 especially the company's nuclear assets. Market conditions remained difficult for the gas-fired generation and gas storage businesses. An increase in taxation in the UK on upstream operations reduced the company's earnings in that segment. However in North America the company's Direct Energy unit showed a strong performance in 2011.

Centrica posted revenues of Â22.8 billion ($36 billion) in 2011 a 2% hike over 2010 revenues primarily because of higher upstream revenue that year due to higher prices. The company also recorded earnings that year of Â421 million ($662 million) plunging about 78% from the previous

year due to a large one-off charge mild weather higher wholesale gas prices and a weak economy. The charge included costs for the revaluation of contracts pension changes and losses on the company's disposals.

HISTORY

William Murdock invented gas lighting in 1792. In 1812 the Gas Light and Coke Company of London was formed as the world's first gas supplier to the public and by 1829 the UK had 200 gas companies.

In the second half of the 19th century the gas industry began looking for new uses for the fuel. Gas stoves were introduced in 1851 the geyser water heater was invented in 1868 and in 1880 the first gas units to heat individual rooms were developed.

Gas companies countered the emerging electricity industry by renting gas stoves at low prices and installing gas fittings (stove pipe and lights) in poor homes with no installation charges or deposits. By 1914 the UK had 1500 gas suppliers.

The electricity industry soon made major strikes against the gas industry's dominance. In 1926 the government began reorganizing the fragmented electricity supply industry building a national power grid and establishing the Central Electricity Generating Board to oversee it.

The gas industry was nationalized in 1949 and 1050 gas suppliers were brought under the control of the British Gas Council. Still the gas industry was losing. Supplying gas was more expensive than generating electricity: Gas was seen as a power supply of the past. The Gas Council sought to change that image through an aggressive marketing campaign in the 1960s touting gas as a modern clean fuel. Other factors played a part in its re-emergence: The Clean Air Act of 1956 steadily reduced the use of coal for home heating liquefied natural gas was discovered in the North Sea and OPEC raised oil prices in the 1970s. When natural gas was introduced most of the old gasworks were demolished and the British Gas Council (which became the British Gas Corp. in 1973) set about converting free of charge every gas appliance in the UK to natural gas.

As Margaret Thatcher's government began privatizing state industries the British Gas Corp. was taken public in 1986. Freed from government control British Gas expanded its international exploration and production activities. When the US gas industry began deregulating British Gas formed joint venture Accord Energy in 1994 with US gas trader Natural Gas Clearinghouse (now NGC) to sell gas on the wholesale market.

With the opening of the UK gas-supply market (which began regionally in 1996 and went nationwide in 1998) British Gas split into two public companies to avoid a conflict of interest between its supply business and its monopoly transportation business. In 1997 it spun off Centrica the retail operations and BG (now BG Group) which received the transportation business and the international exploration and production operations.

The UK electricity supply market began opening up to competition in 1998 and Centrica won 750000 UK electricity customers most of them also gas customers. In 1999 it bought The Automobile Association which it sold to venture capitalists in 2004. In 2000 Centrica began offering telecom services in the UK.

Centrica moved into North America in 2000 by purchasing two Canadian companies: natural gas retailer Direct Energy Marketing and gas production company Avalanche Energy. It gained a 28% stake in US marketing firm Energy America through the Direct Energy transaction and purchased the remaining 72% from US firm Sempra Energy the next year. Continuing its non-domestic strategy Centrica bought a 50% interest in Belgium energy supplier Luminus.

The firm purchased 60% of the 1260-MW Humber Power station in 2001 its first domestic power plant interest. It also acquired the UK operations of Australia's One.Tel and it bought Enron's European retail supply business Enron Direct for $137 million.

In 2002 Centrica purchased the retail energy services business of Canadian pipeline company Enbridge for $637 million; it also agreed to acquire another Enron-controlled company US retail energy supplier NewPower Holdings for $130 million. But Centrica withdrew its offer to buy NewPower a month after the deal was announced because of concerns about NewPower's potential Enron-related liabilities. Later that year Centrica acquired 200000 retail customer accounts in Ohio and Pennsylvania from NewPower.

In 2004 the company brought all its UK upstream activities together under Centrica Energy.

In 2005 Centrica acquired Oxxio the Netherlands #4 energy supplier.

To pursue green energy options in 2007 British Gas launched British Gas New Energy.

In 2007 Centrica acquired Newfield Exploration's North Sea assets for $486 million and in 2008 it acquired its first gas and oil assets in the Norwegian North Sea for $375 million (from Marathon Oil).

Growing it retail business in 2008 Centrica acquired Electricity Direct a UK commercial retail supplier serving nearly 1 million customers.

In 2008 Centrica's British Gas unit acquired 40000 small and mid-sized business customers from UK retail energy provider BizzEnergy in the wake of the latter's sudden financial collapse.

EXECUTIVES

Chairman, Sir Roger M. Carr
CFO and Director, Nick Luff
Managing Director British Gas and Director, Phillip K. (Phil) Bentley, $700,744 total compensation
Chief Executive and Director, W. Samuel H. (Sam) Laidlaw
Managing Director International Downstream, Chris Weston
General Counsel and Company Secretary, Grant Dawson
Managing Director International Upstream, Mark Hanafin
Group Director Human Resources, Jill Shedden
Head of Group Media Relations, Greg Wood
CFO and Director, Nick Luff
Director, Ian K. Meakins
Managing Director British Gas and Director, Phillip K. (Phil) Bentley
Chief Executive and Director, W. Samuel H. (Sam) Laidlaw
Director, Andrew Mackenzie
Managing Director International Downstream, Chris Weston
Director, Paul Rayner, age 59
Managing Director International Upstream, Mark Hanafin
Director, Lesley Knox, age 60
Director, Margherita Della Valle
Director, Mary Francis, age 66
Independent Non-Executive Director, Margherita Margherita Della Valle Valle
Auditors: PricewaterhouseCoopersLLP

LOCATIONS

HQ: Centrica Plc
  Millstream, Maidenhead Road, Windsor, Berkshire SL4 5GD
Phone:
Web: www.centrica.com

Sales

	% of total
UK	69
US	17
Canada	9
Other	5
Total	**100**

PRODUCTS/OPERATIONS

Sales

	% of total
UK	
Downstream	
Residential energy	36
Business energy supply &	12
Residential	7
Upstream	
Gas	13
Power	6
Storage	1
North America	
Business energy	12
Residential energy	10
Residential & business	2
Upstream & wholesale	1
Total	**100**

COMPETITORS

AGL Resources	IBERDROLA
Community Energy	RWE npower
Constellation Energy Group	STASCO
Dominion Resources	Scottish and Southern Energy
E.ON Ruhrgas	Southern Company
E.ON UK	United Utilities
EDF Energy	Viridian Group
Electrabel	Western Power Distribution
Gasunie	
Green Mountain Energy	

HISTORICAL FINANCIALS

Company Type: Public

Income Statement

FYE: December 31

	REVENUE ($ mil.)	NET INCOME ($ mil.)	NET PROFIT MARGIN	EMPLOYEES
12/13	43,910	1,569	3.6%	36,966
12/12	38,591	2,051	5.3%	38,642
12/11	35,259	650	1.8%	39,432
12/10	34,814	3,004	8.6%	34,970
12/09	35,570	1,366	3.8%	34,125
Annual Growth	**5.4%**	**3.5%**		**2.0%**

2013 Year-End Financials

Debt ratio: 42.5%
Return on equity: 17.0%
Cash ($ mil.): 1,188
Current ratio: 0.94
Long-term debt ($ mil.): 8,547
No. of shares (mil.): —
Dividends
  Yield: 4.4%
  Payout: 867.6%
Market value ($ mil.): —

	STOCK PRICE ($) FY Close	P/E High/Low	PER SHARE ($) Earnings	Dividends	Book Value
12/13	23.18	371282	0.30	1.02	1.69
12/12	22.00	239173	0.39	0.96	1.84
12/11	17.82	702504	0.13	2.34	1.67
12/10	20.64	145 90	0.58	0.76	1.75
12/09	18.15	289177	0.27	2.61	1.32
Annual Growth	**6.3%**	**— —**	**3.3%(20.9%)**		**6.3%**

Ceskoslovenska Obchodni Banka A.S. (Czech Republic)

LOCATIONS

HQ: Ceskoslovenska Obchodni Banka A.S. (Czech Republic)
  Radlicka 333/150, Praha 5 150 57
Phone: (420) 224 114 106
Web: www.csob.cz

HISTORICAL FINANCIALS

Company Type: Public

Income Statement

FYE: December 31

	ASSETS ($ mil.)	NET INCOME ($ mil.)	INCOME AS % OF ASSETS	EMPLOYEES
12/13	51,990	686	1.3%	7,553
12/12	49,152	801	1.6%	7,801
12/11	46,933	559	1.2%	7,769
12/10	47,192	718	1.5%	7,641
12/09	46,752	945	2.0%	8,018
Annual Growth	**2.7%**	**(7.7%)**	**—**	**(1.5%)**

2013 Year-End Financials

Return on assets: 1.3%
Return on equity: 17.7%
Long-term debt ($ mil.): —
No. of shares (mil.): 292
Sales ($ mil): 2,127
Dividends
  Yield: —
  Payout: —
Market value ($ mil.): —

Chiba Bank, Ltd

The Chiba Bank based in Japan's Chiba prefecture — located east of Tokyo — operates 175 branches and sub-branches across Japan. The bank boasts more than 39140 ATMs nationwide and operates international offices in Hong Kong London New York Shanghai and Singapore. Its lending focuses on home mortgages regional businesses and residential construction companies. In addition to providing traditional banking services to individuals and businesses The Chiba Bank offers investment trusts credit cards leasing financial consulting annuities and securities. Subsidiaries include Chibagin Accounting Service (cash and securities analysis) and Chibagin Capital (shareholders consultancy).

EXECUTIVES

President, Hidetoshi Sakuma, age 63
Senior Executive Officer, Tetsuya Koike
Senior Executive Officer, Toshikazu Okubo
Senior Executive Officer, Kyoichi Hanashima
Managing Executive Officer, Masao Morimoto
Managing Executive Officer, Osamu Kimura
Managing Executive Officer, Takeshi Kubo
Managing Executive Officer, Toru Nomura
Managing Executive Officer, Shoichi Hatano
Senior Executive Officer Chief Business Operation Unit and Director, Toshio Yoshii, age 62

Managing Executive Officer Treasury Division and Treasury Operation Division and Director, Hidetoshi Sakuma, age 62
Auditors: Ernst&YoungShinNihon

LOCATIONS

HQ: Chiba Bank, Ltd
1-2 Chiba-Minato, Chuo-ku, Chiba 260-8720
Phone: (81) 43 245 1111
Web: www.chibabank.co.jp

COMPETITORS

Aozora Bank	Mizuho Financial
Bank of Nagoya	Mizuho Trust &
Chiba Kogyo Bank	Banking Ltd
Chuo Mitsui Trust	Resona
Keiyo Bank	Shizuoka Bank
Mitsubishi UFJ	Sumitomo Mitsui
Financial Group	

HISTORICAL FINANCIALS
Company Type: Public

Income Statement
FYE: March 31

	ASSETS ($ mil.)	NET INCOME ($ mil.)	INCOME AS % OF ASSETS	EMPLOYEES
03/14	116,486	449	0.4%	4,399
03/13	120,878	469	0.4%	4,454
03/12	133,082	497	0.4%	4,491
03/11	127,441	490	0.4%	4,490
03/10	109,857	402	0.4%	4,403
Annual Growth	1.5%	2.8%	—	(0.0%)

2014 Year-End Financials

Return on assets: 0.4%	Dividends
Return on equity: 6.2%	Yield: —
Long-term debt ($ mil.): —	Payout: —
No. of shares (mil.): 846	Market value ($ mil.): 26,177
Sales ($ mil): 2,111	

	STOCK PRICE ($) FY Close	P/E High/Low	PER SHARE ($) Earnings	Dividends	Book Value
03/14	30.94	— —	0.53	0.00	8.77
03/13	28.90	— —	0.54	0.00	9.01
03/12	29.50	— —	0.57	0.00	9.21
03/11	28.85	— —	0.55	0.00	8.55
Annual Growth	2.4%	— —	(1.2%)	—	0.6%

China Citic Bank Corp Ltd

Commercial enterprises mean money in the bank for China CITIC Bank. One of China's largest commercial banks China CITIC Bank offers corporate small business and retail banking and financial services including business accounts personal savings accounts loans asset management and private banking. The bank operates primarily in China through a network of more than 600 branches many of which are located in China's coastal regions and major economic centers. To a lesser extent China CITIC serves select international markets as well. Founded in 1987 the bank is majority-owned and controlled by state-owned investment firm CITIC Group.

While it is actively expanding its presence throughout China China CITIC Bank has been fo-

cused in recent years on building its international banking business. In late 2009 the bank acquired a controlling stake in CITIC International Financial Holdings Limited (CIFH) which has a presence in China and operates offices in Los Angeles and New York. China CITIC Bank intends to leverage CIFH's international presence to expand into markets in Asia the Americas and other regions.

One of China CITIC Bank's shareholders Banco Bilbao Vizcaya Argentaria (BBVA) has itself been actively investing in some of the bank's other growth efforts. The two banks are collaborating to develop auto financing private banking and other retail banking services for markets in Asia. The relationship is also opening up business opportunities for China CITIC Bank in South America a region in which BBVA has a significant presence.

BBVA has ownership stakes in both China CITIC Bank (15%) and CIFH (30%) and has been increasing its investments in and consequently strengthening its relationship with China CITIC Bank since its initial investment in 2006.

EXECUTIVES

Chairman, Dan Kong, age 67
Vice Chairman, Zhenming Chang, age 58
President, Xiaoxian Chen, age 60
EVP, Beiying Wu, age 64
VP, Qian Ou Yang, age 59
VP, Xiaofan Zhao, age 50
VP, Guoxin Su, age 48
VP, Tong Cao, age 46
Chairman of the Trade Union, Lianfu Wang, age 60
Assistant President Finance Affairs, Guoqiang Cao, age 50
Assistant President, Qiang Zhang, age 51
Secretary, Yan Luo, age 46
Auditors: KPMG

LOCATIONS

HQ: China Citic Bank Corp Ltd
Block C, Fuhua Mansion, No. 8 Chaoyangmen Beidajie, Dongcheng District, Beijing 100027
Phone: (86) 10 65558000   **Fax:** (86) 10 65550809
Web: www.bank.ecitic.com

PRODUCTS/OPERATIONS

2009 Operating Income

	% of total
Whole sale	73
Retail	16
Capital and fund	3
Other	6
Total	**100**

COMPETITORS

Agricultural Bank of China
Bank of Communications
China Construction Bank
China Development Bank
China Merchants Bank
China Minsheng Banking
Hua Xia Bank
Industrial Development Bank of India
Industrial and Commercial Bank of China
Shanghai Pudong Development Bank
Shenzhen Development Bank

HISTORICAL FINANCIALS
Company Type: Public

Income Statement
FYE: December 31

	REVENUE ($ mil.)	NET INCOME ($ mil.)	NET PROFIT MARGIN	EMPLOYEES
12/13	30,388	6,471	21.3%	46,822
12/12	24,705	4,977	20.1%	41,365
12/11	18,945	4,896	25.8%	37,195
12/10	12,332	3,263	26.5%	33,552
12/09	9,025	2,097	23.2%	24,180
Annual Growth	35.5%	32.5%	—	18.0%

2013 Year-End Financials

Debt ratio: —	No. of shares (mil.): —
Return on equity: 18.4%	Dividends
Cash ($ mil.): 82,009	Yield: —
Current ratio: —	Payout: —
Long-term debt ($ mil.): —	Market value ($ mil.): —

	STOCK PRICE ($) FY Close	P/E High/Low	PER SHARE ($) Earnings	Dividends	Book Value
12/13	0.53	0 0	0.14	0.00	0.80
12/12	0.51	0 0	0.11	0.00	0.68
12/11	0.55	0 0	0.11	0.00	0.59
12/10	0.71	0 0	0.08	0.00	0.47
12/09	0.83	0 0	0.05	0.00	0.39
Annual Growth	(10.8%)	— —	26.5%	—	19.5%

China Communications Constructions Group Ltd

If you travel by car ship or train in China chances are you've used one of China Communications Construction Company's (CCCC) structures. One of China's largest infrastructure construction companies CCCC designs and builds sea ports roads bridges railways tunnels and other structures. In addition the company operates a dredging and reclamation business as well as a port machinery (mainly container cranes) and construction machinery manufacturing business. Although China constitutes its largest market CCCC also has substantial operations in Southeast Asia South America Africa and the Middle East. The company which operates through numerous subsidiaries was established in 2006.

Geographic Reach

Beyond China Beijing-based China Communications Construction Company has branches in Cuba Libya Saudi Arabia and Tanzania. The firm has overseas projects in Ethiopia Hong Kong Macao Malaysia Malta Sudan and Uzbekistan among other far flung locals.

Financial Performance

China Communications Construction Company's (CCCC) revenue grew by 8% in 2011 vs. 2010 while net income increased 24% over the same period. CCCC's design dredging and heavy machinery businesses each posted double-digit increases in revenue while construction which accounts for more than three-quarters of the company's total sales saw its revenue increase by a relatively-modest 7% year over year.

Strategy

As part of its growth strategy CCCC intends to bolster its dredging and port machinery manufacturing operations by acquiring and merging with related businesses. The company also plans to acquire businesses in emerging markets in order to grow its overseas business.

EXECUTIVES

President, Qitao Liu
CFO, Junyuan Fu
Auditors: PricewaterhouseCoopers

LOCATIONS

HQ: China Communications Constructions Group Ltd
85 De Sheng Men Wai Street, Xicheng District, Beijing 100088
Phone: (86) 10 8201 6562   **Fax:** (86) 10 8201 6524
Web: www.cccltd.cn

PRODUCTS/OPERATIONS

2011 Revenue

	% of total
Construction	77
Dredging	11
Heavy	7
Design	5
Other	2
Adjustment (2)	—
Total	**100**

Selected Operations

Dredging
Infrastructure construction
    Bridge
    Port
    Railway
    Road
    Other projects
Infrastructure design
Heavy machinery manufacturing
Investment

COMPETITORS

Beijing Urban Construction	Shanghai Construction Skanska
CRCC	VINCI
CSCEC	Zhejiang Expressway
China Railway Engineering	

HISTORICAL FINANCIALS

Company Type: Public

Income Statement

FYE: December 31

	REVENUE ($ mil.)	NET INCOME ($ mil.)	NET PROFIT MARGIN	EMPLOYEES
12/13	54,807	2,076	3.8%	100,874
12/12	47,370	1,964	4.1%	94,629
12/11	46,752	1,869	4.0%	90,674
12/10	41,376	1,496	3.6%	101,030
12/09	33,233	1,054	3.2%	100,461
Annual Growth	13.3%	18.5%	—	0.1%

2013 Year-End Financials

Debt ratio: 5.9%
Return on equity: 13.8%
Cash ($ mil.): 13,419
Current ratio: 1.05
Long-term debt ($ mil.): 16,379
No. of shares (mil.): —
Dividends
    Yield: 2.9%
    Payout: 10.0%
Market value ($ mil.): —

	STOCK PRICE ($) FY Close	P/E High/Low		PER SHARE ($) Earnings	Dividends	Book Value
12/13	16.21	1	0	0.13	0.48	0.97
12/12	19.80	1	0	0.12	0.46	0.86
12/11	15.78	1	0	0.13	0.01	0.75
12/10	17.75	1	1	0.10	0.29	0.62
12/09	19.75	1	1	0.07	0.01	0.54
Annual Growth	(4.8%)	—	—	15.8%	211.3%	15.8%

China Construction Bank (Asia) Corp Ltd

LOCATIONS

HQ: China Construction Bank (Asia) Corp Ltd
G/F, 6 Des Voeux Road Central, Central,
Phone: ( )   **Fax:** ( )
Web: www.asia.ccb.com

HISTORICAL FINANCIALS

Company Type: Public

Income Statement

FYE: December 31

	ASSETS ($ mil.)	NET INCOME ($ mil.)	INCOME AS % OF ASSETS	EMPLOYEES
12/13	53,414	478	0.9%	0
12/12	22,734	99	0.4%	2,000
12/11	17,362	78	0.5%	2,000
12/10	13,216	72	0.5%	2,000
12/09	10,520	114	1.1%	1,700
Annual Growth	50.1%	43.0%	—	—

2013 Year-End Financials

Return on assets: 1.2%
Return on equity: 12.4%
Long-term debt ($ mil.): —
No. of shares (mil.): 602
Sales ($ mil): 1,846
Dividends
    Yield: —
    Payout: —
Market value ($ mil.): —

China Construction Bank Corp

LOCATIONS

HQ: China Construction Bank Corp
No. 25, Financial Street, Xicheng District, Beijing 100033
Phone: (86) 10 6621 5533   **Fax:** (86) 10 6621 8888
Web: www.ccb.com

HISTORICAL FINANCIALS

Company Type: Public

Income Statement

FYE: December 31

	ASSETS ($ mil.)	NET INCOME ($ mil.)	INCOME AS % OF ASSETS	EMPLOYEES
12/13	2,537,740	35,457	1.4%	368,410
12/12	2,241,301	30,986	1.4%	355,290
12/11	1,951,231	26,890	1.4%	329,438
12/10	1,640,014	20,456	1.2%	313,867
12/09	1,409,395	15,635	1.1%	301,537
Annual Growth	15.8%	22.7%	—	5.1%

2013 Year-End Financials

Return on assets: 1.4%
Return on equity: 21.3%
Long-term debt ($ mil.): —
No. of shares (mil.): —
Sales ($ mil) 127,365
Dividends
    Yield: 4.8%
    Payout: 13.8%
Market value ($ mil.): —

	STOCK PRICE ($) FY Close	P/E High/Low		PER SHARE ($) Earnings	Dividends	Book Value
12/13	15.18	1	0	0.14	0.73	0.70
12/12	16.23	1	0	0.12	0.62	0.60
12/11	13.94	1	0	0.11	0.01	0.52
12/10	18.30	2	1	0.08	2.47	0.42
12/09	42.66	2	1	0.07	0.53	0.35
Annual Growth	(22.8%)	—	—	20.5%	8.3%	19.3%

China Life Insurance Co Ltd

EXECUTIVES

President, Ming Yang Wang

LOCATIONS

HQ: China Life Insurance Co Ltd
16 Financial Street, Xicheng District, Beijing 100033
Phone: (86) 10 63633333   **Fax:** (86) 10 66575722
Web: www.e-chinalife.com

PRODUCTS/OPERATIONS

HISTORICAL FINANCIALS

Company Type: Public

Income Statement

FYE: December 31

	ASSETS ($ mil.)	NET INCOME ($ mil.)	INCOME AS % OF ASSETS	EMPLOYEES
12/13	325,896	4,090	1.3%	100,310
12/12	304,594	1,774	0.6%	100,340
12/11	251,637	2,912	1.2%	100,319
12/10	213,996	5,101	2.4%	103,220
12/09	179,592	4,815	2.7%	96,698
Annual Growth	16.1%	(4.0%)	—	0.9%

2013 Year-End Financials

Return on assets: 1.2%
Return on equity: 11.2%
Long-term debt ($ mil.): —
No. of shares (mil.): —
Sales ($ mil) 69,543
Dividends
    Yield: 0.6%
    Payout: 5.3%
Market value ($ mil.): —

	STOCK PRICE ($) FY Close	P/E High/Low		PER SHARE ($) Earnings	Dividends	Book Value
12/13	47.25	2	1	0.15	0.29	1.29
12/12	49.69	3	2	0.06	0.47	1.25
12/11	36.97	2	1	0.10	0.02	1.08
12/10	61.17	1	1	0.18	1.37	1.12
12/09	73.35	1	1	0.17	1.32	1.09
Annual Growth	(10.4%)	—	—	(3.8%)	(31.8%)	4.2%

China Merchants Bank Co Ltd

China Merchants Bank (CMB) is out for the business of corporate and small-time merchants. The bank is one of China's top five banks and with 53 million credit cards its largest issuer. CMB offers businesses and individuals a range of financial services including credit cards savings accounts mortgage loans ATMs foreign exchange trading and on-line banking service. Corporate banking accounts for half of its operating income. CMB targets affluent markets through a network of more than 90 branches and 800 sub-branches and 2680 ATMs in more than 100 cities in China. It also maintains branches in New York City and London. CMB has relationships with more than 1600 banks worldwide.

Geographic Reach

CMB is headquartered in Shenzhen and primarily focuses on the Chinese domestic market. CMB operates a branch and a representative office in New York and also representative offices in London and Taipei.

Operations

CMB divides its operations into three main segments: corporate (or wholesale) banking retail banking and treasury. Corporate banking accounted for 63% of the bank's total revenue in 2011; retail banking 37%. The treasury operations lost money for the bank during its fiscal year 2011.

Financial Performance

Since the end of the global Great Recession CMB has seen four straight years of impressive growth. From 2010 to 2011 its net sales increased by 35% and its net income jumped by 40%.

The growth was attributed to a 34% increase in net interest which was mainly due to improvement in yield of interest-earning assets brought about by better risk pricing and positive re-pricing of assets as a result of rising interest rates and a steady expansion of the volume of interest-earning assets. Net fee and commission revenue also surged by 38% due to the increase in commissions from custody and other trustee businesses bank card commissions settlement and clearing fees and financial consultancy fees.

Net income in 2011 increased mainly due to the increase in net sales partially offset by a 25% increase in operating expenses. Staff costs and other general and administrative expenses increased by 27% due to increased headcounts along with business expansion.

EXECUTIVES

Vice Chairman, Wei Jiafu, age 63
Chairman, Yuning Fu, age 57
President CEO and Director, Ma Weihua
EVP and CFO, Li Hao

Executive Vice President, Tang Zhihong
Executive Vice President, Yin Fenglan
EVP, Zhang Guanghua
Executive Vice President, Ding Wei
CTO, Xu Lianfeng
Executive Vice President, Zhu Qi
Secretary, Lan Qi
Vice Chairman, Wei Jiafu, age 63
Director, Yinquan Li, age 59
Director, Sun Yueying, age 55
Director, Wang Daxiong
President CEO and Director, Ma Weihua
Director, Fu Junyuan
Director, Liu Hongxia
Director, Hong Xiaoyuan
Director, Yi Xiqun
Director, Yan Lan
Director, Chow (Edward) Kwong Fai

LOCATIONS

HQ: China Merchants Bank Co Ltd
7088 Shennan Boulevard, Futian District, Shenzhen, Guangdong Province 518040
Phone: (86) 755 83198888 **Fax:** (86) 755 83195109
Web: www.cmbchina.com

PRODUCTS/OPERATIONS

Sales

Net interest income	79
Other	5
Total	**0** 100

Sales

Corporate banking	63
Total	**0** 100

COMPETITORS

Agricultural Bank of China
Bank of China
Bank of Communications
Bank of East Asia
China Construction Bank
China Development Bank
China Minsheng Banking
Chong Hing Bank
Chuo Mitsui Trust
HSBC
Hang Seng Bank
Hua Xia Bank
Industrial and Commercial Bank of China
Public Financial Holdings
Shanghai Pudong Development Bank

HISTORICAL FINANCIALS

Company Type: Public

Income Statement   FYE: December 31

	ASSETS ($ mil.)	NET INCOME ($ mil.)	INCOME AS % OF ASSETS	EMPLOYEES
12/13	663,440	8,547	1.3%	68,078
12/12	546,693	7,261	1.3%	59,340
12/11	444,040	5,739	1.3%	45,344
12/10	364,480	3,909	1.1%	43,089
12/09	302,861	2,670	0.9%	40,340
Annual Growth	21.7%	33.8%	—	14.0%

2013 Year-End Financials

Return on assets: 1.3%	Dividends
Return on equity: 22.2%	Yield: 37.6%
Long-term debt ($ mil.): —	Payout: 5.0%
No. of shares (mil.): —	Market value ($ mil.): —
Sales ($ mil): 34,668	

	STOCK PRICE ($) FY Close	P/E High/Low		PER SHARE ($) Earnings	Dividends	Book Value
12/13	10.76	0	0	0.38	0.10	1.74
12/12	11.25	0	0	0.34	0.11	1.49
12/11	10.12	0	0	0.27	0.00	1.21
12/10	14.75	0	0	0.19	0.00	0.94
Annual Growth	(10.0%)	—	—	19.5%	—	16.6%

China Minsheng Banking Corp Ltd

LOCATIONS

HQ: China Minsheng Banking Corp Ltd
No. 2, Fuxingmennei Avenue, Xicheng District, Beijing 100031
Phone: (86) 10 58560666 **Fax:** (86) 10 58560690
Web: www.cmbc.com.cn

HISTORICAL FINANCIALS

Company Type: Public

Income Statement   FYE: December 31

	ASSETS ($ mil.)	NET INCOME ($ mil.)	INCOME AS % OF ASSETS	EMPLOYEES
12/13	532,914	6,983	1.3%	54,927
12/12	515,218	6,025	1.2%	49,227
12/11	354,134	4,435	1.3%	40,820
12/10	276,675	2,667	1.0%	31,454
12/09	208,903	1,772	0.8%	26,039
Annual Growth	26.4%	40.9%	—	20.5%

2013 Year-End Financials

Return on assets: 1.3%	Dividends
Return on equity: 23.4%	Yield: 3.6%
Long-term debt ($ mil.): —	Payout: 4.5%
No. of shares (mil.): —	Market value ($ mil.): —
Sales ($ mil): 35,959	

	STOCK PRICE ($) FY Close	P/E High/Low		PER SHARE ($) Earnings	Dividends	Book Value
12/13	11.00	0	0	0.20	0.33	0.96
12/12	11.67	0	0	0.18	0.48	0.77
12/11	8.61	0	0	0.14	0.00	0.64
Annual Growth	13.0%	—	—	9.1%	—	10.6%

China Mobile Limited

China Mobile Limited sees unlimited potential. The company is China's (and the world's) leading wireless operator by subscribers which total some 800 million. In terms of sales it trails UK-based global leader Vodafone Group. China Mobile offers domestic and international phone service text messaging and other mobile data services. In addition to its flagship postpaid GoTone brand the company targets the youth and budget-conscious markets with M-Zone and Easy Own prepaid services. State-controlled China Mobile Communications Corporation (CMCC) indirectly holds a majority stake of 75% through intermediary subsidiary China Mobile (Hong Kong) Group Limited.

Revenue rose more than 7% in 2010 over 2009 thanks mainly to upticks in voice usage volume and value-added business besides the more obvious factor of subscriber growth. In the company's main segment of usage and monthly fees (64% of revenue) revenue went up about 4% in 2010 over 2009 a trend that could continue because of tariff decreases that may bring more business. The value-added services segment (31% of revenue) enjoyed an increase of more than 15% in 2010 over 2009 owing mainly to the launch of new products and other business-development efforts.

Like any other major telecom company 3G (Third Generation) and LTE (Long Term Evolution) development have kept China Mobile Limited buzzing recently. After initiating 3G service in 2009 the company has signed up about 27 million customers for it. Efforts to keep 3G service up to speed could result in significant capital expenditures. In addition to that China Mobile has been helping its parent CMCC roll out the LTE network in six Chinese cities as well as installing a demonstration LTE network in Beijing.

Meanwhile China Mobile Limited's organic growth has been fueled in part by the adoption of mobile communications in rural areas that previously had no wired or wireless telephone services. Additionally the company has catered increasingly to corporate clients in a search for higher-margin contracts.

Other efforts to grow its business include the $35.9 million acquisition in 2011 of China Topssion Communication a seller of mobile phones and other electronic devices to build its distribution and retail operations. China Mobile bought state-run fixed-line carrier China Tietong Telecommunications in 2008 as part of a broader restructuring of the telecom industry in China which also involved former rival China Unicom selling its wireless operations to China Telecom. The previous year it grew globally as well with the acquisition of nearly 90% of Pakistani wireless company Paktel Ltd. for about $284 million.

These purchases continued the company's history of using acquisitions to expand operations. From 1998 to 2004 China Mobile purchased 29 regional telecom service providers. The company acquired China Resources Peoples Telephone (later renamed China Mobile Peoples Telephone) a Hong Kong-based telecom service provider for $436 million in 2006.

EXECUTIVES

Executive Director, Xu Long, age 56
CEO, Li Yue, age 55
VP and CFO, Xue Taohai, age 58
Chairman, Xi Guohua, age 63
Chairman and Executive Director, Wang Jianzhou, age 65
VP and Executive Director, Sha Yuejia, age 56
VP and Executive Director, Liu Aili, age 51
VP and Executive Director, Huang Wenlin, age 60
Director, Lo Ka Shui, age 67
Executive Director, Xu Long, age 56
CEO and Executive Director, Li Yue, age 54
VP and Executive Director, Lu Xiangdong, age 53
VP CFO and Executive Director, Xue Taohai, age 57
Director, Frank K. S. Wong, age 65
Director, Moses M. C. Cheng, age 63
VP and Executive Director, Sha Yuejia, age 55
VP and Executive Director, Liu Aili, age 50
VP and Executive Director, Xin Fanfei, age 56
VP and Executive Director, Huang Wenlin, age 59
Auditors: KPMG

LOCATIONS

HQ: China Mobile Limited
   60th Floor, The Center, 99 Queen's Road Central,
Phone: (852) 3121 8888   **Fax:** (852) 2511 9092
Web: www.chinamobileltd.com

PRODUCTS/OPERATIONS

Sales

	% of total
Usage & monthly	64
Value-added services	31
Other	5
Total	**100**

COMPETITORS

China Telecom Corporation Limited	Hutchison Telecommunications
China Unicom	PCCW Ltd.
City Telecom	Vodafone

HISTORICAL FINANCIALS
Company Type: Public

Income Statement
FYE: December 31

	REVENUE ($ mil.)	NET INCOME ($ mil.)	NET PROFIT MARGIN	EMPLOYEES
12/13	104,094	20,101	19.3%	197,030
12/12	89,892	20,736	23.1%	182,487
12/11	83,883	19,997	23.8%	175,336
12/10	73,613	18,150	24.7%	164,336
12/09	66,213	16,866	25.5%	350,192
Annual Growth	12.0%	4.5%	—	(13.4%)

2013 Year-End Financials

Debt ratio: 0.0%
Return on equity: 16.0%
Cash ($ mil.): 7,421
Current ratio: 1.26
Long-term debt ($ mil.): 824

No. of shares (mil.): —
Dividends
 Yield: 3.8%
 Payout: 5.5%
Market value ($ mil.): —

	STOCK PRICE ($) FY Close	P/E High/Low		PER SHARE ($) Earnings	Dividends	Book Value
12/13	52.29	0	0	0.99	2.02	6.48
12/12	58.72	0	0	1.02	1.96	5.77
12/11	48.49	0	0	0.99	0.05	5.14
12/10	49.62	0	0	0.89	1.66	4.36
12/09	46.43	0	0	0.83	1.60	3.70
Annual Growth	3.0%	—	—	4.4%	6.0%	15.0%

China Pacific Insurance (Group) Co., Ltd.

LOCATIONS

HQ: China Pacific Insurance (Group) Co., Ltd.
   South Tower, Bank of Communications, Financial Building, 190 Central Yincheng Road, Pudong New District, Shanghai 200120
Phone: (86) 21 58767282   **Fax:** (86) 21 68870791
Web: www.cpic.com.cn

HISTORICAL FINANCIALS
Company Type: Public

Income Statement
FYE: December 31

	REVENUE ($ mil.)	NET INCOME ($ mil.)	NET PROFIT MARGIN	EMPLOYEES
12/13	31,750	1,529	4.8%	86,893
12/12	26,812	814	3.0%	85,137
12/11	24,707	1,320	5.3%	82,456
12/10	21,440	1,298	6.1%	74,590
12/09	15,259	1,077	7.1%	0
Annual Growth	20.1%	9.2%	—	—

2013 Year-End Financials

Debt ratio: —
Return on equity: 9.4%
Cash ($ mil.): 2,735
Current ratio: 2.32
Long-term debt ($ mil.): —

No. of shares (mil.): —
Dividends
 Yield: 0.0%
 Payout: 2.9%
Market value ($ mil.): —

	STOCK PRICE ($) FY Close	P/E High/Low		PER SHARE ($) Earnings	Dividends	Book Value
12/13	14.38	0	0	0.17	0.00	1.80
12/12	13.29	1	1	0.09	0.00	1.70
Annual Growth	8.2%	—	—	15.5%	—	1.5%

China Petroleum & Chemical Corp. Inc

China Petroleum and Chemical Corporation (Sinopec Corp.) is China's largest producer and supplier of refined oil products and its second-largest crude oil producer. It is also China's largest petrochemicals producer and distributor and the world's fourth-largest ethylene producer. Operations include oil and gas exploration and production; crude oil processing; oil products trading transportation distribution and marketing; and petrochemicals manufacturing. In 2010 it reported proved reserves of 2.9 billion barrels of oil and 6.5 trillion cu. ft. of natural gas; it also owns more than 29600 gas stations and 34 refineries. China's government controls about 76% of the company through Sinopec Group.

Sinopec Corp. is committed to growing its oil and gas reserves to keep pace with the energy demands from China's booming industrial economy and growing population. The company operates 16 oil and gas production fields in China and also owns vast reserves in Africa. In 2010 the company produced an average of more than 1 billion barrels of oil equivalent per day. For the past few years it has been buying up resources across the globe as it competes with other developing countries for oil and gas reserves.

In late 2011 the company acquired Canada's Daylight Energy for $2.1 billion which gave it access to 69 oil and natural gas assets in the western provinces of British Columbia and Alberta. Daylight is being integrated within an indirect subsidiary of Sinopec Corp. and will operate as Sinopec Daylight Energy. The purchase was made on the heels of the acquisition of OPTI Canada in November by competitor CNOOC another Chinese state-owned company.

In 2013 it purchased a 50% undivided interest in 850000 of Chesapeake's net oil and natural gas leasehold acres in the Mississippi Lime play in northern Oklahoma (425000 acres net to Sinopec) for $1.02 billion.

The acquisitions follow several other purchases Sinopec has made since 2009 including shelling out $7.1 billion for Repsol's assets in Brazil $2.5 billion for Occidental Petroleum's assets in Argentina; $4.7 billion for ConocoPhillips' 9% stake in Syncrude; and $7.5 billion for Addax Petroleum which had reserves in Africa and the Middle East. In late 2010 the company also signed a deal with Chevron to help develop the $6 billion-plus Gendalo-Gehem deepwater natural gas project off the coast of Indonesia.

The shopping spree for oil and gas resources paid off in 2010 when Sinopec Corp. achieved record sales. The company's sales spiked 47% over the previous year and its net income grew by more than 20%. Its exploration and production operations not only grew exponentially but the official launch of the Sichuan-East China Gas project in 2010 also accelerated the company's growth. The pipeline has the capacity to produce about 12 billion cu. meters of gas per year.

Sinopec Corp.'s parent state-owned China Petrochemical (Sinopec Group) reorganized in 2000 and pooled the best of its assets as Sinopec Corp.

EXECUTIVES

Chairman, Su Shulin, age 51
Vice Chairman of the Board; President, Wang Tianpu, age 51, $106,214 total compensation
SVP and Director, Wang Zhigang, age 56, $92,216 total compensation
SVP and Director, Zhang Jianhua, age 49, $89,332 total compensation
SVP and Director, Cai Xiyou, age 52, $105,482 total compensation
Secretary, Chen Ge, age 51, $53,108 total compensation
SVP and Director, Dai Houliang, age 50, $105,482 total compensation
VP and Director General Engineering Department, Zhang Kehua, age 60, $73,681 total compensation
VP, Zhang Haichao, age 56, $65,047 total compensation
VP, Jiao Fangzheng, age 51, $67,148 total compensation
VP and Director General Development and Planning Department, Lei Dianwu, age 51, $52,961 total compensation
Vice Chairman, Zhang Yaocang, age 60
Chief Financial Officer, Wang Xinhua, age 58, $51,937 total compensation
Chairman of the Board of Directors, Fu Chengyu
Director, Liu Yun, age 57
Vice Chairman and President, Wang Tianpu, age 51
SVP and Director, Wang Zhigang, age 56
SVP and Director, Zhang Jianhua, age 49
SVP and Director, Cai Xiyou, age 52
Director, Li Chunguang, age 58
SVP and Director, Dai Houliang, age 50
Director, Ma Weihua
Director, Chen Xiaojin, age 69
Director, Li Deshui, age 70
Vice Chairman, Zhang Yaocang, age 60
Director, Cao Yaofeng, age 60
Director, Xie Zhongyu, age 70
Auditors: KPMGHuazhen

LOCATIONS

HQ: China Petroleum & Chemical Corp. Inc
22 Chaoyangmen North Street, Chaoyang District, Beijing 100728
Phone: (86) 10 5996 0028   **Fax:** (86) 10 5996 0386
Web: www.sinopec.com.cn

PRODUCTS/OPERATIONS

Sales

	% of total
Exploration & production	43
Marketing & distribution	28
Chemicals	14

COMPETITORS

BASF SE	Chevron
BP	Exxon Mobil
Bangchak Petroleum	Furmanite
Public	PetroChina
CNOOC	Royal Dutch Shell
CPC	TOTAL

HISTORICAL FINANCIALS
Company Type: Public

Income Statement
FYE: December 31

	REVENUE ($ mil.)	NET INCOME ($ mil.)	NET PROFIT MARGIN	EMPLOYEES
12/13	475,778	10,923	2.3%	368,953
12/12	446,893	10,246	2.3%	376,201
12/11	398,081	11,633	2.9%	377,235
12/10	290,245	10,892	3.8%	373,375
12/09	196,990	9,045	4.6%	371,333
Annual Growth	24.7%	4.8%	—	(0.2%)

2013 Year-End Financials

Debt ratio: 3.7%
Return on equity: 12.2%
Cash ($ mil.): 2,494
Current ratio: 0.65
Long-term debt ($ mil.): 24,048

No. of shares (mil.): —
Dividends
Yield: 3.9%
Payout: 100.5%
Market value ($ mil.): —

	STOCK PRICE ($) FY Close	P/E High/Low		Earnings	PER SHARE ($) Dividends	Book Value
12/13	82.17	6	3	0.09	3.27	0.81
12/12	114.92	6	4	0.09	4.25	0.73
12/11	105.05	4	3	0.10	0.06	0.67
12/10	95.69	4	3	0.10	2.47	0.56
12/09	88.07	4	2	0.08	2.07	0.49
Annual Growth	(1.7%)			2.4%	12.1%	13.4%

China Railway Construction Corp Ltd

LOCATIONS

HQ: China Railway Construction Corp Ltd
East, No. 40 Fuxing Road, Haidian District, Beijing 100855
Phone: (86) 10 5268 8600   **Fax:** (86) 10 5268 8302
Web: www.crcc.cn

HISTORICAL FINANCIALS
Company Type: Public

Income Statement
FYE: December 31

	REVENUE ($ mil.)	NET INCOME ($ mil.)	NET PROFIT MARGIN	EMPLOYEES
12/13	96,927	1,708	1.8%	246,736
12/12	77,685	1,360	1.8%	244,523
12/11	72,662	1,247	1.7%	241,621
12/10	69,230	644	0.9%	229,070
12/09	50,523	966	1.9%	209,103
Annual Growth	17.7%	15.3%	—	4.2%

2013 Year-End Financials

Debt ratio: 3.9%
Return on equity: 13.5%
Cash ($ mil.): 15,433
Current ratio: 1.21
Long-term debt ($ mil.): 12,391

No. of shares (mil.): —
Dividends
Yield: 1.4%
Payout: —
Market value ($ mil.): —

	STOCK PRICE ($) FY Close	P/E High/Low		Earnings	PER SHARE ($) Dividends	Book Value
12/13	10.00	0	0	0.14	0.14	1.08
12/12	11.39	0	0	0.11	0.00	0.94
12/11	5.29	0	0	0.10	0.00	0.83
12/10	11.90	1	1	0.05	0.00	0.71
12/09	12.70	1	0	0.08	0.12	0.63
Annual Growth	(5.8%)			15.4%	4.8%	14.4%

China Railway Group Ltd

LOCATIONS

HQ: China Railway Group Ltd
No. 1, Xinghuo Road, Fengtai District, Beijing 100070
Phone:
Web: www.crec.cn

HISTORICAL FINANCIALS
Company Type: Public

Income Statement
FYE: December 31

	REVENUE ($ mil.)	NET INCOME ($ mil.)	NET PROFIT MARGIN	EMPLOYEES
12/13	89,263	1,548	1.7%	289,547
12/12	74,688	1,179	1.6%	289,343
12/11	70,255	1,062	1.5%	294,761
12/10	69,194	1,136	1.6%	285,054
12/09	48,840	1,008	2.1%	276,150
Annual Growth	16.3%	11.3%	—	1.2%

2013 Year-End Financials

Debt ratio: 4.9%
Return on equity: 11.3%
Cash ($ mil.): 12,497
Current ratio: 1.20
Long-term debt ($ mil.): 17,237

No. of shares (mil.): —
Dividends
Yield: 1.3%
Payout: —
Market value ($ mil.): —

STOCK PRICE ($) FY Close	P/E High/Low		PER SHARE ($) Earnings	Dividends	Book Value
12/13 12.81	1	1	0.07	0.17	0.67
12/12 14.14	1	1	0.06	0.00	0.59
12/11 7.82	1	0	0.05	0.00	0.54
12/10 17.87	1	1	0.05	0.00	0.47
Annual Growth (10.5%)	—	—	8.0%	151.5%	9.0%

China Shenhua Energy Co., Ltd.

China Shenhua Energy Company (CSEC) is an integrated coal mining company in China. CSEC operates four mining groups —two underground and two surface mining projects —in western and northern China. The Shendong Mines account for close to two-thirds of its total coal production which is more than 180 million tons a year. It also markets coal mined by other companies making a total of more than 230 million tons sold annually. CSEC owns and operates four railway lines and port facilities for the transportation of its coal. The company also operates more than a dozen power plants with a total installed capacity of close to 18000 MW. Shenhua Group holds about 75% of the company.

The group announced in early 2006 that it plans to funnel all of its coal-related activities into Shenhua Energy. Shenhua Group's other businesses include power station construction coal chemicals manufacturing and coal-to-oil production.

EXECUTIVES

Chairman, Zhang Xiwu, age 55
VP Safety Health and Environmental Management and Operational Coordination, Hao Gui, age 51
VP Strategic Planning and Coal Production, Wang Jinli, age 54
VP Transportation, Xue Jilian, age 59
VP Coal Sales and Marketing, Hua Zeqiao, age 62
VP Power Production, Wang Pingang, age 53
Secretary, Huang Qing, age 48
CFO, Zhang Kehui, age 50
Senior Vice President, Dong Li
Senior Vice President, Gui Hao
Vice President, Guiwu Zhai
Senior Vice President; Executive Director, Jianguo Han
Senior Vice President, Jilian Xue
Vice President, Jinli Wang
Chief Financial Officer, Kehui Zhang
Senior Vice President, Pingang Wang
Secretary of the Board, Qing Huang
President; Executive Director, Wen Ling
Senior Vice President, Xiaolin Wang
Chairman of the Board; Executive Director, Xiwu Zhang
Vice Chairman of the Board; Executive Director, Yuzhuo Zhang
Director, Zhang Yuzhuo, age 51
Director, Han Jianguo, age 55
Director, Huazhang Gong, age 68
Non-Executive Director, Benren Liu
Non-Executive Director, Dong Kong
Non-Executive Director, Hongsheng Chen
Independent Non-Executive Director, Peizhang Guo
Non-Executive Director, Songlin Xie

Independent Non-Executive Director, Xulitai Fan
Auditors: KPMG

LOCATIONS

HQ: China Shenhua Energy Co., Ltd.
Shenhua Tower, 22 Xibinhe Road, Andingmen, Dongcheng District, Beijing 100011
Phone: (86) 10 5813 3399   **Fax:** (86) 10 5813 1804
Web: www.csec.com

Sales

	% of total
China	91
Other	9
Total	**100**

COMPETITORS

China Yangtze Power	Yankuang
Peabody Energy	Yanzhou Coal
Rio Tinto Limited	
U.S. China Mining Group	

HISTORICAL FINANCIALS

Company Type: Public

Income Statement

FYE: December 31

	REVENUE ($ mil.)	NET INCOME ($ mil.)	NET PROFIT MARGIN	EMPLOYEES
12/13	46,878	7,446	15.9%	91,487
12/12	40,142	7,837	19.5%	89,144
12/11	33,076	7,256	21.9%	82,260
12/10	23,069	5,784	25.1%	65,154
12/09	17,766	4,643	26.1%	62,286
Annual Growth	27.5%	12.5%	—	10.1%

2013 Year-End Financials

Debt ratio: 2.9%
Return on equity: 16.9%
Cash ($ mil.): 6,331
Current ratio: 0.92
Long-term debt ($ mil.): 6,944

No. of shares (mil.): —
Dividends
  Yield: 4.0%
  Payout: —
Market value ($ mil.): —

STOCK PRICE ($) FY Close	P/E High/Low		PER SHARE ($) Earnings	Dividends	Book Value
12/13 12.60	0	0	0.37	0.51	2.30
12/12 17.90	0	0	0.39	0.49	2.07
12/11 43.03	1	0	0.36	0.01	1.80
12/10 41.45	1	0	0.29	0.27	1.51
12/09 49.00	1	0	0.23	0.01	1.26
Annual Growth (28.8%)	—	—	12.5%	217.4%	16.3%

China Telecom Corp Ltd

China Telecom Corporation Limited is a leading provider of fixed-line (or wireline) phone and Internet broadband services in some 20 provinces and autonomous regions of China. Its principal operations are in four of the most economically developed regions in China including Shanghai and the provinces of Guangdong Jiangsu and Zhejiang. Services include local access domestic and international long-distance Internet access wireless service managed data services leased lines and about 13 million public phones. China Telecom counts 100 million residential landline customers 186 million wireless subscribers 100 million broadband subscribers and about 30 million business wireless subscribers.

Revenues for residential landline customers continue to decrease as fewer households use landlines and instead make their primary phone a cell phone or VoIP service. The number of subscribers dropped 10% in 2009 and the company expects to lose about as many customers in 2010. Enterprise customers however such as corporations and government agencies still require wireline service and that business segment continues to grow by a few million new customers every year. As long as wireline customers switch to a wireless service with China Telecom the company isn't losing anything but the wireless service market is intensely competitive in China. Wireless customers currently make up about 10% of revenue.

Internet service accounts for a quarter of revenue and is the company's second-largest segment. Unlike the US where many customers use their television cable company as an Internet service provider China's television programming is largely state-controlled and thus service is offered through the phone company.

In 2008 the Ministry of Industry and Information the National Development and Reform Commission and the Ministry of Finance reformed the telecommunications industry in China by granting 3G network access to the three main providers — China Telecom China Mobile and China Unicom. As part of the deal China Telecom acquired the CDMA (code division multiple access) mobile communications business from China Unicom and was able to enter the wireless market in order to remain competitive.

China Telecom Corporation Limited is ultimately owned by the Chinese government. It is 71% controlled by the government-owned China Telecommunications Corporation. Chinese law forbids foreign investment and in order to trade on the New York Stock Exchange the company became an operating subsidiary.

EXECUTIVES

Chairman and CEO, Wang Xiaochu, age 56
Executive Director EVP and CFO, Andi Wu, age 59
Executive Director and EVP, Zhang Jiping, age 58
President COO and Director, Shang Bing, age 58
Director, Jianhua Miao, age 62
Executive Director and EVP, Yang Jie, age 52
Executive Director and EVP, Sun Kangmin, age 57
Chairman and General Manager Jiangxi Telecom Company Limited, Ke Ruiwen, age 50
Executive Director and EVP, Yang Xiaowei, age 50
Executive Director and EVP, Zhang Chenshuang, age 62
Director Corporate Strategic Department, Xu Cailiao, age 50
Director Audit Department, Han Fang, age 41
Senior Accountant, Zhu Lihao, age 73
Employee Representative Supervisor, Yuzhu Ma, age 61
Executive Director EVP and CFO, Andi Wu, age 59
Executive Director and EVP, Zhang Jiping, age 58
Director, Qin Xiao, age 67
President COO and Director, Shang Bing, age 58
Director, Jianhua Miao, age 62
Executive Director and EVP, Yang Jie, age 52
Executive Director and EVP, Sun Kangmin, age 57
Director, Aloysius H. Y. Tse, age 66
Executive Director and EVP, Yang Xiaowei, age 50
Executive Director and EVP, Zhang Chenshuang, age 62
Director, Li Jinming, age 62
Director, Prof Xu Erming, age 64
Director, Cha (Laura) May Lung, age 64
Director, Wu Jichuan, age 76
Auditors: KPMG

LOCATIONS

HQ: China Telecom Corp Ltd
31 Jinrong Street, Xicheng District, Beijing 100033
Phone: (86) 10 6642 8166   **Fax:** (86) 10 6601 0728
Web: www.chinatelecom-h.com

PRODUCTS/OPERATIONS

Sales

	% of total
Wireline	38
Broadband	25
Wireless	10
Value-added services (Caller ID text messaging	10
Integrated information application	6
Other	6
Managed data and leased-line	5
Total	**100**

COMPETITORS

China Mobile	China Tietong
Communications	China Unicom
China Netcom Hong Kong	Shanghai Mobile

HISTORICAL FINANCIALS

Company Type: Public

Income Statement
FYE: December 31

	REVENUE ($ mil.)	NET INCOME ($ mil.)	NET PROFIT MARGIN	EMPLOYEES
12/13	53,120	2,898	5.5%	306,545
12/12	45,406	2,394	5.3%	305,676
12/11	38,930	2,621	6.7%	309,799
12/10	33,355	2,390	7.2%	312,322
12/09	30,663	2,112	6.9%	312,520
Annual Growth	**14.7%**	**8.2%**	**—**	**(0.5%)**

2013 Year-End Financials

Debt ratio: 3.3%
Return on equity: 6.4%
Cash ($ mil.): 2,654
Current ratio: 0.26
Long-term debt ($ mil.): 10,343

No. of shares (mil.): —
Dividends
 Yield: 1.9%
 Payout: —
Market value ($ mil.): —

	STOCK PRICE ($) FY Close	P/E High/Low		PER SHARE ($) Earnings	Dividends	Book Value
12/13	50.57	7	6	0.04	0.99	0.57
12/12	56.85	9	6	0.03	0.99	0.53
12/11	57.13	8	6	0.03	0.02	0.50
12/10	52.28	7	5	0.03	0.98	0.43
12/09	41.42	7	4	0.03	0.99	0.40
Annual Growth	**5.1%**	**—**		**8.4%**	**(0.0%)**	**9.0%**

China Unicom (Hong Kong) Ltd

China Unicom (Hong Kong) Limited has brought competition to the world's largest telecommunications market. The Chinese government set up China Unicom in 1994 as the first competitor to another government-owned telecommunications monopoly. The state-controlled company provides 437 million subscribers long-distance broadband data and mobile communications services in 31 provinces cities and other regions throughout China. It is the country's #2 mobile phone operator behind former monopoly China Mobile Communications. China Unicom (Hong Kong) Limited operates primarily in the Chinese northern provinces; major cities served include Beijing and Tianjin.

EXECUTIVES

SVP and Director, Gang Li, age 56
SVP, Pei Aihua, age 64
CFO and Director, Tong Jilu, age 56
SVP and Director, Zuo Xunsheng, age 63
SVP, Zhao Jidong, age 63
Executive Chairman of the Board; Chief Executive Officer, Chang Xiaobing, age 57
SVP and Director, Li Jianguo, age 60
SVP and Director, Junan Zhang, age 57
President; Executive Director, Lu Yimin, age 50
SVP, Li Fushen
SVP, Jiang Zhengxin, age 58
Director, John L. Thornton, age 59
SVP and Director, Gang Li, age 56
CFO and Director, Tong Jilu, age 56
SVP and Director, Zuo Xunsheng, age 63
Director, Wu Jinglian, age 83
Director, Cheung Wing (Linus) Lam, age 64
Director, Cesareo (Cesar) Alierta Izuel, age 68
SVP and Director, Li Jianguo, age 60
SVP and Director, Junan Zhang, age 57
Director, Wong Wai Ming, age 55
President; Executive Director, Lu Yimin, age 50
Director, Timpson Chung Shui Ming, age 61
Auditors: PricewaterhouseCoopers

LOCATIONS

HQ: China Unicom (Hong Kong) Ltd
75th Floor, The Center, 99 Queen's Road Central,
Phone: (852) 2121 3220   **Fax:** (852) 2121 3232
Web: www.chinaunicom.com.hk

PRODUCTS/OPERATIONS

Sales

	% of total
Fixed-line	53
Mobile	47
Total	**100**

COMPETITORS

Beijing Mobile	China Tietong
China Mobile	Hunan Telecom
China Mobile	Hutchison Whampoa
Communications	Pacnet
China Telecom	Shanghai Mobile
Corporation Limited	

HISTORICAL FINANCIALS

Company Type: Public

Income Statement
FYE: December 31

	REVENUE ($ mil.)	NET INCOME ($ mil.)	NET PROFIT MARGIN	EMPLOYEES
12/13	48,735	1,719	3.5%	283,596
12/12	39,928	1,138	2.9%	218,598
12/11	33,230	671	2.0%	297,210
12/10	25,987	584	2.2%	310,030
12/09	22,546	1,399	6.2%	321,772
Annual Growth	**21.3%**	**5.3%**	**—**	**(3.1%)**

2013 Year-End Financials

Debt ratio: 4.4%
Return on equity: 4.8%
Cash ($ mil.): 3,561
Current ratio: 0.18
Long-term debt ($ mil.): 2,279

No. of shares (mil.): —
Dividends
 Yield: 1.1%
 Payout: 6.6%
Market value ($ mil.): —

	STOCK PRICE ($) FY Close	P/E High/Low		PER SHARE ($) Earnings	Dividends	Book Value
12/13	15.06	1	1	0.07	0.17	1.52
12/12	16.29	2	1	0.05	0.14	1.43
12/11	21.13	3	2	0.03	0.00	1.39
12/10	14.25	2	1	0.02	0.47	1.33
12/09	13.11	1	0	0.06	0.26	1.28
Annual Growth	**3.5%**	**—**		**4.9%**	**(9.9%)**	**4.3%**

China United Network Communications Ltd

LOCATIONS

HQ: China United Network Communications Ltd
29th Floor, No. 1033, Changning Road, Changning District, Shanghai 200050
Phone: (86) 21 52732228   **Fax:** (86) 21 52732220
Web: www.chinaunicom-a.com

HISTORICAL FINANCIALS

Company Type: Public

Income Statement
FYE: December 31

	REVENUE ($ mil.)	NET INCOME ($ mil.)	NET PROFIT MARGIN	EMPLOYEES
12/13	50,170	568	1.1%	0
12/12	41,105	379	0.9%	0
12/11	34,239	224	0.7%	215,954
12/10	26,726	186	0.7%	215,815
12/09	23,194	459	2.0%	216,772
Annual Growth	**21.3%**	**5.5%**	**—**	**—**

2013 Year-End Financials

Debt ratio: 3.4%
Return on equity: 4.6%
Cash ($ mil.): 3,566
Current ratio: 0.18
Long-term debt ($ mil.): 2,227

No. of shares (mil.): —
Dividends
 Yield: —
 Payout: —
Market value ($ mil.): —

Christian Dior SA

This is not your grandmere's Christian Dior. Under now former chief designer John Galliano the fashion house had gone from outfitting ladies who lunch to women who rock. The holding company's operating unit Christian Dior Couture designs and makes some of the world's most coveted haute couture as well as luxury ready-to-wear fashion and accessories for men and women. Christian Dior operates more than 235 boutiques worldwide with plans to open more. Don't let the pious name fool you though; Christian Dior is a wolf in tight-fitting clothing due to its roughly 42% stake in luxury goods giant LVMH. Chairman and LVMH CEO Bernard Arnault and family control Christian Dior.
Geographic Reach
Headquartered in France Christian Dior operates more than 235 boutiques worldwide. It sells its upscale items in Europe the US Asia and internationally. Some 37% of its revenue comes from

Asia followed by Europe's 30% and another 22% from the US.

Sales and Marketing

Besides its network of luxury boutiques Christian Dior sells its products online.

Operations

The company which owns a 100% stake in its lucrative Christian Dior Couture operation also runs retail stores under the the the banner names DFS Galleria Sephora Le Bon Marche Ile de Beaute and Ole Henriksen. As part of its business Christian Dior maintains publications that are sold under the Les Echos-Investir and the Royal Van Lent-Feadship titles.

Financial Performance

Christian Dior generated 30.6 billion euros in revenue in fiscal 2013. Its revenue consisted of Fashion and Leather Goods Selective Retailing Wine and Spirits Perfumes and Cosmetics Watches and Jewelry and Christian Dior Couture. Combined Fashion and Leather Goods and Selective Retailing accounted for about 60% of the firm's total revenue. During the same reporting period the luxury retailer posted 1.87 billion euros in profit.

Strategy

Capitalizing on its brand's reputation for timeless elegance the company has been busy growing its network of swank boutiques in markets such as Russia Asia and the Middle East. It plans to continue building its presence in these regions specifically targeting China and Singapore.

In the US Christian Dior plans to open a 10000-sq.-ft. flagship store in San Francisco's Union Square in 2016.

HISTORY

Christian Dior a trained architect opened his own fashion house in 1947 with the backing of flamboyant textile king Marcel Boussac. Dior brightened up a bleak postwar Paris in 1948 when he launched his "New Look" designs. After years of slim cuts (to conserve fabric) and drab colors Dior's looks were feminine glamorous and opulent (skirts often used 40 or more yards of fabric).

Dior opened a store in New York in 1948 and pioneered the concept of licensing with hosiery and ties. Dior died unexpectedly from a stroke in 1957 and was succeeded by 21-year-old assistant Yves Saint-Laurent. By 1960 when Marc Bohan succeeded Saint-Laurent the house of Dior had dressed such famous women as Brigitte Bardot Marlene Dietrich and Eva Peron.

But mismanagement by Boussac took its toll and the company sold its trademark for perfume and cosmetics —potentially its most lucrative licenses —to Moet-Hennessy in 1972. Boussac drained the profits from Dior to finance his company's other struggling divisions and in 1978 the Boussac group was purchased by (also struggling) textile and retailing company Agache-Willot. Agache-Willot wound up in the hands of the French government with the dubious distinction of being France's largest bankruptcy since the war.

In 1984 ambitious but little-known real estate executive Bernard Arnault beat out several more prominent suitors to buy Agache-Willot from the French government; he put up $15 million of his own money and $45 million from investors and re-named the company Financiere Agache. He then laid off 9000 people sold factories and made the company profitable within three years.

Christian Dior SA was born in 1988 when Arnault sold 42% of it to the public to finance his victorious battle for control of newly formed luxury goods conglomerate LVMH Moet Hennessy Louis Vuitton. Meanwhile Arnault had to deal with the fact that Christian Dior's traditional business Dior Couture was losing its luster. Part of the problem

was overlicensing —more than 250 licenses existed for everything Dior from sunglasses to sheets. What's more Dior Couture simply looked dowdy compared to other hot young designers.

To turn things around Arnault lured Beatrice Bongibault from Chanel and made her managing director of Dior Couture. She quickly cut nearly a quarter of the company's licenses and centralized control of those that remained improving quality and cutting costs. (Her techniques were quickly copied by other design houses.) She also replaced designer Bohan with Italian Gianfranco Ferre in 1989. Arnault ousted Bongibault in 1990. Dior Couture accused her of embezzlement but the parties settled out of court.

Dior Couture bought back most of its remaining licenses in 1994 and 1995. In 1996 Dior Couture turned to controversial designer John Galliano —already head of LVMH's house of Givenchy —to capitalize on the publicity that followed Galliano's eccentric sometimes bizarre creations.

Aided by its retail expansion Dior Couture bounced back from a 1997 loss with a profit in 1998. The fashion house opened 19 more boutiques in 2000 and introduced the Dior Homme collection of menswear —designed by Hedi Slimane —in January 2001 (now designed by Kris Van Assche).

In 2005 the company launched the perfume brands Miss Dior Cherie and Dior Homme. Christian Dior reclaimed the Baby Dior business in 2006 which had been operated under license. The fashion house celebrated its 60th anniversary in 2007.

In 2008 Christian Dior Couture acquired 87% of the shares of John Galliano SA a company specializing in the creation and concession of fashions and luxury items by the designer. To mark its entrance into the Chinese market the company hosted a major exhibition in Beijing.

Following allegations of anti-Semitic remarks made by its longtime and lucrative designer Christian Dior in March 2011 parted ways with Galliano.

EXECUTIVES

Chairman and CEO, Bernard Arnault, age 65
Vice Chairman, Eric Guerlain, age 74
Group Managing Director, Sidney Toledano, age 63
Vice Chairman, Eric Guerlain, age 74
Director, Denis Dalibot, age 68
Director, Antoine Bernheim, age 89
Group Managing Director, Sidney Toledano, age 63
Director, Segolene Gallienne
Director, Jaime de Marichalar Y Saenz De Tejada, age 50
Director, Pierre Gode, age 69
Director, Christian De Labriffe, age 66
Director, Alessandro Vallarino Gancia, age 46
Director, Renaud Donnedieu de Vabres, age 59
Auditors: Mazars&Guerard

LOCATIONS

HQ: Christian Dior SA
30, avenue Montaigne, Paris 75008
Phone: (33) 1 44 13 22 22   **Fax:** (33) 1 44 12 22 23
Web: www.dior-finance.com

Sales

	% of total
Asia	
Japan	9
Rest of Europe	25
France	13
Rest of US	22
US	22
Other	9
Total	**100**

PRODUCTS/OPERATIONS

Sales

	% of total
Fashion & leather	36
Selective retailing	25
Perfumes & cosmetics	15
Wines & spirits	15
Watches & jewelry	5
Couture	4
Total	**100**

Principal Holdings
Christian Dior Couture SA
  Accessories
  Haute couture
  Luxury ready-to-wear
LVMH Moet Hennessy Louis Vuitton (42%)
  Fragrances and cosmetics
  Leather and fashion
  Retailing
  Watches and jewelry
  Wine and spirits

COMPETITORS

Armani	L' Oreal
Bill Blass	Oscar de la Renta
Calvin Klein	Prada
Chanel	Puig
Dolce & Gabbana	Ralph Lauren
Escada	Richemont
Estee Lauder	Salvatore Ferragamo
Gianni Versace	Shiseido
Hermes	Valentino Fashion
Kering	Vera Wang
Krizia	

HISTORICAL FINANCIALS

Company Type: Public

Income Statement

FYE: June 30

	REVENUE ($ mil.)	NET INCOME ($ mil.)	NET PROFIT MARGIN	EMPLOYEES
06/14	42,306	1,945	4.6%	117,806
06/13*	6,231	282	4.5%	108,837
04/13	39,076	1,871	4.8%	108,546
04/12	11,888	520	4.4%	100,755
12/11	31,855	1,654	5.2%	101,154
Annual Growth	15.2%	8.5%	—	7.9%

*Fiscal year change

2014 Year-End Financials

Debt ratio: 24.1%	No. of shares (mil.): 178
Return on equity: 12.4%	Dividends
Cash ($ mil.): 3,612	Yield: 0.0%
Current ratio: 1.25	Payout: 17.7%
Long-term debt ($ mil.): 6,007	Market value ($ mil.): 8,884

	STOCK PRICE ($) FY Close	P/E High/Low		PER SHARE ($) Earnings	Dividends	Book Value
06/14	49.70	12	10	10.79	1.91	91.44
06/13*	41.59	65	57	1.57	0.73	80.51
04/13	41.50	10	9	10.33	0.73	80.29
04/12	37.75	29	25	2.86	0.59	74.50
Annual Growth	9.6%			94.4%	79.7%	10.8%

*Fiscal year change

Chubu Electric Power Co., Inc.

Chubu Electric Power is Japan's third-largest electric utility after Tokyo Electric and Kansai Electric. The company supplies power to about 16 million people in central Japan's Chubu region a leading manufacturing region in Japan that includes Nagoya one of the country's largest cities. It has thermal hydroelectric nuclear wind and solar power generating facilities that together have a capacity of more than 32830 GW. It also has power transmission and distribution facilities. In response to deregulation Chubu Electric Power has moved into newer industries including IT natural gas supply real estate management and overseas consulting.

Operations

Chubu Electric Power has about 200 power generation facilities in Japan a transmission line that runs more than 12200 kilometers a distribution line that runs more than 130000 kilometers and nearly 100 transforming substations. The company also maintains major overseas offices in Washington DC London Bangkok and Doha in Qatar.

Financial Performance

Chubu Electric experienced its first operating loss in its history in fiscal 2012 (ends March). While revenues increased just slightly at 5% net income took a steep nose dive from a profit of about $1 billion in fiscal 2011 to a net loss of about $1.1 billion in fiscal 2012 mainly due to swelling thermal power fuel costs attributable to the shutdown of the Hamaoka nuclear power station in mid-2011. Chubu Electric suspended operations at that plant at the request of the national government due to rising concerns over safety after the massive tsunami and Fukushima Daiichi nuclear power plant disaster in March 2011.

Strategy

In order to get its profitability back on track and ensure a stable supply of electricity Chubu Electric is working on a tsunami countermeasure initiative to improve the safety of its power generation facilities including Hamaoka at a cost of about $1.5 billion. Its main efforts to this end are developing flooding prevention measures and enhancing emergency measures.

Although tight conditions at the company are expected to continue until the Hamaoka station resumes operations Chubu Electric's longer-term goals are to continue developing and buying more renewable energy and increase revenues by advancing energy-related infrastructure businesses including power generation in foreign countries.

EXECUTIVES

EVP and Director, Haruhiko Asano
Chairman, Toshio Mita
President, Akihisa Mizuno
EVP, Tomohiko Ohno
EVP, Masatoshi Sakaguchi
EVP, Kazuhiro Matsubara
Corporate Auditor, Hidetaka Tomita
EVP, Satoru Katsuno
Senior Managing Executive Officer, Ryousuke Mizutani
Senior Managing Executive Officer, Yutaka Watanabe
Senior Managing Executive Officer, Satoshi Onoda
Senior Managing Executive Officer, Masanori Matsuura
EVP and Director, Haruhiko Asano

Senior Managing Executive Officer and Director, Toshiyuki Nosaka
EVP and Director, Yoshihito Miyaike
EVP and Director, Norihisa Ito
Director, Hideko Katsumata
Director, Shun Matsushita
Senior Managing Executive Officer and Director, Ryousuke Mizutani
Director, Yuji Kume
President and Director, Akihisa Mizuno
Senior Managing Executive Officer and Director, Masakazu Aida
EVP and Director, Tomohiko Ohno
EVP and Director, Masatoshi Sakaguchi
EVP and Director, Kazuhiro Matsubara
Auditors: KPMGAZSA&Co.

LOCATIONS

HQ: Chubu Electric Power Co., Inc.
1 Higashi-Shincho, Higashi-ku, Nagoya, Aichi 461-8680
Phone: (81) 52 951 8211 **Fax:** (81) 52 962 4624
Web: www.chuden.co.jp

PRODUCTS/OPERATIONS

Sales

	% of total
Electric	81
Energy	2
Other	17
Total	**100**

COMPETITORS

Chugoku Electric Power	Kyushu Electric Power
Hokkaido Electric Power	Osaka Gas
	Shikoku Electric
Hokuriku Electric Power	Tohoku Electric Power
KEPCO	Tokyo Electric
	Tokyo Gas

HISTORICAL FINANCIALS

Company Type: Public

Income Statement

FYE: March 31

	REVENUE ($ mil.)	NET INCOME ($ mil.)	NET PROFIT MARGIN	EMPLOYEES
03/14	27,535	(632)	—	30,888
03/13	28,153	(341)	—	30,847
03/12	29,858	(1,123)	—	29,859
03/11	28,148	1,021	3.6%	29,583
03/10	23,965	1,162	4.8%	29,116
Annual Growth	**3.5%**	**—**		**1.5%**

2014 Year-End Financials

Debt ratio: 0.5%
Return on equity: (-4.5%)
Cash ($ mil.): 1,361
Current ratio: 1.02
Long-term debt ($ mil.): 25,396

No. of shares (mil.): 757
Dividends
  Yield: —
  Payout: —
Market value ($ mil.): —

	STOCK PRICE ($) FY Close	P/E High/Low		PER SHARE ($) Earnings	Dividends	Book Value
03/14	0.00	—	—	(0.84)	0.00	18.38
03/13	0.00	—	—	(0.45)	0.00	20.92
Annual Growth	**—**	**—**	**—**	**—**	**—**	**(3.2%)**

Chugoku Bank, Ltd. (The)

Chugoku Bank hopes to attract individuals and businesses who are looking to bank on the sunny side. The Japanese regional bank serves the Okayama prefecture (known as "the sunny land") and the neighboring areas of Ehime Hiroshima Hyogo Kagawa and Tottori through some 150 offices and a network of ATMs. The bank also boasts overseas operations with offices in China Hong Kong Singapore and the US. Chugoku Bank subsidiaries and affiliates are involved in such businesses as asset management credit cards credit guarantees financing leasing and pre-paid cards. Japan Trustee Services Bank Ltd. owns a majority stake in the bank.

EXECUTIVES

Chairman, Fumihiro Izumi
Senior Managing Director, Hiromichi Tsuboi
President and Director, Masato Miyanaga
Managing Director, Hajime Aoyama
Managing Director, Yoshinori Yamamoto
Managing Director, Hiroyuki Hanazawa
Managing Director, Yoshimasa Asama
Auditors: KPMGAZSA&Co.

LOCATIONS

HQ: Chugoku Bank, Ltd. (The)
1-15-20 Marunouchi, Kita-ku, Okayama 700-8628
Phone: (81) 86 223 3111
Web: www.chugin.co.jp

COMPETITORS

Awa Bank	Norinchukin Bank
Hiroshima Bank	Resona
Hyakujushi Bank	Sumitomo Mitsui
Mitsubishi UFJ Financial Group	Sumitomo Trust and Banking
Mizuho Financial	

HISTORICAL FINANCIALS

Company Type: Public

Income Statement

FYE: March 31

	ASSETS ($ mil.)	NET INCOME ($ mil.)	INCOME AS % OF ASSETS	EMPLOYEES
03/14	67,627	278	0.4%	3,558
03/13	72,051	195	0.3%	3,570
03/12	77,278	232	0.3%	3,574
03/11	75,126	52	0.1%	3,583
03/10	64,948	109	0.2%	3,523
Annual Growth	**1.0%**	**26.2%**	**—**	**0.2%**

2014 Year-End Financials

Return on assets: 0.4%
Return on equity: 6.4%
Long-term debt ($ mil.): —
No. of shares (mil.): 200
Sales ($ mil): 1,291

Dividends
  Yield: —
  Payout: —
Market value ($ mil.): —

CIMB Group Holdings Bhd

CIMB Group is the second-largest financial services firm in Malaysia behind Maybank. It is the holding company for CIMB Bank CIMB Investment Bank and CIMB Islamic which provide retail and commercial banking and financial services to 13 million customers throughout Southeast Asia. While it has a presence in more than 15 countries (including a CIMB Securities office in New York City) the bank's main markets are Malaysia Indonesia Singapore Thailand and Cambodia. Altogether the group has more than 1050 branches. CIMB Group's offerings include corporate and consumer banking investment banking Islamic banking stock brokerage asset management and insurance. It was established in 1924 as Bian Chiang Bank.

Mergers and Acquisitions

CIMB Investment Bank became one of the largest investment banking franchises in Asia in 2012 with the acquisition of most of the Asian investment banking business of the Royal Bank of Scotland. The acquisition gave CIMB a presence in Taiwan and Australia and expanded its operations in Hong Kong India and China. RBS kept its business in South Korea.

LOCATIONS

HQ: CIMB Group Holdings Bhd
Level 13, Menara CIMB, Jalan Stesen Sentral 2, Kuala Lumpur Sentral, Kuala Lumpur 50470
Phone: (60) 3 2261 0085   **Fax:** (60) 3 2261 0099
Web: www.cimb.com

PRODUCTS/OPERATIONS

Selected Businesses
Consumer Banking
Wholesale Banking
Islamic Banking

Selected Subsidiaries
CIMB Group
  CIMB Bank Berhard (commercial banking)
  CIMB Futures Sdn Bhd (futures and options)
  CIMB Investment Bank Berhad (investment banking and securities)
  CIMB Islamic Bank Berhad (Islamic banking and finance)
  CIMB-Mapletree Management Sdn Bhd (real estate investment and management 60%)
  CIMP-Principal Asset Management Berhard (50%)

HISTORICAL FINANCIALS
Company Type: Public

Income Statement
FYE: December 31

	ASSETS ($ mil.)	NET INCOME ($ mil.)	INCOME AS % OF ASSETS	EMPLOYEES
12/13	113,225	1,386	1.2%	40,804
12/12	110,085	1,419	1.3%	41,993
12/11	94,731	1,271	1.3%	40,244
12/10	87,399	1,142	1.3%	36,984
12/09	70,078	819	1.2%	35,922
Annual Growth	12.7%	14.0%	—	3.2%

2013 Year-End Financials
Return on assets: 1.2%
Return on equity: 15.3%
Long-term debt ($ mil.): —
No. of shares (mil.): —
Sales ($ mil): 6,771
Dividends
  Yield: —
  Payout: —
Market value ($ mil.): —

	STOCK PRICE ($) FY Close	P/E High/Low		PER SHARE ($) Earnings	Dividends	Book Value
12/13	2.31	0	0	0.18	0.00	1.20
12/12	2.44	0	0	0.19	0.00	1.26
Annual Growth	(5.5%)	—	—	(1.0%)	—	(1.1%)

Clydesdale Bank PLC (United Kingdom)

LOCATIONS

HQ: Clydesdale Bank PLC (United Kingdom)
  30 St. Vincent Place, Glasgow, Scotland G1 2HL
Phone: (44) 0141 248 7070   **Fax:** (44) 0141 204 0828
Web: www.cbonline.co.uk

HISTORICAL FINANCIALS
Company Type: Public

Income Statement
FYE: September 30

	ASSETS ($ mil.)	NET INCOME ($ mil.)	INCOME AS % OF ASSETS	EMPLOYEES
09/14	60,013	(288)	—	4,521
09/13	58,906	(71)	—	4,570
09/05	39,322	219	0.6%	6,176
09/04	15,873	108	0.7%	6,443
09/03	14,761	184	1.2%	2,881
Annual Growth	13.6%	—	—	4.2%

2014 Year-End Financials
Return on assets: (-0.4%)
Return on equity: (-7.2%)
Long-term debt ($ mil.): —
No. of shares (mil.): —
Sales ($ mil): 2,147
Dividends
  Yield: —
  Payout: —
Market value ($ mil.): —

CNH Industrial N.V.

LOCATIONS

HQ: CNH Industrial N.V.
  Cranes Farm Road, Basildon, Essex SS14 3AD
Phone: (44) 1 268 292 545   **Fax:** (44) 1 268 292 984
Web: www.cnhindustrial.com

HISTORICAL FINANCIALS
Company Type: Public

Income Statement
FYE: December 31

	REVENUE ($ mil.)	NET INCOME ($ mil.)	NET PROFIT MARGIN	EMPLOYEES
12/13	35,489	1,086	3.1%	71,192
12/12	33,985	1,067	3.1%	68,257
12/11	31,416	807	2.6%	66,998
12/10	28,563	456	1.6%	62,123
Annual Growth	7.5%	33.5%	—	4.6%

2013 Year-End Financials
Debt ratio: 73.0%
Return on equity: 15.1%
Cash ($ mil.): 6,477
Current ratio: 8.74
Long-term debt ($ mil.): 29,894
No. of shares (mil.): 1,350
Dividends
  Yield: —
  Payout: —
Market value ($ mil.): 15,323

	STOCK PRICE ($) FY Close	P/E High/Low		PER SHARE ($) Earnings	Dividends	Book Value
12/13	11.35	38	31	0.87	0.00	5.61
12/12	0.00	—	—	0.86	0.00	5.32
Annual Growth	—	—	—	0.4%	—	1.8%

Cnooc Ltd.

CNOOC Limited manages China's offshore oil and gas exploration and production activities in partnership with international oil and gas firms. Under Chinese government-regulated production sharing contracts CNOOC Limited has the sole right to acquire up to 51% of any successful discovery offshore China made by foreign partners. CNOOC Limited has 2.6 billion barrels of oil equivalent in estimated proved reserves primarily in the South China Sea. CNOOC Limited is also engaged in oil refining natural gas processing and refined products marketing. The oil producer has a net production of 469.4 barrels of oil equivalent per day. To grow it global assets in 2012 the company agreed to buy Nexen for $15 billion.

The deal gives CNOOC access to major oil and gas plays including Canadian oil sands and conventional fields in western Canada the North Sea the Gulf of Mexico and Nigeria.

Growin its North American assets in 2010 the company paid about $1.1 billion for a one-third stake in Chesapeake Energy's 600000 oil and natural gas acres in the Eagle Ford shale project in South Texas. It boosted its shale holdings further in 2011 agreeing to spend $570 million to buy a one-third stake in Chesapeake Energy's drilling assets in a shale oil field in northeast Colorado and southeast Wyoming. It also bought oil sands producer OPTI Canada for $2.1 billion.

In another major expansion that year the company acquired a 33% stake in an onshore oilfield in Uganda from Tullow Oil for $1.5 billion.

CNOOC Limited is 64%-owned by China National Offshore Oil Corporation.

EXECUTIVES

Chairman, Chengyu Fu, age 63
Senior Vice President, Wei Chen, age 56
Vice Chairman, Yang Hua, age 53
EVP, Liu Jian, age 56
Compliance Officer and Executive Director, Guangqi Wu, age 57
Executive Vice President, Bi Chen, age 53
Vice President; General Manager - CNOOC International Limited, Zhi Fang, age 52
Executive Vice President, Guangyu Yuan, age 56
SVP and General Manager CNOOC China Limited Shanghai Branch, Guohua Zhang, age 55
Chief Geologist EVP and General Manager Exploration Department, Weilin Zhu, age 59
President; Chief Executive Officer; Executive Director, Fanrong Li, age 52
Company Secretary, Yongzhi Jiang
Chief Financial Officer; Joint Company Secretary, Hua Zhong
Joint Company Secretary, Sik Tsue

General Counsel, Liguo Zhao
Non-Executive Director, Shouwei Zhou, age 64
Vice Chairman, Yang Hua, age 53
Independent Non-Executive Director, Sung Hong Chiu, age 67
Compliance Officer and Executive Director, Guangqi Wu, age 57
Independent Non-Executive Director, Aloysius H. Y. Tse, age 66
Non-Executive Director, Xinghe Cao, age 65
Non-Executive Director, Zhenfang Wu, age 62
Independent Non-Executive Director, Edgar W. K. Cheng, age 71
Independent Non-Executive Director, Lawrence J. Lau, age 70
Independent Non-Executive Director, Tao Wang, age 84
President CEO and Director, Fanrong Li, age 51
Auditors: Ernst&Young

LOCATIONS

HQ: Cnooc Ltd.
   65th Floor, Bank of China Tower, One Garden Road,
Phone: (852) 2213 2500   **Fax:** (852) 2525 9322
Web: www.cnoocltd.com

Sales

	% of total
China	86
Other	14
Total	**100**

PRODUCTS/OPERATIONS

Sales

	% of total
Production sharing	47
Independent	35
Trading	18
Total	**100**

Selected Subsidiaries

CNOOC China Limited (China)
CNOOC Finance (2002) Limited (British Virgin Islands)
CNOOC Finance (2003) Limited (British Virgin Islands)
CNOOC International Limited (British Virgin Islands)
CNOOC Offshore Oil (Singapore) Pte. Ltd.

COMPETITORS

Anadarko Petroleum	Exxon Mobil
Apache	PetroChina
BP	Royal Dutch Shell
Chevron	Sinopec Corp.

HISTORICAL FINANCIALS

Company Type: Public

Income Statement

FYE: December 31

	REVENUE ($ mil.)	NET INCOME ($ mil.)	NET PROFIT MARGIN	EMPLOYEES
12/13	47,218	9,326	19.8%	17,553
12/12	39,720	10,216	25.7%	10,063
12/11	38,279	11,161	29.2%	5,377
12/10	27,770	8,254	29.7%	4,650
12/09	15,406	4,318	28.0%	4,019
Annual Growth	**32.3%**	**21.2%**	—	**44.6%**

2013 Year-End Financials

Debt ratio: 3.5%	No. of shares (mil.): —
Return on equity: 17.3%	Dividends
Cash ($ mil.): 6,695	Yield: 3.5%
Current ratio: 1.14	Payout: 3,150.0%
Long-term debt ($ mil.): 13,546	Market value ($ mil.): —

	STOCK PRICE ($) FY Close	P/E High/Low		PER SHARE ($) Earnings	Dividends	Book Value
12/13	187.66	5	3	0.21	6.62	1.26
12/12	220.00	4	3	0.23	4.99	1.11
12/11	174.68	4	2	0.25	0.14	0.94
12/10	238.37	4	3	0.18	4.74	0.73
12/09	155.45	5	2	0.10	4.64	0.57
Annual Growth	**4.8%**	—	—	**21.1%**	**9.2%**	**22.0%**

CNP Assurances S.A.

Running to the post office and the bank? Buy some insurance while you're out. CNP Assurances is France's top personal life insurer. In addition to life insurance and other savings products it sells health death and disability and other personal risk coverage and pensions. CNP sells its products primarily through the outlets of La Poste the French postal service and Groupe BPCE the state savings banks; together these two channels account for about 65% of CNP's sales. These partners are also shareholders in the company together owning about 35%. Another French paragovernmental organization Caisse des Depots et Consignations owns 40%.

HISTORY

CNP Assurances traces its origins to three government insurance entities established in the mid-19th century. Caisse nationale d'assurance en cas d'accident ("accident insurance") was formed in 1868. Caisse nationale d'assurance en cas de deces ("death and disability insurance") was formed in 1848 while Caisse de retraite pour la vieillesse ("retirement pensions") followed two years later. These two organizations were merged in 1949 forming Caisse nationale d'assurance sur la vie. Ten years later it was merged with the government's accident insurance bureau to form Caisse Nationale de Prevoyance ("provident society"). CNP was put under the domain of the French government's investment banking arm Caisse des Depots et Consignations (CDC).

Over the years CNP earned a reputation for specializing in certain risks introducing a variety of life and personal risk insurance and pension and savings products. During the 1980s the company enjoyed a healthy growth rate around 20% annually as more French individuals and companies began investing in insurance products.

In 1987 CNP became a national public establishment making it independent from though still owned by the government. The next year the company teamed with Centre National des Caisses d'Epargne et de Prevoyance (now La Caisse Nationale des Caisses d'Epargne or Caisses d'Epargne) to form Ecureuil-Vie a joint venture to sell CNP's insurance and savings products in the national savings banks. That year it partnered with Portugal's Caixa Geral de Depositos to create new products.

In the early 1990s CNP was among several entities the government announced it would privatize. To prepare for the change the company reorganized and became CNP Assurances; the government sold a large chunk of the firm to CDC La Poste and Caisses d'Epargne reducing its stake to 42%. During this time CNP passed rival Union des Assurances de Paris (now part of AXA) to become France's top life insurer.

Privatization lurched along until 1995 when it was put on hold for elections; the Socialist government that came to power was less enthusiastic about the sale of government assets than its predecessor. The process hit another snag two years later when some workers protested fearing they'd lose their status as civil servants and the perks associated with it. Also in 1997 CNP became the major shareholder of Polish life insurer Polisa-Zycie when it raised its stake from 26% (purchased 1996) to 46%. By 1998 privatization was back on track and the government sold a 22% stake in CNP to the public. CDC La Poste and Caisses d'Epargne raised their interests to their current levels. Before the year's end CNP bought majority stakes in Portuguese insurers Global and Global Vida.

Expansion abroad continued in 1999 when CNP announced plans to set up operations in China. That year it teamed with the UK's Prudential for cobranded insurance products. In 2000 the company extended its selling arrangement with Caisses d'Epargne to 2005. In 2003 it sold off its share of Italian bancassurance company Carivita.

EXECUTIVES

CEO, Gilles Benoist, age 66
Director Management and Innovation, Jean-Pierre Walbaum, age 68
Director International Operations and Deputy CEO, Xavier Larnaudie-Eiffel
Director Finance and Deputy CEO, Antoine Lissowski
Director Redaction, Agathe Sanson
Head of Investor Relations, Jim Root
Manager Investor Relations, Jean-Yves Icole
Director Programmes Organisation and Information Systems and Deputy CEO, Michel Bois, age 54
Director Internal Auditing and Quality Mission and Secretary, Huguette Rellier, age 59
Auditors: KPMGAudit

LOCATIONS

HQ: CNP Assurances S.A.
   4, place Raoul Dautry, Paris, Cedex 15 75716
Phone: (33) 1 42 18 88 88
Web: www.cnp.fr

2010 Premiums

	% of total
France	81
Italy	8
Brazil	8
Spain	2
Other	1
Total	**100**

PRODUCTS/OPERATIONS

Revenues

	% of total
Premiums	72
Total	**100**

Premiums

	% of total
Life insurance	63
Financial instruments	29

Selected Subsidiaries

Barclays Vida y Pensiones (50% Spain)
Caixa Seguros (52% insurance Brazil)
CNP Europe Life Ltd (Ireland)
CNP Holding Brasil
CNP IAM
CNP Seguros de Vida (76% insurance Argentina)
CNP UniCredit Vita (57% insurance Italy)
CNP Vida (94% insurance Spain)
Global (83% insurance Portugal)
Global Vida (83% insurance Portugal)

ITV
La Banque Postale Prevoyance (50% insurance)
Marfin Insurance Holdings Ltd. (50% insurance Cyprus)
Previposte

COMPETITORS

AXA	BNP Paribas
Allianz	Credit Agricole
April Group	Eureko
Assurances Generales	Groupama
de France	ING

HISTORICAL FINANCIALS

Company Type: Public

Income Statement

FYE: December 31

	ASSETS ($ mil.)	NET INCOME ($ mil.)	INCOME AS % OF ASSETS	EMPLOYEES
12/13	503,862	1,418	0.3%	4,809
12/12	465,555	1,253	0.3%	4,842
12/11	415,211	1,127	0.3%	3,077
12/10	427,755	1,405	0.3%	4,680
12/09	434,874	1,446	0.3%	4,628
Annual Growth	3.7%	(0.5%)	—	1.0%

2013 Year-End Financials

Return on assets: 0.2%	Dividends
Return on equity: 7.1%	Yield: 0.0%
Long-term debt ($ mil.): —	Payout: 28.3%
No. of shares (mil.): 686	Market value ($ mil.): 5,084
Sales ($ mil.): 58,689	

	STOCK PRICE ($) FY Close	P/E High/Low		PER SHARE ($)		
				Earnings	Dividends	Book Value
12/13	7.41	10	9	2.01	0.57	29.35
12/12	7.90	10	6	1.92	0.49	29.03
Annual Growth	(6.2%)	—	—	1.1%	4.0%	0.3%

Co-operative Bank p.l.c. (The) (United Kingdom)

LOCATIONS

HQ: Co-operative Bank p.l.c. (The) (United Kingdom)
 1 Balloon Street, Manchester M60 4EP
Phone: (44) 161 832 3456   **Fax:** (44) 161 829 4475
Web: www.co-operativebank.co.uk

HISTORICAL FINANCIALS

Company Type: Public

Income Statement

FYE: December 31

	ASSETS ($ mil.)	NET INCOME ($ mil.)	INCOME AS % OF ASSETS	EMPLOYEES
12/13	71,715	(1,237)	—	7,526
12/12	79,905	(820)	—	7,754
12/11	75,629	74	0.1%	8,528
12/10*	70,771	56	0.1%	8,746
01/09	22,796	20	0.1%	3,990
Annual Growth	25.8%	—	—	13.5%

*Fiscal year change

2013 Year-End Financials

Return on assets: (-1.6%)	Dividends
Return on equity: (-42.0%)	Yield: —
Long-term debt ($ mil.): —	Payout: —
No. of shares (mil.): 250	Market value ($ mil.): —
Sales ($ mil): 3,242	

Commerzbank AG (Germany, Fed. Rep.)

Sprechen sie Commerz? The second-largest bank in Germany (behind Deutsche Bank) Commerzbank provides retail and commercial banking services from approximately 1200 branches nationwide and from offices in another 50 countries. The bank serves about 15 million customers primarily individuals and small to midsized businesses in Germany and abroad. Mortgage specialist Eurohypo provides commercial and residential real estate lending and public financing services in Europe and the US. Since Dresdner Bank merged into Commerzbank in 2009 the company has been retooling itself and focusing on its core banking operations.

It took two years for Commerzbank to fully integrate Dresdner Bank and its former Dresdner Kleinwort investment banking operations. It was the largest integration project in German banking history.

As a result of the merger Commerzbank scaled back some of its operations and is focused on becoming a leaner more efficient company. It is in the process of selling several private banking divisions including units acquired in the Dresdner Bank transaction. Units sold include Dresdner Bank of Switzerland Kleinwort Benson Private Bank Dresdner Monaco and Austria's Privatinvest Bank. Additionally Commerzbank has shut down or sold investment banking and securities lending units.

In 2010 the company continued to cut non-core assets selling its Montrada credit card processing unit to Equens and its Commerzbank International Trust Singapore fund management unit to Trident Trust. The company also is seeking buyers for Eurohypo (though finding a buyer for the troubled firm may be difficult).

The financial market and economic crisis dragged down performance of Commerzbank during the recession. However by 2010 Commerzbank returned to profit after posting losses in 2009. The increase in profit was attributed to net trading income and lower loan loss provisions. Charges connected to the integration of Dresdner Bank also were not a factor in 2010. With the integration behind Commerzbank it expects to realize synergies and reduce costs helping increase profits even more. The company also plans to reduce risk as a whole by scaling back its activity in commercial real estate and public finance.

As Commerzbank's performance improves one big goal is to repay the German government for the aid it received during the market turmoil. In 2008 the global economic crisis hit Germany and Commerzbank received a government bailout of Å8 billion ($11 billion) to help stimulate lending and promote consumer confidence.

The government stepped in once again in early 2009 with an injection of some Å10 billion ($14 billion) to help ensure the merger between Commerzbank and Dresdner Bank. As part of the intervention in which the government assumed one-fourth ownership of the company.

In 2011 Commerzbank started a two-step process to repay the government.

HISTORY

In 1870 a group of merchants and bankers formed Commerz- und Disconto-Bank in Hamburg. Germany boomed after the Franco-Prussian War and the bank expanded quickly into Frankfurt Berlin and London. Its 1905 purchase of Berliner Bank refocused the bank on the German capital.

After WWI hyperinflation led to a rash of mergers among crippled banks; Commerz absorbed regional players including Mitteldeutsche Privat-Bank (1920) and Mitteldeutsche Creditbank (1929). In the late 1920s the bank partnered with Chase National Bank to bring foreign money into Germany. As the Depression swept Europe the government bought a majority stake and merged it with Barmer Bank-Verein. Commerz became one of Germany's six "Berliner Grossbanken".

The bank took its current name after the government sold its stake in 1940. After WWII the Allies overhauled Germany's banking system and Commerzbank was split into three regional banks in 1952. In the late 1950s the rules barring large banks expired and the Commerz trio had regrouped by 1958 minus the company's prewar eastern German offices.

After rebuilding its domestic operations in the early 1960s Commerzbank expanded into Hong Kong the UK and the US among other countries. During the 1970s it acquired stakes in a variety of nonbanking companies spurred by a government fearful that Middle Eastern oil money would take control of the country's struggling industrial giants. It also diversified its services.

Overexpansion bad loans in Latin America and a bloated staff took their toll in the early 1980s. On the verge of failure Commerzbank brought in banker Walter Seipp to lead a recovery. He cut costs and focused on profit; the bank was back in shape by 1984. It then focused on creating an "allfinanz" group lining up with such firms as insurance provider DBV Versicherungen and savings and loan Leonberger Bausparkasse.

After the Berlin Wall fell in 1989 Commerzbank moved back into eastern Germany and made forays into other Eastern European countries. During the 1990s the bank focused on asset and investment management. It bought UK pension fund manager Jupiter Tyndall Group Martingale Asset Management (US) Montgomery Asset Management (US) and other firms and opened investment management offices in Frankfurt Hong Kong London New York and Tokyo. It added money market funds when they were introduced in Germany in 1994.

In 1996 the bank was embroiled in a tax evasion scandal when regulators charged that it had helped clients move assets to Luxembourg. The company was then hit hard by the Asian financial crisis of 1998 especially after the contagion spread to Russia. But as the situation eased in 1999 Commerzbank formed a joint venture with Bangkok Land to build a mall in Bangkok. That year the company announced an alliance with Assicurazioni Generali (which owns about 9% of Commerzbank) to cross-sell their banking and insurance products.

In 2000 Commerzbank and Dresdner Bank (on the rebound from a failed merger with Deutsche Bank) began merger talks. However after German regulators sought to prevent Commerzbank's largest single shareholder Cobra Beteiligungs from exercising its voting rights the bank's share price fell and the companies could not conclude the merger of equals. Amid swirling rumors of other potential alliances Commerzbank sought to strengthen its pan-European alliances and made connections with retail brokers in Japan. (German insurance giant Allianz bought Dresdner in 2001.)

Later in 2000 Commerzbank announced a restructuring plan that included closing about 150 branches and regrouping the bank's business divisions. The next year Commerzbank entered a strategic alliance with China-based China Southern Securities.

Commerzbank's mortgage bank RheinHyp merged with Dresdner Bank's Deutsche Hypothekenbank and Deutsche Bank's Eurohypo in 2002. The combined company was named Eurohypo.

As chief executive Klaus-Peter Moller launched a more performance-driven strategy for Commerzbank and implemented an Anglo-American style of management in an effort to make the bank competitive.

Commerzbank acquired the struggling Schmidt-Bank in 2004 in response to government pressure for consolidation in the banking industry.

In 2006 Commerzbank which owned about 32% of Eurohypo bought Deutsche Bank's 38% stake and Dresdner Bank's 28% interest for $6.9 billion in 2006 bringing Commerzbank's ownership in the venture to some 98%.

Commerzbank acquired rival Dresdner Bank from Allianz in 2009 cementing its position as Germany's second-largest bank. Commerzbank has boosted its Central and Eastern Europe business. It acquired 60% of Ukraine-based Bank Forum in 2009 and the following year increased its stake to 89%.

EXECUTIVES

Chairman, Klaus-Peter Muller, age 70
Chairman Managing Directors, Martin Blessing, age 51
Chief Risk Officer, Stefan Schmittmann, age 58
Managing Director Private Customers, Martin Zielke, age 51
Chief Operating Officer, Frank Annuscheit, age 52
Managing Director Human Resources and Integration, Ulrich Sieber, age 49
Managing Director Corporate and Markets, Michael Reuther, age 55
Managing Director Mittelstandsbank, Markus Beumer, age 50
Chief Financial Officer, Stephan Engels, age 52
Director, Sergio Balbinot, age 53
Director, Helmut Perlet, age 65
Director, Burckhard Bergmann, age 69
Director, Nikolaus von Bomhard
Director, Edgar Meister
Deputy Chairman, Uwe Tschage, age 44
Director, Otto Happel, age 65
Director, Astrid Evers, age 50
Director, Uwe Foullong, age 54
Director, Daniel Hampel, age 50
Director, Prof Ulrich Middlemann, age 67
Director, Marcus Schenck, age 49
Director, Karin van Brummelen, age 59
Director, Alexandra Krieger, age 41
Director, Barbara Priester, age 54
Director, Hans-Hermann Altenschmidt, age 51
Director, Prof Hans-Peter Keitel, age 64
Director, Beate Hoffmann, age 52
Director, Mark Roach, age 57
Auditors: PwCDeutscheRevisionAG

LOCATIONS

HQ: Commerzbank AG (Germany, Fed. Rep.)
Kaiserplatz, Frankfurt am Main D-60261
Phone: (49) 69 136 20   **Fax:** (49) 69 28 53 89
Web: www.commerzbank.com

PRODUCTS/OPERATIONS

Sales

	% of total
Interest	81
Commissions	19
Total	**100**

Sales by Segment

Private Customers	30
Corporates & Markets	19
Central & Eastern Europe	8
Portfolio restructuring unit	7
Consolidation & other	3

Selected Subsidiaries and Affiliates

AFOG GmbH & Co. KG
BRE Bank Hipoteczny SA (Poland)
comdirect bank Aktiengesellschaft
Commerz (East Asia) Ltd. (Hong Kong)
Commerzbank (Eurasija) SAO (Russia)
Commerzbank Inslandsbanken Holding GmbH
Erste Europaische Pfandbrief- und
  Kommunalkreditbank Aktiengesellschaft in
  Luxemburg
European Bank for Fund Services GmbH
OLEANDRA Grundstucks-Vermietungsgesellschaft
  mbH&Co. Objekt Jupiter KG

COMPETITORS

BayernLB	IKB
Credit Agricole	UBS
Credit Suisse	UniCredit Bank AG
Deutsche Bank	WestLB
Deutsche Postbank	

HISTORICAL FINANCIALS

Company Type: Public

Income Statement

	ASSETS ($ mil.)	NET INCOME ($ mil.)	INCOME AS % OF ASSETS	EMPLOYEES
12/13	756,737	107	0.0%	52,944
12/12	838,118	7	0.0%	53,601
12/11	855,958	825	0.1%	58,160
12/10	1,009,532	1,913	0.2%	59,101
12/09	1,215,989	(6,535)	—	53,231
Annual Growth	(11.2%)	—	—	(0.1%)

FYE: December 31

2013 Year-End Financials

Return on assets: 0.0%	Dividends
Return on equity: 0.3%	Yield: 22.2%
Long-term debt ($ mil.): —	Payout: —
No. of shares (mil.): 1,138	Market value ($ mil.): 18,558
Sales ($ mil): 24,315	

	STOCK PRICE ($) FY Close	P/E High/Low		PER SHARE ($) Earnings	Dividends	Book Value
12/13	16.30	—	—	(0.12)	3.63	31.42
12/12	1.98	—	—	(0.53)	0.00	59.13
12/11	1.69	9	1	2.33	0.00	60.98
12/10	7.36	2	1	16.19	0.00	318.29
12/09	8.45	—	—	(63.39)	0.00	317.36
Annual Growth	17.9% (43.9%)	—	—	—	—	—

Commonwealth Bank of Australia

Commonwealth Bank of Australia (CBA) one of Australia's Big Four banks offers retail and commercial banking insurance and investment services including credit cards home loans deposit accounts and mutual funds. CBA's brands include Bankwest wealth manager Colonial First State master trust services provider FirstChoice online brokerage CommSec ASB Bank which provides banking investment and financial services in New Zealand. CBA has approximately 1100 branch offices in Australia (plus approximately 3700 Australia Post locations) as well as operations that reach Asia Europe and the US. CBA is also one of the largest life insurers in Australia and a leading provider of home loans there.

Geographic Reach

CBA has a growing international presence. It operates retail banks in New Zealand (ASB) and Indonesia (Commonwealth Bank of Indonesia). It has minority investments in two banks in China and one in Vietnam. It also has banking branch offices in London New York Tokyo Hong Kong Shanghai Singapore Auckland Ho Chi Minh City and Mumbai.

Operations

In addition to banking CBA has life insurance operations in New Zealand (Sovereign) Indonesia (Commonwealth Life) and a joint venture in China called BoCommLife. Its investment products include funds offered by CBA or through its master trust product FirstChoice the largest retail platform in Australia. CBA is one of the country's largest managers of Australian funds.

Strategy

CBA is expanding at home and abroad. Its acquisition of BankWestfrom HBOS in 2008 bolstered its position in western Australia. In 2010 CBA entered the Chinese insurance market with the launch of a joint venture with Bank of Communications. The following year the bank opened branches in China India and Indonesia and bought a 20% sake in Vietnam International Bank. The bank continued to strengthen its ties to China signing a referral agreement with Agricultural Bank of China in 2011 to capture potential customers.

Customer service and business banking are also areas of focus for the bank. To improve its banking offerings the company has been migrating its retail clients to a new core operating platform. CBA has also switched from overnight batch processing to real-time banking. In business banking new office openings and personnel have helped the company grow its market share from 12% (2006) to 18% (2011).

HISTORY

The Commonwealth Bank Act of 1911 allowed banks to conduct both savings bank and central bank functions and paved the way for the founding of the Commonwealth Bank of Australia the next year. The bank initially operated through a single main office and in nearly 500 post offices in Victoria; it spread out through the entire country over the next few years.

The young bank was drafted during WWI to help the federal government organize war loans and a merchant shipping fleet. In 1919 the bank took over responsibility for issuing notes from the Federal Treasury. In 1928 it created the Commonwealth Savings Bank from its savings department.

Australia —heavily indebted to British lenders — was devastated by the Great Depression. As banks failed the Commonwealth Bank picked up several other institutions including the state banks in Western Australia and New South Wales. During those years Commonwealth took on more and more of the functions of a central bank.

During WWII the bank again came to the aid of its country acting as an agent for the federal government. After the war when the Australian economy stabilized the bank began offering home loans.

After years of controversy in 1959 two bank acts formally separated the Commonwealth Bank's central bank and savings functions. The Reserve Bank of Australia took over the central bank functions in 1960 and the trading and savings operations were taken over by the new Commonwealth Development Bank later renamed the Commonwealth Banking Corporation (a subsidiary of Commonwealth Bank of Australia).

The bank concentrated on expansion and diversification in the 1970s establishing travel home insurance and financing (CBFC 1978); it set its sights on technology in the 1980s expanding its credit card offerings and introducing electronic banking.

The US's 1987 stock market crash again affected Australia's banks which spent almost a decade recovering. Luckily for Commonwealth Bank it wasn't the hardest hit.

In 1988 Commonwealth Bank moved into life insurance and investment services forming subsidiaries Commonwealth Life and Commonwealth Management Services (now together known as CBA Financial Services). In 1989 the bank bought 75% of New Zealand-based ASB Bank.

Commonwealth faced a bevy of challenges including banking deregulation that began in 1982 foreign competition and 1990's banking-law amendments allowing banks to be publicly traded. All of these factors influenced Commonwealth's decision to reorganize. The government sold approximately 30% of its stake in 1991 in part to help Commonwealth fund its acquisition of the State Bank of Victoria. The government sold the rest of its stake in 1996.

That year the company's push into electronic banking bore fruit —some 60% of all its banking transactions were online; that figure later rose to 80%. The company moved into e-commerce in 1999 putting out a call for an overseas partner; Commonwealth's stated goal was to generate one-quarter of its income outside Australia. Also that year Commonwealth and a division of The Bank of Nova Scotia joined forces to form a commodities trading group specializing in metals. In 2000 the company bought Australian financial services firm Colonial Limited.

In late 2008 the company acquired Australia-based BankWest from British bank HBOS (now part of Lloyds Banking Group). The US$1.5 billion deal included insurer and asset manager St. Andrew's (which was later sold) and bolstered CBA's presence in western Australia.

EXECUTIVES

Chairman, David J. Turner, age 70
Chief Marketing Officer, Andrew Lark
Group Executive - Financial Services; Chief Financial Officer, David Craig
General Counsel, David Cohen
Company Secretary, John D. Hatton
Group Executive Institutional Banking and Markets, Ian Saines
Group Executive Business and Private Banking, Grahame A. Petersen, $395,776 total compensation
General Manager Media and Issues Management, Bryan Fitzgerald

Head of UK and Europe, Paul Orchart
Chief Executive Colonial First State Global Asset Management, Mark J. Lazberger
Company Secretary, Carla F. Collingwood
Group Executive Enterprise Services and CIO, Michael R. Harte, $85,763 total compensation
Chief Executive and Managing Director ASB, Barbara Chapman
Chief Executive Officer; Managing Director; Executive Director, Ian Narev, age 46
Regional Head Asia, Lindsay Mann
Regional General Manager Asia, Stephen Poon
Managing Partner Edinburgh, Stuart Paul
Managing Partner Edinburgh, Angus Tulloch
Group Head Strategy, Rob Jesudason
Chief Risk Officer, Alden Toevs
Group Executive Wealth Management, Annabel F. Spring
Group Executive International Financial Services, Simon Blair
Group Executive Retail Banking Services, Ross McEwan
Director Greater Asia Equities, M. Lau
Managing Director ASB Bank Limited, Charles Pink
China Chief Representative, Paul Au
General Manager China Life ? CMG Asia Life Assurance, Alan Wood
Chief Representative India, Ravi Kushan
President Director PT Bank Commonwealth Indonesia, Nursing Nursing
General Manager Japan, Richard Harris
General Director CBA HCMC Vietnam, Danny Armstrong
General Manager Americas, Ian Phillips
Investor Relations, Louise Amos
Group Executive - Retail Banking Services, Matt Comyn
Group Executive - Human Resources, Melanie Laing
Director, Andrew M. Mohl, age 58
Director, Jane S. Hemstritch, age 61
Director, S. Carolyn H. Kay, age 53
Director, Reginald J. (Reg) Clairs, age 74
Director, Colin R. Galbraith, age 65
Director, Sir John A. Anderson, age 69
Director, Fergus D. Ryan, age 72
Director, Harrison H. Young, age 69
Non-Executive Independent Director, Brian Long
Non-Executive Independent Director, Lorna Inman
Auditors: PricewaterhouseCoopers

LOCATIONS

HQ: Commonwealth Bank of Australia
Ground Floor, Tower 1, 201 Sussex Street, Sydney, New South Wales 2000
Phone: (61) 2 9378 2000   **Fax:** (61) 2 9118 7192
Web: www.commbank.com.au

PRODUCTS/OPERATIONS

Sales by Segment

	% of total
Retail banking	45
Business & private	18
Institutional banking & Bankwest	14
New	10
Other	7
	6
Total	**100**

Sales

	% of total
Banking Interest	77
Other	23
Total	**100**

Selected Brands

ASB (New Zealand)
Bankwest

Colonial First State
CommInsure
CommSec
FirstChoice
Sovereign

COMPETITORS

AMP Limited	Macquarie Group
AXA Asia Pacific	National Australia
Asteron	Bank
Australia and New	QBE
Zealand Banking	Suncorp-Metway
HSBC	Westpac Banking
Lloyds Banking Group	

HISTORICAL FINANCIALS

Company Type: Public

Income Statement

FYE: June 30

	ASSETS ($ mil.)	NET INCOME ($ mil.)	INCOME AS % OF ASSETS	EMPLOYEES
06/14	743,668	8,109	1.1%	44,329
06/13	695,355	7,081	1.0%	44,969
06/12	731,444	7,220	1.0%	44,844
06/11	715,933	6,853	1.0%	46,060
06/10	550,925	4,827	0.9%	45,025
Annual Growth	**7.8%**	**13.8%**	**—**	**(0.4%)**

2014 Year-End Financials

Return on assets: 1.1%
Return on equity: 18.4%
Long-term debt ($ mil.): —
No. of shares (mil.): 1,615
Sales ($ mil): 40,544
Dividends
Yield: 4.6%
Payout: 60.8%
Market value ($ mil.): 123,609

	STOCK PRICE ($) FY Close	P/E High/Low		PER SHARE ($) Earnings	Dividends	Book Value
06/14	76.50	13	10	4.90	3.53	28.38
06/13	63.35	15	10	4.28	3.51	25.82
06/12	53.69	14	9	4.41	3.44	26.37
06/11	54.70	17	9	4.24	3.01	25.38
06/10	41.65	12	8	3.02	0.86	19.37
Annual Growth	**16.4%**	**—**	**—**	**12.9%**	**42.5%**	**10.0%**

Compagnie de Saint-Gobain

One of the world's largest materials groups Compagnie de Saint-Gobain is in a glass by itself. The mega-group develops manufactures and distributes a wide variety of products for construction transportation industrial food storage and solar energy use. Saint-Gobain operates in four primary sectors: Building Distribution Construction Products (insulation roofing and other products) Innovative Materials (Flat Glass and High-Performance Materials such as polymers and glass fabrics) and Packaging (glass bottles). It owns notable brands such as Gyproc Dahl International and Certain-Teed. Saint-Gobain dates to the 1660s when it made mirrors for the Palace of Versailles.

The global economy and slowdown in the construction market hurt Saint-Gobain's performance in 2008 and 2009 (when net income dropped by 85%). To weather the financial crisis the group cut costs and worked to improve operating efficiencies. The cost cutting (along with an increase in sales prices) helped. By 2010 the company began to recover. It returned to growth and reported an increase in sales.

Saint-Gobain which operates in about 65 countries around the world is focused on growing organically by constructing new manufacturing plants. It is keen on investing in emerging countries such as Asia Latin America Africa and the Middle East and Eastern Europe. In 2011 it made acquisitions in Turkey to expand it plasterboard business. It also bought a manufacturer of insulation in Russia and a float glass business in India.

Another key strategy is developing more sustainability technologies to take advantage of increasing interest in environmental issues. Some of its products include self-cleaning windows and green insulation systems and water supply systems. Saint-Gobain has a particular focus on solar power. Its solar unit is dedicated to solar-related products including photovoltaic panels and solar heating systems. The company plans to expand that business by more than ten-fold within five years; to that end Saint-Gobain acquired the 70% of solar roof tiles maker Solarwood Technology it didn't already own in 2010. It also bought the rest of photovoltaic panels maker Avancis from Shell. In another deal that year Saint-Gobain bought 50% of SAGE Electrochromics which manufactures tinted glass products. In 2011 Saint-Gobain agreed to acquire Solar Gard which specializes in manufacturing tinted films used to reduce energy consumption.

As part of a renewed focus on the construction sector Saint-Gobain plans to divest its Verallia packaging arm which makes bottles and jars for food and drinks. Verallia planned an initial public offering but that was delayed due to poor market conditions (and fears surrounding the Greek financial crisis). In another deal aimed at sharpening its focus on the construction sector Saint-Gobain sold its advanced ceramics unit to US specialty manufacturer CoorsTek for $245 million.

However construction isn't getting all of the attention. In 2011 Saint-Gobain announced plans to expand its building distribution segment (which represents more than 40% of sales) with the acquisition of the Build Center network from Wolseley. The deal will include 148 builders merchant branches in the UK as well as the French subsidiary Brossette. Saint-Gobain plans to blend the new locations in with its 500-store Jewson retail network

French holding company Wendel Investissement is Saint-Gobain's largest shareholder with a stake of 18%. Wendel also has three seats on the company's board of directors.

HISTORY

Originally called Dunoyer Saint-Gobain (named after the factory location) was founded in 1665 by order of the Sun King Louis XIV who needed mirrors to adorn his palaces. Because Venice had the monopoly on glass Louis lured Venetian artisans to Paris. Some were poisoned by Italian assassins but enough remained to teach Parisians their secrets. Saint-Gobain glass decorates the Palace of Versailles' Hall of Mirrors.

With its decreed glass monopoly in France the company grew steadily until the French Revolution interrupted its prosperity. By the early 1800s however Saint-Gobain was shining again. It set up a sales office in New York in 1830 and its first foreign subsidiary in Germany in 1857. Under chemist Joseph Gay-Lussac's direction Saint-Gobain began dabbling in chemicals in the mid-1800s.

Expanding to Italy (1889) and Spain (1904) the firm was Europe's leading glassmaker by 1913. Saint-Gobain pioneered the production of tempered security glass in the 1920s; it diversified into glass fiber in the 1930s.

Pilkington a UK competitor developed a glass-making method in 1959 that obviated the need for polishing and therefore slashed production costs. Saint-Gobain refit its factories to use the Pilkington method to keep its 50% EC market share. In 1968 the shareholding Suez Group forced Saint-Gobain to merge with Pont-a-Mousson (now Saint-Gobain Canalizacion) then the world's leading iron pipe maker. The merger led to a much-needed restructuring that included selling Saint-Gobain's chemical interests.

The company acquired a majority interest in US building-material maker CertainTeed in 1976. In 1982 it was forced to divest some of its interests when it was nationalized by France's new socialist government. Despite nationalization the company grew steadily during the 1980s investing in Compagnie Generale des Eaux the world's largest drinking-water distributor.

In 1986 after a change in France's political climate Saint-Gobain became the first company to be reprivatized. Three years later it purchased Generale Francaise de Ceramique (clay tile) and a controlling interest in Vetri (glass containers Italy).

Saint-Gobain bought Norton (the world's leader in abrasives) and UK glassmaker Solaglas in 1990. With the 1991 purchases of German glassmakers GIAG and Oberland Saint-Gobain became the world's #1 glass manufacturer within a year.

After the recession of the early 1990s Saint-Gobain sold its paper and packaging interests to Jefferson Smurfit in 1994 raising more than $1 billion for acquisitions. With Ball Corporation it formed a glass container joint venture Ball-Foster Glass in 1995; the next year it bought Ball's stake. Acquisitions in 1997 included industrial ceramics firms in Germany and France and UK abrasives maker Unicorn International. In 1998 Saint-Gobain bought Bird Corp. (roofing materials US) and CALMAR (plastic pump sprayers US). The next year it bought US-based Furon which was absorbed into a new unit Saint-Gobain Performance Plastics.

In 2000 Saint-Gobain acquired Meyer International (a UK building materials supplier) Raab Karcher (a German building materials distributor) and US-based polymer specialist Chemfab. The following year Saint-Gobain bolstered its ceiling systems operations with the acquisition of the Maars Group's metal ceiling grid business. In 2002 Saint-Gobain acquired the 25% of France-based Lapeyre (doors windows cabinetry) stock it didn't own.

The company's most notable deal of 2004 was the E686 million acquisition of Swedish plumbing products distributor Dahl International. Early in 2005 Saint-Gobain raised its stake in Hankuk Glass Industries a Korean glass maker with sales of more than $250 million from 46% to more than 80%.

In August 2005 the company made a hostile $6.5 billion bid for UK drywall/plasterboard maker BPB after friendly overtures were rejected. BPB with operations in some 60 countries rejected Saint-Gobain's initial offer as too low. Saint-Gobain came back with a sweetened $6.68 billion bid which BPB accepted. The transaction closed in 2006.

Also that year the company formed a joint venture with Owens Corning to merge their reinforcements and composites businesses. Owens Corning bought out Saint-Gobain's 40% stake in the venture for $640 million in 2007.

All told Saint-Gobain acquired around 70 companies in 2007. Its purchases that year included US vinyl siding manufacturer Norandex other building products distribution companies in Europe and the UK medical tubing products maker Consolidated Polymer Technologies (folded into its performance plastics group) and construction materials operations primarily in emerging countries.

Perhaps its biggest deal was its acquisition of HeidelbergCement's industrial mortars division Maxit. The deal made Saint-Gobain the top producer in Germany and Scandinavia and strengthened its position in the rest of Europe.

Although it had embarked on a notable spending spree Saint-Gobain also sold noncore operations to refocus on its core products. In 2007 it sold 80% of its specialty bottle maker Desjonqueres to two investment funds Sagard and Cognetas. It planned to sell its packaging operations but halted those plans when the global financial markets crashed.

Saint-Gobain bought a 44% stake in Japanese insulation maker MAG in 2008. Later that year Saint-Gobain was fined nearly Â900 million ($1.1 billion) by the European Union for alleged price fixing; it was one of the largest fines ever levied against a single firm.

Also in 2008 French holding company Wendel Investissement became Saint-Gobain's largest shareholder with a stake of approximately 20%. Wendel gained two board seats and a third seat in 2009.

EXECUTIVES

VP Construction Products Sector North America, Peter R. Dachowski

General Delegate North America, Gilles Colas

Corporate Secretary, Bernard Field, age 68

SVP and Director Audit and Internal Control, Jean-Francois Phelizon, age 68

Honorary Chairman, Jean-Louis Beffa, age 73, $1,298,696 total compensation

SVP Human Resources, Claire Pedini, age 50

General Delegate Central Europe and Northern Europe, Paul Neeteson

SVP; President Building Distribution Sector, Benoit Bazin, age 46

General Delegate United Kingdom Republic of Ireland and South Africa, Peter Hindle

SVP; President Packaging Sector, Jerome Fessard, age 60

SVP; Director Construction Products Sector, Claude Imauven, age 57

CFO, Laurent Guillot, age 45

SVP International Development; General Delegate Brazil Argentina and Chile, Jean-Claude Breffort, age 66

VP Research and Innovation, Didier Roux

Director; COO Saint- Gobain Eurocoustic, Bernard Cusenier, age 67

VP Communications, Sophie Chevallon

General Delegate for the Nordic and Baltic Countries, Thierry Lambert

SVP; President Innovative Materials Sector (Flat Glass and High-Performance Materials), Jean-Pierre Floris, age 66

VP Marketing, Gerard Aspar

General Delegate Eastern Europe, Olivier Lluansi

General Delegate India, Anand Mahajan

General Delegate Asia-Pacific Region, Emmanuel Normant

General Delegate Spain Portugal and Morocco, Ricardo de Ramon Garcia

General Delegate Mexico Venezuela and Colombia, Guy Rolli

General Delegate Italy Greece and Egypt, Gianni Scotti

VP Corporate Planning, David Molho

Corporate Secretary; Secretary of the Board of Directors; Member of the Management Committee and Executive Committee, Antoine Vignial

General Delegate to Brazil; Argentina and Chile, Benoit dIribarne

General Delegate to North America; Member of the Management Committee, John Crowe

Chairman of the Board and Chief Executive
  Officer; Member of the Management Committee
  and Executive Committee, Pierre-Andre Chalendar
General Delegate to Spain; Portugal and Morocco,
  Ricardo Garcia
General Delegate to Russia; Ukraine and CIS
  countries, Thierry Fournier
Director, Jean-Martin Folz, age 67
Director, Jean-Cyril Spinetta, age 71
Director, Isabelle Bouillot, age 64
Director, Robert Chevrier, age 70
Director, Gerhard Cromme, age 71
Director, Michel Pebereau, age 71
Director, Denis Ranque, age 62
Director, Gerard Mestrallet, age 65
Chairman and CEO, Pierre-Andre de Chalendar, age
  55
Director, Bernard Gautier, age 54
Director, Lady Sylvia Jay, age 67
Director; COO Saint- Gobain Eurocoustic,
  Bernard Cusenier, age 67
Director, Yuko Harayama, age 63
Director, Frederic Lemoine, age 48
Director, Maj. Gilles Schnepp, age 55
Independent Director, Anne-Marie Idrac
Director - Representative of Employee
  Shareholders, Jacques Pestre
Independent Director, Olivia Qiu
Auditors: PricewaterhouseCoopersAudit

LOCATIONS

HQ: Compagnie de Saint-Gobain
  Les Miroirs, 18, avenue d' Alsace, Courbevoie 92400
Phone: (33) 1 47 62 30 00
Web: www.saint-gobain.com

Sales

	% of total
Western Europe	
France	28
Other	43
Asia & emerging	20
North	14
Total	**100**

PRODUCTS/OPERATIONS

Sales by Market

	% of total
Renovation	45
Construction	31
Other	24
Total	**100**

Sales by Segment

	% of total
Building	43
Construction products	
Exterior	14
Interior	13
Innovative materials	
Flat	13
High-performance	10
Packaging &	7
Total	**100**

Selected Segments and Products

Construction products
  Exterior fittings
    Asphalt roofing shingles
    Siding
    Vinyl fences
  Gypsum
    Ceiling tiles
    EPS insulation
    Plaster
    Plasterboard
  Industrial mortars
    Flooring screed
    Interior rendering
    Masonry mortar

Tile adhesive and grouting
    Wall rendering products
  Insulation
    Glass wool
    Insulating foam
    Metal frames
    Rock wool
    Soundproof ceilings
  Pipe
    Complete piping systems
    Ductile cast iron and steel manhole covers
Flat glass
  Construction glass
  Furniture glass
  Automotive glazing
  Photovoltaic systems
  Solar heating systems
  Specialty glass
    Fireproof glass
    Nuclear safety glass
High-performance materials
  Abrasives
    Bonded abrasives
    Superabrasives
    Thin grinding wheels
  Ceramics
    Advanced ceramics
    Crystals
    Diesel particulate filters
    Grains and powders
  Performance plastics
    Bearings and seals
    Films foams and coated fabrics
    Fluid control systems
  Textiles
    Glass fiber yarn
    Reinforcement fabrics for construction and
      manufacturing
Packaging
  Glass bottles and jars

COMPETITORS

3M	Kyocera
Anchor Glass	Lafarge
Asahi Glass	Nippon Electric Glass
Ball Corp.	Nitto Boseki
CRH	Owens-Illinois
DuPont	PPG Industries
Georgia-Pacific	RHI
Gerresheimer Glas	Rexam
Grafton Group	Royal Group
Guardian Industries	SCHOTT
Johns Manville	SIG plc
Knauf Insulation	Travis Perkins
Kubota	Wolseley

HISTORICAL FINANCIALS

Company Type: Public

Income Statement

FYE: December 31

	REVENUE ($ mil.)	NET INCOME ($ mil.)	NET PROFIT MARGIN	EMPLOYEES
12/13	57,857	819	1.4%	185,364
12/12	56,937	1,009	1.8%	191,113
12/11	54,475	1,660	3.0%	194,658
12/10	53,694	1,511	2.8%	189,193
12/09	54,433	291	0.5%	191,442
Annual Growth	**1.5%**	**29.5%**	**—**	**(0.8%)**

2013 Year-End Financials

Debt ratio: 35.8%	No. of shares (mil.): 551
Return on equity: 3.4%	Dividends
Cash ($ mil.): 6,045	Yield: —
Current ratio: 1.39	Payout: —
Long-term debt ($ mil.): 12,934	Market value ($ mil.): 29,481

	STOCK PRICE ($) FY Close	P/E High/Low	PER SHARE ($) Earnings	Dividends	Book Value
12/13	53.46	92 58	1.51	0.00	43.76
12/12	41.95	58 33	1.91	0.00	43.66
12/11	38.00	53 25	3.13	0.00	43.79
12/10	51.50	42 27	2.90	0.00	45.49
12/09	58.10	294 95	0.62	0.00	45.08
Annual Growth	**(2.1%)**	**— —**	**25.0%**	**—**	**(0.7%)**

Compagnie Generale des Etablissements Michelin (France)

The Michelin Man may look like a marshmallow but what he's selling is tires. Behind that fluffy white figure is one of the world's top tire manufacturers Compagnie Generale des Etablissements Michelin which produces more than 175 million tires annually for all kinds of vehicles. The majority of its sales are made from supplying replacement tires to the passenger car and truck markets. It is also a world leader in aircraft and earthmover tires. Michelin sells to both consumers and vehicle manufacturers. Included in its stable are brands recognized regionally (Kleber in Europe Warrior in China) and worldwide (Michelin BF Goodrich). The company also publishes about 10 million maps and travel guides per year.

The company produces its tires at approximately 70 production sites across the Americas Asia Africa and Europe; its sales network is worldwide. North America is Michelin's second-largest market (with 18 manufacturing facilities) generating about one-third of the company's sales annually. With demand up in Europe and North America as well as in Asia and South America Michelin is building three high capacity plants in Brazil India and China; all of which are scheduled to begin production in 2012.

In fact with such a strong demand from these fast-growing emerging regions Michelin is realigning its business to emphasize the three countries. It is also bumping up its research and development investment from E1 billion (about $1.3 billion) to E1.6 billion (more than $2 billion) per year for the next five years. R&D will weigh the needs of the company's main emerging markets and will cater to the regions accordingly.

With its sights focused on China as a burgeoning region Michelin agreed in spring 2011 to form a joint venture (it will take a 40% stake) with China-based tire maker Double Coin and investment firm Shanghai Huayi to manufacture Warrior-brand car and truck tires for the Chinese market.

With resurging demand and new regional market interest Michelin's 2010 passenger and truck tire sales increased 18% and 26% respectively over 2009. With higher volumes sold and cost cutting measures in place the company realized a respectable overall revenue increase in 2010 of almost 12%; however its net income exceeded expectations at almost $1.4 billion representing an increase in excess of 800% over 2009. As tough as it was the company's Horizon 2010 plan did reduce costs and increased plant productivity by 35%; Michelin's cost-cutting measures and plans to improve efficiency showed up as positive cash flow. Higher prices for its tires and lower materials costs also helped the bottom line.

This positive showing comes not so long after the economic downturn that crushed the automotive industry particularly in North America and Europe. The US was at the forefront of the financial impact in 2009 when Michelin was forced to close its 1000-worker BF Goodrich plant in Opelika Alabama. Michelin chose to close the plant in order to focus on the Michelin brand which the company says is more resilient than other brands. Europe was hit hard as well and it suffered a similar fate with 1000 workers laid off in France; this was also part of a company-wide restructuring to focus on its best-selling brands.

HISTORY

After toying with making rubber balls Edouard Daubree and Aristide Barbier formed a partnership in Clermont-Ferrand France in 1863 and entered the rubber business in earnest. Both men soon died but Barbier in-law Andre Michelin a successful businessman took over the company in 1886. Andre recruited his brother Edouard a Parisian artist to run the company and in 1889 it was renamed Compagnie Generale des Etablissements Michelin.

That year Edouard found that air-filled tires made bicycling more comfortable. But pneumatic tires were experimental and because they were glued to the rims required hours to change. In 1891 Edouard made a detachable bicycle tire that took only 15 minutes to change.

The Michelins promoted their tires by persuading cyclists to use them in long-distance races where punctures were likely. They demonstrated the applicability of such tires for cars in an auto race in 1895. In 1898 Andre commented that a stack of tires would look like a man if it had arms a notion that led to the creation of Bibendum the Michelin Man. Andrea launched the "Michelin Guide" for auto tourists in 1900.

Expansion followed as Michelin opened a London office (1905) and began production in Italy (1906) and the US (in New Jersey in 1908). Innovations included detachable rims and spare tires (1906) tubeless tires (1930) treads (1934) and modern low-profile tires (1937). During the Depression Michelin closed its US plant and accepted a stake in Citroen later converted into a minority stake in Peugeot in lieu of payment for tires.

Michelin patented radial tires in 1946. Expansion was largely confined to Europe in the 1950s but thanks to radials increased worldwide in the 1960s. Sears began selling Michelin radials in 1966. Radials took hold during the 1970s and Michelin returned to manufacturing in the US opening a plant in South Carolina in 1975.

Expanding aggressively (Michelin opened or bought a plant every nine months from 1960 to 1990) the company went into the red when economic conditions dipped in the early 1980s and in 1990 and 1991. The company's $1.5 billion purchase of Uniroyal Goodrich in 1990 contributed to the latter losses but improved Michelin's position in the US the world's largest auto market.

In response to the losses Michelin attacked its bloated infrastructure and reinvented itself along nine product lines (according to tire/vehicle type plus travel suspension and primary product manufacturing). It also consolidated facilities and cut about 30000 jobs. The company continued to focus on R&D bringing out new high-performance tires such as its "green" tire designed to help cars save fuel.

Michelin bought a majority interest in a Polish tire maker in 1995 and the next year it bought 90% of Taurus a Hungarian firm that produces most of that country's rubber. Michelin joined German competitor Continental in 1996 to make private-label tires for independent distributors. The next year Michelin introduced a run-flat tire —capable of traveling 50 miles after a puncture —for the automotive aftermarket. The company acquired Icollantas a Colombian tire group with two factories in Bogota and Cali in 1998.

After leading the company for more than 40 years patriarch Francois Michelin stepped down in 1999 leaving his youngest son Edouard in charge. Almost immediately Edouard announced a restructuring that would cut 7500 jobs in Europe including almost 2000 in France. The company benefited somewhat from Firestone's recall woes in 2000 but Michelin still faced rising material costs and difficult market conditions.

The European Commission fined Michelin nearly $20 million in 2001 claiming the company engaged in anticompetitive behavior by abusing its dominant position in Europe. In 2003 Michelin and TRW Automotive created EnTire Solutions a joint venture to develop a tire pressure monitoring system. Michelin announced a licensing agreement in 2004 for Toyo Tire to make sell and promote PAX system tires (run-flat tires).

Former co-managing partner Edouard Michelin the youngest son of patriarch Francois Michelin and the fourth generation of Michelins in the business was killed in a boating accident in May 2006.

The tire market made a huge shift during and after the Great Recession of 2009. While Europe and North American demand faltered emerging countries like China and India as well as countries in South America filled the gap in demand. To take advantage of the burgeoning Asian market Michelin increased its stake in South Korea-based Hankook Tires to about 10% in mid-2008.

EXECUTIVES

Member Supervisory Board, Benoit Potier, age 56
Member Supervisory Board, Louis Gallois, age 69
Member Supervisory Board, Francois Grappotte, age 77
Member Supervisory Board, Barbara M. Dalibard, age 55
Member Supervisory Board, Pierre Michelin, age 64
Member Supervisory Board, Pat Cox, age 60
Member Supervisory Board, Laurence Parisot, age 53
Auditors: PricewaterhouseCoopersAudit

LOCATIONS

HQ: Compagnie Generale des Etablissements Michelin (France)
23, place des Carmes-Dechaux, Clermont-Ferrand, Cedex 9 63040
Phone: (33) 4 73 32 20 00
Web: www.michelin.com

Sales

	% of total
Europe	43
North	34
Other	23
Total	**100**

PRODUCTS/OPERATIONS

Sales

	% of total
Passenger car & light truck tires & related	55
Truck tires & related	32
Specialty	13
Total	**100**

Sales by Market

	% of total
Replacement	75

Original	25
Total	**100**

Selected Products and Services

Agricultural vehicle tires
Aircraft tires
Construction vehicle tires
Engineering consulting for constructors & equipment manufacturers
Heavy-goods vehicle tires
Motorcycle bicycle & scooter tires
Passenger car tires
Sports leisure & work accessories
Travel maps & guides
Truck tires

Selected Brands

BF Goodrich
Encore
Euromaster
Kleber
Kormoran
Michelin
Riken
Taurus
Tigar
Tyre Plus
Uniroyal
Warrior

Selected Subsidiaries

Compagnie Financiere Michelin (Switzerland)
Manufacture Francaise des Pneumatiques Michelin
Michelin Aircraft Tire Company (US)
Michelin Americas Research & Development Corporation (US)
Michelin Asia-Pacific Import-Export (HK) Limited (Hong Kong)
Michelin Corporation (US)
Michelin North America Inc. (US)
Michelin Gummi Compagni A/S (Denmark)

COMPETITORS

Avalon Travel Publishing
Bridgestone
Continental AG
Cooper Tire & Rubber
Fieldens
Goodyear Tire & Rubber

Kumho Tire
Pirelli
Sime Darby
Sumitomo Rubber
Toyo Tire & Rubber
Yokohama Rubber

HISTORICAL FINANCIALS

Company Type: Public

Income Statement

FYE: December 31

	REVENUE ($ mil.)	NET INCOME ($ mil.)	NET PROFIT MARGIN	EMPLOYEES
12/13	27,874	1,551	5.6%	112,199
12/12	28,303	2,069	7.3%	113,443
12/11	26,799	1,891	7.1%	115,000
12/10	23,944	1,402	5.9%	111,090
12/09	21,330	152	0.7%	109,193
Annual Growth	6.9%	78.5%	—	0.7%

2013 Year-End Financials

Debt ratio: 15.3%
Return on equity: 12.7%
Cash ($ mil.): 2,151
Current ratio: 1.92
Long-term debt ($ mil.): 1,992

No. of shares (mil.): 185
Dividends
  Yield: 2.9%
  Payout: 13.5%
Market value ($ mil.): 3,966

	STOCK PRICE ($) FY Close	P/E High/Low		PER SHARE ($) Earnings	Dividends	Book Value
12/13	21.35	7	5	8.23	0.63	68.56
12/12	19.19	4	2	11.08	0.53	61.36
12/11	11.72	5	2	10.31	0.93	58.19
12/10	14.34	5	3	8.89	0.75	61.57
12/09	15.40	52	15	1.02	0.28	53.66
Annual Growth	8.5%			68.4%	22.8%	6.3%

Compass Group PLC (United Kingdom)

Look in almost any direction and you'll likely see a foodservice operation run by this company. Compass Group is the world's largest contract foodservices provider with operations in more than 50 countries. It provides hospitality and foodservice for a variety of businesses and such public-sector clients as cultural institutions hospitals and schools. It also offers vending catering concessions and security services for a number of events and sports venues. Its foodservice brands include Chartwells Crothall and Levy Restaurants. In addition Compass is a franchisee of such well-known chains as Burger King and Starbucks.

Compass became the leader in its industry through aggressive expansion and numerous acquisitions over the years. The company has been especially focused on boosting its presence internationally.

To this end in 2011 Compass acquired the remaining 50% of SOFRA its joint venture in Turkey and entered a deal to buy meal-delivery firm Obasan which serves business in Turkey Bursa and Istanbul. That same year Compass also acquired a pair of companies in India that provide facilities management and foodservice to businesses in Delhi. The twin purchases followed the acquisition of German education and health care foodservices provider Menke Menue for about E5 million (nearly $7 million) in cash and it snapped up a 90% stake in Japanese catering firm Chiyoda Food from Nippon Yusen Kabushiki Kaisha (which retained the remaining shares). In late 2011 Compass acquired UK-based Cygnet Foods a food and support services company for an undisclosed price.

In 2010 the company purchased Australia-based foodservices firm Life's A Party Group for Å14 million ($22 million) and Denmark's IDA Service for Å17 million ($27 million) from OKF Holding A/S and its management. Also that year Compass bought family-owned Tirumala Hospitality Services a leading caterer for corporate and industrial businesses in western India and France's Caterine Restauration a foodservices firm for the country's education and health care sectors.

The company continues to build on its operations back at home as well. Responding to the requests of its clients Compass extended its reach to the safety business in mid-2010 when it acquired VSG Group a security services firm from Lloyds Development Capital for $81 million. VSG supplies manned guarding electronic surveillance and support services to companies in the UK. VSG's security operations are complementary to Compass' cleaning and catering businesses as customers of these services often ask for security support.

While the global recession and credit crisis have caused hardships in many industries the contract foodservices segment has continued to grow as companies look for new ways to outsource and cut costs. As such Compass Group is focused on winning new services contracts and expanding its business relationships with existing customers. In 2009 and 2010 the company won new business from Visa Google Microsoft Nestle and Electrolux.

Compass Group has also been mindful of costs itself pulling out of some unprofitable global markets streamlining operations and strengthening financial controls throughout its expansive network of worldwide subsidiaries. The moves have helped the company to widen its margins.

HISTORY

Compass Group was formed in 1987 when management bought out the catering business of London-based food and spirits giant Grand Metropolitan (now Diageo) for $260 million. The company went public the next year listing on the London Stock Exchange. Gerry Robinson CEO at the time left in 1991 to take a position with British TV programming giant Granada Group (renamed ITV plc in 2004) where he helped that company diversify into food service operations. Finance director Francis Mackay took over as CEO.

Believing that real growth in the catering industry could come from size and economies of scale Mackay orchestrated a $2.5 billion acquisition plan over the next five years. In 1992 Compass bought Traveller's Fare (now Upper Crust) a railway caterer from British Rail. The company expanded into airports the following year with the acquisition of Scandinavian Airlines System's catering operations. Then in 1994 Compass bought Canteen Corporation the US's third-largest vending and food service company.

Compass achieved its goal of becoming the world's largest caterer in 1995 with the acquisition of France's Eurest International putting it ahead of Sodexho Alliance and Granada. Mackay calmed London investors nervous about the pace of Compass' acquisitions by selling off its hospital management operations and paying lip service to focusing on organic growth. Later that year Compass was awarded the world's largest food service contract a $250-million five-year deal with IBM.

By 1996 the company seemed to have forgotten all about organic growth buying Service America and then Daka International and France's SHRM in 1997. French subsidiary Eurest later snatched a $40 million contract from rival Sodexho (later Sodexo) to supply the staff restaurants at Euro Disney one of France's top three catering contracts. The next year Compass solidified its position in the airport markets with a five-year licensing deal for use of the T.G.I. Fridays brand joining Taco Bell Pizza Hut Burger King and Harry Ramsden's fish and chip shops in Compass' quiver of branded airport outlets.

In 1999 CEO Mackay became group chairman leaving the reins to Compass' chief of North American operations Michael Bailey. The company's US acquisitions quickly paid off that year with a contract to serve 90% of the food venues at the 2002 Winter Olympics in Salt Lake City. In 2000 the company merged with UK hospitality giant Granada Group (the combined firm became Granada Compass) which then spun off its media operations as a separate company Granada Media. Late that year it bought Boston-based bakery/cafe chain Au Bon Pain for about $108 million.

The new company got a quick divorce in 2001 when Granada Compass decided to demerge and make Compass Group public again. Compass Group later sold the Le Meridien hotel operations it gained from the Granada merger to Nomura International for nearly $3 billion. (The firm kept the Travelodge chain.) The company then began making purchases including Morrison Management Specialists for $563 million the 66% it didn't already own in Selecta Group UK vending machine company Vendepac and health care services management company Crothall Services. Compass lost seven operating sites during the September 11 terrorist attacks on the World Trade Center. Late in 2001 Compass strengthened its presence in Japan with the $277 million acquisition of Seiyo Food Systems that country's #2 food services group.

In 2002 Compass signed arguably the industry's largest contract ever a $200 million a year deal to feed Chevron employees around the world. In 2003 the company sold its Travelodge motel business and Little Chef diners to private equity firm Permira for $1.14 billion a 5% discount to the asking price. Compass became the first non-Chinese company to provide food in stations and on trains operated by the Shanghai Railway Administration in 2004. In addition the firm bought Creative Host Services in 2004.

In 2005 Compass sold a 75% stake in Au Bon Pain back to a management group retaining a 25% interest in the quick-casual chain. The following year the company sold its travel hospitality businesses including Select Service Partner (now SSP Group) and UK motorway operator Moto to private investors for more than $3 billion. Compass sold its European vending business Selecta to German financial giant Allianz for $1.5 billion in 2007.

In 2009 the firm added the US's Southeast Service Corporation which focuses on education catering for $65 million. Compass also purchased Germany's Plural which provides janitorial and related support services for corporate and health care clients and it took over the remaining 50% of shares it didn't already own in Brazil's GR SA. Touting its expertise in on-the-go food offerings Compass in 2009 purchased about 30 McColls retail locations in UK hospitals from Martin McColl.

EXECUTIVES

Chairman, Sir Roy A. Gardner, age 69
Group Chief Executive and Director, Richard J. Cousins, age 55, $313,000 total compensation
Group Managing Director USA and Canada and Director, Gary R. Green, age 57
General Counsel and Company Secretary, Mark J. White
Group Finance Director and Director, Andrew Martin, age 54, $461,000 total compensation
Director, Sir James R. Crosby, age 58
Group Chief Executive and Director, Richard J. Cousins, age 55
Group Managing Director USA and Canada and Director, Gary R. Green, age 57
Director, Sir Ian Robinson, age 72
Director, Steve Lucas, age 60
Director, Susan E. Murray, age 57
Group Finance Director and Director, Andrew Martin, age 54
Director, Don Robert
Auditors: DeloitteLLP

LOCATIONS

HQ: Compass Group PLC (United Kingdom)
Compass House, Guildford Street, Chertsey, Surrey KT16 9BQ
Phone: (44) 1932 573 000   **Fax:** (44) 1932 569 956
Web: www.compass-group.com

PRODUCTS/OPERATIONS

Selected Operating Units
All Leisure (sports and leisure venues)
Bon Appetit Management Company (on-site dining services)
Canteen (vending services)
Chartwells (education foodservices)
Crothall (health care facilities management)
ESS (offshore and remote foodservices)
Eurest (corporate foodservice)
FLIK (upscale foodservices)
Levy Restaurants (fine dining sports and leisure events)
Medirest (health care services)
Morrison Management Specialists (health care foodservice)
Restaurant Associates Managed Services (corporate dining and sporting and leisure events)
Scolarest (education foodservices)

COMPETITORS

ARAMARK	Healthcare Services
Autogrill	Legion Group
Centerplate	Reliance Security
Delaware North	Securiplan
Elior	Sodexo
Farsight Security Services	

HISTORICAL FINANCIALS

Company Type: Public

Income Statement

FYE: September 30

	REVENUE ($ mil.)	NET INCOME ($ mil.)	NET PROFIT MARGIN	EMPLOYEES
09/14	27,605	1,399	5.1%	514,718
09/13	28,340	692	2.4%	506,699
09/12	27,378	979	3.6%	508,714
09/11	24,662	1,133	4.6%	471,108
09/10	22,986	1,072	4.7%	428,202
Annual Growth	4.7%	6.9%	—	4.7%

2014 Year-End Financials

Debt ratio: 52.5%	No. of shares (mil.): 1,673
Return on equity: 37.4%	Dividends
Cash ($ mil.): 697	Yield: —
Current ratio: 0.77	Payout: —
Long-term debt ($ mil.): 4,087	Market value ($ mil.): 26,899

	STOCK PRICE ($) FY Close	P/E High/Low	PER SHARE ($) Earnings	Dividends	Book Value
09/14	16.07	103 70	0.79	0.00	1.78
09/13	13.71	152 118	0.38	0.00	2.49
09/12	11.05	96 62	0.52	0.00	2.82
09/11	8.02	67 50	0.60	0.00	2.87
09/10	8.50	61 43	0.57	0.00	2.58
Annual Growth	17.3%	— —	8.6%	—	(8.9%)

Continental AG (Germany, Fed. Rep.)

Continental AG keeps rolling along as one of Europe's largest manufacturers of tires for cars trucks bicycles and agricultural products. Its Automotive Group is Continental's largest segment manufacturing brake and traction control systems passive safety products sensors and chassis and powertrain products. The Rubber Group comprises its Tires division (sold under the Continental Uniroyal and General brands) as well as its ContiTech division which produces vibration control and power transmission systems as well as conveyor belts. Germany-based bearing and clutch manufacturer Schaeffler controls 49% of Continental AG's shares.

Continental's Automotive Group generates about 60% of total sales each year while its Rubber Group hauls in the remaining 40%. Automotive comprises the Interior Chassis and Safety and Powertrain segments. Each segment operates through about 50 to 60 production sites located throughout Australia Brazil China Europe India Japan Malaysia Mexico Russia Singapore South Korea Thailand the Philippines and the US.

The Rubber Group comprises Passenger and Light Truck Tires (50 locations spanning 35 countries) and Commercial Vehicle Tires (roughly 45 sites in more than 30 countries). Continental sells its tires to automakers such as BMW Daimler and Ford. Another division within the Rubber Group is ContiTech which operates out of almost 80 locations in some 25 countries. With its several business units ContiTech manufactures products that are also used on rail vehicles and in printing mining wind and power plant petrochemical and navigation markets. In its largest acquisition to date ContiTech acquired the auto air conditioning business owned by a division of Parker Hannifin in mid-2012. The deal gave ContiTech additional plants in China Mexico South Korea and the Czech Republic. In 2014 it inked a deal to buy US rubber and plastics maker Veyance Technologies from financial investment firm Carlyle for about EUR 1.4 billion (or US $1.9 billion) and fold the firm into its ContiTech business.

Like all players in the auto parts industry Continental was hit hard by the painful effects of the recession that decimated the auto construction and transportation sectors. From 2008 to early 2011 the company clamped down on its cost structure by closing plants restructuring reducing its research and development expenses and chipping away at its debt. As a result of an overall increase in demand in the automotive industry and its ability to diversify the product portfolio within its Automotive segment its net revenue rose 17% from 2010 to 2011. Although the 2011 Japan earthquake and European credit crisis negatively affected Continental the company was helped by increases in North American sales and other regions during 2011.

For its growth strategy Continental has identified about 25 of the fastest growing automotive groups including navigation systems turbochargers and systems used for reducing emissions. The decision to diversify product lines is also part of the company's strategy to keep its dependence on the automotive industry in check by generating additional sales in industries other than automotive. To that end ContiTech in late 2010 acquired Tianjin Xinbinhai Conveyor Belt a Chinese maker of conveyor-belts used in various industrial applications.

Continental also intends to tighten its grip in emerging markets in Asia where it already generates about 15% of its total sales. By 2015 the company plans to expand its tire manufacturing capacity by a combined total of more than 22 million tires. To achieve this in 2011 it established new tire plants in China Russia and the US; it also expanded existing ones in Brazil India and the US.

HISTORY

A group of financiers and industrialists with interests in the rubber industry founded Continental-Caoutchouc und Gutta-Percha Compagnie in Hanover Germany in 1871. The company's products included solid tires for carriages and bicycles rubberized fabrics and various consumer items.

In 1892 Continental was the first German maker of pneumatic bicycle tires. During this period the budding automobile and motorcycle industries created fresh demand for solid tires. Continental began producing pneumatic tires for automobiles in 1898.

By 1904 Continental was first to develop a treaded tire. Between 1905 and 1913 Continental expanded into Australia Denmark Italy Norway Romania Sweden and the UK by forming marketing subsidiaries. However the onset of WWI caused a shift to military production and the overseas sales network dissolved.

Poor overall economic conditions atrophied postwar tire industry growth and by the late 1920s the company merged several German rubber firms to create a much larger and stronger Continental. In 1929 the company changed its name to Continental Gummi-Werke AG. The Opel family which had sold its car unit to General Motors bought a substantial stake in the new company.

Emerging from the Great Depression total German tire production doubled between 1934 and 1938 as the Nazi government initiated a program to motorize Germany and reduce unemployment. During WWII the Nazis took over tire and rubber making to meet military needs.

After the war civilian production languished amid occupation and war-damaged factories. To get back on its feet Continental formed a technical assistance alliance with General Tire in 1948.

Between 1950 and 1965 the company tagged along as German car companies mostly Volkswagen expanded overseas. Continental established foreign subsidiaries in Brazil France Italy Portugal South Africa Spain and the UK.

The growth spurt was curtailed by the oil crisis of the 1970s. The company began making fan and conveyor belts in 1975. Continental bought the tire unit of US-based Uniroyal in 1979. In 1981 the company forged a deal with Toyo Rubber Industry Co. (now called Toyo Tire & Rubber Co.) to make Continental tires in Japan. The next year a similar deal was inked in the US with General Tire. By 1987 Continental owned General Tire buying it from GenCorp. The deal gave Continental four factories General's brands a new marketing network and lucrative OEM contracts; expansion into Africa Asia and South America made the deal even sweeter. That year the company's name changed to Continental AG.

In 1991 the company's industrial products segment was reorganized under the ContiTech name. ContiTech joined with Cooper Tire & Rubber in 1995 to collaborate on molded products extrusions and hoses. The following year the company secured the right to use the Uniroyal name in Europe.

Continental bought the automotive brake and chassis unit of ITT Industries for $1.93 billion in 1998; now Continental Teves it is part of Continental's Automotive Systems Group. The next year Continental formed a joint venture with Delco Remy International (now Remy International) to produce motors for integrated starter alternator damper (ISAD) systems.

In 2000 Continental announced that it would recall about 160000 tires fitted on Lincoln Navigators (Ford) in 1998 and 1999: The tires were reportedly prone to lose parts of their treads. The next year Continental announced that it would acquire (60% up front and the rest by 2005) Temic GmbH Daimler AG's automotive-electronics business in a deal worth around $550 million.

Continental announced in 2001 that it would sell off most of its ContiTech division. The same year Continental announced that it would supply Ford with more than 2 million Firestone-replacement tires. In July Ford dropped Continental's General Ameri* 550 AS tire after the NHTSA announced it was launching a probe into all 2.7 million of those tires made since 1995 because the model's tread failure rate was 124 per million (versus nine per million for Firestone's recalled Wilderness AT model).

In 2001 the company's Continental Teves subsidiary acquired a majority interest in Japan-based brake system manufactures Shin-Ei and ShinTec from Mazda Motor Corporation. CEO Stephan Kessel stepped down and was replaced by Manfred Wennemer in September of 2001. Wennemer had been head of ContiTech —Continental's most profitable division —which Kessel had wanted to sell. The German tire maker entered into an agreement in 2002 with Japan-based counterparts Bridgestone and Yokohama to explore run-flat technology. In early 2003 Continental acquired a 30% stake in Malaysia-based Sime Darby's tire business. CGS Tire acquired Continental's agricultural tire business in 2004.

Continental's 2004 acquisition of Phoenix AG strengthened the company's ContiTech division and contributed to its transformation to become a tier-one integrated automotive parts supplier. Likewise its 2006 acquisition of Motorola's automotive division for which it paid about $1 billion greatly expanded Continental's product portfolio with interior electronics controls sensors and telematics operations.

Continuing down the diversification road Continental acquired the 40% of Temic GmbH it didn't already own in 2005.

In 2007 Continental received EU approval to acquire a 51% stake in the conveyor belt tire and rubber machinery operations of Slovakia's Matador Group. Continental moved to enhance its brake offerings when later that year it agreed to buy Automotive Products Italia Srl (AP) from Australia's Pacifica Group for an undisclosed sum. AP which is one of Europe's leading makers of drum brakes had sales of about Å79 million in 2006.

Continental kept up its 2007 international buying spree when it agreed to purchase Zangjiang Fugang Heli Electronics Co. Ltd. a Chinese maker of cooling fan modules and window lift motors. The move marks Continental's first purchase in China the world's fastest-growing car market. The company has also announced plans to relocate a technical center to China as well as build new manufacturing operations in the country (a tire plant in Hefei and a hydraulic brake facility in Changshu).

In 2008 Continental acquired Siemens VDO Automotive (now known as VDO Automotive). The largest acquisition in Continental's 135-plus year history it made the company a top five global automotive supplier and the second largest German parts maker behind Robert Bosch.

Family owned Schaeffler made its hostile takeover bid in 2008; an agreement was made between the two companies in August 2008. As part of the deal changes were made at the top level Changes occurred not only to the business structure but to management as well. Continental CEO Manfred Wennemer stepped down at the end of August 2008. A decision to merge the two companies was abandoned years later and in 2011 Schaeffler lowered the amount of shares it owned in Continental to 49%.

EXECUTIVES

Member Executive Board and Head of Passenger and Light Truck Tires and Commercial Vehicle Tires Division Purchasing and Quality and Environment, Hans-Joachim Nikolin, age 58
Deputy Chairman Supervisory Board, Werner Bischoff, age 67
Head Corporate Quality and the Environment, Thorsten Reese
VP Media Relations, Hannes Boekhoff
SVP Corporate Communications, Felix Gress, age 53
Chairman Executive Board, Elmar Degenhart, age 56
Executive Board Member ContiTech Division, Heinz-Gerhard Wente, age 63
Member Executive Board Chassis and Safety, Ralf Cramer, age 49
Senior Vice President Chassis & Safety NAFTA, Samir Salman
VP Communications ContiTech, Anja Graf
Member Executive Board Interior, Helmut Matschi, age 51
Member Executive Board Tire Division, Nikolai Setzer, age 43
Head of Investor Relations, Rolf Woller
Chairman Supervisory Board, Prof Wolfgang Reitzle

Member Executive Board Finance Controlling Compliance Law and IT, Wolfgang Schafer, age 55
Member Executive Board Powertrain Division, Jose A. Avila, age 59
Vice President Communications, Nicole Geissler
Executive Vice President, Matthias Matic
Senior Vice President Systems & Technology, Peter Rieth
Senior Vice President Human Resources, Rainer Hetzer
Senior Vice President Finance Controlling & Law, Werner Volz
Executive Vice President Business Unit ADAS, Friedrich Angerbauer
Member Supervisory Board, Prof Siegfried Wolf, age 57
Member Supervisory Board, Michael Deister
Member Supervisory Board, Klaus Rosenfeld, age 48
Member Supervisory Board, Prof Hans-Olaf Henkel, age 74
Deputy Chairman Supervisory Board, Werner Bischoff, age 67
Member Supervisory Board, Hartmut Meine
Member Supervisory Board, Erwin Worle
Member Supervisory Board, Jorg Schonfelder
Member Supervisory Board, Michael Iglhaut
Member Supervisory Board, Gunter Dunkel
Member Supervisory Board, Hans Fischl
Member Supervisory Board, Jurgen Gei?inger
Member Supervisory Board, Jorg Kohlinger
Member Supervisory Board, Klaus Mangold
Member Supervisory Board, Dick Nordmann
Member Supervisory Board, Georg F. W. Schaeffler
Member Supervisory Board, Maria-Elisabeth Schaeffler
Member Supervisory Board, Bernd W. Voss, age 75
Auditors: KPMGDeutscheTreuhand-GesellschaftAG

LOCATIONS

HQ: Continental AG (Germany, Fed. Rep.)
Vahrenwalder Strasse 9, Hanover 30165
Phone: (49) 511 938 01   **Fax:** (49) 511 938 81 770
Web: www.continental-corporation.com

Sales

	$ mil.	% of total
Europe		
Other countries		33
Asia		17
Total		**100**

PRODUCTS/OPERATIONS

Sales

	$ mil.	% of total
Automotive Group		
Chassis & safety		21
Rubber Group		
ContiTech		12
Total		**100**

Selected Automotive Group Products

Chassis and Safety
  Chassis components
  Electronic brake systems
  Hydraulic brake systems
  Passive safety and ADAS
  Sensors
Interior
  Body and security
  Commercial vehicles and aftermarket
  Connectivity
  Instrumentation and displays
  Interior modules
  Multimedia
Powertrain
  Engine systems
  Fuel supply
  Hybrid electric vehicle
  Sensors and actuators
  Transmissions

Selected Rubber Group Products

ContiTech
  Air spring systems
  Benecke-Kaliko group
  Conveyor belt group
  Elastomer coatings
  Fluid technology
  Power transmission group
  Vibration control
Tires
  Commercial vehicle
  Passenger and light truck

COMPETITORS

A.G. Simpson	Magna International
AirBoss of America	McLaren Performance
Bridgestone	Meritor
China Enterprises	Michelin
Cooper Tire &	Nokian Tyres
Rubber	Pirelli
DENSO	Robert Bosch
Dana Holding	Standard Motor
Delphi Automotive	Products
Systems	Sumitomo Rubber
Gates Corp.	Tomkins
Goodyear Tire &	Toyo Tire & Rubber
Rubber	Trelleborg
Hankook Tire	Valeo
Johnson Controls	Visteon
Kumho Tire	Yokohama Rubber
Lear Corp	

HISTORICAL FINANCIALS

Company Type: Public

Income Statement

				FYE: December 31
	REVENUE ($ mil.)	NET INCOME ($ mil.)	NET PROFIT MARGIN	EMPLOYEES
12/13	45,887	2,647	5.8%	177,762
12/12	43,147	2,482	5.8%	169,639
12/11	39,456	1,606	4.1%	163,788
12/10	34,860	770	2.2%	148,228
12/09	28,949	(2,375)	—	134,434
Annual Growth	**12.2%**	**—**		**7.2%**

2013 Year-End Financials

Debt ratio: 34.0%   No. of shares (mil.): 200
Return on equity: 21.6%   Dividends
Cash ($ mil.): 2,815   Yield: 0.9%
Current ratio: 1.17   Payout: 5.7%
Long-term debt ($ mil.): 6,940   Market value ($ mil.): 8,884

	STOCK PRICE ($) FY Close	P/E High/Low		PER SHARE ($)		
				Earnings	Dividends	Book Value
12/13	44.42	43	9	13.24	0.43	62.03
12/12	117.10	22	12	12.42	0.29	57.78
12/11	62.00	33	14	8.03	0.00	46.21
12/10	78.10	59	25	3.85	0.73	39.21
12/09	53.00	—	—	(14.06)	0.00	32.16
Annual Growth	**(4.3%)**	**—**	**—**	**—**	**—**	**17.8%**

Coop Switzerland (Switzerland)

LOCATIONS

HQ: Coop Switzerland (Switzerland)
Thiersteinerallee 12, Postfach 2550, Basel CH-4002
Phone: (41) 61 336 66 66   **Fax:** (41) 61 336 60 40
Web: www.coop.ch

HISTORICAL FINANCIALS
Company Type: Public

Income Statement
FYE: December 31

	REVENUE ($ mil.)	NET INCOME ($ mil.)	NET PROFIT MARGIN	EMPLOYEES
12/13	30,264	518	1.7%	74,955
12/12	29,160	493	1.7%	75,309
12/11	28,316	459	1.6%	75,296
12/10	20,266	502	2.5%	53,559
12/09	18,171	417	2.3%	44,154
Annual Growth	13.6%	5.6%	—	14.1%

Cosmo Oil Co., Ltd.

Cosmopolitan Cosmo Oil is one of Japan's top oil refiners and a major petroleum distributor. Cosmo Oil has four refineries; it markets its petroleum products through a network of almost 3500 gas stations. It has a refining and distribution joint venture with Nippon Oil that controls 40% of Japan's oil refining market. The company is also a major petrochemical producer. Cosmo Oil has exploration and production operations and imports crude oil from the Middle East and has affiliates in Singapore the UK and the US. Cosmo Oil has its refineries located near areas of large consumption: Tokyo Nagoya and Osaka.

Geographic Reach

The company serves petroleum product customers across Japan and petrochemical customers in Japan and South Korea.

In the United Arab Emirates and Qatar Cosmo Oil is engaged in oil exploration and production through Abu Dhabi Oil United Petroleum Development and Qatar Petroleum Development. The company is also conducting oil exploration in Australia.

Cosmo Oil operates through nine offices in Japan: Sapporo Sendai Tokyo Kanto-Minami Nagoya Osaka Hiroshima Takamatsu and Fukuoka.

Operations

The company's primary oil refining and petroleum product businesses is supported by two others: oil exploration and production and petrochemicals.

Cosmo Oil's petrochemical business with affiliate Maruzen Petrochemical produces ethylene and functional chemicals and subsidiaries CM Aromatics and Cosmo Matsuyama Oil produce mixed xylene. In addition Hyundai Cosmo Petrochemical a joint venture with Hyundai Oilbank produces and sales paraxylene. Petrochemical products are made and sold by Cosmo Matsuyama Oil CM Aromatics and Maruzen Petrochemical Co. Ltd. Also Hyundai

Cosmo Petrochemical produces and sells petrochemical products in South Korea.

Its other businesses includes EcoPower Co. Ltd. which operates a wind power generation business in Japan and Cosmo Oil Group which is engaged in the construction of petroleum-related facilities leasing and insurance sales.

Financial Performance

The company's revenues increased by 12% in fiscal year 2012 thanks to positive results from its petroleum business. Product prices rose in tandem with an increase in the purchase price of crude oil. Higher fuel demand by thermal power plants following the shutting down of Japan's nuclear power plants led to an increase in sales volume of heavy fuel oil C used for electric power generation. Such growth was offset by sales volumes decline for gasoline kerosene naphtha jet fuel and heavy fuel oil A owing to the structural factors of improving fuel efficiency and the conversion to alternative fuels as well as the slow pace of economic recovery. The export volume of middle distillates (diesel fuel and jet fuel) declined due to the shutdown of the Chiba Refinery.

Cosmo Oil's net loss in fiscal 2012 (131% change over the previous year) which was attributed to The Great East Japan Earthquake which caused the shut down of the Chiba Refinery. Also tax system revisions led to a partial reversal of deferred tax assets.

Strategy

In 2013 the company diversified its business by entering into the mega-solar business with joint venture partners Showa Shell Sekiyu K.K and Development Bank of Japan. The new joint venture CSD Solar will operate and manage solar power generation facilities and sales of generated power to the general electricity utility companies. (Responding to the Japanese government's commitment to reduce carbon emissions and as part of its own push to diversify its operations in 2010 Cosmo made its first move into wind power buying Japan's #4 wind power company Eco Power which has 25 wind farms operating in Japan).

To further strengthen its competitiveness by expanding its network in Japan in 2012 Cosmo Oil bought 97% of Sojitz Energy from Sojitz Corporation. It is looking to leverage the numerous procurement sources loyal customers talented personnel and know-how of Sojitz Energy to beef up Cosmo Oil's domestic marketing strategy creating significant synergies in its supply stability and logistics network.

A major earthquake in 2011 badly damaged the Chiba refinery (40% of the company's total refining output) forcing Cosmo Oil to shut it down for repairs for an entire year.

To meet increased demand in Asia Cosmo Oil is investing more in these refineries and is expanding its petrochemical operations. The company is also looking to expand its operations in the Middle East where it has been involved in petroleum development in the United Arab Emirates for more than 30 years. In 2010 Cosmo Oil agreed to terms for renewing its license for three operating fields and gained a new concession area in Abu Dhabi. It is also looking to generate oil production from Australia.

The company is also pruning back its chain of service stations in order to be more efficient.

EXECUTIVES

Chairman, Yaichi Kimura
Chairman and Representative Director, Keiichiro Okabe
President, Keizo Morikawa
Managing Director, Kaoru Kawana
Senior Executive Officer Finance, Satoshi Miyamoto

Senior Executive Officer Refining and Technology Maintenance & Engineering and Safety and Environment Control, Hideto Matsumura
Senior Executive Officer General Affairs Affiliate Relations Information System Planning and Purchasing Center, Atsuto Tamura
Senior Executive Officer General Manager Chiba Refinery, Katsuhisa Ohtaki
Senior Executive Officer Petroleum E&P International Ventures Crude Oil and Tanker and Petroleum Products Trading, Isao Kusakabe
General Manager Secretariat Office, Hideo Suzuki
Senior Executive Officer Sales Wholesale Marketing Industrial Fuel Marketing and Distribution, Hisashi Kobayash
President and Representative Director, Yaichi Kimura
Director, Mohamed D. Al Hamli
Director, Nasser A. Alsowaidi
EVP and Representative Director, Keizo Morikawa
Senior Executive Officer and Director, Satoshi Miyamoto
Senior Executive Officer Refining and Technology Maintenance & Engineering and Safety and Environment Control, Hideto Matsumura
Senior Executive Officer General Affairs Affiliate Relations Information System Planning and Purchasing Center, Atsuto Tamura
Senior Executive Officer and Director, Hisashi Kobayashi
Senior Executive Officer and Director, Isao Kusakabe
Auditors: KPMGAZSA&Co.

LOCATIONS

HQ: Cosmo Oil Co., Ltd.
1-1-1 Shibaura, Minato-ku, Tokyo 105-8528
Phone: (81) 3 3798 3243   **Fax:** (81) 3 3798 3237
Web: www.cosmo-oil.co.jp

PRODUCTS/OPERATIONS

Sales

	% of total
Petroleum	94
Oil exploration &	3
Petrochemicals	1
Other	2
Total	**100**

COMPETITORS

Exxon Mobil
Idemitsu Kosan
JX Holdings
JX Nippon Oil & Energy
Showa Shell Sekiyu
Singapore Petroleum

HISTORICAL FINANCIALS
Company Type: Public

Income Statement
FYE: March 31

	REVENUE ($ mil.)	NET INCOME ($ mil.)	NET PROFIT MARGIN	EMPLOYEES
03/14	34,274	42	0.1%	6,491
03/13	33,655	(912)	—	6,496
03/12	37,909	(110)	—	6,247
03/11	33,469	349	1.0%	6,366
03/10	27,965	(114)	—	6,418
Annual Growth	5.2%	—		0.3%

2014 Year-End Financials

Debt ratio: 0.4%	No. of shares (mil.): 846
Return on equity: 1.8%	Dividends
Cash ($ mil.): 1,360	Yield: —
Current ratio: 1.15	Payout: —
Long-term debt ($ mil.): 5,118	Market value ($ mil.): 6,415

	STOCK PRICE ($) FY Close	P/E High/Low		PER SHARE ($) Earnings	Dividends	Book Value
03/14	7.58	—	—	0.05	0.00	2.99
03/13	8.70	—	—	(1.08)	0.00	3.23
Annual Growth	(12.9%)	—	—	—	—	(1.9%)

Credit Agricole SA

The name suggests a country farmer's credit union but Credit Agricole's scope is much greater. France's largest bank Credit Agricole owns a 25% stake each in about 40 regional banks which in turn own more than half of Credit Agricole. It offers retail and business banking lending and deposit services at more than 9000 locations throughout the country including those of subsidiary Le Credit Lyonnais (LCL). The company is also involved in investment banking and capital markets (through its Credit Agricole CIB unit) in addition to insurance leasing and private banking. Credit Agricole combined its asset management operations with those of rival French bank Societe Generale to form Amundi in late 2009.

Credit Agricole owns 75% of the new unit which has more than Â690 billion (more than $973 billion) of client assets under management. Credit Agricole has renamed and restructured other units as well in an effort to strengthen its brand: In 2010 its Calyon became Credit Agricole Corporate and Investment Bank and consumer finance company Sofinco and private-label card issuer Finaref were combined to create Credit Agricole Consumer Finance. Credit Agricole also has specialized units devoted to real estate factoring and asset servicing.

Beyond France Credit Agricole has a presence in some 70 nations worldwide. It operates retail banks Cariparma and FriulAdria which were acquired from Intesa Sanpaolo in 2007; they have more than 750 branches in Italy. In 2011 Credit Agricole acquired additional locations in Cariparma's and FriulAdria's markets as well as sole control of Cassa di Risparmio della Spezia (Carispe) all from Intesa Sanpaolo. Additionally Credit Agricole owns about two-thirds of Emporiki Bank of Greece and has stakes in banks in Poland Serbia and the Ukraine. The bank is active in several African nations as well. International activities account for about half of the company's net income.

In 2011 Credit Agricole acquired Centea Belgium for Â527 million ($735 million). The deal will further grow and diversify Credit Agricole. Centea is one of the largest savings banks in Belgium with more than 650 points of sale. Credit Agricole also sold a 20% stake in its Asian and European brokerage units to China's CITIC Securities for some $374 million. It hopes to use the partnership with CITIC to help secure further growth in Asia.

In efforts to boost its capital ratios and trim its balance sheet Credit Agricole has sold some assets and made some cuts. In 2011 it agreed to sell its private equity unit to UK-based Coller Capital.

Georges Pauget stepped down as CEO in 2010. He was replaced by Jean-Paul Chifflet who was deputy chairman of both Credit Agricole and SAS Rue La Boetie which controls a majority of the bank's voting rights.

HISTORY

In the mid-1800s France's farmers were suffering from crop failures and a lack of credit. The government tried to meet the credit crunch without much success until in 1894 it created an agricultural credit company Credit Agricole that was tax-exempt and provided state-subsidized farm loans (a monopoly it enjoyed until 1989). Five years later the government established the regional banks as intermediaries between it and the local banks. By the turn of the century Credit Agricole's three-tiered structure was in place.

The first 30 years of the 20th century were a time of growth for the bank. The government allowed Credit Agricole to expand its lending to include long-term personal loans to encourage the growth of rural farming (1910) and loans to businesses involved in other industries (1919). The bank survived WWI and the drop in farm production largely through government support. After the war Credit Agricole funded rural electrification and other infrastructure.

After WWII the bank grew as it issued loans to finance the modernization of France's farms. In 1959 the government allowed Credit Agricole to begin writing mortgages; expansion of the bank's operations continued in the 1960s as it was permitted to broaden its lending scope and create subsidiaries including one to finance individual investments (Union d'Etudes et d'Investissements). In 1967 it began keeping deposits (previously it had transferred them to the French Treasury) and used the assets to fuel its national growth.

The early 1970s saw the bank continue to expand its lending operations. Its diversification came under fire from both the government which wanted the bank to focus on agriculture and rival banks which resented their tax-exempt competitor. Credit Agricole expanded beyond France in the mid-1970s offering mainly agricultural loans and funds to export firms. It opened its first international office in Chicago in 1979.

In the early 1980s the government continued to allow Credit Agricole to broaden its lending scope but at a price: The bank lost its tax-exempt status. It continued diversifying; it established such subsidiaries as Predica (life insurance 1986) and bought stakes in two brokerage firms (1988). As the 1980s closed Credit Agricole became a mutual company when the government sold 90% of the bank to the regional banks.

In 1991 the last restrictions on Credit Agricole's lending were removed and the bank began transforming itself into a financial services firm. It expanded its lending operations around the world and added subsidiaries offering a variety of financial services. In 1996 it bought Banque Indosuez (which became Credit Agricole Indosuez) fueling its growth in international wholesale banking. In the late 1990s the bank sought partnerships to expand its operations.

Its expansion was slowed by financial turmoil in Russia and Asia and the bank closed its emerging markets business. The next year Credit Agricole teamed with Spain's Banco Bilbao Vizcaya Argentaria and Commercial Bank of Greece as part of its plans to expand its presence in the Mediterranean and southern Europe; it already owned sizable stakes in Italy's Banca Intesa (now IntesaBci) and major banks in Lebanon Morocco and Portugal.

In 2000 the bank bought a majority share in Poland-based Europejski Fundusz Leasingowy but declined an offer to become the controlling shareholder of fellow French bank Credit Lyonnais which it eventually acquired in 2003. Credit Agricole went public on the Euronext Paris Exchange at the end of 2001.

Under pressure from the US government Credit Lyonnais admitted in 2003 to illegally acquiring

Executive Life the Californian insurance company in the early 1990s. Credit Lyonnais agreed to pay a fine of nearly $772 million to avoid criminal prosecution. It was allowed to keep its US banking license.

Credit Agricole acquired Italian retail banks Cariparma and FriulAdria from Intesa Sanpaolo in 2007.

In 2008 Credit Agricole found itself ensnared along with its colleagues in the worsening economic crisis and credit crunch. To encourage banks to loosen their purse strings the French government acquired billions of euros worth of debt securities from Credit Agricole and five of its peers.

LOCATIONS

HQ: Credit Agricole SA
12 place des Etat-Unis, Montrouge, Cedex 92127
Phone: (33) 1 43 23 52 02
Web: www.credit-agricole.com

PRODUCTS/OPERATIONS

Sales

	% of total
Asset management insurance & private	32
Corporate & investment	21
Regional	21
LCL	14
Specialized financial	12
Total	**100**

HISTORICAL FINANCIALS
Company Type: Public

Income Statement
FYE: December 31

	ASSETS ($ mil.)	NET INCOME ($ mil.)	INCOME AS % OF ASSETS	EMPLOYEES
12/13	2,115,867	3,448	0.2%	75,529
12/12	2,428,322	(8,529)	—	79,282
12/11	2,229,404	(1,901)	—	87,451
12/10	2,132,735	1,690	0.1%	87,520
12/09	2,243,459	1,620	0.1%	89,172
Annual Growth	(1.5%)	20.8%	—	(4.1%)

2013 Year-End Financials

Return on assets: 0.1%
Return on equity: 6.1%
Long-term debt ($ mil.): —
No. of shares (mil.): —
Sales ($ mil): 98,724

Dividends
Yield: —
Payout: —
Market value ($ mil.): —

	STOCK PRICE ($) FY Close	P/E High/Low		PER SHARE ($) Earnings	Dividends	Book Value
12/13	6.42	12	7	1.39	0.00	23.33
12/12	4.05	—	—	(3.44)	0.00	21.02
12/11	2.74	—	—	(0.78)	0.58	22.22
12/10	6.37	35	14	0.72	0.28	25.55
12/09	8.85	49	13	0.72	0.31	28.36
Annual Growth	(7.7%)	—	—	17.9%	—	(4.8%)

Credit Suisse Group

Credit Suisse is one of Switzerland's top financial services firms though a distant second to behemoth rival UBS. The group provides investment management private banking and asset management services to clients worldwide. Its investment banking offerings include debt and equity underwriting M&A advisory and other securities services. The group provides wealth management services in Switzerland through subsidiary Clariden Leu; internationally it operates under the Credit Suisse brand. Credit Suisse offers asset management services to individual institutional and government clients. With more than 200 retail branches in Switzerland it operates in more than 50 countries (including the US and UK).

Credit Suisse is working to rebound from the global economic meltdown. The group suffered hefty losses at the height of the crisis (in 2008) and subsequent legislation and market turmoil has continued to make it challenging for Credit Suisse. New regulation such as the Dodd-Frank Act enacted in 2010 to prevent risky activities in the financial industry impacted financial institutions like Credit Suisse by limiting proprietary trading and raising capital requirements. To this end the group has been reducing its investment banking operations and focusing on its client-focused businesses which are less volatile. In 2011 Credit Suisse exited proprietary trading and other businesses that were a drain on capital. In 2013 the firm also sold its exchange traded funds (ETFs) business to private equity giant BlackRock Inc.

Its three primary businesses —Private Banking Investment Banking and Asset Management —are increasingly collaborating to increase the group's efficiency. In 2011 Credit Suisse cut 3500 jobs (or 7% or its workforce) in an effort to reduce costs. It was part of a bigger plan to cut around 8% in total costs.

Credit Suisse's strategy as the economy recovers includes expanding its roster of high-net-worth customers around the world and in Switzerland adding commercial clients of all sizes. In investment banking Credit Suisse is focused on reducing its risky assets and cutting costs. In asset management the company is working in collaboration with its private banking and investment banking arms to grow revenues by expanding its product line. The asset management segment (which concentrates on alternative investments including private equity hedge funds and real estate) is growing in markets such as Brazil southeast Asia China and Russia.

The company continues to make strategic acquisitions in order to grow the business. In late 2010 the company acquired a 30% stake in US hedge fund York Capital Management. The following year it acquired Fortis' Nederland's Prime Fund Solutions business which will strengthen its hedge fund offerings. In 2012 the company acquired HSBC's private banking operations in Japan.

Results in 2011 were impacted by the struggling economy and new regulations within the financial services industry. Credit Suisse reported a 62% drop in net revenues in 2011. Results in the investment banking business were particularly hurt due to macroeconomic uncertainties political strife and regulatory changes. The company also is transitioning itself to operate within new global banking rules by ridding itself of risk and improving its capital ratios.

In 2012 Credit Suisse handed over information to the US government as part of an investigation into hidden Swiss bank accounts that are used by wealthy Americans to evade taxes. Credit Suisse was among other Swiss banks that were being investigated. Swiss privacy laws have typically protected wealthy individuals who funnel money through offshore accounts.

HISTORY

In 1856 shortly after the creation of the Swiss federation Alfred Escher opened Credit Suisse (CS) in Zurich. Primarily a venture capital firm CS helped fund Swiss railroads and other industries. It later opened offices in Italy and helped establish the Swiss Bank Corporation.

CS shifted its focus to commercial banking in 1867 and sold most of its stock holdings. By 1871 it was Switzerland's largest bank buoyed by the nation's swift industrialization. In 1895 CS helped create the predecessor of Swiss utility Electrowatt. Foreign activity grew in the 1920s. A run on banks in the Depression forced CS to sell assets at a loss and dip into reserves of unreported retained profits.

Trade declined in WWII but neutrality left Switzerland's institutions intact and made it a major banking center partly due to CS's role as a conduit for the Nazis' plundered gold. Foreign exchange and gold trading became important activities for CS after WWII. Mortgage and consumer credit acquisitions fueled domestic growth in the 1970s.

In 1978 the bank took a stake in US investment bank First Boston and with it formed London-based Credit Suisse-First Boston (CSFB). CS created 44%-owned holding company Credit Suisse First Boston to own First Boston CSFB and Tokyo-based CS First Boston Pacific.

The stock market crash of 1987 led a damaged First Boston to merge with CSFB the next year. In 1990 CS (renamed CS Holding) injected $300 million into CSFB and shifted $470 million in bad loans from its books becoming the first foreign owner of a major Wall Street investment bank.

In the early 1990s CS Holding strengthened its insurance business with a Winterthur Insurance alliance. In 1993 and 1994 acquisitions helped it gain share in its overbanked home market.

In 1996 CS Holding reorganized as Credit Suisse Group and grew internationally including further merging the daredevil US investment banking operations into Credit Suisse's more staid and relationship-oriented corporate banking. It bought Winterthur (Switzerland's #2 insurer) in 1997 as well as Barclays' European investment banking business.

Credit Suisse and other Swiss banks came under fire in 1996 for refusing to relinquish assets from Jewish bank accounts from the Holocaust era and for gold trading with the Nazi regime. In 1997 the banks agreed to establish a humanitarian fund for Holocaust victims. A stream of lawsuits by American heirs and boycott threats from US states and cities led in 1998 to a tentative $1.25 billion settlement (unpopular in Switzerland) with Credit Suisse on the hook for about a third of that.

CS in 1998 expanded its investment banking by buying Brazil's Banco de Investimentos Garantia; it also moved to expand US money management operations by allying with New York-based Warburg Pincus Asset Management. By 1999 that joint venture —which was to give the investment firm access to CS's mutual fund distribution channels in Europe and Asia —had morphed into CS's $650 million purchase of Warburg Pincus Asset Management.

Japan revoked the license of the company's financial products unit for obstructing an investigation (the harshest penalty ever given to a foreign firm at the time); it also accused the company of helping 60 others hide losses and cover up evidence.

In 2000 the company started a mortgage and home-buying Web site and decided to allow searches of Holocaust-era accounts. The next year as a part of its European expansion Credit Suisse acquired Spanish broker and asset manager General de Valores y Cambios.

Under former chairman and CEO Lukas Mohlemann the company expanded Credit Suisse First Boston when it bought US investment firm Donaldson Lufkin & Jenrette in 2000 and renamed it Credit Suisse First Boston (USA).

The collapse of Credit Suisse's share price along with what proved to be an over-ambitious acquisition strategy brought about the downfall of Mohlemann who was pressured out by shareholders in 2002.

In 2005 Credit Suisse merged with its Credit Suisse First Boston subsidiary creating a global Credit Suisse brand and in 2006 reorganized into three distinct operating segments —investment banking private banking and asset management along with insurance.

Credit Suisse sold insurance subsidiary Winterthur to AXA in 2006 for nearly $10 billion. A Winterthur sale had been on Credit Suisse's agenda for a while as a plan to divest noncore operations. Also that year Credit Suisse and General Electric jointly acquired a 50% stake in London City Airport which serves about 2 million travelers a year. The following year as a cost-saving measure Credit Suisse combined four private banks and one securities dealer into Clariden Leu.

The company named Brady Dougan CEO in 2007. Dugan was the first non-German speaker to hold the position.

Globally the investment banking industry was hit hard by the US subprime mortgage crisis and Credit Suisse was no exception. The company reported a net loss of Å5.4 billion in 2008 the worst in its history. Credit Suisse turned down a bailout offer from the Swiss government in 2008 but it did receive a capital injection of CHF10 billion ($8.7 billion) from private investors. However the capital infusion couldn't prevent losses as global credit markets froze and consumer and shareholder confidence fell.

The company cut more than 5000 jobs or some 11% of its workforce mostly from its investment banking unit. It also reviewed its results for 2007 and among its findings discovered rogue traders in its ranks a la the beleaguered Societe Generale. Credit Suisse reduced its results accordingly.

In 2008 it bought an 80% stake in US firm Asset Management Finance Corporation a division of National Bank of Canada. Also in 2008 it expanded its Middle East franchise when it bought majority ownership in joint venture Saudi Swiss Securities which it renamed Credit Suisse Saudi Arabia. It has added Shariah-compliant banking for Islamic clients and has expanded in other markets including Brazil Kazakhstan and Turkey.

The following year Credit Suisse sold certain fund management assets and businesses to Aberdeen Asset Management in exchange for about 25% of Aberdeen's shares.

EXECUTIVES

Chief Risk Officer, Tobias Guldimann, age 53
Vice Chairman, Peter Brabeck-Letmathe, age 70
Honorary Chairman of the Board of Directors, Rainer E. Gut, age 82
Independent Member of the Board, Walter B. Kielholz, age 63
CEO, Brady W. Dougan, age 55
Chief Talent Branding and Communications Officer, Pamela A. Thomas-Graham, age 51
Corporate Secretary, Pierre Schreiber
Head Private Banking and Wealth Management; CEO Region Americas, Robert S. (Rob) Shafir, age 57
Chairman, Urs Rohner, age 55
CEO Investment Bank; CEORegion Asia Pacific, Eric Varvel, age 51
CEO Private Banking and Credit Suisse Switzerland, Hans-Ulrich Meister
Chairman Private Banking, Walter Berchtold, age 52
CIO and Director, Karl Landert, age 56

CEO Europe Middle East and Africa, Fawzi
Kyriakos-Saad
Chief Risk Officer Clariden Leu, Jean-Pierre
Colombara
Head Mergers and Acquisitions Middle East and
North Africa, Anthony Armstrong
CFO, David Mathers, age 50
General Counsel, Romeo Cerutti, age 52
CEO Americas, Antonio Quintella
CEO Asia Pacific, Osama Abbasi
Independent Member of the Board of Directors,
Anton Anton van Rossum Rossum
Member of the Board of Directors, Jassim Jassim Al
Thani Thani
Secretary of the Board, Joan Joan Belzer Belzer
Head Investment Banking; CEO Region Europe
Middle East & Africa (EMEA), Gael de Boissard
Vice Chairman, Peter Brabeck-Letmathe, age 70
Director, Richard E. Thornburgh, age 63
Independent Member of the Board of Directors,
Robert H. (Bob) Benmosche, age 69
Independent Member of the Board, Walter B.
Kielholz, age 63
Director, Ernst Tanner, age 67
Director, Jean Lanier, age 68
Director, Anton van Rossum, age 68
Director, Aziz R.D. Syriani, age 71
Director, Andreas N. Koopmann, age 63
CIO and Director, Karl Landert, age 56
Director, Noreen Doyle, age 64
Director, David W. Syz, age 70
Director, Peter F. Weibel, age 72
Director, John Tiner, age 57
Auditors: KPMGAG

LOCATIONS

HQ: Credit Suisse Group
Paradeplatz 8, Zurich CH 8070
Phone: (41) 44 212 16 16   Fax: (41) 44 333 25 87
Web: www.credit-suisse.com

PRODUCTS/OPERATIONS

Sales

	% of total
Interest and dividend	53
Commissions &	30
Trading	12
Other	5
Total	100

COMPETITORS

AEGON	JPMorgan Chase
Barclays	Mitsubishi UFJ
Citigroup	Financial Group
Deutsche Bank	Mizuho Financial
Goldman Sachs	Morgan Stanley
Grupo Santander	Nomura Securities
HSBC	TD Bank
ING	UBS

HISTORICAL FINANCIALS

Company Type: Public

Income Statement

FYE: December 31

	ASSETS ($ mil.)	NET INCOME ($ mil.)	INCOME AS % OF ASSETS	EMPLOYEES
12/13	979,520	2,610	0.3%	46,000
12/12	1,008,171	1,617	0.2%	47,400
12/11	1,115,189	2,075	0.2%	49,700
12/10	1,102,816	5,447	0.5%	50,100
12/09	1,001,389	6,528	0.7%	47,600
Annual Growth	(0.6%)	(20.5%)	—	(0.9%)

2013 Year-End Financials

Return on assets: 0.2%
Return on equity: 5.9%
Long-term debt ($ mil.): —
No. of shares (mil.): 1,590
Sales ($ mil): 29,017

Dividends
Yield: 0.4%
Payout: 8.1%
Market value ($ mil.): 49,383

	STOCK PRICE ($) FY Close	P/E High/Low	PER SHARE ($) Earnings	Dividends	Book Value
12/13	31.04	35 25	1.37	0.14	29.74
12/12	24.56	39 20	0.98	0.82	30.04
12/11	23.48	41 18	1.45	1.82	29.33
12/10	40.41	15 9	4.16	1.78	30.30
12/09	49.16	11 3	4.99	0.09	31.15
Annual Growth	(10.9%)	—	(27.6%)	11.4%	(1.2%)

CTBC Financial Holdings Ltd

Chinatrust Financial Holding (CFHC) is one of Taiwan's largest financial services groups. It operates Chinatrust Commercial Bank which has more than 140 domestic branches and more than 70 overseas. The group provides general banking services including corporate and consumer loans financial consulting checking and savings accounts letters of credit commercial drafts collections and payments and credit cards. It also offers property/casualty insurance life insurance investments and other related financial services. Overseas the bank operates subsidiaries in the US Canada the Philippines and Indonesia. The predecessor to the family-owned CFHC was founded in 1966.

EXECUTIVES

President Retail Banking Group, Oliver Shang
SVP, Miao-Chiu Hsu
President Institutional Banking Group and
Director, James Chen
EVP; Managing Director Investment Banking
Group, Larry Hsu
EVP; Managing Director Retail Banking Group,
Su Kuo Huang
Managing Director General Administration,
Thomas K. S. Chen
EVP; Managing Director Consumer Finance
Group, Eric Wu
EVP; Managing Director Risk Management Group,
Jack T. K. Cheng
EVP; Managing Director Audit Management
Division, Julie L. Yang
EVP, Jason Wang
EVP, Albert Shiung
SVP, Connie Lin
Chief Executive Officer-Banking Business,
DeNoma Michael
Chief Executive Officer-China Business, Lianfu
Luo
Chairman of the Board, Liansong Gu
Chief Administrative Officer, Renjie Gao
Chief Information Officer, Rutian Zhang
Chief Risk Officer, Taike Zheng
Chief Executive Officer-Insurance Business,
Yinbao Ling
President Institutional Banking Group and
Director, James Chen
Director, Jeffrey L. S. Koo
Independent Director, Wenzhi Li

Independent Director, Zhihong Li

LOCATIONS

HQ: CTBC Financial Holdings Ltd
17F, No.3, Sung Shou Road, Taipei
Phone: (886) 2 2722 2002   Fax: (886) 2 2723 7883
Web: www.ctbcholding.com

PRODUCTS/OPERATIONS

Sales

	% of total
Institutional	38
Retail	34
Consumer	28
Total	100

COMPETITORS

Cathay Financial Holding	Fubon Financial
Chang Hwa Bank	Hua Nan Financial
E.Sun	Mega Financial
East West Bancorp	Shin Kong
First Financial Holding	SinoPac Holdings
	Taishin
	Taiwan Business Bank

HISTORICAL FINANCIALS

Company Type: Public

Income Statement

FYE: December 31

	ASSETS ($ mil.)	NET INCOME ($ mil.)	INCOME AS % OF ASSETS	EMPLOYEES
12/13	81,308	721	0.9%	0
12/12	72,825	733	1.0%	13,107
12/11	66,632	603	0.9%	12,568
12/10	62,359	485	0.8%	11,562
12/09	55,032	76	0.1%	9,983
Annual Growth	10.3%	75.4%	—	—

2013 Year-End Financials

Return on assets: 0.9%
Return on equity: 11.8%
Long-term debt ($ mil.): —
No. of shares (mil.): —
Sales ($ mil): 4,826

Dividends
Yield: —
Payout: —
Market value ($ mil.): —

Dai-ichi Life Insurance Co Ltd

Trying its best to live up to its name (Dai-ichi means "first") Dai-ichi Life Insurance Company is one of Japan's top insurers. The firm sells individual and group life insurance annuities and supplemental medical coverage as well as individual and group pension products. Dai-ichi Life also provides nonlife insurance products through its partnership with Sompo Japan Insurance as well as cancer insurance through a partnership with Aflac. Other services include asset management and risk management. Dai-ichi Life sells its products through its network of thousands of sales representatives.

Sales and Marketing

Dai-ichi Life markets its products through sales representatives at a number of locations —including retail stores call centers and administration centers —as well as through online and direct mail programs.

Strategy

The company has responded to increased competition in the Japanese market by expanding its product offerings including lifetime supplemental medical coverage and annuity products. In expanding its financial services segment the company has become one of the top institutional investors in Japan.

Mergers and Acquisitions

Dai-ichi Life is also investing in overseas subsidiaries in a bid to increase its presence outside of Japan. In mid-2011 it strengthened its international presence by acquiring the balance of Tower Australia Group. (It first purchase a stake in the Australian life insurer in 2008.) Dai-Ichi Life has also made moves into Thailand and Vietnam.

Ownership

Previously named Dai-ichi Mutual Life Insurance the company jumped on the demutualization bandwagon and made its IPO on the Tokyo stock exchange in early 2010. The listing for the renamed Dai-ichi Life Insurance raised some Â1 trillion ($11 billion) and the proceeds were used to pad the company's coffers after the drop in value of its securities during the economic recession.

EXECUTIVES

Chairman, Katsutoshi Saito, age 71
Deputy President, Hideto Masaki
Senior Managing Executive Officer and Director, Shinsuke Kume
President, Koichiro Watanabe
Senior Managing Executive Officer, Ryoji Yajima
Senior Managing Executive Officer, Satoru Ueno
Senior Managing Executive Officer, Kazuma Ishii
Senior Managing Executive Officer, Shigeo Tsuyuki
Managing Executive Officer, Takahiro Inaba
Managing Executive Officer, Takehide Itonaga
Senior Managing Executive Officer, Norimitsu Horio
Managing Executive Officer and Director, Tomoyasu Asano
Managing Executive Officer and Director, Yoshio Takeyama
Executive Officer, Hiroshi Kanai
Executive Officer, Akio Tanaka
Executive Officer, Kenji Sakurai
Executive Officer, Morinobu Nagahama
Executive Officer, Hideo Teramoto
Executive Officer, Takashi Kawashima
Chairman Dai-ichi Life Insurance Company of Vietnam, Takashi Fujii
CEO and Managing Director Dai-ichi Life Australia, Jim Minto
Chairman Ocean Life Insurance, Kirati Assakul
Chief Representative Beijing, Zhao Ke Fei
Chief Representative Taipei, Hajime Namba
Executive Officer; Chief Director of Investment, Atsushi Nagayama
Executive Officer; Chief Director of Eastern Japan Sales, Atsushi Takahashi
Executive Officer; Chief Director of Underwriting; Director of Business Affaris Planning, Masao Taketomi
Executive Officer; President of Sapporo General Office; Director of Hokkaido Sales, Nobuyuki Akimoto
Executive Officer, Shinichi Aizawa
President Dai-ichi Life International (U.S.A.), Shigeru Mori
Managing Director Dai-ichi Life International (Europe), Shinichiro Masunaga
CEO Star Union Dai-ichi Life Insurance, Girish Kulkarni
Managing Director Dai-ichi Life International (AsiaPacific), Tatsusaburo Yamamoto
Chief Representative Shanghai, Tomoki Sugizaki
President and Board Member, Katsutoshi Saito, age 69

Senior Managing Executive Officer and Director, Hideto Masaki
Senior Managing Executive Officer and Director, Shinsuke Kume
Senior Managing Executive Officer and Director, Koichiro Watanabe
Director, Nobuya Minami
Managing Executive Officer and Director, Ryoji Yajima
Managing Executive Officer and Director, Kazuma Ishii
Managing Executive Officer and Director, Shigeo Tsuyuki
Managing Executive Officer and Director, Tomoyasu Asano
Senior Managing Executive Officer and Director, Kimio Oiso
Managing Executive Officer and Director, Yoshio Takeyama
Director, Haruo Funabashi
Independent Director, Michiko Miyamoto
Auditors: Ernst&YoungShinNihon

LOCATIONS

HQ: Dai-ichi Life Insurance Co Ltd
1-13-1 Yuraku-cho, Chiyoda-ku, Tokyo 100-8411
Phone: (81) 3 3216 1211
Web: www.dai-ichi-life.co.jp

COMPETITORS

AXA Life Insurance	Meiji Yasuda Life
Asahi Mutual Life	Mitsui Life
Daido Life	Nippon Life Insurance
Fukoku Mutual	Sumitomo Life
Gibraltar Life Insurance	Taiyo Life

HISTORICAL FINANCIALS

Company Type: Public

Income Statement

FYE: March 31

	REVENUE ($ mil.)	NET INCOME ($ mil.)	NET PROFIT MARGIN	EMPLOYEES
03/14	54,963	755	1.4%	59,512
03/13	52,947	344	0.7%	60,771
03/12	55,775	248	0.4%	60,305
03/11	51,146	231	0.5%	59,356
03/10	53,009	595	1.1%	60,061
Annual Growth	0.9%	6.1%	—	(0.2%)

2014 Year-End Financials

Debt ratio: 0.0%
Return on equity: 4.3%
Cash ($ mil.): 7,411
Current ratio: 0.13
Long-term debt ($ mil.): 1,042

No. of shares (mil.): 1,000
Dividends
Yield: —
Payout: —
Market value ($ mil.): 15,301

	STOCK PRICE ($) FY Close	P/E High/Low	PER SHARE ($) Earnings	Dividends	Book Value
03/14	15.30	— —	0.76	0.00	18.87
Annual Growth	—		—	—	—

Daimler AG

Daimler's cars may stop on a dime but they cost a little more than that. Daimler's passenger car business Mercedes-Benz includes luxury brands Mercedes and Maybach as well as compact hybrid and electric models including its smart and B-Class

F-Cell brands. Its Daimler Trucks North America unit manufactures heavy-trucks in the US and with its Fuso Mercedes-Benz and Sprinter brands Daimler is the world's leading maker of commercial vehicles. The Atego BlueTecHybrid truck was launched in 2011. The company holds a 22% stake in aerospace and defense consortium Airbus and 60% in Formula One team Mercedes-Benz Grand Prix. Daimler sells its vehicles in 40 countries but Europe represents 40% of its sales.

What a difference a year makes. Daimler followed the global post-recession automotive trend with a 24% boost in its 2010 revenues over 2009. Its net income went from a negative Â4.4 billion (more than $6 billion) to a positive Â5.6 billion (almost $8 billion). China which is where Mercedes-Benz is the fastest growing premium brand posted a sales increase of almost 140% over 2009. Overall the company's vehicle sales increased by 27% trucks by 37% and vans 35% over 2009. Daimler expects a positive trajectory in 2011 sales but not at the level of 2010.

The global automotive markets started to recover in the second half of 2010 fueled by government incentive programs designed to stimulate car sales. Prior to that Daimler made certain that it was in the driver's seat when it came to navigating the economic gridlock of 2008 and 2009.

Daimler implemented restructuring and efficiency initiatives to bring production in line with demand. In addition it refined its strategy to develop environmentally friendly compact cars along with strengthening its luxury brand by engineering models adapted for regional markets such as Asia. Recognizing a change in investor behavior the company delisted and deregistered from the New York Stock Exchange (NYSE Euronext) and the SEC in mid-2010. Delisting saves on administrative expenses and fees for financial reporting.

Daimler also used 2010 to ally itself with companies to increase scale reduce expenses share in developing advanced technology as well as to expand geographically. To that end the company entered a partnership agreement with Nissan and Renault to share small-car technology and powertrains and work together to develop electric cars anticipating the ability to compete with global giants Toyota and VW. Through this alliance Daimler will also acquire technology for its next smart fortwo model (which will be developed alongside Renault's Twingo model) to help make the car profitable. The first jointly developed smart fortwo and Twingo models possibly including all-electric versions are expected to be launched in 2013. Additionally the company will have access to diesel engines and transmissions for its Mercedes-Benz Vito van. For its part Daimler will provide engines from its Mercedes division for use in Nissan's Infiniti luxury car model.

As part of the three-way deal the companies will take equity stakes in each other. Renault and Nissan will each acquire a 1.55% stake ; the combined 3.1% stake in Daimler is estimated to be worth about Â1.2 billion ($1.6 billion). Daimler will acquire a 3.1% stake in each of Renault and Nissan. The equity investments are intended to encourage ongoing collaboration among the three companies.

Another way Daimler took advantage of the economic slowdown was to develop new products and get involved in markets with developing economies with a particular eye on Brazil China India and Russia. In mid-2010 the company formed a joint venture with Chinese automaker BYD to develop electric vehicles for the Chinese market. BYD's expertise in battery technology complements Daimler's knowledge of electric vehicle architecture. (Daimler has applied for more than 600 patents related to electric vehicle technology over the past 30 years.) The companies plan to launch the Chinese car by 2013. Daimler also partnered with China's Beiqi Foton Motor Co. to create a joint venture to produce heavy trucks.

On the Eastern front in late 2010 Daimler and Russian truck maker Kamaz expanded their existing partnership; Daimler supplies axles to Kamaz as well as makes Mercedes-Benz and Setra truck brands in Russia while Kamaz supplies axle components to Daimler. The two companies plan to invest about Å50 million (more than $66 million) in axle production. Earlier Daimler's 89% owned Mitsubishi Fuso unit formed a joint venture with Kamaz to import produce and sell the light-duty Fuso Canter brand trucks. Daimler owns an approximate 15% stake in Kamaz.

On its heels Daimler formed a joint venture in 2010 with Uzavtosanoat an automotive holding company. The venture assembles and sells a range of bus models under the Mercedes-Benz brand to the Uzbekistan and neighboring markets. Subsidiary Mercedes-Benz Buses Central Asia holds a 51% interest in the partnership and Uzavtosanoat 49%.

India is another area of interest where Daimler is looking to go-it-alone with its commercial truck operations. To that end Daimler shed its approximate 5% state in Tata Motors Ltd. for an estimated $410 million in 2010. The deal provided a cash infusion for Daimler and repositioned the company to capture truck sales which are being fueled by a rise in government-backed urban renewal projects. India's Hero Group conglomerate withdrew from a truck-building partnership with another automotive maker transferring its 40% interest to Daimler. The company's trucks made in India are due to be released in 2012 and will carry the BharatBenz brand.

Domestically Daimler and Rolls-Royce announced plans in 2011 to acquire Tognum a Germany-based engine and powertrain supplier for distributed power generation and marine propulsion markets. Daimler is interested in the company's engines and powertrains for off-highway applications and for local power generators. After acquiring nearly a 60% stake Daimler and Rolls Royce upped the offer by just over 8% in mid-2011 with the goal of acquiring at least 75%. The takeover would give the companies rights to Tognum's intellectual property. If successful Daimler and Rolls Royce will own an equal stake in Tognum.

In the meanwhile Daimler for its part in developing more electric and hybrid automobiles is conducting large-scale field tests for electric vehicles — called e-mobility projects —in London (since 2007) and Berlin (since 2009) using battery-powered fortwo electric drive cars. In spring 2011 Daimler and Robert Bosch set up a 50/50 joint ventures to produce electrical vehicle engines that are to be used in Mercedes-Benz smart vehicles; production is set to start in 2012. In Berlin the company partnered with electricity provider RWE AG to set up 500 charging stations; Daimler is developing global standards for charging plugs and sockets for the power infrastructure. Daimler also plans to begin production of its own lithium-ion batteries for use by other automotive manufacturers with commercial production of the batteries scheduled for 2014.

Daimler in the same spirit made an equity investment in Tesla Motors the developer of an all-electric sports car taking a stake of nearly 10% in 2009. The companies previously collaborated on integrating Tesla's lithium-ion battery packs and charging electronics into the first 1000 units of Daimler's electric smart car. Although later that year Daimler sold part of its Tesla stake to Abu Dhabi-based Aabar Investments Daimler and Tesla continue to cooperate on development of battery systems electric drive and other projects.

In addition to Renault-Nissan's 3.1% stake in Daimler Aabar Investments holds an equity share of about 9% in the automaker making it the largest shareholder in Daimler. Aabar Investments also holds a 40% stake in Mercedes-Benz Grand Prix a UK-based Formula One racing team. The government of Kuwait owns almost 7% of the company.

After nearly 10 years of irreconcilable differences Daimler and Chrysler called it quits. They joined forces in 1998 in a $37 billion deal but the marriage never worked. In 2007 Daimler sold 80% of Chrysler to Cerberus Capital for $7.4 billion.

HISTORY

Daimler-Benz was formed by the merger of two German motor companies —Daimler and Benz —in 1926. Daimler-Benz bought Auto Union (Audi) in 1958 (sold to Volkswagen in 1966). The company's Mercedes cars gained international fame and sales expanded worldwide in the 1970s.

Daimler-Benz diversified in the 1980s buying aerospace heavy truck (Freightliner) and consumer and industrial electrical companies. Although diversification continued sales slowed. Losses at its aerospace unit forced Daimler-Benz into the red in 1995. Also that year the company and ABB Asea Brown Boveri (now ABB) formed joint venture Adtranz the #1 train maker in the world and Jorgen Schrempp became chairman of the management board (CEO).

In 1998 Daimler-Benz acquired Chrysler and introduced a subcompact car the smart in Europe. DaimlerChrysler rolled both companies' financial services units into DaimlerChrysler Interservices (DEBIS) and acquired the remaining shares of Adtranz in 1999.

North American influence in the company began to fade in 2000 with the exit of US management including co-chairman Robert Eaton. Prior to his retirement Eaton announced DaimlerChrysler's goal to become the world's #1 carmaker through partnerships or acquisitions.

In 2000 DaimlerChrysler agreed to buy a controlling $2.1 billion stake (34%) in Mitsubishi Motors (later upped to 37% when it acquired 3.3% from Volvo). It took a minority stake in South Korea-based Hyundai Motor (sold in 2004) and the two bid jointly on Daewoo Motor (now named GM Daewoo Auto & Technology; South Korea) but Ford was named exclusive bidder (although it later withdrew). DaimlerChrysler bought Canada-based truck maker Western Star Holdings for $456 million and paid about $473 million for the 79% of Detroit Diesel (heavy-duty truck engines) that it didn't already own. The company also agreed to sell its rail systems unit Adtranz to Bombardier (completed in 2001 for about $1.1 billion).

Also in 2000 in an effort to turn things around at its money-losing Chrysler division James Holden was replaced with Dieter Zetsche who immediately began making personnel changes. Days after Zetsche was installed billionaire investor Kirk Kerkorian filed an $8 billion lawsuit seeking to undo the 1998 Daimler-Benz/Chrysler merger on grounds that portraying the deal as a "merger of equals" was misrepresentative.

Zetsche announced early in 2001 that Chrysler would eliminate almost 26000 North American jobs over three years (largely through retirement and attrition) and make wholesale changes in the group's senior management positions overseeing the Chrysler and Mercedes divisions.

Early in 2003 in an effort to bolster its worldwide commercial vehicle ambitions DaimlerChrysler took a 43% stake in MFTBC. Mitsubishi Motors held a 20% stake and other Mitsubishi group companies controlled the rest of MFTBC. Early in 2004 DaimlerChrysler increased its stake in MFTBC to 65%.

Later that year mounting problems concerning poor quality and cover-ups plagued Mitsubishi and continued to cause problems at DaimlerChrysler when CEO Jorgen Schrempp's plan to infuse the ailing Japanese carmaker with $7 billion met with fierce resistance by many of Schrempp's fellow members of the management board including Schrempp's protege former Chrysler COO Wolfgang Bernhard. Bernhard had been slated to take over as chief of the Mercedes Group but his disloyalty to Schrempp and his heavy-handed management style blocked his promotion (soon afterward Bernhard left DaimlerChrysler and later was hired by VW).

In 2004 DaimlerChrysler created a joint venture with Magna International for the purposes of eventually selling DaimlerChrysler's driveline subsidiary New Venture Gear to Magna for about $435 million. The deal which received European Commission approval that year created a new company New Process Gear. Also in 2004 DaimlerChrysler sold its 10% stake in Hyundai Motor but the two companies said they would maintain a joint-development relationship on a project-by-project basis.

Late in 2004 DaimlerChrysler received Chinese regulatory approval to build cars in China with joint venture partner Beijing Automotive Industry Holding Co. Ltd. (BAIC).

Early in 2005 the problems with Mitsubishi came to a head when it was revealed that known truck defects at MFTBC had been covered up since 1974. A deal was struck whereby DaimlerChrysler got Mitsubishi Motors' 20% in MFTBC reducing Mitsubishi Motors' stake to zero. Also in 2005 joint venture Beijing Benz-DaimlerChrysler Automotive Co. Ltd. (with partner Beijing Automotive Industry Holding Company) got a license to build Mercedes-Benz C- and E- Class cars. Chinese Jeep production was also moved to this new facility. Late that year DaimlerChrysler sold its remaining 12% stake in Mitsubishi Motors to Goldman Sachs marking the end of the companies' previous cooperation. Goldman Sachs sold all but 0.01% of the stake on the open market the following day. DaimlerChrysler began offering passenger car and commercial vehicle financing in China through DaimlerChrysler Automotive Finance (China) Ltd. as 2005 wound down.

Early in 2006 DaimlerChrysler said it would eliminate 6000 administrative jobs or 20% of its worldwide administrative workforce in order to streamline operations. Later that year the company formed a joint venture with Chinese Fujian Motor Industry Group and Taiwanese China Motor Corporation for the manufacture of the Mercedes-Benz Sprinter and Vito vans for the Chinese market.

In early 2007 after Chrysler losses topping $1.5 billion in 2006 Daimler admitted for the first time that it was rethinking the wisdom of the merger with Chrysler and was looking at all options. Reports later emerged that Chrysler might be sold and that interested parties included General Motors Magna International and some private equity concerns including a team led by The Blackstone Group and Centerbridge Partners as well as Cerberus Capital Management. Through his investment firm Tracinda Corp. billionaire and former Chrysler and GM activist investor Kirk Kerkorian later threw his hat into the ring with a bid of $4.5 billion for Chrysler.

Cerberus won out over its rivals and struck a deal to buy roughly 80% of Chrysler for about $7.4 billion. Daimler retained about a 20% equity stake and the two companies continued to cooperate on alternative drive systems sales and financial services and purchasing outside North America. Daimler officially changed its name from DaimlerChrysler to Daimler AG two months after the Cerberus deal was completed.

The company reduced its 15% stake in EADS by selling 7% early in 2007 to German state-owned development bank KfW. Daimler however retained the stake's voting rights. In 2008 Daimler spent $1.5 billion to bring the smart fortwo minicar to the US. The cars are sold and serviced through Roger Penske's Penske Automotive Group (formerly United Auto Group) network of new-car franchises.

Despite negotiation with Cerberus to sell its remaining stake in Chrysler in 2008 Cerberus accused Daimler of concealing material facts about Chrysler –particularly the Chrysler Financial lending business –and the talks broke off. Daimler remained interested in selling its stake in Chrysler which received an emergency loan of $4 billion from the US government in early 2009 to continue operating. Chrysler –like Ford and General Motors –was struggling with too much capacity too few models that impress consumers and high costs for parts and labor. Ultimately in 2009 Daimler agreed to give up its remaining stake in Chrysler to Cerberus and to forgive loans to Chrysler. Cerberus and Chrysler in exchange agreed to waive any legal claims against Daimler. Chrysler and Daimler retained only a customer-supplier relationship for certain parts and technology. Daimler also agreed with the federal Pension Benefit Guaranty Corporation to make payments of $600 million over three years into Chrysler's pension plans.

To generate cash in 2009 Daimler sold an equity stake of about 9% to Aabar Investments for nearly Â2 billion ($2.7 billion). Aabar controlled by the International Petroleum Investment Company (IPIC) of Abu Dhabi became Daimler's largest shareholder as a result overtaking the government of Kuwait which owns almost 7% of the automaker.

EXECUTIVES

Chairman Management Board; Head Mercedes-Benz Cars, Dieter Zetsche, age 61, $2,252,007 total compensation

Chairman Supervisory Board, Manfred Bischoff, age 72

Deputy Chairman Supervisory Board, Erich Klemm, age 60

Member of the Management Board; Mercedes-Benz Cars Production and Procurement; Mercedes-Benz Vans, Wolfgang Bernhard, age 54

Member Management Board Finance and Controlling Daimler Financial Services, Bodo Uebber, age 54, $874,632 total compensation

Member Management Board Group Research and Mercedes-Benz Cars Development, Thomas Weber, age 60, $802,185 total compensation

Member Management Board; Head Daimler Trucks, Andreas Renschler, age 56, $846,342 total compensation

Chairman Daimler Financial Services, Klaus Entenmann, age 58

Member Management Board Daimler Financial Services Africa and Asia/Pacific Region, Richard A. Howard

Sales and Marketing Mercedes-Benz Cars, Joachim Schmidt, age 65

Finance Controlling and Strategic Planning Mercedes-Benz Cars, Stephan Engels, age 52

Member Management Board Daimler Financial Services AG Europe Africa and Asia/Pacific, Alwin Epple, age 51

Member Management Board Daimler Financial Services Human Resources Sales and Financial Services, Dieter Buhl, age 58

Head Development Mercedes-Benz Vans, Sascha Paasche, age 57

Head Daimler Buses; CEO EvoBus GmbH, Hartmut Schick, age 51

Member Management Board Human Resources and Director Labor Relations, Wilfried Porth, age 56, $547,482 total compensation

Head Daimler Trucks Asia; President and CEO Mitsubishi Fuso Truck & Bus Corporation, Albert Kirchmann

Head Daimler Trucks North America, Martin Daum, age 54

Head Finance Controlling Business and Product Planning Daimler Trucks & Buses, Frank Lindenberg, age 50

Managing Director Mercedes-Benz Vans, Volker Mornhinweg, age 54

Member Management Board Intergrity and Legal Affairs, Christine Hohmann-Dennhardt, age 64

Senior Manager Institutional Investors and Analysts, Lutz Deus

Manager Institutional Investors and Analysts, Alexander Vollmer

Senior Manager Private Investors and Internet Investor Relations, Rolf Bassermann

Member of the Board of Management of Daimler AG, Hubertus Troska

Truck Product Engineering Daimler Trucks, Geor Weiberg

Procurement Trucks and Buses and Truck Powertrain Operations and Manufacturing Engineering, Stefan E. Buchner

Head Production Mercedes-Benz Vans, Heinrich Weiss

Head Sales and Marketing Mercedes-Benz Vans, Andreas Burkhart

Head Finance and Controlling Mercedes-Benz Vans, Martin Schad

Head Human Resources Mercedes-Benz Vans, Dietmar Meder

Head Procurement Mercedes-Benz Vans, Klaus Gritsch

Head Product Engineering Daimler Buses, Richard Averbeck

Head Marketing Sales and After Sales Daimler Buses, Holger Suffel

Member Supervisory Board, Lloyd G. Trotter, age 68

Member Supervisory Board, Clemens A. H. Borsig, age 65

Member Supervisory Board, Paul Achleitner, age 57

Member Supervisory Board, Sari M. Baldauf, age 58

Member Supervisory Board, Lynton R. Wilson, age 74

Member Supervisory Board, Bernhard Walter, age 71

Deputy Chairman Supervisory Board, Erich Klemm, age 60

Member Supervisory Board, Jurgen Hambrecht, age 67

Member Supervisory Board, Stefan Schwaab, age 62

Member Supervisory Board, Petraea Heynike, age 67

Member Supervisory Board, Jorg Hofmann, age 58

Member Supervisory Board, Gerard J. Kleisterlee, age 68

Member Supervisory Board, Heinrich Flegel, age 65

Member Supervisory Board, Thomas Klebe, age 66

Member Supervisory Board, Jurgen Langer, age 59

Member Supervisory Board, Valter Sanches, age 50

Member Supervisory Board, Uwe Werner, age 62

Member Supervisory Board, Ansgar Osseforth, age 67

Member Supervisory Board, Jorg Spies, age 52

Member of the Supervisory Board, Clemens Clemens Boersig Boersig

Auditors: KPMGDeutscheTreuhand-GesellschaftAG

LOCATIONS

HQ: Daimler AG
Mercedesstrasse 137, Stuttgart D-70327
Phone: (49) 711 17 97875   **Fax:** (49) 711 17 94075
Web: www.daimler.com

Sales

	% of total
Western Europe	
Germany	20
Other	20
Americas	
US	21
Other	9
Asia	20
Other	10
Total	**100**

PRODUCTS/OPERATIONS

Sales by Vehicle

	% of total
Mercedes-Benz	53
Daimler	22
Daimler Financial	12
Mercedes-Benz	8
Daimler	5
Total	**100**

Sales by Segment

	% of total
Vehicles	86
Rental & Daimler Financial	10
	3
Automotive	1
Total	**100**

Selected Divisions and Brands

Mercedes-Benz Cars
  Maybach
  Mercedes-Benz
  smart
Daimler Trucks
  Freightliner
  Mitsubishi Fuso
  Mercedez-Benz
  Western Star Trucks
Daimler Financial Services
  Banking (Mercedes-Benz Bank)
  Fleet management
  Insurance
  Leasing and financing
Mercedes-Benz Vans
Daimler Buses
  Mercedes-Benz (city buses coaches interurban minibuses)
  Mercedes-Benz chassis
  Mitsubishi Fuso (large buses midi-sized buses minibuses)
  Orion (city buses)
  Setra (coaches interurban buses)
  Thomas Built Buses (hybrid school bus school and activity buses)

COMPETITORS

BMW	PACCAR
Fiat	PROTON Holdings
Ford Motor	Peugeot
Fuji Heavy Industries	Porsche
General Motors	Renault
Honda	Saab Automobile
Isuzu	Scania
Land Rover	Toyota
MAN	Volkswagen
Navistar International	Volvo
Nissan	ZAP

HISTORICAL FINANCIALS

Company Type: Public

Income Statement

FYE: December 31

	REVENUE ($ mil.)	NET INCOME ($ mil.)	NET PROFIT MARGIN	EMPLOYEES
12/13	162,430	9,419	5.8%	274,616
12/12	150,649	8,033	5.3%	275,087
12/11	137,804	7,329	5.3%	271,370
12/10	130,840	6,020	4.6%	260,100
12/09	113,695	(3,803)	—	256,407
Annual Growth	9.3%	—	—	1.7%

2013 Year-End Financials

Debt ratio: 63.5%	No. of shares (mil.): 1,069
Return on equity: 15.8%	Dividends
Cash ($ mil.): 15,217	Yield: 2.5%
Current ratio: 1.19	Payout: 26.8%
Long-term debt ($ mil.): 61,603	Market value ($ mil.): 92,985

	STOCK PRICE ($) FY Close	P/E High/Low		PER SHARE ($) Earnings	Dividends	Book Value
12/13	86.92	26	14	8.81	2.89	54.93
12/12	54.97	20	12	7.53	2.88	54.17
12/11	43.86	28	13	6.87	0.00	48.07
12/10	67.58	32	18	5.73	0.00	45.68
12/09	53.30	—	—	(3.79)	0.80	42.63
Annual Growth	13.0%	—	—	—	38.0%	6.5%

Danone

You say Danone I say Dannon; let's call the whole thing one of the largest dairy food and water producers in the world. The company is organized around its core activities: fresh dairy products water and infant and medical nutrition. The company #1 maker of fresh dairy products worldwide offers dozens of worldwide and regional yogurt brands including Dannon and Activia and the organic and Greek yogurt brands Stonyfield Farm and Oikos. The company's Evian Volvic Aqua and other water brands make it #2 worldwide in bottled water. Danone became a player in the baby-food sector with its purchase of Royal Numico and is now the world's #2 baby nutrition company. Its medical nutrition products are #1 in Europe.

HISTORY

In 1965 Antoine Riboud replaced his uncle as chairman of family-run Souchon-Neuvesel a Lyons France-based maker of glass bottles. Antoine quickly made a mark in this field —he merged the firm with Boussois a major French flat-glass manufacturer creating BSN in 1966.

Antoine enlarged BSN's glass business and filled the company's bottles by acquiring well-established beverage and food concerns. In 1970 BSN purchased Brasseries Kronenbourg (France's largest brewer) Societe Europeenne de Brasseries (another French brewer) and Evian (mineral water France). The 1972 acquisition of Glaverbel (Belgium) gave BSN 50% of Europe's flat-glass market. The next year BSN merged with France's Gervais Danone (yogurt cheese Panzani pasta; founded in 1919 and named after founder Isaac Carasso's son Daniel). This moved the company into pan-European brand-name foods.

Increasing energy costs depressed flat-glass earnings so BSN began divesting its flat-glass busi-

nesses. In the late 1970s it acquired interests in brewers in Belgium Spain and Italy.

BSN bought Dannon the leading US yogurt maker (co-founded by Daniel Carasso who had continued making Danone yogurt in France until WWII) in 1982. It established a strong presence in the Italian pasta market by buying stakes in Ponte (1985) and Agnesi (1986). BSN also purchased Generale Biscuit the world's #3 biscuit maker (1986) and RJR Nabisco's European cookie and snack-food business (1989).

In a series of acquisitions starting in 1986 BSN took over Italy and Spain's largest mineral water companies and several European pasta makers and other food companies. Adopting the name of its leading international brand BSN became Groupe Danone in 1994.

Antoine's son Franck succeeded him as chairman in 1996 and restructured the company to focus on three core businesses: dairy beverages (specifically water and beer) and biscuits. By 1997 Danone had begun shedding non-core grocery products. The company simultaneously stepped up acquisitions of dairy beer biscuit and water companies in developing markets.

The 1998 purchase of AquaPenn Spring Water for $112 million doubled its US water-bottling production capacity. Danone in 1999 completed a merger and subsequent sale of part of its BSN Emballage glass-packaging unit to UK buyout firm CVC Capital Partners for $1.2 billion; Danone retained 44% ownership. Thirsty for the #2 spot in US bottled water sales Danone gulped down McKesson Water (the #3 bottled water firm in the US after Nestle and Suntory) for $1.1 billion in 2000.

Also in 2000 Danone's joint venture Finalrealm (which includes several European equity firms) along with Burlington Biscuits Nabisco and HM Capital Partners (then called Hicks Muse Tate & Furst) acquired 87% of leading UK biscuit maker United Biscuits. Danone then bought Naya (bottled water Canada) and sold its brewing operations (#2 in Europe) to Scottish & Newcastle (later acquired by Heineken and Carlsberg) for more than $2.6 billion.

During 2001 Danone announced restructuring would shutter two LU biscuit plants and eliminate about 1800 jobs; the move met with strikes and legal battles. That same year having been bumped to the #2 spot in the US yogurt market (after General Mills' Yoplait brand) Danone acquired 40% of Stonyfield Farm the #4 yogurt brand in the US and ultimately came to own 84% of the company.

The company launched 2002 with a series of beverage acquisitions including Frucor (New Zealand) and Zywiec Zdroj (the top brand of water in Poland). Danone then struck a deal handing Coca-Cola the distribution and marketing of Evian in North America and formed a joint venture with Coke to distribute its lower-end water brands. Antoine Riboud died that same year at the age of 83.

Danone divested noncore companies during 2002 including the sale of its Italian meat and cheese business Galbani and its Kro Beer Brands (Kronenbourg 1664 brands) to Scottish & Newcastle. Then typical of its consolidation strategy later in 2002 Danone acquired the home and office water delivery companies Chateaud'eau (France) Patrimoine des Eaux du Quebec (Canada) and Canada's Sparkling Spring (now Aquaterra).

In 2004 Danone sold its 10% interest in the Australian dairy firm National Foods. Later that year it announced an alliance with Japanese dairy group Yakult Honsha to focus both companies' efforts with probiotics. Danone is a 20% shareholder of Yakult and has agreed not to increase its share holdings of Yakult for five years and not to pursue majority control for another five. Also in 2004

Danone acquired the Mexican bottled water company Arco Iris.

While its dairy and water businesses bubbled along nicely Danone found its cookies crumbling. Opting for a new recipe in 2004 it joined with Argentine food giant ARCOR Group to merge both companies' biscuits operations in South America. Later that same year Danone sold off its W&R Jacob Ltd. biscuits operations in Ireland to local company Fruitfield Foods. It also sold Italaquae its Italian bottled water business to LGR Holding.

Long after its departure from brewing in 2004 Danone was fined Â1.5 million for forming a beer distribution cartel along with Heineken in 1996. In 2005 Danone and Coca-Cola ended their 2002 water-distribution joint venture with Coke buying out Danone's 49% share for about $100 million.

In 2005 Danone got out of the brewing business altogether with the sale of its 33% stake in Spanish brewer Mahou. It sold its HP Foods Group including Amoy Lea & Perrins and HP sauce brands to Heinz and its biscuits businesses in the UK and Ireland. That year it sold its US home and office water-delivery company DS Waters of America to investment firm Kelso & Company. Danone has increased its ownership of Russian dairy and beverage company Wimm-Bill-Dann Foods to almost 20%.

Due to slow sales for its chilled products and competition from lower-priced brands in 2006 Danone introduced Senja (a soy-based yogurt) in France. It acquired Egyptian fresh dairy products company Olait (which it renamed Danone Dairy Egypt) and Algerian bottled water company Tessala. On the Asian front Danone acquired 23% of fruit-drink company China Huiyuan Juice Group and 51% of Wahaha. (It sold its interest in Huiyuan Juice in 2010.) In the Ukraine it bought fresh dairy company JSC Molochnyi Zavod. In the US it launched the Activia brand yogurt.

Because it wants to introduce more organic products in Europe in 2006 Danone announced the spending of $66 million on the expansion of its subsidiary Stonyfield Farm's New Hampshire production plant. (That year Stonyfield bought a 34% interest in Irish organic dairy Glenisk.)

In 2006 Danone sold its Amoy Asian sauce and chilled foods business to Ajinomoto exiting the sauce business altogether. It then sold virtually all of its grocery activities glass-container business its cheese and cured meat activities (Galbani) and its beer activities in Europe. It also sold New Zealand biscuits maker Griffins Food to investment firm Pacific Equity Partners.

Danone paid Â12 billion (about $16 billion) for Numico maker of infant food and medical nutrition (nutritional bars and shakes) in 2007. The Numico products (Cow & Gate Dumex Mellin milupa NUTRICIA) joined Danone's bledina baby-food brand to create a wide array of well-known nutritional products for babies and adults. The purchase made Danone the largest baby-food maker in Europe.

Prior to announcing the Numico purchase Danone announced the sale of its cookie business to Kraft Foods; that deal closed in late 2007. At the time some analysts saw Danone as ripe for a takeover; hence the Numico deal was construed as a way for Danone to remain independent. (The acquisition was viewed as helping ward off predators who might have been attracted to the cash that Danone accrued as a result of the Kraft deal.) As part of its strategy to divest itself of all biscuit/cookie activities in 2009 the company ended its Indian joint venture with the Wadia Group. Danone sold its 50% interest in the operation ABI Holdings to Wadia.

Strengthening its business in Asia in 2007 Danone acquired all of the Japanese joint venture with Ajinomoto and Calpis that it did not already own. Renamed Danone Japan the operation manufactures fresh products for the expanding Japanese dairy market.

Saying it wanted to "regain room for maneuver[ing]" in 2007 it sold off its 20% stake in and terminated its distribution agreement with Shanghai-based Bright Dairy. Danone cited no specifics surrounding the move but the company has had legal disputes with various joint-venture partners in China and India recently relating to how its brands are marketed and produced.

In late 2007 the company exited its joint venture with Chinese company Mengniu Dairy Group citing time frame and other condition difficulties. (Both companies agreed to the termination of the venture which was initiated in 2006.) Turning to South America that same year Danone acquired a 70% holding in Chile's fresh dairy company Vialat.

Among its divestments in 2008 in order to fulfill European Union requirements for its acquisition of Numico the company sold off its French baby milk and baby drinks businesses to Groupe Lactalis. That year it also sold its subsidiary Frucor a maker of non-alcoholic beverages in New Zealand and Australia as well as its international brands V and Mizone (with the exception of in China and Indonesia) to Suntory for some Â600 million ($780 million).

Danone took full control of its South African joint venture Danone Clover in 2009. It purchased Clover's 45% stake for R1085 ($145 million). (Clover is one of South Africa's largest dairy companies.) Other partnerships include a joint venture with Weight Watchers formed in 2008. The 51% Weight Watchers-49% Danone operation provides weight-management services to the People's Republic of China.

Following its acquisition of a controlling interest in a venture with Russia's Unimilk in 2010 Danone sold its 18.4% stake in Wimm-Bill-Dann Foods back to the Russian dairy and juice producer for $470 million.

EXECUTIVES

Vice Chairman and Co-COO, Jacques Vincent, age 67, $2,192,509 total compensation
Chairman and CEO, Franck Riboud, age 59, $3,494,439 total compensation
EVP Fresh Dairy Products, Thomas Kunz, age 57
Deputy General Manager and Co-COO; Director, Emmanuel Faber, age 51, $1,968,672 total compensation
Chairman President and CEO Stonyfield Farm, Gary Hirshberg
Deputy General Manager and Co-COO; Director, Bernard Hours, age 58, $4,036,272 total compensation
EVP Waters, Francisco Camacho, age 48
EVP Baby Nutrition, Felix Martin Garcia, age 54
General Manager Medical Nutrition, Flemming Morgan, age 58
Director Investor Relations, Antoine Guttinger
EVP Research and Development, Jean-Philippe Pare, age 56
Exec. VP Baby Nutrition; Member of the Executive Committee, Felix Garcia
Executive Vice President - Research & Development; Member of the Executive Committee, Jean-Philippe Pare
Executive VP HR and Chair of the Board of the Danone Ecosystem Fund; M. of Ex. Com., Muriel Penicaud
Chief Financial Officer; Member of the Executive Committee, Pierre-Andre Terisse
Vice Chairman and Co-COO, Jacques Vincent, age 67
Director, Michel David-Weill, age 82
Director, Bruno Bonnell, age 56
Director, Guylaine Saucier, age 68

Director, Benoit Potier, age 57
Director, Jean Gaston Pierre Marie Victor Laurent, age 69
Director, Baron Richard Goblet d'Alviella, age 66
Director, H?kan Mogren, age 70
Deputy General Manager and Co-COO; Director, Bernard Hours, age 58
Director, Christian Laubie, age 76
Director, Jacques-Alexandre Nahmias, age 66
Director, Naomasa Tsuritani, age 69
Independent Director, Richard dAlviella
Auditors: Mazars

LOCATIONS

HQ: Danone
17, Boulevard Haussmann, Paris 75009
Phone: (33) 1 44 35 20 20   **Fax:** (33) 1 44 35 26 95
Web: www.danone.com

Sales

	% of total
Europe	60
Asia	12
Rest of the	28
Total	**100**

Production Sites

	% of total
No. of plants	
Europe	
Western	36
Central	19
Asia/Pacific	50
Africa & Middle East	15
North America	6
Total	**126**

PRODUCTS/OPERATIONS

Sales

	% of total
Fresh	57
Water	17
Baby	20
Medical	6
Total	**100**

Selected Products and Brands

Fresh dairy
  Africa (Clover)
  Argentina (La Serenissima Ser)
  China (Bright Dairy)
  France (Danette Danone Senja)
  International (Actimel Danone)
  Japan (Danone Yakult)
  Latin America (Corpus La Serenisima Mastellone)
  US (Activia Dannon Stonyfield Farm YoCream)
Bottled water
  Argentina (Villa del Sur)
  Asia/Pacific (Aqua)
  Canada (Crystal Springs Evian Labrador Naya)
  France (Badoit Salvetat Arvie)
  International (Evian Volvic)
  Mexico (Bonafont)
  Spain (Font Vella)
  Turkey (Hayat)
  US (Dannon Evian)
Baby nutrition
  Bebelac
  bledina
  Cow & Gate
  Dumex
  Gallia
  Mellin
  milupa
  NUTRICIA
Medical nutrition
  FortiCare
  Fortimel
  Fortisip
  Neocate
  Nutricia
  Nutrini

COMPETITORS

Abbott Nutrition	HP Hood
Ajinomoto	Heinz
Arla Foods	Irish Dairy Board
Associated British Foods	Kellogg
Beech-Nut	Kerry Group
Blue Bell	Lactalis
China Mengniu Dairy	Leche Pascual
Coca-Cola	Mead Johnson
Dairy Crest	Metagenics
Dairy Farm International	Mondelez International
Dairygold	Nestle
Dean Foods	Novartis
Dr Pepper Snapple Group	Parmalat
Dreyer's	PepsiCo
Feihe	Pfizer
Fonterra	Shanghai Bright Dairy & Food
FrieslandCampina	Sodiaal
General Mills	Unilever NV
Gerber Products	Wells' Dairy
Glanbia plc	Wessanen
Granarolo	WhiteWave
	Wimm-Bill-Dann
	Yili Group

HISTORICAL FINANCIALS

Company Type: Public

Income Statement

FYE: December 31

	REVENUE ($ mil.)	NET INCOME ($ mil.)	NET PROFIT MARGIN	EMPLOYEES
12/13	29,321	1,957	6.7%	104,642
12/12	27,506	2,203	8.0%	102,401
12/11	24,986	2,161	8.7%	101,885
12/10	22,765	2,502	11.0%	100,995
12/09	21,582	1,960	9.1%	80,976
Annual Growth	8.0%	(0.0%)	—	6.6%

2013 Year-End Financials

Debt ratio: 53.0%
Return on equity: 12.4%
Cash ($ mil.): 1,334
Current ratio: 0.74
Long-term debt ($ mil.): 9,726

No. of shares (mil.): 586
Dividends
  Yield: 2.6%
  Payout: 20.5%
Market value ($ mil.): 8,515

	STOCK PRICE ($) FY Close	P/E High/Low		PER SHARE ($) Earnings	Dividends	Book Value
12/13	14.52	12	10	3.33	0.38	25.11
12/12	13.39	9	7	3.65	0.36	27.08
12/11	12.64	10	7	3.58	0.71	26.06
12/10	12.65	8	5	4.07	0.89	26.11
12/09	12.19	11	6	3.57	0.92	31.13
Annual Growth (5.2%)	4.5%	—	—	(1.7%)	(19.9%)	

Danske Bank AS (Denmark)

When you're the largest bank in Denmark there's nowhere to grow but out. Danske Bank serves 3.7 million consumers and businesses through a network of 159 branches in Denmark; 45 branches in Finland (where it operates Sampo Bank); 39 branches in Sweden (Ostgota Enskilda Bank); 32 in Norway (Fokus Bank); and more than 50 branches in Ireland and Northern Ireland where it owns National Irish Bank and Northern Bank respectively. The company also has operations in

Germany Poland Russia and the Baltic states. In addition to standard deposit and lending services Danske Bank offers asset management insurance leasing securities trading and research and real estate brokerage services.

HISTORY

Leathersmith-turned-stock trader Gottlieb Gedalia founded Den Danske Landmandsbank Hypothek- og Vexelbank i Kjøbenhavn (The Danish Farmer's Bank Mortgage and Exchange Bank of Copenhagen. It would change its name four times before finally settling on the less-verbose Danske Bank.

Even in its early years Danske Bank never restricted itself to purely agricultural concerns preferring to offer a wide range of banking services that appealed to farmers merchants and businessmen alike. Isak Glockstadt who managed the bank from 1872 until his death in 1910 guided the bank to prominence in Copenhagen's corporate landscape where it became a leading commercial bank. Glockstadt's son Emil succeeded his father as managing director in 1910. Despite his best efforts Danske Bank could not cope with the strains of WWI and the Depression; the Danish government had to rescue the firm from bankruptcy. But the bank survived German occupation during WWII mostly unscathed.

During the 1960s and 1970s Denmark's government encouraged Danish banks to expand internationally. Danske Bank pounced on the opportunity by forming consortium banks with such Nordic neighbors as Skandinaviska Enskilda Banken (aka S-E-Banken). Danske Bank stayed ahead of its competitors through acquisitions including the purchase of two large Danish banks in 1990 making it Denmark's largest bank.

By 1990 the bank also had made its presence felt worldwide but Asian economic crises in the early 1990s caused the bank's international subsidiaries to fall short of expectations. After restructuring its international business the bank focused more energy on its Nordic customers. It bought Sweden's Ostgota Enskilda in 1998 and Norway's Fokus Bank in 1999. In 2000 Danske bought fellow Danish Bank BG Bank. Danske also added a Finnish asset management company and a majority interest in Pol-Can Bank of Poland in the same year. In 2001 Danske and BG trimmed down redundant branches.

Danske Bank bought the banking operations of Finnish insurer Sampo for more than $5 billion in 2007. The acquisition brought in more than 150 branches in Finland Estonia Latvia and Lithuania. It followed Danske Bank's 2005 acquisitions of National Irish Bank and Northern Bank from National Australia Bank for some $1.8 billion.

EXECUTIVES

EVP and Executive Board Secretariat, Erik Sevaldsen
SEVP International Banking, Mads Jacobsen
Chairman of Executive Board, Peter Straarup, age 63
Managing Director Sampo Bank, Ilkka Hallavo, age 58
Chairman home; CEO R?lkredit Danmark, Sven Holm
Head Danske Markets, Henrik Normann, age 60
Group CEO, Thomas F. Borgen, age 50
Chairman Nordania, Jakob Brogaard, age 67
Vice Chairman, Niels B. Christiansen, age 48
COO and Executive Board Member, Georg Schubiger
Executive Board Member and Head Group Credits, Per Damborg Skovhus, age 54

Member of the Executive Board and head of Personal Banking, Tonny Thierry Andersen, age 50
Head of Investor Relations, Martin Gottlob
Chief Executive National Irish Bank, Andrew Healy
Member of the Executive Board and head of Business Banking, Lars Stensgaard M?rch, age 42
Chairman of the Executive Board, Eivind Kolding, age 55
Group Treasury, Steen Blaafalk
SEVP Danske Capital; Chairman Dansk Bank International Luxembourg, Niels-Ulrik Mousten
Director; Chairman Dansk kreds, Per Alling Toubro, age 61
Personal Customer Advisor and Director, Charlotte Hoffmann, age 46
Chief Executive Northern Bank, Gerry Mallon
Member of the Executive Board and Chief Financial Officer, Henrik Ramlau-Hansen, age 58
Managing Director Danske Private Equity, John Danielsen
Managing Director Nordania, Henrik Bech-Hansen
Managing Director Danske Bank International Luxembourg, Klaus M. Pedersen
Chairman, Ole Gjesso Andersen, age 58
EVP, Lars Andreasen
SEVP and Head Credit Portfolio Management, Bo Sonne Ravn
EVP and Head Credit Methods and Process, Sune Visti Petersen
EVP and Head Credits Denmark, Henrik Hoffmann
Chief Actuary, Danske Bank
Member of the Board of Directors and Employee Representative, Carsten Carsten Eilertsen Eilertsen
Member of the Board of Directors and Employee Representative, Helle Helle Broendum Broendum
Head of Business Banking; Member of the Executive Board, Lars Lars Moerch Moerch
Member of the Executive Board and Head of Group Risk Management, Robert Endersby, age 55
Member of the Board of Directors and Employee Representative, Susanne Susanne Arboe Arboe
Director, Michael E. (Mike) Fairey, age 65
Director, Sten Scheibye, age 62
Director, Peter H?jland, age 63
Director, Prof Majken Schultz, age 55
Director, Prof Claus Vastrup, age 72
Director, Birgit Aagaard-Svendsen, age 58
Director; Chairman Dansk kreds, Per Alling Toubro, age 61
Assistant VP and Director, Verner Usbeck, age 63
Bank Clerk and Director, Helle Br?ndum, age 61
Personal Customer Advisor and Director, Charlotte Hoffmann, age 46
Director; Vice Chairman Dansk Kreds, Solveig ?rteby, age 48
Director, Mats Jansson, age 62
Auditors: GrantThornton

LOCATIONS

HQ: Danske Bank AS (Denmark)
Holmens Kanal 2-12, Copenhagen K DK-1092
Phone: (45) 33 44 00 00   **Fax:** 212 370-9564
Web: www.danskebank.com

PRODUCTS/OPERATIONS

Sales

	% of total
Interest	51
Net	19
Net trading	17
Fee	8
Net income from insurance	5
Total	**100**

Sales by Segment

	% of total
Banking	72
Danske	14
Danica	7

Danske	4
Other	3
Total	**100**

COMPETITORS

ABN AMRO Group	ING
Citigroup	Jyske
Credit Agricole	Nordea Bank
Credit Suisse	SEB AB
Deutsche Bank	Svenska Handelsbanken
DnB NOR	UniCredit Bank AG

HISTORICAL FINANCIALS
Company Type: Public

Income Statement
FYE: December 31

	ASSETS ($ mil.)	NET INCOME ($ mil.)	INCOME AS % OF ASSETS	EMPLOYEES
12/13	595,590	1,313	0.2%	19,122
12/12	615,733	838	0.1%	20,308
12/11	595,800	297	0.1%	21,320
12/10	577,066	657	0.1%	21,522
12/09	599,780	334	0.1%	22,093
Annual Growth	(0.2%)	40.8%	—	(3.5%)

2013 Year-End Financials

Return on assets: 0.2%	Dividends
Return on equity: 5.0%	Yield: —
Long-term debt ($ mil.): —	Payout: —
No. of shares (mil.): 1,000	Market value ($ mil.): —
Sales ($ mil): 21,677	

DBS Group Holdings Ltd.

DBS Group is the holding company for DBS Bank the largest bank in Singapore and a significant presence throughout Southeast Asia. DBS Bank offers personal and private banking in addition to commercial banking services to small and midsized companies through some 80 branches in its home country. The company also has around 50 locations in Hong Kong plus operations in China India Indonesia Malaysia The Philippines Taiwan and Thailand. DBS Group owns a 20% stake in the Bank of the Philippine Islands (that country's second-largest bank) as well. Other activities include capital markets brokerage fund management private equity and equipment and trade finance.

DBS intends to continue its expansion in Asia. It has opened new branches in India and Indonesia and was the first Singapore bank to establish a local subsidiary in China. In 2011 the company bought the retail and commercial banking operations of Royal Bank of Scotland in China and plans to more than double its presence in that country by 2013.

In 2012 DBS announced plans to acquire PT Bank Danamon Indonesia. The deal would greatly expand DBS' presence in Indonesia and add about 1400 branches.

In addition to expanding geographically DBS is also placing more emphasis on small and midsized businesses large corporations and affluent consumers. Areas of focus include transaction services treasury and markets and wealth management.

The Singapore government (through Temasek) owns more than a quarter of DBS Group.

EXECUTIVES

Managing Director and Head Capital Markets DBS Bank, Eric T. L. Ang
Group Executive Institutional Banking Group DBS Bank, Jeanette Wong
CFO DBS Bank, Chng Sok Hui
Vice Chairman DBS Bank (China) Limited, Teresa Lin
Managing Director and Head Group Strategic Marketing and Communications DBS Bank, Karen Ngui
CEO DBS Bank (Hong Kong); Managing Director & Head Wealth Management DBS Bank, Amy Yip
Chief Risk Officer DBS Bank, Elbert Pattijn
Managing Director and Head Enterprise Banking Singapore and South & SEA Corporate and Investment Banking DBS Bank, Edwin Khoo
President Director DBS Indonesia, Hendra Gunawan, age 44
CEO and Director, Piyush Gupta, age 54
Chairman, Peter L. H. Seah, age 67
Secretary, Linda Hoon
Managing Director and Head Group Technology and Operations DBS Bank, David Gledhill
Group Executive Treasury and Markets Wholesale Banking DBS Bank, Andrew Ng
President Commissioner PT Bank DBS Indonesia, Bernard Tan
Executive Director and CEO DBS Bank China, Melvin T. W. Teo
Managing Director and Head Wealth Management DBS Bank, Tan Su Shan, age 46
Director, Bart Joseph Broadman, age 53
Director, Euleen Y. K. Goh, age 58
Director, Christopher W. C. Cheng, age 66
Director, Kwa Chong Seng, age 67
CEO and Director, Piyush Gupta, age 54
Auditors: PricewaterhouseCoopersLLP

LOCATIONS

HQ: DBS Group Holdings Ltd.
  12 Marina Boulevard, Marina Bay Financial Centre Tower 3, 018982
Phone: (65) 6878 8888   **Fax:** 213 627-0228
Web: www.dbs.com

PRODUCTS/OPERATIONS

Selected Subsidiaries
DBS Bank
  Bank of the Philippines Islands (20.3%)
  Cholamandalam DBS Finance Limited (37.4%)
  DBS Asia Capital Limited
  DBS Asset Management Ltd
  DBS Diamond Holdings Ltd
    DBS Bank (Hong Kong) LimitedHutchison DBS Card Ltd (50%)
  DBSN Services Pte. Ltd.
  DBS Vickers Securities (Singapore) Pte Ltd
  The Islamic Bank of Asia Limited (50%)
  PT Bank DBS Indonesia (99%)

COMPETITORS

AmBank Group	Hong Leong Finance
Amara	Maybank
Bangkok Bank	Maybank Kim Eng
Bank Central Asia	Metropolitan Bank and
Bank Mandiri	Trust
Bank Rakyat	OCBC Bank
Bank of China	Standard Chartered
HSBC	United Overseas Bank

HISTORICAL FINANCIALS
Company Type: Public

Income Statement
FYE: December 31

	ASSETS ($ mil.)	NET INCOME ($ mil.)	INCOME AS % OF ASSETS	EMPLOYEES
12/13	318,213	2,906	0.9%	0
12/12	288,638	3,114	1.1%	0
12/11	262,255	2,335	0.9%	0
12/10	221,253	1,272	0.6%	0
12/09	184,532	1,456	0.8%	0
Annual Growth	14.6%	18.9%	—	—

2013 Year-End Financials

Return on assets: 0.9%	Dividends
Return on equity: 11.1%	Yield: 3.2%
Long-term debt ($ mil.): —	Payout: 93.4%
No. of shares (mil.): —	Market value ($ mil.): —
Sales ($ mil) 9,177	

	STOCK PRICE ($) FY Close	P/E High/Low	Earnings	PER SHARE ($) Dividends	Book Value
12/13	54.27	25 19	1.17	1.73	11.09
12/12	49.06	21 15	1.28	1.74	10.66
12/11	35.42	25 15	0.97	1.08	9.47
12/10	44.94	39 29	0.53	1.62	9.01
12/09	44.00	25 8	0.62	5.46	7.96
Annual Growth	5.4%	— —	17.2%	(24.9%)	8.7%

Dekabank Deutsche Girozentrale

LOCATIONS

HQ: Dekabank Deutsche Girozentrale
  Mainzer Landstrasse 16, Frankfurt 60325
Phone: (49) 69 7147 0   **Fax:** (49) 69 7147 1376
Web: www.dekabank.de

HISTORICAL FINANCIALS
Company Type: Public

Income Statement
FYE: December 31

	ASSETS ($ mil.)	NET INCOME ($ mil.)	INCOME AS % OF ASSETS	EMPLOYEES
12/13	159,801	407	0.3%	4,035
12/12	171,009	375	0.2%	4,040
12/11	172,983	337	0.2%	3,957
12/10	174,395	866	0.5%	3,683
12/09	192,003	556	0.3%	3,667
Annual Growth	(4.5%)	(7.5%)	—	2.4%

2013 Year-End Financials

Return on assets: 0.2%	Dividends
Return on equity: 8.0%	Yield: —
Long-term debt ($ mil.): —	Payout: —
No. of shares (mil.): 191	Market value ($ mil.): —
Sales ($ mil) 6,477	

Denso Corp. (Japan)

DENSO knows: When building cars the whole is very little without its parts. Among the world's largest automotive parts manufacturers DENSO supplies OEM and aftermarket components and systems for most of the world's carmakers. Its six product groups make systems for powertrain control information and safety electric electronic small motors and thermal systems. Its lines range from automotive air conditioning systems to radiators and spark plugs. The Information and Safety Systems arm develops car navigation and collision avoidance systems. Non-auto industrial systems and consumer products are also made; subsidiary DENSO WAVE makes bar code readers industrial robots and programmable logic controllers.

DENSO's holistic perspective is demonstrated in all aspects of its automotive business from product development and design to manufacturing and sales. The company touts collaborative efforts with local car manufacturers and suppliers that support each customer's specific regional requirements. Although the company has a global presence with more than 185 subsidiaries and operations in 35 countries more than half of its sales depend on Japanese manufacturers. US operations are overseen by DENSO International America which accounted for 14% of sales in fiscal 2011.

DENSO was spun off from Toyota Motor Corporation in 1949; its former parent remains the largest shareholder owning a 25% stake. Toyota Industries Corporation owns almost 9% while an affiliate of German auto parts giant Robert Bosch owns another 6%. Toyota Motor Corporation is also its largest customer accounting for about 30% of sales in 2011.

Like other auto parts manufacturers DENSO is looking to expand in emerging markets in Brazil China and India. It built a new plant for car air conditioners in Changchun a city in northeast China that is also home to the China FAW Group. The plant will supply AC units to Toyota and Volkswagen models built by China FAW and is expected to open by 2013. It also expanded its car air conditioner and radiator plant in Brazil to increase production capacity and established a joint venture with Indian air conditioning company Subros. It introduced four low-cost heat exchangers for the Indian market. Elsewhere DENSO bought CTR an Italian company that sells air conditioners to aftermarket customers and opened its first sales office in Dubai for customers in the Middle East and North Africa.

With international operations representing about a quarter of overall sales the company is pinning its future growth foremost on product research and development to boost fuel efficiency and reduce carbon dioxide emissions. New products include engines for hybrid and electric vehicles. DENSO is working on cutting costs and improving performance in key products such as inverters DC-DC converters battery monitoring units and electric compressors. It is also developing new products such as battery packs that integrate motor generators batteries battery monitoring units and cooling fans. Its intelligent sensing monitoring and navigation technologies are advancing too with components that promise to help reduce car accidents.

Cost-control measures are playing an equally dominant role in DENSO's operations. The company is shifting its concentration from products for mature markets and premium vehicles to producing low-cost lines that cater to rising demand in developing markets particularly for compact cars which are common in Asia. Business systems at DENSO are evolving as well; more projects are addressed on an interdepartmental basis allowing resources to be pooled and leveraged. The company set a goal to halve the manufacturing costs of 23 key products sold in emerging markets by buying local parts and materials. For fiscal 2011 DENSO managed to cut costs by 40%.

HISTORY

Originally the in-house parts supplier for Toyota Nippondenso Co. (the predecessor to DENSO) was spun off by Toyota in 1949 because Toyota no longer wanted the burden of Nippondenso's troubled financial performance. Nippondenso remained dependent upon Toyota for sales and members of Toyota's controlling family the Toyodas remained involved in management. Nippondenso established a technological partnership with Germany's Robert Bosch in 1953.

As part of its plan to become a major supplier to North American carmakers in 1966 Nippondenso established a sales office in Chicago and branch offices in Los Angeles and Detroit. It then turned to Europe establishing a branch office in Stuttgart Germany in 1970. The following year the company established its first overseas subsidiary Nippondenso of Los Angeles (now DENSO Sales California). In 1972 the company established three more foreign subsidiaries in Australia Canada and Thailand. A European subsidiary (now DENSO Europe) was established in the Netherlands in 1973.

Nippondenso began consignment production for what is now known as Asmo Co. a maker of electric motors in 1978. In 1984 the company joined with Allen Bradley Co. (US) to develop factory automation equipment. That year the predecessor to DENSO Manufacturing Michigan one of the company's largest international subsidiaries was established. Nippondenso expanded into Spain in 1989 by opening a plant in Barcelona.

In 1990 the company formed NDM Manufacturing (now DENSO Manufacturing UK) a joint venture (25%-owned) with Magneti Marelli of Italy for the manufacture of automotive air conditioning and heating systems. The following year Nippondenso and AT&T formed a joint venture for the development of integrated circuit (IC) cards.

Nippondenso established several Chinese manufacturing joint ventures during the mid-1990s. In 1994 the company was recognized by the "Guinness Book of Records" as the maker of the world's smallest car the DENSO Micro Car.

The company changed its name to DENSO CORPORATION in 1996. In 1999 it acquired the rotating machines business of Magneti Marelli. The next year DENSO agreed to buy out Magneti Marelli's share in the companies' automotive air conditioning and heating joint venture (the deal was completed in 2001).

In 2001 DENSO ceased production of wireless phones in order to focus on making onboard car information systems. Also in 2001 the company merged its industrial equipment subsidiaries (bar code scanners and factory automation robots) and spun them off as majority-owned subsidiary DENSO Wave.

DENSO joined forces with Robert Bosch GmbH in 2003 to form a joint venture for the development of car navigation and multimedia systems.

In 2006 DENSO added four new Chinese production facilities that make navigation systems air conditioner compressors instrument panels and oil filters. It has also established technical centers in China and Thailand.

EXECUTIVES

Managing Officer, Akio (Alex) Shikamura
EVP, Koji Kobayashi
EVP, Hiromi Tokuda
President and CEO, Nobuaki Katoh
Senior Managing Director Overall Production Affairs and Production Promotion Center and Board Member, Sojiro Tsuchiya
EVP, Hikaru Sugi
Managing Officer; President DENSO International Asia, Yasushi Nei
Managing Officer, Mitsuhiko Masegi
EVP, Masahiko Miyaki
Managing Officer, Haruya Maruyama
Managing Officer, Akio Tajima
Managing Officer, Yasushi Yamanaka
Senior Executive Directors Member of the Board, Michio Adachi
Managing Officer, Hiroyuki Wakabayashi
Managing Officer, Akihiro Yukawa
Managing Officer, Yoshihiro Saka
Managing Officer, Sadahiro Usui
Managing Officer; President and CEO DENSO International America, Yoshiki (Steve) Sekiguchi
Managing Officer, Hiroyuki Murayama
Managing Officer, Hitoshi Tasaka
COO DENSO International America, Kazumasa Kimura
Director, Shoichiro Toyoda, age 88
Senior Managing Director Overall Electronic Business and Director, Mitsuharu Kato
Senior Managing Director Corporate Center Procurement Group and North America Region and Board Member, Koji Kobayashi
EVP and Director, Hiromi Tokuda
EVP and Director, Kenji Ohya
Senior Managing Director Sales Group and Board Member, Kazuo Hironaka
Senior Managing Director Overall Production Affairs and Production Promotion Center and Board Member, Sojiro Tsuchiya
President, Hikaru Sugi
Senior Managing Director Electronic Systems Business Group and Board Member, Shinji Shirasaki
Auditors: DeloitteToucheTohmatsu

LOCATIONS

HQ: Denso Corp. (Japan)
1-1 Showa-cho, Kariya, Aichi 448-8661
Phone: (81) 566 25 5850   **Fax:** (81) 566 25 4913
Web: www.denso.co.jp

Sales

	% of total
Japan	56
Rest of North	17
America	14
Europe	11
Other	2
Total	**100**

PRODUCTS/OPERATIONS

Sales

	% of total
Automotive	
Thermal	31
Powertrain control	25
Information & safety	17
Electronic	9
Electric	9
Small	7
Industrial systems & consumer	1
Total	**100**

Selected Products

Automotive
Thermal systems
  Air conditioning systems
  Air purifiers
  Cooling fans
  Cooling modules
  Front end modules
  Oil coolers
  Radiators
  Truck refrigeration units
Powertrain control systems
  Diesel engine management systems
  Gasoline engine management systems
  Transmission control components
Information and safety systems
  Multi-information display
  Radar system for detecting obstacles in front of vehicle
  Remote touch controller
Electronic systems
  Car security systems
  Instrument clusters
  Integrated climate control panels
  Rear and corner sonars
  Remote keyless entry controllers
  Smart keys
Electric systems
  ABS actuators
  Airbag sensors
  Alternators
  Electric power steering motors
  Starters
Small motors
  Power window motors
  Windshield washer systems
  Windshield wiper systems
Industrial and Consumer
  Bar code readers
  Industrial robots
  Programmable logic controllers

COMPETITORS

APM Automotive	NGK SPARK PLUG
Adept Technology	Prestolite Electric
Aisin Seiki	Remy International
Delphi Automotive	Robert Bosch
Systems	Standard Motor
Garmin	Products
JTEKT	TRW Automotive
Johnson Controls	Valeo
KUKA	Visteon
Key Safety Systems	Yazaki

HISTORICAL FINANCIALS

Company Type: Public

Income Statement

FYE: March 31

	REVENUE ($ mil.)	NET INCOME ($ mil.)	NET PROFIT MARGIN	EMPLOYEES
03/14	39,681	2,784	7.0%	139,842
03/13	38,057	1,930	5.1%	132,276
03/12	38,456	1,088	2.8%	126,036
03/11	37,816	1,727	4.6%	123,165
03/10	31,868	786	2.5%	120,812
Annual Growth	5.6%	37.2%	—	3.7%

2014 Year-End Financials

Debt ratio: 0.1%   No. of shares (mil.): 797
Return on equity: 11.5%   Dividends
Cash ($ mil.): 5,886   Yield: 1.7%
Current ratio: 2.27   Payout: —
Long-term debt ($ mil.): 2,989   Market value ($ mil.): 19,124

	STOCK PRICE ($) FY Close	P/E High/Low	Earnings	Dividends	Book Value
03/14	23.99	— —	3.49	0.42	34.31
03/13	21.24	— —	2.41	0.00	32.43
03/12	16.82	— —	1.35	0.00	32.03
03/11	16.45	— —	2.14	0.21	31.06
03/10	118.51	— —	0.98	0.14	27.00
Annual Growth	(32.9%)	— —	37.6%	31.1%	6.2%

Deutsche Bahn AG

One of Europe's largest transportation providers Deutsche Bahn gets freight and passengers from Punkt A to Punkt B. The company's DB Mobility Logistics group encompasses logistics and rail operations. About half of the company's sales come from freight transport and logistics led by Schenker AG. Its railway division carries 2.2-plus billion passengers yearly throughout Germany and into neighboring countries over a network of about 33.4 million km of track. Deutsche Bahn operates bus services in Germany and holds interests in passenger rail franchises dotting Europe. It also manage train stations and infrastructure services. State-owned Deutsche Bahn operates a handful of offices around the world.

HISTORY

In 1989 the Federal Cabinet of West Germany adopted a resolution to set up an independent government railway commission. That year the wall between East Germany and West Germany came down and the two nations were united into the Federal Republic of Germany in 1990.

In 1993 the cabinet endorsed a railway reform plan submitted by the federal minister of transport and later that year the plan won approval from the German Parliament and the Federal Council. Deutsche Bahn was then established in 1994 to unify Germany's western (Deutsche Bundesbahn) and eastern (Deutsche Reichsbahn) railway systems as a public company. The Federal Republic of Germany was sole shareholder.

The next year Deutsche Bahn created a subsidiary DBKom to offer telecom services in competition with Deutsche Telekom. In 1996 a consortium led by German conglomerate Mannesmann bought a 50% stake in DBKom. By 1997 Deutsche Bahn had been transformed from a government department into a registered company and split into four operating units: tracks freight local passenger services and intercity passenger services. That year Deutsche Bahn also bought Lufthansa's 33% stake in tour operator Deutsches Reiseboro (DER) giving it full ownership of the company as well as DER's 20% stake in tour group TUI.

Trouble came in 1998: Deutsche Bahn sent its 59 first-generation high-speed InterCityExpress (ICE) trains for inspections after one of the trains crashed and killed 98 passengers. Investigators believed a broken wheel caused the crash.

Deutsche Bahn and French state-owned railway SNCF announced plans in 1999 to develop a high-speed train capable of traveling up to 320 km (198 miles) per hour. Also that year Hartmut Mehdorn credited with turning around printing equipment manufacturer Heidelberger Druck and Daimler-Chrysler's aerospace unit became Deutsche Bahn's new CEO. Tasked with improving the railway's punctuality Mehdorn pledged to make Deutsche Bahn more efficient by cutting losses and raising productivity. That year the company sold its stake in TUI to conglomerate Preussag and its DER unit to supermarket giant Rewe.

In 2000 the company's DB Cargo unit and Dutch rail freight company N.S. Cargo formed a new group Railion (joined by Danish State Railways' freight unit DSB Gods in 2001). Also in 2000 Germany's transport minister postponed plans to float Deutsche Bahn after it posted losses for the first time since 1994.

Hoping to take advantage of Deutsche Bahn's financial troubles Connex then a subsidiary of French conglomerate Vivendi offered in 2001 to acquire Deutsche Bahn's long-distance express passenger trains. But Mehdorn refused the offer saying the company did not want to give up its long-distance traffic. Deutsche Bahn did agree in 2001 to form a railway telematics (communications system) joint venture with Mannesmann Arcor a company controlled by Vodafone. The agreement called for Deutsche Bahn to keep its 18% stake in Arcor but lose its minority veto rights which Deutsche Bahn had used earlier that year to block an Arcor IPO.

The company in 2002 bought the 65% stake in logistics provider Stinnes held by E.ON. The next year Deutsche Bahn took full ownership of Stinnes.

In 2004 Deutsche Bahn partnered with two UK companies Stagecoach Group and Virgin Group to bid on UK rail franchises. Deutsche Bahn withdrew from the venture before the bidding got very far however.

Deutsche Bahn sold its 83% stake in bus unit Deutsche Touring GmbH to Eurosur SA of Spain for an undisclosed amount in 2005.

Deutsche Bahn enhanced its logistics business in 2006 by acquiring US-based freight forwarder BAX Global. Buying BAX Global expanded Deutsche Bahn's logistics network in the Americas as well as the Asia/Pacific region positioning the company to benefit from Asian and transpacific trade.

Deutsche Bahn began expanding its passenger transportation business into the UK in 2007 by purchasing English Welsh & Scottish Railway (now DB Schenker Rail UK). In 2008 it acquired Laing Rail from construction firm John Laing. The company gained interests in three rail operations including full ownership of Chiltern Railways which operates the main artery between London and Birmingham. It rebranded it DB Schenker Rail UK.

Raising cash through privatization has been a long-held goal for Deutsche Bahn. In preparation for an IPO the company's passenger and freight transportation and logistics businesses were spun off as DB Mobility Logistics in 2008. (The split comprised almost all former operations; DB Mobility Logistics accounts for more than 90% of Deutsche Bahn's revenue.) Plans called for just under 25% of DB Mobility Logistics to be sold to the public while parent Deutsche Bahn —and thus the German government —would maintain a controlling stake. However the IPO was halted due to the international financial crisis. The business climate worsened in 2009; Deutsche Bahn's operating profit plummeted by more than 70% from 2008 levels pressured by declining revenues of about 13%.

In addition Deutsche Bahn in 2008 acquired a majority stake in Spanish logistics company Transportes Ferroviarios Especiales (Transfesa) which specializes in arranging the transportation of freight by rail and by road. The deal bolstered Deutsche Bahn's presence in Western Europe and the Iberian Peninsula. The company has also moved to extend its rail freight operations which are conducted primarily under the DB Schenker Rail brand.

In May 2009 Rodiger Grube took over as chairman of the company's management board and CEO replacing Hartmut Mehdorn. Grube has served on the boards of Daimler and Airbus. Grube's arrival fell on the heels of accusations that Deutsche Bahn management spied on its employees tarnishing the company's image among employees stakeholders and the general public.

With plans to capitalize on the liberalization of the European transportation industry Deutsche Bahn paid around Â2.8 billion (approximately $3.7 billion) in 2010 to buy Arriva one of the UK's largest bus and rail operators. European antitrust laws however are dashing Deutsche Bahn's hopes and forcing it to divest Arriva's German bus and rail business along with other German activities.

Late in the year Deutsche Bahn agreed to sell the bus and rail unit to Italy's national railway company Trenitalia (a division of Ferrovie dello Stato) to comply with European Union law.

LOCATIONS

HQ: Deutsche Bahn AG
Potsdamer Platz 2, Berlin D-10785
Phone: (49) 30 297 61676   **Fax:** (49) 30 297 61983
Web: www.deutschebahn.com

Sales

	% of total
Europe	
Other countries	23
North America	6
Total	**100**

PRODUCTS/OPERATIONS

Sales

	% of total
Transport & logistics	
Rail freight	14
Regional	20
Local	5
Track infrastructure	2
Passenger stations	1
Total	**100**

HISTORICAL FINANCIALS

Company Type: Public

Income Statement

FYE: December 31

	REVENUE ($ mil.)	NET INCOME ($ mil.)	NET PROFIT MARGIN	EMPLOYEES
12/13	57,486	904	1.6%	307,589
12/12	55,239	1,938	3.5%	299,005
12/11	52,302	1,706	3.3%	294,733
12/10	49,007	1,390	2.8%	285,977
12/09	45,048	1,182	2.6%	239,382
Annual Growth	**6.3%**	**(6.5%)**	**—**	**6.5%**

2013 Year-End Financials

Debt ratio: 50.2%	No. of shares (mil.): 430
Return on equity: 4.3%	Dividends
Cash ($ mil.): 3,938	Yield: —
Current ratio: 0.76	Payout: —
Long-term debt ($ mil.): 24,872	Market value ($ mil.): —

Deutsche Bank AG

LOCATIONS

HQ: Deutsche Bank AG
Taunusanlage 12, Frankfurt am Main D-60325
Phone: (49) 69 910 00   **Fax:** (49) 69 910 34 225
Web: www.deutsche-bank.com

HISTORICAL FINANCIALS
Company Type: Public

Income Statement
FYE: December 31

	ASSETS ($ mil.)	NET INCOME ($ mil.)	INCOME AS % OF ASSETS	EMPLOYEES
12/13	2,218,471	916	0.0%	98,254
12/12	2,652,349	312	0.0%	98,219
12/11	2,799,163	5,344	0.2%	100,996
12/10	2,550,442	3,091	0.1%	102,062
12/09	2,161,810	7,163	0.3%	77,053
Annual Growth	0.6%	(40.2%)	—	6.3%

2013 Year-End Financials

Return on assets: 0.0%
Return on equity: 1.2%
Long-term debt ($ mil.): —
No. of shares (mil.): 1,019
Sales ($ mil): 58,761

Dividends
Yield: 1.5%
Payout: 84.2%
Market value ($ mil.): 49,172

	STOCK PRICE ($) FY Close	P/E High/Low		PER SHARE ($) Earnings	Dividends	Book Value
12/13	48.24	148	102	0.89	0.97	73.91
12/12	44.29	364	175	0.33	0.92	76.60
12/11	37.86	28	12	5.56	0.00	76.34
12/10	52.05	48	27	3.91	0.93	71.13
12/09	70.91	23	5	10.93	0.70	85.13
Annual Growth	(9.2%)	—	—	(46.5%)	8.7%	(3.5%)

Deutsche Bank Luxembourg S.A.

LOCATIONS

HQ: Deutsche Bank Luxembourg S.A.
2, boulevard Konrad Adenauer, Luxembourg L-1115
Phone: (352) 4 21 22 1   **Fax:** (352) 4 21 22 449
Web: www.dbcom/luxembourg

HISTORICAL FINANCIALS
Company Type: Public

Income Statement
FYE: December 31

	ASSETS ($ mil.)	NET INCOME ($ mil.)	INCOME AS % OF ASSETS	EMPLOYEES
12/13	122,866	260	0.2%	299
12/12	112,468	330	0.3%	307
12/11	124,099	229	0.2%	330
12/10	116,752	453	0.4%	331
12/09	98,585	187	0.2%	352
Annual Growth	5.7%	8.6%	—	(4.0%)

2013 Year-End Financials

Return on assets: 0.2%
Return on equity: 3.8%
Long-term debt ($ mil.): —
No. of shares (mil.): 15
Sales ($ mil): 1,669

Dividends
Yield: —
Payout: —
Market value ($ mil.): —

Deutsche Bundesbank (Germany, Fed. Rep.)

Deutsche Bundesbank is not your local burg's bank. The central bank of Germany Deutsche Bundesbank is a major part of the European System of Central Banks (ESCB). Deutsche Bundesbank supervises the German banking system manages the country's monetary supply collects and publishes economic statistics advises the German government on monetary policy and settles cross-border euro transactions. With the ESCB it participates in monetary decisions for the European Union. Deutsche Bundesbank has nine regional offices and about 50 branches throughout Germany.

EXECUTIVES

Member Executive Board Controlling Accounting and Organisation Department, Hans Georg Fabritius
Member Executive Board Information Technology and Markets, Hans-Helmut Kotz
VP, Prof Franz-Christoph Zeitler
Member Executive Board Economics Department Statistics Department and the Economic Research Centre, Prof Hermann Remsperger
Member Executive Board, Hans Reckers
Chairman Executive Board and President, Jens Weidmann, age 45
VP, Sabine Lautenschlaeger-Peiter
Auditors:
PricewaterhouseCoopersAGWirtschaftsprufungsgesellschaft

LOCATIONS

HQ: Deutsche Bundesbank (Germany, Fed. Rep.)
Wilhelm-Epstein-Strasse 14, Frankfurt am Main D-60431
Phone: (49) 69 9566 0   **Fax:** (49) 69 9566 3077
Web: www.bundesbank.de

COMPETITORS

Bank of England	Reserve Bank of
Federal Reserve	Australia

HISTORICAL FINANCIALS
Company Type: Public

Income Statement
FYE: December 31

	ASSETS ($ mil.)	NET INCOME ($ mil.)	INCOME AS % OF ASSETS	EMPLOYEES
12/13	1,102,810	6,320	0.6%	10,822
12/12	1,351,404	875	0.1%	10,825
12/11	1,083,451	831	0.1%	9,743
12/10	898,394	2,952	0.3%	9,560
12/09	847,116	5,974	0.7%	9,822
Annual Growth	6.8%	1.4%	—	2.5%

2013 Year-End Financials

Return on assets: 0.5%
Return on equity: 3.8%
Long-term debt ($ mil.): —
No. of shares (mil.): —
Sales ($ mil): 11,184

Dividends
Yield: —
Payout: —
Market value ($ mil.): —

Deutsche Genossenschafts-Hypothekenbank (Germany, Fed. Rep.)

LOCATIONS

HQ: Deutsche Genossenschafts-Hypothekenbank (Germany, Fed. Rep.)
Rosenstrasse 2, P.O. Box 10 14 46, Hamburg D-20009
Phone: (49) 40 33 34 0   **Fax:** (49) 40 33 34 11 11
Web: www.dghyp.de

HISTORICAL FINANCIALS
Company Type: Public

Income Statement
FYE: December 31

	ASSETS ($ mil.)	NET INCOME ($ mil.)	INCOME AS % OF ASSETS	EMPLOYEES
12/13	68,445	0	—	438
12/12	71,659	0	—	372
12/11	75,041	0	—	433
12/10	84,910	0	—	454
12/09	98,067	0	—	459
Annual Growth	(8.6%)	—	—	(1.2%)

Deutsche Lufthansa AG (Germany, Fed. Rep.)

Germany's air ambassador Deutsche Lufthansa rivals the world's largest airlines. Operating through some 400 subsidiaries and affiliated companies the global aviation group runs Europe's largest passenger airline. It operates a fleet of more than 700 aircraft flying passengers to some 280 destinations in more than 100 countries worldwide not counting those served by code-sharing. Its logistics segment is also a market leader in international airfreight transportation through Lufthansa Cargo. The group's other main business segments deal in maintenance repair and overhaul (MRO) services through Lufthansa Technik; airline catering services through LSG Sky Chefs; and IT services through Lufthansa Systems.

Lufthansa's passenger airline business segment consists of Lufthansa (which includes Lufthansa Regional and Lufthansa Italia) Austrian Airlines SWISS and Germanwings as well as equity stakes in Brussels Airlines JetBlue and SunExpress. The company is considered to be a leading European premium carrier with hubs in Brussels Frankfurt Munich Vienna and Zurich.

The company is quickly expanding the number of destinations that its passenger airlines reach through code-sharing partnerships with other airlines. It is a member of the Star Alliance a group of 27 member airlines and counting that together cover more than 1100 destinations across the globe and of Atlantic++ the largest transatlantic joint venture which was founded by Lufthansa Air

Canada Continental Airlines and United Air Lines. With about 280 daily transatlantic flights Atlantic++ establishes a route network to North America from Europe the Middle East and Africa.

After being hit hard on all fronts by the global recession in fiscal 2010 Lufthansa began seeing clear signs of recovery as total revenues were the highest they had been in five years. Its passenger airline segment in particular saw passenger numbers rise sharply and it experienced strong performance in all regions. Capacity was up by about 20% in Europe (geographically its largest market) 17% in the Middle East and Africa regions and 8% in the Asia/Pacific region largely due to airline consolidation in those areas. Overall capacity was up 13% and total passenger airline sales were up roughly 15% for the fiscal period.

This positive uptick in passenger air travel is expected to help Lufthansa return to normal economic growth. A fleet modernization program may also prove fruitful over the long-term as Lufthansa ordered more than 50 new aircraft to be delivered starting in 2012. At the same time although it has a hedging strategy in place the company anticipates that it will continue to contend with ongoing increases in oil prices. It will also face a burdensome air traffic tax that the German and Austrian governments have introduced which may offset some of its growth.

Lufthansa Cargo one of the largest cargo airlines in the world is seeing a dramatic earnings turnaround due to the recovering global economy and a boom in German exports. With a fleet of about 18 freighters Lufthansa Cargo is adding freight capacity through its joint ventures AeroLogic (50/50 held with DHL Express) and Jade Cargo International (majority held by Shenzhen Airlines). The Asia/Pacific region is Lufthansa Cargo's most important sales market generating about half of its total traffic revenue. Outside of China Japanese airline JAL withdrew its freighter service as a result of the recession causing freighter service opportunities to Japan to expand substantially for other cargo carriers.

Lufthansa Technik serves its parent as one of the world's leading providers of MRO services for commercial aircraft. It provides maintenance aircraft overhaul technical support for engines components and landing gear and special maintenance services for VIP aircraft. Lufthansa Technik launched a multitude of products in 2010 including a new in-flight camera surveillance system and a kit that enables airlines to turn part of an aircraft cabin into an exclusive VIP compartment for VIP and business travel customers. Although it reported modest growth in 2010 Lufthansa Technik anticipates that the MRO market will continue to grow as a result of aircraft fleets being modernized and becoming larger around the world.

HISTORY

The Weimar government created Deutsche Luft Hansa (DLH) in 1926 by merging private German airlines Deutscher Aero Lloyd (founded 1919) and Junkers Luftverkehr (formed in 1921 by aircraft manufacturer Junkers Flugzeugwerke). DLH built what would become Europe's most comprehensive air route network by 1931. It served the USSR through Deruluft (formed 1921; dissolved 1941) an airline jointly owned by DLH and the Soviet government. In 1930 DLH and the Chinese government formed Eurasia Aviation Corporation to develop air transport in China.

DLH established the world's first trans-Atlantic airmail service from Berlin to Buenos Aires in 1934 and went on to develop air transport throughout South America. The outbreak of WWII ended operations in Europe and the Chinese government seized Eurasia Aviation in 1941. Klaus Bonhoef-

fer head of DLH's legal department led an unsuccessful coup against the Nazi leadership and was executed in 1945. Soon afterward all DLH operations ceased.

In 1954 the Allies allowed the recapitalization of Deutsche Lufthansa. The airline started with domestic routes returned to London and Paris (1955) and then re-entered South America (1956). In 1958 it made its first nonstop flight between Germany and New York and initiated service to Tokyo and Cairo. Meanwhile it started a charter airline with several partners in 1955. Lufthansa bought out its partners in 1959 and renamed the unit Condor two years later.

The carrier resumed service behind the Iron Curtain in 1966 with flights to Prague. The stable West German economy helped Lufthansa maintain profitability through most of the 1970s.

The reunification of Germany in 1990 ended Allied control over Berlin airspace allowing Lufthansa which had bought Pan Am's Berlin routes to fly there under its own colors for the first time since the end of WWII. The company began seeking international partners in 1991 but that year European air travel suffered its first-ever slowdown forcing Lufthansa into the red for the first time since 1973.

The company restructured in 1994 into a group of new business units: Lufthansa Technik Lufthansa Cargo and Lufthansa Systems. In 1995 the carrier began to face increased domestic competition from Deutsche BA a British Airways affiliate.

The airline formed a code-sharing agreement with Air Canada in 1996. In 1997 the Star Alliance was formed and Lufthansa signed a pact with Singapore Airlines. That year the German government sold its remaining 38% stake in Lufthansa. In 1998 Lufthansa and All Nippon Airways (later renamed ANA Holdings) formed a code-sharing alliance and Condor was combined with Karstadt's tour company NUR Touristic to form C&N Touristic. (After buying UK-based travel operator Thomas Cook in 2000 C&N Touristic changed its name to Thomas Cook in 2001.)

In a plan to gain more access to London's Heathrow Airport Lufthansa took a 20% stake in British Midland which was admitted into the Star Alliance in 2000 along with Mexicana Airlines. In 2001 the airline bought the 52% of Texas-based Sky Chefs it did not already own and formed a new unit LSG Sky Chefs International to hold its catering operations.

Lufthansa said goodbye to its 24% stake in delivery firm DHL when it sold its share to Deutsche Post in 2002. In 2004 the company sold its facilities management division Lufthansa Gebaudemanagement (LGM) to German construction company HOCHTIEF.

To facilitate international expansion and to respond to the acquisition of KLM by Air France in 2007 Lufthansa took full ownership of SWISS Switzerland's primary international airline. The carriers agreed to the deal in 2005 but issues related to international air traffic rights delayed the completion of the transaction. SWISS operates under its own brand and the carrier's Zurich headquarters became a third major hub for Lufthansa.

Lufthansa exited the leisure travel services business in 2006 by selling its 50% stake in Thomas Cook to German retailer Karstadt Quelle which owned the other half.

Lufthansa acquired a 45% stake in SN Airholding parent of Brussels Airlines in 2008. In 2009 Lufthansa completed its acquisition of UK-based airline bmi. It then sold it to International Airlines Group in 2012.

EXECUTIVES

Member Executive Board; Chief Officer Group Airlines and Corporate Human Resources; Chairman British Midland Airways, Stefan Lauer, age 59, $824,090 total compensation

Chairman Supervisory Board, Jurgen Weber, age 73

Honorary Chairman Supervisory Board, Wolfgang Roller

Chairman British Midland Airways, Nigel Turner

CEO, Christoph Franz, age 54, $453,215 total compensation

CEO Swiss International Air Lines, Harry Hohmeister, age 50

CEO British Midland Airways, Wolfgang Prock-Schauer, age 58

Deputy Chairman Supervisory Board, Frank Bsirske

Chairman LSG Lufthansa Service Holding, Walter N. Gehl, age 61

Operations and Sales LSG Lufthansa Service Holding, Thomas Nagel, age 64

Marketing and Sales Solutions LSG Lufthansa Service Holding, Jochen Muller, age 52

EVP Marketing and Sales Lufthansa Passenger Airlines, Thierry Antinori, age 52

Chief Executive Officer, Carsten Spohr, age 48

Member Executive Board; CFO and Head Aviation Services; Chairman LSG Lufthansa Service Lufthansa Cargo Lufthansa Technik, Stephan Gemkow, age 54, $824,090 total compensation

CEO Lufthansa Technik, August-Wilhelm Henningsen, age 64

Product and Service Lufthansa Technik, Thomas Stuger, age 58

CFO Lufthansa Technik, Peter Jansen, age 60

Marketing and Sales Lufthansa Systems, Gunter Kuchler

Group Representative and Head of Hub Management Munich, Thomas Kluhr, age 51

Director Public Affairs The Americas, Natalie A. Hartman

Chairman and CEO Cargo, Karl U. Garnadt, age 58

Director Corporate Communications The Americas, Martin Riecken

VP The Americas, Jens Bischof, age 49

Human Resources Lufthansa Technik, Uwe Mukrasch, age 53

EVP Operations Lufthansa Passenger Airlines, Jurgen Raps, age 63

General Director Argentina Chile Paraguay and Uruguay, Annette Taeuber

Regional Director Saint-Petersburg and North-Western Region of the Russian Federation, Bart Buyse, age 41

CEO Ukraine and Armenia, Harald Hahn

Manager Leisure and Specialist Sales UK and Ireland, Becky Schmidt

Chief Marketing and Strategy Officer Swiss International Air Lines, Christoph Beckmann

SVP and Head Corporate Communications, Klaus Walther

Head Media Relations, Andreas Bartels

Head Corporate Communications Europe, Aage Dunhaupt

Chairman Executive Board and CEO Lufthansa Systems, Stefan Hansen, age 50

Manager Media Communications North America, Christina Semmel

Member Supervisory Board, Klaus G. Schlede

Chairman Supervisory Board, Jurgen Weber, age 73

Member Supervisory Board, Werner Brandt, age 60

Member Supervisory Board, Michael Wollstadt

Member Supervisory Board, Jurgen Hambrecht, age 68

Member Supervisory Board, Jacques Aigrain, age 60

Deputy Chairman Supervisory Board, Frank Bsirske

Member Supervisory Board, Jurgen Erwert

Member Supervisory Board, Nicola Leibinger-Kammuller, age 55

LOCATIONS

HQ: Deutsche Lufthansa AG (Germany, Fed. Rep.)
Lufthansa Aviation Center, Airportring, Frankfurt
60546
Phone: (49) 69 696 28008   **Fax:** (49) 69 696 90990
Web: www.lufthansa.com

Sales

	% of total
Europe	65
Asia/Pacific	14
North	14
Middle	3
Africa	2
Central & South	2
Total	**100**

PRODUCTS/OPERATIONS

Sales

	% of total
Passenger airline	75
Maintenance repair &	10
Logistics	8
Catering	6
IT	1
Total	**100**

COMPETITORS

AAR Corp.	IAG
Aer Lingus	ITA Software
Air Berlin	Japan Airlines
Air France-KLM	Jeppesen Sanderson
Alitalia	Korean Air
Amadeus IT	Qantas
American Airlines	Ryanair
Group	SR Technics
Aviall	TIMCO Aviation
British Airways	Virgin Atlantic
Delta Air Lines	Airways
Deutsche Bahn	easyJet
Gate Gourmet	

HISTORICAL FINANCIALS

Company Type: Public

Income Statement
FYE: December 31

	REVENUE ($ mil.)	NET INCOME ($ mil.)	NET PROFIT MARGIN	EMPLOYEES
12/13	41,558	430	1.0%	118,214
12/12	39,868	1,304	3.3%	116,957
12/11	37,345	(16)	—	120,055
12/10	36,790	1,513	4.1%	117,019
12/09	32,424	(161)	—	117,521
Annual Growth	**6.4%**	**—**	**—**	**0.1%**

2013 Year-End Financials

Debt ratio: 30.0%	No. of shares (mil.): 461
Return on equity: 4.3%	Dividends
Cash ($ mil.): 2,133	Yield: —
Current ratio: 0.88	Payout: —
Long-term debt ($ mil.): 6,640	Market value ($ mil.): 9,861

STOCK PRICE ($) FY Close	P/E High/Low	PER SHARE ($) Earnings	Dividends	Book Value
12/13 21.39	60 45	0.94	0.00	18.08
12/12 19.29	15 8	2.85	0.22	23.61
12/11 11.78	— —	(0.04)	1.22	22.45
12/10 21.76	18 8	3.31	0.00	24.09
12/09 16.90	— —	(0.35)	0.65	19.17
Annual Growth 6.1%	— —	—	—	(1.4%)

Deutsche Post AG

LOCATIONS

HQ: Deutsche Post AG
Charles-de-Gaulle-Strasse 20, Bonn D-53113
Phone: (49) 228 182 0   **Fax:** (49) 228 14 88 72
Web: www.dpwn.de

Sales

	% of total
Europe	
Other countries	33
Asia/Pacific	14
Total	**100**

PRODUCTS/OPERATIONS

Sales

	% of total
Mail	27
Supply Chain	25

Selected Services
Air freight
Contract logistics
Dialog marketing services
European road freight
International express
National and international mail and parcel services
Ocean freight
Outsourcing and system solutions for the mail business

HISTORICAL FINANCIALS

Company Type: Public

Income Statement
FYE: December 31

	REVENUE ($ mil.)	NET INCOME ($ mil.)	NET PROFIT MARGIN	EMPLOYEES
12/13	75,837	2,878	3.8%	480,006
12/12	73,167	2,185	3.0%	472,321
12/11	68,331	1,504	2.2%	467,188
12/10	68,900	3,400	4.9%	464,471
12/09	66,555	927	1.4%	488,518
Annual Growth	**3.3%**	**32.7%**	**—**	**(0.4%)**

2013 Year-End Financials

Debt ratio: —	No. of shares (mil.): 1,209
Return on equity: 19.1%	Dividends
Cash ($ mil.): 4,704	Yield: 2.4%
Current ratio: 1.02	Payout: 69.2%
Long-term debt ($ mil.): —	Market value ($ mil.): 44,371

Deutsche Post RG

LOCATIONS

HQ: Deutsche Post RG
Charles-de-Gaulle-Str. 20, Bonn 53113
Phone: (49) 228 182 0   **Fax:** (49) 228 182 98 80
Web: www.dp-dhl.com

HISTORICAL FINANCIALS

Company Type: Public

Income Statement
FYE: December 31

	REVENUE ($ mil.)	NET INCOME ($ mil.)	NET PROFIT MARGIN	EMPLOYEES
12/13	75,837	2,878	3.8%	480,006
12/12	73,167	2,185	3.0%	473,626
12/11	68,331	1,504	2.2%	471,654
Annual Growth	**5.3%**	**38.3%**	**—**	**0.9%**

2013 Year-End Financials

Debt ratio: —	No. of shares (mil.): 1,209
Return on equity: 19.1%	Dividends
Cash ($ mil.): 4,704	Yield: —
Current ratio: 1.02	Payout: —
Long-term debt ($ mil.): —	Market value ($ mil.): —

STOCK PRICE ($) FY Close	P/E High/Low	PER SHARE ($) Earnings	Dividends	Book Value
12/13 0.00	— —	2.29	0.00	11.22
12/12 0.00	— —	1.74	0.00	13.03
Annual Growth	— —	14.6%	—	(7.2%)

STOCK PRICE ($) FY Close	P/E High/Low	PER SHARE ($) Earnings	Dividends	Book Value
12/13 36.70	41 23	2.29	0.89	11.22
12/12 22.12	28 19	1.74	0.87	13.03
12/11 15.42	40 22	1.24	1.63	11.78
12/10 17.09	19 11	2.81	0.76	11.64
12/09 19.40	82 28	0.76	0.76	9.74
Annual Growth 17.3%	— —	31.5%	4.0%	3.6%

Deutsche Postbank AG

Deutsche Postbank is claiming its post as one of Germany's leading retail banks. Spun off from postal service provider Deutsche Post in 2004 the bank offers deposits loans and mortgages asset management insurance and commercial finance including factoring and leasing services through more than 850 branches; it also offers some services through post office locations. The bank performs payment processing services as well with rivals including Deutsche Bank among its biggest customers. Outside Germany Deutsche Postbank offers banking services in Luxembourg and structured finance products to companies in North America. Deutsche Bank controls just over half of the bank.

In 2008 there was renewed interest in the acquisition of Deutsche Postbank as its former parent company Deutsche Post sought to sell the bank in order to focus on mail express deliveries and logistics. German banking giant Deutsche Bank acquired 25% of Deutsche Postbank for some $4 billion in 2009; it later upped its stake to more than 50% the next year.

Stefan Juette was named CEO of Deutsche Postbank in 2009. He followed Wolfgang Klein who resigned following a clash with members of the board. Juette was a Deutsche Postbank board member responsible for lending and credit management.

EXECUTIVES

Chairman Supervisory Board, Frank Appel, age 53
Member Management Board Human Resources Legal Affairs and Real Estate Management, Ralf Stemmer, $527,720 total compensation
Member Management Board Services, Mario Daberkow, age 45, $55,015 total compensation
Member Management Board Retail Sales, Hans-Peter Schmid, $571,653 total compensation
CFO and General Manager, Marc Hess
Member Management Board Product Marketing, Michael Meyer, age 50
Vice Chairman of the Supervisory Board, Frank Bsirske
Chairman of the Management Board, Frank Strauss
Member of the Management Board; Chief Risk Officer, Hanns-Peter Storr
Member of the Management Board; Responsible for Financial Markets; Treasurer, Horst Kuepker
Chairman of the Supervisory Board, Rainer Neske
Auditors: PricewaterhouseCoopersAG

LOCATIONS

HQ: Deutsche Postbank AG
Friedrich-Ebert-Allee 114-126, Bonn D-53113
Phone: (49) 228 920 0   **Fax:** (49) 228 920 35151
Web: www.postbank.com

Sales

	% of total
Europe	
Germany	94
Other	4
US &	2
Total	**100**

PRODUCTS/OPERATIONS

Sales by Segment

	% of total
Retail	77
Corporate	9
Transaction	8
Financial	6
Total	**100**

COMPETITORS

ABN AMRO Group	Erste Bank
Commerzbank	HSBC
DZ BANK	UniCredit Bank AG
Deutsche Bank	

Company Type: Public

Income Statement

FYE: December 31

	ASSETS ($ mil.)	NET INCOME ($ mil.)	INCOME AS % OF ASSETS	EMPLOYEES
12/13	222,351	454	0.2%	18,223
12/12	255,466	367	0.1%	18,599
12/11	248,319	143	0.1%	19,232
12/10	287,327	184	0.1%	20,361
12/09	326,446	109	0.0%	20,860
Annual Growth	**(9.2%)**	**42.7%**	**—**	**(3.3%)**

2013 Year-End Financials

Return on assets: 0.1%
Return on equity: 5.2%
Long-term debt ($ mil.): —
No. of shares (mil.): 218
Sales ($ mil): 9,477
Dividends
  Yield: —
  Payout: —
Market value ($ mil.): 9,124

	STOCK PRICE ($) FY Close	P/E High/Low	PER SHARE ($) Earnings	Dividends	Book Value
12/13	41.70	50 50	2.08	0.00	39.06
12/12	42.20	57 52	1.69	0.00	37.98
12/11	30.10	113 99	0.66	0.00	33.73
12/10	34.52	112 71	0.84	0.00	34.40
12/09	33.00	233 47	0.50	0.00	34.55
Annual Growth	**6.0%**	**— —**	**42.5%**	**—**	**3.1%**

Deutsche Telekom AG

Operating the autobahn on the global information superhighway Deutsche Telekom (DT) is a leading telecom company in Europe and one of the largest carriers in the world. The company's core business is its services and products for fixed-network and mobile communications services as well as for enterprise information and communication technology (ICT). Germany's #1 fixed-line telephone operator it provides domestic and international long-distance voice services. It is a leading ISP offering other data and multimedia services such as its Entertain-branded Internet television. DT's T-Systems International delivers ICT services for businesses. About three-quarters of sales come from Europe.

Geographic Reach
Deutsche Telekom (DT) operates through its subsidiary in more than 50 countries worldwide. The company gets more than half of its revenue from outside Germany. While DT has an impressive global reach customers in Germany still comprise its largest single market accounting for almost 45% of sales; its customers in Europe are essentially in Eastern European countries.

Operations
DT offers goods & services through subsidiaries in 15 European countries including Austria Croatia the Czech Republic Greece (through a 30% stake in OTE) Hungary (Magyar Telekom) the Netherlands and Poland (Polska Telefonia Cyfrowa).

Outside Germany and Eastern Europe the company's key international wireless subsidiaries are T-Mobile USA and T-Mobile (UK). The UK is the group's third-largest market with about 17 million subscribers.

Financial Performance
Net revenue in fiscal 2012 was down by 1% compared with the prior year. Intense competition price changes imposed by regulatory authorities and the strained economic situation in most countries in its Europe operating segment had a negative effect.

Mergers and Acquisitions
In 2012 DT and MetroPCS Communications signed a definitive agreement to combine T-Mobile USA and MetroPCS. The transaction which is expected to close in mid-2013 will create a leading carrier in the US wireless marketplace.

Ownership
The German government and German state-owned development bank KfW together own about 32% of Deutsche Telekom.

HISTORY

Deutsche Telekom was formed by the 1989 separation of West Germany's telecommunications services from the nation's postal system Deutsche Post. Dating back to the 15th century (when the Thurn und Taxis private postal system was created for German principalities) the service expanded to cover Austria France the Netherlands and most of Germany by the 1850s. After the 1866 Austro-Prussian War it became part of the North German Postal Confederation. When the German Empire was formed in 1871 the postal operation became the Deutsche Reichspost (later the Bundespost). Shortly thereafter the newly invented telephone was introduced in Germany.

Post-WWI inflation shook the Bundespost and the government allowed it to try new organizational structures. A 1924 law allowed the state-run service to operate as a quasi-commercial company. After WWII the American-British zone returned postal authority to Germans and in 1949 the USSR established the state of East Germany.

Only by the 1960s did West Germany's postal and phone services meet modern standards. Privatization of the Bundespost became a political cause when many complained about the monopoly's cost and inefficiency. Efforts to privatize the agency (named Deutsche Telekom in 1989) intensified with the 1990 German reunification. Faced with updating the antiquated phone system of the former East Germany however political opposition to taking Deutsche Telekom public faded.

The company began operating T-D1 its mobile phone network in 1992 and the next year it launched T-Online now Germany's largest online service provider. In 1996 Deutsche Telekom finally went public and raised more than $13 billion in Europe's largest IPO. It also launched Global One with France Telecom (renamed Orange) and Sprint (now Sprint Nextel); as part of the partnership Deutsche Telekom took a 10% stake in Sprint.

In 1998 European Union (EU) member countries opened their phone markets to competition and Deutsche Telekom's long-distance market share quickly eroded. Under EU pressure in 1999 the company said it would sell its cable network which it divided into nine regional units.

Deutsche Telekom's plan to merge with Telecom Italia in 1999 blew up in its face: Olivetti butted in and took over Telecom Italia while an angry France Telecom filed a lawsuit claiming that Deutsche Telekom's merger plan violated their agreements (the case was settled in 2000).

Undaunted Deutsche Telekom forged ahead with its international expansion plans buying French fixed-line carrier SIRIS and UK wireless provider One 2 One (now T-Mobile UK). In 2000 the company sold its stake in Global One to France Telecom as did Sprint. In the fallout from the unwinding of the Global One partnership Deutsche Telekom in 2001 sold its stake in Sprint PCS and its interest in France Telecom the next year.

T-Mobile International moved into the US mobile phone market in 2001 with the acquisitions of

VoiceStream Wireless and Powertel now known as T-Mobile USA. The German government's stake in Deutsche Telekom decreased largely to accommodate US regulators for the VoiceStream and Powertel acquisitions.

With competition flourishing in Germany Deutsche Telekom worked hard to lose its bureaucratic image and reposition itself as a slimmer customer-friendly organization. To cut costs and eliminate debt it reduced its workforce by 22000 jobs nearly 10% over two years.

As the company's share price slumped amid the general telecom industry downturn CEO Ron Sommer was forced to resign in 2002. That year the company announced plans to sell its phone directory unit (DeTeMedien) saying it hoped to raise Â1 billion but reversed that decision a year later after making progress at reducing its debt burden. Also in 2003 the company announced plans to acquire the 51% of Polish wireless operator Polska Telefonia Cyfrowa (PTC) that it did not own from Vivendi and Elektrim. But the company pulled out of the deal which was valued at $1.26 billion after Elektrim officials sought a higher price. Nearly a decade later Vivendi and Deutsche Telekom closed an agreement that gave Deutsche Telekom full control of PTC in exchange for a payment of about Â1 billion (around $1.3 billion).

Until 2003 Deutsche Telekom was Germany's #1 cable provider through the company's six regional cable TV operations which it sold for nearly $2 billion to a group of US investors that included Apax Partners the Goldman Sachs Group and Providence Equity Partners. The deal represented a substantial discount from a 2001 agreement to sell the cable networks to US-based Liberty Media for about $5 billion. But German regulatory authorities blocked that sale. Deutsche Telekom previously sold controlling stakes in three other regional networks.

The company boosted its T-Mobile USA holdings through the acquisition in 2005 of wireless networks serving California and Nevada from Cingular Wireless (which became AT&T Mobility). The deal valued at $2.5 billion included the end of an agreement in which the two companies used each other's networks.

Faced with plummeting profits caused largely by operational inefficiencies Deutsche Telekom in 2007 began to reduce costs by cutting the pay and extending the hours of about 50000 or one-third of its employees. Also that year Deutsche Telekom sold is Ya.com unit to France Telecom for about $432 million. Acquisitions for the year included the cell phone unit of France Telecom and ISP Orange Netherlands.

Deutsche Telekom had previously said that it might combine IT services subsidiary T-Systems with a future acquisition. In 2008 it formed a partnership with US-based IT services provider Cognizant in order to cut operational costs and to expand T-Systems' potential European customer base for systems integration services. The deal included the transfer of staff from T-Systems' unit in India to Cognizant's Indian operations.

In 2009 T-Systems acquired about 90 hosting customers from enterprise applications giant and partner SAP. The deal saw T-Systems assume SAP software systems infrastructure and services support for these medium and large-sized corporate clients at its data centers. That year it also bought Strato the Web-hosting services unit of freenet for Â275 million (about $385 million) to boost its presence in the data network services market. The deal helped Deutsche Telekom to gain ground on market leader United Internet.

Also that year the company absorbed its T-Mobile International subsidiary which formerly oversaw the operations of its US and UK wireless businesses in a move to simplify both its corporate structure and its sales and marketing efforts. The reorganization resulted in the US and UK businesses coming under the direct supervision of Deutsche Telekom. Furthermore wireless operations in Germany were combined with the domestic landline operations T-Home unit under the simplified T brand early the next year.

In 2010 it bought UK-based online payment services provider ClickandBuy used by more than 16000 Web retailers.

EXECUTIVES

Member Management Board Data Privacy Legal Affairs and Compliance, Manfred Balz, age 70, $660,000 total compensation
SEVP Corporate Communications, Philipp Schindera, age 43
Director, Prof Ulrich Middelmann, age 68
Director, Hubertus von Grunberg, age 71
Director, Bernhard Walter, age 70
Director, Wulf H. Bernotat, age 64
Director, Lawrence H. Guffey, age 45
Director, Ulrich Hocker
Director, Monika Brandl
Director, Lothar Holzwarth
Director, Waltraud Litzenberger
Director, Michael Loffler
Director, Michael Sommer
Deputy Chairman, Lothar Schroder
Director, Hermann-Josef Becker
Director, Sylvia Kuhnast
Director, Ulrich Schroder, age 61
Director, Jorg Asmussen
Director, Hans Martin Bury
Director, Hans-Jurgen Kallmeier
Director, Sibylle Spoo
Auditors:
Ernst&YoungWirtschaftsprufungsgesellschaft

LOCATIONS

HQ: Deutsche Telekom AG
Friedrich-Ebert-Allee 140, Bonn D-53113
Phone: (49) 228 181 4949   **Fax:** (49) 228 181 94004
Web: www.telekom.com

Sale

	% of total
Europe	
Other European countries	27
Other countries	1

PRODUCTS/OPERATIONS

Sales

	% of total
Telecommunications	88
Total	**100**

COMPETITORS

BT	Tele Columbus
Belgacom	Tele2
COLT Group	Telecom Italia
Cable & Wireless	Telefonica
Freenet	Telefonica O2 Germany
HP Enterprise Services	Telekom Austria
Invitel	Telenor
KPN	TeliaSonera
Orange	United Internet
QSC	Versatel
Swisscom	Vodafone
TDC	Vodafone D2

HISTORICAL FINANCIALS

Company Type: Public

Income Statement

FYE: December 31

	REVENUE ($ mil.)	NET INCOME ($ mil.)	NET PROFIT MARGIN	EMPLOYEES
12/13	82,785	1,280	1.5%	228,596
12/12	76,669	(6,926)	—	229,686
12/11	75,864	720	0.9%	235,132
12/10	83,542	2,268	2.7%	246,777
12/09	93,063	508	0.5%	259,920
Annual Growth	(2.9%)	26.0%	—	(3.2%)

2013 Year-End Financials

Debt ratio: 60.1%
Return on equity: 3.7%
Cash ($ mil.): 10,972
Current ratio: 0.98
Long-term debt ($ mil.): 60,174

No. of shares (mil.): —
Dividends
Yield: 5.1%
Payout: 114.9%
Market value ($ mil.): —

	STOCK PRICE ($) FY Close	P/E High/Low		PER SHARE ($) Earnings	Dividends	Book Value
12/13	17.26	157	88	0.29	0.90	7.39
12/12	11.36	—	—	(1.61)	0.85	7.91
12/11	11.45	246	146	0.17	1.79	10.56
12/10	12.80	75	44	0.52	1.03	11.78
12/09	14.70	424	254	0.12	1.04	12.01
Annual Growth (11.4%)	4.1%			—	25.9%	(3.6%)

Deutscher Sparkassen- und Giroverband e.V. (Germany, Fed. Rep.)

LOCATIONS

HQ: Deutscher Sparkassen-und Giroverband e.V. (Germany, Fed. Rep.)
Charlottenstrasse 47, Berlin 10117
Phone: (49) 30 20225 0   **Fax:** (49) 30 20225 250
Web: www.dsgv.de

HISTORICAL FINANCIALS

Company Type: Public

Income Statement

FYE: December 31

	REVENUE ($ mil.)	NET INCOME ($ mil.)	NET PROFIT MARGIN	EMPLOYEES
12/13	58,289	2,292	3.9%	349,500
12/12	56,879	2,763	4.9%	354,500
12/11	59,202	2,100	3.5%	360,300
12/10	60,843	8,071	13.3%	363,000
12/09	67,894	(3,340)	—	366,500
Annual Growth	(3.7%)	—	—	(1.2%)

2013 Year-End Financials

Debt ratio: —
Return on equity: 1.0%
Cash ($ mil.): 31,658
Current ratio: —
Long-term debt ($ mil.): —

No. of shares (mil.): —
Dividends
Yield: —
Payout: —
Market value ($ mil.): —

Dexia Bank Belgium S.A. (Belgium)

LOCATIONS

HQ: Dexia Bank Belgium S.A. (Belgium)
Boulevard Pacheco 44, Brussels B-1000
Phone: (32) 2 222 45 50   **Fax:** (32) 2 222 40 38
Web: www.dexia.be

HISTORICAL FINANCIALS

Company Type: Public

Income Statement

FYE: December 31

	ASSETS ($ mil.)	NET INCOME ($ mil.)	INCOME AS % OF ASSETS	EMPLOYEES
12/13	251,636	612	0.2%	7,058
12/12	280,674	547	0.2%	7,175
12/11	300,739	(1,767)	—	7,428
12/10	331,785	907	0.3%	7,859
12/09	365,574	607	0.2%	8,541
Annual Growth	(8.9%)	0.2%	—	(4.7%)

2013 Year-End Financials

Return on assets: 0.2%	Dividends
Return on equity: 7.4%	Yield: —
Long-term debt ($ mil.): —	Payout: —
No. of shares (mil.): 359	Market value ($ mil.): —
Sales ($ mil): 11,865	

Dexia S.A.

Dexia is sorting out some big issues stemming from the European debt crisis. The company has traditionally offered retail banking public and wholesale banking and asset management services through some 1300 branches in Belgium Luxembourg France and Turkey. Dexia is best known for European public and semi-public finance. It funds municipal buildings social housing and infrastructure projects and is active in Europe and North America. However the troubled company is undergoing a massive restructuring. It has been selling off units as it splits itself up.

Operations

The company's lending activities to European governments left Dexia in dire straits. The company was heavily exposed to European debt (Greece Italy Portugal) and when that debt went south Dexia's ability to secure funding also deteriorated. The company reported a record loss of Â11.6 billion ($15.4 billion) in 2011. The huge loss was attributed mainly to write-offs of its Greek bond portfolio and costs tied to its restructuring.

The company which has been ailing since 2008 announced plans to split itself up in October 2011. In conjunction with that announcement the governments of France Belgium and Luxembourg pitched in with a second rescue (the first came in 2008 during the global financial crisis). The countries pledged state guarantees of up to Â90 billion ($118 billion) over 10 years. In return Dexia is selling its Luxembourg operations to private investors and the Luxembourg government. Dexia's Belgian retail banking unit was nationalized and the company created a "bad bank" that holds its riskiest assets. In 2012 the company sold its

healthier Turkish retail bank subsidiary Denizbank to Russian bank Sberbank. Also that year Royal Bank of Canada bought out Dexia in its RBC Dexia Investor Services (now RBC Investor Services) venture. In 2013 Dexia SA agreed to sell its asset management unit to New York Life for Â380 million ($512 million).

Once all of its assets are sold Dexia will likely remain holding a portfolio of illiquid loans and eurozone soveriegn debt. The bank also will be able to make loans using guarantees from Belgium France and Luxembourg.

Strategy

Dexia announced in 2011 that it is suing Deutsche Bank for more than $1 billion in losses it suffered as a result of residential mortgage-backed securities it bought during the global credit crisis of 2008. Dexia also is seeking similar repayment from Bank of America and others for losses tied to mortgage-backed securities.

Ownership

Caisse des Depots et Consignations is Dexia's largest single shareholder with an 18% stake.

HISTORY

Dexia which is Greek for both "right" and "treaty" is the product of the Maastricht Treaty of 1991 which called for full economic union within the European Economic Community.

Dexia's earliest antecedent the still-powerful Caisse des Depots et Consignations (CDC) was formed in 1816 by the restored French monarchy to manage funds for institutions and government entities. It used the funds to finance public infrastructure projects.

In 1860 the Belgian government formed Credit Communal de Belgique (known to Flemings as Gemeentekrediet) to provide banking services particularly loans to local governments.

Both banks were state-owned until the 1990s. In 1987 CDC under fire for being too powerful separated its savings and asset management functions from municipal lending packaging the latter into Credit Local of which it sold 20% in 1991 (CDC now owns 18%). While France was beginning to deal with its chaotic banking system Belgium was content with its bewildering array of specialty banks until the move toward European economic union forced it to reduce its national debt which stood at 137% of GDP in 1993. Part of the solution was to offload debt through privatization so in 1996 Belgium floated Credit Communal.

As European banks began to consolidate both Credit Communal and Credit Local began looking for ways to grow. Credit Local made acquisitions in Germany and the UK and Credit Communal linked with Banque Internationale a Luxembourg (BIL formed in 1856 to help finance industrial development throughout Europe).

In 1996 the two companies agreed on a merger modeled on Fortis a cross-border pairing of insurers AG 1824 (Belgian) and AMEV (Dutch). Dexia spent 1997 assimilating its operations but not streamlining them: Both companies retained their full management and directorial rosters. Dexia made acquisitions in Spain and Italy and began adding new services including debt security underwriting; deposit accounting and cash management services; and asset management (using BIL as the nucleus for asset management offerings).

In 1999 Dexia expanded its asset management services into Asia and South America and increased its interest in BIL from about 60% to 99%. It also abandoned its unusual ownership structure merging Dexia France and Dexia Belgium into a single Belgian holding company.

In 2000 the company bought US bond insurer Financial Security Assurance Holdings. It also

boosted its private banking operations with the purchase of Dutch bank Labouchere from AEGON N.V..

In 2001 Dexia bought Artesia Banking a private Belgian financial services company. The move bolstered Dexia's already notable size in Belgium. During the merger Dexia closed about 30% of its branches bringing its total down from 1500 to about 1000.

Dexia acquired around 75% of Turkey's DenizBank in 2006. Denizbank offers retail and commercial banking as well as public finance in one of Europe's fastest-growing markets. DenizBank was positioned to be a major growth engine for Dexia. The bank wanted to take advantage of the growing Turkish market by establishing an additional 300 branches there and generating 27% of its income from Turkey.

Dexia was hurt by the global financial crisis which exposed the group to an increase in mortgage defaults (through its former Financial Securities Assurance Holdings arm (FSA)). The company lost billions when a loan to Germany's DEPFA BANK went sour. The governments of Belgium France and Luxembourg first stepped in to bail the bank out in 2008. They injected some Â6.5 billion ($9.3 billion) in capital and provided state guarantees for its liabilities. In 2010 Dexia freed itself from the state guarantees and tried to improve liquidity and refocus on financial activities that rely less on capital and reserves.

As part of the rescue Dexia's chairman Pierre Richard and CEO Axel Miller were both fired. Jean-Luc Dehaene and Pierre Mariani were named as their respective replacements.

As Dexia restructured it sold off assets that no longer fit with its mission and cut costs. First off it sold its troubled FSA to Assured Guaranty and cut some 900 jobs. It also halted noncore public-finance operations in Asia North America Europe and Australia.

Next the group sold its Dexia Epargne Pension life insurance subsidiary to a unit of BNP Paribas in early 2010. Also that year Dexia sold its Slovak unit (Slovensko) to Penta Investments in order to meet requirements by the European Commission and sold its majority stake in IT services unit Adinfo. In 2011 Bank of Jerusalem bid $150 million for Dexia's Israeli unit.

LOCATIONS

HQ: Dexia S.A.
Place Rogier 11, Brussels B-1210
Phone: (32) 2 213 50 81
Web: www.dexia.com

Sales

	% of total
Belgium	45
Turkey	18
Luxembourg	12
France	6
Other	19
Total	**100**

PRODUCTS/OPERATIONS

Sales

	% of total
Retail & commercial banking	54
Legacy portfolio management and other	8

HISTORICAL FINANCIALS

Company Type: Public

Income Statement

FYE: December 31

	ASSETS ($ mil.)	NET INCOME ($ mil.)	INCOME AS % OF ASSETS	EMPLOYEES
12/13	306,923	(1,491)	—	1,405
12/12	470,820	(3,777)	—	3,373
12/11	533,884	(15,054)	—	14,181
12/10	758,502	967	0.1%	27,148
12/09	832,116	1,454	0.2%	35,234
Annual Growth	(22.1%)	—	—	(55.3%)

2013 Year-End Financials

Return on assets: (-0.3%)
Return on equity: (-34.1%)
Long-term debt ($ mil.): —
No. of shares (mil.): 1,948
Sales ($ mil): 19,299

Dividends
Yield: —
Payout: —
Market value ($ mil.): 1

	STOCK PRICE ($) FY Close	P/E High/Low		PER SHARE ($) Earnings	Dividends	Book Value
12/13	0.00	—	—	(0.77)	0.00	2.46
12/12	0.00	—	—	(1.94)	0.00	1.93
12/11	0.50	—	—	(7.72)	0.00	(1.34)
Annual Growth	(97.6%)	—	—	—	—	—

DNB ASA

Financial services 'n real estate are what DnB NOR is for. One of the largest banks in Norway the company serves retail and corporate clients at more than 150 locations in 20 countries operating under the DnB NOR Bank Nordlandsbanken and Postbanken banners. In addition to traditional banking services such as deposits and loans it also provides life and pension insurance (through its Vital subsidiary) credit cards (through Cresco) and mutual funds and institutional asset management in Norway and Sweden (through DnB NOR Asset Management) as well as real estate brokerage and capital markets services. The Norwegian government owns about a third of DnB Nor.

DnB NOR also has banking and insurance operations in Sweden where it operates through Svensk Fastighetsformedling and SalusAnsvar. Elsewhere it provides banking services in Poland Denmark and the Baltic States through DnB NORD and in Russia through DnB NOR Monchebank. The group's strategy for international growth is focused on large corporate clients particularly in the energy shipping and seafood industries. DnB NOR also has limited operations in the US and Asia.

The company acquired the 49% it didn't already own in DnB NORD from German venture partner Norddeutsche Landesbank Girozentrale (NordLB) in late 2010. NordLB had considered buying out DnB NOR in the Baltic venture which had been hit hard by the global economic crisis but ultimately chose not to. DnB NOR instead took over the unit. DnB NORD is still reeling from the downturn but its 2010 losses were about a third of 2009's.

To strengthen the group's identity and streamline operations DnB NOR is uniting itself under one brand. Among its planned changes is the eventual phasing out of the Postbanken name.

Also DnB NOR discontinued its mortgage lending business in Sweden in 2011. It sold its retail customer mortgage loan portfolio to SEB that year.

The Norwegian government owns about a third of DnB NOR.

EXECUTIVES

Group EVP Retailing, ?smund Sk?r, age 55, $507,375 total compensation
Head Investor Relations and Long-Term Funding, Per Sagbakken
Director; Chairman DnB NOR Bank, Bent Pedersen, age 72
Group Audit, Harald J?gtnes
Director; Chairman DnB NOR Bank, Bent Pedersen, age 72
Director, Trine S?ther Romuld, age 46
Director, J?rn O. Kvilhaug, age 64
Director, Per Hoffmann, age 64
Auditors: PricewaterhouseCoopersAS

LOCATIONS

HQ: DNB ASA
  Dronning Eufemias gate 30, Oslo NO-0021
Phone: (47) 915 03000   **Fax:** 212 681-4121
Web: www.dnb.no

PRODUCTS/OPERATIONS

Sales by Segment

	% of total
Retail Banking	47
Large Corporates & International	24
DnB NOR Markets	14
DnB NORD	5
Insurance & Asset Management	10
Total	**100**

COMPETITORS

ABN AMRO Group
BNP Paribas
Credit Suisse
Danske Bank
Deutsche Bank
Grupo Santander
HSBC
Nordea Bank
SEB AB
Svenska Handelsbanken
UBS

HISTORICAL FINANCIALS

Company Type: Public

Income Statement

FYE: December 31

	ASSETS ($ mil.)	NET INCOME ($ mil.)	INCOME AS % OF ASSETS	EMPLOYEES
12/13	393,236	2,884	0.7%	12,016
12/12	404,904	2,441	0.6%	13,291
12/11	353,609	2,158	0.6%	13,620
12/10	319,028	2,538	0.8%	13,021
12/09	316,505	1,490	0.5%	13,317
Annual Growth	5.6%	18.0%	—	(2.5%)

2013 Year-End Financials

Return on assets: 0.7%
Return on equity: 12.9%
Long-term debt ($ mil.): —
No. of shares (mil.): 1,628
Sales ($ mil): 16,367

Dividends
Yield: 2.0%
Payout: 25.0%
Market value ($ mil.): 28,276

	STOCK PRICE ($) FY Close	P/E High/Low		PER SHARE ($) Earnings	Dividends	Book Value
12/13	17.36	0	0	1.77	3.61	14.37
12/12	12.65	0	0	1.49	3.42	14.05
12/11	9.85	0	0	1.33	0.33	12.03
12/10	13.95	0	0	1.48	0.69	11.70
12/09	10.65	0	0	1.11	0.30	10.51
Annual Growth	13.0%	—	—	12.5%	85.6%	8.1%

DZ Bank AG Deutsche Zentral-Genossenschaftsbank

DZ BANK is the central institution for some 1100 local cooperative banks which serve 30 million customers from a combined 12000 branch offices across Germany. It provides administrative services for its member banks which are also the company's owners. Additionally DZ BANK provides corporate banking services including commercial lending for small to midsized businesses investment banking structured financing and private banking. GZ-Bank and DG Bank —Germany's primary central institutions for cooperative lenders — merged in 2001 to create today's DZ BANK.

Subsidiary Union Investment is one of Germany's top fund managers and has some E177 million (approximately $2324 million) in assets under management. ReiseBank another unit provides foreign cash exchange and transfers from about 100 locations around Germany. Other divisions offer credit processing for financial companies and specialist consumer financing.

In the aftermath of the global financial crisis DZ BANK has renewed its focus on its core business —serving the cooperative bank network. It has thus started reducing its corporate banking and structured finance activities. As a result pre-tax profits rose in 2010 and the following fiscal year improved even more. As a result of heightened capital and liquidity requirements amid concerns surrounding European sovereign debt the company has also improved its capital base levels.

In 2009 DZ BANK and WGZ BANK the second-largest central institution for Germany's cooperative banking network postponed merger discussions for the fourth time in three years. The deal would have created the third-largest bank in Germany. However the two companies have combined certain operations such as their investment advisory and private banking units.

HISTORY

Created as a public entity in 1895 DG Bank began as the Preussische Central Genossenschafts-Kasse (Preussenkasse). The bank controlled liquidity and also managed cashless payment transfers and securities business for central cooperative banks. By 1905 regional co-op banks had taken equity stakes in the Preussenkasse. In the years that followed more central banks began to work with the company and its influence spread to all areas of the cooperative movement as well as outside Prussian borders.

Even the German government took an interest in the Preussenkasse and by 1932 had taken it under its control and renamed it the Deutsche Zentralgenossenschaftskasse. The partition of Germany following WWII affected the bank in two ways: assets of companies in the Soviet zone were seized and the bank's headquarters located in the Soviet-occupied portion of Berlin had to be moved. The bank operated from Marburg and Hamburg until a new headquarters was chosen in 1949. This new bank was based in Frankfurt and called Deutsche Genossenschaftskasse. The entity had a similar structure and public mandate to Preussenkasse and Deutsche Zentralgenossenschaftskasse.

In the following decades the bank started accepting deposits and received trust investment status

(1954) began issuing securities (1957) and expanded its investment portfolio. The Deutsche Genossenschaftsbank Act of 1975 formalized the company's development into a commercial bank and gave it the new name Deutsche Genossenschaftsbank to reflect this.

Throughout the late 1980s the bank underwent mergers that expanded its abilities as a cooperative central institution. During this time the bank arose as the central bank of Bavaria northern Germany and parts of Hesse. In 1987 the bank approached the trade union-owned Volksfursorge Group about merging with the R&V Versicherungsgruppe to form an insurance group in an effort to boost bank and insurance cross-marketing. The next year DG solicited a possible merger among West Germany's five cooperative banks. It also took a stake in its Spanish counterpart Cajas Rurales. Both offers fell through in 1989 as some of the other cooperatives dissented and management decided against acquiring a 75% stake in Volksfursorge.

In 1990 several French banks cried outrage over $3.5 billion in bonds that had sunk in value by about $350 million. Inflation and fears over the currency integration with East Germany were the culprits for the devaluation. A vice chairman of the company took responsibility for the dispute and resigned. By 1991 three key DG Bank executive had left or announced their resignations from the company. Bernd Thiemann took the helm to restore credibility to the company which had alienated itself from other cooperative banks and whose plans to be a universal bank made it overextend itself.

With the reunification of Germany in the early 1990s DG assumed the role of the central bank for former East German cooperatives as well as East Germany's Bank for Landwirtschaft und Nahrungsgoterwirtschaft der DDR (Agriculture and Food Industry Bank).

In 1995 the bank started to look outside Germany for expansion and by 1997 it was ready to open an office in Hong Kong. In addition DG purchased a majority stake in Magyar Takarekszovethezeti Bank of Hungary. That year DG Bank along with other state-owned banks in Germany came under fire from the European Commission for receiving illegal public aid.

DG became a publicly traded company in 1998. Early that year the bank began discussions with Rabobank and Credit Agricole (similarly organized banks in the Netherlands and France) about establishing a European cooperative bank.

In 2000 DG Bank began to securitize mortgages originated by its DG Hypothekenbank unit and scrapped its planned merger with the Netherlands-based Rabobank. DG Bank then found a merger partner in the fellow German cooperative bank GZ Bank. They formed DZ BANK in 2001.

EXECUTIVES

Managing Director, Albrecht Merz
CEO, Wolfgang Kirsch
Managing Director, Thomas Duhnkrack
President DZ Financial Markets, Gerhard Summerer
General Manager London, Holger Wessling
General Manager Singapore, Klaus G. Borig
Managing Director DZ BANK Ireland, Mark Jacob
Chairman of the Supervisory Board, Rolf Hildner
Managing Director and Head of Project and Structured Finance Europe Middle East and Africa, Jonathan Bullock
Global Product Head Project Finance, Bill Roos
Managing Director DZ BANK Ireland, Tilmann Gerhards
General Manager DZ PRIVATBANK Schweiz, Richard Manger

General Manager DZ PRIVATBANK Schweiz, Marion Pester
Divisional Head Communication and Marketing, Martin Roth
Deputy Chairman of the Supervisory Board, Helmut Gottschalk
Managing Director, Frank Westhoff, age 53
Founder of the commercial cooperative system, Hermann Schulze-Delitzsch
Deputy Chairman of the Supervisory Board, Wolfgang Apitzsch
Deputy Chairman of the Supervisory Board, Helmut Gottschalk
Auditors: Ernst&YoungGmbH

LOCATIONS

HQ: DZ Bank AG Deutsche Zentral-Genossenschaftsbank
Platz der Republik, Frankfurt am Main 60265
Phone: (49) 69 7447 01   **Fax:** (49) 69 7447 1685
Web: www.dzbank.com

PRODUCTS/OPERATIONS

Sales

	% of total
Insurance premiums	58
Net	16
Fees &	13
Gains on trading	2
Other	11
Total	**100**

Selected Subsidiaries

Bausparkasse Schwabisch Hall
Deutsche Genossenschafts-Hypothekenbank AG (DYG HYP)
DZ PRIVATBANK Group
R+V Versicherung AG
TeamBank
Union Investment Group
VR LEASING

COMPETITORS

BNP Paribas	HSBC
Barclays	KBC
BayernLB	UniCredit Bank AG
Citibank	WGZ BANK
Commerzbank	WestLB
Deutsche Bank	

HISTORICAL FINANCIALS

Company Type: Public

Income Statement

FYE: December 31

	REVENUE ($ mil.)	NET INCOME ($ mil.)	NET PROFIT MARGIN	EMPLOYEES
12/13	37,220	1,609	4.3%	28,962
12/12	34,534	910	2.6%	28,227
12/11	31,051	497	1.6%	27,825
12/10	33,971	1,160	3.4%	26,800
12/09	35,870	193	0.5%	25,636
Annual Growth	0.9%	69.9%	—	3.1%

2013 Year-End Financials

Debt ratio: —
Return on equity: 13.5%
Cash ($ mil.): 5,248
Current ratio: —
Long-term debt ($ mil.): —

No. of shares (mil.): 1,215
Dividends
  Yield: —
  Payout: —
  Market value ($ mil.): —

E F G Eurobank Ergasias SA

LOCATIONS

HQ: E F G Eurobank Ergasias SA
8 Othonos Street, Athens 105 57
Phone: (30) 210 333 7000   **Fax:** (30) 210 323 3866
Web: www.eurobank.gr

HISTORICAL FINANCIALS

Company Type: Public

Income Statement

FYE: December 31

	ASSETS ($ mil.)	NET INCOME ($ mil.)	INCOME AS % OF ASSETS	EMPLOYEES
12/13	106,815	(1,588)	—	20,053
12/12	89,170	(1,915)	—	17,662
12/11	99,365	(7,124)	—	19,156
12/10	116,690	91	0.1%	22,717
12/09	121,395	439	0.4%	23,578
Annual Growth	(3.1%)	—		(4.0%)

2013 Year-End Financials

Return on assets: (-1.5%)
Return on equity: (-69.7%)
Long-term debt ($ mil.): —
No. of shares (mil.): —
Sales ($ mil): 4,548

Dividends
  Yield: —
  Payout: —
  Market value ($ mil.): —

	STOCK PRICE ($) FY Close	P/E High/Low		PER SHARE ($) Earnings	Dividends	Book Value
12/13	0.11	—	—	(0.56)	0.00	1.07
12/12	0.30	—	—	(3.03)	0.00	(2.23)
12/11	0.18	—	—	(13.10)	0.00	1.40
12/10	2.60	—	—	(0.20)	0.00	14.37
12/09	5.59	50	10	0.59	0.00	16.17
Annual Growth	(62.4%) (49.3%)	—	—	—	—	—

E.ON SE

E.ON has transformed itself from a regional conglomerate into a multi-utility and a global player with 26 million customers. Its diversified business consists of power generation natural gas energy trading retail and distribution operations. Subsidiary E.ON Energie is one of Germany's top two power companies (running neck and neck with RWE) with some 17 million electricity gas and water customers; the unit also has about 69000 MW of electric generating capacity across Germany and Central Europe. E.ON operates E.ON Ruhrgas Germany's #1 natural gas supplier. Non-German utility subsidiaries include E.ON UK and E.ON Nordic.

Geographic Reach

E.ON operates in Bulgaria the Czech Republic France Germany Hungary Italy the Netherlands Romania Russia Slovakia Spain Sweden and the UK.

Financial Analysis

In 2011 the company reported revenue growth of 22% thanks to a 2% increase in Generation revenue as a result of higher sales volume higher average transfer prices and positive currency-translation effects in Sweden's Nuclear sales. Other factors included high Fossil segment sales a 26% increase in the Renewables segment and an 8% increase in the Gas segment as a result of positive energy price developments. There was also a 50% jump in the Trading segment as a result of an increase in trading activity in power and gas and a 29% increase in Russian sales as a result of a growth in generating capacity coupled with higher power prices.

E.ON has a net loss of 130% in 2011 attributable to the 58% decrease in Net book gains compared to 2010 and E3 billion ($4.2 billion) in impairment charges on assets and goodwill mainly at its generation businesses. It also had impairment charges of E1.9 billion ($2.7 billion) in Spain and Italy due to poor regional economic forecasts for the long-term development of power prices regulatory intervention and reduced use of gas-fired and coal-fired power stations.

Strategy

The company is focusing on realigning its businesses to create greater efficiencies putting more emphasis on developing its renewable power operations and reducing its debt.

In response to tightening European regulations regarding carbon emissions E.ON has announced plans to obtain 24% of its generating capacity from renewable energy sources by 2030.

In 2012 the company started building the Wysoka (Wysoka 1 und 2) onshore wind farm in Poland growing E.ON's position as one of the leading players on the Polish wind energy market.

Creating a foothold in Brazil in 2012 the company formed a power generation joint venture with Brazilian company MPX to develop 20000 MW of capacity in Brazil and Chile.

E.ON is seeking to generate about E15 billion ($21 billion) through divestments by the end of 2013. Paying down debt in 2012 E.ON sold Open Grid Europe its gas transmission company in Germany to a consortium led by Macquarie European Infrastructure Fund 4 for about E3.2 billion ($4.5 billion).

In 2011 it sold its Italian natural gas distribution network unit (E.ON Rete) to a group of Italian and French investors for EUR290 million (US$392.3 million). It also sold its UK-based Central Networks unit to PPL for $5.7 billion

HISTORY

VEBA (originally Vereinigte Elektrizitats-und Bergwerks AG) was formed in 1929 in Berlin to consolidate Germany's state-owned electricity and mining interests. These operations included PreussenElektra an electric utility formed by the German government in 1927; Hibernia a coal mining firm founded in 1873; and Preussag a mining and smelting company founded in 1923.

In the 1930s VEBA produced synthetic gasoline (essential to the German war machine) from coal at its Hibernia plant. In 1938 the company and chemical cartel I. G. Farben set up Chemische Werke Hols to make synthetic rubber. After WWII VEBA's assets in western Germany were transferred to the government and several executives were arrested. Preussag was spun off in 1959.

In 1965 the government spun off VEBA to the public. That year the company entered trading and transportation by buying Stinnes one of West Germany's largest industrial companies. In 1969 VEBA transferred its coal mining interests to Ruhrkohle and a few years later moved into oil exploration and development. The company shortened its name to VEBA in 1970.

The West German government sold its remaining stake in VEBA in 1987. In a changed regulatory environment large investors were able to ac-

cumulate big portions of stock and their dissatisfaction with the company's lackluster results made it a takeover target. In response new chairman Ulrich Hartmann began cutting noncore businesses and reducing staff.

In 1990 VEBA began accumulating mobile communications networking and cable TV companies. It allied with the UK's Cable and Wireless (C&W) in 1995 to develop a European mobile phone business but in 1997 C&W sold its interest to VEBA (as part of the deal VEBA gained a 10% stake in C&W which it sold in 1999). In anticipation of the 1998 deregulation of the German telecom market VEBA and RWE merged their German telecom businesses in 1997.

VEBA acquired a 36% stake in Degussa a specialty chemicals company in 1997; two years later Degussa merged with Hols to form a separately traded chemical company called Degussa-Hols in which VEBA took a 62% stake. VEBA sold a 30% stake in Stinnes to the public in 1999. The company's telecom venture sold its fixed-line telephone business its cable TV unit and its stake in mobile phone operator E-Plus.

These moves however were just the prelude to a bigger deal: a $14 billion merger agreement between VEBA and fellow German conglomerate VIAG. The partners announced plans to dump noncore businesses and beef up their energy and chemicals holdings. VEBA and VIAG completed their merger in 2000 and the combined company adopted the name E.ON. The companies' utilities businesses were combined into E.ON Energie and their chemicals units were brought together as Degussa.

To gain regulatory approval to form E.ON VEBA and VIAG agreed to sell their stakes in German electric utilities Bewag and VEAG and coal producer LAUBAG. E.ON sold its VEAG and LAUBAG interests along with semiconductor and electronics distribution units in 2000 and sold Bewag in 2001.

In 2001 E.ON agreed to acquire UK electricity generator Powergen (now E.ON UK) and it sold off nonutility operations including Degussa and Veba Oel. E.ON swapped a 51% stake in Veba Oel for BP's 26% stake in German natural gas supplier Ruhrgas (now E.ON Ruhrgas). E.ON also sold Klockner to UK steel trader Balli and sold its stake in silicon wafer maker MEMC to buyout firm Texas Pacific Group.

In 2002 E.ON sold its VAW Aluminum unit to Norwegian conglomerate Norsk Hydro in a $2.8 billion deal. Regulators moved to prevent E.ON from acquiring BP's stake in Ruhrgas in 2002 but BP agreed to pay for the Veba Oel stake in cash if necessary and the swap was completed later that year. E.ON also acquired Vodafone and ThyssenKrupp's stakes in Ruhrgas in 2002 and it sold its remaining stake in Veba Oel to BP.

Also in 2002 E.ON completed its purchase of Powergen (which included its US subsidiary LG&E Energy) for about $8 billion and it sold its 65% stake in logistics company Stinnes to German railroad operator Deutsche Bahn. In late 2002 E.ON acquired the UK energy supply and generation businesses of TXU Europe in a $2.5 billion deal.

The following year E.ON swapped its majority stake in chemical maker Degussa with coal group RAG for RAG's 18% interest in Ruhrgas. It completed its acquisition of Ruhrgas by purchasing the combined 40% stake held by Royal Dutch Shell Exxon Mobil and TUI (formerly Preussag). It also sold subsidiary Viterra's energy services unit (gas and water meters) to CVC Capital Partners.

In 2005 the company acquired the Enfield power station in the UK for $250.2 million.

In 2007 E.ON acquired Ireland-based wind farm company Airtricity for $1.4 billion.

Pursuing growth in new geographic markets in 2007 E.ON acquired Russia-based power utility OGK-4 for almost $6 billion. Outmaneuvered by its rivals in 2008 it dropped its $56 billion bid to buy Endesa S.A. Spain's largest electric utility settling for the purchase of a number of Endesa's generation assets in Spain and Italy.

In 2009 to counter EDF's acquisition of British Energy E.ON and RWE formed a joint venture to develop 6000 MW of nuclear power capacity in the UK.

That year prompted by the regulatory requirements of the European Commission E.ON and GDF SUEZ agreed to swap generating assets to allow for more competition in their major markets. It sold 860 MW of Germany-based conventional power plants 132 MW of hydroelectric plants and access to 770 MW of nuclear power. In return GDF SUEZ sold to E.ON a similar amount of power generation capacity in France and the Benelux countries. In 2010 also to meet EU anti-monopoly regulations it sold grid operator Transpower to Dutch giant TenneT for $1.1 billion and it swapped 5000 MW of generation capacity with EDF and EnBW.

In 2010 the company sold E.ON U.S. which operates Kentucky's two major utilities for $7.6 billion. Its US assets were no longer considered a core part of its growth strategy and the sale helped to pay down debt. To raise cash that year it also sold its 3.5% stake in Gazprom to Russian investment bank Vnesheconombank for $4.4 billion.

EXECUTIVES

Chairman Supervisory Board, Werner Wenning, age 68

EVP Corporate Responsibility and Health Safety & Environment, Peter Blau

Press Spokesperson, Josef Nelles

SVP Investor Relations, Sascha Bibert

Chief Commercial Officer E.ON Energy Tradign, Gareth Griffiths

Chairman Chief Executive Officer CEO, Johannes Teyssen, age 55

CEO E.ON UK, Tony Cocker

Member Board of Management Regional Units Distribution & Retail, Bernhard Reutersberg, age 60

Member Board of Management Group Human Resources IT Group Procurement Legal and Compliance Corporate Incident and Crisis Management Real Estate/Mining Facility Management and E.ON Academy, Regine Stachelhaus, age 59

Member Board of Management Finance Accounting Controlling and Corporate Planning Mergers & Acquisitions Tax, Marcus Schenck, age 49

Sales E.ON Energie, Stefan Vogg, age 52

Member Board of Management Research and Development New Build and Technology Corporate Responsibility Health/Safety and Environment, Klaus-Dieter Maubach, age 52

CEO E.ON Sverige, Jonas Abrahamsson

Member of the Board of Management Commercial Operations & Analysis Optimization & Trading Exploration & Production, J?rgen Kildahl, age 51

CEO E.ON Espa?a; President E.ON Italia, Miguel Anto?anzas

Chairman E.ON Energie, Ingo Luge, age 56

VP Corporate Responsibility, Anette Bickmeyer

Press Spokesperson, Carsten Thomsen-Bendixen

Member of the Board of Management Corporate Incident & Crisis Management Health/Safety & Environment Engineering & Major Projects Technology & Innovation, Michael (Mike) Winkel, age 43

CEO E.ON Climate & Renewables, Steve Trenholm

Director, Ulrich Lehner, age 68

LOCATIONS

HQ: E.ON SE
E.ON-Platz 1, Duesseldorf D-40479
Phone: (49) 211 45 79 0   **Fax:** (49) 211 45 79 5 01
Web: www.eon.com

Sales

	% of total
Europe	
Germany	42
UK	28
Sweden	4
Other	25
Other	1
Total	**100**

PRODUCTS/OPERATIONS

Sales

	% of total
Electricity	53
Gas	41
Other	6
Total	**100**

Selected Business Areas

Power Generation
Energy Mix
Coal
Natural Gas and Oil
Nuclear
Water
Wind
Solar
Bio Energy
Gas Supply & Production
Exploration & Production
LNG
Sources of Supply
Security of Supply
Gas Storage & Transportation
Underground Storage Facilities
Nord Stream Pipeline
Trading
Power and Emissions Trading
Gas and Oil Trading
Coal Biofuels and Freight Trading
Market Activity
Market Development
Distribution
Power Distribution
Gas Distribution
Technology of the Future

COMPETITORS

BASF SE	EnBW
Bayer AG	Endesa S.A.
Business Group Benelux	Enel
Deutsche Telekom	Eni
Dow Chemical	GDF SUEZ
DuPont	Orange
EVN	RWE
Electricite de France	Vattenfall

HISTORICAL FINANCIALS

Company Type: Public

Income Statement

FYE: December 31

	REVENUE ($ mil.)	NET INCOME ($ mil.)	NET PROFIT MARGIN	EMPLOYEES
12/13	169,067	2,948	1.7%	62,239
12/12	174,687	2,922	1.7%	72,083
12/11	146,751	(2,870)	—	78,889
12/10	125,181	7,833	6.3%	83,105
12/09	118,691	12,095	10.2%	88,227
Annual Growth	**9.2%**	**(29.7%)**	**—**	**(8.4%)**

2013 Year-End Financials

Debt ratio: 24.5%
Return on equity: 6.2%
Cash ($ mil.): 10,069
Current ratio: 1.08
Long-term debt ($ mil.): 25,107

No. of shares (mil.): 1,907
Dividends
　Yield: 0.0%
　Payout: 124.8%
Market value ($ mil.): 35,256

	STOCK PRICE ($) FY Close	P/E High/Low	PER SHARE ($) Earnings	Dividends	Book Value
12/13	18.48	32 24	1.54	1.92	24.15
12/12	18.79	38 25	1.53	0.96	24.16
12/11	21.39	— —	(1.50)	3.04	24.26
12/10	30.41	27 14	4.11	1.40	29.26
12/09	41.75	21 10	6.35	1.48	30.50
Annual Growth	**(18.4%)**	**— —**	**(29.8%)**	**6.9%**	**(5.7%)**

Ecopetrol SA

Ecopetrol performs crude oil and natural gas exploration production refining and transportation. The largest company in Colombia (where it accounts for 60% of national production and is one of the world's 40 largest oil companies) Ecopetrol has two large refineries (Barrancabermeja and Cartagena) strategically located to supply the domestic market and to export oil and oil products to the southern US. Ecopetrol explores for oil and gas across Colombia and is expanding internationally through exploration partnerships in Brazil Peru and the US Gulf of Mexico. In 2013 the company reported proved reserves of more than 1.4 billion barrels of oil equivalent.

Geographic Reach

Headquartered in Bogota Colombia the company has exploration and production activities in Brazil Peru and the US (Gulf of Mexico). In 2013 it derived almost 40% of its revenues from Colombia and nearly 30% from the US.

Sales and Marketing

The company's crude oil export sales are made both in the spot market and through long-term contracts primarily to refiners in the US Gulf Coast Far East Europe and the U. West Coast. It sell natural gas to distribution companies through take-or-pay or swing contracts.

Strategy

The company has ambitious expansion plans including the doubling of refining capacity and the emergence of Ecopetrol as a leader in biofuels production. The company's goal is to produce 1 million barrels of oil equivalent per day by 2015 and 1.3 million of oil equivalent per day in 2020. Ecopetrol's strategy is focused on supplying the local market and exporting crude oil refined products petrochemical products and natural gas to end-users including refineries and wholesalers in order to improve its margins. It also intends to increase its market participation in crude oil and refined products in Asia and Europe.

In an effort to enhance the strategic and logistical framework of Colombia's oil industry in response to the increase in hydrocarbon production and higher sales of crudes and refined products both within Colombia and on the international markets in 2012 the company established Cenit as a wholly-owned subsidiary specializing in logistics and transportation of hydrocarbons within Colombia.

During 2012 the company acquired 23908 kilometers of additional seismic equivalent which includes 13908 kilometers in the US Gulf Coast and 10000 kilometers in Brazil. During the first quarter of 2013 it drilled five stratigraphic wells out of which two exhibited evidence of hydrocarbons (Segua 1 and Circe 1).

EXECUTIVES

President of the Board, Fabio Echeverri Correa, age 81
General Secretary, Margarita Obregon Triana
Executive Vice President of Exploration and Production, Hector Manosalva Rojas
VP Legal, Mauricio Echeverry Gutierrez, age 58
VP Exploration, Enrique Velazquez Convers, age 61
EVP Downstream, Pedro Alfonso Rosales Navarro, age 51
VP Refining and Petrochemicals, Federico Maya Molina
President, Javier G. Gutierrez Pemberthy, age 63
CFO, Adriana M. Echeverri, age 43
VP Strategy and Growth, Camilo Marulanda, age 35
VP Human Talent, Martha Cecilia Casta?o
VP Transporacion, Alvaro Castaneda Caro
Disciplinary Control Office, Adriana Marcela Neira
VP Production, Hector Castano Aristizabal, age 52
VP Services and Technology, Oscar A. Villadiego, age 50
VP Supply and Marketing, Claudia L. Castellanos R.
President of the Board, Fabio Echeverri Correa, age 81
Director, Ignacio Sanin Bernal, age 65
Director, Joaquin Moreno, age 65
Director, Maria E. Velasquez, age 56
Director, Amilkar Acosta Medina, age 61
Director, Mauricio Cardenas, age 52
Director, Carlos Rodado Noriega
Director, Hernando J. Gomez
Auditors: Ernst&YoungAudit

LOCATIONS

HQ: Ecopetrol SA
Carrera 13 No. 36 ? 24, Bogota
Phone: (57) 1 234 5190   **Fax:** (57) 1 234 5628
Web: www.ecopetrol.com.co

Sales

	% of total
Colombia	40
Other	60
Total	**100**

PRODUCTS/OPERATIONS

Sales

	% of total
Crude	52
Refined petroleum products and	48
Total	**100**

COMPETITORS

Apco Oil and Gas International	Hunt Oil
BP	Nexen
Exxon Mobil	Pacific Rubiales
Gran Tierra Energy	Petrobank Energy and Resources

HISTORICAL FINANCIALS

Company Type: Public

Income Statement
FYE: December 31

	REVENUE ($ mil.)	NET INCOME ($ mil.)	NET PROFIT MARGIN	EMPLOYEES
12/13	36,501	6,792	18.6%	10,686
12/12	38,801	8,328	21.5%	9,701
12/11	33,928	7,973	23.5%	8,729
12/10	21,097	4,095	19.4%	7,575
12/09	14,858	2,508	16.9%	7,395
Annual Growth	25.2%	28.3%	—	9.6%

2013 Year-End Financials

Debt ratio: 0.0%
Return on equity: 19.2%
Cash ($ mil.): 4,582
Current ratio: 1.29
Long-term debt ($ mil.): 11,103

No. of shares (mil.): —
Dividends
Yield: 7.1%
Payout: —
Market value ($ mil.): —

	STOCK PRICE ($) FY Close	P/E High/Low	PER SHARE ($) Earnings	Dividends	Book Value
12/13	38.45	— —	0.17	3.15	0.90
12/12	59.67	— —	0.20	4.38	0.89
12/11	44.52	— —	0.20	0.00	0.69
12/10	43.62	— —	0.10	0.93	0.51
12/09	24.26	— —	0.06	2.05	0.39
Annual Growth	12.2%	— —	27.8%	11.3%	22.9%

Electricite de France

While France has been slow to open its own doors to competition in the utilities industry state-owned Electricite de France (EDF) has been quick to expand into global deregulated markets. One of the world's top electric utilities (as well as one of the last major state-controlled energy giants in Europe) EDF has a generating capacity of more than 628 TWh (primarily from nuclear energy sources) and provides power to 28 million French customers and 10 million customers in other countries (primarily in Europe). Its EDF Trading unit trades a range of energy products.

Geographic Reach

The company operates power plants in Europe Africa the Americas Asia and the Middle East.

Operations

EDF operates in three major segments: Generation/Supply –energy generation and energy sales to industry local authorities small businesses and residential consumers. This segment also includes commodity trading activities; Distribution –the management of the low and medium-voltage public distribution network; and Other –energy services (district heating thermal energy services etc.) for industry and local authorities and new businesses mainly aimed at boosting electricity generation through cogeneration and renewable energy sources.

Nuclear plants provide the vast majority of EDF's domestic power supply; other sources include hydroelectric and fossil-fueled plants. Making use of its extensive experience especially in developing nuclear power EDF builds power plants and provides plant management and consulting services worldwide.

Financial Performance

The company's revenues increased by 11% in 2012 due to the recovering global economy increasing demand spurring revenue growth in all of EDF's segments.

Net income increased by 5% in 2012 due to an increase in operating income resulting from the French regulator's decision of October 9 2012 setting the final charge for the TaRTAM transition tariff system and increase in other items including E347 million corresponding to the effects of the rulings in Edison's favor in the litigations over price revisions for the long-term gas supply contracts with Rasgas (Qatar) and ENI (Libya).

Strategy

EDF is investing aggressively abroad. In 2012 EDF acquired the Italy-based energy group Edison by purchasing Delmi's entire investment (50%) in Transalpina Di Energia for a total of E784 million. Following this acquisition the Group held 78.96% of the capital and 80.64% of the voting rights in Edison.

Not to be left out in the competitive renewable energy market EDF is seeking to boost its wind and solar energy output from a few hundred MW in 2008 to 4000 MW (in 2012) and higher in 2013.

The company is working on a E6 billion Flamanville EPR construction project in France. In early 2013 the civil engineering work was 94% complete and 39% of the electro-mechanical equipment was in place. Its other projects included French offshore projects at Saint-Nazaire Courseulles-sur-Mer and Fecamp.

To help pay down debt to pay for its expansion in 2010 Hong Kong's Cheung Kong Infrastructure and Hongkong Electric both controlled by Hong Kong-based billionaire Li Ka-shing acquired EDF's three UK distribution UK grids in a deal valued at about $9 billion. In 2011 EDF sold its 45% stake in German power utility Energie Baden-Worttemberg for $6.1 billion.

Ownership

The French government owns 85% of the company.

HISTORY

The French government nationalized hundreds of regional private firms to form Electricite de France (EDF) in 1946 as part of an effort to rebuild the nation's badly shaken post-war economy. This was a marked difference from the notoriously complex and inefficient pre-war electrical industry.

By the 1950s EDF had taken advantage of the centralized control and developed massive hydroelectric projects. Hydroelectric power would account for more than 70% of EDF's power.

But in France as elsewhere hydro wasn't enough to keep up with the growing demand for electricity and fossil fuels became an increasingly important power source. Then came the oil shortages of the 1970s and France –with limited domestic supplies of oil and gas –began searching for alternatives to fossil-fueled plants. Nuclear power was determined to be the answer.

The government moved to invest billions of dollars in developing its relatively small nuclear power production facilities. Muddled with Malthusian predictions of power shortages and a preoccupation with having enough energy to be self-reliant France found its nuclear operations left the government with more energy than it could use and more debt than it wanted. The company began to build a cable connecting the Continent to the UK in 1981. With the power grids of the two countries connected in 1986 EDF was finally able to start exporting its power to the Brits.

The 1990s brought with them deregulation. EDF fought to keep the UK-France grid closed to other energy sellers. After the government forbade the utility from diversifying into areas other than electricity in 1995 the company turned its attention to foreign investment especially in Latin America.

The company faced increasing deregulatory pressures from without in the late 1990s. The newly formed European Union required open competition from member states. Begrudgingly and behind schedule EDF opened about 30% of its market to competition in 2000.

Other members of the EU complained that EDF was trying to play it both ways: It was making aggressive acquisitions in the UK liberalized market (it bought London Electricity in 1999) while resisting a competition-enabling breakup or even allowing a foreign competitor to buy a stake in the French market.

EDF in 2001 expanded its stake in Italy's Montedison a conglomerate with substantial energy holdings by forming a consortium (Italenergia) with Italian automaker Fiat and some Italian banks to wrest control of Montedison from Italian bank MEDIOBANCA. Although the consortium owns 94% of Montedison EDF has only 2% of voting rights. (Montedison changed its name to Edison in 2002.)

EDF also purchased a 35% interest in German utility Energie Baden-Worttemberg in 2001 and it merged its energy services unit with Dalkia a unit of Vivendi Environnement (now Veolia Environnement) taking a 34% stake in Dalkia (which will eventually be increased to 50%). EDF subsidiary London Electricity agreed to buy $2.4 billion in UK assets from TXU Europe that year including a 2000 MW power plant TXU's Eastern Electricity distribution unit and its interest in TXU/EDF joint venture 24seven; the deals were completed in 2001 and 2002.

In 2002 EDF increased its stake in Brazilian utility Light Servicos de Eletricidade to 88% by swapping Light's interest in S o Paulo utility Eletropaulo for AES's 24% interest in Light. Later that year EDF purchased UK electric and gas utility SEEBOARD (1.9 million customers) from US utility AEP in a $2.2 billion deal.

Deregulation of 70% of the French market took effect in July 2004. Between 2000 and 2004 only 30% of the market was deregulated just more than the percentage required by European Union (EU) rulings.

EDF acquired Edison SpA (Italy's second-largest power group) in partnership with Italian utility company AEM SpA in 2005 for an estimated $15.4 billion.

Expanding its presence and its position as a nuclear power provider in the US in 2009 EDF unit EDF Development acquired 49.99% of Constellation Energy's Constellation Energy Nuclear Group LLC for $4.5 billion. (However another joint venture between these two parties aimed at developing new nuclear power plants in the US was terminated in 2010 after strategic disagreements between the principals).

In a move to boost its position as both a major energy and a nuclear power player in Europe in 2009 EDF acquired British Energy with its 1.1 million customer accounts for about $18 billion.

In 2010 EDF signed two new agreements with China National Nuclear Corporation and China Guangdong Nuclear Power Holding Company solidifying its role as a long term partner in China's nuclear development program. (The company has worked in China for 25 years).

LOCATIONS

HQ: Electricite de France
22-30 avenue de Wagram, Paris, Cedex 08 75382
Phone: (33) 1 40 42 22 22   **Fax:** (33) 1 40 42 32 17
Web: www.edf.com

Sales

	% of total
France	54
Italy	14
UK	13
Other	11
Other	8
Total	**100**

PRODUCTS/OPERATIONS

HISTORICAL FINANCIALS

Company Type: Public

Income Statement

FYE: December 31

	REVENUE ($ mil.)	NET INCOME ($ mil.)	NET PROFIT MARGIN	EMPLOYEES
12/13	104,072	4,841	4.7%	158,467
12/12	95,860	4,370	4.6%	159,740
12/11	84,471	3,893	4.6%	156,168
12/10	87,215	1,365	1.6%	158,842
12/09	95,561	5,625	5.9%	169,139
Annual Growth	**2.2%**	**(3.7%)**	**—**	**(1.6%)**

2013 Year-End Financials

Debt ratio: 28.5%
Return on equity: 11.7%
Cash ($ mil.): 7,515
Current ratio: 1.20
Long-term debt ($ mil.): 57,857

No. of shares (mil.): 1,858
Dividends
  Yield: 4.7%
  Payout: 23.9%
Market value ($ mil.): 13,026

	STOCK PRICE ($) FY Close	P/E High/Low		PER SHARE ($) Earnings	Dividends	Book Value
12/13	7.01	8	4	2.53	0.33	25.34
12/12	3.71	5	3	2.37	0.29	18.46
12/11	4.81	10	5	2.11	0.57	21.40
12/10	8.30	43	23	0.74	0.29	22.68
12/09	11.82	12	6	3.08	0.16	21.78
Annual Growth	**(12.2%)**	**—**	**—**	**(4.8%)**	**20.3%**	**3.9%**

Enbridge Inc

Cold spells heated business for Enbridge in North America. Gas Pipelines Processing and Energy Services is Enbridge's largest segment but it also has interests in Gas Distribution Liquids Pipelines and Sponsored Investments. Its gas utilities provide natural gas to about 2 million customers primarily in Ontario and New York. A major crude oil and liquids transporter Enbridge moves about 2.5 million barrels of crude oil a day and operates thousands of miles of natural gas pipeline including a 1500 mile system connecting Alberta and British Columbia to the Chicago area. Its Sponsored Investments business consists of the firm's holdings in Enbridge Energy Partners (25%) and Enbridge Income Fund (72%).

Enbridge operates the world's longest crude oil and liquids pipeline system and transports 65% Western Canada's crude oil exports. It has natural gas gathering transmission and midstream operations and a power transmission business. The company also owns Canada's largest natural gas distribution operations. To meet clean air regula-

tions Enbridge is also investing in geothermal hybrid fuel cell solar and wind power projects and has about 1000 MW of renewable and alternative energy generating capacity.

Enbridge operates in Canada and the US. It has gas distribution customers in Ontario Quebec New Brunswick and New York. Outside of North America the company provides natural gas distribution consulting services in more than 30 countries.

Embridge reported a 26% jump in revenues in 2011 thanks to an improving economy increased product sales and higher commodity oil and natural gas liquids prices. However net income grew by only 1.5% as higher gas commodity costs related to its gas pipelines processing and energy services segment trimmed back its profits.

In North America the company is investing heavily in pipeline construction to expand the reach of its oil and gas assets. In 2012 it teamed up with Spectra Energy and DTE Energy to develop the NEXUS Gas Transmission system a 250-mile pipeline to move natural gas from the Ohio Utica shale to markets in the US Midwest and Ontario. In 2011 Enbridge was eyeing $30 billion in growth opportunities under development extending pipelines from Canadian gas and oil sources for heavily populated markets in the Midwest and Southern US. In 2010 alone Enbridge put into service some $6.5 billion of growth projects including the $3.5 billion Alberta Clipper project the largest liquids pipeline project in the Enbridge's history which provides service between Hardisty Alberta and Superior Wisconsin.

In a major expansion in 2011 Enbridge acquired ConocoPhillips' 50% stake in the Seaway Crude Pipeline System for $1.15 billion and plans to reverse the direction of crude oil flows on the pipeline to enable it to ship oil from Cushing Oklahoma to Gulf Coast refineries.

In 2011 the company acquired Tonbridge Power for $20 million. Tonbridge Power is developing the Montana-Alberta Tie-Line power transmission project a 345-km transmission line from Great Falls Montana to Lethbridge Alberta.

Embridge has also agreed to work with PetroChina International Company to develop the Gateway Pipeline. The proposed pipeline would move 525000 barrels per day of oil sands production from Edmonton Alberta to a port in British Columbia where it would be shipped to California and on to China and other Asian markets.

Enbridge has cut back on its direct investments in international pipeline projects in order to focus on the growing demand and surer financing for pipeline expansion closer to home. (In 2009 Enbridge sold its quarter stake in Colombian pipeline operator Oleoducto Central S.A. to that country's national oil company Ecopetrol for $400 million. Cash from the deal was designated to fund North American crude oil pipeline expansion projects.)

EXECUTIVES

Chairman, David A. Arledge, age 69
VP Investor Relations and Enterprise Risk, Jody L. Balko, age 53
EVP Corporate Development and CFO, J. Richard Bird, age 65, $441,612 total compensation
President - Liquids Pipelines and Major Projects, Stephen J. (Steve) Wuori, age 57, $566,887 total compensation
Senior Vice President President EEP, Mark A. Maki, age 50
SVP and Controller, John K. Whelen
SVP Green Energy, James A. (Jim) Schultz
President and CEO, Al Monaco, age 55, $437,413 total compensation
EVP People and Partners, Karen L. Radford, age 45
Executive Vice President; Chief Legal Officer, David T. Robottom

Media Relations, Jennifer Varey
VP Investor Relations and Enterprise Risk, Vern D. Yu
EVP Western Access, Janet A. Holder
VP Corporate Secretary and Chief Compliance Officer, Alison T. Love
VP Alternative and Emerging Technology, Chuck J. Szmurlo
VP Treasury and Tax, Colin K. Gruending
VP Public Government and Aboriginal Affairs, D'Arcy L. Levesque
VP Financial Partnerships, L. M. Luison
VP Corporate Law and Deputy General Counsel, R. F. Carpenter
VP Corporate Development and Planning, W. Opheim
Manager Investor Relations, Pat Murray
President Enbridge Gas Distribution, Guy Jarvis
Senior Vice President - Major Projects, Byron Neiles
Director Investor Relations, Jonathan Gould
Senior Vice President - Enterprise Safety & Operational Reliability, Cynthia Hansen
President - Gas Pipelines, Leon Zupan
VP Chief Legal Officer, David T. Q.C
Executive Vice President Chief Legal Officer, David T. Qc
President Enbridge Gas Distribution, Glenn Beaumont
Chief Sustainability Officer, Linda Coady
Director, Dan C. Tutcher, age 66
CEO and Director, Patrick D. Daniel, age 66
Director, George K. Petty, age 73
Director, J. Lorne Braithwaite, age 72
Director, James J. Blanchard, age 71
Director, Cathy L. Williams, age 64
President and CEO, Al Monaco, age 55
Director, Charles E. Shultz, age 74
Director, David A. Leslie, age 70
Director, J. Herbert (Herb) England, age 68
Director, Charlie W. Fischer, age 64
Independent Director, Maureen Darkes
Auditors: PricewaterhouseCoopersLLP

LOCATIONS

HQ: Enbridge Inc
3000, 425 - 1st Street S.W., Calgary, Alberta T2P 3L8
Phone: 403 231-3900   **Fax:** 403 231-3920
Web: www.enbridge.com

Sales

	% of total
Canada	65
US	35
Total	**100**

PRODUCTS/OPERATIONS

Sales

	% of total
Gas pipelines processing and energy	75
Gas	13
Liquids	10
Spnsored	2
Total	**100**

Selected Subsidiaries and Affiliates

Gas Pipelines Processing and Energy Services
  Aux Sable Liquids Products Inc. (43%)
  Alliance Pipeline Limited Partnership (50%)
  Tlbury Solar Project
  Vector Pipeline Limited Partnership (60%)
Gas Distribution
  Enbridge Gas Distribution
  Enbridge Gas New Brunswick (63%)
  Gazifere Inc.
  Niagara Gas Transmission Limited
Liquids Pipelines
  Chicap Pipe Line Company (44%)
  Enbridge Energy Partners L.P. (13%)
  Enbridge Pipelines (Athabasca) Inc.
  Enbridge Pipelines (North Dakota) Inc.

Enbridge Pipelines (NW) Inc.
Enbridge Pipelines (Toledo) Inc.
Enbridge Pipelines Inc.
Frontier Pipeline Company (78%)
Mustang Pipe Line Partners (30%)
Olympic Pipe Line (85%)
Sponsored Investments
Enbridge Income Fund (72%)
Enbridge Energy Partners L.P. (25.5%)
Corporate
Noverco Inc. (39%)
Gaz Metropolitain and Company Limited Partnership
(71%)Vermont Gas Systems Inc.

COMPETITORS

Con Edison	New York Power
Dynegy	Authority
El Paso Corporation	ONEOK Partners
Hydro One	TransCanada
Koch Industries Inc.	Williams Companies
National Fuel Gas	

HISTORICAL FINANCIALS
Company Type: Public

Income Statement
FYE: December 31

	REVENUE ($ mil.)	NET INCOME ($ mil.)	NET PROFIT MARGIN	EMPLOYEES
12/13	30,957	591	1.9%	10,000
12/12	25,444	718	2.8%	7,828
12/11	19,019	984	5.2%	0
12/10	15,159	972	6.4%	6,357
12/09	11,890	1,489	12.5%	6,065
Annual Growth	27.0%	(20.6%)	—	13.3%

2013 Year-End Financials

Debt ratio: 42.2%	No. of shares (mil.): 831
Return on equity: 5.2%	Dividends
Cash ($ mil.): 710	Yield: 2.8%
Current ratio: 0.65	Payout: 122.3%
Long-term debt ($ mil.): 21,025	Market value ($ mil.): 36,298

	STOCK PRICE ($) FY Close	P/E High/Low		PER SHARE ($) Earnings	Dividends	Book Value
12/13	43.68	81	65	0.52	1.23	15.27
12/12	43.32	56	44	0.78	1.13	13.11
12/11	37.41	51	22	1.27	0.96	11.10
12/10	56.40	44	31	1.29	0.83	9.85
12/09	46.22	20	10	2.03	0.65	10.08
Annual Growth	(1.4%)	—	—	(28.9%)	17.1%	11.0%

ENBW Energie Baden-Wuerttemberg AG

One of Germany's largest utilities Energie Baden-Worttemberg (EnBW) is bathing its namesake region with light. EnBW distributes electricity in the state of Baden-Worttemberg; the company also provides natural gas and energy and environmental services. The company markets power to retail customers throughout Germany under subsidiary Yello Strom. EnBW also generates distributes and markets energy across Central Europe. The company has 6 million energy customers and about 15500 MW of electric generating capacity. EnBW is focusing on energy diversity improving the energy-efficiency of its fossil-fuel powered generation facilities while expanding its renewable power sources.

As part of this green energy push in 2010 EnBW completed its Baltic 1 wind farm (which has 21 turbines and an installed output of 50 MW) just off of Germany's north coast. The company has additional wind farms under construction or in the planning stage.

It is also growing its renewables by acquisition. In 2011 EnBW acquired a 6 MW wind farm from ABO Wind AG through its renewable energy unit EnBW Erneuerbare Energien GmbH. The company had previously acquired a 15 MW wind farm from ABO Wind in 2010.

EnBW has also made selective international energy acquisitions (including renewable sources) to balance the growth of its core German operations. The company moved into Sweden in 2007 via Yello Strom. In 2008 EnBW made a domestic acquisition when it acquired a 26% stake in German gas and electricity distributor EWE for about $3 billion. It also bought stakes in two German coal-fired power plants from E.ON in 2009.

Moving into the Turkish market in 2009 the company announced plans to build up generation capacities of 2000 MW of primarily renewable energy powered plants by 2020 in collaboration with Turkish industrial conglomerate Borusan Holding.

In 2010 with the global economy bouncing back the company benefitted from higher commodity prices and greater industrial demand. EnBW saw its revenues and income grow robustly that year led by a 100% jump in its power generating and trading segment revenues.

Electricite de France (EDF) and Oberschwabische Elektrizitatswerke once each owned 45% of EnBW but in early 2011 EDF sold its stake to the state of Baden-Worttemberg for $6.1 billion to raise cash. Baden-Worttemberg increased its holdings to 47% in March 2011 through the acquisition of minority stakes.

LOCATIONS

HQ: ENBW Energie Baden-Wuerttemberg AG
Durlacher Allee 93, Karlsruhe D-76131
Phone: (49) 721 63 00   **Fax:** (49) 721 63 127 25
Web: www.enbw.com

PRODUCTS/OPERATIONS

Sales

	% of total
Electricity grid &	58
Electricity generation &	28
Gas	10
Energy & environmental	4
Total	**100**

Selected Subsidiaries
EnBW Gas GmbH (natural gas distribution)
EnBW Vertriebs- und Servicegesellschaft mbH
(electricity energy and environmental services)
EnBW Kraftwerke AG (electricity generation)
EnBW Regional AG (electricity distribution)
EnBW Trading GmbH (energy marketing)
EnBW Transportnetze AG (electricity transmission)
Yello Strom GmbH (electricity supply)
Gasversorgung Suddeutschland GmbH (GVS district heating and natural gas transmission and supply)

HISTORICAL FINANCIALS
Company Type: Public

Income Statement
FYE: December 31

	REVENUE ($ mil.)	NET INCOME ($ mil.)	NET PROFIT MARGIN	EMPLOYEES
12/13	28,356	70	0.2%	19,822
12/12	25,410	624	2.5%	20,098
12/11	24,420	(1,121)	—	20,959
12/10	23,531	1,566	6.7%	20,450
12/09	22,518	1,106	4.9%	20,914
Annual Growth	5.9%	(49.8%)	—	(1.3%)

2013 Year-End Financials

Debt ratio: 21.9%	No. of shares (mil.): 270
Return on equity: 0.9%	Dividends
Cash ($ mil.): 3,333	Yield: —
Current ratio: 1.19	Payout: —
Long-term debt ($ mil.): 7,637	Market value ($ mil.): —

Endesa S.A.

Endesa provides power to more than 26 million customers in 11 countries (50% customers in Spain) on three continents. A subsidiary of Italian power giant Enel Endesa is Spain's #1 electric utility and has a generating capacity of 39562 MW from nuclear fossil-fueled hydroelectric and renewable energy plants. Endesa is the primary electricity company in Chile Argentina Colombia and Peru and also operates in Brazil. It is a major player in the Mediterranean region especially Italy and is active in other countries. Endesa also serves natural gas customers in Spain. The company is also investing heavily in renewable energy to meet Spain's commitment to greenhouse gas reduction.

HISTORY

When dictator Francisco Franco set about rebuilding Spain after the Civil War Empresa Nacional de Electricidad (Endesa) was formed in 1944 under the state-run Instituto Nacional de Industria (INI). The nation's lack of power facilities sparked the company into building hydroelectric plants. In the 1950s the US fighting the Cold War financed Spain's industrial boom which Endesa aided by building coal-fired plants including Compostilla (on line in 1961).

When inflation plagued Spain in the late 1950s the government cut off INI's funding. INI and its companies then borrowed heavily from banks. Spain then passed the Stabilization Act in 1959 to make INI companies self-financing though they were still government-owned. In the 1960s many of Spain's rural areas were undeveloped so the government instituted and funded a plan to build power infrastructure.

In 1972 Endesa acquired the As Pontel and Teruel facilities where it began constructing fossil fuel plants. However the energy crisis of the early 1970s kept the plants from operating until 1976 and 1979 respectively.

After Franco's death in 1975 King Juan Carlos moved Spain into Europe's free market union. In preparation for the liberalization of the energy markets INI and Endesa reorganized in 1983 and shifted INI's holdings in regional electric utilities (Eneco Enher Gesa and Unelco) to Endesa.

After the government halted its nuclear power program in 1984 many private electric companies were left with bad investments. Endesa was brought in to bail them out by taking over power plants; to repay Endesa they were forced to buy Endesa's electricity. The 1985 asset swaps also brought regional power companies Erz and Fecsa into Endesa's grasp.

In 1986 Spain joined the European Community; two years later the government sold 20% of Endesa to the public. In the early 1990s Endesa went into coal production when it purchased EN-CASUR (1990) and it continued buying interests in private power companies including Viesgo and Sevillana.

The government floated more of the company in 1997 and the utility became Endesa S.A. Its eye on Latin American opportunity Endesa bought a 29% stake in Chile's largest power company Enersis. It also branched into telecommunications by grabbing a small stake in Retevision.

Endesa was fully privatized in 1998 the year Spain's deregulation process began. The next year Endesa paid some $2.6 billion to buy the outstanding shares of its regional units and merge them into the company as part of its larger effort to reorganize and cut its costs and workforce. Endesa also increased its stake in Enersis to more than 60%.

In 2000 Endesa began restructuring its regional electric utilities into separate generation and distribution units. Also that year Endesa Telecom Italia and Union Fenosa combined their Spanish telecom holdings to form the Auna joint venture. (Telecom Italia later sold its stake to Santander Central Hispano.) Endesa also agreed to acquire rival Spanish utility Iberdrola but the companies cancelled the transaction in 2001.

In 2001 Endesa completed the purchase of a 30% interest in French generation company SNET. The company also acquired one of Italian utility Enel's power production units (Elettrogen). Endesa sold its New Viesgo unit (a spinoff composed of regional electric utility Electra de Viesgo which served 500000 customers and had 2400 MW of generation assets) to Enel in 2002.

Endesa branched out into new territories to prepare for the deregulation of Spain's electric utility market which took full effect in 2003.

In 2005 Endesa sold its major stake in Auna to France Telecom (since renamed Orange).

The company found itself the target of takeover bids by other European power companies seeking to bulk up in the wake of the deregulation of the European power and gas markets. In 2007 E.ON and Gas Natural made bids of $47-plus billion and $26-plus billion respectively for Endesa. That year Enel and Acciona jumped into the fray buying about 70% and 25% of the company respectively when Gas Natural dropped out of the bidding. E.ON dropped out in 2008 in return for buying some power plants and shareholdings in Italy Spain and France from Endesa. In 2009 Enel bought Acciona's stake.

In 2009 Endesa had a generating capacity of more than 3700 MW of wind power or about 10% of the Spanish wind power market. In another major move to promote renewable energy in 2010 the company agreed to develop about 550 recharging locations in Barcelona Madrid and Seville to power electric cars.

EXECUTIVES

Director, Valentin Montoya Moya, age 59
CEO and Director, Rafael Miranda Robredo, age 64
Director, Andrea Brentan, age 64
Director, Claudio Machetti, age 55
Director, Fernando d'Ornellas Silva, age 56
Director and Deputy CEO, Esteban Morras Andres, age 55
Director, Maria del Carmen Becerril Martinez

Director, Luigi Ferraris, age 51
Auditors: DeloitteSL

LOCATIONS

HQ: Endesa S.A.
 calle Ribera del Loira, 60, Madrid 28042
Phone: (34) 91 213 10 00   **Fax:** (34) 91 563 81 81
Web: www.endesa.es

Sales

	% of total
Europe	
Spain &	68
Latin	32
Total	**100**

COMPETITORS

AES	International Power
Business Group Benelux	PPL Corporation
E.ON	RWE
Edison	Red Electrica de
Electricite de France	Espa?a
Energias de Portugal	Sempra Energy
Gas Natural SDG	Telefonica
HC Energia	Tractebel Engineering
IBERDROLA	Vattenfall

HISTORICAL FINANCIALS

Company Type: Public

Income Statement

FYE: December 31

	REVENUE ($ mil.)	NET INCOME ($ mil.)	NET PROFIT MARGIN	EMPLOYEES
12/13	42,958	2,586	6.0%	22,995
12/12	44,725	2,680	6.0%	22,807
12/11	42,277	2,861	6.8%	22,877
12/10	41,726	5,526	13.2%	24,732
12/09	37,011	4,941	13.4%	26,305
Annual Growth	3.8%	(14.9%)	—	(3.3%)

2013 Year-End Financials

Debt ratio: 21.2%
Return on equity: 9.1%
Cash ($ mil.): 5,968
Current ratio: 1.21
Long-term debt ($ mil.): 10,395

No. of shares (mil.): 1,058
Dividends
 Yield: —
 Payout: —
Market value ($ mil.): 33,351

	STOCK PRICE ($) FY Close	P/E High/Low	PER SHARE ($) Earnings	Dividends	Book Value
12/13	31.50	34 22	2.44	0.00	26.68
12/12	22.74	21 12	2.53	0.00	25.71
12/11	19.75	33 16	2.70	0.00	23.57
12/10	25.05	17 9	5.22	0.00	22.47
12/09	34.00	23 11	4.67	0.00	19.36
Annual Growth	(1.9%)	—	(15.0%)	—	8.3%

Enel Societa Per Azioni

Arrivederci monopolio! Buongiorno diversified energy player. Italy's largest electric utility Enel has given up its monopoly status and raced into the deregulated global power marketplace. Operating in 40 countries Enel distributes electricity and gas to about 61 million customers and has more than 96000 MW of primarily fossil-fueled and hydroelectric generating capacity. The second largest gas distributor in Italy (after Italgas) Enel serves 3.2 million customers in Italy. It also has renewable and international power generation assets. The Italian government owns about a third of Enel.

Geographic Reach

Internationally Enel has built and acquired independent power plants primarily in Europe and the Americas. The company operates in 40 countries across four continents.

In 2011 Italy accounted for 40% of the company's revenues.

Operations

Enel operates through a number of segments. Its Sales Division sells to high-value mass market segments acquiring new electricity and gas customers. Italy-focused Enel Energia serves about 7.1 million customers: 3.9 million electricity customers and 3.2 million gas customers. The company's Generation and Energy Management Division generates about 67.2 TWh of power (23% of the Italian market) a year.

The Engineering and Innovation Division carries out numerous research and development initiatives and plant construction projects. The Infrastructure and Networks Division is engaged in energy distribution The Iberia and Latin America Division serve market in Spain and Portugal and South America.

Enel also has an Upstream Gas segment to secure long-term gas supply an International Division and a Renewable Energy Division (with total net generation of 22.5 TWh in 2011.)

Financial Performance

The company's revenues increased by 8% in 2011 thanks to stronger revenues from generation and electricity and fuel trading as well as greater revenues from the sale of electricity to end users in markets outside of Italy. Enel also made revenues gains from the sale of a number of equity investments and from the remeasurement at fair value of the assets and liabilities of certain companies.

Net income decreased by 6% in 2011 due to rise in the tax liability for the year an increase in depreciation amortization and impairment losses due to increase in depreciation and amortization (the result of the rise in the installed renewables generation capacity) and impairment (caused by an increase in the impairment losses on the value of the electricity distribution grids in Argentina) and on the goodwill allocated to the cash generating units of Enel Green Power Hellas and Marcinelle Energie.

Strategy

The company is also growing its non-traditional power assets to meet EU regulation on carbon emissions. In 2012 Enel Green Power consolidated its position in the Greek renewable industry through the launching of two new plants - a wind farm and a photovoltaic plant - both located in the Peloponnese region.

Ownership

The Italian government owns about a third of Enel. Italy's Ministry of Economy and Finance directly owns approximately 14% of Enel; it owns another 17% indirectly through the government-controlled bank Cassa Depositi e Prestiti.

HISTORY

Italy's energy consumption doubled in the 1950s as the country experienced a period of rapid industrialization and urbanization. A tight-knit oligopoly controlled the electric power industry and included Edison SADE La Centale SME and Finelettrica. The economic boom pushed into the 1960s and the Italian government created Enel (Ente Nazionale per l'Energia Elettrica) in 1962 to nationalize the power industry. In 1963 Enel began gradually buying some 1250 electric utilities. About 160 municipal utilities and the larger independents such as Edison were left out of the takeover.

The company spent the late 1960s and early 1970s connecting Italy's unwieldy transmission network and building new power plants including the La Spezia thermoelectric plant (600 MW). Construction costs coupled with the high prices Enel was required to pay for its takeover targets caused the utility to become steeped in debt. The Arab oil embargoes of the early 1970s made matters worse and the Italian government helped Enel with an endowment in 1973.

The energy crisis also prompted Enel to build its first nuclear power plant Caorso which came on line in 1980. However nuclear power was short-lived in Italy: After the 1986 Chernobyl accident a national referendum forced Enel to deactivate its nukes in 1987. The firm also stepped up its development of renewable energy sources in the 1980s.

Meanwhile Enel opened its Centro Nazionale de Controllo (CNC) in Rome in 1985 to supervise Italy's power grid. The next year the company turned its first profit.

To begin disassembling Enel's monopoly the Italian government in 1992 opened the power generation market to outside producers and converted Enel into a joint stock company (with the state holding all of the shares). Following the European Union's 1997 directive to deregulate Europe's power industry Enel unbundled its utility activities and began trimming its staff.

Italy's Bersani Decree (passed in 1999) outlined the restructuring process: Enel was ordered to divest 25% of its capacity (15000 MW) and turn over a portion of its municipal distribution networks to local governments to enhance competition in the country's power market. Accordingly it transferred management of the national transmission grid to an independent government-owned operator Gestore della Rete di Trasmissione Nazionale (GRTN) and reduced its customer count by approximately 1 million through municipal distribution asset sales.

Enel had already begun to diversify. It started Wind Telecomunicazioni a joint venture with France Telecom —later renamed Orange —and Deutsche Telekom in 1998. (Deutsche Telekom sold its stake to the other partners in 2000.) Wind first offered fixed-line and mobile telecom services to corporations; it extended the services to residential users in 1999. In addition Enel began building water infrastructure to serve local distributors and purchased three water operations in southern Italy.

Also in 1999 the government floated 32% of Enel in one of the world's largest IPOs at the time. The next year the company bought Colombo Gas (a northern Italian gas distributor with about 75000 customers) and it transferred control of its transmission network to Gestore della Rete di Trasmissione Nazionale (an independent government-owned operator) while retaining ownership of the assets.

Enel bought fixed-line telephone company Infostrada from Vodafone in 2001 acquired two more Italian gas distributors and sold its 5400-MW Elettrogen generation unit to Spain's Endesa for $2.3 billion. That year Enel put its 7000-MW Eurogen generation unit on the auction block. The high bidder with a $2.6 billion offer was a consortium backed by Fiat and Electricite de France; the sale was completed in 2002.

Also in 2002 Enel merged Infostrada into Wind Telecomunicazioni to create one of Italy's top telecom companies it purchased Camuzzi Gazometri's gas distribution business (Italy's second-largest) for $870 million from Mill Hill Investments and it bought Endesa's Viesgo unit (2400 MW of generating capacity and 500000 power customers) for about $1.8 billion.

Enel sold its final generation divestment company Interpower (2600 MW) to a consortium of utilities (including Belgian utility Electrabel and Italian utility ACEA) for about $880 million in 2003.

That year Enel purchased France Telecom 's 27% stake in Wind for $1.4 billion making the unit a wholly owned subsidiary. (Enel had flirted with the idea of taking Wind public but instead sold the unit in 2006 to the Egypt-based Weather Investments consortium which had the backing of Orascom Telecom 's chairman and CEO Naguib Sawiris.)

The Italian government began the second round of Enel's privatization process in 2003 by selling a 7% stake to Morgan Stanley for more than $2.3 billion. In 2004 the government further reduced its stake by nearly 20% through a public offering of shares.

In 2005 it acquired power distribution and sales businesses in Romania and in 2006 in Slovakia.

With Italian regulators requiring that Enel divest 80% of its Terna subsidiary (which holds the company's power transmission assets) by 2007 Enel spun off 50% of the unit in an IPO in 2004. The following year it divested another 44% and the company reduced its holding to about 5% by January 2006. Grid management and operational functions were also transferred from GRTN back to Terna.

In 2008 the company set Enel Green Power to develop wind solar geothermal and biomass projects. By 2009 it was operating alternative energy plants worldwide with a generating capacity of 4700 MW. In 2010 Enel Green Power acquired Pagoda Wind Power which is developing 4000 MW of wind projects in California.

In what could have been a large cross-border deal Enel considered making a bid for France's SUEZ (now GDF SUEZ) utility company. Perhaps in reaction to the news of Enel's interest France's Gaz de France made a bid for SUEZ (consummated in 2008) a move that Italy called protectionist.

Unperturbed by its failure to secure SUEZ the company took control of Spain's power giant Endesa in 2007 increasing its market share as a European power player. Hoping to pay down what had become a heavy debt load the company in 2009 sold an 80% stake in gas distributor Enel Rete Gas for $666 million.

LOCATIONS

HQ: Enel Societa Per Azioni
Viale Regina Margherita, 137, Rome I-00198
Phone: (39) 6 8509 3184   **Fax:** (39) 6 8509 5810
Web: www.enel.it

Sales

	% of total
Europe	
Italy	40
Other EU	43
Non-EU	4
Americas	13
Total	**100**

PRODUCTS/OPERATIONS

Sales

	% of total
Iberia & Latin	35
Generation & energy management	25
Sales	19
International	8
Infrastructure & networks	8
Renewable	3
Other	2
Total	**100**

HISTORICAL FINANCIALS

Company Type: Public

Income Statement

FYE: December 31

	REVENUE ($ mil.)	NET INCOME ($ mil.)	NET PROFIT MARGIN	EMPLOYEES
12/13	110,875	4,453	4.0%	71,394
12/12	111,966	313	0.3%	73,702
12/11	102,847	5,365	5.2%	75,360
12/10	98,205	5,875	6.0%	78,313
12/09	92,246	7,771	8.4%	81,208
Annual Growth	4.7%	(13.0%)	—	(3.2%)

2013 Year-End Financials

Debt ratio: 48.9%   No. of shares (mil.): —
Return on equity: 9.0%   Dividends
Cash ($ mil.): 11,055   Yield: 3.1%
Current ratio: 1.04   Payout: 52.3%
Long-term debt ($ mil.): 70,369   Market value ($ mil.): —

	STOCK PRICE ($) FY Close	P/E High/Low	PER SHARE ($) Earnings	Dividends	Book Value
12/13	4.34	25 16	0.47	0.14	5.26
12/12	4.14	254 128	0.04	0.22	5.01
12/11	4.00	31 14	0.57	0.44	5.34
12/10	4.96	25 14	0.63	0.18	5.39
12/09	5.85	24 13	0.82	0.92	4.98
Annual Growth	(7.2%)	—	—(13.1%)	(38.0%)	1.4%

ENI S.p.A.

It's not teeny it's Eni —and it's huge. One of Italy's largest companies Eni operates in the oil and natural gas petrochemicals and oil field services industries and has expanded into power generation. Its main subsidiaries and affiliates include EniPower (power generation) Italgas (natural gas transmission) Saipem (oil field services) pipeline operator Snam Rete Gas and Snamprogetti (contracting engineering). As one of the world's leading oil enterprises in 2010 Eni had proved reserves of 6.8 billion barrels of oil equivalent most of it in Italy and in Africa. The Italian government owns 27% of Eni.

The company's oil and gas holdings and exploration and production efforts extend into more than 30 countries on five continents. Eni has expanded outside its traditional bases of Africa and Italy with ventures in the Americas the Asia/Pacific region Europe and the Middle East.

In response to the opening up of Italy's energy markets Eni is increasing its natural gas holdings and adding electricity generating power units. In 2007 the company bought Dominion Resources' US oil and gas assets in the Gulf of Mexico for $4.75 billion. To expand its Asian and Algerian holdings in 2008 Eni acquired Burren Energy and First Calgary Petroleums. It was able to benefit from SUEZ's acquisition of Gaz de France by buying up GDF SUEZ's majority stake in Belgian gas company Distrigas. Eni now owns 100% of Distrigas.

In 2009 to raise cash to pay down debt the company sold its 20% stake in Gazprom Neft to strategic partner Gazprom for $4.2 billion. To save operating costs that year Eni consolidated its gas divisions and sold Italgas and Stogit (gas storage) to subsidiary Snam Rete Gas.

Expanding its Central European market share in 2010 it acquired Exxon Mobil's 135 gas stations and other downstream assets in Austria.

In the wake of the global recession the company saw its revenues and income bounce back in 2010 thanks to higher commodity prices and stronger demand. The unrest in Libya in 2011 had a material impact of Eni which gets 15% of it production from the North African country. To compensate the company is investing heavily in growing production in other areas. Looking to expand in China in 2011 Eni signed a strategic alliance with Chinese oil major PetroChina.

In order to comply with an EU anti-trust ruling in 2011 the company sold its 89% stake in the TAG Pipeline (which transports gas from Russia to Italy) to Cassa Depositi e Prestiti for $986 million.

HISTORY

Although the Italian parliament formed Ente Nazionale Idrocarburi (National Hydrocarbon Agency) in 1953 Enrico Mattei is the true father of Eni. In 1945 Mattei a partisan leader during WWII was appointed northern commissioner of Agip a state-owned petroleum company founded in 1926 by Mussolini and ordered to liquidate the company. Mattei instead ordered the exploration of the Po Valley where workers found methane gas deposits in 1946.

When Eni was created in 1953 Mattei was named president. His job was to find energy resources for an oil-poor country. He initiated a series of joint ventures with several Middle Eastern and African nations offering better deals than his large oil company rivals which he dubbed the Seven Sisters.

Mattei didn't stick to energy: By the time he died in a mysterious plane crash in 1962 Eni had acquired machinery manufacturer Pignone finance company Sofid Milan newspaper "Il Giorno" and textile company Lane Rossi. Eni grew during the 1960s partly because of a deal made for Soviet crude in 1958 and a joint venture with Esso in 1963. It also expanded its chemical activities.

By the early 1970s losses in Eni's chemical and textile operations the oil crisis and the Italian government's dumping of unprofitable companies on Eni hurt its bottom line. Former finance minister Franco Reviglio took over in 1983 and began cutting inefficient operations.

EniChem merged with Montedison Italy's largest private chemical company in 1988 but clashes between the public agency and the private company made Montedison sell back its stake in 1990. Eni became a joint stock company in 1992 but the government retained a majority stake.

Franco Bernabe took over Eni following a 1993 bribery scandal and began cutting noncore businesses. The Italian government began selling Eni stock in 1995. In 1996 Eni signed on to develop Libyan gas resources and build a pipeline to Italy. A year later the company merged its Agipa exploration and production subsidiary into its main operations. Eni also took a 35% stake in Italian telecom company Albacom (which has since been sold to British Telecom Group).

The government cut its stake in Eni from 51% to 38% in 1998. That year Vittorio Mincato a company veteran succeeded Bernabe as CEO. In 1999 Eni and Russia's RAO Gazprom the world's largest natural gas production firm agreed to build a controversial $3 billion natural gas pipeline stretching from Russia to Turkey. Eni agreed to invest $5.5 billion to develop oil and gas reserves in Libya; it also sold interests in Saipem and Nuovo Pignone as well as some of its Italian service stations.

In 2000 Eni paid about $910 million for a 33% stake in Galp a Portuguese oil and gas company

that also has natural gas utility operations. Also that year Eni bought British-Borneo Oil & Gas in a $1.2 billion deal and in 2001 it paid $4 billion for UK independent exploration and production company LASMO topping a bid by US-based Amerada Hess.

The Italian government sold off another 5% of Eni in 2001 reducing its stake to about 30% and announced that it was considering selling its entire investment. In an effort to reduce noncore holdings the company sold property management subsidiary Immobiliare Metanopoli to Goldman Sachs. Also that year Eni sold a minority stake in its gas pipeline unit Snam Rete Gas to the public.

In 2002 Eni entered discussions to acquire Enterprise Oil but lost out to a rival bid from Royal Dutch Shell. Later that year Eni's oil field services unit Saipem gained control of Bouygues Offshore.

In 2006 Eni and Gazprom formed an international alliance to launch joint mid and downstream gas projects and collaborate in upstream and in technological activities.

EXECUTIVES

CEO, Paolo Scaroni, age 68
COO, Salvatore Sardo, age 63
CFO, Alessandro Bernini, age 54
SEVP Public Affairs and Communication, Stefano Lucchini, age 52
EVP External Communication, Gianni Di Giovanni
SEVP Corporate Affairs and Governance and Secretary, Roberto Ulissi, age 52
COO Gas and Power, Umberto Vergine, age 57
SEVP Legal Affairs and General Counsel, Massimo Mantovani, age 51
COO Exploration and Production Division, Claudio Descalzi, age 59
COO Refining and Marketing, Angelo Fanelli, age 63
Chairman, Giuseppe Recchi, age 50
Chairman Syndial, Leonardo Bellodi
SEVP Midstream, Marco Alvera
EVP Research and Technological Innovation, Salvatore Meli
EVP Internal Audit, Marco Petracchini
Senior Vice President Media Relations, Camilla Palladino
Director of Human Resources and Organization, Pierluigi Pierluigi Renzi Renzi
Executive Assistant to the Chief Executive Officer, Raffaella Raffaella Leone Leone
CFO, Massimo Mondazzi
Director, Alberto Clo, age 66
Director, Francesco Taranto, age 74
Director, Mario Resca, age 69
Director, Pierluigi Scibetta, age 55
Director, Marco Reboa, age 59
Director, Paolo Andrea Colombo, age 54
Director, Paolo Marchioni, age 45
Independent Director, Alessandro Alessandro Lorenzi Lorenzi
Independent Director, Alessandro Alessandro Profumo Profumo
Independent Director, Carlo Carlo Gatto Gatto
Independent Director, Roberto Roberto Petri Petri
Auditors: RecontaErnst&YoungS.p.A.

LOCATIONS

HQ: ENI S.p.A.
 1, piazzale Enrico Mattei, Rome 00144
Phone: (39) 2 52041730   **Fax:** (39) 2 52041765
Web: www.eni.com

Sales

	% of total
Europe	
Italy	49
Other EU	21
Other	4
Africa	13

Americas	7
Asia	6
Total	**100**

PRODUCTS/OPERATIONS

Sales

	% of total
Refining &	42
Gas &	29
Exploration &	13
Engineering &	9
Petrochemicals	6
Corporate &	1
Total	**100**

Selected Subsidiaries and Affiliates

Distrigas NV (gas Belgium)
EniPower SpA (power generation)
Italgas SpA (natural gas supply)
Saipem SpA (42.9% oil field services)
Snam Rete Gas SpA (52.5% gas pipeline)
Snamprogetti SpA (contracting and engineering)

COMPETITORS

A2A	Hellenic Petroleum
Ashland Inc.	Marathon Oil
BASF SE	Occidental Petroleum
BG Group	PEMEX
BP	PETROBRAS
Chevron	Petroleos de Venezuela
ConocoPhillips	Royal Dutch Shell
ERG S.p.A.	Sunoco
Edison	TOTAL
Exxon Mobil	

HISTORICAL FINANCIALS

Company Type: Public

Income Statement

	REVENUE ($ mil.)	NET INCOME ($ mil.)	NET PROFIT MARGIN	EMPLOYEES
12/13	159,816	7,103	4.4%	83,887
12/12	169,719	10,264	6.0%	77,838
12/11	142,954	8,873	6.2%	78,686
12/10	133,139	8,455	6.4%	79,941
12/09	121,504	6,290	5.2%	78,417
Annual Growth	7.1%	3.1%	—	1.7%

FYE: December 31

2013 Year-End Financials

Debt ratio: 25.4%	No. of shares (mil.): —
Return on equity: 8.7%	Dividends
Cash ($ mil.): 7,477	Yield: 4.7%
Current ratio: 1.54	Payout: 111.1%
Long-term debt ($ mil.): 28,739	Market value ($ mil.): —

	STOCK PRICE ($) FY Close	P/E High/Low		PER SHARE ($) Earnings	Dividends	Book Value
12/13	48.49	68	51	1.95	2.31	22.12
12/12	49.14	40	27	2.83	2.14	21.54
12/11	41.27	55	30	2.44	3.67	19.81
12/10	43.74	60	33	2.33	1.87	18.92
12/09	50.61	97	47	1.74	2.37	18.32
Annual Growth	(1.1%)	—	—	2.9%	(0.7%)	4.8%

Ericsson

Ericsson opens all lines of communication. The world's leading maker of mobile broadband infrastructure gear provides the equipment that telecom carriers use to build and expand their networks.

The company also provides wireline broadband metro area Ethernet LTE modems and optical transport equipment. Its services unit handles operations ranging from systems integration to network deployment and management. Ericsson's multimedia arm provides content-related products including Internet television systems. The company traces its roots back to 1876 when Lars Magnus Ericsson opened up a telegraph repair shop in Stockholm.

Operations

Ericsson's core business comprises three segments: networks professional services and support solutions. The networks segment which accounts for more than half of the company's sales develops and deploys the latest generation of mobile broadband networks (LTE) and maintains and refines older networks (GSM WCDMA etc.) for its network operator customers. The segment also provides equipment for Internet protocol (IP) microwave transport and core networks including IP routers core routers and switches cables and interconnect products microwave radio links optical transport components radio base stations and wireline network access equipment.

Serving network operators Ericsson's professional services segment supports its customers network operations through its consulting customer support network design and integration and training services. The segment also offers managed services like application hosting and network operations. The growing professional services unit is supported by four global service centers in India China Mexico and Romania. The services segment accounts for about 40% of the company's net sales.

The company's multimedia support solutions segment offers software for consumer-facing applications including mobile and Internet television messaging and music as well as billing support systems for telecommunications network operators.

Financial Performance

For 2012 Ericsson reported modest revenue growth and a 50% drop in its net income from 2011 levels. While its networks segment struggled its growing professional services segment finished strong in 2012. The company attributed the group-wide drop in profitability to operating losses in its ST-Ericsson joint venture (which it dissolved in late 2013) as well as to high research and development and other costs tied to the ongoing modernization of its networks product line. Geographically North America and northeast Asia were Ericsson's strongest markets where demand for mobile products continues to climb.

Strategy

Capitalizing on the booming mobile communications industry Ericsson's is focusing on growing its broadband network equipment and services businesses while divesting non-core businesses. In 2012 Ericsson sold its 50% stake in Sony Ericsson to Sony for more than Å1 billion (about $1.5 billion) in cash. Ericsson which is now focused on global wireless connectivity surrendered the handset portion of the Sony Ericsson business to Sony. Sony and Ericsson plan to work together on a wireless connectivity initiative Ericsson's primary expertise and a pivotal component of Sony's device convergence strategy.

In 2013 semiconductor manufacturer STMicroelectronics (ST) sold its stake in ST-Ericsson a now-dissolved joint venture with Ericsson. The two companies split the joint venture's assets with Ericsson taking over the development and sales of the newer LTE multimedia thin modems (which complement its mobile broadband business) and ST taking a portion of the existing ST-Ericsson modem product line. Other assets including a global navigation satellite system were sold to third parties.

Mergers and Acquisitions

Ericsson is using acquisitions to bolster its product portfolio and expand further into international markets to capitalize on demand for the mobile broadband services that its equipment supports and fuel the growth of its global services organization. The company bought New Jersey-based Telcordia in 2012 for more than $1 billion in cash to expand its mobile broadband and business communications software holdings particularly in the areas of operations support systems and business support systems applications and to further expand its North American business. Telcordia brought in about $740 million in revenue for its 2011 fiscal year.

Ericsson kept pouring money into boosting its wireless portfolio with the 2012 purchase of BelAir Networks which provides carrier-grade Wi-Fi equipment in North America. Ericsson also established a stronger presence as a provider of managed services for broadcasters that year when it bought a related division from Technicolor for nearly Å20 million (about $25 million). The acquisition extended its reach beyond Sweden into France the Netherlands and the UK and became a leading provider in Europe.

HISTORY

Lars Magnus Ericsson opened a telegraph repair shop in Stockholm in 1876 the same year Alexander Graham Bell applied for a US patent on the telephone. Within two years Ericsson was making telephones. His company grew rapidly supplying equipment first to Swedish phone companies and later to other European companies. In 1885 Ericsson crafted a combination receiver-speaker in one handset.

In 1911 Ericsson and SAT the Stockholm telephone company merged under the Ericsson banner. The company adopted its present name in 1926. In 1930 international financier Ivar "The Match King" Kreuger owner of the Swedish Match Co. won control of Ericsson. His triumph was short-lived. Krueger committed suicide in 1932 and one of his creditors Sosthenes Behn's ITT took over.

ITT in 1960 sold its interest in Ericsson to the top Swedish industrialist family the Wallenbergs. In 1975 Ericsson introduced its computer-controlled exchange called AXE. Buoyed by AXE's success the company unveiled the "office of the future" in the early 1980s diversifying into computers and office furniture.

However Ericsson's timing was off: The demand for office automation never materialized and profits plunged. Electrolux chairman Hans Werthen was recruited to split his time between the two companies and rescue Ericsson. The company sold its computer business to Nokia in 1988 and refocused on telephone equipment. It dusted off its aging AXE system for the burgeoning cellular market and quickly won key contracts.

The company and aircraft maker Saab merged their military aviation electronics operations as Ericsson Saab Avionics in 1996. (It was dissolved in 1998.) In 1998 manager Sven-Christer Nilsson was appointed CEO. He reorganized the company and laid off 14000 workers.

After Ericsson fought bitterly with rival QUALCOMM over wireless standards and patents the companies settled in 1999 agreeing to push for the standardization of third-generation technology based on QUALCOMM's code-division multiple access (CDMA) technology. As a part of the deal Ericsson purchased QUALCOMM's infrastructure business. To expand its Internet offerings Ericsson bought Internet router maker Torrent and Internet telephony company Touchwave.

By 1999 Nilsson was pushed out for moving too slowly on restructuring plans and was replaced as CEO by chairman Lars Ramqvist who put many of the duties on president Kurt Hellstrom. Hellstrom immediately set out to simplify the company's managerial and accounting structure trim its workforce and slow-growth businesses and push new phone models to market.

The next year Ericsson sold noncore businesses including its private radio systems power supply and equipment shelter operations. The company also agreed to develop a standard for secure wireless transactions with Nokia and Motorola and formed a joint venture with Web router maker Juniper Networks to sell routers for mobile Internet applications.

Fierce competition an industrywide slowdown in handset sales and manufacturing glitches led Ericsson to outsource the manufacture of its phones to Flextronics and form a joint venture (Sony Ericsson Mobile Communications) with Sony to link the development and marketing of their handsets in 2001. Ericsson also sold its direct enterprise sales and service unit outsourced IT operations in Europe to Electronic Data Systems (which later became HP Enterprise Services) and cut more than 20000 jobs that year. Hellstrom became CEO in 2001.

Chairman Ramqvist became honorary chairman in 2002; Electrolux CEO Michael Treschow was named as the acting chairman. Ericsson announced 20000 more layoffs in 2002. That year the company sold its semiconductor unit to Infineon for about $380 million.

Ericsson sold its optoelectronic components business in 2003. Hellstrom retired later that year and Carl-Henric Svanberg former CEO of Assa Abloy was appointed as company president and CEO. In 2005 Ericsson acquired certain telecom hardware assets from troubled Marconi (later renamed telent) for about $2.1 billion.

The company acquired seven companies in 2007 the largest of which were Redback Networks ($1.9 billion) and TANDBERG Television ($1.4 billion). The Redback buy gained Ericsson broadband IP routers while the TANDBERG Television purchase brought software and services for the cable television market. It also picked up fiber-access technology company Entrisphere in an effort to expand its broadband access offerings in North America.

Looking to broaden its multimedia offerings the company purchased Mobeon a Swedish provider of IP-based voice and video mail. Other 2007 acquisitions included German customer care software provider LHS Swedish mobile service deliver platform developer Drutt and Spanish IPTV specialist HyC. In an effort to refocus its multimedia operations on key areas such as service delivery and provisioning Ericsson sold its enterprise PBX products business to Aastra Technologies for about $100 million in 2008.

To expand its North American business Ericsson bought bankrupt Nortel Network's CDMA and LTE-based wireless business there in 2009 for $1.1 billion. The deal significantly boosted its profile as a provider of mobile networking gear to wireless carriers on the continent. The company's other acquisitions that year complemented its manufacturing and services activities. These purchases included the manufacturing operations of Estonian electronics maker Elcoteq as well as Turkish systems integrator Bizitek.

In 2010 EVP/CFO Hans Vestberg took over as president and CEO of Ericsson succeeding Carl-Henric Svanberg who resigned to become chairman of BP.

EXECUTIVES

VP and CTO Sony Ericsson, Jan Uddenfeldt
Chairman, Leif Johansson, age 63
SVP and Head Sales and Marketing, Jan Wareby, age 58
Deputy Chairman, Jacob Wallenberg, age 59
EVP and Head Global Services, Magnus Mandersson, age 52
VP Investor Relations, Gary Pinkham
President CEO and Director, Hans Vestberg, age 49, $2,321,550 total compensation
VP Communications Americas, Kathy Egan Wummer
President Sony Ericsson Mobile Communications, Bert Nordberg
Head North America Region; President and CEO Ericsson North America, Angel Ruiz
Head Human Resources China and North East Asia, Marita Hellberg, age 58
Deputy Chairman, Sverker Martin-Lof, age 72
Head Middle East, Anders Lindblad
EVP and CFO, Jan Frykhammar, age 49
SVP and Head Strategy, Douglas L. Gilstrap, age 51
SVP; Head of Business Unit Support Solutions, Per G. Borgklint, age 37
VP and Head Investor and Analyst Relations, ?se Lindskog
Head Corporate Public and Media Relations, Ola Rembe
Head Greater China and North East Asia, Mats H. Olsson, age 60
Deputy Chairman, Marcus Wallenberg, age 58
Head Vodafone Global Customers, Torbjorn Possne, age 60
Head Western and Central Europe, Anders Runevad
EVP and Head Networks, Johan Wibergh, age 51
Senior Vice President Strategic Projects, Rima Qureshi, age 49
Head Sub-Saharan Africa, Lars Linden
Head South East Asia and Oceania, Arun Bansal
Head Latin America, Sergio Quiroga da Cunha
Head Mediterranean, Nunzio Mirtillo
SVP and Head Human Resources and Organization, Bina Chaurasia
SVP General Counsel and Head Legal Affairs, Nina Macpherson
SVP CTO and Head Technology and Portfolio Management, Ulf Ewaldsson
SVP and CIO; Head Group Function Business Excellence and Common Functions, Anders Thulin
Director, Roxanne S. Austin, age 53
Director, Carl-Henric Svanberg
Deputy Chairman, Jacob Wallenberg, age 59
President CEO and Director, Hans Vestberg, age 49
Director, Jan Hedlund, age 68
Director, Ulf J. Johansson, age 69
Director, Nancy McKinstry, age 55
Director, Sir Peter L. Bonfield, age 69
Deputy Chairman, Sverker Martin-Lof, age 72
Director, Anders Nyren, age 59
Director, E. Borje Ekholm, age 50
Deputy Chairman, Marcus Wallenberg, age 58
Director, Kristina Davidsson, age 59
Director, Karin ?berg, age 54
Director, Michelangelo (Mike) Volpi, age 48
Director, Pehr Claesson, age 48
Auditors: PricewaterhouseCoopersAB

LOCATIONS

HQ: Ericsson
Torshamnsgatan 23, Kista, Stockholm SE-164 83
Phone: (46) 10 719 0000
Web: www.ericsson.com

Sales

	% of total
North	25
China & North East	16
Mediterranean	10
Latin	10
Western & Central	8
Middle	7
South East Asia &	7
Northern Europe & Central	6
Sub-Saharan	5
India	3
Other	3
Total	**100**

PRODUCTS/OPERATIONS

Sales

	% of total
Networks	51
Services	43
Support	6
Total	**100**

COMPETITORS

Accenture	LG Electronics
Alcatel-Lucent	Motorola Mobility
Amdocs	Nokia Siemens Networks
Cisco Systems	Oracle
Comverse Technology	QUALCOMM
HP Enterprise Services	Samsung Electronics
HTC Corporation	Sharp Corp.
Harmonic	Tata Consultancy
Huawei Technologies	Tech Mahindra
IBM	Technicolor
Juniper Networks	ZTE

HISTORICAL FINANCIALS

Company Type: Public

Income Statement

FYE: December 31

	REVENUE ($ mil.)	NET INCOME ($ mil.)	NET PROFIT MARGIN	EMPLOYEES
12/13	35,465	1,872	5.3%	114,340
12/12	34,964	886	2.5%	110,255
12/11	32,901	1,768	5.4%	104,525
12/10	30,325	1,662	5.5%	90,261
12/09	28,991	515	1.8%	82,493
Annual Growth	**5.2%**	**38.0%**	**—**	**8.5%**

2013 Year-End Financials

Debt ratio: 1.7%	No. of shares (mil.): —
Return on equity: 8.6%	Dividends
Cash ($ mil.): 6,565	Yield: 6.2%
Current ratio: 2.09	Payout: —
Long-term debt ($ mil.): 3,441	Market value ($ mil.): —

	STOCK PRICE ($) FY Close	P/E High/Low		PER SHARE ($) Earnings	Dividends	Book Value
12/13	12.24	0	0	0.58	0.77	6.77
12/12	10.10	0	0	0.27	0.35	6.52
12/11	10.13	0	0	0.55	0.00	6.46
12/10	11.53	0	0	0.52	0.28	6.76
12/09	9.19	0	0	0.16	0.23	6.15
Annual Growth	**7.4%**	**—**	**—**	**37.7%**	**35.3%**	**2.4%**

Erste Group Bank AG

First there was Erste. Erste Group Bank is the holding company of Erste Bank Austria's first savings bank founded in 1819. However the company has grown beyond its home country to number some 2800 branches throughout Central and Eastern European that serve some 16.5 million customers. The company has operating subsidiaries in Austria Croatia the Czech Republic Montenegro Moldova Romania Serbia Slovakia and Hungary. Erste Group banks provide financial services such as savings and lending to individuals and small to medium-size businesses. It also has a private banking arm. Erste Bank is Austria's largest lender.

As Austrian banks consolidated the group increased its presence in surrounding nations. Since the early 2000s the holding company has expanded its market by purchasing stakes in or acquiring outright banks in Austria Bosnia Russia and the Ukraine. Each of its subsidiaries is focused on local operations.

Erste Group slowed its acquisitions during the economic downturn and focused instead on cutting costs and making good lending decisions. The choices helped the company weather the financial crisis rather well. Over the long term Central and Eastern European countries are expected to record economic growth. Erste Group expects loan growth and an increased demand for asset management services in those emerging countries.

The company has sharpened its focus on its core banking activities by selling non-core insurance subsidiaries. It sold most its insurance brokerage operations to Austrian firm GrECo International in 2010.

In 2011 Erste Group made its first acquisitions in several years when it took control of Intermarket Bank —the largest factoring bank in Austria. Erste Group already owned more than 20% of Intermarket Bank and it acquired an additional 56%. The transaction was part of Erste Group's strategy to offer broad services to corporate customers. Also in 2011 Erste offered to buy the rest of majority-held Romanian unit Banca Comerciala Romana it doesn't already own.

HISTORY

In 1819 a bank was born and its name was Erste oesterreichische Spar-Cassa. Called Die Erste for short the bank was Austria's first commercial and savings bank. Unlike Austria's community savings banks Die Erste was independent —not backed by government guarantees.

For more than 150 years Die Erste operated as a local savings bank serving Vienna. Then in 1979 the Austrian government passed a law that would alter the face of the banking industry in that country. The Banking Act of 1979 placed banks and savings institutions in direct competition with each other by allowing them both to take part in all aspects of the banking business. As a result of the enhanced competition Die Erste began expanding its domestic branch network.

Meanwhile the Austrian savings banks had established their own central institution in 1937 and called it Girovereinigung der osterreichischen Sparkassen or Girozentrale for short. Girozentrale focused on managing the liquidity reserves of the savings banks and helping them with their syndication and securities businesses. The bank also endeavored to improve the non-cash payment system and to promote mortgage savings. Concentrating on international and investment banking rather than retail banking Girozentrale eventually became the country's third-largest bank.

Throughout the late 1980s and into the 1990s rumors began to spread about a possible merger between Girozentrale and Die Erste (both were associated with the nation's conservative People's Party). In 1992 Girozentrale merged with Osterreichisches Credit-Institut (OCI) to create GiroCredit giving the central savings bank a branch network for the first time. But it also made GiroCredit a direct competitor with its two largest shareholders — Bank Austria (now part of HypoVereinsbank) and

Die Erste who were also fierce competitors with each other.

Between 1992 and 1994 Die Erste and Bank Austria struggled to find a solution to the problem of GiroCredit's ownership. In 1994 Bank Austria emerged the victor by winning the majority stake in GiroCredit in a move that was characterized by Die Erste as "unfriendly."

Throughout the next two years Die Erste attempted to secure a stake in Creditanstalt Austria's second-biggest bank as the Austrian government began moves to privatize it. Die Erste acted as a part of a consortium of Austrian German and Italian entities interested in obtaining stakes in the bank. But in 1997 Bank Austria won that battle too managing to take over Creditanstalt. In turn Die Erste bought Bank Austria's majority stake in GiroCredit. The resulting company was given the name Erste Bank which went public that year in the largest stock issue in Austrian history. In 1998 it became the first major Austrian company to allow for the election of small shareholder representatives to its supervisory board.

In 2000 Erste Bank bought a majority stake in Ceska Sporitelna the largest retail bank in the Czech Republic from the Czech government. Later in the year the Slovak government allowed Erste Bank to become a major shareholder in the previously state-owned Slovenska sporitel'na. Erste Bank was also one of several Austrian banks to be accused by the European Commission of fixing foreign exchange fees.

In 2001 Erste Bank took control of Slovenska Sporitel'na and acquired majority ownership of Tiroler Sparkasse Bank AG. The following year Erste Bank took full control of Czech Republic-based Czeska Sporitelna. Ever acquisitive in 2005 the company completed its acquisition of Serbia's Novosadska banka.

Erste in 2006 acquiered Romanian bank Banca Comerciala Romana the largest bank in that country and previously state-owned.

Erste switched to a holding company structure in 2008. That year the company also sold most of its insurance business to Vienna Insurance Group.

EXECUTIVES

Deputy Chairman Management Board and Deputy CEO, Franz Hochstrasser, $1,115,030 total compensation

Chairman Management Board and CEO, Andreas Treichl, $1,452,791 total compensation

Second VP Supervisory Board, Theresa Jordis, age 65

Member of the Management Board and Chief Risk Officer, Bernhard Spalt, $93,670 total compensation

Member Management Board Corporate and Investment Banking, Gernot Mittendorfer, age 50

Member Management Board and COO, Herbert Juranek

First VP Supervisory Board, Georg Winckler, age 71

Head of Investor Relations, Thomas Sommerauer

Chairman of the Management Board, Pavel Kysilka

Member Supervisory Board, Wilhelm G. Rasinger

Second VP Supervisory Board, Theresa Jordis, age 65

Member Supervisory Board, Juan Maria Nin Genova, age 60

First VP Supervisory Board, Georg Winckler, age 71

Member Supervisory Board, Brian D. O'Neill
Member Supervisory Board, Friedrich Rodler
Member Supervisory Board, John James Stack
Member Supervisory Board, Werner Tessmar-Pfohl
Auditors: Sparkassen-PrufungsverbandAuditingAgency

LOCATIONS

HQ: Erste Group Bank AG
Milchgasse 1, Vienna A-1010
Phone: (43) 50100 17 693   **Fax:** (43) 50100 9 13112
Web: www.erstegroup.com

PRODUCTS/OPERATIONS

Sales

	% of total
Interest	69
Fees and commissions	25
Trading and other	6
Total	**100**

Selected Subsidiaries

Banca Comerciala Romana S.A. (BCR)
Ceska Sporitelna (Czech Republic)
Erste Bank a.d. Novi Sad (Serbia)
Erste Bank Croatia (Erste & Steiermarkische Bank d.d.)
Erste Bank der oesterreichen Sparkassen AG
  Autoleasing EBV
  Sparkasse Salzburg
  Wohnbaubank
Erst Bank Hungary Nyrt.
Erste Bank Ukraine (formerly Bank Prestige)
Slovenska sporitelna a.s. (Slovakia)

COMPETITORS

BAWAG	Erste &
Banca Comerciala	Steiermarkische Bank
Romana	Investkredit
Bank Austria	OTP Bank
Credit Suisse	Oberbank AG
Deutsche Bank	RZB Group
Deutsche Post	UBS
Deutsche Postbank	UniCredit Bank AG

HISTORICAL FINANCIALS

Company Type: Public

Income Statement

FYE: December 31

	ASSETS ($ mil.)	NET INCOME ($ mil.)	INCOME AS % OF ASSETS	EMPLOYEES
12/13	275,176	83	0.0%	45,670
12/12	281,830	637	0.2%	49,381
12/11	271,633	(929)	—	50,452
12/10	275,621	1,359	0.5%	50,272
12/09	290,577	1,301	0.4%	50,488
Annual Growth	(1.4%)	(49.6%)	—	(2.5%)

2013 Year-End Financials

Return on assets: 0.0%
Return on equity: 0.5%
Long-term debt ($ mil.): —
No. of shares (mil.): 415
Sales ($ mil): 14,019
Dividends
Yield: 1.2%
Payout: —
Market value ($ mil.): 7,305

	STOCK PRICE ($) FY Close	P/E High/Low		PER SHARE ($) Earnings	Dividends	Book Value
12/13	17.60	—	—	(0.08)	0.21	37.56
12/12	16.05	32	15	1.15	0.00	45.10
12/11	8.65	—	—	(2.95)	0.00	41.92
12/10	23.77	20	10	3.11	0.28	50.23
12/09	18.84	21	3	3.41	0.32	51.54
Annual Growth	(1.7%)			—	(9.6%)	(7.6%)

Espirito Santo Financial Group S.A. (Luxembourg)

Espirito Santo Financial Group (ESFG) wields its earthly powers via two main entities: Banco Espirito Santo (BES) and Companhia de Seguros Tranquilidade one of Portugal's top insurance firms. BES is the largest commercial bank in Portugal where it has a 20% market share. Its Banco Espirito Santo de Investimento offers investment banking; Espirito Santo Activos Financeiros is a fund management firm. Although most of its operations are in Portugal ESFG has financial services and insurance interests across Europe Africa Brazil the Caribbean the Middle East and the US where it owns Espirito Santo Bank in Florida. Entities associated with the founding Espirito Santo family are ESFG's major shareholders.

In 2008 ESFG established a partnership with Danish company Saxo Bank acquiring a 5% stake in the bank with an option to buy an additional 5%. Saxo Bank specializes in online trading and will partner with ESFG's majority owned asset management trading firm Banco BEST to provide integrated products and services.

The group provides private banking services primarily in Switzerland (through Banque Privee Espirito Santo) the US and Portugal. Its ES Bankers (Dubai) unit offers asset management services in the United Arab Emirates.

HISTORY

The Espirito Santo financial empire traces its roots to a bank founded by Jose Maria de Espirito Santo Silva in Lisbon in 1884. After WWI Portugal underwent a major banking expansion and in 1920 the Espirito Santo family established Banco Espirito Santo which grew rapidly thanks to postwar expansion and speculation.

After Jose Maria's oldest son Jose fled the bank and the country in scandal his brother Ricardo led the massive growth of both the bank and the family's fortune. During the 1930s the Espirito Santos acquired a major interest in insurance company Tranquilidade and in 1937 Banco Espirito Santo merged with Banco Comercial de Lisboa (founded 1875) to create Banco Espirito Santo e Comercial de Lisboa.

The family's fortunes were aided by dictator Antonio de Oliveira Salazar who came to power in 1933. During WWII Salazar declared Portugal neutral and the country became a sanctuary for many of Europe's elite who brought the Espirito Santos business and contacts.

The Espirito Santo empire was fostered by Salazar's postwar protectionist policies. Banco Espirito Santo became one of Portugal's largest banks and Tranquilidade one of its largest insurance companies. The family also acquired large coffee sugar and palm-oil plantations in Portugal's colonies Angola and Mozambique. At their peak the Espirito Santo holdings were valued at $4 billion.

But the family's fortunes turned with political upheaval in Portugal during the 1970s. In 1974 the military overthrew Salazar's successor Marcelo Caetano. A year later the leftist government nationalized Portugal's major corporations including Banco Espirito Santo and Tranquilidade.

The family fled to London and pooled their savings to create a new company in Luxembourg Espirito Santo Financial Holding (ESFH). In the late 1970s they got a banking license in Brazil and later set up a fund management company in Switzerland and banks in Miami and Paris. The family's name attracted business and investors.

The Portuguese government reprivatized financial services organizations in 1986. That year ESFH and France's Credit Agricole opened Banco Internacional de Credito in Portugal. After raising money on the Eurobond market ESFH bought back control of Tranquilidade in 1990. A year later the company and a group of investors including Credit Agricole reacquired control of Banco Espirito Santo.

In 1993 ESFH reduced its interest in Banco Internacional de Credito to 47% (it regained 100% control in 1997). Since then the company has concentrated on Portugal. In the early 1990s recession rocked the economy –and the company. But in the mid-1990s despite poor commercial demand consumer-related services rebounded.

ESFH expanded its commercial banking network in 1995 and 1996. In 1997 the company and Brazil's Monteiro Aranha bought more than 60% of that country's Banco Boavista. The company also dropped "Holding" in favor of "Group" and the next year ESFG in a vote of confidence in Banco Boavista moved to raise its holdings in Banco Boavista.

In 1999 amid a flurry of speculation about Spanish/Portuguese banking mergers the company agreed to buy a majority interest in Spanish brokerage Benito y Monjardin. The company also moved to bolster its asset management operations by inking a deal to buy Portugal-based fund manager Gescapital.

In 2000 ESFG bought the majority stake of French credit institution Via Banque from BNP Paribas (it acquired the rest of Via Banque in 2001). The next year ESFG in conjunction with Portugal Telecom launched Banco Electronico de Servico Total (Banco Best) as a technologically integrated banking investment and brokerage service.

ESFG had sold the lion's share of Tranquilidade's insurance pension and investment products through its bank offices but the company reorganized in 2006 to separate the bank and non-bank distribution networks. The two bancassurance distribution units BES Vida (life insurance) and BES Seguros (non-life insurance) are now controlled and managed by Credit Agricole. Tranquilidade's non-life insurance business that is not distributed through banks remains with ESFG.

EXECUTIVES

Vice Chairman, Jose Manuel Pinheiro Espirito Santo Silva, age 68
Director, Patrick Monteiro de Barros, age 68
Director, Robert Studer, age 75
Director, Manuel Guerrero Peman, age 64
Director, Mario Mosqueira do Amaral, age 81
Director, Manuel Fernando de Moniz Galv?o Espirito Santo Silva, age 55
Director, Jackson B. Gilbert, age 81
Director, Philippe Guiral, age 65
Director, Manuel Antonio Ribeiro Serzedelo de Almeida, age 70
Director, Jose Maria Espirito Santo Silva Ricciardi, age 59
Director, Pedro Guilherme Beauvillain de Brito e Cunha, age 62
Director, Carlos Augusto Machado de Almeida Freitas, age 63
Director, Anibal da Costa Reis Oliveira, age 78
Director, Juan Villalonga Navarro, age 60
Director, Othman Benjelloun, age 81
Director, Jose Pedro Torres Garcia Caldeira da Silva, age 54

Director, Fernando Pedro Braga Pereira Coutinho, age 66
Director, Yves Alain Marie Morvan, age 74
Director, Alexandre da Paix?o Coelho, age 71
Controller and Director, Jose Carlos Cardoso Castella, age 64
Director, Horacio Lisboa Afonso, age 64
Director, Bernard Basecqz, age 68
CEO and Director, Gerard Laffineur Petracchini, age 51
Auditors: KPMG

LOCATIONS

HQ: Espirito Santo Financial Group S.A. (Luxembourg)
22-24 Boulevard Royal, Luxembourg L-2449
Phone: 212 270-3400   **Fax:** 212 980-1777
Web: www.esfg.com

PRODUCTS/OPERATIONS

Selected Subsidiaries

AdvanceCare - Gest?o de Servicos (health insurance)
Banco Espirito Santo de Investimento SA (investment bank)
Banco Espirito Santo SA (BES) (commercial bank)
Banque Privee Espirito Santo S.A. (private bank in Switzerland)
BES Investimento do Brasil (investment bank branch in Brazil)
Companhia de Seguros Tranquilidade SA (non-life insurance)
ES Bankers (Dubai) Limited (private bank in Dubai)
Espirito Santo Activos Financeiros (asset management)
Espirito Santo Saude (private health care provider in Portugal)
Seeguros LOGO (non-life insurance)
T-Vida (life insurance)

COMPETITORS

BBVA	Deutsche Bank
BNP Paribas	Grupo Santander
Banco Comercial Portugues	Itausa
Caixa Geral de Depositos	JPMorgan Chase
	Societe Generale
Citigroup	UBS
Credit Suisse	Zurich Insurance Group

HISTORICAL FINANCIALS

Company Type: Public

Income Statement

FYE: December 31

	ASSETS ($ mil.)	NET INCOME ($ mil.)	INCOME AS % OF ASSETS	EMPLOYEES
12/13	116,815	(1,189)	—	12,282
12/12	115,426	413	0.4%	12,036
12/11	108,675	156	0.1%	14,889
12/10	116,639	163	0.1%	14,813
12/09	122,905	226	0.2%	13,758
Annual Growth	(1.3%)	—	—	(2.8%)

2013 Year-End Financials

Return on assets: (-1.0%)
Return on equity: (-49.6%)
Long-term debt ($ mil.): —
No. of shares (mil.): 207
Sales ($ mil): 7,544

Dividends
 Yield: —
 Payout: —
Market value ($ mil.): 1,398

	STOCK PRICE ($) FY Close	P/E High/Low		PER SHARE ($) Earnings	Dividends	Book Value
12/13	6.75	—	—	(5.82)	0.00	8.54
12/12	6.75	6	2	2.45	0.00	14.00
12/11	6.50	15	2	3.25	0.00	15.60
12/10	15.00	36	14	1.39	0.00	26.50
12/09	22.65	31	15	2.30	0.00	28.70
Annual Growth	(26.1%)	—	—	—	—	(26.2%)

Etablissements Delhaize Freres et Cie Le Lion S.A. (Belgium)

This Belgian's roar can be heard from Brussels to Bali to Baltimore. Food retailer Delhaize Group runs about 3500 stores –including flagship banner Delhaize Le Lion –in the US Southeastern Europe and Asia. Food retailing accounts for a lion's share of the company's profits but it also engages in food wholesaling and the sale of pet food and pet products in Belgium. Delhaize Group's sales network consists of company-operated affiliated and franchised stores 85% of which conform to the supermarket format. Other store formats include neighborhood convenience and specialty stores. US subsidiary Delhaize America is one of the largest supermarket operators on the East Coast from Maine to Florida.

The operation of retail supermarkets accounts for nearly 90% of Delhaize Group's sales. Its US subsidiary Delhaize America is the third-largest operator of grocery stores along the East Coast of the US where it operates some 1500 stores in 17 states from Maine to Florida. Stores banners include Food Lion and Hannaford. It also operates two of fast-growing off-price formats: Bloom and the Bottom Dollar chain of limited-assortment discount supermarkets. In its home market of Belgium (including the Grand Duchy of Luxembourg) Delhaize operates a multi-format network of about 820 stores under about a half a dozen banners. It does business in Greece through some 250 Alfa-Beta stores and in five Balkan countries through the recently-acquired Delta Maxi chain of supermarkets. In Indonesia its 51%-owned PT Lion Super Indo chain operates stores on the island of Java where it has about an 11% share of the retail food market. Beyond retailing Delhaize supplies food to affiliated stores and independent customers. The company also sells pet food and pet products at about 135 Tom & Co. stores in Belgium.

Brussels-based Delhaize rings up nearly two-thirds of its sales and earns more than 60% of its operating profit in the US where it operates about 1650 supermarkets. Belgium and Luxembourg account for more than 20% of sales with Southern Europe (Albania Bosnia and Herzegovina Bulgaria Greece Montenegro Romania and Serbia) and Indonesia making up the rest.

Despite continued shaky economic conditions in Europe (including an economic catastrophe in Greece) and parts of the US Delhaize Group rang up more than Â21 billion ($29.4 billion) in sales in 2011 a 1.3% increase vs. 2010. The company's operating profit fell 21% over the same period. The US operation outperformed Belgium with sales up more than 2% vs. 1% respectively. While growth in the US was modest it was an improvement over the past few years when Delhaize America posted declining annual sales comparisons. Delhaize's Southeastern Europe and Asia segment saw sales climb by nearly a third driven by the acquisition half way through the year of Delta Maxi's 485 retail stores in the Baltic states and expansion in Indonesia. Looking ahead Delhaize expects Delta Maxi to generate approximately Â1.3 billion in revenues in 2012.

To grow Delhaize Group is setting its sights on newer and faster growing opportunities. The purchase of the Delta Maxi stores in Southeastern Europe fits the bill. Delhaize in July 2011 it acquired

Serbia's leading food retail chain for about Â630 million (nearly $875 million) from businessman Miroslav Miskovic. Delta Maxi operates about 485 retail stores in Albania Bosnia Bulgaria Montenegro and Serbia. Combined with its existing operations in Greece where it owns the #2 food retailer Alfa-Beta and Romania (Mega Image) the Belgian retailer is now a leading player with about 850 grocery stores in the seven countries. Fast-growing Indonesia is another focus of growth for the Belgian retailer. In 2011 the company added 16 new stores bringing the total to about 90 supermarkets there. Other growth formats include limited-assortment low-cost supermarkets: Bottom Dollar in the US and Red Market (launched in 2009) in Europe.

HISTORY

Two brothers and a brother-in-law —all teachers —founded Delhaize in 1867 in Charleroi Belgium. A professor of commercial sciences Jules Delhaize wanted to try out his ideas about food retailing such as creating a network of stores and a centralized warehouse and charging set prices for items. He enlisted the aid of his brother Edouard and his brother-in-law Jules Vieujant. The trio picked the symbol that has become synonymous with the company —the lion because it represented strength and it was the emblem of their native country. A third brother Adolphe later started his own food-retailing operation also with multiple branches. (His operations were merged into Delhaize in 1950.)

The company moved to Brussels in 1871. In the early 1880s the company moved closer to a rail line for better transportation services opened a large warehouse and other operations and began setting up factories to produce its own brand-name foods and beverages.

Although it still had stores only in Belgium (more than 500 by 1914) the company had an international presence because of its appearance at exhibitions such as the St. Louis World's Fair in 1904. After WWI the company began investigating possibilities for international trade by sending a delegation to the US and Canada.

At the beginning of WWII Delhaize had 744 branches and 1500 affiliated shops including several in the Belgian Congo. At war's end Delhaize started closing some of its factories although it kept a few.

Taking a page from the American supermarkets it had been studying Delhaize in 1957 opened Europe's first full self-serve supermarket complete with pre-packaged meat frozen foods and fresh produce and the look of American stores —bright colors checkout stands and fluorescent lighting. Delhaize went public in 1962 as S.A. Delhaize Freres et Cie "Le Lion."

In 1972 Jacques LeClercq the great-grandson of Jules Delhaize persuaded the Delhaize board that future opportunities for growth lay in the US. Two years later with the enactment of "padlock laws" to halt the spread of hypermarkets in Belgium and similar restrictions occurring elsewhere in Europe the company bought 32% of Food Town an American chain with 19 stores. (Delhaize bought a controlling interest in Food Town in 1976.) A few years later Delhaize bought Food Giant in Atlanta and began expanding beyond the supermarket in Belgium setting up the Di body care shops and in 1981 the AD (Delhaize Affiliates) chain to offer wholesale and management advice services.

Food Town became Food Lion in 1983. Two years later Delhaize opened a new chain Cub Food in Atlanta. In 1989 it set up Caddy-Home a home-delivery service and Tom & Co stores selling pet foods and supplies.

International expansion was the byword for the 1990s. Delhaize set up Delvita in 1991 in the Czech Republic. Further acquisitions included controlling interests in Alfa-Beta Vassilopoulos (Greece 1992) the Kash n' Karry chain (US 1996) and interests in supermarket chains in Thailand and Indonesia (1997). Acquisitions in 1999 included 49% of Shop n Save (Singapore) and 28 Farmer Jack stores (US).

Expansion continued in 2000 with further acquisitions in Thailand and Romania and the mid-year US acquisition of Hannaford Bros. In April 2001 Delhaize acquired all of Delhaize America merging its US operations and listing on the New York Stock Exchange (the only Belgian company on that august body). In late 2001 the company shut down its Atlanta-based joint venture 19 Super Discount Markets in which it held a 60% ownership stake.

In October 2003 Delhaize Group completed the acquisition of 43 Harveys supermarkets in Florida and central and southern Georgia filling in an area where Food Lion has a limited presence. Following the acquisition Harveys became the Delhaize Group's fourth US banner. In November Delhaize agreed to sell its 49% stake in Singapore food retailer Shop N Save to Cold Storage Singapore for Â21.9.

Delhaize Group shut down its Food Lion Thailand operation in August 2004 with the sale of 20 stores there to Central Food Retail Co. and the closure of its remaining locations. In November the company —through its US subsidiary Hannaford Bros. —acquired the 19-store Victory Super Markets chain Massachusetts and New Hampshire for $175 million. At year end Baron Gui de Vaucleroy retired down as chairman of the board and was succeeded by Georges Jacobs.

In May 2005 Delhaize Group completed the acquisition of Cash Fresh a chain of 43 supermarkets mainly in northeastern Belgium for about Â169 million (including real estate). In June the company sold all 11 Delvita stores in Slovakia to Germany's Rewe exiting that market.

Stiff competition in its home market from discounters including ALDI Lidl and French hypermarket operator Carrefour led Delhaize Group to cut prices on some 1000 items in early 2006.

The following year the Belgian grocer sold its Delvita stores in the Czech Republic also to Rewe. Also the last of the company's Kash n' Karry stores in Florida were converted to the Sweetbay banner.

In April 2008 Delhaize through its Alfa-Beta subsidiary in Greece acquired 34 Plus Hellas supermarkets there from Germany's Tengelmann for about $108 million. Mega Image in 2008 nearly doubled its store network through acquisitions including the purchase of the 14-store La Fourmi chain for Â19 million (about $26 million).

To streamline its European operations the company in July 2009 sold its four stores in Germany to rival REWE. (Delhaize entered the German market in 2003.)

In 2010 the company added 110 new stores: 40 in the US 28 in Belgium 14 in Greece 21 in Romania and seven in Indonesia. Delhaize acquired all of the minority shares in Alfa-Beta and delisted the company from the Athens Stock Market in 2010.

In July 2011 Delhaize acquired Serbia's Delta Maxi chain of stores from businessman Miroslav Miskovic for about Â630 million (nearly $875 million). Delta Maxi is Serbia's #1 food retailer with 365 stores there. The grocery chain operates about 100 other stores in Bulgaria Bosnia and Herzegovina Montenegro and Albania.

In June 2014 Delhaize sold its Sweetbay Reid's and Harveys chains in the southeastern US to rival BI-LO Holding for $246 million. In a separate transaction the company sold its distribution center in Plant city Florida to C&S Wholesale Grocers for $28 million.

EXECUTIVES

Executive Vice President General Counsel and General Secretary, Maura Abeln Smith, age 58
EVP; President and CEO Delhaize America, Roland C. Smith, age 59
Executive Vice President and Chief Financial Officer, Pierre B. Bouchut, age 59
President and CEO, Frans W.H. Muller, age 53
EVP Human Resources and Organizational Development, Nicolas Hollanders, age 53
Chairman, Mats Jansson, age 63
Vice President Delhaize America, Greg Amoroso
Vice President Treasury Delhaize Group, Miguel Gonzales
Executive Vice President of Delhaize Group and Chief Executive Officer Southeastern Europe, Kostas Macheras
Board Member, Jack J. Stahl, age 60
Board Member, Claire H. Babrowski, age 55
Board Member, Robert J. Murray, age 71
Group President CEO and Board Member, Pierre-Olivier Beckers, age 53
Board Member, Hugh G. Farrington, age 68
Board Member, Didier Smits, age 51
Board Member, Jacques de Vaucleroy, age 52
Board Member, Baron Luc Vansteenkiste, age 66
Auditors: DeloitteBedrijfsrevisorenBV

LOCATIONS

HQ: Etablissements Delhaize Freres et Cie Le Lion S.A. (Belgium)
Square Marie Curie 40, Brussels 1070
Phone: (32) 2 412 22 11   **Fax:** (32) 2 412 22 22
Web: www.delhaizegroup.com

Sales

	% of total
US	65
Belgium &	23
Southeast Europe &	12
Total	**100**

2011 Stores

	No.
US	1,650
Belgium &	821
Greece	251
Romania	105
Indonesia	89
Serbia	366
Bosnia and	44
Bulgaria	42
Montenegro	22
Albania	18
Total	**3,408**

PRODUCTS/OPERATIONS

Sales

	% of total
Retail	
Perishable	38
Non-perishable	36
Nonfood	15
Wholesale	11
Total	**100**

Selected Store Banners

Belgium
  AD Delhaize
  Delhaize Le Lion
  Proxy Delhaize
  Red Market
  Shop 'n Go
  Tom & Co
Greece
  Alfa-Beta
Indonesia

Super Indo
Romania
  La Fourmi
  Mega Image
Serbia
  Delta Maxi
US
  Bloom
  Bottom Dollar Food
  Food Lion
  Hannaford Bros. Co.
  Harveys Supermarket
  Sweetbay Supermarket

COMPETITORS

ALDI	ITM Entreprises
Ahold U.S.A.	Kroger
Albertsons	METRO AG
Auchan	Migros
BI-LO	Publix
Carrefour	REWE
Casino Guichard	Royal Ahold
Coop	Shaw's
Costco Wholesale	Tengelmann
DeMoulas Super Markets	Tesco
Golub	Wal-Mart
Harris Teeter	Winn-Dixie

HISTORICAL FINANCIALS
Company Type: Public

Income Statement
FYE: December 31

	REVENUE ($ mil.)	NET INCOME ($ mil.)	NET PROFIT MARGIN	EMPLOYEES
12/13	29,060	246	0.8%	161,000
12/12	29,968	138	0.5%	158,000
12/11	27,316	614	2.2%	160,000
12/10	27,905	768	2.8%	138,622
12/09	28,722	740	2.6%	138,119
Annual Growth	0.3%	(24.0%)	—	3.9%

2013 Year-End Financials

Debt ratio: 33.2%	No. of shares (mil.): 101
Return on equity: 3.4%	Dividends
Cash ($ mil.): 1,581	Yield: 2.2%
Current ratio: 1.17	Payout: 24.6%
Long-term debt ($ mil.): 3,451	Market value ($ mil.): 6,016

	STOCK PRICE ($) FY Close	P/E High/Low		PER SHARE ($) Earnings	Dividends	Book Value
12/13	59.42	73	41	2.42	0.33	68.94
12/12	40.55	96	50	1.37	0.41	67.82
12/11	56.35	36	20	6.05	0.88	69.56
12/10	73.71	27	20	7.60	0.36	67.45
12/09	76.72	33	19	7.32	0.39	63.32
Annual Growth	(6.2%)	—	—	(24.1%)	(3.8%)	2.1%

European Investment Bank

The biggest international lovefest since Esperanto the European Investment Bank (EIB) is the financial backbone of the European Union (EU). Led by finance ministers from EU countries the bank makes loans for trans-European enterprise and infrastructure projects focusing on less-developed EU countries. About 90% of the loans go to projects located within the EU; major loan categories are transportation and energy. The bank

also offers development aid to some non-European countries. The EIB owns a majority of the European Investment Fund (EIF) which invests in venture capital funds and debt financing for small businesses in the EU.

The EIB provides loans and finances the development of infrastructure and businesses according to the policies of the EU. Loan categories also include health care organizations educational ventures and housing throughout the EU and beyond. Most of the 150 non-European countries it makes loans to are former colonies of European countries. The EIB which loans more money annually than the World Bank has lending policies geared to foster economic integration and social cohesion among current and potential EU member nations.

A board of governors (consisting of EU member states' finance ministers) appoints a 28-person board of directors (along with 18 alternates) to manage the bank's affairs. One director and one alternate represent the European Commission. The board of directors meets once a month to approve loans review policies and suggest changes in the EIB's credit policy. The EIB also employs an audit committee and a management committee to oversee daily functions. The bank's president chairs the management committee's meetings.

Although the EIB enjoys unique legal and financial autonomy within the EU it must also remain competitive with private banks in the international market. The bank's concerns for economic parity among member nations sometimes pit it against the EU which seeks to bring Europe's poorer cousins of the east into the Union's political fold. Watchdog groups have called for the bank to be more open in its decision-making process and policies arguing that large infrastructure projects funded by EIB loans have a substantial environmental impact.

The EIB's clients include public entities EU and non-EU governments and large private corporations.

HISTORY

The European Investment Bank (EIB) has its roots in the Messina Conference of 1955 when the soon-to-be members of the European Economic Community (EEC) proposed a central public body to oversee the spread of wealth between rich and poor European nations.

In 1958 the Treaty of Rome established the EEC and the EIB was founded to make and guarantee loans that helped develop infrastructure and improvements in member countries. The six founding countries were Belgium France Italy Luxembourg the Netherlands and West Germany.

The Yaounde (Cameroon) Convention of 1963 saw the EIB expand its lending activities to 17 African former colonies of European countries. Under the Yaounde Convention these nations were provided financial aid and trading advantages.

In 1973 the UK Denmark and Ireland joined the EEC and the EIB grew in size assets and lending power. The Lome (Togo) Convention of 1975 expanded the Yaounde Convention to include 70 more African Caribbean and Pacific countries. Meanwhile the EEC continued to grow adding Greece (1981) and Spain and Portugal (1986). It became the more fully integrated European Union (EU) in 1993 (Finland Austria and Sweden were added in 1995). The bank's loans first exceeded those of the World Bank in 1992.

In 1994 the European Investment Fund (EIF) was created by the EIB the EU and private European banks to invest in venture capital funds and to guarantee financed debt.

Environmental groups denounced the EIB for loans they considered ecologically damaging in the mid-1990s; those included loans for a Sweden-

Denmark bridge a gold mine in Papua New Guinea a water project in Lesotho (Africa) and a gas pipeline between Bolivia and Brazil.

In 2000 EIF realigned itself as the EIB's specialist risk capital arm while the EIB raised its stake to more then 50% of the fund.

EXECUTIVES

Chairman and President, Philippe Maystadt, age 66
Director General Credit Risk, Pierluigi Gilibert
Director General Lending Operations - Other Countries, Jean-Louis Biancarelli
VP, Philippe de Fontaine Vive Curtaz, age 55
Chairman Board of Governors, Charilaos Stavrakis, age 58
VP, Ploutarchos K. Sakellaris
VP, Dario Scannapieco, age 46
VP, Simon Brooks, age 60
VP, Carlos da Silva Costa
VP, Matthias Kollatz-Ahnen
VP, Eva Srejber
VP, Marta Gajecka
Auditors: KPMGAuditS.a.r.l.

LOCATIONS

HQ: European Investment Bank
98-100, Boulevard Konrad Adenauer, Luxembourg L-2950
Phone: (352) 43 79 1   **Fax:** (352) 43 77 04
Web: www.eib.org
The EIB has offices in Australia Austria Belgium Egypt Finland France the French Caribbean Germany Greece Italy Kenya Luxembourg Morocco Poland Portugal Romania Senegal South Africa Spain Tunisia and the UK.

COMPETITORS

BNP Paribas	Deutsche Bank
Banco Comercial Portugues	National Bank of Greece
Banco Popular Espa?ol	Royal Bank of Scotland
Citigroup	UniCredit Bank AG

HISTORICAL FINANCIALS
Company Type: Public

Income Statement
FYE: December 31

	REVENUE ($ mil.)	NET INCOME ($ mil.)	NET PROFIT MARGIN	EMPLOYEES
12/13	32,068	3,505	10.9%	0
12/12	34,301	3,611	10.5%	0
12/11	32,379	2,964	9.2%	0
12/10	26,578	3,539	13.3%	2,077
12/09	19,156	(3,285)	—	1,896
Annual Growth	13.7%	—	—	—

2013 Year-End Financials

Debt ratio: —	No. of shares (mil.): —
Return on equity: 4.4%	Dividends
Cash ($ mil.): 36,652	Yield: —
Current ratio: 1.45	Payout: —
Long-term debt ($ mil.): —	Market value ($ mil.): —

Fiat Chrysler Automobiles NV

LOCATIONS

HQ: Fiat Chrysler Automobiles NV
25 St. James' Street, London SW1A 1HA
Phone: (44) 20 776 0311
Web: www.fcagroup.com

HISTORICAL FINANCIALS

Company Type: Public

Income Statement

FYE: December 31

	REVENUE ($ mil.)	NET INCOME ($ mil.)	NET PROFIT MARGIN	EMPLOYEES
12/13	119,258	1,244	1.0%	229,053
12/12	110,406	57	0.1%	218,311
12/11	77,036	1,550	2.0%	197,021
Annual Growth	24.4%	(10.4%)	—	7.8%

2013 Year-End Financials

Debt ratio: 47.8%
Return on equity: 12.4%
Cash ($ mil.): 26,784
Current ratio: 1.49
Long-term debt ($ mil.): 41,691

No. of shares (mil.): 1,216
Dividends
  Yield: —
  Payout: —
Market value ($ mil.): —

	STOCK PRICE ($) FY Close	P/E High/Low		PER SHARE ($) Earnings	Dividends	Book Value
12/13	0.00	—	—	1.01	0.00	9.43
12/12	0.00	—	—	0.05	0.00	6.71
Annual Growth	—	—	—	362.1%	—	18.5%

First Gulf Bank

LOCATIONS

HQ: First Gulf Bank
P.O. Box 6316, Abu Dhabi
Phone: (971) 2 681 6666   **Fax:** (971) 2 681 3169
Web: www.firstgulfbank.ae

HISTORICAL FINANCIALS

Company Type: Public

Income Statement

FYE: December 31

	ASSETS ($ mil.)	NET INCOME ($ mil.)	INCOME AS % OF ASSETS	EMPLOYEES
12/14	57,767	1,539	2.7%	0
12/13	53,098	1,299	2.4%	1,452
12/12	47,650	1,130	2.4%	1,112
12/11	42,874	1,009	2.4%	930
12/10	38,321	931	2.4%	956
Annual Growth	10.8%	13.4%	—	—

2014 Year-End Financials

Return on assets: 2.7%
Return on equity: 17.3%
Long-term debt ($ mil.): —
No. of shares (mil.): —
Sales ($ mil): 3,000

Dividends
  Yield: —
  Payout: —
Market value ($ mil.): —

Formosa Petrochemical Corp

Formosa Petrochemical Corporation (FPCC) is second only to Chinese Petroleum Corporation for oil refining in Taiwan. The company produces refined petroleum products (jet fuel liquid petroleum gas and gasoline) and petrochemicals (ethylene propylene and butadiene) from its naphtha cracking operations. It owns gas stations through subsidiary Formosa Oil. FPCC also sells electricity and steam from its co-generation plants. Its engineering and maintenance divisions carry out planning construction and daily maintenance services on behalf of group companies.

Geographic Segment

FPCC sells its products worldwide. In 2011 Taiwan accounted for 58% of the company's revenues.

Sales and Marketing

In 2011 Formosa Chemicals & Fibers accounted for 19% of sales; Formosa Plastics 13%.

Financial Performance

FPCC's revenues increased by 7% in 2011 and its net income decreased by 45%.

Strategy

In 2011 the company restarted its 700000 tons-per-year No. 1 naphtha cracker after a four-month shutdown due to a fire.

Ownership

Formosa Plastics owns 29% of FPCC; affiliates Formosa Chemicals & Fibers and Nan Ya Plastics also own 25% and 24% respectively.

Company Background

The three group companies formed FPCC in 1992 to build and run a giant integrated petrochemicals facility called the No. 6 Naphtha Cracking Project.

EXECUTIVES

Executive Director, Wilfred Wang
Senior Vice President Hang, C. Y. Su
SVP and Director, Han-Ting Chen
Vice President President's Office, Keh-Yen Lin
Chief Financial Officer, Ming-Hsiung Shih
Vice President of Engineering, Ja-Tao Huang
Vice President of Maintenance, Tsai-Shan Kao
Chairman, Chen Bao-Lang
SVP and Director, Han-Ting Chen
Director, Chi-Tong Lo
Director, C. P. Chang
Auditors: DiwanErnst&Young

LOCATIONS

HQ: Formosa Petrochemical Corp
No. 1-1, Taisu Industrial Park, Mailiao Township, Yunlin County 638
Phone: (886) 5 6812345
Web: www.fpcc.com.tw

Sales

	% of total
Taiwan	58
Singapore	8
China	3
Korea	1
Other	30
Total	**100**

PRODUCTS/OPERATIONS

Sales

	% of total
Petrochemical	29
Diesel	25
Gasoline	15
Jet	6
Electricity	3
Steam	2
Other petrochemical	20
Total	**100**

COMPETITORS

BASF-YPC	OCI Company
CPC	Total Petrochemicals
ExxonMobil Chemical	

HISTORICAL FINANCIALS

Company Type: Public

Income Statement

FYE: December 31

	REVENUE ($ mil.)	NET INCOME ($ mil.)	NET PROFIT MARGIN	EMPLOYEES
12/13	31,230	900	2.9%	3,978
12/12	30,817	93	0.3%	6,507
12/11	0	0	—	6,426
12/10	25,736	1,406	5.5%	5,604
12/09	19,867	1,225	6.2%	6,275
Annual Growth	12.0%	(7.4%)	—	(10.8%)

2013 Year-End Financials

Debt ratio: 1.4%
Return on equity: 12.0%
Cash ($ mil.): 558
Current ratio: 2.16
Long-term debt ($ mil.): 3,945

No. of shares (mil.): —
Dividends
  Yield: —
  Payout: —
Market value ($ mil.): —

Fresenius SE & Co KGaA

Fresenius SE takes a free hand with dialysis and infusion products and services. The company offers a wide range of health products and services through its four core business segments: Fresenius Medical Care Fresenius Kabi Fresenius Helios and Fresenius Vamed. The company's Medical Care division specializes in treating chronic kidney failure at some 3250 dialysis clinics worldwide. Fresenius Kabi provides nutrition infusion and IV therapies and related equipment. Fresenius Helios operates private hospitals in Germany while Fresenius Vamed offers facility management project development and other services to hospitals and health facilities. Fresenius SE has operations in more than 100 countries.

Geographic Reach

North America and Europe are the German health care company's largest markets contributing 42% and 40% of annual revenue respectively. The Asia-Pacific region (China Japan) accounts for about 10% of revenue followed by Latin America (6%) and South Africa (2%).

Financial Performance

Fresenius reported sales of Â20.3 billion in 2013 a 5% increase versus 2012. Net income rose 12% over the same period to $1.05 billion. The company's largest business Medical Care (54% of 2013 revenue) posted a 2% gain in revenue while Fresenius Kabi's sales rose 10% year over year. The company's Vamed unit posted a 21% gain in revenue.

Strategy

The company has been aggressively expanding its core operating segments through both organic growth and acquisitions. Its majority owned Fresenius Medical Care subsidiary which accounts for more than half of the firm's revenues has expanded its dialysis service and its equipment manufacturing operations through acquisitions. Though Fresenius Medical Care primarily grows through purchases of single clinics or small dialysis groups it occasionally makes larger acquisitions. For instance in 2010 the business acquired Asia Renal Care which operates about 100 clinics throughout Asia. It also added 70 European clinics in 2011 by purchasing International Dialysis Centers (IDC) and it acquired some 260 clinics in the US through the 2012 purchase of Liberty Dialysis (including the Renal Advantage unit). The division is also widening its operations in the fields of home dialysis and renal pharmaceuticals.

Fresenius has also expanded Fresenius Kabi's operations through a number of acquisitions in recent years. In 2014 for instance Kabi acquired the privately-held Brazilian pharmaceutical company Novafarma Industria Farmaceutica Ltda. to further its strategy to expand its market presence in emerging markets. Previously Kabi purchased Fenwal a developer and manufacturer of blood collection separation and transfusion technologies for some $1.1 billion in 2012. In addition Fresenius Kabi is working to expand in the generic injectables market by developing and releasing new IV pharmaceutical products and expanding distribution of existing drugs both in the US and international markets. Kabi is also working to increase its offerings of infusion and nutrition equipment such as feeding tubes and drug delivery pumps.

Fresenius Vamed provides hospitals with engineering equipment planning and other upkeep-related services. Helios is seeking to increase brand recognition and add more facilities as Germany's hospitals become increasingly privatized while Vamed is focused on growth of engineering and other specialty services. A hard-won acquisition in 2014 of a rival German hospital operator has made Fresenius Helios the leading private hospital operator in Europe with 117 hospitals across Germany.

Mergers and Acquisitions

In a move that created the largest private hospital operator in Europe in February 2014 Fresenius Helios acquired 38 hospitals and 11 outpatient facilities from Rhon-Klinikum AGfor $4.1 billion. The purchase gave Fresenius Helios 117 hospitals across Germany. The deal came a year after Fresenius attempted to acquire all of Rhon-Klinikum but failed. The purchase will add about Â2 billion in annual sales.

This action followed steps taken in 2011 when the Helios unit expanded its hospital network by acquiring a majority stake in the Damp Hospital Group in northern Germany. The purchase added seven acute care hospitals and four rehabilitation hospitals with a total of more than 4100 beds to the Helios network. A maximum care hospital in Duisburg was also added to the regional network that year.

HISTORY

Fresenius was founded as the Hirsch Pharmacy in 1462. The Fresenius family took over its ownership in the 18th century and converted it into a pharmaceutical manufacturing entity in 1912.

Fresenius entered the dialysis equipment market in 1966. The company formed its Fresenius Medical Care unit in 1996 when it merged its dialysis systems division with National Medical Care (NMC).

In 1999 Fresenius formed its Fresenius Kabi division by combining its infusion pharmaceutical operations with the former infusion solution business of drugmaker Pharmacia & Upjohn which it acquired the previous year.

The company conducted a number of expansion efforts within the Kabi division in the following decade including the 2007 purchase of IV drug

manufacturing firms Labesfal (Portugal) and Filaxis (Argentina) as well as German medical device maker Clinico. Also that year the company bought the artificial colloid product business of Kyorin to build up a presence in the Tokyo market.

It then purchased Indian oncology drug manufacturer Dabur Pharma in 2008. Also that year the unit expanded its reach in the US market for injectable drugs by acquiring US generics maker APP Pharmaceuticals for $3.7 billion plus debt.

Following the acquisition of German private clinic operator Helios Kliniken Fresenius refreshed its acute care operations by separating its hospital division (Fresenius ProServe) into two business segments Fresenius Helios and Fresenius Vamed in 2008.

EXECUTIVES

Deputy Chairman, Gerhard Rupprecht, age 66
CEO Fresenius Medical Care, Ben J. Lipps, age 74
SVP Investor Relations, Birgit Grund
Chairman Managing Board, Ulf M. (Mark) Schneider, age 49
CEO Fresenius Kabi, Rainer Baule, age 66
Chairman, Dieter Schenk, age 62
SVP Corporate Communications and Public Affairs, Joachim Weith
CFO, Stephan Sturm, age 51
CEO Fresenius Helios, Francesco De Meo, age 51
CEO Fresenius Vamed, Ernst Wastler, age 55
Director of Corporate Communications, Matthias Link
Vice President Investor Relations, Leslie Iltgen
Member of the Management Board; CEO Fresenius Helios, Francesco Meo
Chief Legal and Compliance Officer; Labor Relations Director; Member of the Management Board, Juergen Goetz
Deputy Chairman of the Supervisory Board; Employee Representative, Niko Stumpfoegger
Deputy Chairman, Gerhard Rupprecht, age 66
Director, Gerhard Roggemann
Director, Klaus-Peter Muller
Deputy Chairman, Niko Stumpfogger
Director, H. C. Roland Berger
Director, Dario Ilossi
Director, Konrad Kolbl
Director, Stefan Schubert
Director, Rainer Stein
Director, D. Michael Albrecht
Director, Dieter Reu?
Member of the Supervisory Board, Dieter Reuss
Member of the Supervisory Board, Klaus-Peter Mueller
Member of the Supervisory Board, Konrad Koelbl
Auditors: KPMGDeutscheTreuhand-GesellschaftAG

LOCATIONS

HQ: Fresenius SE & Co KGaA
Else-Kroener-Strasse 1, Bad Homburg D-61352
Phone: (49) 6172 608 0   **Fax:** (49) 6172 608 2488
Web: www.fresenius.com

Sales

	% of total
North	43
Europe	42
Asia	8
Latin America & other	7
Total	**100**

PRODUCTS/OPERATIONS

Sales

	% of total
Fresenius Medical Care	57
Fresenius Helios	17
Total	**100**

Selected Services

Fresenius Medical Care
  Dialysis facility operation
  Disease management
  Disposable dialysis supplies
  Hemodialysis equipment
  Peritoneal dialysis equipment
Fresenius Kabi
  Blood volume replacement
  Enteral nutrition
  Infusion and IV devices
  Infusion therapies
  IV generic drugs
  Parenteral nutrition
  Tranfusion products
Fresenius Helios
  HELIOS Kliniken Group (61 private hospitals Germany)
Fresenius Vamed
  Construction management
  Facility planning
  Maintenance services
  Operational management
  Project development
  Staff recruitment and training

COMPETITORS

Asahi Kasei	Hospira
B. Braun Melsungen	Johnson & Johnson
Baxter International	NxStage
Becton Dickinson	Ranbaxy Laboratories
Ben Venue	Renal Advantage
Bio-Reference Labs	Terumo
DaVita	Teva
Dialysis Clinic Inc	

HISTORICAL FINANCIALS

Company Type: Public

Income Statement

FYE: December 31

	REVENUE ($ mil.)	NET INCOME ($ mil.)	NET PROFIT MARGIN	EMPLOYEES
12/13	27,990	1,391	5.0%	178,337
12/12	25,425	1,220	4.8%	169,324
12/11	21,370	892	4.2%	149,351
12/10	21,376	832	3.9%	127,552
12/09	20,404	711	3.5%	130,510
Annual Growth	**8.2%**	**18.3%**	**—**	**8.1%**

2013 Year-End Financials

Debt ratio: 53.7%
Return on equity: 13.5%
Cash ($ mil.): 1,189
Current ratio: 1.32
Long-term debt ($ mil.): 15,122

No. of shares (mil.): 539
Dividends
  Yield: 0.9%
  Payout: 2.3%
Market value ($ mil.): 10,429

	STOCK PRICE ($) FY Close	P/E High/Low	PER SHARE ($) Earnings	Dividends	Book Value
12/13	19.35	19 13	2.58	0.12	20.93
12/12	14.40	15 10	2.32	0.10	18.82
12/11	11.70	14 14	1.80	0.00	15.77
Annual Growth	**28.6%**	**— —**	**9.4%**	**—**	**7.3%**

Fujitsu Ltd.

Fujitsu Limited's supply of high-tech offerings seems almost limitless. The company provides customers worldwide with products ranging from computers and electronic components to air conditioners and bar code scanners. Fujitsu's computer products include PCs servers storage systems and peripherals. One of the top IT services firms in the world it provides consulting infrastructure management and systems integration. Other lines include a wide range of software telecommunications transmission equipment consumer electronics and semiconductors. Fujitsu also owns Nifty one of Japan's leading ISPs. The company gets the vast majority of its sales in Japan.

Already struggling amid the global economic slump —with a year-over-year decline in net sales of 3% in 2010 —Fujitsu booked an extraordinary loss of Å11.6 billion ($150.8 million) and operating income fell Å13 billion ($169 million) primarily as a result of the Great East Japan Earthquake in March 2011. Year-over-year net sales were again down 3% in 2011 but rose 1.4% to $55.4 billion the following year.

The company's Technology Solutions unit generates the largest portion of its revenue. In addition to consulting and outsourcing this division provides systems integration application development hardware installation and other services. Fujitsu Services is among the company's key IT services subsidiaries. Fujitsu's software offerings include customer relationship management (CRM) supply chain management (SCM) and enterprise resource planning (ERP) applications. Revenue for technology solutions declined about 4% in 2011.

Fujitsu's ubiquitous solutions division includes PCs tablets mobile phones and audio and navigation equipment. Ubiquitous solutions (22% of sales) rose 0.5% in 2011. The device solutions segment which includes LSI devices and electronic components and represents 12% of revenue rose 7% in 2011.

In 2012 Fujitsu spun off its access network business as a new company called Access Network Technology Ltd. The venture is 52.8% owned by Fujitsu with the remainder held by NTT DoCoMo (19.9%) NEC (17.8%) and Fujitsu Semiconductor (9.5%). The joint venture will develop chips that control wireless communications and signals but will outsource production of those chips. The move is intended to take take on industry leader QUALCOMM in the fast-growing market for mobile communications chips used smartphones and tablets.

The Access Network Technology venture was the result of a failed attempt by the company to establish a partnership with NTT Docomo Fujitsu Semiconductor NEC Panasonic Mobile Communications and Samsung Electronics earlier in 2012. Intended to give the companies a way to develop and market their own cellphone chips the venture was abandoned after the partners were unable to come to an agreement over details.

In 2010 the company combined its cell phone business with that of key rival Toshiba in hopes that the new business (anticipated to be the largest cell phone maker in Japan) would be better able to compete with global industry leaders. Fujitsu carried an 80% stake in the new company Fujitsu Toshiba Mobile Communications Limited until it bought Toshiba's remaining 20% in 2012 making the company a subsidiary Fujitsu Mobile Communications Limited.

Fujitsu generates most of its revenues in Japan but its growth strategy includes strengthening its international operations with a goal of increasing the percentage of sales outside Japan to 40%. To increase its international operations the company acquired KAZ Group the IT arm of Australian telecom giant Telstra in 2009. It also bought out Siemens' stake in their European computer joint venture Fujitsu Siemens for E450 million ($570 million) in 2009. The unit is now called Fujitsu Technology Solutions.

Fujitsu's efforts to strengthen its North American operations have included consolidating a number of its subsidiaries in the region. In 2009 the company combined three of its US-based subsidiaries —Fujitsu Consulting Fujitsu Computer Systems and Fujitsu Transaction Solutions —to form Fujitsu America.

HISTORY

Furukawa Electric and Siemens created Fuji Electric in 1923 to produce electrical equipment. Fuji Electric spun off Fujitsu its communications division in 1935. Originally a maker of telephone equipment Fujitsu produced anti-aircraft weapons during WWII. After the war it became one of four major suppliers to state-owned monopoly Nippon Telegraph and Telephone (NTT) and continued to benefit from Japan's rapid economic recovery in the 1950s and 1960s.

With encouragement from Japan's Ministry of International Trade and Industry (MITI) Fujitsu developed the country's first commercial computer in 1954. MITI erected trade barriers to protect Japan's computer industry and in the early 1960s sponsored the production of mainframe computers directing Fujitsu to develop the central processing unit. The company expanded into semiconductor production and factory automation in the late 1960s. Its factory automation business was spun off as Fujitsu Fanuc in 1972.

Fujitsu gained badly needed technology when it bought 30% of IBM-plug-compatible manufacturer Amdahl in 1972. By 1979 Fujitsu had passed IBM to become Japan's #1 computer manufacturer. In Europe Fujitsu entered into computer marketing ventures with Siemens (1978) and UK mainframe maker ICL (1981). In the US it teamed with TRW to sell point-of-sale systems (1980) assuming full control of the operation in 1983. Fujitsu released its first supercomputer in 1982.

Fujitsu bought 80% of ICL (from the UK's Standard Telephones & Cables) in 1990 for $1.3 billion. In 1993 it formed a joint venture with Advanced Micro Devices to make flash memory products.

The company doubled its share of Japan's PC market in 1995 to more than 18% and the next year expanded its PC business globally. In 1997 Fujitsu paid about $878 million for the 58% of Amdahl it didn't already own. The next year it bought the 10% of ICL it didn't own. Fujitsu's 1998 earnings suffered from a slump in the semiconductor market Amdahl-related expenses and a weak Asian economy.

Also in 1998 Naoyuki Akikusa son of a former NTT president became head of Fujitsu. He began trimming some operations while ramping up the company's Internet activities. Fujitsu in 1999 became full owner of online services provider Nifty Serve making it Japan's largest Internet service provider. It merged Nifty with the operations of another ISP called InfoWeb. Also that year Siemens and Fujitsu combined their European computer operations in a 50-50 joint venture (Fujitsu Siemens Computers) as one part of a larger global alliance. A restructuring of Fujitsu's semiconductor operations caused losses for 1999.

Akikusa's reorganization continued in 2000. Fujitsu overhauled its server business (subsidiary Amdahl ceased production of IBM-compatible mainframes) and accelerated production of flash memory. Responding to a global slump in its markets in 2001 Fujitsu announced that it would cut more than 16000 jobs —about 10% of its workforce —to control costs. Soon after it announced the cutting of an additional 4500 jobs.

In 2002 Fujitsu moved to outsource its semiconductor test and assembly operations when it agreed to sell its Kyushu Fujitsu Electronics subsidiary to Amkor Technology; the deal was terminated however when Amkor and Fujitsu were unable to agree to terms.

In 2003 the company formed a joint venture with AMD called Fujitsu AMD Semiconductor Ltd.

or FASL to manufacture flash memory. (Renamed Spansion in 2004 the company went public in 2005 filed for Chapter 11 in 2009 and emerged from bankruptcy reorganization in 2010.)

In 2005 Fujitsu sold Hitachi its stake in Fujitsu Hitachi Plasma Display a company it formed with Hitachi to develop plasma display panels for televisions. Fujitsu sold its LCD business Fujitsu Display Technologies to Sharp in 2005.

Fujitsu spun off its advanced semiconductor business as a separate subsidiary Fujitsu Microelectronics (now Fujitsu Semiconductor) in 2008. The following year it sold its hard-disk drive business to Toshiba but retained about a 20% stake in the business which was renamed Toshiba Storage Device. Late in 2010 Toshiba bought Fujitsu's remaining shares.

EXECUTIVES

Chairman, Michiyoshi Mazuka, age 71
EVP, Kazuhiko Kato
President and CEO Fujitsu America, Anthony P. (Tony) Doye, age 56
SVP, Akira Yamanaka
President, Masami Yamamoto, age 61
EVP, Rod Vawdrey
CEO UK & Ireland, Duncan Tait
EVP, Hirokazu Uejima
Corporate Executive Vice President Director, Kenji Ikegai
SVP, Tsuneo Kawatsuma
SVP, Masaaki Hamaba
SEVP, Masami Fujita
SVP, Takashi Mori
SEVP, Hideyuki Saso
SVP, Bunmei Shimojima
SVP, Kazuhiro Igarashi
SVP, Norihiko Taniguchi
EVP, Chikafumi Urakawa
SVP, Noriyuki Toyoki
CEO Fujitsu Australia and New Zealand, Mike Foster
SVP, Yoshihiko Hanada
Vice Chairman, Masahiro Koezuka
SVP, Nobuo Otani
EVP and Director, Masahiro Koezuka
Executive Officer; Chief Director of Social Base System, Atsuo Atsuo Yatagai Yatagai
Executive Officer; Chief Director of IA Server Business, Hiroaki Hiroaki Kondo Kondo
Executive Officer; Chief Director of Health Care Solution Business, Hirofumi Hirofumi Goda Goda
Executive Officer; Chief Director of Mobile Phone Business, Katsumi Katsumi Takada Takada
Executive Officer, Kazuhiko Kazuhiko Ogawa Ogawa
Executive Officer; Chief Director of Cloud Platform Development, Kazuo Kazuo Imada Imada
Senior Manager of Corporate Affairs, Koji Koji Shiseki Shiseki
Executive Officer; Chief Director of Automobile Business, Motoyuki Motoyuki Ozawa Ozawa
Managing Executive Officer, Nobuo Nobuo Ohtani Ohtani
Executive Officer; Chief Director of Network Service Business, Shingo Shingo Kagawa Kagawa
Executive Officer; Chief Director of Network Business Group Business Planning, Tango Tango Matsumoto Matsumoto
EVP, Yoshikazu Kudo
Executive Officer; Chief Director of Solution Business Promotion, Yoshiki Yoshiki Kondo Kondo
Executive Vice President, Ryosuke Mori
Executive Vice President Enterprise Business Services, Alexandre Attal
Sr. Vice President Operations Fujitsu America, David Berry
Executive Vice President Platform Products, Bill King
Corporate Vice President, Jiro Otsuki

Chief Information Officer, Timothy L. Branham
CEO President Fujitsu America, Robert D. Pryor
Senior Vice President Chief Financial Officer,
 Richard Deranleau
Director, Hiroshi Oura, age 78
EVP and Director, Kazuhiko Kato
SEVP and Director, Kazuo Ishida
Independent Director, Takashi Okimoto
Director, Haruo Ito
SEVP and Director, Masami Fujita
Director, Yoko Ishikura
Vice Chairman, Masahiro Koezuka
Director, Ryosei Kokubun
EVP and Director, Masahiro Koezuka
Independent Director, Shotaro Yachi
Auditors: Ernst&YoungShinNihon

LOCATIONS

HQ: Fujitsu Ltd.
 Shiodome City Center, 1-5-2 Higashi-Shimbashi,
 Minato-ku, Tokyo 105-7123
Phone: (81) 3 6252 2220
Web: www.fujitsu.com

Sales

	% of total
Asia/Pacific	
Japan	65
Other	9
EMEA	19
Americas	7
Total	**100**

PRODUCTS/OPERATIONS

Sales

	% of total
Technology solutions	
Services	53
System	12
Ubiquitous solutions	
Personal computers & mobile	16
Mobileware	6
Device solutions	
LSI	6
Electronic	6
Other	1
Total	**100**

Selected Products and Services

Technology Solutions
 Services
  Infrastructure services
  Systems integration
 System platforms
  Network products
  System products
Ubiquitous Product Solutions
 Hard disk drives
 Mobile phones
 PCs
Device Solutions
 Electronic components
 LSI devices

COMPETITORS

Alcatel-Lucent	NTT DATA
CASIO COMPUTER	Nokia
Canon	Nortel Networks
Cisco Systems	Oki Electric
Dell	Oracle
EMC	Panasonic Corp
Epson	Philips Electronics
Ericsson	Ricoh Company
FUJIFILM	STMicroelectronics
Hewlett-Packard	Samsung Electronics
Hitachi	Seagate Technology
IBM	Sharp Corp.
Infineon Technologies	Siemens AG
Intel	Sony
Micron Technology	TDK
Microsoft	Texas Instruments
Mitsubishi Electric	Toshiba
Motorola Solutions	Unisys
NCR	Western Digital
NEC	

HISTORICAL FINANCIALS
Company Type: Public

Income Statement
FYE: March 31

	REVENUE ($ mil.)	NET INCOME ($ mil.)	NET PROFIT MARGIN	EMPLOYEES
03/14	46,139	470	1.0%	162,393
03/13	46,568	(774)	—	168,733
03/12	54,462	520	1.0%	173,155
03/11	54,686	665	1.2%	172,336
03/10	50,097	996	2.0%	172,438
Annual Growth	**(2.0%)**	**(17.1%)**		**(1.5%)**

2014 Year-End Financials

Debt ratio: 0.1%
Return on equity: 7.1%
Cash ($ mil.): 2,272
Current ratio: 1.28
Long-term debt ($ mil.): 4,050

No. of shares (mil.): 2,069
Dividends
 Yield: —
 Payout: —
Market value ($ mil.): 62,733

	STOCK PRICE ($) FY Close	P/E High/Low	PER SHARE ($) Earnings	Dividends	Book Value
03/14	30.32	— —	0.23	0.00	3.29
03/13	21.05	— —	(0.37)	0.00	4.67
03/12	26.44	— —	0.25	0.00	5.69
03/11	28.00	— —	0.31	0.57	5.57
03/10	32.63	— —	0.45	0.33	4.92
Annual Growth	**(1.8%)**	**— —**	**(15.7%)**		**(9.6%)**

Fukoku Mutual Life Insurance Co (Japan)

Fukoku Mutual Life Insurance Company is one of Japan's major life insurers. As part of its business it sells products through a network of nearly 11000 agents as well as through more than 60 branch locations and about 470 field offices. It operates primarily through half a dozen subsidiaries that extends its reach to London New York and Singapore. Fukoku Mutal sells both face-to-face in the field and through call centers offering life and nonlife insurance products (such as medical and nursing care insurance) as well as a variety of financial products and services. Fukoku Mutal's typical clients include private individuals and business owners. Fukoku Mutual was founded in 1923.

Fukoku Mutual's traditional strategies —investing conservatively and targeting government agencies as customers —have earned it a reputation as one of the more stable insurers in an industry experiencing heavy losses primarily stemming from the weak economy and slumping stock markets. As Japan's economy recovers Fukoku Mutual and other insurers have been increasing their exposure to riskier investments including real estate.

EXECUTIVES

Chairman, Tomofumi Akiyama
Deputy President and Executive Officer,
 Katsumasa Furuya
President and CEO, Yoshiteru Yoneyama
Director and Managing Executive Officer, Hitoshi
 Sakai
Director and Managing Executive Officer,
 Toshihiro Hayashi
Director and Managing Executive Officer, Kenji
 Hirai
Director and Managing Executive Officer, Tadashi
 Akikawa
Deputy President and Executive Officer, Mikio
 Yamamoto
Deputy President and Executive Officer,
 Katsumasa Furuya
President and CEO, Yoshiteru Yoneyama
Director and Managing Executive Officer, Hitoshi
 Sakai
Director and Managing Executive Officer,
 Toshihiro Hayashi
Director and Managing Executive Officer, Kenji
 Hirai
Director and Managing Executive Officer, Tadashi
 Akikawa
Auditors: KisaragiAuditCorporation

LOCATIONS

HQ: Fukoku Mutual Life Insurance Co (Japan)
 2-2-2 Uchisaiwaisho, Chiyoda-ku, Tokyo, injike- 100-0011
Phone: (81) 3 3508 1101 **Fax:** (81) 3 3591 6446
Web: www.fukoku-life.co.jp

PRODUCTS/OPERATIONS

Selected Subsidiaries and Affiliates

Fukoku Capital Management Inc.
Fukoku Information Systems Co. Ltd.
Fukoku Life International (America) Inc.
Fukoku Life International (U.K.) Limited
Fukoku Shinyo Hosho Company Limited
Fukokushinrai Life Insurance Company

COMPETITORS

Asahi Mutual Life	Mitsui Life
Dai-ichi Life	Nippon Life Insurance
Daido Life	Sony Financial
Gibraltar Life	Sumitomo Life
Insurance	T&D Holdings
Meiji Yasuda Life	Taiyo Life

HISTORICAL FINANCIALS
Company Type: Public

Income Statement
FYE: March 31

	ASSETS ($ mil.)	NET INCOME ($ mil.)	INCOME AS % OF ASSETS	EMPLOYEES
03/14	75,738	0	—	12,999
03/13	80,122	0	—	13,488
03/12	85,745	0	—	13,502
03/11	80,553	0	—	13,702
03/10	65,177	0	—	14,207
Annual Growth	**3.8%**		**—**	**(2.2%)**

2014 Year-End Financials

Return on assets: —
Return on equity: —
Long-term debt ($ mil.): —
No. of shares (mil.): —
Sales ($ mil): 9,083

Dividends
 Yield: —
 Payout: —
Market value ($ mil.): —

Galp Energia, SGPS, SA

LOCATIONS

HQ: Galp Energia, SGPS, SA
Rua Tomas de Fonseca, Torre C, Edificio Galp Energia,
Lisbon 1600-209
Phone: (351) 21 240 866   **Fax:** (351) 21 242 965
Web: www.galpenergia.com

HISTORICAL FINANCIALS

Company Type: Public

Income Statement

	REVENUE ($ mil.)	NET INCOME ($ mil.)	NET PROFIT MARGIN	EMPLOYEES
12/13	27,210	259	1.0%	6,968
12/12	24,573	452	1.8%	7,241
12/11	21,972	559	2.5%	7,381
12/10	19,040	590	3.1%	7,311
12/09	17,486	500	2.9%	7,493
Annual Growth	11.7%	(15.1%)	—	(1.8%)

FYE: December 31

2013 Year-End Financials

Debt ratio: 36.9%
Return on equity: 3.5%
Cash ($ mil.): 2,069
Current ratio: 1.98
Long-term debt ($ mil.): 4,548
No. of shares (mil.): 829
Dividends
Yield: 0.0%
Payout: —
Market value ($ mil.): 6,750

	STOCK PRICE ($) FY Close	P/E High/Low		PER SHARE ($) Earnings	Dividends	Book Value
12/13	8.14	68	57	0.32	0.17	8.57
12/12	7.82	39	23	0.54	0.21	8.58
12/11	8.53	43	25	0.67	0.11	4.50
12/10	9.50	36	23	0.71	0.56	4.32
12/09	7.75	38	32	0.61	0.07	4.10
Annual Growth	1.2%	—	—	(14.9%)	26.1%	20.2%

Gas Natural SDG, S.A.

A latter-day Spanish "conquistador" Gas Natural is venturing into markets in both the Old World and the New. Gas Natural operates a group of energy companies that supply natural gas and electricity serving 20 million customers primarily in Spain but also in France Italy and Latin America. The largest natural gas supplier in Spain Gas Natural is also a leading liquefied natural gas (LNG) supplier. The company has a generating capacity of 15400 MW (including 4400 MW in Latin America). In 2009 Gas Natural greatly expanded its power business acquiring Spanish utility Union Fenosa in a $26 billion deal and in 2010 adopted Gas Natural Fenosa as its new corporate brand name.

EXECUTIVES

General Director of Gas Regulated Business, Antoni Mingot
General Director of Strategy and Development, Antonio Tena
Vice Chairman of the Board, Antonio Niubo
Chief Corporate Officer; General Director of Resources, Antonio Gabas
Chief Financial-Economy Officer, Carlos Fernandez

General Director of Energy Retail Business, Daniel Jorda
General Director of Communication and Chairmans Office, Jordi Tabernero
General Director of Regulated Power Business, Jose Lopez
General Director of Generation Division, Jose Martinez
General Director of Energy Planning, Jose Krauel
General Director of Energy Wholesale Business, Manuel Alvarez
General Director of Legal Services, Manuel Cobaleda
Chief Executive Officer; Director, Rafael Marco
General Director of Latin America Unit, Sergio Moreno
CEO and Director, Rafael Villaseca Marco, age 62
Vice Chairman, Antonio Brufau Niubo, age 65
Independent Director, Carlos Marrodan
Independent Director, Emiliano Achurra
Independent Director, Felipe Marquez
Independent Director, Miguel Maseda
Independent Director, Santiago Cobo
Auditors: PricewaterhouseCoopersAuditoresS.L.

LOCATIONS

HQ: Gas Natural SDG, S.A.
Placa del Gas, 1, Barcelona 08003
Phone: (34) 93 219 9199   **Fax:** (34) 93 402 5870
Web: www.gasnatural.com

Sales

	% of total
Europe	
Spain	63
Other	6
Latin	27
North America	
USA	2
Puerto	1
Other	1
Total	**100**

PRODUCTS/OPERATIONS

Sales

	% of total
Wholesale &	39
Electricity	25
Gas	20
Electricity	11
Upstream &	2
Other	3
Total	**100**

COMPETITORS

BG Group	IBERDROLA
BP	Italgas
CEPSA	MetroGAS
Endesa S.A.	Royal Dutch Shell
HC Energia	TGS

HISTORICAL FINANCIALS

Company Type: Public

Income Statement

	REVENUE ($ mil.)	NET INCOME ($ mil.)	NET PROFIT MARGIN	EMPLOYEES
12/13	34,375	1,989	5.8%	14,982
12/12	32,824	1,899	5.8%	15,959
12/11	27,260	1,713	6.3%	16,202
12/10	26,272	1,607	6.1%	17,347
12/09	21,434	1,721	8.0%	18,314
Annual Growth	12.5%	3.7%	—	(4.9%)

FYE: December 31

2013 Year-End Financials

Debt ratio: 57.4%
Return on equity: 10.8%
Cash ($ mil.): 5,853
Current ratio: 1.25
Long-term debt ($ mil.): 21,124
No. of shares (mil.): 1,000
Dividends
Yield: —
Payout: —
Market value ($ mil.): 24,667

	STOCK PRICE ($) FY Close	P/E High/Low		PER SHARE ($) Earnings	Dividends	Book Value
12/13	24.65	33	22	1.98	0.00	18.50
12/12	14.94	20	14	1.91	0.00	17.47
12/11	17.60	28	21	1.80	0.00	16.68
12/10	15.28	33	17	1.74	0.00	16.53
12/09	20.50	38	18	2.13	0.00	16.69
Annual Growth	4.7%	—	—	(1.8%)	—	2.6%

Gazprom Neft

One of Russia's largest integrated oil companies and its third largest refiner Gazprom Neft explores for produces refines and markets petroleum products. Its retail operations include about 1750 gas stations. The company with proved reserves of 9.7 billion barrels of oil equivalent controls refineries in Moscow Mozyr Noyabrsk and Omsk that produce more than 45.7 million tonnes of petroleum products per year. It refines about 80% of the oil it produces a high ratio for Russia. Gazprom Neft also shares ownership of major natural gas project SeverEnergia with NOVATEK the country's largest independent gas producer. State-owned gas giant Gazprom controls Gazprom Neft.

HISTORY

In the aftermath of the fall of the Soviet Union in the early 1990s Sibneft was formed in 1995 as part of Russia's privatization of state industries. Sibneft included western Siberian oil producer Noyabrskneftegas and the Omsk oil refinery. The Russian government was to retain a 51% stake for three years while limiting foreign ownership to 15%. Finance Oil Company (FNK) controlled by business oligarch Boris Berezovsky the man reportedly behind Sibneft's formation gained a controlling stake in Sibneft. The new integrated oil company's prize asset was the Omsk refinery. Built in the mid-1980s it was Russia's largest and most modern refinery.

In 1997 Sibneft became the first Russian company to issue a Eurobond. Despite an economic crisis in 1998 Sibneft continued to service all of its financial obligations. That year Sibneft made plans to merge with rival oil company Yukos (controlled by oligarch Mikhail Khodorkovsky) but falling oil prices led the two firms to scuttle the proposed union.

Also in 1998 Sibneft published a corporate governance charter compiled by leading European experts to bring the company in line with international practices. This move was followed up with the appointment of three non-executives to the company's board of nine directors. A year later Sibneft became the first major Russian oil company to publish its financial accounts (audited by Arthur Andersen) according to US generally accepted accounting principles. In 1999 Sibneft also formed alliances with two Western oil services firms US-based Schlumberger and Canadian-based BJ Services to enhance its extraction of oil and gas.

During the 1999 Russian Duma elections reclusive oligarch Roman Abramovich (who had acquired a 12% stake in Sibneft in 1996) claimed to control Sibneft whereas Berezovsky (also elected to the Duma) was said to have only a background role in Sibneft.

The company announced plans in 2000 to invest $52 million to modernize the Omsk refinery upgrading its capacity to produce lead-free gasoline. That year Sibneft also agreed to acquire majority stakes in two refined products retailers in the Urals region which together controlled 132 service stations and 20 storage sites.

Sibneft lost out in its bid to gain control of Onako another former state-owned oil company that was privatized in 2000. Sibneft had teamed up with two other oil companies Yukos and Stroitransgaz (a unit of Russian gas giant Gazprom) to bid for Onako but lost out to rival Tyumen Oil Co. (TNK). However Sibneft which had gained control of a 40% stake in Onako's main oil producing subsidiary Orenburgneft reportedly made an arrangement with TNK to swap its Orenburgneft shares for a minority stake in Onako. Also in 2000 Sibneft and other Russian oil companies were investigated by Russian authorities after allegations of tax evasion.

In 2001 the company announced plans to search for oil in the Chukotka autonomous district. (Abramovich is the governor of Chukotka). This unexplored area has a similar geological structure to Alaska's oil-rich North Slope. Later that year Sibneft acquired a 36% stake in a Moscow refinery from oil giant LUKOIL allowing the company to supply markets in European Russia.

In 2002 Sibneft opened its first gas station in Moscow.

Gazprom Neft (as Sibneft) was once controlled by UK-residing Chelsea soccer club-owning Russian oligarch Roman Abramovich through investment company Millhouse Capital. In 2005 Gazprom bought its majority stake in Sibneft from Millhouse Capital for $11 billion. The company changed its name to Gazprom Neft the next year and ENI acquired 20% of Gazprom Neft in 2007 following the bankruptcy of Yukos. Gazprom had the option to buy ENI's stake within two years and exercised that right in 2009 paying just more than $4 billion to ENI. Gazprom now directly owns or indirectly controls through subsidiaries about 95% of Gazprom Neft.

EXECUTIVES

Chairman, Alexey B. Miller, age 53
Deputy CEO Corporate Communications, Alexander Dybal, age 48
CEO and Director, Alexander V. Dyukov, age 46
Deputy Chairman and Deputy CEO for Logistics Processing and Sales, Anatoly Cherner, age 61
Deputy CEO Foreign Asset Management, Kirill Kravchenko, age 37
CFO, Vadim Yakovlev, age 44
Deputy General Director for Legal and Corporate Affairs, Elena A. Ilyukhina, age 46
Head Investor Relations, Anna Sidorkina
Executive Vice President Strategy and Business Development, Mikhail Slobodin
Director, Vasiliy Podyuk, age 66
Director, Andrey V. Kruglov, age 46
Director, Kirill Gennadievich Seleznev, age 37
Director, Olga P. Pavlova, age 61
CEO and Director, Alexander V. Dyukov, age 46
Director, Claudio Descalzi, age 58
Director, Dubik Nikolai Nikolaevich
Director, Valery Golubev, age 62
Director, Marco Alvera, age 37
Auditors: ZAOPricewaterhouseCoopersAudit

LOCATIONS

HQ: Gazprom Neft
G3-5 Pochtamtskaya St., St. Petersburg 190000
Phone: (7) 812 363 31 52   **Fax:** (7) 812 363 31 51
Web: www.gazprom-neft.ru

Sales

	% of total
Refining marketing &	99
Exploration &	1
Total	**100**

COMPETITORS

BP	Occidental Petroleum
Devon Energy	Rosneft
Exxon Mobil	Royal Dutch Shell
JX Nippon Oil &	Surgutneftegas
Energy	TOTAL
LUKOIL	Tatneft
Mitsui	Transneft

HISTORICAL FINANCIALS

Company Type: Public

Income Statement

FYE: December 31

	REVENUE ($ mil.)	NET INCOME ($ mil.)	NET PROFIT MARGIN	EMPLOYEES
12/13	38,569	5,413	14.0%	0
12/12	40,415	5,791	14.3%	0
12/11	44,172	5,352	12.1%	0
12/10	32,772	3,148	9.6%	0
12/09	24,166	3,013	12.5%	0
Annual Growth	**12.4%**	**15.8%**	—	—

2013 Year-End Financials

Debt ratio: 0.6%
Return on equity: 19.9%
Cash ($ mil.): 2,771
Current ratio: 2.08
Long-term debt ($ mil.): 7,955

No. of shares (mil.): —
Dividends
Yield: 7.5%
Payout: 0.1%
Market value ($ mil.): —

	STOCK PRICE ($) FY Close	P/E High/Low		PER SHARE ($) Earnings	Dividends	Book Value
12/13	22.60	0	0	1.15	1.70	6.14
12/12	23.76	0	0	1.23	0.95	5.81
12/11	23.33	24	15	1.13	0.66	4.98
12/10	20.95	44	24	0.67	0.47	3.96
12/09	27.35	47	15	0.64	0.74	3.42
Annual Growth	**(4.7%)**	—	—	**15.7%**	**23.1%**	**15.7%**

Gazprom OAO

Gazprom Russia's largest company has proved and probable oil and gas reserves of 29.2 billion tons of coal equivalent and produces about 513 billion cu. meters of natural gas a year. With 18% of the world's gas reserves it is also the world's largest gas producer. The company is engaged in oil and gas exploration processing transport and marketing. It operates Russia's domestic gas pipeline network and delivers gas to countries across Central Asia and Europe. Gazprom relies heavily on Western exports. It also holds stakes in Russian financial institutions a polypropylene plant and its own telecom network and produces 17% of Russia's electricity. Gazprom accounts for about 25% of Russia's tax revenues.

Exports to Europe are critical to Gazprom which is burdened by debt because of the insolvency of Russian consumers and hordes of nonpaying cus-

tomers. Gazprom holds strategic partnerships with Western energy companies including Germany's E.ON Ruhrgas. Other partners include Royal Dutch Shell Eni of Italy and Finland's Fortum. In addition Gazprom has a deal with German chemical conglomerate BASF that grants BASF minority shares in both the proposed North Europe Gas Pipeline and the West Siberia field that will feed it. The company is also working on the South Stream Pipeline a massive project aimed at linking Russia's southern gas fields to Western markets via Bulgaria.

Establishing a major new market (China) in 2014 the company tied up a 30-year $400 billion-plus gas supply deal with China National Petroleum.

In addition to natural gas Gazprom holds a 5% global share of the production of liquefied natural gas (LNG). It also holds 79% of oil producer Gazprom Neft. It also holds stakes in Russian financial institutions a polypropylene plant and its own telecom network and produces 17% of Russia's electric power.

Gazprom exports gas to more than 30 countries within and beyond the borders of the former Soviet Union. The company has offices in Algiers Astana Ashkhabad Bishkek Dokha Ekaterinburg Kiev Kishinev Krasnodar Minsk Moscow Novy Urengoy Peking Riga Rio de Janeiro Samara St. Petersburg Tehran Tomsk Khabarovsk and Yuzhno-Sakhalinsk.

In 2011 Gazprom reported a 29% spike in revenues (in local currency) driven by expanded capacity higher oil and gas prices and by a 16% jump in demand for gas from former Soviet Union countries (where the company has invested heavily in building infrastructure). Net profit rose further to 30% as rapid revenue growth outstripped an increase in operating costs and other expenses. An improving economy and a related increase in the volume and price of natural gas also drove up revenues and operating profits in 2010.

To expand its gas supply in 2012 the company announced that it planned to spend 43 billion rubles (US $1.4 billion) that year to develop gas infrastructure projects (gas fields and pipelines) in the Sakhalin region of Eastern Russia. In 2011 Gazprom acquired TNK-BP's east Siberian Kovykta gas field for about $770 million. The purchase opens up the possibility of a major supply agreement with China.

While natural gas is its core asset the company is also ramping up its other segments as part of a diversification drive to broaden its revenue base and enhance its profile as an integrated energy producer. In 2011 it installed 1.9 GW of combined heat and power generation units and deployed an offshore production platform at the Prirazlomnoye oil field in the Pechora Sea in the Arctic.

Expanding its energy footprint in 2011 Gazprom agreed to acquire power generation KES Holding (which owns four power companies) to create Russia's largest power company. KES Holding will hold 25% of the new joint venture.

In 2010 the company made its first entry into the US gas market when it began trading and marketing natural gas though Gazprom Marketing & Trading USA. It also signed a strategic partnership with Royal Dutch Shell to develop oil and gas assets in Russian Siberia and the Far East and process and market products in Russia and Europe.

To raise cash to pay down debt in 2010 the company sold its controlling stake in SeverEnergia (a natural gas project partly owned by ENI) to a joint venture owned by Gazprom Neft and OAO Novatek for $1.5 billion. To raise cash it sold 9% of its 19% stake in Novatek to Gazprombank for $2.8 billion.

Over time the Russian government has boosted its stake in Gazprom from 38% to more than 50%.

HISTORY

Following the breakup of the Soviet Union in the early 1990s one of the first priorities of the Russian government was to move some state monopolies toward a free-market economic system. A presidential decree in 1992 moved the company toward privatization by calling for the formation of a Russian joint-stock company to explore for and produce gas gas condensates and oil; provide for gas processing; operate gas wells; and build gas pipelines and storage facilities.

By 1993 the government had converted its natural gas monopoly Gazprom into a joint-stock company; the company had dated back to the 1940s and the USSR Ministry of the Gas Industry had kept all of its assets when it became a corporation in 1989.

The new Gazprom was 15%-owned by Gazprom workers and 28% by people living in Russia's gas-producing regions. The state retained about a 40% share (boosted to 51% in 2003). The company inherited all of the former Soviet republics' export contracts to Western and Central Europe.

Thanks to the power of Viktor Chernomyrdin (Gazprom's former Soviet boss and gas industry minister who became Russia's prime minister in 1992) the company was able to enjoy large tax breaks and maintain its role as a monopoly —even as other industries were being more deeply privatized. However the privatization of Gazprom was later attacked as being manipulated to profit the company's top management including Chernomyrdin. Top managers were rumored to have each received 1%-5% of shares —holdings potentially worth $1.2 billion-$10 billion each.

Needing to raise cash in 1996 Gazprom offered 1% of its stock to foreigners the first sale of stock to foreign investors. In 1997 Gazprom and Royal Dutch/Shell formally became partners. That year Gazprom began building its Blue Stream pipeline across the Black Sea to Turkey. Italian group Eni helped back the project and became a partner by 1999.

In 1998 Gazprom acquired a stake in Promstroibank Russia's fourth-largest financial institution. German energy powerhouse Ruhrgas acquired a 3% stake in Gazprom in 1998 which it increased to nearly 4% the next year. Also in 1999 Gazprom started building its Yamal-Europe pipeline which was to stretch to Germany for exports to Europe.

The next year an attempt by Gazprom to muscle into Hungary's chemicals sector by offering cheaper raw materials was blocked by Hungary's TVK and Borsodchem and their allies. Also in 2000 Gazprom became embroiled in a politically controversial issue when it called for the country's leading private media holding group Media-MOST to sell shares to the gas giant in order to settle millions of dollars of debt. Because Media-MOST held NTV television a major critic of Russian President Vladimir Putin the deal was alleged to have been directed by the Kremlin. A government probe into the deal was later ordered. (By 2002 Gazprom owned a significant stake in NTV which it sold that year so it could focus on its core energy businesses.)

The alignment of Gazprom's board changed in 2000 after the annual shareholder's meeting. For the first time in Gazprom's history company managers did not have a majority of seats. A new chairman Dmitri Medvedev second in command to Putin was elected to replace Chernomyrdin. In 2001 the board fired CEO Rem Vyakhirev and replaced him with Deputy Energy Minister Alexei Miller a Putin ally.

Gazprom had announced plans in 2004 to acquire Rosneft (effectively giving the Russian government control of Gazprom) though the deal was complicated by Rosneft's acquisition of the Yugansk assets acquired from YUKOS. In 2005 Gazprom abandoned plans to merge with Rosneft and acquired Sibneft in an effort to add significant oil operations to its business. Millhouse Capital a holding company controlled by Russian oligarch Roman Abramovich sold its majority stake in what was then a major exploration and production company called Sibneft (now Gazprom Neft) to Gazprom for a reported $13 billion. At the time Sibneft was Russia's fifth-largest oil company.

In 2006 Gazprom signed long-term contracts for gas deliveries with Austrian energy giant OMV. That year Royal Dutch/Shell agreed to give control of the $22 billion Sakhalin-2 project (run by Sakhalin Energy Investment) in Russia's Far East to Gazprom.

Former Gazprom chairman Dmitri Medvedev was elected president of Russia in 2008.

The company became embroiled in a pricing dispute with neighbor Ukraine in 2009 resulting in the disruption of gas supplies to Ukraine and because of its transnational pipelines to dozens of other countries in Europe.

Wanting to expand its Russian and international assets and diversify its profile in 2009 Gazprom acquired Italian energy titan ENI's 20% share in oil producer Gazprom Neft raising the Russian giant's direct ownership to 79%. ENI had acquired its stake in 2007 following the bankruptcy of YUKOS. Gazprom had the option to buy ENI's stake within two years and exercised that right in 2009 paying just more than $4 billion to ENI. Gazprom directly owns or indirectly controls through subsidiaries about 95% of Gazprom Neft.

EXECUTIVES

Deputy Chairman and CEO, Alexey B. Miller, age 53
Deputy Chairman Management Committee; Director General OOO Gazprom export, Alexander I. Medvedev, age 59
Deputy Chairman Management Committee and Chief Accountant, Elena A. Vasilyeva, age 55
Deputy Chairman Management Committee and Head Finance and Economics Department, Andrey V. Kruglov, age 46
Deputy Chairman Management Committee, Valery A. Golubev, age 62
Member Management Committee; Head Strategic Development Department, Vlada V. Rusakova, age 61
Member Management Committee; Head Marketing and Processing of Gas and Liquid Hydrocarbons Department; Director General OOO Mezhregiongaz, Kirill Gennadievich Seleznev, age 37
Director; Deputy Chairman and Head Administration Management Committee, Mikhail L. Sereda, age 44
Deputy Chairman Management Committee, Alexander N. Kozlov, age 62
Member Management Committee; Head Legal Department, Nikolay N. Dubik, age 43
Chairman, Victor A. Zubkov, age 73
Deputy Chairman Management Committee; Director General Gazprom Corporate Security Service, Sergey F Khomyakov
Member Management Committee; Director General OOO Gazprom komplektatsiya, Igor Y. Fyodorov, age 49
Member Management Committee; Head Investment and Construction Department, Yaroslav Y. Golko, age 53
Head Information Policy Department, Alexander D. Bespalov, age 64

Member Management Committee and Head Department Gas Transportation Underground Storage and Utilization Department, Oleg E. Aksyutin
Head Central Production and Dispatch Department, Boris S. Posyagin, age 70
Head Technological Process Control Systems Automation Department, Nikolai F. Stolyar, age 62
Director General Gazprom dobycha Krasnoyarsk, Mikhail Sirotkin, age 42
Deputy Chairman Management Committee, Vitaly Markelov, age 51
Member Management Committee; Head Gas Gas Condensate and Oil Production, Vsevolod Cherepanov, age 48
Member Management Committee; Head Dept. of Goverment Relations, Vladimir Markov, age 59
Member Management Committee; Head Asset Management and Corporate Relations, Elena Mikhailova, age 37
Deputy Chairman of the Management Board, Aleksandr Kozlov
Deputy Chairman of the Management Board, Aleksandr Medvedev
Chairman of the Management Board; Deputy Chairman of the Board; General Director, Aleksey Miller
Member of Management Board; Head of Asset Management and Corporate Relations Department, Elena Mikhaylova
Deputy Chairwoman of the Management Board; Chief Accounting Officer, Elena Vasileva
Management Board Member, Igor Fedorov
Chairman of the Board, Viktor Zubkov
Head of the Department for Pricing and Economic Expert Analysis Department; Director, Yelena Karpel
Director, Burckhard Bergmann, age 68
Deputy Chairman and CEO, Alexey B. Miller, age 53
Director; Deputy Chairman Management Committee, Alexander G. Ananenkov, age 60
Director; Deputy Chairman and Head Administration Management Committee, Mikhail L. Sereda, age 44
Director, Farit R. Gazizullin, age 68
Director, Elena E. Karpel, age 70
Director, Igor K. Yusufov, age 58
Chairman, Victor A. Zubkov, age 73
Director, Elvira Nabiullina, age 50
Director, Valery A. Musin, age 75
Director, Sergey I. Shmatko, age 46
Auditors: ZAOPricewaterhouseCoopersAudit

LOCATIONS

HQ: Gazprom OAO
Nametkina St., 16, V-420, GSP-7, Moscow 117997
Phone: (7) 495 719 3001   **Fax:** (7) 495 719 8333
Web: www.gazprom.com

PRODUCTS/OPERATIONS

Sales

	% of total
Gas	59
Oil & refined	27
Gas transportation power &	14
Total	**100**

COMPETITORS

BP	Qatar Petroleum
Centrica	Rosneft
E.ON Ruhrgas	Sakhalin Energy
Gasunie	Surgutneftegas
LUKOIL	Tatneft

Company Type: Public

Income Statement

FYE: December 31

	REVENUE ($ mil.)	NET INCOME ($ mil.)	NET PROFIT MARGIN	EMPLOYEES
12/13	159,918	34,664	21.7%	459,500
12/12	156,607	38,850	24.8%	417,000
12/11	143,741	40,490	28.2%	401,000
12/10	118,085	31,741	26.9%	393,000
12/09	98,941	25,717	26.0%	386,000
Annual Growth	12.8%	7.7%	—	4.5%

2013 Year-End Financials

Debt ratio: 0.4%
Return on equity: 12.8%
Cash ($ mil.): 20,968
Current ratio: 2.06
Long-term debt ($ mil.): 44,727

No. of shares (mil.): —
Dividends
Yield: 3.3%
Payout: 0.0%
Market value ($ mil.): —

	STOCK PRICE ($) FY Close	P/E High/Low		PER SHARE ($) Earnings	Dividends	Book Value
12/13	8.65	0	0	1.51	0.29	12.34
12/12	9.73	0	0	1.69	0.46	12.00
12/11	10.68	0	0	1.76	0.00	10.06
12/10	25.44	0	0	1.38	0.12	8.91
12/09	25.05	0	0	1.09	0.15	7.65
Annual Growth	(23.3%)	—	—	8.4%	17.4%	12.7%

GDF SUEZ

GDF SUEZ channels its energy as Europe's top power gas and infrastructure players. It is engaged in the purchasing production and marketing of natural gas and electricity; the development and maintenance of major natural gas and electricity infrastructures; and the creation and marketing of energy and environmental services. With operations in about 70 countries power producer GDF SUEZ had 118200 MW of installed capacity in 2011. It is Europe's top importer of liquefied natural gas (LNG) its largest supplier of natural gas the continent's leading supplier of multi-technical energy services and a leading global supplier of water and waste management services.

Geographic Reach

GDF SUEZ operates around the world. Europe accounted for 80% of the company's revenues in 2011.

Operations

The company has expertise in four key sectors: liquefied natural gas energy efficiency services independent power production and environmental services. Its environmental services segment offers water management and waste treatment and recovery through its subsidiary SUEZ Environnement.

In 2011 GDF SUEZ operated more than 1200 water production sites producing around 4.5 billion metric meters of drinking water in 2011. In sanitation services it biologically treated around 3.2 billion metric meters of waste water. Internationally in the waste segment it operates 120 composting platforms 48 incineration sites (including 45 that recover energy) 645 sorting and transfer stations and 130 storage centers.

In the renewable energy sector GDF SUEZ had an installed capacity of 16121 MW at the end of 2011. At 11332 MW the company is a hydroelectric operator in France and Brazil where it is continuing to develop large-scale projects. It also has a production capacity of 918 MW in biomass and biogas in Europe the US and Latin America. Wind energy is also a priority with capacity of 3792 MW making the Group the leading operator on the French and Belgian markets and the second in Portugal.

Financial Performance

Despite unfavorable weather conditions and flat natural gas prices in France the company's revenues grew by 7% in 2011. In Europe water revenues increased by 3% and waste by 7.1%. Internationally sales from both of these sectors went up by 3.7% that year.

Strategy

GDF SUEZ is looking to harness its global size and its presence in a mix of energy areas (nuclear natural gas LNG coal and renewables) with its water sanitation and waste management expertise to deliver energy in a way that preserves the environment. The company is constructing 11800 MW of installed power-production capacity. (To raise capital to help fund its expansion between 2011 and 2013 the company sold stakes in power projects in Slovakia Canada and the UK and elsewhere).

In 2013 GDF SUEZ announced the construction of the 300 MW Tarfaya wind farm in Morocco which will be the largest wind project in Africa. The project is owned in partnership with Nareva Holding a Moroccan energy company. GDF SUEZ is also developng Cyberjaya Malaysia's premier cybercity through a joint venture with local partner Cyberview Sdn Bhd of Cyberjaya's district cooling network.

In 2012 GDF SUEZ and its International Power subsidiary expanded its power generation of Tihama power sites in Saudi Arabia by 532 MW following an award from Saudi Aramco.

Dramatically boosting its power generation assets in 2011 the company's GDF SUEZ Energy International merged with UK-based International Power. The $21.5 billion deal created one of the world's largest global independent power generation companies. GDF SUEZ held 70% of International Power which has generation capacity of 66000 MW in 2011 and bought out the other 30% in 2012 for about $2.2 billion to gain full ownership.

Later than year International Power formed a joint venture with Supreme Energy and Marubeni Corporation to develop the Rantau Dedap geothermal project located in Sumatra.The 220 MW geothermal plant is part of the Indonesian government's long-term plan meet its country's needs with renewable power.

Ownership

In 2012 the French government owned about 37% of GDF SUEZ. In mid-2014 France announced that it was selling a 3% stake in the gas utility.

HISTORY

The first canal in Egypt was dug in the 13th century BC but it was Napoleon who revived the idea of a shorter trade route to India: a canal through Egypt linking the Gulf of Suez with the Mediterranean. Former French diplomat and engineer Ferdinand de Lesseps formed Compagnie Universelle du Canal Maritime de Suez in 1858 to build and eventually operate the canal which opened 11 years later. Egypt's modernization had pushed it into debt and increased its ties to the British government which by 1875 had acquired a 44% stake in the company.

For more than 80 years the Suez Canal was a foreign enclave protected by the British Army since 1936. After Egypt's puppet government fell and as Gamal Abd Al-Nasser assumed power in 1956 British troops exited the Canal Zone which Egypt quickly nationalized. Israel Britain and France attacked but the United Nations arranged a truce and foreign forces withdrew leaving the Suez in Egypt's control.

With no canal to operate Universelle du Canal Maritime de Suez became Compagnie Financiere de Suez in 1958. A year later it created a bank (which became Banque Indosuez in 1974).

In 1967 Financiere de Suez became the largest shareholder in Societe Lyonnaise des Eaux et de L'Eclairage a leading French water company. Formed in 1880 Lyonnaise des Eaux had stakes in water (Northumbrian Water) and energy (Elyo). After France's energy firms were nationalized in 1946 Lyonnaise des Eaux dipped deeper into the water industry by acquiring Degremont (now Ondeo-Degremont) in 1972. It also purchased stakes in waste management (SITA 1970) and heating systems (Cofreth 1975).

In the 1980s Lyonnaise des Eaux expanded in Spain the UK and the US and diversified into cable TV (1986) and broadcast TV (1987). It merged with construction firm Dumez in 1990.

Meanwhile Financiere de Suez became a financial power when it won a controlling stake in Societe Generale de Belgique (SGB) in 1988 and bought Groupe Victoire in 1989. But the two buys left the firm (renamed Compagnie de Suez in 1990) deeply in debt.

Losing money Compagnie de Suez disposed of Victoire (1994) and then the valuable Banque Indosuez (1996). In 1996 the company bought a controlling stake in Belgium's top utility Tractebel (now SUEZ-TRACTEBEL). Compagnie de Suez and Lyonnaise des Eaux merged in 1997 to create Suez Lyonnaise des Eaux. The following year Suez Lyonnaise acquired the rest of SGB and bought the European and Asian operations of waste management giant Browning-Ferris Industries; it also began divesting noncore operations.

Suez Lyonnaise in 1999 expanded its core businesses primarily in the US. The company bought Calgon (water treatment US) and Nalco Chemical (water treatment chemicals US) then merged Calgon into Nalco to form Ondeo Nalco. (The company's name was changed back to Nalco when it was divested in 2003.)

In 2000 Suez Lyonnaise bought United Water Resources (now United Water) and acquired the rest of SITA. Through its Elyo subsidiary Suez Lyonnaise bought out minority shareholders in US-based Trigen Energy. The company also merged its construction unit Groupe GTM with French construction rival VINCI; Suez Lyonnaise then sold the VINCI shares that it received from the transaction.

The next year the company shortened its name to Suez (later modified to SUEZ) as part of a global rebranding effort. It also united its water services operations under the ONDEO brand. In 2002 SUEZ made Tractebel a wholly owned subsidiary by purchasing the remaining publicly held shares. Also in 2002 SUEZ sold minority stakes in communications equipment manufacturer Sagem (now SAFRAN) steelmaker Arcelor and motorway operator Autopistas Concesionaria Espanola (ACESA).

SUEZ divested most of its 11% stake in Belgian insurance firm Fortis for nearly $2 billion in 2003. It also sold its 79% stake in cable company Coditel that year. In 2003 the company merged Tractebel and SGB (Tractebel's former holding company) to form SUEZ-TRACTEBEL. Gaz de France was founded in 1946 by the French government to consolidate the more than 500 (mostly coal-fired) gas works that had existed before WWII. From 1949 on Gaz de France focused on upgrading gas plants and local transmission networks. Its first long-distance pipeline was built in 1953 linking Paris to the Lorraine coal gas fields. With the development of the Lacq gas field in southwestern France annual gas sales increased by 300% between 1957 and 1962.

By 1965 nearly half of the French population was supplied with natural gas. Spurred on by the loss of its Algerian colony which held major oil and gas assets the French government pushed for new gas supplies to supplement its Lacq resources. Gaz de France was able to secure a contract with Algerian natural gas supplier Sonatrach in 1965 and in 1967 it signed an import contract with Dutch supplier Gasunie. The company also diversified in the 1960s helping to build a natural gas liquefaction plant in Algeria and a receiving terminal in Le Havre. It also helped pioneer gas storage engineering.

Following the price shock of the Arab oil embargo of the early 1970s Gaz de France stepped up its search for alternative suppliers including contracts with Russia's largest gas producer Soyouzgazexport (in 1976 1980 and 1984) and four separate Norwegian producers Efofisk (1977) Stafjord (1985) Heimdal (1986) and Gullfaks (1987). The company also renewed contracts with its Dutch and Algerian suppliers.

During the 1990s Gaz de France expanded its international operations as deregulation in the industry accelerated. In 1994 the company gained a foothold in eastern Germany's gas sector by buying gas production and storage company Erdgas Erdol GmbH (EEG). Three years later Gaz de France acquired Italian heating and related services firm Agip Servizi and was awarded a joint venture contract to distribute gas in Berlin in 1997 and in the suburbs of Mexico City in 1998.

Through contracts for North Sea oil and gas with Elf Aquitaine (now owned by TOTAL FINA ELF) British-Borneo and Ruhrgas in 1999 the company increased its natural gas supplies. It also established new gas supply contracts with Nigeria and Qatar.

For the first time in its history Gaz de France became an offshore field operator in 2000 by acquiring exploration and production company TransCanada International Netherlands and a 39% stake in Noordgastransport BV an offshore gas pipeline operator.

In 2001 through the purchase of a 10% interest in Petronet LNG Gaz de France embarked on a project to import liquefied natural gas from Qatar to India.

France's energy and environmental services giants came together when SUEZ merged with Gaz de France in 2008 to form GDF SUEZ. As part of the merger agreement and in order to clear hurdles set up by the EU competition policy SUEZ then spun off its waste and water unit SUEZ Environnement.

Following the 2008 merger of Gaz de France with SUEZ in a move to expand geographically GDF SUEZ acquired a 90% stake in Izmit Gaz Dagitim San Ve Tic AS (Turkey's third-largest natural gas distributor) for $232 million.

In 2009 the company made further geographic realignments prompted by the regulatory requirements of the European Commission for GDF SUEZ and Germany's E.ON to allow for more competition in their major markets by swapping some generation capacity. It acquired from E.ON 860 MW of Germany-based conventional power plants 132 MW of hydroelectric plants and through subsidiary Electrabel access to 770 MW of nuclear power. In return GDF SUEZ sold to E.ON a similar amount of power generation capacity in France and the Benelux countries.

Ramping up its nuclear assets in 2011 GDF SUEZ formed a joint venture with IBERDROLA and Scottish and Southern Energy. NuGeneration planned to develop up to 3600 MW of nuclear

power in the UK. Late in 2011 SSE announced plans to sell its 25 percent in NuGen to GDF SUEZ and IBERDROLA and return to its renewable energy strategy.

EXECUTIVES

Executive Vice-President Energy Service, Jerome Tolot, age 63

Executive Member Senior Managers Department, Emmanuel van Innis, age 66

President Energy Policy Committee, Jean-Pierre Hansen, age 65

EVP Global Gas and LNG Business Line, Jean-Marie Dauger, age 62

Executive Vice-President Communications Marketing and Sustainable Development, Valerie Bernis, age 56

Chairman and CEO; Chairman SUEZ-TRACTEBEL GDF SUEZ Energy Services and SUEZ Environnement, Gerard Mestrallet, age 65

Executive Vice-President Energy International Business, Dirk Beeuwsaert, age 67

Executive Member Human Resources, Philippe Saimpert, age 60

Executive Member Energy Europe and International, Pierre Clavel, age 54

Executive Member Business Strategy and Sustainable Development, Alain Chaigneau, age 62

Executive Member and General Secretary, Yves de Gaulle, age 62

Executive Vice-President Environment Business, Jean-Louis Chaussade, age 63

Vice Chairman and President, Jean-Francois Cirelli, age 56

Executive Vice-President Chief Financial Officer, Isabelle Kocher, age 46

CEO of GDF SUEZ Energy International, Willem van Twembeke, age 49

Executive Member Audit and Risks, Philippe Jeunet, age 60

Executive Vice-President Group Human Resources, Henri Ducre, age 58

Executive Vice-President Infrastructures, Jean-Claude Depail, age 66

Chief Executive Officer, Activites Nucleaires

Director of Group Purchasing, Claire Brabec-Lagrange

Director of the Group Sales and Marketing, Jean-Louis Blanc

Director of Information Systems, Veronique Durand-Charlot

Vice-President in charge of Group Human Resources, Henri Ducra

Director, Jean-Louis Beffa, age 72

Director, Anne Lauvergeon, age 54

Director, Paul Desmarais Jr., age 59

Director, Edmond Alphandery, age 70

Director, Baron Albert Frere, age 87

Director, Aldo Cardoso, age 58

Director, Rene Carron, age 71

Director, Jean-Paul Bailly, age 67

Director, Pierre Graff, age 66

Vice Chairman and President, Jean-Francois Cirelli, age 56

Director, Thierry de Rudder, age 64

Director, Pierre-Franck Chevet, age 52

Director, Ramon Fernandez, age 46

Director, Alain Beullier, age 50

Director, Patrick Petitjean, age 61

Director, Anne-Marie Mourer, age 55

Director, Gabrielle Prune, age 57

Director, Olivier Bourges, age 46

Director, Lord Simon of Highbury, age 74

Director, Pierre Mongin, age 59

Auditors: Mazars

LOCATIONS

HQ: GDF SUEZ
1, Place Samuel de Champlain, Courbevoie 92400
Phone: (33) 1 44 22 00 00
Web: www.gdfsuez.com

Sales

	% of total
Europe	80
Asia Pacific & Middle	8
North	6
Latin	5
Africa	1
Total	**1**

PRODUCTS/OPERATIONS

Sales

	% of total
Electricity	33
Environmental	33
Natural gas &	34
Total	**100**

COMPETITORS

BG Group	Eni
Bouygues	Gas Natural SDG
CANAL+	Gasunie
Centrica	Gazprom
Covanta	Italgas
Dragados	National Grid
E.ON	RWE
Electricite de France	SABESP
Electricite de Strasbourg	United Utilities
	Vattenfall
Enel	Veolia Environnement

HISTORICAL FINANCIALS

Company Type: Public

Income Statement

FYE: December 31

	REVENUE ($ mil.)	NET INCOME ($ mil.)	NET PROFIT MARGIN	EMPLOYEES
12/13	122,942	(12,788)	—	147,199
12/12	127,900	2,042	1.6%	139,781
12/11	117,281	5,177	4.4%	240,303
12/10	113,063	6,177	5.5%	236,116
12/09	115,113	6,449	5.6%	242,714
Annual Growth	**1.7%**	**—**	**—**	**(11.8%)**

2013 Year-End Financials

Debt ratio: 34.4%	No. of shares (mil.): —
Return on equity: (-17.2%)	Dividends
Cash ($ mil.): 11,965	Yield: 8.4%
Current ratio: 1.07	Payout: —
Long-term debt ($ mil.): 40,509	Market value ($ mil.): —

	STOCK PRICE ($) FY Close	P/E High/Low	PER SHARE ($) Earnings	Dividends	Book Value
12/13	23.67	— —	(5.38)	1.99	27.97
12/12	21.04	73 47	0.88	3.00	33.41
12/11	27.17	44 23	2.33	3.75	36.77
12/10	36.04	41 22	2.81	3.07	37.43
12/09	42.80	49 25	2.92	3.09	39.19
Annual Growth	**(13.8%)**	**— —**	**—(10.4%)**	**(8.1%)**	

GlaxoSmithKline Plc

GlaxoSmithKline (GSK) gives anxiety asthma and other ailments the ax. One of the top five pharmaceutical firms in the world GSK's bestsellers include respiratory neurological cardiovascular and dermatology drugs as well as vaccines and antivirals. Its top product is asthma medication Advair (aka Seretide) which combines two of its other asthma products Flovent and Serevent. Other bestsellers include epilepsy treatment Lamictal cholesterol medicine Lovaza prostate enlargement drug Avodart and antibiotic Augmentin as well as Cervarix and Pediarix vaccines. The company's consumer products include Tums dental care products Aquafresh and Sensodyne and smoking-cessation products NicoDerm and Nicorette.

The company markets its products directly to hospitals pharmacies doctors and other health care consumers; it also uses wholesale distributors in some markets and serves customers in more than 100 countries overall. Pharmaceuticals account for two-thirds of sales with vaccines and consumer health products making up the remainder of revenues. Respiratory drugs are the company's largest sales category primarily due to blockbuster Advair which brings in more than Â5 billion ($6.7 billion) annually. GSK also has a strong presence in the central nervous system cardiovascular urogenital dermatology (through its Stiefel division) virology infectious disease oncology and metabolism treatment markets.

As sales in GSK's largest market the US account for more than a third of pharmaceutical sales maintaining a rich portfolio of US patent-protected products can make or break the company's future. Examples of GSK drugs that have experienced sales slumps due to patent losses include its bestselling herpes drug Valtrex which began facing generic competition in 2009 and accounted for a 5% to 10% drop in US and European pharmaceutical sales in both 2010 and 2011. Other recent patent losses include cardiovascular drug Arixtra and oncology drug Hycamtin both of which began facing generic competition in 2011.

The development of new potential blockbusters is the best way to alleviate these losses and GSK's development efforts include about 100 different clinical stage projects. Its major R&D centers are located in the UK the US Spain Belgium and China. GSK has some 30 candidates in late-phase trials for conditions such as HIV pulmonary conditions Parkinson's disease type-2 diabetes heart disease and various cancers. One candidate Benlysta became the first lupus therapy approved by the FDA in more than 50 years in 2011; the drug was developed with Human Genome Sciences(HGS) and was also approved in Europe that year. Other drugs launched in 2011 include epilepsy treatment Potiga (also known as Trobalt) and restless leg syndrome medication Horizant.

GSK is also working to pump potential new blockbusters into its pipeline by acquiring promising research firms and forming development agreements with other drug companies. For instance the company is developing cancer drug Arzerra for additional indications with biotech firm Genmab. It also has development deals with OncoMed (for new cancer treatments) and Theravance (respiratory drugs). GSK is also working with Pfizer on HIV medications; many of the company's HIV and vaccine development programs aim to provide affordable disease preventions and treatments to developing countries.

To further solidify its R&D relationships in 2012 the company increased its minority stake in development partner Theravance from 19% to 27% acquired a 15% stake in companion diagnostic test provider and partner Response Genetics Inc. (RGI) and fully acquired HGS for some $3 billion. In acquiring HGS GSK gained full access to Benlysta and other partnered development candidates.

A major trend among pharmaceutical companies is to focus on growing in emerging markets which represent an opportunity for big sales be-

cause of a relatively untapped consumer base. Towards that end GSK owns a minority stake (about 20%) in South African generic drugmaker Aspen Pharmacare; it has also established a presence in select Asian African Latin American and Middle Eastern nations. In 2010 the company spent about Â174 million ($250 million) to expand in Latin America with the buy of Laboratorios Phoenix an Argentinean drug manufacturer and marketer.

GSK also expanded its Asian operations by acquiring Nanjing MeiRui Pharma a Chinese manufacturer of allergy and urology products in 2010 and by buying out its Chinese partner Neptunus in a joint venture to manufacture influenza vaccines in 2011. The following year GSK formed a joint venture with Daiichi Sankyo to make and sell vaccines in Japan a market where GSK has seen rapid growth in recent years.

CEO Andrew Witty is intent on keeping the company focused on small strategic acquisitions and expansion in fast-growing markets including vaccines biopharmaceuticals and consumer health products. He is also carrying forth the company's ongoing cost-cutting measures which aim to reduce operational expenses through measures such as simplifying its administrative infrastructure narrowing its R&D programs and consolidating its drug development and manufacturing sites. To focus on its top selling drugs and R&D investments the company is also divesting assets where it sees fit.

For instance GSK sold a penicillin manufacturing site in Bristol Tennessee to Dr. Reddy's Laboratories for an undisclosed price in 2011. The sale also included the rights to the Augmentin and Amoxil brands in the US. GSK kept the rights to those brands outside the US. The firm also sold its minority stake (about 20%) in laboratory services firm Quest Diagnostics (which provides clinical trial testing to GSK) for some Â585 million ($1.1 billion) and it sold North American rights back to Valeant Pharmaceuticals for antiviral cream Zovirax.

Still in the mood to divest GSK also announced plans to sell some noncore consumer health brands. In early 2012 it completed the sale of a portfolio of North American OTC brands including BC Beano Ecotrin Fiber Choice Goody's and Tagamet to Prestige Brands Holdings for some Â426 million ($660 million). Later in 2012 GSK reached agreements to sell its noncore OTC offerings in Europe and other international markets including Solpadeine and Zantac; European rights will go to Omega Pharma for some Â391 million ($614 million) and rights in other international markets will be sold to Aspen Pharmacare for some Â164 million ($263 million). GSK also plans to divest global rights to its OTC weight loss product alli.

In 2014 it paid Novartis $7.1 billion for its vaccine business while collecting up to $16 billion for handing over its oncology line. The two companies are also combining their consumer products lines. The deal is expected to add Â1.3 billion to its bottom line and strengthen its core OTC and vaccine businesses.

The company has faced some trouble in recent years over diabetes drug Avandia which was linked to heart attack risks in 2007. GSK has since withdrawn sales of the drug in most markets; the European Medicines Agency suspended marketing authorization for Avandia in 2010 and the FDA placed use of the drug under a strict risk evaluation and mitigation strategy (REMS) program that same year. In addition the firm is working to settle a large number of patient lawsuits related to Avandia.

GSK paid $3 billion in 2012 to settle numerous fraud charges by the US Justice Department and other federal and state autorities including for failing to report safety data on Avandia. The agree-

ment which was the largest such drugmaker settlement to date also covered lawsuits over improper sales and marketing practices for several other products as well as improper Medicaid reimbursement activities.

Overall revenues declined 1% in 2011 to Â27.4 billion ($43.4 billion) as GSK worked to stabilize its operations following the Valtrex patent loss. (Sales had decreased 3% the previous year largely due to the increase in generic competition.) Other factors impacting the firm's revenues in 2010 and 2011 include decreased sales of Avandia and a drop in demand for pandemic flu vaccines and flu-related antivirals. Net income also fell in 2010 to some Â1.6 billion ($2.5 billion) due to legal expenses but in 2011 profits bounced back to previous levels of more than Â5 billion ($8 billion). Sales from new product launches as well as increased revenues in emerging and Asian markets have helped to offset the impact of competition and other factors causing flat or decreased sales in the US and Europe.

HISTORY

Englishman Joseph Nathan started an import-export business in New Zealand in 1873. He obtained the rights to a process for drying milk and began making powdered milk in New Zealand selling it as baby food Glaxo.

Nathan's son Alec dispatched to London to oversee baby food sales in Britain increased Glaxo's name recognition by publishing the Glaxo Baby Book a guide to child care. After WWI the company began distribution in India and South America.

In the 1920s Glaxo launched vitamin D-fortified formulations. It entered the pharmaceutical business with its 1927 introduction of Ostelin a liquid vitamin D concentrate and continued to grow globally in the 1930s introducing Ostermilk (vitamin-fortified milk).

Glaxo began making penicillin and anesthetics during WWII; it went public in 1947. A steep drop in antibiotic prices in the mid-1950s led Glaxo to diversify; it bought veterinary medical instrument and drug distribution firms.

In the 1970s the British Monopolies Commission quashed both a hostile takeover attempt by Beecham and a proposed merger with retailer and drugmaker Boots. Glaxo launched US operations in 1978.

Glaxo shed nondrug operations in the 1980s to concentrate on pharmaceuticals. A 1981 marketing blitz launched antiulcer drug Zantac (to vie with SmithKline's Tagamet) in the US where Glaxo's sales had been small. The company boosted outreach by contracting to use Hoffmann-La Roche's sales staff. The Zantac sales assault gave Glaxo leadership in US antiulcer drug sales.

Under CEO Sir Richard Sykes Glaxo in 1995 made a surprise bid for UK rival Wellcome. Founded in 1880 by Americans Silas Burroughs and Henry Wellcome to sell McKesson-Robbins' products outside the US Burroughs Wellcome and Co. began making its own products two years later. By the 1990s the company which fostered Nobel Prize-winning researchers led the world in antiviral medicines. Its primary drug products were Zovirax (launched 1981) and Retrovir (1987).

Though an earlier bid by Glaxo had been rejected Sykes won the takeover with backing from Wellcome Trust Wellcome's largest shareholder.

In 1997 the company formed a new genetics division buying Spectra Biomedical and its gene variation technology. That year the company pulled diabetes drug Romozin (Rezulin in the US) from the UK market over concerns that it caused liver damage.

Glaxo in 1998 ended its joint venture with Warner-Lambert (begun 1993) selling its former partner the Canadian and US marketing rights to acid blocker Zantac 75.

In 1999 Glaxo trimmed its product line pulling hepatitis treatment Wellferon because of slow sales and selling the US rights to several anesthesia products. It also cut some 3400 jobs (half from the UK). Also that year Glaxo threatened to leave the UK after the National Health Service opted not to cover antiflu inhalant Relenza claiming the drug is not cost-effective.

The FDA in 2000 approved Glaxo's Lotronex for irritable bowel syndrome but several hospitalizations linked to the drug prompted the FDA to ask the company to withdraw it from the US market. Later that year Glaxo completed its merger with former UK rival SmithKline Beecham to create GlaxoSmithKline (GSK); Jean-Pierre Garnier took over as CEO.

Although GSK has largely escaped the flurry of patent worries afflicting other druggernauts in 2001 a US court declared invalid three patents protecting Augmentin from generics until 2017 and opened the door for cheaper rivals.

GSK returned European and international marketing rights for erectile dysfunction drug Levitra back to its developer Bayer HealthCare in late 2004 after it umm failed to perform. (It still markets the drug with Schering-Plough in the US.)

In 2005 the company expanded its vaccine operations through the acquisition of Corixa; that purchase gained the company a factory engaged in producing Monophosphoral Lipid A a key ingredient in a number of the company's vaccines and vaccine-related products. Later its acquisition of ID Biomedical a Canadian vaccine producer bolstered GSK's influenza vaccine production capability. The company also increased its flu vaccine capacity five-fold by building a new production facility in Dresden Germany; a $633 million production facility in France; and a vaccine plant in Singapore.

The fall of 2005 saw the sale of the company's US dermatology business (part of GlaxoSmithKline Consumer Healthcare) to the PharmaDerm division of ALTANA Inc. (which later became Nycomed US and then Fougera Pharmaceuticals); products involved in the deal included Alcovate Cutivate Emgel Oxistat and Temovate. In 2006 GSK sold its unbranded generic drug businesses in Spain and Italy to India's pharma giant Ranbaxy.

In 2006 GSK settled a tax dispute with the IRS for $3.1 billion the largest single tax payment in IRS history over international profit allocation in taxes filed by Glaxo Wellcome (prior to the 2001 Glaxo Wellcome/ SmithKline Beecham merger) from 1989 through 2000. The payment also includes taxes owed from 2001 through 2005.

GSK boosted its development pipeline in 2006 with the acquisition of the research operations of PLIVA Eastern Europe's largest pharmaceutical maker (the remainder of which was bought by Barr Pharmaceuticals) which focused on research into macrolide antibiotics (it developed blockbuster antibiotic Zithromax sold by Pfizer). That same year GSK acquired private biotech Domantis Ltd which specialized in laboratory-engineered monoclonal antibodies. The additions which cost the company more than $450 million nearly doubled the size of GSK's research capabilities. GSK also expanded its consumer products operations by purchasing CNS the maker of Breathe Right nasal strips in late 2006.

Tykerb an orally administered breast-cancer treatment gained FDA approval in 2007 and EU approval the following year. Human papillomavirus (HPV) vaccine Cervarix was also approved for sale in the EU in 2007.

Diabetes treatment Avandia another new drug that was a top seller in 2006 experienced a decrease in sales in 2007 after its safety was disputed by scientific studies that linked the drug to a risk of heart attack. GSK updated Avandia's warning labels and began conducting further studies on the drug. As a result of Avandia's troubles and increased generic competition GSK announced a cost-cutting program towards the end of 2007 to streamline manufacturing operations and marketing programs.

GSK acquired Reliant Pharmaceuticals for $1.65 billion to expand its cardiovascular product line (including coronary artery disease treatment Lovaza) in December 2007; GSK integrated Reliant's operations shortly after.

The company launched an operational excellence restructuring program in 2007 that aimed to reduce costs across the GSK organization. In 2008 Jean-Pierre Garnier was replaced as CEO by Andrew Witty who had been with the company for over 20 years and was previously president of GSK's European pharmaceuticals division.

In 2008 GSK acquired biotech firm Sirtris Pharmaceuticals for Å362 million ($720 million). Following the purchase the acquired firm operated as an independent drug discovery subsidiary focused on the areas of metabolism immunology inflammation and neurology.

GSK's added a line of dermatology products when it acquired Stiefel Laboratories from the Stiefel family and other investors (including the Blackstone Group) for some $2.9 billion in 2009. The acquisition added prescription and over-the-counter medications for conditions including acne psoriasis dandruff and fungal infections. Stiefel was combined with the existing GSK prescription dermatology and OTC operations into a new business unit under the Stiefel name. Also in 2009 GSK acquired a portfolio of international prescription products from UCB for some Å477 million to expand in Africa the Middle East Latin America and the Asia/Pacific region.

GSK sold US marketing rights to antidepressant Wellbutrin XL in 2009 after it began facing generic competition in 2006 and has thus seen lower sales volumes to fellow drugmaker Valeant Pharmaceuticals (formerly Biovail) for $510 million. GSK retained international marketing rights for the drug.

A highlight for GSK's development and commercialization programs in 2009 came from its pandemic vaccine program which delivered vaccines for H1N1 or swine flu. (It also previously developed a vaccine for H5N1 avian bird flu.) GSK also pooled its HIV/AIDS assets with Pfizer's in 2009 to form ViiV Healthcare a joint venture aiming to develop and sell affordable HIV therapies.

EXECUTIVES

Chairman, Sir Christopher Charles (Chris) Gent, age 66

President Asia Pacific and Japan, Marc Dunoyer

CEO and Director, Sir Andrew Witty, age 50, $1,230,205 total compensation

President Global Manufacturing and Supply, David Pulman

SVP Human Resources, Claire Thomas

President Consumer Healthcare Worldwide, Emma Walmsley

President North America Pharmaceuticals, Deirdre P. Connelly, age 53

SVP Governance Ethics and Assurance, Simon M. Bicknell

SVP Global Communications, Philip (Phil) Thomson

Chairman Research and Development and Director, Moncef Slaoui, age 54, $825,000 total compensation

President - Pharmaceuticals R&D, Patrick Vallance

President Emerging Markets and Asia Pacific, Abbas Hussain

SVP Core Business Services and Chief Information Officer, Bill Louv

President Pharmaceuticals Europe, Eddie Gray

Chief Strategy Officer, David Redfern

SVP and General Counsel, Dan Troy

CFO and Director, Simon Dingemans

Senior Vice President Global Communications, Phil Thomson

Senior Vice President; General Counsel, Daniel Troy

President - Global Manufacturing & Supply, Roger Connor

President - Vaccines, Christophe Weber

Director, Sir Deryck Maughan, age 66

Director, James R. Murdoch, age 41

Director, Tom de Swaan, age 69

Director, H. Lawrence (Larry) Culp Jr., age 51

Director, Judy C. Lewent, age 65

Director, Sir Robert P. Wilson, age 71

Director, Stacey Cartwright, age 50

Director, Sir Crispin Davis, age 64

Director, Stephanie A. Burns, age 59

CEO and Director, Sir Andrew Witty, age 50

Chairman Research and Development and Director, Moncef Slaoui, age 54

Director, Daniel K. Podolsky, age 60

Director, Sir Roy Anderson, age 67

CFO and Director, Simon Dingemans

Auditors: PricewaterhouseCoopersLLP

LOCATIONS

HQ: GlaxoSmithKline Plc
980 Great West Road, Brentford, Middlesex TW8 9GS
Phone: (44) 20 8047 5000   **Fax:** (44) 20 8047 7807
Web: www.gsk.com

Sales

	% of total
US	32
Emerging markets	19
Asia/Pacific	7
Other	4
Total	**100**

PRODUCTS/OPERATIONS

Sales

	$ mil.	% of total
Pharmaceuticals		
Cardiovascular & urogenital		10
ViiV Healthcare (HIV)		6
Antibacterials		5
Dermatology		4
Antivirals (non-HIV)		3
Oncology & emesis		2
Other		4
Consumer Healthcare		
OTC medicines		9
Oral health care		6
Nutritional health care		4
Total		**100**

Selected Products

Pharmaceuticals
Respiratory
Beconase (allergies)
Becotide/Beclovent (asthma and chronic obstructive pulmonary disease)
Flixonase/Flonase (allergies)
Flixotide/Flovent (asthma and chronic obstructive pulmonary disease)
Seretide/Advair (asthma and chronic obstructive pulmonary disease)
Serevent (asthma and chronic obstructive pulmonary disease)
Ventolin (asthma and chronic obstructive pulmonary disease)
Veramyst/Avamys (rhinitis)
Cardiovascular and urogenital
Arixtra (deep vein thrombosis and pulmonary embolism)
Avodart (prostatic hyperplasia)
Benlysta (systemic lupus erychematosus with HGS)
Coreg CR (heart failure and hypertension)
Fraxiparine (deep vein thrombosis and pulmonary

embolism)
Levitra (erectile dysfunction with Bayer)
Lovaza (coronary heart disease)
Vesicare (overactive bladder)
Volibris (pulmonary hypertension)
Central nervous system disorders
Horizant (post-herpetic neuralgia or restless leg syndrome)
Imigran/Imitrex (migraines)
Lamictal (epilepsy and bipolar disorder)
Potiga/Trobalt (epilepsy and partial seizures)
Requip (Parkinson's disease)
Seroxat/Paxil (depression)
Treximet (migraine)
Wellbutrin SR (depression)
ViiV Healthcare (HIV with Pfizer)
Combivir/Biovir (reverse transcriptase inhibitor for HIV/AIDS)
Epivir/3TC (reverse transcriptase inhibitor for HIV/AIDS)
Epizicom/Kivexa (combination of Epivir and Ziagen for HIV/AIDS)
Lexiva/Telzir (protease inhibitor for HIV/AIDS)
Selzentry (HIV)
Trizivir (three reverse transcriptase inhibitors for HIV/AIDS)
Antibacterials
Amoxil and Augmentin (antibiotics non-US only)
Dermatology
Bactroban (skin infections)
Duac (acne vulgaris)
Zovirax (herpes infections shingles chicken pox and cold sores)
Antivirals
Relenza (influenza)
Hepsera (hepatitis B)
Valtrex/Zelitrex (shingles and genital herpes)
Zeffix/Septavir/Heptodin/Epivir HBV (hepatitis B)
Vaccines
Cervarix (human papilloma virus)
Fluarix (influenza)
FluLaval (influenza)
Infanrix/Pediarix (diphtheria tetanus pertussis polio and hepatitis B)
Rotarix (rotavirus)
Synflorix (pneumonia)
Twinrix (hepatitis A and hepatitis B)
Metabolic
Avandia Avandamet (type 2 diabetes)
Boniva/Bonviva (osteoporosis with Roche)
Oncology and emesis
Arzerra (refractory chronic lymphocytic leukemia)
Hycamtin (ovarian cervical and small cell-lung cancers)
Promacta/Revolade (blood therapy)
Tykerb/Tyverb (advanced and metastatic breast cancer)
Votrient (metastatic renal cell carcinoma)
Consumer products
Over-the-counter medicines
Abreva (cold sores)
alli (weight loss)
Breathe Right (nasal strips)
Citrucel (laxative)
Commit (smoking-cessation)
Contac (respiratory product)
Nicabate/NicoDerm/NiQuitin CQ (smoking-cessation)
Nicorette (smoking-cessation)
Panadol (analgesic)
Tums (antacid)
Oral care
Aquafresh (toothpaste and toothbrushes)
Corega (denture care)
Dr Best (toothbrushes)
Macleans (toothpaste)
Odol (toothpaste)
Polident (denture cleaner)
Poli-Grip (denture adhesive)
Sensodyne (toothpaste)
Nutritional health care
Horlicks (milk-based malted food and chocolate drinks)
Lucozade (glucose energy drink)
Ribena (line of juice drinks rich in vitamin C)

COMPETITORS

Abbott Labs	Merck
Amgen	Mylan
AstraZeneca	Novartis
Bayer AG	Novo Nordisk
Biogen Idec	Pfizer
Bristol-Myers Squibb	Procter & Gamble

Colgate-Palmolive	Ranbaxy Laboratories
Dr. Reddy' s	Reckitt Benckiser
Elan	Roche Holding
Eli Lilly	Sanofi
Forest Labs	Takeda Pharmaceutical
Gilead Sciences	Teva
Johnson & Johnson	UCB

HISTORICAL FINANCIALS
Company Type: Public

Income Statement
FYE: December 31

	REVENUE ($ mil.)	NET INCOME ($ mil.)	NET PROFIT MARGIN	EMPLOYEES
12/13	43,801	8,983	20.5%	99,817
12/12	42,603	7,358	17.3%	99,488
12/11	42,308	8,127	19.2%	97,389
12/10	44,082	2,537	5.8%	96,461
12/09	45,944	8,957	19.5%	99,913
Annual Growth	(1.2%)	0.1%	—	(0.0%)

2013 Year-End Financials

Debt ratio: 71.6%	No. of shares (mil.): —
Return on equity: 84.8%	Dividends
Cash ($ mil.): 9,145	Yield: 4.5%
Current ratio: 1.11	Payout: 191.1%
Long-term debt ($ mil.): 25,542	Market value ($ mil.): —

	STOCK PRICE ($) FY Close	P/E High/Low		PER SHARE ($) Earnings	Dividends	Book Value
12/13	53.39	129	98	1.83	2.41	2.38
12/12	43.47	133	115	1.47	2.48	1.91
12/11	45.63	109	85	1.59	5.53	2.46
12/10	39.22	337	225	0.50	2.00	2.66
12/09	42.25	106	56	1.75	1.85	3.12
Annual Growth	6.0%	—	—	1.0%	6.8%	(6.5%)

Glencore PLC

LOCATIONS
HQ: Glencore PLC
Baarermattstrasse 3, P.O. Box 777, Baar CH-6340
Phone: (41) 41 709 2000   **Fax:** (41) 41 709 3000
Web: www.glencorexstrata.com

HISTORICAL FINANCIALS
Company Type: Public

Income Statement
FYE: December 31

	REVENUE ($ mil.)	NET INCOME ($ mil.)	NET PROFIT MARGIN	EMPLOYEES
12/13	232,694	(7,402)	—	0
12/12	214,436	1,004	0.5%	0
12/11	186,152	4,048	2.2%	0
12/10	144,978	1,291	0.9%	0
12/09	106,364	983	0.9%	0
Annual Growth	21.6%	—	—	—

2013 Year-End Financials

Debt ratio: 35.6%	No. of shares (mil.): —
Return on equity: (-18.2%)	Dividends
Cash ($ mil.): 2,849	Yield: 0.0%
Current ratio: 1.27	Payout: —
Long-term debt ($ mil.): 38,724	Market value ($ mil.): —

	STOCK PRICE ($) FY Close	P/E High/Low		PER SHARE ($) Earnings	Dividends	Book Value
12/13	10.42	—	—	(0.67)	0.29	3.81
12/12	11.67	112	66	0.14	0.28	4.40
12/11	12.14	20	16	0.69	0.09	4.23
Annual Growth	(7.4%)	—	—	—	33.4%	(2.6%)

Great-West Lifeco Inc.

Great-West writes policies for the Great White North and beyond. Holding company Great-West Lifeco majority-owned by Power Financial is one of Canada's largest insurance organizations but its reach extends to the US and to Europe. Through subsidiaries (including Great-West Life Assurance in Canada and Great-West Life & Annuity in the US) the company offers a range of individual and group life and health insurance retirement savings and investment products reinsurance and services to financial institutions. Great-West Life Assurance's two major subsidiaries Canada Life and London Life Insurance provide individual insurance and wealth-management products in Canada Germany Ireland and the UK.

Operations
In the US Great-West Life & Annuity (GWL&A) provides retirement savings plans to employers. Great-West Lifeco's companies also provide reinsurance to niche markets in the US and Europe. Great-West Lifeco has more than $705 billion in assets under administration.

The company divides its business geographically: it offers financial services and asset management in the US its largest market individual and group insurance and wealth management services in Canada and insurance and annuities along with reinsurance in Europe. Its US asset management line of business brings in the largest part of revenue at 40%.

Financial Performance
A decline in European results balanced with increases in Canada and the US sales to result in flat revenue for 2012. Net income dropped due to higher commissions and general expenses.

Strategy
Going forward Great-West Lifeco intends to keep expanding geographically and across product lines. It believes multiple brands and distribution channels positions it well for growth. It continues to seek unique opportunities to support larger and more complex accounts especially in its wealth management business which is developing retirement income products as that segment of the population grows.

Mergers and Acquisitions
In 2013 Great-West Lifeco acquired Irish Life Group Limited for some Â1.3 billion ($1.75 million) from the Irish government. The purchase gives Great-West a leading position in life insurance pension and investment management markets in Ireland. Following the transaction Great-West Lifeco moved its existing Irish subsidiary Canada Life (Ireland) into the Irish Life division.

EXECUTIVES
President and CEO Putnam Investments, Robert L. (Bob) Reynolds, age 62

Chairman of the Board; Chairman of the Board Great-West Life; London Life Canada Life; Great-West Life and Annuity, Raymond L. McFeetors, age 68

Chairman, R. Jeffrey Orr

Chief Financial Officer; Executive Vice President, William W. Lovatt

President CEO and Director; President and CEO Great-West Life Assurance London Life Insurance and Canada Life Assurance, D. Allen Loney

President and CEO Great-West Life & Annuity Insurance, Mitchell T. G. Graye, age 58

Senior Vice President & General Counsel; Canada & Europe, Andrew D. Brands

Senior Vice President and Chief Risk Officer, Alexandre J. Guertin

SVP and General Counsel US, Richard G. Schultz, age 53

EVP Capital Management, Arshil Jamal

VP and Corporate Secretary, Laurie A. Speers

President and CEO, Paul A. Mahon

Senior Vice President - Capital Management, Garry MacNicholas

Senior Vice President and Chief Internal Auditor; SVP & Chief Internal Auditor of Great-West; London Life & Canada Life, Helen Kasdorf

Chief Compliance Officer; Canada, Anne Toal

Senior Vice-President and Chief Internal Auditor, Douglas Tkach

President and COO Canada of Great -West Life London Life and Canada Life, J. Dave Johnston

Director, R. Jeffrey Orr

Corporate Director, Marcel R. Coutu, age 60

Director, Andre R. Desmarais, age 56

Corporate Director, Raymond Royer, age 75

Director, Michel Plessis-Belair, age 71

Director, Paul Desmarais Jr., age 60

Corporate Director, David A. Nield, age 75

President CEO and Director; President and CEO Great-West Life Assurance London Life Insurance and Canada Life Assurance, D. Allen Loney

Director, Henri-Paul Rousseau, age 65

Director, Michael L. Hepher, age 71

Director, Rt. Hon. Donald F. (Don) Mazankowski, age 77

Director, Jerry E. A. Nickerson, age 78

Director, Emoke J. E. Szathmary

Director, Brian E. Walsh, age 60

Director, Philip K. Ryan, age 57

Director, H. David Graves

Director, Chaviva M. Hosek

Corporate Director, George S. Bain

Independent Director, Emoke Szathmary

Independent Director, Michel Plessis-Belair

Auditors: Deloitte&ToucheLLP

LOCATIONS

HQ: Great-West Lifeco Inc.
100 Osborne Street North, Winnipeg, Manitoba R3C 1V3
Phone: 204 946-1190 **Fax:** 204 946-4139
Web: www.greatwestlifeco.com

PRODUCTS/OPERATIONS

2009 Premiums

	% of total
Proprietary mutual funds	38
Life insurance guaranteed annuities & insured health	32
Segregated deposits	
Group	15
Individual	11
Self-funded premium equivalents (ASO	4
Total	**100**

Selected Subsidiaries & Affiliates

The Great-West Life Assurance Company
Canada Life Financial Corporation

The Canada Life Assurance CompanyCanada Life
  Capital Corporation Inc.The Canada Life Group (U.K.)
  LimitedCanada Life International Re LimitedCanada
  Life Irish Holding Company Limited
Crown Life Insurance Company
Laketon Investment Management Ltd.
London Insurance GroupLondon Life Insurance
  CompanyLondon Reinsurance Group Inc.
GWL&A Financial Inc. (US)
  Great-West Life & Annuity Insurance Company
  Advised Assets Group LLC
  FASCore LLC

COMPETITORS

AXA Financial
CIBC
Industrial Alliance Insurance and Financial Servic
John Hancock Financial Services
Liberty Mutual
Manulife Financial
Nationwide Financial
Prudential
RBC Financial Group
RBC Insurance
Sun Life

HISTORICAL FINANCIALS

Company Type: Public

Income Statement
FYE: December 31

	ASSETS ($ mil.)	NET INCOME ($ mil.)	INCOME AS % OF ASSETS	EMPLOYEES
12/14	308,036	2,303	0.7%	0
12/13	306,494	2,264	0.7%	20,970
12/12	255,102	1,940	0.8%	17,870
12/11	234,062	2,076	0.9%	17,350
12/10	229,909	1,704	0.7%	17,450
Annual Growth	**7.6%**	**7.8%**	—	—

2014 Year-End Financials

Return on assets: 0.7%	Dividends
Return on equity: 14.4%	Yield: 0.0%
Long-term debt ($ mil.): —	Payout: 48.3%
No. of shares (mil.): 996	Market value ($ mil.): 28,925
Sales ($ mil): 33,834	

	STOCK PRICE ($) FY Close	P/E High/Low	Earnings	PER SHARE ($) Dividends	Book Value
12/14	29.02	10 8	2.20	1.06	16.68
12/13	30.70	12 10	2.16	1.16	16.60
12/12	24.42	14 10	1.91	1.24	15.95
12/11	20.04	14 8	2.07	1.21	14.32
12/10	26.50	17 12	1.70	1.23	13.49
Annual Growth	**2.3%**	—	**6.7%**	**(3.7%)**	**5.4%**

Grupo Financiero Banorte S.A. BDE C V

Grupo Financiero Banorte is one of Mexico's leading bank groups and the largest bank not owned by a foreign company. Banorte provides banking lending investment and money exchange services through more than 1100 branches. It serves the retail corporate and government markets; loans for the retail and manufacturing industries make up a large part of its lending portfolio. The group also has a microlending unit. Banorte subsidiaries offer pension management insurance annuities leasing and factoring services. The group

has grown quickly through big-ticket bank acquisitions including Bancrecer Bancentro and the state-controlled Banpais. It also owns South Texas-based Inter National Bank.

Mergers and Acquisitions

In early 2013 Banorte acquired Afore Bancomer from Spanish bank Banco Bilbao Vizcaya Argentaria (BBVA) for roughly $1.6 billion to would create Mexico's largest pension fund. Later in the year the company purchased Ixe Grupo Financiero.

Prior to that in 2011 Banorte bought IXE a boutique bank based in Mexico City that specializes in serving wealthy clients. The acquisition made the bank the third-largest in terms of assets.

LOCATIONS

HQ: Grupo Financiero Banorte S.A. BDE C V
Prolongacion Reforma 1230, Col. Cruz Manca Santa Fe, Mexico, Distrito Federal 05300
Phone: (52) 55 1103 4000
Web: www.banorte.com

PRODUCTS/OPERATIONS

HISTORICAL FINANCIALS

Company Type: Public

Income Statement
FYE: December 31

	ASSETS ($ mil.)	NET INCOME ($ mil.)	INCOME AS % OF ASSETS	EMPLOYEES
12/13	76,883	1,031	1.3%	0
12/12	70,538	837	1.2%	0
12/11	59,365	609	1.0%	24,027
12/10	47,636	540	1.1%	19,759
12/09	43,320	447	1.0%	19,327
Annual Growth	**15.4%**	**23.2%**	—	—

2013 Year-End Financials

Return on assets: 1.4%	Dividends
Return on equity: 14.3%	Yield: 1.1%
Long-term debt ($ mil.): —	Payout: —
No. of shares (mil.): —	Market value ($ mil.): —
Sales ($ mil): 8,221	

	STOCK PRICE ($) FY Close	P/E High/Low	Earnings	PER SHARE ($) Dividends	Book Value
12/13	35.04	— —	0.41	0.39	2.94
12/12	32.51	— —	0.36	0.18	2.71
12/11	15.17	— —	0.27	0.00	2.19
12/10	23.49	— —	0.27	0.00	1.84
12/09	18.35	— —	0.22	0.06	1.57
Annual Growth	**17.6%**	— —	**16.5%**	**59.2%**	**17.0%**

Gunma Bank, Ltd. (The) (Japan)

Gunma Bank hopes that you have more than just a yen for its services. Through more than 140 branches The Gunma Bank provides banking services in the Gunma prefecture and surrounding areas of Japan through some 150 branches. The Gunma Bank also operates a subsidiary in Hong Kong and a branch in New York City. As the company's name might imply the Gunma prefecture (known for its industry and agriculture-based economy) accounts for more than 80% of deposits. Besides deposits Gunma Bank's services include loans to companies individuals and the government securities insurance and exchange. The Gunma Bank was founded in 1932.

Auditors: Ernst&YoungShinNihon

LOCATIONS

HQ: Gunma Bank, Ltd. (The) (Japan)
194 Motosoja-machi, Maebashi, Gunma 371-8611
Phone: (81) 27 252 1111
Web: www.gunmabank.co.jp

COMPETITORS

77 Bank   Ito-Yokado
Hachijuni Bank   Japan Post

HISTORICAL FINANCIALS
Company Type: Public

Income Statement

	ASSETS ($ mil.)	NET INCOME ($ mil.)	INCOME AS % OF ASSETS	EMPLOYEES
03/14	69,189	192	0.3%	3,405
03/13	72,746	218	0.3%	3,405
03/12	78,760	228	0.3%	3,399
03/11	75,207	209	0.3%	3,347
03/10	66,031	194	0.3%	3,359
Annual Growth	1.2%	(0.3%)	—	0.3%

FYE: March 31

2014 Year-End Financials

Return on assets: 0.2%
Return on equity: 4.4%
Long-term debt ($ mil.): —
No. of shares (mil.): 469
Sales ($ mil): 1,264

Dividends
Yield: —
Payout: —
Market value ($ mil.): —

	STOCK PRICE ($) FY Close	P/E High/Low	PER SHARE ($) Earnings	Dividends	Book Value
03/14	0.00	— —	0.41	0.00	9.65
03/13	0.00	— —	0.46	0.00	10.01
03/12	5.46	— —	0.47	0.00	10.21
Annual Growth	—	— —	(3.4%)	—	(1.4%)

Hachijuni Bank, Ltd. (Japan)

The Hachijuni Bank operates more than 150 branches in Japan primarily in the central prefecture of Nagano. It serves individuals and businesses with traditional products as deposit services and loans. The bank also owns subsidiaries active in financial services including leasing consumer loan guarantee investment advisory venture capital for high-tech firms and credit cards. Overseas Hachijuni has a branch in Hong Kong and representative offices in China Singapore and Thailand. The company was founded in Nagano City in 1931.

The Hachijuni Bank is looking to expand both through opening additional offices and through beefing up its offerings in such areas as investment production sales and consultation services.

EXECUTIVES

President and Director, Yoshiyuki Yamaura
Managing Director, Yoshio Horigome
Deputy President and Director, Sadayuki Koide
Managing Director, Tadashige Maeyama

Managing Director, Yoshio Horigome
Deputy President and Director, Sadayuki Koide
Managing Director, Tadashige Maeyama
Auditors: DeloitteToucheTohmatsu

LOCATIONS

HQ: Hachijuni Bank, Ltd. (Japan)
178-8 Aza Okada, Oaza Nakagosho, Nagano 380-8682
Phone: (81) 26 227 1182
Web: www.82bank.co.jp

PRODUCTS/OPERATIONS

COMPETITORS

Daishi Bank   Mizuho Financial
Gunma Bank   Musashino Bank
Hokuetsu Bank Ltd.   Resona
Mitsubishi UFJ   Sumitomo Mitsui
  Financial Group   Towa Bank

HISTORICAL FINANCIALS
Company Type: Public

Income Statement

	ASSETS ($ mil.)	NET INCOME ($ mil.)	INCOME AS % OF ASSETS	EMPLOYEES
03/14	73,510	256	0.3%	3,713
03/13	77,105	235	0.3%	3,756
03/12	80,473	211	0.3%	3,800
03/11	76,006	244	0.3%	3,862
03/10	65,939	180	0.3%	3,851
Annual Growth	2.8%	9.2%	—	(0.9%)

FYE: March 31

2014 Year-End Financials

Return on assets: 0.3%
Return on equity: 4.7%
Long-term debt ($ mil.): —
No. of shares (mil.): 506
Sales ($ mil): 1,640

Dividends
Yield: 1.9%
Payout: 193.9%
Market value ($ mil.): 29,307

	STOCK PRICE ($) FY Close	P/E High/Low	PER SHARE ($) Earnings	Dividends	Book Value
03/14	57.89	— —	0.51	1.14	11.37
03/13	59.46	— —	0.46	0.00	11.83
03/12	58.85	— —	0.41	0.00	11.75
03/11	57.56	— —	0.47	0.75	10.99
03/10	56.60	— —	0.34	0.54	9.53
Annual Growth	0.6%	— —	10.1%	20.6%	4.5%

Haci Omer Sabanci Holding A.S.

Haci Omer Sabanci is one of Turkey's largest industrial and financial conglomerates with interests in the energy banking retail cement textile and other industries. Its primary holding is a stake in Turkish banking firm Akbank which provides commercial retail and private banking as well as investment and foreign trade services. Other holdings include stakes in domestic energy company Enerjisa and supermarket operator Carrefoursa a joint venture with Carrefour. Sabanci's portfolio spans some 20 countries in Europe Africa Asia and the Americas. It also has several partnerships with multinationals such as Bridgestoneand Philip Mor-

ris. The wealthy Sabanci family owns 60% of the company.

HISTORY

Haci Omer Sabanci's eponymous empire traces back to the 1930s. Sabanci left his native village Akcakaya at the age of 14 to become a laborer in a cotton plantation in the Adana region of Turkey in 1921. By 1932 he had become a shareholder in a cotton ginning plant. During the next decade he grabbed stakes in two vegetable oil plants: Tork Nebati Yaglar Fabrikasi (1943) and Marsa (1946; renamed in 1993 as Marsa KJS a joint venture with Kraft).

Quickly broadening his portfolio Sabanci along with more than 80 citizens of Adana and surrounding regions became a founding shareholder in Akbank (named for Sabanci's native village) in 1948. He further diversified with investments in Bossa a flour and cotton ginning mill in 1951. Sabanci's second financial holding the Aksigorta insurance business was formed in 1960 as a subsidiary of Akbank.

By the time Sabanci died in 1966 Akbank had opened its 100th branch office. Sabanci's five sons took the helm of their father's companies and moved the group's headquarters to the more cosmopolitan Istanbul in 1974 in accordance with Sabanci's growing stance as a global entity. Domestic operations continued to grow however; fabric producer Yonsa was founded in 1973 and the Cimsa unit began producing cement two years later.

The 1980s marked the Haci Omer Sabanci group's emergence as a multinational and the beginnings of its signature business style: growth through partnerships with major players. In 1985 Akbank joined with Banque Nationale de Paris (now BNP Paribas) to create BNP-Ak Bank; leading German bank Dresdner joined the companies three years later to form BNP-Ak-Dresdner Bank. A joint venture with DuPont in 1987 created nylon yarn producer Dusa. The following year the company renamed its Lassa tire manufacturing concern Brisa after sealing a deal with Bridgestone of Japan. By the end of the decade the Sabanci family were billionaires.

The group continued developing powerful partnerships in the next decade. Two joint ventures with Philip Morris (1991 and 1994) involved Haci Omer Sabanci in the manufacturing marketing and selling of the maker's cigarettes in Turkey. A trinational deal in 1997 with US conglomerate Koch Industries and Mexican billionaire Isaac Saba's Imasab created Sakosa a polyester tire cord and industrial yarn manufacturer. Another joint venture with DuPont in 1999 (DuPontsa BV) linked the companies' operations to create Europe's largest polyester producer.

An attempt to break into telecommunications stalled that year when the almost $3 billion price tag in Turkey's mobile phone license auction proved too steep for the Sabanci group. However the company was able to purchase Turk.Net Turkey's largest ISP for $25 million. By 2000 Haci Omer Sabanci had ceased seeking out partnerships and ventures in disparate sectors planning instead to narrow its focus to select industries including energy the Internet and telecommunications.

In 2001 the company teamed up with DuPont to form global nylon industrial yarn and tire cord joint venture DUSA International. It also sold its stake in automotive joint venture Toyotasa to partner Toyota.

Chairman Sakip Sabanci's lifelong dream of creating a world-class museum in Turkey was realized in 2002 with the opening of the Sakip Sabanci Museum. Sabanci died two years later.

Also in 2004 Sabanci bought BNP Paribas and Dresdner Bank out of their BNP-Ak-Dresdner Bank venture.

Belgian partner Bekaert bought out Sabanci's share of their Beksa steel cord and metal fiber joint venture in 2008. Sabanci sold stakes in other holdings including its edible oils operations financial services companies and another joint venture with Toyota.

The group teamed up with Austria-based Verbund to own and operate a regional electricity distributor in Turkey in 2008. The landmark $1 billion deal was part of the Turkish government's plan to privatize and transform the country's power industry.

LOCATIONS

HQ: Haci Omer Sabanci Holding A.S.
Sabanci Center 4, Levent, Istanbul 34330
Phone: (90) 212 385 80 80   **Fax:** (90) 212 385 88 88
Web: www.sabanci.com

PRODUCTS/OPERATIONS

Selected Investments
Cement
  Akcansa
  Cimsa
Energy
  Enerjisa
Financial services
  Akbank
  Aksigorta
Retail
  Carrefoursa
  Teknosa
Industrial
  Brisa
  Kordsa Global
  Temsa
  Sasa
  Yunsa
Other
  Bimsa
  Philip Morrissa
  Philsa
  Tursa

HISTORICAL FINANCIALS

Company Type: Public

Income Statement

	ASSETS ($ mil.)	NET INCOME ($ mil.)	INCOME AS % OF ASSETS	EMPLOYEES
12/13	96,571	809	0.8%	58,907
12/12	97,929	1,036	1.1%	57,556
12/11	80,059	994	1.2%	57,374
12/10	84,258	1,077	1.3%	57,209
12/09	74,725	2,030	2.7%	55,201
Annual Growth	6.6%	(20.5%)	—	1.6%

2013 Year-End Financials

Return on assets: 0.9%
Return on equity: 10.4%
Long-term debt ($ mil.): —
No. of shares (mil.): —
Sales ($ mil): 11,718

Dividends
  Yield: —
  Payout: —
Market value ($ mil.): —

	STOCK PRICE ($) FY Close	P/E High/Low		Earnings	PER SHARE ($) Dividends	Book Value
12/13	4.30	0	0	3.97	0.00	0.04
12/12	4.28	0	0	5.08	0.00	0.04
12/11	3.94	0	0	4.87	0.00	0.04
12/10	1.78	—	—	5.28	0.00	(0.00)
12/09	1.78	0	0	4.29	0.00	0.07
Annual Growth	24.6% (14.4%)	—	—	(1.9%)	—	

Hamburger Sparkasse (Germany, Fed. Rep.)

LOCATIONS

HQ: Hamburger Sparkasse (Germany, Fed. Rep.)
Ecke Adolphsplatz/Grosser Burstah, Hamburg D-20457
Phone: (49) 40 35 79 0   **Fax:** (49) 40 35 79 3418
Web: www.haspa.de

HISTORICAL FINANCIALS

Company Type: Public

Income Statement

FYE: December 31

	ASSETS ($ mil.)	NET INCOME ($ mil.)	INCOME AS % OF ASSETS	EMPLOYEES
12/13	55,786	0	—	4,855
12/12	52,159	0	—	4,526
12/11	49,895	0	—	3,931
12/10	51,170	0	—	3,887
12/09	54,041	0	—	0
Annual Growth	0.8%	—	—	—

2013 Year-End Financials

Return on assets: —
Return on equity: —
Long-term debt ($ mil.): —
No. of shares (mil.): —
Sales ($ mil): 2,228

Dividends
  Yield: —
  Payout: —
Market value ($ mil.): —

Hang Seng Bank Ltd.

Hang Seng Bank whose name means "ever-growing" in Chinese is one of Hong Kong's largest banks. It has more than 220 branches and automated banking centers —including one in every subway station —throughout the city. It also boasts more than 45 outlets in mainland China and has locations in Macao Singapore and Taiwan. The bank provides corporate and retail banking services such as deposit accounts credit cards mortgages business and personal loans and insurance as well as investment products and services the likes of securities trading and mutual funds. With total assets of HK$1.1 billion at the end of 2013 it also offers personal wealth management and private banking services.

EXECUTIVES

Chairman, Raymond K. F. Ch'ien, age 61
Director and Head of Personal Banking, William Wing Cheung Leung, age 59
Director; Vice Chairman and Chief Executive Hang Seng Bank (China) Limited, Dorothy K. Y. P. Sit, age 62
General Manager and Head Investment and Insurance, Andrew H. C. Fung
Vice Chairman and CEO, Margaret K. M. Y. Leung, age 63
Deputy General Manager and CFO, Andrew Leung, age 51
Director, Alexander A. (Sandy) Flockhart, age 62
Director and Head of Personal Banking, William Wing Cheung Leung, age 59

Director; Vice Chairman and Chief Executive Hang Seng Bank (China) Limited, Dorothy K. Y. P. Sit, age 62
Director, Iain J. Mackay, age 52
Vice Chairman and CEO, Margaret K. M. Y. Leung, age 63
Director, Tung Shun (Peter) Wong
Director, Yat Sun (Richard) Tang, age 61
Director, Hong Sui (Vincent) Lo
Director, LI Ka (Eric) Cheung, age 60
Director, Ting Chang (Peter) Lee, age 59
Director, Jenki Hui, age 69
Director, Kin Tung (Marvin) Wong, age 66
Director, Cho Chak (John) Chan, age 71
Auditors: KPMG

LOCATIONS

HQ: Hang Seng Bank Ltd.
83 Des Voeux Road Central,
Phone: (852) 2198 1111   **Fax:** (852) 2868 4047
Web: www.hangseng.com

COMPETITORS

Bank of China (Hong Kong)
Bank of Communications
Bank of East Asia
CITIC International Financial
China Development Bank
China Merchants Bank
China Minsheng Banking
Chong Hing Bank
Dah Sing Financial Holdings Limited
Public Financial Holdings
Shanghai Pudong Development Bank
Standard Chartered

HISTORICAL FINANCIALS

Company Type: Public

Income Statement

FYE: December 31

	ASSETS ($ mil.)	NET INCOME ($ mil.)	INCOME AS % OF ASSETS	EMPLOYEES
12/13	147,504	3,440	2.3%	9,856
12/12	138,949	2,506	1.8%	9,680
12/11	125,572	2,147	1.7%	9,834
12/10	117,967	1,919	1.6%	9,642
12/09	106,516	1,704	1.6%	9,342
Annual Growth	8.5%	19.2%	—	1.3%

2013 Year-End Financials

Return on assets: 2.4%
Return on equity: 26.6%
Long-term debt ($ mil.): —
No. of shares (mil.): 1,911
Sales ($ mil): 7,297

Dividends
  Yield: 3.7%
  Payout: —
Market value ($ mil.): 31,125

	STOCK PRICE ($) FY Close	P/E High/Low		Earnings	PER SHARE ($) Dividends	Book Value
12/13	16.28	0	0	1.80	0.61	7.27
12/12	15.49	0	0	1.31	0.72	6.23
12/11	11.80	0	0	1.12	0.01	5.30
12/10	16.49	0	0	1.00	0.60	4.71
12/09	14.88	0	0	0.89	0.74	3.93
Annual Growth	2.3%	—	—	19.2%	(4.7%)	16.6%

Hannover Rueckversicherung SE

Who insures insurance companies over and over? Hannover! Hannover Rock (Hannover Re) is the second-largest German reinsurance company (Munich Re is #1) and the fourth-largest such company in the world. Through more than 100 subsidiaries the company provides property and casualty (Hannover Re's largest segment) financial life and health reinsurance products in about 150 countries worldwide. Financial reinsurance is provided through Hannover Re Advanced Solutions a Dublin-based consortium managed jointly with HDI Reinsurance (Ireland); both Hannover Re and HDI Reinsurance (Ireland) are subsidiaries of HDI Haftpflichtverband der Deutschen Industrie.

Hannover Re is 50%-owned by German mutual insurance group Talanx AG part of HDI Haftpflichtverband der Deutschen Industrie.

Like nearly all other insurers Hannover Re saw its investment income for 2008 shrink significantly. But an uptick in demand for reinsurance in 2009 along with a decrease in catastrophe losses and a more than 300% increase in investment returns put group results back in line with pre-financial crisis levels. In the second quarter of 2010 however the company experienced higher-than-expected major losses with the sinking of the Deepwater Horizon oil rig operated by BP.

The property/casualty unit of the ever-diversifying Hannover Re accounts for more than 55% of all premiums and is geared toward markets in the US Germany and Japan. Its life/health business is marketed through subsidiary Hannover Life Re and focuses on treaty (groups of risks) rather than facultative (individual risk) policies.

To boost its presence in the US the company purchased a portfolio of life reinsurance from Scottish Re in 2009. The deal gave Hannover a business it attempted to buy from ING Groep in 2004 but lost out to Scottish Re. In 2011 Scottish Re offloaded another chunk of life reinsurance which Hannover Re readily purchased.

While Hannover Re's traditional "brot und butter" has been property and casualty reinsurance the firm has expanded its life and health lines which are contributing closer and closer to half of all premiums. Hannover Re has also adopted American accounting practices and become more transparent in order to remain a compelling stock in investors' eyes.

HISTORY

Hannover Re was founded in 1966 as the Aktiengesellschaft for Transport und Rockversicherung (ATR) by the Feuerschadenverband Rheinisch-Westfaelischer Zechen (FSV) a mutual insurer specializing in fire damage in the town of Bochum. Within five years ATR had expanded into international reinsurance markets. In 1970 FSV merged with another mutual HDI Haftpflichtverband der Deutschen Industrie which owned reinsurer Eisen und Stahl Rockversicherungs-AG. ATR's headquarters relocated to Hannover and six years later it was renamed Hannover Rockversicherungs-Gesellschaft.

Jointly managed by HDI Hannover Re and Eisen und Stahl operated separately until 1996: Hannover Re targeted international markets while Eisen und Stahl operated mostly within Germany.

Hannover Re maintained its foreign focus throughout the 1970s and 80s expanding in Europe and South Africa and making its first forays into the US. In 1990 the firm acquired US life insurer Reassurance Company of Hannover.

Hannover Re went public in 1994 selling 25% of its stock. Also that year the firm formed an Australian subsidiary. The next year Hannover Re acquired Eisen und Stahl (renamed E+S Ruck 1996) which then assumed total control of the company's domestic business.

In 1998 Hannover Re became the first reinsurer to securitize life insurance business (reinsurers often securitize non-life policies to protect against natural catastrophe risks) through an agreement with Interpolis an Irish reinsurance subsidiary of the Netherlands' Rabobank. Also that year the firm expanded its financial reinsurance business reorganizing the Irish consortium it formed with another subsidiary of HDI into Hannover Re Advanced Solutions.

As various natural disasters offset earnings in Hannover Re's property & casualty division in 1998 and 1999 its life and health segment boomed. To facilitate further growth the firm restructured these operations into a new subsidiary Hannover Life Re. Also in 1999 the firm acquired the Clarendon Insurance Group of New York. In 2001 Hannover Re joined Inreon an online reinsurance trading exchange set up by rivals Munich Re and Swiss Re. Also in 2001 the company established a Bermuda-based subsidiary focused on catastrophe business. The following year Hannover Re split its stock in order to stimulate demand and become a more widely held company.

Like many other insurers the company was hit hard by the attacks of September 11 2001 falling stock markets and in 2005 damages in the Gulf of Mexico caused by hurricanes Katrina and Rita.

Late in 2006 China loosened its regulation of a number of industries and insurance was one of them —Hannover Re was one of the first to gain permission to enter the Chinese market for life and health reinsurance.

At about the same time the company announced plans to cut down on its noncore business operations. The first move in this direction was the sale of its US-based Praetorian Group subsidiary to QBE's US-based subsidiary for a sum in excess of $800 million. Hannover Re used the proceeds to shore up its property/casualty and life/health reinsurance businesses.

EXECUTIVES

CEO Hannover Life Re, Wolf Becke, age 67
Deputy Chairman Supervisory Board, Klaus Sturany, age 68, $67,254 total compensation
Executive Board Member Non-life, Michael Pickel, age 54
Executive Board Member Non-Life, Andre Arrago, age 65
Chairman of the Executive Board, Ulrich Wallin, age 53
Chief Public Relations Manager, Gabriele Handrick
CFO, Roland Vogel
Senior Manager Investor Relations, Klaus Paesler
Head Corporate Communications, Karl Steinle, age 44
Executive Board Member Hanover Life Re Northern and Central Europe, Klaus Miller, age 54
Chief Risk Officer, Eberhard Muller
CFO, Elke A. K?nig
Member of the Executive Board, Claude Chevre
Member of the Executive Board, Juergen Graeber
Chief Executive Officer, Nick Parr
Director, Herbert K. Haas, age 60
Director, Karl H. Midunsky
Director, Immo Querner
Deputy Chairman Supervisory Board, Klaus Sturany, age 68
Director, Uwe Kramp
Director, Otto Muller
Director, Erhard Schipporeit
Director, Gert Wachtler
Member of the Supervisory Board, Andrea Pollak
Member of the Supervisory Board; Employee Representative, Gert Waechtler
Member of the Supervisory Board; Employee Representative, Otto Mueller
Member of the Supervisory Board, Wolf-Dieter Baumgartl
Auditors: KPMGAGWirtschaftsprufungsgesellschaft

LOCATIONS

HQ: Hannover Rueckversicherung SE
Karl-Wiechert-Allee 50, Hannover D-30625
Phone: (49) 511 5604 0   **Fax:** (49) 511 5604 1188
Web: www.hannover-re.com

2009 Premiums Written

	% of total
Europe	
Germany	13
UK	17
France	5
Other	12
North America	
US	28
Other	4
Asia	8
Australia	4
Africa	3
Other	6
Total	**100**

COMPETITORS

Everest Re	Reinsurance Group of
General Re	America
Lloyd's	SCOR
Munich Re Group	Swiss Re
PartnerRe	XL Group plc

HISTORICAL FINANCIALS
Company Type: Public

Income Statement
FYE: December 31

	ASSETS ($ mil.)	NET INCOME ($ mil.)	INCOME AS % OF ASSETS	EMPLOYEES
12/13	74,227	1,232	1.7%	2,419
12/12	72,244	1,131	1.6%	2,312
12/11	64,500	783	1.2%	2,217
12/10	62,535	1,002	1.6%	2,192
12/09	60,884	1,053	1.7%	2,069
Annual Growth	**5.1%**	**4.0%**	**—**	**4.0%**

2013 Year-End Financials

Return on assets: 1.6%	Dividends
Return on equity: 14.9%	Yield: 3.3%
Long-term debt ($ mil.): —	Payout: 16.3%
No. of shares (mil.): 120	Market value ($ mil.): 5,212
Sales ($ mil): 18,946	

	STOCK PRICE ($) FY Close	P/E High/Low		Earnings	PER SHARE ($) Dividends	Book Value
12/13	43.22	11	8	10.23	1.43	67.22
12/12	38.93	10	6	9.38	0.98	66.19
12/11	24.82	12	7	6.49	2.35	53.31
12/10	26.70	8	5	8.31	0.96	50.04
12/09	23.60	9	4	8.73	0.00	44.34
Annual Growth	**16.3%**	**—**	**—**	**4.0%**	**—**	**11.0%**

Hanwha Corp

LOCATIONS

HQ: Hanwha Corp
86 Cheonggyecheon-ro Jung-gu, Seoul 100-220
Phone: (82) 2 729 1881   **Fax:** (82) 2 729 1762
Web: www.hanwhacorp.co.kr

HISTORICAL FINANCIALS

Company Type: Public

Income Statement

FYE: December 31

	REVENUE ($ mil.)	NET INCOME ($ mil.)	NET PROFIT MARGIN	EMPLOYEES
12/13	36,823	123	0.3%	3,801
12/12	10,773	290	2.7%	3,840
12/11	10,516	116	1.1%	3,642
12/10	12,906	1,024	7.9%	3,422
12/09	25,939	483	1.9%	3,164
Annual Growth	9.2%	(28.9%)	—	4.7%

2013 Year-End Financials

Debt ratio: 0.0%
Return on equity: 2.8%
Cash ($ mil.): 1,284
Current ratio: 1.04
Long-term debt ($ mil.): 5,413

No. of shares (mil.): 69
Dividends
  Yield: —
  Payout: —
Market value ($ mil.): —

HDFC Bank Ltd

HDFC Bank serves nearly 30 million customers worldwide and provides a variety of wholesale retail and depository financial services through more than 3400 branches and some 11500 ATMs throughout India. Established by financial institution Housing Development Finance Corporation in 1994 the bank offers deposit accounts loans credit cards insurance investments and related services. Subsidiary HDFC Securities provides online brokerage services. HDFC Bank targets individual customers in the middle and upper-class as well as trusts small businesses and not-for-profit organizations in the country.

EXECUTIVES

Managing Director, Aditya Puri, age 63
Head Wholesale Banking and Director, Harish Engineer, age 65
Head Audit Compliance Vigilance, G. Subramanian, age 66
Head Credit and Market Risk and Human Resources and Director, Paresh Sukthankar, age 51
Head Equities and Private Banking, Abhay Aima, age 51
Head Wholesale Credit Market Risk and Retail Risk Policy, Kaizad Bharucha, age 48
Head Retaill Assets, Pralay Mondal, age 48
Member of Senior Management, Bhavesh Zaveri, age 48
Head Branch Banking, Navin Puri, age 55
Member of Senior Management, Jimmy Tata, age 46
Head Finance, Sashi Jagdishan, age 49
Member of Senior Management, Rajender Sehgal, age 58
Treasury, Ashish Parthasarthy, age 46
Head Retail Liabilities Marketing and Phone Banking, Rahul N. Bhagat, age 50
Executive Vice President - Legal; Compliance Officer; Company Secretary, Sanjay Dongre
Member of Senior Management, Anil Jaggia
Director, Arvind Pande, age 71
Managing Director, Aditya Puri, age 63
Director, Keki M. Mistry, age 59
Director, Renu S. Karnad, age 61
Head Wholesale Banking and Director, Harish Engineer, age 65
Head Credit and Market Risk and Human Resources and Director, Paresh Sukthankar, age 51
Director, Ashim Samanta, age 59

Director, C.M. Vasudev, age 70
Director, Pandit Palande, age 52
Director, Partho Datta
Non-Executive Independent Director, Bobby Parikh
Non-Executive Independent Director, Anami Roy
Auditors: Haribhakti&Co.

LOCATIONS

HQ: HDFC Bank Ltd
HDFC Bank House, Senapati Bapat Marg, Lower Parel, Mumbai 400 013
Phone: (91) 22 66521000   **Fax:** (91) 22 24960737
Web: www.hdfcbank.com

PRODUCTS/OPERATIONS

Sales By Segment

	% of total
Retail	51
Wholesale	27
Treasury	15
Other	7
Total	**100**

COMPETITORS

Bank of Baroda
Bank of India
Canara Bank
ICICI Bank

Industrial Development Bank of India
State Bank of India

HISTORICAL FINANCIALS

Company Type: Public

Income Statement

FYE: March 31

	ASSETS ($ mil.)	NET INCOME ($ mil.)	INCOME AS % OF ASSETS	EMPLOYEES
03/14	85,359	1,321	1.5%	68,165
03/13	80,517	1,138	1.4%	69,065
03/12	70,194	978	1.4%	66,076
03/11 55,752	0	924	***************%	
03/10	49,549	656	1.3%	51,888
Annual Growth	14.6%	19.1%	—	7.1%

2014 Year-End Financials

Return on assets: 1.6%
Return on equity: 15.8%
Long-term debt ($ mil.): —
No. of shares (mil.): —
Sales ($ mil): 8,211

Dividends
  Yield: 0.6%
  Payout: 0.0%
Market value ($ mil.): —

	STOCK PRICE ($) FY Close	P/E High/Low		PER SHARE ($) Earnings	Dividends	Book Value
03/14	41.03	0	0	0.55	0.26	3.69
03/13	37.42	0	0	0.48	0.00	3.63
03/12	34.10	0	0	0.42	0.00	3.31
03/11	169.94	0	0	0.39	0.15	(0.00)
03/10	139.39	—	—	0.30	0.12	2.09
Annual Growth	(26.3%)	—	—	16.5%	20.9%	15.2%

Hindustan Petroleum Corp., Ltd. (India)

Hindustan Petroleum is one of India's top oil refiners (along with Indian Oil and Bharat Petroleum) and accounts for 10% of the country's total refining requirements. The company has two major

refineries —one in Mumbai the other in the southern Indian city of Vishakhapatnam —and produces lubricants aviation fuel liquefied petroleum gas and light diesel oil. Hindustan Petroleum also holds a 17% stake in a refinery at Mangalore. Other businesses include pipelines a lube refinery (with a 40% share of the lube oil market) and more than 11250 retail outlets nationwide. The Indian government owns 51% of the company.

Geographic Reach

The company's marketing network consists of 13 zonal offices in major cities and 101 regional offices. It has a major refinery in Mumbai on India's west coast and in Vishakhapatnam on the east coast and 17% of Mangalore Refinery & Petrochemicals Limited in the south of India and a joint venture refinery in the Punjab in the north.

Operations

Hindustan Petroleum has a refining capacity of more than 15 million metric tonnes per year. Its refineries produce a wide variety of petroleum fuels and specialty products. Its supply and distribution infrastructure includes terminals pipeline networks aviation service stations LPG bottling plants inland relay depots and retail outlets lube and LPG distributorships.

Financial Performance

Higher prices and demand help to lift the company's revenues by 33% in 2011.

Net income decreased by 90% in 2011 due to increase in depreciation and amortization expenses other expenses transshipping expenses purchase in stock-in-trade and cost of materials consumed.

Strategy

Hindustan Petroleum in addition investing heavily in the modernization and expansion of its major refineries is opening new retail outlets to keep up with the growing population. In 2011 the company commissioned 1056 retail outlets including 329 in rural areas.

To stay competitive the company has been diversifying by entering into exploration and production as well as into the supply of liquefied natural gas (LNG) and compressed natural gas (CNG). In 2011 the company held minority stakes in oil and gas fields in Australia Egypt India and Oman.

Ownership

The company is controlled by the Government of India.

EXECUTIVES

Chairman and Managing Director, S. Roy Choudhury
Human Resources Director, V. Vizia Saradhi
Finance Director, Bhaswar Mukherjee
Refineries Director, K. Murali
Marketing Director, Nishi Vasudeva
Auditors: B.K.Khare&Co.

LOCATIONS

HQ: Hindustan Petroleum Corp., Ltd. (India) Petroleum House, 17, Jamshedji Tata Road, Mumbai 400020
Phone:
Web: www.hindustanpetroleum.com

COMPETITORS

Bharat Petroleum
Essar Group

Exxon Mobil
Indian Oil

HISTORICAL FINANCIALS

Company Type: Public

Income Statement

FYE: March 31

	REVENUE ($ mil.)	NET INCOME ($ mil.)	NET PROFIT MARGIN	EMPLOYEES
03/13	40,014	92	0.2%	11,027
03/12	36,620	34	0.1%	11,226
03/11	31,400	381	1.2%	11,248
03/10	25,235	0	—	11,291
03/09	25,548	0	—	11,246
Annual Growth	11.9%	—	—	(0.5%)

2013 Year-End Financials

Debt ratio: 0.5%
Return on equity: 3.7%
Cash ($ mil.): 159
Current ratio: 0.57
Long-term debt ($ mil.): —
No. of shares (mil.): 338
Dividends
  Yield: —
  Payout: —
Market value ($ mil.): —

Hiroshima Bank, Ltd. (The) (Japan)

Few banks have deeper roots in the Hiroshima Prefecture than the Hiroshima Bank. Established in 1878 the bank serves Japan's Chugoku and Shikoku regions through more than 175 offices and 830 ATMs. Hiroshima organizes its business approach into three distinct areas: financial intermediation risk management assistance and information provision. It offers the traditional array of financial services including investment and private banking products real estate appraisal banking software venture capital support and assistance with corporate restructuring.

EXECUTIVES

President, Isao Sumihiro
Executive Officer, Hideo Yamashita
Executive Officer, Makoto Tsukamoto
Executive Officer, Hironori Kawasaki
Executive Officer, Hiroshi Matsushige
Auditors: KPMGAZSA&Co.

LOCATIONS

HQ: Hiroshima Bank, Ltd. (The) (Japan)
1-3-8 Kamiya-cho, Naka-ku, Hiroshima 730-0031
Phone: (81) 82 247 5151   **Fax:** (81) 82 247 5234
Web: www.hirogin.co.jp

COMPETITORS

Aozora Bank	Miyazaki Bank
Chugoku Bank	Shizuoka Bank
Higo Bank	
Mitsubishi UFJ Financial Group	

HISTORICAL FINANCIALS

Company Type: Public

Income Statement

FYE: March 31

	ASSETS ($ mil.)	NET INCOME ($ mil.)	INCOME AS % OF ASSETS	EMPLOYEES
03/14	69,808	221	0.3%	3,187
03/13	75,050	184	0.2%	3,207
03/12	81,075	168	0.2%	3,274
03/11	77,165	166	0.2%	3,371
03/10	68,151	118	0.2%	3,385
Annual Growth	0.6%	16.9%	—	(1.5%)

2014 Year-End Financials

Return on assets: 0.3%
Return on equity: 6.5%
Long-term debt ($ mil.): —
No. of shares (mil.): 621
Sales ($ mil): 1,393
Dividends
  Yield: —
  Payout: —
Market value ($ mil.): —

Hitachi, Ltd.

Hitachi which means "risen sun" is looking for a new dawn of profits from its galaxy of businesses. The company's Information & Telecommunications Systems (semiconductors servers mainframes ATMs) brings in the most revenue followed by Social Infrastructure (elevators escalators industrial machinery) and High Functional Materials (wire cables specialty steel circuit boards). Its Electronic Systems & Equipment segment includes specialized manufacturing equipment and power tools. The company is a world leader in consumer goods ranging from TVs to washing machines and in power generation equipment. Hitachi also has operations in financial services automotive systems and construction machinery.

Operations

Responding to such IT changes as cloud computing and business globalization the company announced it would merge Information & Telecommunication Systems' units Hitachi Electronics Services (HES) and Hitachi Information Systems (Hitachi Joho) to create Hitachi Systems. Effective in 2011 the combination is designed to strengthen the company's data center services business in Japan. The move follows Hitachi's efforts to focus on its most profitable segments and streamline sector management.

Financial Analysis

When the company announced fiscal 2011 results it showed improved revenue on the strength of an increase in global demand amid economic recovery and the company's restructuring and cost-cutting measures. Revenue had declined 10% the prior year due to falling demand though belt tightening in 2009 had begun to have a positive effect on net income.

Strategy

Hitachi plans to put many of its eggs in the Social Innovation basket where its Social Infrastructure unit works with its other four leading business units –Information & Telecom Power Construction Machinery and High Functional Materials –to create IT power and transportation systems for urban and industrial segments. The eggs in the basket are about Â2.6 trillion in capital expenditures strategic investments and R&D spending on Social Innovation through fiscal 2014. Other targets include improving Hitachi's overall business structure and expanding globally especially in China Germany and the US.

In a move aimed at improving its ability to compete in an increasingly global marketplace in early 2011 Hitachi formed an alliance with Mitsubishi Heavy Industries (MHI) and Mitsubishi Electric Corp to spin off and integrate their hydroelectric power businesses. The joint venture 98% owned by Hitachi with 1% for each of the other partners is tentatively named HM Hydro. The companies' variable-speed technology could give them an advantage over other power players if smart grids continue to expand in global markets. The joint venture is a way for Hitachi and its partners to better compete for international projects against market leaders such as Toshiba and Voith Hydro (a joint venture between Voith and Siemens). The domestic market for hydroelectric power systems in Japan has stopped growing which has forced companies there to rely on maintenance services to stay afloat.

An increasingly competitive climate along with expected growth in the small and midsized display market prompted another alliance in this case with Sony and Toshiba. Each of the three companies will integrate their businesses in this niche under a new company to be set up and run by Innovation Network Corporation of Japan (INCJ). INCJ will hold 70% of the voting stock in the company while the remaining shares will be evenly divided among the other three companies.

As part of its strategy to refocus on its infrastructure businesses in 2012 Hitachi sold its Hitachi Global Storage Technologies (HGST) disk drive subsidiary to Western Digital in a $4.3 billion cash and stock transaction. The deal gave Hitachi a 10% stake in Western Digital and board representation along with an estimated $3.5 billion in cash. Hitachi originally planned on an IPO for HGST which became profitable in 2011 after five years of losses. HGST was not considered core to ongoing operations. Also in 2012 Hitachi's display business was folded into a new joint venture with Sony and Toshiba called Japan Display Inc. The company was launched on the same day as South Korea-based rival Samsung Display Co. Ltd. and focuses on small and midsized displays for mobile devices automotive and industrial applications.

Mergers and Acquisitions

In 2012 Hitachi announced it would buy the UK Horizon nuclear project from Germany's E.ON and RWE for $1.12 billion to build four to six new nuclear power stations. It hopes to have the first of the 1300 megawatt (MW) nuclear power plants operations by the mid-2020s. Together the plants could provide electricity to 14 million homes for more than 60 years. Hitachi along with British companies Babcock International and Rolls-Royce will use Horizon to create a strong and permanent base of nuclear skills in the UK.

HISTORY

Namihei Odaira an employee of Kuhara Mining in the Japanese coastal city of Hitachi wanted to prove that Japan did not have to depend on foreigners for technology. In 1910 he began building electric motors in Kuhara's engineering and repair shop. Japanese power companies were forced to buy Odaira's generators when WWI made imports scarce. Impressed they reordered and in 1920 Hitachi (meaning "risen sun") became an independent company.

During the 1920s acquisitions and growth turned Hitachi into a major manufacturer of electrical equipment and machinery. In the 1930s and 1940s Hitachi developed vacuum tubes and light bulbs and produced radar and sonar for the Japanese war effort. Postwar occupation forces removed Odaira and closed 19 Hitachi plants. Reeling from the plant closures war damage and labor strife Hitachi was saved from bankruptcy by US military contracts during the Korean War.

In the 1950s Hitachi became a supplier to Nippon Telegraph and Telephone (NTT) the state-owned telecommunications monopoly. Japan's economic recovery led to strong demand for the company's communications and electrical equipment. Hitachi began mass-producing home appliances radios TVs and transistors. The group spun off Hitachi Metals and Hitachi Cable in 1956 and Hitachi Chemical in 1963.

With the help of NTT the Ministry of International Trade and Industry and technology licensed from RCA (bought by General Electric in 1986) Hitachi produced its first computer in 1965. Hitachi built factories in Southeast Asia and started manufacturing integrated circuits.

Hitachi launched an IBM-compatible computer in 1974. The company sold its computers in the US through Itel until 1979 when Itel was bought by National Semiconductor and afterward through National Semi's National Advanced Systems (NAS) unit. In 1982 FBI agents caught Hitachi staff buying documents allegedly containing IBM software secrets. Settlement of a civil lawsuit required Hitachi to make payments to IBM for eight years as compensation for the use of IBM's software.

When the rising Japanese yen hurt exports Hitachi focused on its domestic market and invested heavily in factory automation in the late 1980s. But a recession at home caused earnings to fall. In 1988 the company and Texas Instruments joined in the costly development and production of 16-megabyte DRAMs. In 1989 Hitachi bought 80% of NAS giving it direct control of its US distribution.

Despite its rivalry with IBM in 1991 Hitachi began to resell IBM notebook PCs under its own name in Japan. In a major move to combat sluggish consumer electronics sales in 1994 Hitachi merged with its marketing subsidiary Hitachi Sales Corp. Hitachi used joint ventures to beef up its international presence including a 1995 agreement with India's Tata Group.

Tokyo police in 1997 began investigating Hitachi charging that the company and others had paid off a corporate racketeer. A slump in semiconductor prices coupled with the Asian economic turmoil hurt Hitachi in 1998. Etsuhiko Shoyama became president the next year replacing Tsutomu Kanai who became chairman. Hitachi posted its then-worst loss in history in 1999; the firm combined some subsidiaries and announced layoffs. It also formed a joint venture with Fujitsu to make plasma display panels. The JV was called Fujitsu Hitachi Plasma Display (FHP).

Hitachi spun off its DRAM business into Elpida Memory a joint venture with NEC that began operations in 2000. That year Hitachi launched the Internet & Network Services Group to focus on Internet business development; in 2001 it joined with NEC to develop semiconductors for LCD panels and cell phone displays.

Hitachi teamed with Sun Microsystems in 2002 in a multibillion-dollar storage software distribution and cross-licensing agreement. The company also formed a joint venture with IBM for Hitachi to acquire IBM's disk drive operations which was launched the following year as Hitachi Global Storage Technologies.

In 2002 Hitachi merged its system chip unit with that of Mitsubishi Electric to form a new company Renesas Technology.

In early 2003 the company unveiled a three-year program to reorganize its businesses known as Hitachi Plan II. The plan called for the company to exit certain businesses and to focus on targeted businesses using a process it called "future inspiration value."

In 2003 the company unveiled a finger vein authentication system for use in confirming user identities. Hitachi also increased its investment in Elpida Memory by $80 million along with NEC and added Intel as an investor in the memory semiconductor business. Intel put in $100 million. Later that year Hitachi merged Hitachi netBusiness (established 2000) with Hitachi Information Systems.

It sold its Hitachi Printing Solutions subsidiary to Ricoh in 2004. To strengthen its automotive business Hitachi merged its TOKICO affiliate with its Hitachi Unisia Automotive subsidiary consolidating the operations within the company. Hitachi also announced plans for an LCD television joint venture with Toshiba and Matsushita Electric in 2004 and a plasma television JV with Matsushita Electric in 2005. It collaborated with NEC again on forming another ALAXALA Networks to make backbone routers and switches for communications networks. Hitachi took a 60% interest in ALAXALA.

In early 2005 Hitachi assumed control of Fujitsu Hitachi Plasma Display by buying 30% of FHP from Fujitsu leaving Hitachi with 80% of the JV. That year the company sold shares in Elpida Memory reducing its ownership to nearly 20%. Hitachi launched a computer server systems business in North America as part of Hitachi America. Hitachi Plant Engineering & Construction Hitachi Kiden Kogyo and Hitachi Industries merged in 2006 along with part of Hitachi's Industrial Systems Group to become Hitachi Plant Technologies. Hitachi Mobile in which Hitachi held an equity stake of about 65% became a wholly owned subsidiary of Hitachi. Hitachi Mobile was established in 1950 to repair automobiles and to sell car parts; it later offered auto and mobile communication equipment.

Hitachi Renesas and Toshiba set up a joint-venture planning company in early 2006 to study whether the three chip makers should go into the silicon foundry business (contract manufacturing of semiconductors) together. By midyear however Hitachi concluded that such a move was not feasible under industry conditions at the time. The three chip makers along with NEC Electronics agreed on standardizing technology among them for fabricating semiconductors with features as small as 45 nanometers.

Etsuhiko Shoyama president and CEO of Hitachi since mid-2003 became chairman of the company in early 2006. EVP Kazuo Furukawa was promoted to president and CEO at the same time.

In late 2006 Hitachi took control of Clarion a manufacturer of audio and navigation systems for motor vehicles. In 2000 the company had established a joint venture with Clarion HCX and in 2004 Hitachi became Clarion's largest shareholder buying nearly 15% of the company. Through a tender offer Hitachi increased its ownership to nearly 64% spending almost Â32 billion (about $260 million). The acquisition was expected to strengthen its position in the car information systems market.

Hitachi decided to exit the consumer PC market in late 2007. The company scaled back production of PCs at its factory in Toyokawa Japan to focus on manufacturing computer servers for business applications. Hitachi had previously contracted out some PC production to Hewlett-Packard. According to MM Research Institute Hitachi was eighth in the Japanese PC market with a share of only 4.5% well behind competitors Dell Fujitsu NEC and Toshiba.

The economic downturn and slow recovery forced change across Hitachi's businesses. In 2009 Renesas Technology Corp. a joint venture between Hitachi and Mitsubishi Electric merged with NEC Electronics. Yasushi Akao Renesas president took the reins as president of the merged company. It also created a joint venture with NEC Corp. and CASIO COMPUTER to compete in the growing global cell phone market.

Continuing the streamlining in 2009 Hitachi established new units designed to take advantage of synergies. It created a Battery Systems Division bringing together its work in lithium-ion batteries and a Renewable Energy & Smart Grid Division both in the Power Systems Group. The company launched a Material Resource Recycling Office in the Business Incubation Division for recycling home appliances and other products. It also merged communication subsidiaries in the US to create Hitachi Communication Technologies America.

In 2012 Hitachi sold its Hitachi Global Storage Technologies disk drive subsidiary to Western Digital in a cash and stock deal valued at around $4.3 billion. The move was part of Hitachi's plan to focus on its social infrastructure businesses.

EXECUTIVES

Chairman, Takashi Kawamura, age 75

SVP and Executive Officer, Shinjiro Iwata, age 66

SVP and Executive Officer, Masahide Tanigaki, age 64

Representative Executive Officer and President General Manager, Hiroaki Nakanishi, age 68

SVP and Executive Officer, Makoto Ebata, age 64

EVP and Executive Officer, Kazuhiro Mori, age 65

EVP Representative Executive Officer and Director, Takashi Miyoshi, age 66

EVP and Representative Executive Officer, Junzo Nakajima, age 66

EVP and Representative Executive Officer, Koji Tanaka

VP and Executive Officer, Toshiaki Higashihara

Executive Vice President and Executive Officer, Toyoaki Nakamura, age 62

Senior Vice President and Executive Officer, Toshiaki Kuzuoka, age 60

VP and Executive Officer; Management Strategies, Toshikazu Nishino

VP and Executive Officer; Information and Telecommunication Systems Business, Kaichiro Sakuma, age 60

Executive Vice President and Executive Officer, Shigeru Azuhata, age 65

EVP and Representative Executive Officer, Nobuo Mochida, age 67

SVP and Executive Officer, Yutaka Saito, age 60

VP and Executive Officer; Information and Telecommunication Systems Business, Yoshihiko Mogami, age 61

VP and Executive Officer, Ryuichi Kitayama, age 62

VP and Executive Officer; Urban Planning and Development Systems Business, Toshio Ikemura

VP and Executive Officer; Power Systems Business, Tatsuro Ishizuka

VP and Executive Officer, Yoshifumi Kanda

VP and Executive Officer, Kazuhiro Kurihara

VP and Executive Officer; Government and External Relations, Yasuo Tanabe

VP and Executive Officer; Power Systems Business (Nuclear Power Systems Business Promotion), Masaharu Hanyu

VP and Executive Officer; Human Capital, Naoki Mitarai

Vice President and Executive Officer, Shinichiro Omori

Vice President and Executive Officer, Hiroshi Nakayama

Vice President and Executive Officer, Kaoru Kawano

Vice President and Executive Officer, Masaya Watanabe

Vice President and Executive Officer, Keiji Kojima

Vice President and Executive Officer, Yoshihito Kitamatsu

Director, Mitsuo Ohashi, age 78

Director, Isao Ono

President Representative Executive Officer and
 Director, Hiroaki Nakanishi, age 68
EVP Representative Executive Officer and
 Director, Takashi Miyoshi, age 66
Director, Sir Stephen Gomersall, age 66
Director, Tohru Motobayashi, age 76
Auditors: Ernst&YoungShinNihon

LOCATIONS

HQ: Hitachi, Ltd.
 1-6-6 Marunouchi, Chiyoda-ku, Tokyo 100-8280
Phone: (81) 3 3258 1111
Web: www.hitachi.co.jp

Sales

	% of total
Asia/Pacific	
Japan	57
Other	22
Europe	8
North	8
Other	5
Total	**100**

PRODUCTS/OPERATIONS

Sales

	% of total
Information & Telecom	16
High Functional Materials &	13
Social Infrastructure & Industrial	11
Electronic Systems &	10
Digital Media & Consumer	9
Components &	8
Power	8
Automotive	7
Construction	7
Financial	4
Other	7
Total	**100**

Selected Products and Services

Digital media and consumer products
 Batteries
 Fluorescent lamps
 Kitchen appliances
 LCD projectors
 Mobile phones
 Refrigerators
 Room air conditioners
 TVs
 VCRs
 Videotapes
 Washing machines
Electronic devices
 LCDs
 Medical electronics equipment
 Memories
 Multipurpose semiconductors
 Semiconductor manufacturing equipment
 System LSIs
 Testing and measurement equipment
Financial services
 Insurance services
 Leasing
 Loan guarantees
High-functional materials and components
 Cables
 Carbon products
 Chemical products
 Components
 Copper products
 Electrical insulating materials
 Fine ceramics
 Magnetic materials
 Malleable cast-iron products
 Printed circuit boards
 Specialty steels
 Synthetic resins
 Wires
Information and telecommunication systems
 Computer peripherals
 Fiber-optic components
 Mainframes
 Servers
 Software
 Switches

 Systems integration
Power and industrial systems
 Air-conditioning equipment
 Automotive equipment
 Construction machinery
 Elevators
 Environmental control systems
 Escalators
 Hydroelectric power plants
 Industrial machinery and plant construction
 Nuclear power plants
 Rolling stock
 Thermal power plants
Logistics services and other
 General trading
 Property management
 Transportation

Selected Acquisitions

Mica-AVA (Guangzhou) Material Co. (2011 75%
 advanced laminate products)
Aptivo Consulting S.A. (2011; financial- public sector-
 and telecom-focused IT consulting)
Sierra Atlantic (2011 offshore IT outsourcing)
Telco Construction Equipment Co. Ltd. (2010; 60%;
 hydraulic excavators backhoe loaders wheel loaders)
Wenco International Mining Systems Ltd. (2009 fleet
 management systems)
Aqua-Tech Engineering and Supplies Pte. Ltd. (2009
 water-treatment systems)
Astral Meditech GmbH (2008 70% ultrasound probe
 cables)
M-Tech Information Technology Inc. (2008 67% identity
 management software)
Tanaka Kogyo (2007 power generation equipment)
Clarion (2006 64% audio and navigation systems for
 motor vehicles)

COMPETITORS

ALSTOM
AREVA
Alcatel-Lucent
Applied Materials
Babcock & Wilcox
Canon
Dell
Ericsson
Fluor
Fujitsu
GE
Hewlett-Packard
IBM
Johnson Controls
Kyocera
LG Group
McDermott
Micron Technology
Mitsubishi Electric
Mitsubishi Heavy Industries
NEC
Nippon Steel & Sumitomo Metal Corporation
Nokia
Nortel Networks
Oki Electric
Panasonic Corp
Philips Electronics
SANYO
Samsung Group
Sharp Corp.
Siemens AG
Sony
TDK
Texas Instruments
Toshiba
Truly International
Unisys
United Technologies
Whirlpool

HISTORICAL FINANCIALS

Company Type: Public

Income Statement

FYE: March 31

	REVENUE ($ mil.)	NET INCOME ($ mil.)	NET PROFIT MARGIN	EMPLOYEES
03/14	93,162	2,567	2.8%	369,116
03/13	96,087	1,863	1.9%	374,775
03/12	117,833	4,232	3.6%	369,722
03/11	112,500	2,884	2.6%	406,149
03/10	96,015	(1,145)	—	399,308
Annual Growth	**(0.8%)**	**—**	**—**	**(1.9%)**

2014 Year-End Financials

Debt ratio: 0.2%
Return on equity: 11.2%
Cash ($ mil.): 5,408
Current ratio: 1.33
Long-term debt ($ mil.): 14,655

No. of shares (mil.): —
Dividends
 Yield: 136.0%
 Payout: 19.1%
Market value ($ mil.): —

	STOCK PRICE ($) FY Close	P/E High/Low		PER SHARE ($) Earnings	Dividends	Book Value
03/14	7.35	0	0	0.53	0.10	5.32
03/13	5.87	0	0	0.39	0.11	4.58
03/12	6.46	0	0	0.88	0.10	4.66
03/11	5.17	0	0	0.60	0.06	3.85
03/10	3.45	—	—	(0.31)	0.00	3.07
Annual Growth	**20.8%**	**—**	**—**	**—**	**—**	**14.7%**

Hochtief AG

HOCHTIEF is a giant in Germany and beyond. In addition to doing business throughout Europe the construction-related services provider operates in the Americas and the Asia/Pacific region and is among the world's largest general builders. US subsidiaries Turner and Flatiron provide building and infrastructure construction. Leighton Holdings based in Australia provides engineering and construction services for the infrastructure and mining industries. The group also operates in such European countries as the Czech Republic Poland Russia and the UK. All of HOCHTIEF's businesses focus on the Americas Asia Pacific Europe and concessions.

Spanish construction group Actividades de Construcciones y Servicios (ACS) is HOCHTIEF's largest shareholder controlling more than 45% of its capital (and more than 50% voting rights); a Qatar sovereign wealth fund owns some 10%. ACS has been building up its ownership for several months and in late 2010 bid to buy the company outright. HOCHTIEF management initially fought off the acquisition but gave up the fight in 2011 clinching the takeover. Then-chairman and CEO Herbert Lotkestratkotter stepped down as did CFO Burkhard Lohr and four supervisory board members. ACS board member Frank Stieler succeeded Lotkestratkotter.

HOCHTIEF aims to provide services that span the lifecycle of a construction project. The company is known for building private projects such as warehouses and retail complexes. But its growing concessions and public-private partnership (PPP) division works on major federal state and municipal projects such as power plants toll roads tunnels and water treatment facilities. HOCHTIEF is continually growing and has its sights set on areas of growth especially in places where the PPP market is expanding as it is in North America. Other growth areas include the wind power market. Geographically HOCTIEF plans to expand into India.

Through its concessions division the group also is active in airport projects and it runs public buildings such as schools hospitals and prisons. HOCHTIEF AirPort has grown to become one of the world's largest independent airport managers. The division also takes ownership stakes in projects; its portfolio encompasses principal airports in Athens; Budapest Hungary; Dosseldorf and Hamburg Germany; Sydney; and Tirana Albania. HOCHTIEF in 2013 agreed however to sell its airport portfolio to Public Sector Pension Investment Board of Canada. The deal values the business at 1.5 billion Euros ($2 billion) giving HOCHTIEF about 1.1 billion Euros after its other business partners are paid. Also in 2011 HOCHTIEF sold several of its Leighton mining assets in Australia as a way to boost profit.

The company's former real estate and services divisions merged into the Europe division in 2011. The restructuring helped streamline business and save the company money. The Europe division includes HOCHTIEF Solutions which plans develops and markets large real estate properties such as hotels office buildings and retail and residential projects in Europe.

In addition to building and developing properties HOCHTIEF also makes sure those properties stay running. Its services division includes facility management and energy management providers. The division specializes in servicing the automotive industry chemical and pharmaceutical plants financial services facilities airports and health care and event facilities.

HISTORY

Brothers Philipp and Balthasar Helfmann mill and farm workers from Kelsterbach Germany started construction company Fa. Gebr. Helfmann Bauunternehmer in Frankfurt am Main in 1875. The firm primarily built houses until 1878 when it was contracted to build the university at Giessen.

In 1884 the company was made a general partnership. Projects of this era included Frankfurt's Hotel Continental and Wiesbaden's Hotel Kaiserhof. When Balthasar died in 1896 Philipp converted the business to a joint stock company and renamed it Actien-Gesellschaft for Hoch- und Tiefbauten. Three years later with new capital for expansion the company won its first contract abroad —construction of a pneumatic conveyer-equipped granary in the harbor at Genoa (its first reinforced-concrete project).

Philipp Helfmann died in 1899 but the company continued operating. The battlefields of WWI took away most of the workforce and construction slowed to a near halt. But in the years following the war the company grew. In 1921 German industrialist Hugo Stinnes began buying stakes in the company and was its major shareholder by 1923. The company decided in 1922 to relocate to Essen closer to the Stinnes Group's operations and in 1923 it was renamed HOCHTIEF Aktiengesellschaft for Hoch- und Tiefbauten vorm. Gebr. Helfmann.

Stinnes died in 1924 and two years later his empire collapsed. But German banks helped keep HOCHTIEF alive and operating as an independent company. That year Rheinisch-Westfalische-Elektrizitatswerke AG (RWE) the electric utility that Stinnes helped create became the main shareholder in HOCHTIEF with a 31% stake.

Many of RWE's facilities were damaged during WWII including its Essen headquarters and the RWE staff used the HOCHTIEF building until 1961. Postwar reconstruction kept the company active including Germany's first nuclear reactor built by HOCHTIEF and commissioned in 1966.

After the war RWE began increasing its stake in HOCHTIEF until it became the majority shareholder (56%) in 1989.

As a division of the RWE Group HOCHTIEF began acquiring former state-owned companies throughout Germany. By 1996 it had added financing and operation of major projects to its services. That year it led a consortium to build and operate an international airport in Athens. In 1997 it teamed with Ireland's Aer Rianta to build new terminals and manage the airport in Dosseldorf Germany. The next year HOCHTIEF won a bid to build and operate Berlin's new airport but a rival's allegations of bidding irregularities led to a raid by prosecutors on HOCHTIEF's headquarters. Charges were dismissed but the company was disqualified from the project.

The company sought to expand internationally with an agreement to take a 49% stake in the US holdings of its main rival Philipp Holzmann (1997). But when these plans failed and HOCHTIEF was blocked by regulators from increasing its 20% stake in the competitor (held since 1981) it lost interest and relinquished its shares.

HOCHTIEF like many of its competitors expanded abroad in 1999 by helping engineer Canadian firm Armbro's takeover of rival BFC (and then grabbing a 49% share in the merged firm now Aecon Group) and by acquiring US construction giant Turner. The company suffered a $75 million operating loss in 2000 because of a slowdown in the German construction industry and expenses related to acquisitions.

It secured a contract to build a rail tunnel under the River Thames in London in 2001. Also that year it merged its building and civil units into HOCHTIEF Construction and made plans to join former rival IVG Immobilien to bid on building Berlin's new airport Berlin-Brandenburg. HOCHTIEF reorganized in 2001 to reflect its increasingly international operations.

By 2002 Philipp Holzmann was in insolvency and HOCHTIEF initially made plans to bid on its former rival's technical services group HSG. However after reviewing the unit's prospectus HOCHTIEF withdrew from the bidding.

Longtime shareholder and German energy giant RWE sold its 56% stake in HOCHTIEF in 2004 to European and US institutional investors. It was the largest such transaction involving a German stock.

HOCHTIEF subsidiary Leighton and joint venture partner Downer EDI won a Â100 million contract to build a four-lane highway in New Zealand in 2006. The project is expected to be finished in 2010.

In 2007 the company acquired the energy contracting business of Vattenfall Europe adding to its existing service portfolio of energy contracting and management operations. Also that year HOCHTIEF acquired Flatiron Construction from Royal BAM Group. That deal provided the group with entry into infrastructure PPP markets in the US and Canada.

EXECUTIVES

President and CEO Turner Construction, Peter J. Davoren, age 59
CEO Flatiron Construction, John A. DiCiurcio, age 59
Chairman and CEO, Marcelino F. Verdes, age 58
CEO Flatiron Construction, Tom Rademacher
CFO and Member Executive Board, Peter Sassenfeld, age 48
Chief Executive Officer CEO, Rainer Eichholz, age 58
CEO Leighton Holdings Limited, Hamish G. Tyrwhitt, age 50
Head Investor Relations, Ulrike Kroner

Senior Vice President Corporate Communications, Bernd Putter
Chairman of the Executive Board CEO of HOCHTIEF Solutions AG, Rainer Eicholz
Head of Investor Relations, Ulrike Ulrike Kroener Kroener
Member Supervisory Board, Angel Garcia Altozano
Member Supervisory Board, Gerrit Pennings
Member Supervisory Board, Marcelino F. Verdes
Member Supervisory Board, Klaus Wiesehugel
Member Supervisory Board, Gregor Asshoff
Deputy Chairman Supervisory Board, Ulrich Best
Member of the Supervisory Board, Abdulla Abdulla Al-Subaie Al-Subaie
Member of the Supervisory Board, Eggert Eggert Voscherau Voscherau
Member of the Supervisory Board; Employee Representative, Johannes Johannes Howorka Howorka
Member of the Supervisory Board, Jose Jose Luis del Valle Perez Perez
Member of the Supervisory Board; Employee Representative, Klaus Klaus Wiesehuegel Wiesehuegel
Member of the Supervisory Board; Employee Representative, Nikolaus Nikolaus Graf von Matuschka Matuschka
Member of the Supervisory Board; Employee Representative, Olaf Olaf Wendler Wendler
Member of the Supervisory Board, Pedro Pedro Jose Lopez Jimenez Jimenez
Auditors: Deloitte&ToucheGmbH

LOCATIONS

HQ: Hochtief AG
Opernplatz 2, Essen D-45128
Phone: (49) 201 824 0   **Fax:** (49) 201 824 2777
Web: www.hochtief.com

Sales

	% of total
Australia	41
Americas	34
Europe	
Germany	8
Other	5
Asia	12
Total	**100**

Sales

	% of total
Americas	37
Australia	35
Europe	
Germany	12
Other	6
Asia	10
Total	**100**

PRODUCTS/OPERATIONS

Sales

	% of total
Asia/Pacific	54
Americas	29
Europe	11
Services	3
Real	2
Concessions	1
Total	**100**

Selected Subsidiaries and Associates

Airport
  HOCHTIEF AirPort Capital Verwaltungs GmbH & Co. KG
  HOCHTIEF AirPort GmbH
Construction Services Americas
  Flatiron Construction Corp. (US)
  HOCHTIEF Americas GmbH
  HOCHTIEF do Brasil S.A. (92%)
  The Turner Corporation (US)
Construction Services Asia Pacific

HOCTHIEF Asia Pacific GmbH
Construction Services Europe
   DURST-BAU GmbH (Austria)
   HOCHTIEF Construction AG
Development
   Deutsche Bau-und Siedlungs-Gesellschaft mbH
   HOCHTIEF Aurestis Beteiligungsgesellschaft mbH

COMPETITORS

Acciona	Fluor
Avionic Services	KBR Building Group
International	PCL Employees Holdings
BAA	Parsons Corporation
Bechtel	Peter Kiewit Sons'
Bilfinger Berger	STRABAG SE
Bouygues	Skanska
Cheung Kong	Tutor Perini
Infrastructure	VINCI
Dragados	

HISTORICAL FINANCIALS
Company Type: Public

Income Statement
FYE: December 31

	REVENUE ($ mil.)	NET INCOME ($ mil.)	NET PROFIT MARGIN	EMPLOYEES
12/13	35,265	235	0.7%	80,912
12/12	33,767	208	0.6%	79,987
12/11	29,928	(207)	—	75,449
12/10	27,187	385	1.4%	70,657
12/09	26,215	281	1.1%	66,178
Annual Growth	7.7%	(4.3%)	—	5.2%

2013 Year-End Financials

Debt ratio: 31.2%
Return on equity: 6.9%
Cash ($ mil.): 2,802
Current ratio: 1.40
Long-term debt ($ mil.): 3,668

No. of shares (mil.): 77
Dividends
   Yield: —
   Payout: —
Market value ($ mil.): 6,564

	STOCK PRICE ($) FY Close	P/E High/Low	Earnings	PER SHARE ($) Dividends	Book Value
12/13	85.25	68 47	3.26	0.00	40.51
12/12	51.91	58 33	2.83	0.00	45.20
12/11	57.60	— —	(2.82)	0.00	43.65
12/10	84.00	37 24	5.77	0.00	51.58
12/09	76.25	58 20	4.22	0.00	47.85
Annual Growth	2.8%	— —	(6.2%)	—	(4.1%)

Hokuhoku Financial Group Inc

Short on cash and passing through the Hokuriku or Hokkaido districts of Japan? You might want to check in with this group. The Hokuhoku Financial Group's core business is banking primarily through its chief subsidiaries: The Hokuriku Bank and The Hokkaido Bank. Through both banks' approximately 325 branches the financial services group targets the Toyama Ishikawa and Fukui Prefectures. In addition to banking Hokuhoku Financial Group provides credit cards leasing services venture capital and financing products. Hokuriku Bank (founded in 1877) merged with Hokkaido Bank in 2004 to form Hokuhoku Financial Group which today operates in the Hokuriku and Hokkaido district and Tokyo Osaka and Nagoya.

EXECUTIVES

President Hokuhoku Financial Group and The Hokuriku Bank, Shigeo Takagi
Chairman, Yoshihiro Sekihachi
Senior Managing Director The Hokuriku Bank, Tatsuya Kaseda
President, Eishin Ihori
Senior Managing Director The Hokuriku Bank, Tetsuji Mitsuzuka
Senior Managing Director The Hokuriku Bank, Takashi Nakano

LOCATIONS

HQ: Hokuhoku Financial Group Inc
1-2-26 Tsutsumicho-dori, Toyama 930-8637
Phone: (81) 76 423 7331
Web: www.hokuhoku-fg.co.jp

2013 Branches

	No.
Hokuriku	149
Hokkaido	158
Other major metro	17
Other	4
Total	**328**

PRODUCTS/OPERATIONS

Selected Subsidiaries and Affiliated Companies

Hokugin Lease Co. Ltd.
Hokugin Software Co. Ltd.
Hokuriku Capital Co. Ltd.
Hokuriku Card Co. Ltd.
Hokuriku Hosho Services Co. Ltd.
Nihonkai Services Co. Ltd.
The Hokkaido Bank Ltd.
   Dogin Business Service Ltd.
   Dogin Card Co. Ltd.
The Hokuriku Bank Ltd.
   Hokugin Business Services Co. Ltd.
   Hokugin Corporate Co. Ltd.
   Hokugin Office Services Co. Ltd.
   Hokugin Real Estate Services Co. Ltd.
   Hokugin Shisankanri Co. Ltd.
   Hokuriku International Cayman Limited

COMPETITORS

Bank of Nagoya	Mitsubishi UFJ
Hachijuni Bank	Financial Group
Hokkoku Bank	Sapporo Hokuyo
Hyakujushi Bank	

HISTORICAL FINANCIALS
Company Type: Public

Income Statement
FYE: March 31

	ASSETS ($ mil.)	NET INCOME ($ mil.)	INCOME AS % OF ASSETS	EMPLOYEES
03/14	107,681	264	0.2%	5,510
03/13	116,686	192	0.2%	5,569
03/12	129,578	172	0.1%	5,573
03/11	127,828	222	0.2%	5,447
03/10	108,205	205	0.2%	5,044
Annual Growth	(0.1%)	6.5%	—	2.2%

2014 Year-End Financials

Return on assets: 0.2%
Return on equity: 5.5%
Long-term debt ($ mil.): —
No. of shares (mil.): 1,339
Sales ($ mil): 1,851

Dividends
   Yield: —
   Payout: —
Market value ($ mil.): —

	STOCK PRICE ($) FY Close	P/E High/Low	Earnings	PER SHARE ($) Dividends	Book Value
03/14	0.00	—	0.19	0.00	3.65
03/13	0.00	—	0.13	0.00	3.82
03/12	1.91	—	0.11	0.00	3.95
Annual Growth	—	— —	14.1%	—	(2.0%)

Hon Hai Precision Industry Co., Ltd.

Hon Hai Precision Industry may be the biggest electronics company you never heard of. The company more commonly known by its trade name Foxconn is the world's largest contract electronics manufacturer. It manufactures computers consumer electronics communications and other products including connectors cable assemblies enclosures flat-panel displays game consoles motherboards servers and televisions. Hon Hai also provides design engineering and mechanical tooling services. The global company's customers include Apple Cisco Dell Nokia and Sony. Chairman Terry Gou founded Hon Hai in 1974 to make plastic switches for TVs.

Hon Hai's operations are closely tied to consumer demand for computers and consumer electronics. Because of its size the company is able to take on significant new orders in a relatively short time. The company was tapped by Microsoft in 2009 to supply Xbox consoles for the holiday shopping season shortly after Hon Hai landed the contract to provide Sony with PS3 consoles. The company's sales also increased after Microsoft released its Windows 7 operating system. It also makes several products for Apple —the iPod Nano music player the iPhone the iPad and the iMac — all products that are in greater demand during the holiday season.

After having a 30% growth rate for years in 2010 the company lowered its growth forecasts. Computer sales are predicted to slow throughout 2011 and demand for iPhones and iPads has not offset shrinking PC sales. In 2011 the company's sales were up just 11% to $113 billion and its net income rose a mere 2%.

Hon Hai has tried to expand its focus beyond consumer electronics with biotechnology nanotechnology and media content mentioned as industries the company is interested in as it tries to sustain growth. The company is also targeting the budding automotive market in China (the company makes automotive connectors) smartbooks (mini-laptops that use smartphone technology) and e-book readers for the Taiwan market. (Hon Hai already makes about 80% of e-book readers made globally including the Amazon Kindle reader.)

In another move aimed at expanding its reach Hon Hai has tried to reach a deal with Sharp which is spiraling downward along with prices for flat-panel TVs. Sharp which has had too narrow a focus on TVs in the last few years also makes displays for Hon Hai's Apple products something Hon Hai is eager to get its hands on. In 2012 Hon Hai offered to buy nearly 10% of Sharp for around $1.7 billion. But Sharp's market value plummeted as it later widened expectations for a record loss and its credit was downgraded to junk status. Hon Hai wants to renegotiate the initial deal including lowering the price and having a hand in Sharp's operations. Chairman Gou left negotiations in Japan a day early and without a deal when Sharp's management balked at the idea. Hon Hai is also looking at buying plants in Mexico and China from Sharp; the two companies are joint owners in the Sakai LCD panel factory which has been running below capacity and contributed to the losses at Sharp.

Hon Hai focuses more on internal development than growth through acquisitions stating that it had paid too much for some acquisitions. The company has expanded its product lines and design capabilities through a number of select acquisitions including Finland-based Eimo renamed Foxconn Oy which makes plastic moldings for cell phone components. It also bought Taiwan-based Ambit Microsystems for $1.1 billion; Ambit makes routers modems and networking equipment. Hon Hai has also boosted its manufacturing capacity through acquisitions such as its purchase of the PC manufacturing assets in Hungary Mexico and the US with associated logistics services from rival Sanmina-SCI which is getting out of the PC-making business.

Hon Hai subsidiary INNOLUX Display acquired flat-panel display manufacturer Chi Mei Optoelectronics through a share swap in 2010 creating a company called Chimei Innolux. Through Chimei Innolux Hon Hai will compete with big display makers in South Korea and Taiwan which dominate the market.

Outside of acquisitions Hon Hai grows organically by investing in new manufacturing facilities as it prepares to enter new markets. The company is investing about $1 billion to build a new manufacturing facility in China as part of its environmental protection technology initiative. The plant will develop and make products for the alternative energy market including LED (light-emitting diode) backlights and LCD display modules. Hon Hai subsidiary Foxsemicon is working with semiconductor manufacturing equipment maker Applied Materials to develop products for solar energy manufacturing equipment.

A spate of suicides by workers at its Shenzhen production facilities sent Hon Hai reeling in 2010. The company responded by increasing wages at its largest facilities and relocating some production facilities inland closer to the hometowns of much of the workforce. It has also hired a significant number of employees (in 2011 the number of employees rose by 85%) and restricted the number of hours that can be worked. The moves increased production costs for Hon Hai not all of which could be recouped by raising the prices charged to manufacturers. After reports of poor working conditions at some facilities Apple took heat for continuing to source products from Hon Hai.

A Hon Hai affiliate Foxconn International Holdings (FIH) has struggled after handset orders from major clients declined. The company makes handsets for companies including Nokia which are losing market share to smartphones like the iPhone and devices based on Google's Android operating system. FIH which began relocating some of its Chinese facilities in 2007 also moved some production to northern China and to India to lower costs.

In 2013 Hon Hai embarked on an extensive restructuring effort to create more nimble business units and streamline decision-making. The company may spin off one or more of its business units as part of the initiative.

EXECUTIVES

Chairman, Terry T.M. Gou
Investor Relations Contact, Arthur Huang
Auditors: PricewaterhouseCoopers

LOCATIONS

HQ: Hon Hai Precision Industry Co., Ltd.
  No. 66, Zhongshan Road, Tucheng Industrial Zone, Tucheng District, New Taipei 236
Phone: (886) 2 2268 3466
Web: www.foxconn.com

PRODUCTS/OPERATIONS

Selected Products

Cable assemblies
CD-ROMs
Connectors
E-book readers
Enclosures
Flat-panel displays
Game consoles
Handsets
Keyboards
LCD (liquid-crystal display) TVs
Mobile phones
Motherboards
Personal computers
Servers
Smartphones
Switches
Tablets
Thermal products

COMPETITORS

ASUSTeK	MiTAC
Amphenol	Molex
BenQ	Nam Tai
Cal-Comp Electronics	Quanta Computer
Celestica	Sanmina
First International Computer	TPV Technology
	Universal Scientific
Flextronics	Venture Corp.
Hosiden	WBL Corp.
Inventec	Wistron
Jabil	

HISTORICAL FINANCIALS

Company Type: Public

Income Statement

FYE: December 31

	REVENUE ($ mil.)	NET INCOME ($ mil.)	NET PROFIT MARGIN	EMPLOYEES
12/13	132,534	3,577	2.7%	0
12/12	134,567	3,261	2.4%	1,290,000
12/11	113,912	2,703	2.4%	961,000
12/10	103,000	2,593	2.5%	836,000
12/09	61,239	2,387	3.9%	611,000
Annual Growth	21.3%	10.6%	—	—

2013 Year-End Financials

Debt ratio: 0.7%
Return on equity: 15.1%
Cash ($ mil.): 23,273
Current ratio: 1.33
Long-term debt ($ mil.): 4,431
No. of shares (mil.): —
Dividends
  Yield: 1.1%
  Payout: 0.0%
Market value ($ mil.): —

	STOCK PRICE ($) FY Close	P/E High/Low		Earnings	PER SHARE ($) Dividends	Book Value
12/13	5.10	0	0	0.24	0.06	1.74
12/12	5.82	0	0	0.22	0.00	1.52
12/11	5.27	—	—	0.18	0.00	1.40
12/10	8.00	—	—	0.18	0.06	1.23
12/09	9.25	—	—	0.16	0.09	1.04
Annual Growth	(13.8%)	—	—	9.9%	(12.3%)	13.9%

Honda Motor Co., Ltd.(Honda Giken Kogyo Kabushiki Kaisha) (Japan)

According to Honda you might be in your Element if you do you Civic duty and get Fit. Honda Motor is Japan's #2 automaker (after Toyota) and the world's largest motorcycle producer. The company's car models include the Accord CR-V Civic Element and Fit; gasoline-electric hybrid versions of the Civic and Accord; and seven models of the luxury Acura line. Honda's line of motorcycles includes everything from scooters to superbikes. The company also makes a line of ATVs and personal watercraft. Honda's power products division makes commercial and residential machinery (lawn mowers snow blowers and tillers); portable generators; and outboard motors. Almost 70% of Honda Motor sales come from outside Japan.

The company's strong sales in fiscal 2011 left the days of the global economic recession in Honda's rearview mirror. Sales were down in both fiscal 2009 and 2010 while the automotive industry took a hit. However as the economy improved and the value of the Japanese yen grew stronger Honda saw its overall sales grow 4% in its native currency and 16% in US dollars. The company sold 3.5 million passenger vehicles (up 3%) and more than 11 million motorcycles (up 18%) in fiscal 2011. To top it off profits doubled to $6 billion.

Unfortunately fiscal 2012 was affected by two major natural disasters in Asia. The tsunami and earthquake that rattled Japan in March 2011 killed one worker and injured more than a dozen others. Honda and other car manufacturers in the country were forced to cease production for about a month before resorting to operating at reduced capacity due to a shortage of parts. Then in October its auto parts manufacturing plants in Thailand were damaged by floods. The Thai plant supplied parts to the US and Canada and Honda had to reduce North America production until the damage in Thailand could be assessed and the plants can be repaired. Production was down more than 30% for the first half of 2012.

Like its rival Toyota Honda is facing questions about the quality of its cars. The company recalled some 2.5 million vehicles in August 2011 over software in the automatic transmission that could cause the vehicle to stall and make it difficult to put the car into park.

Automotive sales account for more than 75% of Honda's revenues. In its home region of Asia Honda's automotive focus is the same as everyone else's —China and India. Unit sales in the region for 2011 grew by 32% and revenue increased more than 20%. To meet the increasing demand Honda added capacity to one of its Chinese factories and opened new facilities in both India and Thailand. Its Dongfeng Honda Automobile unit a 50/50 joint venture with Dongfeng Motor is building a second factory in China to keep up with surging demand. The plant which is expected to open sometime in 2012 is expected to produce 100000 units a year by 2012. The car company's 50/50 joint venture with Denway Motors known as Guangqi Honda Automobile should produce 480000 units annually by the end of 2011. Altogether Honda's total production capacity in China will reach 890000 vehicles by 2013.

With a desire to concentrate on its own growth strategy in the India market Honda sold its 26% stake in Hero Honda Motors (renamed Hero MotoCorp Ltd. in mid-2011) a joint venture between Honda and Hero Group which is run by the Munjal family. Though the exact amount of the 2011 transaction was not reported Hero indicated earlier in the year that it would buy the shares for approximately $853 million. Hero Group now owns about 52% of Hero MotoCorp.

Honda is enjoying brisk motorcycle sales particularly in Asia where motorcycles are a popular mode of transportation. Motorcycle sales account for almost 15% of revenues. The company is beefing up production capacity in India to keep up with demand. Honda is adding on to its two existing Indian factories and is building a third one. Indonesia is the world's third-largest market for motorcycles (after China and India). Although high gas prices triggered inflation in Indonesia and the ensuing credit crunch put a damper on sales demand for motorcycles in the region remains high. To that end Honda has announced plans to expand its plant and increase motorcycle production in Indonesia to 4 million in 2012. The company is also expanding its plant in Vietnam to produce 2 million bikes. Motorcycle sales in South America (particularly Brazil) are zooming along; however sales in North America and Europe slowed in 2011. North American motorcycle sales were hurt by rising gas prices and interest rates. Sales of ATVs also declined in North America as economic jitters prompted consumers to postpone purchases of expensive recreational goods.

HISTORY

Soichiro Honda spent six years as an apprentice at Tokyo service station Art Shokai before opening his own branch of the repair shop in Hamamatsu in 1928. He also raced cars and in 1931 received a patent for metal spokes that replaced wood in wheels.

Honda started a piston ring company in 1937. During WWII the company produced metal propellers for Japanese bombers. When bombs and an earthquake destroyed most of his factory Honda sold it to Toyota in 1945.

In 1946 Honda began motorizing bicycles with war-surplus engines. When this proved popular Honda began making engines. The company was renamed Honda Motor Co. in 1948 and began producing motorcycles. Soichiro Honda hired Takeo Fujisawa in 1949 to manage the company so Honda could focus on engineering. Honda's innovative overhead valve design made its early 1950s Dream model a runaway success. In 1952 the smaller Cub sold through bicycle dealers accounted for 70% of Japan's motorcycle production.

Funded by a 1954 public offering and Mitsubishi Bank Honda expanded capacity and began exporting. American Honda Motor Company was formed in Los Angeles in 1959 accompanied by the slogan "You meet the nicest people on a Honda" in a campaign crafted to counter the stereotypical biker image. Honda added overseas factories in the 1960s and began producing lightweight trucks sports cars and minicars.

The company began selling its tiny 600 model in the US in 1970 but it was the Civic introduced in 1973 that first scored with the US car market. Three years later Honda introduced the Accord which featured an innovative frame adaptable for many models. In 1982 Accord production started at the company's Ohio plant.

Ex-Honda engineer Nobuhiko Kawamoto was named president in 1990 a year before Soichiro Honda died. Kawamoto cut costs and continued to expand the company internationally. That year the Big Three US automakers (General Motors Ford and Chrysler) clamoring for trade sanctions against Japanese carmakers threw Honda out of the US carmakers' trade association.

In 1997 Honda bought Peugeot's plant in Guangzhou China and boosted its US vehicle production by opening an all-terrain vehicle (ATV) plant in South Carolina in 1998. American Honda agreed in 1998 to pay $330 million to settle a class-action lawsuit filed by 1800 dealers who accused Honda of delivering popular models only to dealers who paid bribes (18 executives from American Honda were convicted). That year Hiroyuki Yoshino an engineer with US management experience succeeded Kawamoto as CEO.

Honda and GM agreed in 1999 to a deal in which Honda would supply low-emission V6 engines and automatic transmissions to GM while Isuzu a GM affiliate would supply Honda with diesel engines. True to Honda's go-it-alone style the deal had no equity component.

In 2000 Honda announced that its super-low-emission engine (as called for by US regulators) would make its mass-market debut in 2001 well ahead of competitor versions. Also Honda recalled 500000 cars in Japan due to problems with audio systems and engine oil seals.

Honda announced in 2001 that it would introduce diesel-powered vehicles in Europe by 2003. Later that year Honda's R&D unit set up a solar-powered hydrogen production station in California as part of its efforts to develop renewable-energy fuel-cell vehicles.

In 2006 Honda announced it would enter the aviation market with the introduction of what Honda CEO Takeo Fukui called the "Honda Civic of the sky." Honda began taking orders for the six-passenger twin-engine HondaJet that year and the planes became available in 2011 through Honda Aero.

In 2008 Honda's car sales especially diesel models in Eastern Europe and Russia surpassed those from the previous year. Two years earlier diesel engines officially became the European preference when diesels outsold gas engines for the first time. Honda began shipping diesel-equipped Accords to Europe in 2004 and is working to keep up with demand (Honda has since added diesel versions of the CR-V the FR-V and the Civic).

As vehicle sales slowed in 2008 however Honda cut production by 12% in Japan and North America. The company also quit its participation in Formula One racing to devote corporate resources to its core car business.

Honda began marketing its FCX Clarity a zero-emissions hydrogen fuel cell sedan in 2008. It also introduced the Insight Hybrid at the Paris Motor Show that year. The Insight is Honda's answer to Toyota's popular Prius. Honda executives are acting on their belief that dedicated hybrid vehicles like the Insight will perform better than hybridized current models. The company began selling the Insight in Europe Japan and the US in 2009.

In 2009 Honda increased its commitment to hybrid vehicles by signing a joint venture contract with GS Yuasa to establish a new company Blue Energy. GS Yuasa Power Supply a wholly owned subsidiary of GS Yuasa owns a 51% stake and Honda Motor owns a 49% stake. The two companies decided that Blue Energy will manufacture lithium-ion batteries and drive sales and R&D. Lithium-ion batteries are lighter and hold almost double the energy of a standard battery which may optimize the performance of next-generation hybrid vehicles. With the increasing interest in low-emission vehicles worldwide and many governments' plans to promote green efforts by automakers the venture spurs Honda's lineup of hybrid vehicles as well as its position in the US market for its Insight model.

EXECUTIVES

Chairman, Koichi Kondo, age 67

Corporate Auditor, Toru Onda, age 65

President and CEO, Takanobu Ito, age 61

Senior Managing Director and Board Member; President and Director Honda Motor Europe; COO Regional Operations (Europe Middle East and Africa), Shigeru Takagi, age 62

EVP Executive Officer and Director; COO Production Operations, Akio Hamada, age 66

EVP; President Honda North America, Tetsuo Iwamura, age 63

Senior Managing Director and Board Member; COO Motorcycle Operations; Chief Officer of Driving Safety Promotion Center, Tatsuhiro Oyama, age 64

Chairman, Fumihiko Ike, age 62

Corporate Auditor, Koukei Higuchi, age 78

Corporate Auditor, Fumihiko Saito, age 69

Senior Managing Officer, Takashi Yamamoto

Managing Officer; EVP and Director Honda Motor Europe; President and Director; Honda U.K. Manufacturing, Suguru Kanazawa

Managing Officer; President Honda Motor Europe, Manabu Nishimae

Managing Director COO Purchasing Operations and Board Member, Masaya Yamashita, age 61

Managing Officer; President Asian Honda Motor, Hiroshi Kobayashi, age 60

Senior Managing Officer, Sho Minekawa, age 60

Senior Managing Officer; President and CEO Honda North America Services, Hidenobu Iwata

Managing Officer Quality Certification and Regulation Compliance, Koichi Fukuo

Managing Executive Officer, Takuji Yamada, age 58

Operating Officer; President and CEO Honda Engineering, Hiroshi Sasamoto

Corporate Auditor, Hideki Okada, age 61

COO Automobile Operations and Board Member, Tsuneo Tanai, age 57

Executive Officer; President of Subsidiary, Takashi Sekiguchi

COO Business Management Operations and Board Member, Yoichi Hojo, age 58

Managing Executive Officer; President Honda South America, Masahiro Takedagawa

Managing Officer; President Honda Motor India, Yoshiyuki Matsumoto

Operating Officer; President and Director Honda Engineering, Eiji Okawara

Operating Officer and General Manager Saitama Factory of Production Operations, Ko Katayama

COO Business Support Operations and Board Member, Masahiro Yoshida, age 57

Operating Officer; President Honda Motor (China) Investment, Seiji Kuraishi, age 56

Operating Officer; President and Director Honda Siel Cars India and Honda Motor India, Takashi Nagai

Operating Officer; General Manager Kumamoto Factory of Production Operations, Katsushi Watanabe

Operating Officer; President Guangqi Honda Automobile, Toshiaki Mikoshiba

Operating Officer Production Operations and Production for Regional Operations (China), Yoshi Yamane

Operating Officer General Manager Automobile Purchasing Division 2 in Purchasing Operations, Takahiro Hachigo

Managing Executive Officer, Chitoshi Yokota

Operating Officer; President Honda Aircraft, Michimasa Fujino

Managing Director and Board Member; President and Director Honda R&D, Tomohiko Kawanabe, age 62

Corporate Auditor, Yuji Matsuda, age 63

Senior Managing Officer; President and CEO Honda R&D, Yoshiharu Yamamoto

Operating Officer; President Honda R&D Europe (U.K.), Soichiro Takizawa
Operating Officer; COO Motorcycle Operations, Shinji Aoyama
Board Member, Takeo Fukui, age 70
Board Member, Nobuo Kuroyanagi, age 73
President CEO and Director; COO Automobile Operations, Takanobu Ito, age 60
Senior Managing Director Government and Industrial Affairs and Compliance Officer and Board Member, Mikio Yoshimi, age 66
Senior Managing Director and Board Member; President and Director Honda Motor Europe; COO Regional Operations (Europe Middle East and Africa), Shigeru Takagi, age 62
Board Member, Kensaku Hogen, age 73
Senior Managing Director and Board Member; President and Director Honda North America; COO Regional Operations North America, Tetsuo Iwamura, age 63
Senior Managing Director and Board Member; COO Motorcycle Operations; Chief Officer of Driving Safety Promotion Center, Tatsuhiro Oyama, age 64
Board Member; President and Director Asian Honda Motor COO Regional Operations Asia and Oceania, Fumihiko Ike, age 61
Managing Director COO Purchasing Operations and Board Member, Masaya Yamashita, age 61
Board Member; COO Regional Sales Operations (Japan), Hiroshi Kobayashi, age 60
Board Member; COO Regional Operations Latin America; President and Director Honda South America Moto Honda da Amazonia and Honda Automoveis do Brasil, Sho Minekawa, age 60
Managing Executive Officer, Takuji Yamada, age 58
COO Automobile Operations and Board Member, Tsuneo Tanai, age 57
COO Business Management Operations and Board Member, Yoichi Hojo, age 58
COO Business Support Operations and Board Member, Masahiro Yoshida, age 57
Board Member, Seiji Kuraishi, age 56
Board Member, Hiroyuki Yamada, age 58
Managing Director and Board Member; President and Director Honda R&D, Tomohiko Kawanabe, age 62
Auditors: KPMGAZSA&Co.

LOCATIONS

HQ: Honda Motor Co., Ltd.(Honda Giken Kogyo Kabushiki Kaisha) (Japan)
1-1, Minami-Aoyama 2-chome, Minato-ku, Tokyo 107-8556
Phone: (81) 3 3423 1111   Fax: (81) 3 5412 1515
Web: www.honda.co.jp

Sales

	% of total
North	37
Asia	
Japan	32
Other	16
Europe	6
Other	9
Total	100

PRODUCTS/OPERATIONS

Sales

	% of total
Automobiles	76
Motorcycles	14
Financial	6
Power products &	4
Total	100

Selected Acura Models
CSX (Canada)
MDX
RDX
RL
TL
TSX
ZDX

Selected Honda Car and Truck Models
Passenger cars
  Accord
  City
  Civic
  Insight
  Inspire
  Legend
Minivans Multi-wagons Sport Utility Vehicles
  Airwave
  Crossroad
  CR-V
  CR-Z
  Element
  Elysion
  Fit
  FREED
  FR-V
  Jazz
  Odyssey
  Partner Pilot
  Ridgeline
  Step Wagon
  Stream
Mini cars
  Acty
  Life
  Vamos
  Zest

Selected Motorcycle Models
CBR600RR
CBR1000RR
Elite (scooter)
Fury
Gold Wing
Interstate
NT700V
Nighthawk
PCX (scooter)
Ruckus (scooter)
Sabre
SH150i (scooter)
Shadow RS
Silver Wing (scooter)
Stateline
ST1300
VFR1200F

Selected ATVs
Utility ATVs
  FourTrax Foreman 4x4
  FourTrax Rancher
  FourTrax Rancher AT
  FourTrax Recon
  FourTrax Rincon
Multipurpose Utility Vehicles
  Big Red

Selected Personal Watercraft
AquaTrax F-15
AquaTrax F-15X

Selected Power Products
Cogeneration Units
Commercial mowers
Engines
Lawn mowers
Marine motors
Portable generators
Pumps
Snowblowers
Tillers

COMPETITORS

BMW	Kia Motors
Briggs & Stratton	Land Rover
Brunswick Corp.	Mahindra Renault
Caterpillar	Mazda
Chrysler	Mitsubishi Motors
Daihatsu	Nissan
Daimler	Peugeot
Deere	Renault
Exmark Manufacturing	Saab Automobile
Fiat	Suzuki Motor
Ford Motor	Tata Motors
Fuji Heavy Industries	Textron
General Motors	Toro Company
Harley-Davidson	Toyota
Hyundai Motor	Triumph Motorcycles
Indian Motorcycle	Viper Motorcycle
Isuzu	Volkswagen
Kawasaki Heavy Industries	Volvo
	Yamaha Motor

HISTORICAL FINANCIALS
Company Type: Public

Income Statement
FYE: March 31

	REVENUE ($ mil.)	NET INCOME ($ mil.)	NET PROFIT MARGIN	EMPLOYEES
03/14	114,730	5,562	4.8%	198,561
03/13	104,981	3,902	3.7%	190,338
03/12	96,892	2,578	2.7%	187,094
03/11	107,924	6,449	6.0%	179,060
03/10	91,846	2,873	3.1%	176,815
Annual Growth	5.7%	18.0%	—	2.9%

2014 Year-End Financials

Debt ratio: 0.3%
Return on equity: 10.4%
Cash ($ mil.): 11,324
Current ratio: 1.22
Long-term debt ($ mil.): 31,331
No. of shares (mil.): 1,802
Dividends
  Yield: 2.8%
  Payout: 44.1%
Market value ($ mil.): 63,693

	STOCK PRICE ($) FY Close	P/E High/Low		PER SHARE ($) Earnings	Dividends	Book Value
03/14	35.34	0	0	3.09	0.99	31.82
03/13	38.26	0	0	2.17	0.00	29.71
03/12	38.43	0	0	1.43	0.00	29.78
03/11	37.51	0	0	3.57	0.60	29.82
03/10	35.29	0	0	1.58	0.37	25.54
Annual Growth	0.0%	—	—	18.2%	27.9%	5.6%

Hong Leong Bank Berhad

LOCATIONS

HQ: Hong Leong Bank Berhad
Level 8, Wisma Hong Leong, 18 Jalan Perak, Kuala Lumpur 50450
Phone: (60) 3 2164 8228   Fax: (60) 3 2164 2503
Web: www.hlb.com.my

PRODUCTS/OPERATIONS

HISTORICAL FINANCIALS
Company Type: Public

Income Statement
FYE: June 30

	ASSETS ($ mil.)	NET INCOME ($ mil.)	INCOME AS % OF ASSETS	EMPLOYEES
06/14	53,048	654	1.2%	0
06/13	51,775	587	1.1%	0
06/12	49,668	518	1.0%	0
06/11	48,145	375	0.8%	0
06/10	25,939	302	1.2%	0
Annual Growth	19.6%	21.3%	—	—

2014 Year-End Financials

Return on assets: 1.2%	Dividends
Return on equity: 15.2%	Yield: —
Long-term debt ($ mil.): —	Payout: —
No. of shares (mil.): 1,798	Market value ($ mil.): —
Sales ($ mil): 2,306	

HSBC Bank Canada

HSBC Bank Canada is one of the largest foreign-owned banks in Canada. Through approximately 250 locations including some 140 bank branches it provides a range of commercial and retail financial services including deposit accounts loans and mortgages import and export financing equipment leasing and investment capital financing. Through subsidiaries the bank also offers brokerage services insurance mutual funds merchant banking trust services and portfolio management and investment counseling. HSBC Bank Canada is controlled by one of the largest banks on the planet UK-based financial services heavyweight HSBC Holdings.

The bank's loan portfolio is dominated by residential mortgages and real estate loans to businesses and government entities. Nearly half of all the bank's loans are originated in British Columbia.

HSBC Bank Canada's operations fall into four segments: retail banking and wealth management commercial banking global banking and markets and consumer finance (which is being wound down). The retail banking and wealth management segment has seen growth by providing specialized services for high-net-worth individuals and families. In commercial banking the company's growth centers around clients including small businesses and midsized Canadian companies doing business overseas. HSBC Banks Canada's global banking and markets segment is also focused on international growth offering trading and investment banking services.

The final segment consumer finance provided products including mortgages loans specialty insurance and credit cards through subsidiary HSBC Financial. In 2012 as part of parent HSBC's restructuring efforts to create a leaner group HSBC Bank Canada announced plans to wind down the consumer finance segment. The decision was made after no buyer could be found for the business.

The closure follows the 2011 sale of the full-service investment advisory business of HSBC Securities (Canada) to National Bank of Canada. Both divestitures reflect the group's strategy to focus on commercial banking retail banking and wealth management.

HSBC Bank Canada's profits rose 14% from 2010 to 2011 as the company reported lower loan impairment charges and fee income grew. The growth was slightly offset by decreased interest income (primarily due to lower interest rates) and net trading income. The company also recorded a one-time charge for a write down in the value of investment property which lowered its other operating income by about half.

EXECUTIVES

Chairman, Samuel (Sam) Minzberg, age 64
President and CEO, Paulo Maia
VP Corporate Affairs, Ernest Yee
Assistant VP Public Affairs, Sharon Wilks
EVP Commercial Banking; Regional President Central and Eastern Canada, Linda Seymour

COO, Sandra Stuart
EVP Personal Financial Services and Wealth Management, Margaret Willis
Co-Head Global Markets, Jason Henderson
Chief Risk Officer, Ralph Hilton
Senior Administrative Assistant, Edith Ho
Director of Operations, Craig Shearer
CFO, Jacques Fleurant
Director, Michael A. Grandin, age 69
Director, Timothy R. (Tim) Price, age 72
Director, Beth Horowitz
Director, Caleb Chan
Auditors: KPMGLLP

LOCATIONS

HQ: HSBC Bank Canada
885 West Georgia Street, Vancouver, British Columbia V6C 3E8
Phone: 604 685-1000 **Fax:** 604 641-3098
Web: www.hsbc.ca

PRODUCTS/OPERATIONS

Sales

	% of total
Interest	
Loans	47
Financial	12
HSBC Financial	10
Noninterest	
Fees	22
Net trading	5
Net gains from financial	1
Other	3
Total	**100**

Selected Subsidiaries

Household Trust Company
HSBC Capital (Canada) Inc.
HSBC Financial Corporation Limited
HSBC Global Asset Management (Canada) Limited
HSBC Investment Funds (Canada) Inc.
HSBC Loan Corporation (Canada)
HSBC Mortgage Corporation (Canada)
HSBC Securities (Canada) Inc.
HSBC South Point Investments (Barbados) LLP
HSBC Trust Company (Canada)

COMPETITORS

BMO Financial Group	National Bank of
CIBC	Canada
Canadian Western Bank	RBC Financial Group
IGM Financial	Scotiabank
Laurentian Bank	TD Bank

HISTORICAL FINANCIALS

Company Type: Public

Income Statement

FYE: December 31

	ASSETS ($ mil.)	NET INCOME ($ mil.)	INCOME AS % OF ASSETS	EMPLOYEES
12/13	79,241	579	0.7%	6,050
12/12	81,154	693	0.9%	0
12/11	78,418	620	0.8%	7,900
12/10*	78,183	532	0.7%	8,200
01/10	74,882	0	—	0
Annual Growth	**1.4%**	—	—	—

*Fiscal year change

2013 Year-End Financials

Return on assets: 0.7%	Dividends
Return on equity: 12.3%	Yield: 5.1%
Long-term debt ($ mil.): —	Payout: —
No. of shares (mil.): 498	Market value ($ mil.): 11,959
Sales ($ mil): 2,856	

Stock Price / Per Share

	STOCK PRICE ($) FY Close	P/E High/Low	PER SHARE ($) Earnings	Dividends	Book Value
12/13	23.98	21 19	1.17	1.23	9.21
12/12	26.77	20 19	1.39	1.28	10.35
12/11	26.85	22 20	1.24	1.62	9.78
12/10*	27.72	27 25	1.06	1.65	8.89
01/10	26.80	— —	(0.00)	1.14	(0.00)
Annual Growth	**(2.7%)**	—	—	1.9%	

*Fiscal year change

HSBC Bank Plc (United Kingdom)

LOCATIONS

HQ: HSBC Bank Plc (United Kingdom)
8 Canada Square, London E14 5HQ
Phone:
Web: www.hsbc.co.uk

HISTORICAL FINANCIALS

Company Type: Public

Income Statement

FYE: December 31

	ASSETS ($ mil.)	NET INCOME ($ mil.)	INCOME AS % OF ASSETS	EMPLOYEES
12/13	1,341,390	4,123	0.3%	69,824
12/12	1,314,446	3,842	0.3%	74,190
12/11	1,279,092	3,597	0.3%	80,013
12/10	1,239,773	4,594	0.4%	77,932
12/09	1,217,808	5,007	0.4%	82,296
Annual Growth	**2.4%**	**(4.7%)**	—	**(4.0%)**

2013 Year-End Financials

Return on assets: 0.3%	Dividends
Return on equity: 7.7%	Yield: —
Long-term debt ($ mil.): —	Payout: —
No. of shares (mil.): 796	Market value ($ mil.): —
Sales ($ mil): 33,550	

HSBC Holdings Plc

HSBC would be a real alphabet soup if the company's name reflected its geographic diversity. One of the world's largest banking groups by assets (and the leader in customer deposits with more than $1 trillion) HSBC Holdings owns subsidiaries throughout Europe Hong Kong and the rest of the Asia/Pacific region the Middle East and Africa and the Americas. All told the company has some 7200 locations in more than 80 countries. Its activities include consumer and commercial banking credit cards private banking investment banking and leasing. Its North American operations include HSBC USA HSBC Bank Canada HSBC Bank Bermuda and Grupo Financiero HSBC in Mexico.

Operations

HSBC has always had a bent toward international expansion even from its inception. Founded in Hong Kong in 1865 HSBC owns all or parts of The Hongkong and Shanghai Banking Corporation HSBC France The Saudi British Bank and Hong Kong's Hang Seng Bank. The company was also one of the first foreign banks to receive regulatory approval to incorporate in China. It owns about 20% of Bank of Communications one of the largest commercial banks in the country.

Strategy

With market instability prevalent in the US and Europe HSBC has been increasingly looking toward emerging markets in Asia and Latin America for growth. The company believes that over the next few decades the global economy will shift toward those markets and it plans to be in place to provide them with cross-border services.

However the global financial crisis is forcing HSBC to rethink its expansion strategy and make some big cuts in some markets. In 2014 HSBC reported that it had sold or closed more than 60 businesses worldwide since top executives set out a new strategy for the bank in May 2011. As part of the effort HSBC in 2014 is selling its UK pensions business to ReAssure Limited part of Admin Re Group and Swiss Re Group. The company also sold off its 15.6% stake in Chinese insurer Ping An to Thailand's CP Group for $9.4 billion. The strategy also involves cutting costs (including 30000 jobs) and trimming low-growth markets. In Latin America for instance HSBC is focusing on its core growth markets of Brazil Argentina and Mexico after a series of disposals in other countries in the region. In 2014 it's also delaying the sale of its direct-investment unit until year-end; it's considering its options one which includes retaining the 2 billion-pound ($3.4 billion) division.

In Asia HSBC sold its private banking operations in Japan to Credit Suisse in 2012. It also shut down its retail banking operations in Japan though it continues to offer corporate banking there.

HSBC sold its US credit card portfolio worth some $30 billion to Capital One in 2012 and is selling 195 US bank branches mainly in upstate New York to First Niagara Financial Group for Â613 million ($1 billion).

In the private equity realm HSBC is divesting five of its private equity fund management businesses to their management teams to conform to new regulations that put limits on banks' trading activities. The first to go was HSBC's Private Equity (Asia) now Heartland Capital Partners which the company sold to unit's management.

Financial Performance

They're the latest moves the company has made to recover from bad loans in the US. The belt tightening paid off in 2010 as HSBC turned a profit in each of its geographic regions and business lines for the first time in four years including North America and Personal Financial Services which had been weighed down by the consumer credit woes. Earnings continued to recover in 2011 with 26% growth in revenues and 15% growth in profits before taxation. However factors such as concerns over European sovereign debt and the possibility of a double-dip recession on the continent have had a negative impact on the group's trading revenues.

HISTORY

Scotsman Thomas Sutherland and other businessmen in 1865 opened the doors to Hongkong & Shanghai Bank financing and promoting British imperial trade in opium silk and tea in East Asia. It soon established a London office and created an international branch network emphasizing China and East Asia. It claims to have been the first bank in Thailand (1888).

War repeatedly disrupted but never demolished the bank's operations. During WWII the headquarters were temporarily moved to London. (They moved back on a permanent basis in 1991.) The

bank's chief prewar manager Sir Vandeleur Grayborn died in a Japanese POW camp. After the Communists took power in China in 1949 the bank gradually withdrew; by 1955 only its Shanghai office remained and it was later closed. The bank played a key role in Hong Kong's postwar growth by financing industrialists who fled there from China.

In the late 1950s Hongkong & Shanghai Bank's acquisitions included the British Bank of the Middle East (founded 1889; now The Saudi British Bank) and Mercantile Bank (with offices in India and Southeast Asia). In 1965 the company bought 62% of Hang Seng Hong Kong's #2 bank. It also added new subsidiaries including Wayfoong (mortgage and small-business finance 1960) and Wardley (investment banking Hong Kong 1972).

In the late 1970s and into the 1980s China began opening to foreign business. The bank added operations in North America to capitalize on business between China and the US and Canada. Acquisitions included Marine Midland Bank (US 1980) Hongkong Bank of Canada (1981) 51% of treasury securities dealer Carroll McEntee & McGinley (US 1983) most of the assets and liabilities of the Bank of British Columbia (1986) and Lloyds Bank Canada (1990).

Following the 1984 agreement to return Hong Kong to China Hongkong & Shanghai Bank began beefing up in the UK buying London securities dealer James Capel & Co. (1986) and the UK's #3 bank Midland plc (1992). In 1993 the company formed London-based HSBC Holdings and divested assets most notably its interest in Hong Kong-based Cathay Pacific Airways.

HSBC then began expanding in Asia again particularly in Malaysia where its Hongkong Bank Malaysia became the country's first locally incorporated foreign bank. The company returned to China with offices in Beijing and Guangzhou. It also added new European branches.

Latin American banks acquired in 1997 were among the non-Asian operations that cushioned HSBC from the worst of 1998's economic crises. Nonetheless The Hong Kong Monetary Authority took a stake in the bank to shore up the stock exchange and foil short-sellers.

In 1999 China's government made HSBC a loan for mainland expansion. That year the company was foiled in its attempt to buy South Korea's government-owned Seoulbank but did buy the late Edmond Safra's Republic New York Corporation and his international bank holding company Safra Republic Holdings (it negotiated a $450 million discount on the $10 billion deal after a Japanese probe of Republic's securities division caused delays).

The company unveiled several online initiatives in 2000 including Internet ventures with Cheung Kong (Holdings) and Merrill Lynch and bought CCF (then called Credit Commercial de France now HSBC France). However HSBC's plans to buy a controlling stake in Bangkok Metropolitan Bank fell through before the year's end.

In 2001 HSBC agreed to pick up Barclays Bank's fund management operations in Greece. Later in response to the slowing economy it froze the salaries of 14000 employees. Argentina's 2001 peso devaluation cost the company half a billion dollars in currency conversion losses alone. Total charges pertaining to Argentina equaled more than $1 billion that year.

HSBC expanded its consumer finance operations with the purchase of US-based Household International (now HSBC Finance) in 2003.

The next year HSBC acquired The Bank of Bermuda as well as Marks and Spencer Financial Services (aka M&S Money) one of the UK's leading credit card issuers. It bought US credit card company Metris the following year.

HSBC's Latin American operations at this point were primarily in Argentina Brazil and Mexico. The company expanded its presence in Central America and the Caribbean with the 2006 purchase of Panama-based Banistmo a banking group with offices in the Bahamas Colombia Costa Rica El Salvador Honduras and Nicaragua.

HSBC asold its regional banking operations in France to Banque Populaire in 2008. The deal included eight banks with around 400 branches. Also that year the company canceled its proposed $6 billion acquisition of Lone Star's 51% stake in Korea Exchange Bank a deal that had been held up for months by an investigation by the South Korean government. HSBC cited weakened asset values in the global financial markets for the cancellation.

Beset by mortgage defaults the group closed its Decision One US-based wholesale subprime lending unit in 2007. In 2009 it shuttered its North American consumer lending business placing related portfolios (excluding credit cards) in run-off. To further reduce its exposure to consumer credit it sold a $4 billion car loan portfolio and servicing platform to an affiliate of Santander USA.

The company acquired a majority stake in Indonesian lender Bank Ekonomi in 2009 doubling its presence in the nation.

In 2010 HSBC sold HSBC Insurance Brokers to Marsh & McLennan in a Â135 million ($218 million) cash-and-stock deal. As part of the transaction the companies entered into a strategic partnership under which Marsh markets insurance and risk management services to HSBC's corporate and private clients ahead of other providers.

In late 2011 the Financial Services Authority (the UK regulator of financial services providers) fined HSBC Â10.3 million after it was found that salespeople at its NHFA Limited subsidiary had sold inappropriate and unsuitable five-year bonds to nearly 3000 elderly customers. HSBC which had alerted the FSA once it was made aware of the issue closed NHFA to new business that year.

EXECUTIVES

Group Company Secretary; Group General Manager, Ralph G. Barber, age 63

Chairman, Douglas J. Flint, age 59, $1,237,440 total compensation

Group General Manager and Group General Counsel, R. E. T. Bennett, age 62

Chairman of the Board Chief Executive Officer, Patrick J. (Pat) Burke, age 52

Group Managing Director and Global Head Personal Financial Services and Marketing; Chairman HSBC Bank A.S., Alexander C. (Alex) Hungate, age 46

Group Chief Executive; Group Managing Director; Executive Director, Stuart T. Gulliver, age 54, $1,236,240 total compensation

CEO Global Private Banking, Krishna Patel, age 65

Group Managing Director and Chief Executive Global Banking, Samir Assaf, age 54

Group Press Office, Patrick McGuinness

Group Managing Director; CEO HSBC North America, Niall S. K. Booker, age 55

Group General Manager and Head Operational Risk, M. J. W. King, age 57

Group Managing Director; Chief Executive of HSBC Bank plc, Brian Robertson, age 59

Group Managing Director; CEO Retail Banking and Wealth Management, Paul A. Thurston, age 60

Group General Manager and Director Communications, Richard S. Beck, age 48

Group Managing Director; Chief Executive Asia Pacific; Chairman HSBC Bank (China), Peter T. S. Wong, age 63

CEO HSBC France, Christophe de Backer, age 49

Group General Manager; CEO Continental Europe; Deputy Chairman HSBC France, Peter W. Boyles, age 58
Group General Manager; Chairman HFC Bank, David C. Budd, age 60
Deputy CEO and Director HSBC UK, Joe D. Garner, age 44
Deputy Chairman, Sir Simon Robertson, age 72
Group Managing Director and Chief Risk Officer, Marc Moses
EVP Corporate Affairs North America, Lisa M. Sodeika, age 50
Co-Head Global Banking, Kevin Adeson, age 50
Co-Head Global Markets, Spencer Lake, age 54
Group General Manager and Group Head Audit, Paul J. Lawrence, age 52
CEO Asia Pacific Asset Management, Joanna Munro
Group Director Finance, Iain J. Mackay, age 52
Director, Laura M. L. Cha, age 64
Group General Manager and Head of Global Transaction Banking, Andrew P. Long, age 58
Group Managing Director and Head Latin America and the Caribbean, Emilson Alonso, age 58
Group Managing Director and Group Head Human Resources, Ann Almeida, age 57
Group General Manager; President and CEO HSBC Bank USA, I. M. Dorner, age 59
Group Managing Director and Global Head Commercial Banking, Alan M. Keir, age 55
Group General Manager; CEO Hang Seng Bank, Margaret K. M. Y. Leung, age 63
Group General Manager; Deputy CEO Continental Europe, A. M. Mahoney, age 51
SEVP and Chief Auditor, Mark Martinelli, age 54
President and CEO HSBC Bank Canada, Paulo Maia
General Manager and Head of Global Markets, S. Assaf, age 54
Group General Manager; Chairman and CEO HSBC Egypt, A. S. El Anwar, age 68
Group General Manager and Group Head Insurance, D. L. Fried, age 53
CEO HSBC Hong Kong, Anita Y. M. Fung, age 54
Group General Manager; Head HSBC Amanah; CEO Malaysia, M. M. Hussain, age 54
Head Group Public Affairs Asia, David Hall
Head Public Affairs Mexico, Roy Caple
Head Marketing and Communications HSBC Private Bank (UK), Tony Joyce
Manager Investor Relations, Alastair Brown
Head Investor Relations Asia, Hugh Pye
Senior Manager External Relations Asia-Pacific/Hong Kong, Gareth Hewett
Deputy CEO Continental Europe, Tony Mahoney
U.S Chief Economist Global Banking and Markets, Kevin Logan
CEO China, Helen Wong
Director Marketing and Communications HSBC Private Bank (UK), John Dore
Senior Media Relations Manager Global Banking & Markets, Charles Clarke
Global Head Media Relations Global Banking & Markets, Jezz Farr
Communications Director Brazil, Helio Duarte
Communications Manager Regional Communications Middle East, Ahmad Othman
CEO Global Asset Management, John Flint
CEO Europe Asset Management, Rudolf Apenbrink
COO Asia Pacific Asset Management, Edmund Stokes
Co-Head Global Banking, Robin Phillips, age 56
Co-Head Global Markets, Jose-Luis Guerrero, age 49
Head of Commercial Banking Asia Pacific, Noel Quinn
Chief Investment Officer Global Asset Management Asia, Bill Maldonado
Head of Human Resources, Udi Agnon
Head of Private Banking, Raz Lerman
Head of Marketing, Michal Karnibad

Head of Treasury, Harel Cordova
Head of Legal and Compliance, Mira Gladstone
Chief Risk Officer, Bentzi Guetta
Chief Financial Officer Israel, Alon Jannai
Head of Corporate Banking, Carol Shaked
Head of Turkish Desk, Emmanuel Lion
Head Of Operations, Erik Wedborn
Head of Trade, Liliana Drozdovsky
Investor Relations Manager, Guy Lewis
Chief Legal Officer; Group Managing Director, Stuart Levey
Director; Chairman HSBC North America Holdings, John L. Thornton, age 60
Director, Rona A. Fairhead, age 52
Director, Gwyn Morgan, age 68
Director, Alexander A. (Sandy) Flockhart, age 62
Director, James W. J. Hughes-Hallett, age 64
Director, Safra A. Catz, age 52
CEO and Director, Stuart T. Gulliver, age 53
Director, W. Samuel H. (Sam) Laidlaw
Director, Rachel Lomax, age 68
Director, Sir Brian Williamson, age 69
Director, Marvin K.T. Cheung, age 66
Director, John D. Coombe, age 69
Deputy Chairman, Sir Simon Robertson, age 72
Director, Laura M. L. Cha, age 64
Director, N. R. Narayana Murthy, age 68
Independent Non-Executive Director, Joachim Faber
Independent Non-Executive Director, John Lipsky
Auditors: KPMGAuditPlc

LOCATIONS

HQ: HSBC Holdings Plc
8 Canada Square, London E14 5HQ
Phone: (44) 20 7991 8888   Fax: (44) 20 7992 4880
Web: www.hsbc.com

PRODUCTS/OPERATIONS

Sales

	% of total
Interest	57
Fees	19
Net earned insurance	12
Net trading	6
Other	6
Total	**100**

Sales by Segment

	% of total
Retail banking & wealth	42
Global banking &	20
Commercial	19
Global private	7
Other	12
Total	**100**

Selected Subsidiaries

Hang Seng Bank Limited (62% Hong Kong)
The Hong Kong and Shanghai Banking Corporation Limited
HSBC Asset Finance (UK) Ltd.
HSBC Bank Argentina S.A. (99.9%)
HSBC Bank A.S. (Turkey)
HSBC Bank Australia Limited
HSBC Bank Bermuda Limited
HSBC Bank Brasil S.A. - Banco Multiplo
HSBC Bank Canada
HSBC Bank (China) Company Limited
HSBC Bank Egypt S.A.E. (95%)
HSBC Bank International Limited (Jersey)
HSBC Bank Malaysia Berhad
HSBC Bank Malta p.l.c. (70%)
HSBC Bank Middle East Limited
HSBC Bank (Panama) S.A.
HSBC Bank plc
HSBC Bank USA N.A.
HSBC Finance Corporation (US)
HSBC France
HSBC Mexico S.A. Institucion de Banca Multiplo Grupo Financiero HSBC (99.9%)

HSBC Private Banking Holdings (Suisse) S.A. (Switzerland)
HSBC Securities (USA) Inc.
HSBC Trinkaus & Burkhardt AG (80% Germany)
Marks and Spencer Retail Financial Services Holdings Limited

COMPETITORS

BBVA	JPMorgan Chase
Bank of America	Lloyds Banking Group
Bank of China	Mitsubishi UFJ
Barclays	Financial Group
CIBC	Mizuho Financial
Citigroup	Prudential plc
Credit Suisse	RBC Financial Group
Deutsche Bank	Royal Bank of Scotland
Hutchison Whampoa	Standard Chartered
Intesa Sanpaolo	UBS

HISTORICAL FINANCIALS

Company Type: Public

Income Statement

FYE: December 31

	ASSETS ($ mil.)	NET INCOME ($ mil.)	INCOME AS % OF ASSETS	EMPLOYEES
12/13	2,671,318	16,204	0.6%	263,000
12/12	2,692,538	14,027	0.5%	270,000
12/11	2,555,579	16,797	0.7%	298,000
12/10	2,454,689	13,159	0.5%	307,000
12/09	2,364,452	5,834	0.2%	302,000
Annual Growth	**3.1%**	**29.1%**	**—**	**(3.4%)**

2013 Year-End Financials

Return on assets: 0.6%	Dividends
Return on equity: 9.0%	Yield: 4.3%
Long-term debt ($ mil.): —	Payout: 285.7%
No. of shares (mil.): —	Market value ($ mil.): —
Sales ($ mil): 99,854	

	STOCK PRICE ($) FY Close	P/E High/Low	Earnings	PER SHARE ($) Dividends	Book Value
12/13	55.13	70 60	0.84	2.40	9.66
12/12	53.07	72 52	0.74	2.50	9.48
12/11	38.10	64 39	0.91	1.95	8.88
12/10	51.04	81 61	0.72	1.70	8.35
12/09	57.09	188 69	0.34	1.70	7.37
Annual Growth	**(0.9%)**	**— —**	**25.4%**	**9.0%**	**7.0%**

Hutchison Whampoa Ltd.

Hutchison Whampoa has a hand in just about everything in Hong Kong. The company one of Hong Kong's oldest "hongs" (trading companies) has extensive holdings in retailing (A.S. Watson & Co) ports energy (Hongkong Electric Husky Energy) telecommunications (3G mobile phone and paging services) and infrastructure (power plants toll roads and construction materials). In addition Hutchison Whampoa owns hotels and a sizable portfolio of Hong Kong properties. Outside Hong Kong the company has operations in about 55 countries including China and elsewhere in the Asia/Pacific region as well as in Europe and the Americas. Hutchison Whampoa is controlled by Li Ka-shing one of the world's wealthiest men.

Although it took awhile the global recession and concurrent decline in consumer demand and trade caught up with Hutchison Whampoa in 2009. Total revenue at the diversified company declined 14% in 2009 vs. 2008. With the exception strong performances from the property and hotels business (up 33%) and its telecommunications business in Hong Kong (up 6%) all of its other businesses declined. Retail the company's largest business segment was down just 2%. The poor performance in 2009 was a reversal from 2008 and 2007 when the company was propped up by strong demand and growth in China and the Asia/Pacific region.

Hutchison Whampoa's retail and manufacturing subsidiary A.S. Watson & Co. (ASW) accounts for more than 45% of revenues (from established businesses) with more than 8900 retail stores spread among a dozen chains. Operations include supermarkets (Park'N Shop) health and beauty stores (Watson's Your Personal Store Drogas Kruidvat) Fortress electrical appliance stores in Hong Kong soft drink and water bottling operations and wine retailing (Watson's Wine Cellar). Already the world's largest operator of health and beauty stores (by store count) with outlets throughout Europe and Asia ASW has expanded its health and beauty business with the acquisition of the French retail perfume chain Marionnaud Parfumeries and the 120-door The Perfume Shop chain in the UK. Its Chinese retail arm Watsons China operates about 400 stores in some 65 cities on the Mainland.

Hutchison Port Holdings (HPH) is the world's leading port investor developer and operator with 300-plus berths in some 50 ports. HPH operates in about 25 countries and in six of the nine busiest container ports in the world including three key ports on Britain's east coast and ports on both ends of the Panama Canal. In addition to owning a controlling interest in Hongkong International Terminals which handles traffic passing through Hong Kong's container port HPH has large investments in terminal operations in southern China. In March 2011 Hutchison launched an IPO for its port operations in the Pearl River Delta which includes Hong Kong and Shenzhen in an initial public offering of Hutchison Port Holdings Trust. Hutchison says it expects to raise as much as $5.8 billion in the offering and will use the proceeds to retire debt and for possible acquisitions and growth within its diverse businesses.

Hutchison Whampoa is a leading competitor in mobile telecommunications offering wireless service to some 16 million customers throughout Australia Europe and Hong Kong. Subsidiary company Hutchison Telecommunications International Limited (HTIL) provides fixed-line and mobile communications services to customers primarily in Southeast Asia (Indonesia Sri Lanka Thailand and Vietnam). Its services include voice calling and broadband Internet access as well as the sale of wireless handsets and accessories. Hutchison Whampoa HTIL's biggest shareholder took the business private in mid-2010.

In an effort to shore up its share value the company's Husky Energy division announced plans to spin off its oil and gas assets in Southeast Asia into a separate publicly traded firm. (Hutchison Whampoa owns a 34% stake in Husky Energy; the division's largest shareholder L.F. Investments holds a 36% share.) The plan however is in an early stage of development. The move could raise up to $1 billion for the spinoff unit which is valued at about $4 billion.

Hutchison Whampoa has strong connections to the Chinese government thanks to its rags-to-riches chairman Li who has spent years building business relationships inside China. His Cheung Kong (Holdings) Limited is a substantial shareholder in Hutchison Whampoa. In turn Hutchison

Whampoa owns about 85% of Cheung Kong Infrastructure.

HISTORY

Hongkong and Whampoa Dock was the first registered company in Hong Kong. The enterprise was founded in 1861 when it bought dry docks in Whampoa (near present-day Guangzhou China) after the kidnapping and disappearance of the docks' owner John Couper during the Second Opium War (1856-60). It bought docks in Hong Kong in 1865.

Founded in 1880 by John Hutchison Hutchison International became a major Hong Kong consumer goods importer and wholesaler. It took control of Hongkong and Whampoa Dock and of A.S. Watson (drugstores supermarkets soft drinks) during an acquisition spree in the 1960s. The purchases entailed a complex web of deals that fell apart in the mid-1970s. To save Hutchison International the Hongkong & Shanghai Bank took a large stake in the company and brought in Australian turnaround specialist Bill Wyllie. Wyllie slashed expenses sold 103 companies in 1976 and bought the rest of Hongkong and Whampoa Dock in 1977. The company became Hutchison Whampoa that year.

In a surprise move in 1979 Hongkong & Shanghai Bank sold its 23% stake in Hutchison to Cheung Kong Holdings: Cheung Kong founder Li Ka-shing who began his career at age 14 by selling plastic flowers became the first Chinese to control a British-style "hong". Wyllie left in 1981.

In the 1980s Hutchison redeveloped its older dockyard sites which had become prime real estate. The company's International Terminals unit grew with Hong Kong's container traffic into the world's largest privately owned container terminal operator. In the 1980s the firm diversified into energy (buying stakes in utility Hongkong Electric and Canada-based Husky Oil) and precious metals and mining. It also moved into telecommunications buying Australian paging and UK mobile telephone units in 1989.

The following year the "hong" launched the AsiaSat I satellite in a venture with Cable & Wireless (C&W) and China International Trust & Investment. More acquisitions followed including European mobile phone businesses and telecom equipment makers. In 1996 the firm reorganized its Hong Kong telecom operations into Hutchison Telecommunications and launched its European wireless operations as a new public company Orange. In 1998 Hutchison Telecommunications made a move into the US when it bought a 20% stake in Western Wireless' digital PCS unit VoiceStream.

In 1999 the company and C&W sold their stakes in AsiaSat. Hutchison Whampoa also traded its stake in Orange to Mannesmann acquiring 10% of the German conglomerate which was later acquired by Vodafone. It recorded a profit that year of more than $15 billion on its investment in Orange. Also in 1999 Hutchison Whampoa and Global Crossing formed a $1.2 billion telecom joint venture to build a fiber-optic network in China (in 2002 the company purchased the remaining 50% of the venture from the beleaguered telecommunications company and renamed it Hutchison Global Communications).

Hutchison Whampoa Dutch phone company KPN and Japanese mobile phone giant NTT DoCoMo (which had purchased a 19% stake in Hutchison Whampoa in 1999) formed an alliance in 2000 to bid on next-generation mobile phone licenses in Europe.

In 2001 Hutchison Whampoa sold its 18% stake in US-based mobile phone operator VoiceStream to Deutsche Telekom for $5.1 billion in cash and

stocks and purchased a 15% stake in travel website Priceline. The next year its A.S. Watson Group bought the Netherlands-based health-and-beauty retail chain Kruidvat Group which operates about 1900 stores in six European countries. Also in 2002 supermarket chain PARKnSHOP opened four large stores in southern China.

In April 2003 Hutchison Telecommunications backed out of a joint bid to invest $125 million in bankrupt Global Crossing citing regulatory difficulties. In November the company sold $5 billion worth of bonds (a record global bond sale) to finance its heavy investment in high-speed mobile phone networks in Europe. In March 2004 Hutchison Whampoa sold its Hong Kong fixed-line business to Vanda Systems & Communications Holdings. In June the company sold the remaining 20% stake in its joint venture in China with household-products-giant Procter & Gamble to P&G for $1.8 billion.

In March 2004 Hutchison Whampoa's fixed-line telecommunications group acquired Vanda Systems and became a listed company on the Hong Kong Stock exchange under the new name Hutchison Global Communications Holdings (HGCH). In October the company combined its 52% stake in HGCH with its interests in the 2G cellular businesses under a single parent company Hutchison Telecommunications International Limited (HTIL) and took it public on the Hong Kong and New York stock exchanges. In the interim Hutchison Whampoa's retail arm the A.S. Watson Group acquired a leading health and beauty chain in Latvia and Lithuania Drogas in June marking its entry into the Baltic region. In August Watson acquired a 40% stake in German health and beauty chain Rossmann which operates more than 1100 stores throughout the Czech Republic Germany Hungary and Poland.

In May 2008 Hutchison Whampoa launched a new division Hutchison Water a provider of water production and treatment solutions.

EXECUTIVES

Group Finance Director and Executive Director, Frank J. Sixt, age 62

Executive Director; Deputy Managing Director Cheung Kong (Holdings); Group Managing Director Cheung Kong Infrastructure Holdings; President and CEO CK Life Sciences International, Kam Hing Lam, age 68

Deputy Group Managing Director and Executive Director, Susan M. F. Chow Woo, age 60

Deputy Chairman and Executive Director, Victor T. K. Li, age 50

Chairman, Li Ka-shing, age 85

Executive Director; Deputy Chairman Hutchison Harbour Ring;, Dominic K. M. Lai, age 60

Company Secretary, Edith Shih, age 61

Corporate Communications, Laura Cheung

Corporate Communications, Jeremy Lau

Corporate Communications, Hans Leung

Deputy Group Managing Director; Executive Director, Mo Woo

Group Finance Director and Executive Director, Frank J. Sixt, age 62

Executive Director; Deputy Managing Director Cheung Kong (Holdings); Group Managing Director Cheung Kong Infrastructure Holdings; President and CEO CK Life Sciences International, Kam Hing Lam, age 68

Deputy Group Managing Director and Executive Director, Susan M. F. Chow Woo, age 60

Deputy Chairman and Executive Director, Victor T. K. Li, age 50

Group Managing Director and Executive Director, Canning K. N. Fok, age 61

Director, Sir Michael D. Kadoorie, age 73

Director, George C. Magnus, age 79

Director, William E. Mocatta, age 61
Director, William Shurniak, age 82
Director, Holger Kluge, age 72
Director, Wong Chung Hin, age 79
Director, Margaret K. M. Y. Leung, age 63
Non-Executive Independent Director, May Ko
Auditors: PricewaterhouseCoopers

LOCATIONS

HQ: Hutchison Whampoa Ltd.
22nd Floor, Hutchison House, 10 Harcourt Road,
Phone: (852) 2128 1188   **Fax:** (852) 2128 1705
Web: www.hutchison-whampoa.com

Sales

	% of total
Europe	41
Hong	18
Asia &	13
Americas & other	16
China	12
Total	**100**

PRODUCTS/OPERATIONS

Sales

	% of total
Retail	38
320	
Husky	14
Ports & related	11
Cheung Kong	5
Property &	5
Hutchison Telecommunications Hong	3
Hutchison Asia	1
Finance &	1
Other	2
Total	**100**

Selected Subsidiaries and Affiliates

Retail
  A/S Drogras (Latvia)
  A.S. Watson & Company Limited
  Dirk Rossmann GmbH (40% Germany)
  Fortress Limited
  Guangzhou Watson's Food and Beverages Co.
    Ltd. (95% China)
  Kruidvat Retail B.V. (The Netherlands)
  Marionnaud Parfumeries SA (perfumes France)
  Nuance-Watson (Singapore) Pte Ltd. (50% duty-free
    shops)
  Park' N Shop Limited (supermarkets)
  The Perfume Shop Limited (UK)
  Savers Health and Beauty Limited (UK)
  Superdrug Stores plc (UK)
  Watson's Personal Care Stores (Taiwan) Co.
    Limited
Energy and infrastructure
  Cheung Kong Infrastructure Holdings Limited (85%)
  Hongkong Electric Holdings Limited (33% utility)
  Husky Energy Inc. (35% oil and gas investment
    Canada)
Ports and related services
  Hongkong International Terminals Limited (53%
    container terminal operations)
  Hongkong United Dockyards Limited (50% ship repair
    and general engineering)
  Shanghai Mingdong Container Terminals Limited
    (40% China)
  Yantian International Container Terminals Limited
    (38% China)
Telecommunications
  3 Italia S.p.A. (97% 3G mobile multimedia services)
  Hutchison 3G UK Limited (3G mobile multimedia
    services)
  Hutchison Telecommunications (Australia) Limited
    (52% holding company and multimedia services)
  Hutchison Telecommunications (Hong Kong) Limited
    (60%)
Property and hotels
  Harbour Plaza Hotel Management (International)
    Limited (50%)
  Hutchison Whampoa Properties Limited (holding
    company)
Finance and investments
  Hutchison Whampoa (Europe) Limited (consulting
    services UK)

Other
  TOM Group Limited (24% Internet portal)

COMPETITORS

AT&T	KP
Aldeasa	Orange
Alliance Boots	Orange
BT	Orient Overseas
Cable & Wireless	PCCW Ltd.
Carrefour	PSA International
China Mobile	Road King
China Unicom	Infrastructure
DFS Group	Schlecker
DP World	Sime Darby
Dairy Farm	SkyTel
International	Sprint Communications
Deutsche Telekom	Swire Pacific
Hopewell Holdings	Verizon
Jardine Matheson	Wharf

HISTORICAL FINANCIALS

Company Type: Public

Income Statement

FYE: December 31

	REVENUE ($ mil.)	NET INCOME ($ mil.)	NET PROFIT MARGIN	EMPLOYEES
12/13	33,046	4,012	12.1%	260,000
12/12	31,359	3,370	10.7%	250,000
12/11	30,084	7,211	24.0%	250,000
12/10	26,912	2,578	9.6%	240,000
12/09	26,927	1,827	6.8%	0
Annual Growth	5.3%	21.7%	—	—

2013 Year-End Financials

Debt ratio: 3.5%	No. of shares (mil.): —
Return on equity: 7.6%	Dividends
Cash ($ mil.): 11,046	Yield: 1.7%
Current ratio: 1.62	Payout: —
Long-term debt ($ mil.): 26,721	Market value ($ mil.): —

	STOCK PRICE ($) FY Close	P/E High	P/E Low	PER SHARE ($) Earnings	Dividends	Book Value
12/13	27.20	0	0	0.94	0.48	12.91
12/12	21.18	0	0	0.79	0.48	11.85
12/11	16.58	0	0	1.69	0.01	10.86
12/10	51.41	0	0	0.60	0.43	9.34
12/09	34.40	0	0	0.43	0.43	8.58
Annual Growth	(5.7%)	—	—	21.8%	2.7%	10.8%

Hyundai Heavy Industries Co., Ltd.

Not afraid to play the heavy Hyundai Heavy Industries (HHI) is the world's largest shipbuilder and among the top five manufacturers in other heavy industries. Started in 1972 HHI's shipbuilding division (15% global market share) builds containerships tankers bulk/petrochemical carriers drillships and specialty vessels. HHI also offers offshore construction and exploration services and has expanded into robotic systems and large industrial pumps and presses. Additionally HHI makes diesel engines and engine parts for industrial and marine applications. Other HHI offerings include electric systems (circuit breakers switchgear transformers) and construction equipment (excavators forklifts and loaders).

Operations

HHI operates through seven business divisions: Construction Equipment Electro Electric System Engine and Machinery Green Energy Industrial Plant and Engineering Offshore and Engineering and its bread and butter Shipbuilding.

The Construction Equipment segment is capitalizing on China's infrastructure market flooded with government stimulus funding. HHI's excavators claim more than a 10% share of China's excavator market. The company operates manufacturing plants in China as well as India that position HHI to capture an increasing share of the countries' construction equipment growth.

The Offshore and Engineering business operates a 230-acre offshore yard and fabrication shop for engineering and construction of offshore oil and gas facility projects. The Industrial Plant and Engineering business works on industrial plant projects for power generation desalination and oil and gas processing and capitalizes on bourgeoning work in the Middle East and South America. Despite a drop in marine engine and power engine demand pressured by the slow economy the Engine and Machinery business continues to benefit from HHI's move into China India and other developing markets.

Another small business of HHI is its Electro Electric Systems segment which manufactures and installs electrical systems in power plants locomotives subways and marine vessels. The business' performance is buoyed by the increase in replacement electrical equipment for renovating and upgrading power transformers and other facilities in North America as well as building new facilities in the Middle East and other rapidly modernizing regions.

Financial Performance

Research and development is also bolstering HHI's reach into profitable niche markets related to its established presence. Shipbuilding HHI's largest business represents roughly 40% of sales and revenues. From 2010 to 2011 its revenues increase by 44% but its net income decreased by 38% during that same time period.

Strategy

Responding to slow economy the company is diversifying its vessel offerings by concentrating resources on specialized energy-related vessels such as FSRU (floating storage and regasification unit) drillships and LNG and LNG-FPSO (floating production storage and offloading) facilities. (HHI introduced the world's largest FPSO in late 2010.) In addition it is partnering with shipbuilders around the world in an effort to court local relationships.

EXECUTIVES

Director, Jin-won Park
Director, Jae-kye Lee
Director, Young-june Park
Director, Man-woo Lee
Auditors: KPMGSamjongAccountingCorp.

LOCATIONS

HQ: Hyundai Heavy Industries Co., Ltd.
1000, Bangeojinsunhwando-ro Dong-gu, Ulsan 682-792
Phone: (82) 52 202 2114   **Fax:** (82) 52 202 3432
Web: www.hhi.co.kr

PRODUCTS/OPERATIONS

Selected Divisions Products and Services

Construction Equipment
  Excavators
  Forklifts
  Skid loaders
  Wheel loaders

Electro Electric Systems
  Low- and Medium-voltage circuit breakers
  Power electronics and control systems
  Rotating machinery
  Transformers gas insulated switchgear switchgear
Engine and Machinery
  Diesel and gas power plant engines
  Industrial and marine pumps industrial robots side
    thrusters
  Propellers and crankshafts
  Presses conveyor systems steel strip process lines
  Steam turbines and turbochargers
  Two-stroke diesel engines four-stroke (HiMSEN)
    engines
Green Energy
Industrial Plant and Engineering
  Plant equipment
  Power plants
  Process plants
Offshore and Engineering
  Floating units
  Fix platforms
  Land-based modules
  Offshore installations
  Pipelines and subsea facilities
Shipbuilding
  Containerships bulk carriers OBO carriers
  Drillships
  LNG carriers LPG carriers
  Ro-pax ships ro-ro ships pure car carriers
    tankers/VLCCs
  Submarines destroyers frigates
  VLCCs tankers product carriers chemical tankers

COMPETITORS

ALSTOM
Aker Solutions
Babcock & Wilcox
Baltija Shipbuilding
Bechtel
Bharat Heavy Electricals
Caterpillar
China State Shipbuilding
China Yuchai
Crown Equipment
DSME
Doosan Infracore
Ebara
Evergreen Marine
General Dynamics
Gulf Island Fabrication
Hanjin Heavy Industries & Construction
Harbison-Fischer
Hitachi Zosen
Huntington Ingalls
KBR
Kawasaki Heavy Industries
Komatsu
McDermott
Mitsubishi Heavy Industries
Mitsui Engineering & Shipbuilding
NASSCO
Oceaneering International
Samsung Heavy Industries
Siemens Industry Automation
Stolt-Nielsen
Sumitomo Heavy Industries
Technip USA

HISTORICAL FINANCIALS
Company Type: Public

Income Statement
FYE: December 31

	REVENUE ($ mil.)	NET INCOME ($ mil.)	NET PROFIT MARGIN	EMPLOYEES
12/13	51,526	265	0.5%	27,246
12/12	51,487	921	1.8%	26,255
12/11	46,355	2,208	4.8%	24,948
12/10	33,303	3,704	11.1%	24,222
12/09	25,283	1,850	7.3%	24,982
Annual Growth	19.5%	(38.5%)	—	2.2%

2013 Year-End Financials

Debt ratio: 0.0%   No. of shares (mil.): 61
Return on equity: 1.6%   Dividends
Cash ($ mil.): 1,270   Yield: —
Current ratio: 1.10   Payout: —
Long-term debt ($ mil.): 5,327   Market value ($ mil.): —

Hyundai Mobis Co. (South Korea)

South Korean auto parts giant Hyundai Mobis keeps drivers mobile with automotive modules and systems including chassis brakes air bags telematics and electronic devices. Established as a container manufacturer in 1977 the Hyundai (HMC) affiliate has since reinvented itself as a leading auto parts manufacturer supplying components in all Hyundai and Kia vehicles; other customers include BMW GM and Chrysler. The company has taken aggressive steps toward expanding beyond its Korean borders with forays into Japan China and Eastern Europe. Mobis markets its products in North America Australia Southeast Asia the Middle East and Europe.

Geographic Reach
Hyundai Mobis' main markets are Korea and China which collectively account for 70% of its total annual revenue. The US generates around 15% while the continent of Europe accounts for roughly 10%.

Operations
Hyundai Mobis has two reportable segments: auto parts (80% of total sales) and after sales services (20%).

Financial Performance
The company's net revenues increased 19% from 2010 to 2011 while its profits jumped by 11% over that same period. It was helped by a 16% surge in demand for its auto parts in Korea and a 19% increase in China.

Ownership
Kia Motors owns nearly 17% of Hyundai Mobis.

EXECUTIVES

Vice Chairman and CEO, Suk Soo Chung, age 62
Auditors: SamilPricewaterhousecoopers

LOCATIONS

HQ: Hyundai Mobis Co. (South Korea)
  203 Teheran-ro Gangnam-gu, Seoul 135-916
Phone: (82) 2 2018 5114   **Fax:** (82) 2 2018 6000
Web: www.mobis.co.kr

Sales

	% of total
Korea	50
China	21
US	15
Europe	10
Other	4
Total	100

PRODUCTS/OPERATIONS

Sales

	% of total
Auto	80
After sales	20
Total	100

Selected Products

Airbags
Brake systems
Chassis modules
Cockpit modules
Wheel and deck assemblies

COMPETITORS

Autoliv
Dana Holding
Delphi Automotive
  Systems
Johnson Controls
Robert Bosch
TRW Automotive
Visteon

HISTORICAL FINANCIALS
Company Type: Public

Income Statement
FYE: December 31

	REVENUE ($ mil.)	NET INCOME ($ mil.)	NET PROFIT MARGIN	EMPLOYEES
12/13	32,519	3,253	10.0%	7,615
12/12	28,836	3,332	11.6%	7,085
12/11	22,693	2,608	11.5%	6,663
12/10*	19,748	2,419	12.3%	6,244
01/10	0	0	—	0
Annual Growth	—	—	—	—

*Fiscal year change

2013 Year-End Financials

Debt ratio: 0.0%   No. of shares (mil.): 95
Return on equity: 18.4%   Dividends
Cash ($ mil.): 2,354   Yield: —
Current ratio: 2.12   Payout: —
Long-term debt ($ mil.): 1,141   Market value ($ mil.): —

Hyundai Motor Co., Ltd.

Hyundai vehicles run the gamut from budget cars to luxury sedans to commercial trucks. South Korea's leading carmaker Hyundai Motor produces compact and luxury cars SUVs minivans trucks buses and other commercial vehicles. Its cars are sold in 180 countries through some 6000 dealerships. Hyundai generates about half of its sales in South Korea but its vehicles are also popular in emerging markets such as China and India. The company operates a dozen manufacturing plants in China the Czech Republic India Russia South Korea Turkey and the US. It sold 3.6 million passenger cars in 2010 but only 500000 in the US where it does business as Hyundai Motor America. Hyundai also owns a 34% stake in Kia Motors.

Although South Korea accounts for half of Hyundai's sales and vehicle production capabilities the company is focused on growth in other markets. China's two plants now account for about 20% of production and construction on a third plant began in 2011. The plant a 50/50 joint venture with Beijing Automotive Industry Holding Co. Ltd. will be the company's largest in China capable of producing 400000 small and mid-size vehicles specifically designed for the Chinese market. (Hyundai's other two plants can make 300000 cars per year each). When the plant opens in 2012 Hyundai will be manufacturing 1 million cars a year in China.

Hyundai also established a second 50/50 joint venture in spring 2011 to begin making commercial trucks and buses in China. Both Hyundai and Sichuan Nanjun Automobile are investing about $275 million each to build Sichuan Hyundai a plant with an annual production capacity of 160000 units (150000 trucks and 10000 buses) starting in 2013. Sichuan Hyundai will make two types of trucks –value models sold under the Nanjun brand and higher-priced models sold under the Hyundai brand. Still the market for commercial vehicles in China is very tight and Hyundai only expects to sell 160000 trucks and buses per year by 2015 for a market share of 3%. A previous joint venture with Baotou Bei Ben Heavy-Duty Truck signed in late 2009 fell through.

To keep pace with markets in Europe Hyundai has manufacturing plants in the Czech Republic Russia and Turkey. The Russian plant opened in early 2011 and can manufacture 150000 Solaris sedans a model specifically designed to withstand Russia's cold climate. Hyundai exports another 10 models to Russia including the Elantra sedan the Sonata sedan and the Santa Fe SUV. Together the company's plants in the Czech Republic and Turkey produce about 7% of Hyundai's vehicles while all of Europe accounts for about 15% of sales.

The company is also setting up shop in Brazil to target the fast-growing Latin American market. Construction on a $600 million manufacturing plant began in early 2011 with the government providing Hyundai with free land and tax breaks. The plant will first produce a small hatchback specifically designed for the market with a goal of manufacturing 150000 ethanol flex-fuel cars per year. Currently top models for the Brazilian market include the compact i30 the Azera and Sonata sedans and the Veracruz and ix35 SUVs.

Hyundai is a leading brand in India as well trailing domestic players Maruti Suzuki India and Tata Motors. India accounts for more than 15% of the company's total production and is the company's international base for economy vehicles. Its newest compact vehicle for India the Eon launched in October 2011.

HISTORY

Hyundai Motor Company was established in 1967 and it initially began manufacturing cars and light trucks through a technology collaboration with Ford's UK operations. By the early 1970s Hyundai was ready to build cars under its own nameplate. The company debuted the subcompact Hyundai Pony in 1974 at Italy's annual Turin Motor Show.

The Pony was an instant domestic success and soon propelled Hyundai to the top spot among South Korea's carmakers. During the mid-1970s the company began exporting the Pony to El Salvador and Guatemala.

By the 1980s Hyundai was ready to shift into high gear and begin high-volume production in anticipation of penetrating more overseas markets. The company began exporting to Canada in 1983.

Hyundai introduced the Hyundai Excel in 1985. That year the company established its US subsidiary Hyundai Motor America. By 1986 Hyundai was exporting Excels for sale in the US. Sales of the Excel soared the next year so Hyundai decided to build a factory in Bromont Quebec.

But by the time the factory was finished in 1989 consumers were tiring of the aging compact car and the quality problems that came with it. Hyundai closed the plant after just four years of operation.

The company introduced its first sports car the Scoupe in 1990. The following year it developed the first Hyundai-designed engine called the Alpha. Two years later the carmaker unveiled its second-generation proprietary engine the Beta.

By 1998 Hyundai was beginning to feel the pinch of the Asian economic crisis as domestic demand dropped drastically. However the decrease in Korean demand was largely offset by exports. That year Hyundai took a controlling stake in Korean competitor Kia Motors.

In hopes of increasing its share of the Asian automotive market Daimler AG took a 10% stake in Hyundai in 2000 (sold 2004). The deal included the establishment of a joint venture to manufacture commercial vehicles as well as an agreement among Hyundai Daimler and Mitsubishi Motors to develop small cars for the global market.

In 2001 Hyundai decreased its stake in Kia Motors to about 46%.

The following year Daimler announced it would exercise its option to take a 50% stake in Hyundai's heavy truck business.

In 2004 Hyundai CEO Kim Dong-Jin was indicted in South Korea on charges that he violated campaign finance laws and engaged in managerial negligence. The charges stemmed from a general crackdown on campaign finance violations during which more than a dozen members of South Korea's parliament were either indicted or detained. Later in 2004 Kim was convicted of the charges against him and sentenced to a suspended two-year prison term.

To increase its presence in the US Hyundai completed construction of a new manufacturing plant Hyundai Motor Manufacturing Alabama in 2005. The plant's annual production was about 300000 cars.

In 2006 Hyundai's legal woes persisted when two executives were arrested as part of a Korean bribery investigation. The pair were accused of creating a slush fund that was allegedly used to fund a lobbyist who sought favors for Hyundai from the South Korean government. Officials were also investigating whether the slush fund was created at the behest of Hyundai chairman Chung Mong-Koo.

Chung then was indicted and arrested on charges that he embezzled Hyundai company cash to finance bribes for Korean government officials in exchange for corporate favors. After two months of incarceration Chung was released from jail on $1 million bail.

He was convicted early in 2007. Under Korean law Chung faced a potential life sentence but received only a three-year prison term as the judge in the case said Chung contributed hugely to the development of the Korean economy. During his trial Chung admitted some wrongdoing when he said "I admit to my guilt to some extent." However Chung appealed the conviction. Three other Hyundai officials were also convicted but they received suspended sentences. Chung's son Kia Motors boss Chung Eui-Sun also was under investigation but prosecutors did not indict him.

Later in 2007 Chung's three-year prison sentence was suspended by an appeals court with a three-judge panel citing his importance to Korea's economy. The appellate judges however required the Hyundai executive to maintain a clean record for five years to avoid prison and to fulfill a promise he made to donate $1.1 billion of his personal assets to society.

EXECUTIVES

Chairman, Chung Mong-Koo, age 65
Vice Chairman, Chung Eui-Sun, age 43
President CEO and Director, Kim Eok-Jo
Vice Chairman, Chung Eui-Sun, age 43
Director, Kwang-Nyun Kim
Director, Il-Hyung Kang
Director, Young-chul Yim
Director, Sung-Il Nam
Director, Young-Rok Lim
President CEO and Director, Kim Eok-Jo
Auditors: DeloitteAnjinLLC

LOCATIONS

HQ: Hyundai Motor Co., Ltd.
12, Heolleung-ro Seocho-gu, Seoul 137-938
Phone: (82) 2 3464 1114   **Fax:** (82) 2 3463 3484
Web: www.hyundai-motor.com

Sales

	% of total
South	49
North	22
Rest of	15
Europe	14
Total	**100**

PRODUCTS/OPERATIONS

Sales

	% of total
Automotive	95
Financial	5
Total	**100**

Selected Models

Commercial vehicles
  Aero (large city bus)
  Aero Town (medium bus)
  County (small bus)
  e-Mighty (light commercial truck)
  Super Aero City (bus)
  Universe (large coach bus)
Passenger cars
  Accent (compact coupe)
  Atos Prime (subcompact)
  Avante XD
  Azera (sedan)
  Elantra (sedan)
  Entourage (minivan)
  Equus/Centennial (premium sedan)
  Genesis (premium coupe)
  Getz (compact sedan)
  Santa Fe (SUV)
  Sonata (sedan)
  Tiburon (coupe)
  Tucson (SUV)
  Trajet (SUV)
  Veracruz (SUV)

COMPETITORS

BYD	Honda
Chery Automobile	Isuzu
Chrysler	Maruti Suzuki
Daihatsu	Mazda
Daimler	Nissan
Dongfeng Motor	Peugeot
Fiat	Renault
Ford Motor	Ssangyong Motor
GM Korea	Tata Motors
General Motors	Toyota
Hindustan Motors	Volkswagen

HISTORICAL FINANCIALS

Company Type: Public

Income Statement

FYE: December 31

	REVENUE ($ mil.)	NET INCOME ($ mil.)	NET PROFIT MARGIN	EMPLOYEES
12/13	83,019	8,122	9.8%	63,099
12/12	79,113	8,018	10.1%	59,831
12/11	67,142	6,607	9.8%	57,105
12/10	59,740	4,964	8.3%	56,137
12/09	79,048	2,569	3.3%	55,984
Annual Growth	**1.2%**	**33.3%**	**—**	**3.0%**

2013 Year-End Financials

Debt ratio: 0.0%	No. of shares (mil.): 209
Return on equity: 17.8%	Dividends
Cash ($ mil.): 6,534	Yield: 1.4%
Current ratio: 1.84	Payout: —
Long-term debt ($ mil.): 32,319	Market value ($ mil.): 12,138

| STOCK PRICE ($) | | P/E | | PER SHARE ($) | | |
FY Close		High/Low	Earnings	Dividends	Book Value
12/13	58.00	— —	29.90	0.86	235.97
12/12	30.15	— —	29.52	0.00	197.10
12/11	25.25	— —	24.34	0.00	153.06
12/10	27.69	— —	18.30	0.00	(0.00)
12/09	17.00	— —	9.46	0.00	89.55
Annual Growth	35.9%	— —	33.3%	—	27.4%

Iberdrola SA

Once just a force in Spain IBERDROLA has established itself as a major global player in the power industry over the past few years. In 2012 it was serving 31 million customers in Europe and the Americas and it owned hydroelectric fossil-fueled nuclear and renewable power generation facilities with a capacity of about 46590 MW (56% of which was derived from hydrolectric or other green energy sources). It also has gas distribution operations in Spain. The company is putting a major focus on being the world leader in developing renewable energy plants primarily wind power facilities and had some 13000 MW of installed capacity in 2011 and a project pipeline of more than 62610 MW.

IBERDROLA owns hydroelectric fossil-fueled nuclear and renewable power generation facilities. It also has gas distribution operations in Spain.

In 2012 the company's installed electric generating capacity included 25700 MW in Spain 7250 MW in the UK 6380 MW in the US and 5880 MW in Latin America.

In 2011 IBERDROLA reported a 4% rise in revenues (in Euros). A weakening of regional economies led to 3% lower power demand in Spain and the UK. US demand stayed flat while Brazil reported a 3% rise in power use. However higher power pricing enabled the company to produce a gain in revenues. Net profits fell by 2% (in Euros) due to higher operating and fuel costs and higher taxation. In a move to improve its financial condition in 2011 the company took its IBERDROLA RENOVABLES subsidiary private (citing that unit's underperformance on the stock market since its was spun off in 2007 and assimilated it).

The company's long term strategy is to focus on the development on its portfolio of clean energy plants and to upgrade its network of transmission and distribution grids to more efficiently harness the new power coming online. It is also focusing on strengthening its presence in Brazil Mexico the US and the UK. With Spain's economy in a serious slump the company needs growth markets in North and South America to sustain its financial performance.

Growing its green energy portfolio in 2011 it acquired 20% of US-based Westec Environmental Solutions which develops carbon dioxide capture and storage technologies. As part of its renewable energy push that year the company announced plans to invest about $2.6 billion in its first offshore wind farm located off the west coast of England. The wind farm (with about 390 MW capacity) is scheduled to come online in 2014.

A possible merger between IBERDROLA and German power player RWE fell through in 2011 due to market and political concerns (resistance to the reduction of competition in the EU market).

In 2010 IBERDROLA secured a contract with partner Vattenfall to build one of the world's largest marine wind farms in the world (in offshore UK) with a capacity of 7200 MW capable of supplying clean energy to 5 million homes. Further boosting in presence in the UK in 2010 the company formed NuGeneration a nuclear joint venture (with GDF SUEZ and Scottish and Southern Energy) which aims to develop up to 3600 MW of nuclear power. (In late 2011 SSE withdrew from the joint ventures as it returned to its renewable energy strategy). In 2012 NuGeneration applied for a license to generate power in the UK.

HISTORY

The 1992 merger of two private utilities –Hidroelectrica Espanola (Hidrola) and Hidroelectrica Iberia Iberduero — created IBERDROLA. Iberduero's forebear Hidroelectrica Iberica was born in 1901 in Spain's industrialized north; its first power plant began operations in 1904.

In 1918 Saltos del Duero began producing hydroelectric power along the Duero River. The two companies merged to become Iberduero in 1944 five years after the reign of Gen. Francisco Franco began. Neither Iberduero nor Hidrola (founded in 1907 to electrify Madrid and Valencia) grew much during Spain's isolationist years.

Hoping to make friends the US pumped money into Spain in the 1950s. As industrial production picked up both Hidrola and Iberduero completed construction on several large power plants between 1957 and 1969.

Dependent on imported oil Spain was shaken by the 1970s oil crisis. In 1975 a few months before Franco died the government began to promote nuclear energy. Both firms invested heavily in nukes but by 1984 overcapacity high building costs and inflation led the government to freeze nuclear construction. Hidrola Iberduero and other private utilities were left deeply in debt.

In the late 1980s the government arranged nuclear and hydro asset swaps to spread the debt around. Ultimately more power was shifted to the state utility Endesa. In 1992 with Endesa gobbling up smaller utilities and European deregulation in the wings Iberduero and Hidrola merged in self-defense. The result was IBERDROLA Spain's largest privately owned utility and Endesa's only real competition. IBERDROLA and Endesa stayed at odds particularly over stranded costs from the stalled nuclear program and the government's mandate that the private utilities buy Endesa's energy to repay Endesa for taking over their power plants. Finally in 1996 the government agreed to issue bonds to cover most of the debt.

IBERDROLA began piling up Latin American interests in 1992 by buying stakes in Argentina's Gas Litoral and the Goemes power plant. It soon grabbed holdings in Bolivian electricity distributors Electropaz and Elfeo (1995) two Chilean utilities (1996) gas and electric companies in Brazil and a gas company in Colombia (1997).

To create a more horizontal business structure in 1995 IBERDROLA created Iberinco an engineering firm and Iberener to manage Latin American energy holdings. It formed telecom joint venture Utilitel with Telefonica in 1997 and founded data management firm Iberdrola Sistemas in 1998.

IBERDROLA agreed to cooperate with oil company Repsol on developing energy projects in 1997 a year before Spain's deregulation began. With Electricidade de Portugal and the US's TECO Energy it acquired Guatemala's Empresa Electrica in 1998 and with Telefonica bought interests in Brazilian wireless phone companies.

In 1999 IBERDROLA took over US company Energy Works (which managed electricity buys for industrial customers) allied with German giant RWE to compete throughout Europe and made plans to exit the Utilitel venture.

IBERDROLA bought Brazilian electric distributor CELPE for $1 billion in 2000. Later that year the company itself agreed to be acquired by rival Endesa for $12.9 billion but the deal was abandoned in 2001. Also in 2001 IBERDROLA sold its Latin American telecommunications interests to Telefonica.

In 2002 the company sold controlling stakes in its Spanish water utilities (Pridesa and Ondagua) to RWE's Thames Water unit for $96 million. IBERDROLA also sold its power transmission assets to Infraestructuras de Alta Tension (INALTA) which is owned by CVC Capital Partners (75%) and Red Electrica de Espana (25%).

IBERDROLA expanded in Latin America to include electric generation and distribution companies in Brazil Bolivia Chile Guatemala and Mexico.

The company sold off noncore assets including some domestic water utility and real estate assets its Latin American gas businesses and two Chilean hydroelectric plants. Spanish construction giant ACS acquired 10% of IBERDROLA in 2006 for $2.7 billion. That year the company acquired two UK-based wind power projects with a combined power capacity of more than 20MW its first such acquisition in the UK.

IBERDROLA became a major global force in 2007 with the friendly takeover of Scottish Power for $22.5 billion. Scottish Power was the third-largest electricity distributor and largest wind power producer in the UK. In 2008 in a major move into the US power market IBERDROLA acquired Energy East (now Iberdrola USA) for $4.5 billion. Iberdrola USA distributes and markets power and natural gas to Connecticut Maine Massachusetts New Hampshire and New York.

EXECUTIVES

CFO, Jose Sainz Armada
Director Development, Pedro Azagra Blazquez
Chief Executive Officer of Iberdrola Ingenier?a, Alberto Sicre
Head Renewables, Xabier Viteri
Head Non Energy Business, Pedro Velasco
Director Iberia and Latin America, Jose Luis San Pedro
Board Member, Braulio Medel Camara, age 66
Board Member, Jose I. Berroeta Echevarria, age 74
Board Member, Julio de Miguel Aynat, age 71
Board Member, Sebastian Battaner Arias, age 74
Board Member, Xabier de Irala Estevez, age 67
Board Member, I?igo V. de Oriol Ibarra, age 51
Board Member, Ines Macho Stadler, age 54
Vice Chairman, Victor de Urrutia Vallejo, age 71
Board Member, Ricardo Alvarez Isasi, age 74
Board Member, Jose Luis Olivas Martinez, age 63
Board Member, Samantha Barber, age 44
Board Member, Santiago Martinez-Lage, age 69
Board Member, Maria Helena Antolin Raybaud, age 46
Auditors: Ernst&YoungS.L.

LOCATIONS

HQ: Iberdrola SA
Tomas Redondo, 1, Madrid 28033
Phone: (34) 91 784 2742   **Fax:** (34) 91 784 2977
Web: www.iberdrola.es

Sales

	% of total
Europe	
Spain	48
UK	27
Other	1
South	14
US	10
Total	**100**

PRODUCTS/OPERATIONS

Sales

	% of total
Deregulated	67
Network	16
Renewables	5
Other	12
Total	**100**

COMPETITORS

AES	Enersis
CEPSA	Ezentis
Cemig	Gas Natural SDG
Constellation Energy	HC Energia
Group	International Power
E.ON UK	Navitas Energy
ELETROBRAS	PPL Corporation
Edison	Plambeck Neue Energien
Electricite de France	Red Electrica de
EnBW	Espa?a
Endesa S.A.	Sempra Energy
Enel	Tractebel Engineering
Energias de Portugal	

HISTORICAL FINANCIALS

Company Type: Public

Income Statement
FYE: December 31

	REVENUE ($ mil.)	NET INCOME ($ mil.)	NET PROFIT MARGIN	EMPLOYEES
12/13	45,167	3,540	7.8%	30,678
12/12	45,078	3,744	8.3%	31,338
12/11	40,935	3,627	8.9%	31,885
12/10	40,728	3,842	9.4%	31,344
12/09	35,378	4,068	11.5%	32,711
Annual Growth	**6.3%**	**(3.4%)**	**—**	**(1.6%)**

2013 Year-End Financials

Debt ratio: 44.8%
Return on equity: 7.4%
Cash ($ mil.): 2,353
Current ratio: 0.94
Long-term debt ($ mil.): 35,687

No. of shares (mil.): —
Dividends
Yield: 4.7%
Payout: —
Market value ($ mil.): —

	STOCK PRICE ($) FY Close	P/E High/Low	PER SHARE ($) Earnings	Dividends	Book Value
12/13	25.55	120 81	0.56	1.22	7.80
12/12	21.32	96 45	0.60	0.99	7.25
12/11	24.10	148 81	0.62	0.00	7.23
12/10	30.65	143 70	0.71	2.26	7.10
12/09	37.85	154 72	0.80	1.48	7.31
Annual Growth	**(9.4%)**	**— —**	**(8.7%)**	**(4.6%)**	**1.6%**

ICICI Bank Ltd (India)

You see ICICI Bank is India's #2 bank (after State Bank of India) and its largest private bank with some Rs. 6 trillion in assets. The bank has some 2700 branches nationwide; it also has locations in about 20 other countries. The retail banking group offers lending and deposit services to small businesses and individuals; larger businesses are served by the corporate banking group which offers finance services and treasury products. The rural and government banking unit offers microloans and agricultural banking. Foreign operations as well as services related to international trade finance and expatriate Indians fall under international banking. The bank also offers life and property/casualty insurance.

Key subsidiaries include ICICI Prudential Life Insurance (the largest private sector life insurer in the country) ICICI Lombard General Insurance (property/casualty coverage) ICICI Prudential Asset Management (mutual funds) ICICI Securities (investment banking and brokerage) and ICICI Venture Funds Management (venture capital).

Consumer loans including mortgages auto loans credit card receivables and commercial business loans account for more than half of the bank's lending portfolio. The company also offers commercial and agricultural loans and leasing. It extends credit to small business and entrepreneurs especially rural residents requiring micro-financing.

Although it has seen a rise in nonperforming loans ICICI Bank remained relatively unscathed from the global financial crisis. At the height of the crisis the company focused on cutting costs and tightening its lending practices. Since then it has again worked on building up its loan portfolio especially with such assets as mortgages project finance and secured retail loans. The growth has helped stimulate the company's earnings: In 2012 the bank's revenues grew 8% and net income grew 26% largely due a 21% increase in net interest income and a 45% decrease in loan loss provisions. However noninterest income fell 9% as insurance and brokerage earnings dipped.

Founded by the World Bank as a development financial institution in the 1950s ICICI has since become a full-fledged financial services company offering a range of products and services. Its insurance business which recently turned its first profit has helped ICICI as it broadens its revenue streams. The company's growth strategy includes seeking ways to enhance its retail and corporate banking operations while strengthening its insurance securities and asset management units. ICICI is also a leader in technology innovation: It was India's first bank to offer mobile banking services and it plans to continue driving the growth of that offering.

The bank also has large cash reserves and knows how to use them: It plans on making strategic international investments over the next few years but will focus largely on its domestic banking and related operations. In particular retail lending including credit cards and secured loans are a key to ICICI's long-term growth. In 2010 the company acquired Bank of Rajasthan expanding its retail network by about 500 branches.

Deutsche Bank Trust owns 27% of ICICI Bank.

EXECUTIVES

Chairman, Kundapur V. (K. V.) Kamath, age 67, $394,454 total compensation
Deputy Managing Director Rural Banking Government Banking and Global Markets and Director, Nachiket Mor, age 52, $258,600 total compensation
Chief Financial Officer; Wholetime Director, N. S. Kannan, age 49, $72,340 total compensation
Executive Director and Chief Human Resources Officer, Krishnaswamy Ramkumar, age 53, $233,443 total compensation
CTO and Director, Pravir Vohra, age 61, $234,686 total compensation
Group Executive Wholesale Banking, Zarin Daruwala
Group Compliance Officer; Company Secretary; Senior General Manager, Sandeep Batra, age 49, $38,700 total compensation
Joint General Manager, Rajiv Arora, age 48, $76,675 total compensation
Head of Cards Product Group, Sachin Khandelwa
Head of Corporate Communications, Charudatta Deshpande

Investor Relations, Rupesh Kumar
Executive Director, Rajiv Sabharwal
President, Vijay Chandok
Investor Relations Officer, Rakesh Mookim
Director, Lakshmi N. Mittal, age 63
Director, M. S. Ramachandran, age 69
Executive Director and Chief Human Resources Officer, Krishnaswamy Ramkumar, age 53
Director, Prof Marti G. Subrahmanyam, age 66
Director, Sridar A. Iyengar, age 67
CTO and Director, Pravir Vohra, age 61
Director, V. Sridar
Director, Homi R. Khusrokhan
Director, Mahendra Kumar Sharma, age 67
Director, T. S. Vijayan, age 60
Managing Director and CEO ICICI Life and Board Member, Sandeep Bakhshi, age 53
Director, Anup K. Pujari, age 68
Director, Prof Marti Gurunath, age 67
Independent Director, Swati Piramal
Independent Director, Tushaar Shah
Auditors: KPMGLLP

LOCATIONS

HQ: ICICI Bank Ltd (India)
ICICI Towers, Bandra-Kurla Complex, Mumbai 400 051
Phone: (91) 22 2653 1414   **Fax:** (91) 22 2653 1122
Web: www.icicibank.com

PRODUCTS/OPERATIONS

Sales by Segment

	% of total
Treasury	29
Wholesale	25
Retail	19
Life	17
General	4
Venture Fund	-
Other	3
Other	3
Total	**100**

Sales

	% of total
Interest	
Advances &	37
Investments	17
Other	3
Noninterest	
Premium & other insurance	31
Commissions exchange &	9
Other	3
Total	**100**

COMPETITORS

BNP Paribas	ING
Bank of Baroda	Industrial Development
Bank of India	Bank of India
Canara Bank	Punjab National Bank
Citigroup	Standard Chartered
GE Money India	State Bank of India
HSBC	UCO Bank

HISTORICAL FINANCIALS

Company Type: Public

Income Statement
FYE: March 31

	ASSETS ($ mil.)	NET INCOME ($ mil.)	INCOME AS % OF ASSETS	EMPLOYEES
03/14	124,494	1,838	1.5%	94,204
03/13	124,309	1,769	1.4%	85,217
03/12	118,759	1,502	1.3%	81,254
03/11	119,719	1,366	1.1%	79,978
03/10	108,994	1,040	1.0%	74,056
Annual Growth	**3.4%**	**15.3%**	**—**	**6.2%**

2014 Year-End Financials

Return on assets: 1.5%	Dividends	
Return on equity: 15.2%	Yield: 1.5%	
Long-term debt ($ mil.): —	Payout: 42.2%	
No. of shares (mil.): 1,155	Market value ($ mil.): 50,593	
Sales ($ mil): 13,144		

	STOCK PRICE ($) FY Close	P/E High/Low	PER SHARE ($) Earnings	Dividends	Book Value
03/14	43.80	— —	1.58	0.13	11.02
03/13	42.90	— —	1.53	0.00	10.98
03/12	34.87	— —	1.30	0.00	10.45
03/11	49.83	— —	1.19	0.10	10.77
03/10	42.70	— —	0.93	0.19	10.25
Annual Growth	0.6%	— —	14.3%	(9.0%)	1.8%

Idemitsu Kosan Co Ltd

As long as Japanese drive Toyotas there will be a role for Idemitsu Kosan. The company is the #2 oil refiner in Japan (behind Nippon Oil). At its four refineries in Japan (processing 640000 barrels per day) Idemitsu Kosan produces petroleum products such as gasoline and other fuels kerosene and lubricants. It markets its fuel products through a network of 4600 service stations. Idemitsu Kosan sells heavy oil and jet fuels to industries and kerosene and liquefied petroleum gas (LPG) to the residential sector. The company also has interests in oil exploration and production as well as coal and uranium.

Operations

Idemitsu Kosan has three reportable segments: Its petroleum products business includes fuel oil and petrochemical products. Its petrochemical products operations consist of the basic chemicals business which jointly operates an ethylene complex with Mitsui Chemicals and the functional materials business which develops functional flexible polypropylene. The company's resources businesses is engaged in exploration activities to expand its oil reserves.

In addition to its oil and gas businesses the company has a number of New Growth activities including agro-business (pesticides) and green energy (wind solar and geothermal). Idemitsu Kosan is also developing electronic materials (organic light-emitting diode luminous materials with Sony Corporation) and lithium battery development.

Geographic Reach

Idemitsu Kosan has offices in Africa Asia (East South East and South West) Australia Europe (including Russia) the Middle East and North and South America.

Financial Performance

In 2012 the company's revenues increased by 18% due to increases in the prices of crude oil and naphtha significant rises in coal prices and an increase in the volume of products sold. Japan accounted for 84% of the company's revenues that year.

Net income increased by 6% in 2012 thanks to higher revenues and the result of progress in streamlining activities in production sales and distribution as well as improved product margins for petrochemical products despite a contraction of margins for petroleum products.

Business Strategy

To meet increased demand Idemitsu Kosan is enhancing its petroleum products business in the growing overseas markets centered on the Pacific

Rim. As part of this process in 2012 it acquired Freedom an independent Australian petroleum products distributor that sells petroleum products wholesale and operates about 40 gas stations on Australia's east coast.

That year it also opened an office in China formed a joint venture in Taiwan and set up a lubricant manufacturing and sales company in Vietnam.

Idemitsu Kosan unified its ethylene production with Mitsui Chemicals in 2010 to promote efficiency.

Company Background

Pooling their LPG resources and expertise in 2006 Idemitsu Kosan merged its LPG operations with those of Mitsubishi to form Astomos Energy.

EXECUTIVES

Chairman, Akihiko Tembo
EVP, Kenichi Matsui
President, Kazuhisa Nakano, age 66
Managing Director, Seiji Fukunaga
Managing Director, Akiro Nishiyori
Managing Director, Junjiro Kuramochi
EVP, Takashi Tsukioka
Managing Director, Yasunori Maeda
Managing Director, Osamu Kamimae
EVP, Yoshihisa Matsumoto
Managing Executive Officer, Kiyotsugu Suita
Executive Officer, Yasuo Kushihashi
Executive Officer, Hiroaki Muko
Executive Officer, Daisuke Seki
Executive Officer, Hiroshi Seki
Executive Officer, Kiyonobu Kobayashi
Executive Officer, Sakugoro Matsuda
Executive Officer, Yasuhiro Haba
Executive Officer, Ryuhei Masumoto
Executive Officer, Shigeki Nakajima
Managing Director, Kenichi Matsui
President and Director, Kazuhisa Nakano, age 66
EVP and Director, Shuichi Omiya
Managing Director, Takahisa Hiruma
Managing Director, Yoshinori Kawamoto
Managing Director, Zenichi Suda
Managing Director, Seiji Fukunaga
Managing Director, Akiro Nishiyori
Director, Mitsuru Soneda
Director, Junjiro Kuramochi
Director, Takashi Tsukioka
Director, Yasunori Maeda
Director; President Idemitsu Snorre Oil Development, Osamu Kamimae
Auditors: DeloitteToucheTohmatsuLLC

LOCATIONS

HQ: Idemitsu Kosan Co Ltd
3-1-1 Marunouchi, Chiyoda-ku, Tokyo 100-8321
Phone: (81) 3 3213 3150
Web: www.idemitsu.co.jp

Sales

	% of total
Japan	84
Asia & North	8
North	5
Europe	2
Other	1
Total	**100**

PRODUCTS/OPERATIONS

Sales

	% of total
Petroleum	83
Petrochemical	12
Resources	4
Other	1
Adjustments	-
Total	**100**

Selected Subsidiaries

Apollo Service Co. Ltd.
Idemitsu Apollo Corp. (US)
Idemitsu Engineering Co. Ltd.
Idemitsu International (Asia) Pte. Ltd. (Singapore)
Idemitsu International (Europe) PLC (UK)
Idemitsu Oil & Gas Co. Ltd.
Idemitsu Oil Development Co Ltd.
Idemitsu Oita Chinetsu Co. Ltd.
Idemitsu Petrochemical Co. Ltd.
IS Electrode Materials Co. Ltd.
Munakata Shipping Co. Ltd.

COMPETITORS

Cosmo Oil
JX Holdings
JX Nippon Mining & Metals
JX Nippon Oil & Energy
SK Innovation
Showa Shell Sekiyu

HISTORICAL FINANCIALS

Company Type: Public

Income Statement

FYE: March 31

	REVENUE ($ mil.)	NET INCOME ($ mil.)	NET PROFIT MARGIN	EMPLOYEES
03/14	48,779	351	0.7%	8,749
03/13	46,493	533	1.1%	8,684
03/12	52,545	784	1.5%	8,243
03/11	44,190	732	1.7%	8,201
03/10	33,319	63	0.2%	8,330
Annual Growth	10.0%	53.1%		1.2%

2014 Year-End Financials

Debt ratio: 0.3%	No. of shares (mil.): 159	
Return on equity: 5.3%	Dividends	
Cash ($ mil.): 1,564	Yield: —	
Current ratio: 1.09	Payout: —	
Long-term debt ($ mil.): 5,663	Market value ($ mil.): 1,686	

	STOCK PRICE ($) FY Close	P/E High/Low	PER SHARE ($) Earnings	Dividends	Book Value
03/14	10.54	— —	2.20	0.00	45.05
03/13	21.97	— —	3.33	0.00	45.71
03/12	26.72	— —	4.91	0.00	46.83
03/11	29.45	— —	4.58	0.00	40.83
03/10	18.80	— —	0.40	0.40	33.28
Annual Growth	(13.5%)	— —	53.1%	—	7.9%

Imperial Oil Ltd.

Imperial Oil Canada's second-largest oil integrated company behind Suncor Energy holds sway over a vast empire of oil and gas resources. Imperial is one of Canada's top natural gas producers a leading refiner and marketer of petroleum products and a major supplier of petrochemicals. It sells petroleum products including gasoline heating oil and diesel fuel under the Esso name and other brand names. The company reported proved reserves in 2013 of 3.6 billion barrels of oil-equivalent including 62 million barrels of liquids 678 billion cu. ft. of natural gas 579 million barrels of synthetic oil and 2.9 billion barrels of bitumen. Exxon Mobil owns about 70% of Imperial.

Geographic Reach

Most of the company's production comes from fields in Alberta and the Northwest Territories.

Operations

Imperial has three main segments: Upstream Downstream and Chemical. Upstream operations include the exploration for and production of crude oil natural gas synthetic oil and bitumen; Downstream operations consist of the transportation and refining of crude oil blending of refined products and the distribution and marketing of those products; and its Chemical operations consist of the manufacturing and marketing of various petrochemicals such as ethylene benzene aromatic and aliphatic solvents plasticizer intermediates and polyethylene resin.

In addition to its conventional upstream operations Imperial owns 25% of Syncrude Canada which operates the world's largest oil sands development with synthetic oil and bitumen/heavy oil end products.

The Downstream segment owns and operates three refineries. The Strathcona and Sarnia refineries process Canadian crude oil and the Nanticoke refinery processes a combination of Canadian and foreign crude oil. The Strathcona refinery operates lubricating oil production facilities. The company maintains a nationwide distribution system including 22 primary terminals to handle bulk and packaged petroleum products moving from refineries to market by pipeline tanker rail and road transport. It also owns and operates natural gas liquids and products pipelines in Alberta Manitoba and Ontario and has interests in the capital stock of one crude oil and two products pipeline companies.

Sales and Marketing

The company sells gasoline to motorists at more than 1700 primarily Esso-branded gas stations across Canada.

It markets more than 550 petroleum products throughout Canada to all types of customers. It also serves the Canadian agriculture residential heating and small commercial markets through 28 branded resellers and sells petroleum products to large industrial and commercial accounts as well as to other refiners and marketers.

Financial Performance

Imperial's revenues grew by 6% in 2013 primarily due to increased Upstream sales partially offset by lower Downstream and Chemical sales.Upstream segment revenue growth was fueled by higher production of both conventional crude oil and natural gas (as the result of the Celtic acquisition and the Horn River pilot which more than offset normal field decline) as well as priced. The improvement was partially offset by lower production of Cold Lake bitumen.Downstream segment revenues declined due to reduced refinery throughput of 426000 barrels per day in 2013 (compared to 435000 barrels per day in 2012) as well as the closing of its Dartmouth refinery. This was partially offset by increased production higher product sales and reduced maintenance activities.The chemical segment revenue decline was due to a lower volume of petrochemical sales in 2013.Imperial's net income declined by 25% in 2013 due to significantly lower industry refining margins higher Kearl bitumen project costs (as production contribution was more than offset by start-up and operating costs) lower volumes at Syncrude and a lower contribution from Cold Lake as well as an after-tax charge associated with the conversion of the Dartmouth refinery to a terminal.

Cash flow generated from operating activities decreased by $1.4 billion in 2013 primarily due to lower net income and working capital effects.

Strategy

Reorganizing its portfolio in 2014 Imperial sold its interests in assets located in Boundary Lake Cynthia/West Pembina and Rocky Mountain House in Western Canada to Whitecap Resources Inc. for C$855 million (US$785 million).

In 2013 the company converted its underperforming Dartmouth refinery to a fuels terminal. That year Imperial invested about $8 billion in capital and exploration expenditures primarily in the

Upstream segment related to Celtic and Clyden acquisitions and post-acquisition investments and the advancement of the Kearl expansion and Nabiye projects. In 2012 the company entered into a $2 billion expansion of the company's Cold Lake operation in northeastern Alberta. The expansion called Nabiye will bring on additional commercial bitumen production of more than 40000 barrels per day at Cold Lake. The project (which has access to 280 million barrels of recoverable reserves) is expected to start up by the end of 2014.In 2013 the company's research expenditures were $199 million and were mainly targeted on developing technologies to reduce the environmental impact and improve bitumen recovery in the upstream segment and for supporting environmental and process improvements in the refineries as well as accessing Exxon Mobil's data worldwide.

Mergers and Acquisitions

In 2013 following the acquisition of Celtic Exploration by ExxonMobil Canada Imperial acquired 50% of Celtic from ExxonMobil Canada for $1.6 billion. A general partnership was formed to hold and operate the assets of Celtic under the name of XTO Energy Canada.That year Imperial and ExxonMobil Canada also acquired ConocoPhillips' interest in the Clyden oil sands lease.

HISTORY

London Ontario boomed from the discovery of oil in the 1860s and 1870s but when the market for Canadian kerosene became saturated in 1880 16 refiners banded together to form the Imperial Oil Company.

The company refined sulfurous Canadian oil nicknamed "skunk oil" for its powerful smell. Imperial faced tough competition from America's Standard Oil which marketed kerosene made from lighter less-odorous Pennsylvania crude. Guided by American expatriate Jacob Englehart Imperial built a better refinery and hired a chemist to develop a process to clean sulfur from the crude.

By the mid-1890s Imperial had expanded from coast to Canadian coast. Cash-starved from its expansion the company turned to old nemesis Standard Oil which bought a controlling interest in Imperial in 1898. That interest is today held by Exxon Mobil.

After the turn of the century Imperial began producing gasoline to serve the new automobiles. The horseless carriages were spooking the workhorses at the warehouse where fuel was sold so an Imperial manager in Vancouver opened the first Canadian service station in 1907. The company marketed its gas under the Esso banner borrowed from Standard Oil.

An Imperial crew discovered oil in 1920 at Norman Wells in the remote Northwest Territories. In 1924 a subsidiary sparked a new boom with a gas well discovery in the Turner Valley area northeast of Edmonton. But soon Imperial's luck ran as dry as the holes it was drilling; it came away empty from the next 133 consecutive wells. That string ended in 1947 when it struck oil in Alberta at the Leduc No. 1. To get the oil to market Imperial invested in the Interprovincial Pipe Line from Alberta to Superior Wisconsin.

The company began research in 1964 to extract bitumen from the oil sands in Cold Lake Alberta. During the 1970s oil crisis Imperial continued to search for oil in northern Canada. It found crude on land near the Beaufort Sea (1970) and in its icy waters (1972). The company formed its Esso Resources Canadian Ltd. subsidiary in 1978 to oversee natural resources production.

In 1989 Texaco (acquired by Chevron in 2001) still reeling from a court battle with Pennzoil sold Texaco Canada to Imperial. To diminish debt and comply with regulators Imperial agreed to sell

some of Texaco Canada's refining and marketing assets in Atlantic Canada its interests in Interhome Energy and oil and gas properties in western Canada.

Imperial reorganized in 1992 centralizing several units and in 1993 closed its refinery at Port Moody British Columbia. It sold most of its fertilizer business in 1994 disposed of 339 unprofitable gas stations in 1995 and the next year closed down Canada's northernmost oil refinery at Norman Wells.

In 1997 Imperial announced an ambitious program to expand Syncrude's oil sands bitumen upgrading plant. In 1998 Exxon agreed to buy Mobil which had substantial Canadian oil assets. In 1999 Canada preapproved the potential merger of Imperial Oil and Mobil Canada. Later that year Exxon completed its purchase of Mobil to form Exxon Mobil.

Expanding its exploration and production assets in 2007 Imperial and ExxonMobil Canada acquired exploration rights for a development parcel in the Beaufort Sea and in 2008 in the Horn River area of northeastern British Columbia.

EXECUTIVES

Vice President; General Counsel; Corporate Secretary, Brian W. Livingston, $349,191 total compensation

Chairman President and CEO, R. M. (Rich) Kruger

Chairman President Chief Executive Officer, Bruce H. March, age 57, $392,299 total compensation

Controller, Sean R. Carleton

Director Corporate Planning, George E. Bezaire

VP; General Manager Fuels Marketing, Simon M. Smith, $334,880 total compensation

Investor Relations, Mark Stumpf

Senior Vice President - Finance and Administration; Controller, Paul J. Masschelin, age 59

Senior Vice President - Resources, T. G. (Glenn) Scott

Vice President and General Manager - Refining and Supply, Gilles Courtemanche

Treasurer, Phil Dranse

Director, Roger Phillips, age 74

Director, Sheelagh D. Whittaker, age 67

Director, Krystyna T. Hoeg, age 64

Director, Victor L. Young, age 69

Director, J. M. (Jack) Mintz, age 63

Chairman President Chief Executive Officer, Bruce H. March, age 57

Director, Robert C. Olsen, age 64

Independent Director, David Sutherland

Auditors: PricewaterhouseCoopersLLP

LOCATIONS

HQ: Imperial Oil Ltd.
237 Fourth Avenue S.W., Calgary, Alberta T2P 3M9
Phone: 416 968-8145   **Fax:** 416 968-5345
Web: www.imperialoil.ca

PRODUCTS/OPERATIONS

Sales

	% of total
Refining &	78
Exploration &	17
Chemicals	4
Total	**100**

COMPETITORS

Abraxas Petroleum	Koch Industries Inc.
Ashland Inc.	Marathon Oil
BHP Billiton	Murphy Oil
BP	Occidental Petroleum
Barnwell Industries	PEMEX

Canadian Natural PETROBRAS
ConocoPhillips Petroleos de Venezuela
Devon Energy Pioneer Natural
Dominion Resources Resources
DuPont Royal Dutch Shell
Encana Suncor
Eni Sunoco
Hunting TOTAL
Husky Energy Talisman Energy

HISTORICAL FINANCIALS
Company Type: Public

Income Statement
FYE: December 31

	REVENUE ($ mil.)	NET INCOME ($ mil.)	NET PROFIT MARGIN	EMPLOYEES
12/13	30,967	2,659	8.6%	5,300
12/12	31,358	3,786	12.1%	5,100
12/11	30,108	3,304	11.0%	5,085
12/10	25,145	2,214	8.8%	4,970
12/09	20,410	1,506	7.4%	5,015
Annual Growth	11.0%	15.3%	—	1.4%

2013 Year-End Financials

Debt ratio: 11.2%
Return on equity: 15.7%
Cash ($ mil.): 255
Current ratio: 0.60
Long-term debt ($ mil.): 4,179

No. of shares (mil.): 847
Dividends
  Yield: 1.1%
  Payout: 15.1%
Market value ($ mil.): 37,489

	STOCK PRICE ($) FY Close	P/E High/Low		PER SHARE ($) Earnings	Dividends	Book Value
12/13	44.23	13	10	3.12	0.47	21.66
12/12	43.00	11	8	4.44	0.48	19.43
12/11	44.48	14	8	3.87	0.43	15.41
12/10	40.52	17	13	2.60	0.41	13.21
12/09	38.66	21	12	1.76	0.38	10.62
Annual Growth	3.4%	—		15.5%	5.3%	19.5%

Imperial Tobacco Group Plc

The UK's #1 cigarette maker Imperial Tobacco Group eyes an even larger throne. The group has lavished billions on brand-building acquisitions — including Spain's Altadis (2008) Commonwealth Brands in the US (2007) and Germany's Reemtsma (Davidoff and West cigarettes 2002) — to extend its reign across Europe Africa the Middle East and Asia/Pacific region and North America. In addition to Davidoff major brands include Gauloises JPS Rizla Montecristo cigars and Skruf snus. Imperial Tobacco operates some 50 cigarette and tobacco product and processing plants worldwide as well as a logistics business. Products are sold in 160-plus countries; emerging markets account for 60% of cigarettes sold.

An expanding global reach helped the group post a slight uptick in net tobacco revenue in 2011 over 2010 albeit less than previous years. It managed nonetheless a rough 125% bounce in earnings over the prior year thanks to significantly lower finance costs among various factors. Sales in emerging markets on top of demand for fine-cut tobacco and Habanos cigars and price hikes also fueled momentum amid a decline in smoking in the group's mature markets. In Spain Imperial Tobacco holds more than a quarter of the market but a ban on smoking in public places and a rise in

taxes on already cash-strapped Spaniards hurt sales. Market sales further deteriorated when rival British American Tobacco (BAT) slashed prices sparking a price war. In England a ban on tobacco sales from vending machines threatens to reduce cigarette purchases. (The move was unsuccessfully challenged by Sinclair Collis Imperial Tobacco's vending machine subsidiary.)

Known largely for its premium brands (Davidoff West and Gauloise) Imperial Tobacco's strategy includes diversifying its portfolio in order to boost revenues through sales of lower-priced tobacco products in mature markets. (In a troubled economy Imperial Tobacco saw an improving trend as more smokers traded down in order to maintain their habit.) The group controls almost half of the shrinking UK cigarette market which accounts for 10% of the tobacco giant's sales volumes.

Concurrently Imperial Tobacco is rolling out regional and local luxury tobacco brands with some success in emerging markets particularly the Asia/Pacific region but also Eastern Europe Africa and the Middle East. In China Imperial Tobacco has signed a 10-year pact to produce and sell cigarettes. Snus brands Skruf and Knox hold more than 5% of total snus sales volumes in Sweden and Norway.

Size however remains a strategic advantage. The addition of Altadis owner of the world's largest cigar maker to the group's portfolio created the fourth-largest tobacco company worldwide by volume (behind BAT). Imperial Tobacco boasts some of the most popular cigar brands in the US including Romeo y Julieta and Montecristo which have a loyal following despite the recession and their extreme regulation. As part of the deal for Altadis Imperial Tobacco disposed of its fine cut tobacco brand Interval and several other brands to Philip Morris International. Proceeds were used in part to reduce debt a top priority for the group.

Government regulation in the UK and abroad coupled with rising health concerns are spurring the group to broaden its horizons. Like competitors BAT and Gallaher (now owned by Japan Tobacco) Imperial Tobacco is eager to distance itself from litigious tobacco issues. The group opened a smoking balcony at Birmingham Airport in mid-2012 as part of its Smoking Allowed campaign. In a follow-on purchase to Altadis Imperial Tobacco acquired separately listed distribution unit Cia. de Distribucion Integral Logista bolting on a new business segment to support activities. Logista delivers tobacco and other products for international manufacturers to tobacconists and other retail outlets across Southern Europe.

Imperial Tobacco has stayed relevant as well by acquiring Sweden's Skruf snus business (2005) a product positioned toward younger men as less harmful. Since then Imperial Tobacco has gained an impressive share of the smokeless tobacco market.

HISTORY

Imperial Tobacco Group was formed in 1901 to fight American Tobacco's invasion of the UK. American Tobacco had become the dominant US tobacco company partly by using a large cash reserve to undercut competitors. When it bought UK tobacco and cigarette factory Ogden's that year 13 UK tobacco firms responded by registering as The Imperial Tobacco Company. The firms (including Wills Lambert & Butler and John Player & Sons) continued to make and sell their products separately.

As expected American Tobacco cut prices and Imperial fought back acquiring the Salmon & Cluckstein tobacco shop chain and offering bonuses to retailers that sold its products. When

Imperial threatened US expansion in 1902 American Tobacco surrendered: It gave Ogden's to Imperial and halted its Ireland and Great Britain business in exchange for Imperial's pledge to stay out of the US (except for buying tobacco leaf). The two formed the British American Tobacco Company (BAT) to sell both firms' cigarettes overseas. But when American Tobacco split into four companies in 1911 and sold its BAT interest the agreement was modified to let Imperial sell some of its brands in the US.

By the 1950s Imperial controlled more than 80% of the UK tobacco market but its share decreased during the 1960s due to competition from Gallaher Group (Benson & Hedges). Imperial diversified buying companies such as Golden Wonder Crisps snack food (1961) and the Courage & Barclay brewery (1972).

In 1973 BAT and Imperial agreed that each firm would control its own brands in the UK and Continental Europe. Imperial sold the last of its stake in BAT in 1980. Conglomerate Hanson Trust paid $4.3 billion for Imperial in a 1986 hostile takeover. Hanson reduced Imperial's tobacco brands from more than 100 to five brand families (a move that decreased its UK market share to 33% by 1990). It also sold Imperial's drinks unit including Courage and John Smith beer to Elders IXL (now Foster's Brewing). Between 1986 and 1993 Hanson cut Imperial's tobacco operations from five factories and 7500 employees to three factories and 2600 employees; it also sold Imperial's restaurant and food operations.

As UK cigarette consumption dropped Imperial began expanding overseas in 1994. By 1996 exports had risen to 15% of sales. That year Gareth Davis became CEO of Imperial.

Facing further declining UK cigarette sales and a government tax hike Imperial bought the world's #1 cigarette paper brand Rizla (1997) and Sara Lee's cut-tobacco unit Douwe Egberts Van Nelle (1998) which it renamed Van Nelle Tabak. That acquisition added Drum hand-rolling tobacco and Amphora pipe tobacco to Imperial's brands. In 1999 the company added a bevy of Australian and New Zealand brands (Horizon Brandon Flagship Peter Stuyvesant) from BAT.

In 2000 Imperial acquired paper maker EFKA (Germany Canada) and tobacco maker Baelen (Belgium). That year Imperial tripled its cigarette vending operations by acquiring Mayfield Vending (27000 UK locations).

Imperial expanded operations in Africa in 2001 with the acquisition of 75% of Tobaccor. It also began distributing the Marlboro brand in the UK.

The company bought 90% of Reemtsma in 2002; the deal at the time was valued at $5.1 billion.

In 2004 Imperial cut 940 jobs as it closed manufacturing plants in Hungary Slovakia and Slovenia. The company shifted production to Germany and Poland. In 2005 Imperial restructured its European production resulting in the closure of its operations in Dublin Ireland and nearly 100 job cuts. In late 2005 Imperial acquired the Swedish snus manufacturer Skruf to get a foothold in the popular niche of the tobacco market) and Norwegian tobacco product distributor Gunnar Stenberg.

In February 2007 Imperial Tobacco acquired the Commonwealth Brands cigarette division of Houchens Industries for $1.9 billion. Commonwealth Brands which makes 14 billion cigarettes each year rang up nearly $350 million in sales in 2006.

In January 2008 the company completed the purchase of Altadis for $18.2 billion. In May it completed the purchase of Altadis's Logista tobacco and tobacco products distribution business. In April Imperial sold its nearly 50% stake in the Aldeasa a duty-free retailer based in Spain to Autogrill Espana for about E355 million ($496 million).

In May 2010 Alison Cooper succeeded the retiring Gareth Davis as CEO of the company.

EXECUTIVES

Finance Director and Director, Robert (Bob) Dyrbus, age 63, $1,098,038 total compensation
Chief Executive and Director, Alison J. Cooper, age 48, $791,831 total compensation
Group Corporate Legal Affairs Director Secretary and Director, Matthew Phillips, age 44
Director Corporate Communications, Alex Parsons
Chairman, Iain J. G. Napier, age 65, $859,614 total compensation
Director Investor Communications, Gerry Gallagher
Company Secretary, John Downing
Director, Michael H. C. Herlihy, age 61
Director, Pierre H. Jungels, age 69
Finance Director and Director, Robert (Bob) Dyrbus, age 63
Director, Susan E. Murray, age 57
Director, Ken Burnett, age 62
Chief Executive and Director, Alison J. Cooper, age 48
Director, Mark Williamson, age 56
Group Corporate Legal Affairs Director Secretary and Director, Matthew Phillips, age 44
Director, Berge Setrakian, age 65
Independent Non-Executive Director, David Haines
Independent Non-Executive Director, Malcolm Wyman
Auditors: PricewaterhouseCoopersLLP

LOCATIONS

HQ: Imperial Tobacco Group Plc
121 Winterstoke Road, Bristol BS3 2LL
Phone: (44) 117 963 6636   **Fax:** (44) 117 933 7430
Web: www.imperial-tobacco.com

2011 Tobacco Sales

	% of total
EU	
Germany	13
UK	12
Spain	8
Other	22
Americas	11
Other	34
Total	**100**

PRODUCTS/OPERATIONS

Sales

	% of total
Tobacco (manufacturing marketing &	88
Logistics (distribution of tobacco & other	12
Total	**100**

Sales (volumes)

	% of total
White stick	50
Cigarettes	44
Fine cut	6
Total	**100**

Selected Products and Brands

Cigarettes
Balkan Star
Bonus
Classic
Davidoff (global strategic cigarette brand)
Drum (roll-your-own tobacco)
Ducados Rubio
Excellence
Fine
Fortuna
Gauloises Bondes (global strategic cigarette brand)
Gitanes
Golden Virginia
John Player Special (JPS)

Lambert & Butler (discount brand)
Marquise
Maxim
Paramount
Richmond (discount brand)
Rizla (rolling paper)
Route 66 (American blend sold in France Belgium and Eastern Europe)
Sonoma
Style
USA Gold
West (global strategic cigarette brand)
Windsor Blue
Cigars
Antonio y Cleopatra
Cadena
Castella
Classic
Cohiba
Dutch Masters cigarillos
Farias
Hav-A-Tampa
Montecristo
Phillies cigarillos
Panama
Romeo y Julieta
Rolling paper and tobacco
Amphora
Drum
Rizla (rolling paper)
St Bruno
Snus
Knox
Skruf

COMPETITORS

Altria	Lorillard
British American Tobacco	Philip Morris International
General Cigar	Reynolds American
Gudang Garam	Swedish Match
JT International	Swisher International
Japan Tobacco	UST llc

HISTORICAL FINANCIALS
Company Type: Public

Income Statement
FYE: September 30

	REVENUE ($ mil.)	NET INCOME ($ mil.)	NET PROFIT MARGIN	EMPLOYEES
09/14	43,088	2,301	5.3%	33,900
09/13	45,631	1,512	3.3%	35,300
09/12	46,277	1,098	2.4%	37,200
09/11	45,520	2,797	6.1%	38,200
09/10	44,759	2,391	5.3%	38,300
Annual Growth	**(0.9%)**	**(1.0%)**	**—**	**(3.0%)**

2014 Year-End Financials

Debt ratio: 61.8%
Return on equity: 26.6%
Cash ($ mil.): 2,315
Current ratio: 0.94
Long-term debt ($ mil.): 15,316
No. of shares (mil.): 957
Dividends
  Yield: 4.6%
  Payout: 449.3%
Market value ($ mil.): 83,048

	STOCK PRICE ($) FY Close	P/E High/Low	PER SHARE ($) Earnings	Dividends	Book Value
09/14	86.77	176121	2.40	4.00	8.56
09/13	74.15	221170	1.55	3.38	9.31
09/12	74.04	323241	1.10	7.78	9.87
09/11	67.10	105 79	2.75	2.86	11.80
09/10	59.40	119 77	2.35	2.35	10.97
Annual Growth	**9.9%**	**— —**	**0.5%**	**14.2%**	**(6.0%)**

Indian Oil Corp., Ltd. (India)

LOCATIONS

HQ: Indian Oil Corp., Ltd. (India)
3079/3, Sadiq Nagar, J.B. Tito Marg, New Delhi 110049
Phone: (91) 11 26260000   **Fax:** (91) 22 2642 7384
Web: www.iocl.com

HISTORICAL FINANCIALS
Company Type: Public

Income Statement
FYE: March 31

	REVENUE ($ mil.)	NET INCOME ($ mil.)	NET PROFIT MARGIN	EMPLOYEES
03/13	83,007	0		34,084
03/12	81,004	830	1.0%	34,233
03/11	71,602	1,756	2.5%	34,105
03/10	58,567	2,449	4.2%	34,363
03/09	56,638	470	0.8%	33,998
Annual Growth	**10.0%**	**—**	**—**	**0.1%**

2013 Year-End Financials

Debt ratio: 0.4%
Return on equity: —
Cash ($ mil.): 92
Current ratio: 0.86
Long-term debt ($ mil.): —
No. of shares (mil.): —
Dividends
  Yield: —
  Payout: —
Market value ($ mil.): —

Industrial and Commercial Bank of China (Asia) Limited

LOCATIONS

HQ: Industrial and Commercial Bank of China (Asia) Limited
33/F., ICBC Tower, 3 Garden Road, Central,
Phone: (852) 2588 1188   **Fax:** (852) 2805 1166
Web: www.icbcasia.com

HISTORICAL FINANCIALS
Company Type: Public

Income Statement
FYE: December 31

	ASSETS ($ mil.)	NET INCOME ($ mil.)	INCOME AS % OF ASSETS	EMPLOYEES
12/13	73,480	677	0.9%	2,317
12/12	54,914	517	0.9%	1,845
12/11	52,131	405	0.8%	0
12/10	34,343	386	1.1%	1,543
12/09	27,823	325	1.2%	1,425
Annual Growth	**27.5%**	**20.1%**	**—**	**12.9%**

2013 Year-End Financials

Return on assets: 1.0%
Return on equity: 12.4%
Long-term debt ($ mil.): —
No. of shares (mil.): 2,064
Sales ($ mil): 2,017
Dividends
  Yield: —
  Payout: —
Market value ($ mil.): —

Industrial and Commercial Bank of China Ltd

In the event not every young man wants to go west Industrial and Commercial Bank of China (ICBC) is able to finance trips elsewhere. The firm is one of China's biggest banks —and one of the largest in the world. ICBC manages more than 16000 domestic branches and more than 200 overseas branches and offices. The bank's financial services offered in Chinese renminbi and foreign currencies include wholesale retail and international banking for more than 4 million corporate clients and some 280 million individuals. It oversees about a quarter of the total domestic assets owned by China's commercial banks. The Chinese government controls about 70% of ICBC.

ICBC makes more than half of its earnings through its corporate banking segment. To support the world's sluggish financial recovery the bank has increased its lending activities for large corporate concerns as well as small to micro businesses. The bank has also made significant inroads into expansion abroad and now has some 1700 correspondent banks around the world.

The company has been gaining steadily since its record-setting 2006 IPO. In 2011 ICBC's operating income grew 24% from the previous year while profits rose 26%. Both interest and noninterest earnings grew —net fee and commission income grew by nearly 40% that year. Assets have also been growing and the bank is considered the world's largest by market capitalization and customer deposits. Conversely ICBC's portfolio of non-performing loans has been shrinking.

Although it doesn't have the international presence of fellow Chinese group Bank of China ICBC does have its eyes on growth abroad. In 2011 the bank established operations in about a dozen new international markets. The bank's targeted markets for growth include Russia Vietnam Pakistan the Middle East and the Americas. ICBC owns most of Bank Halim Indonesia a minority stake in South Africa-based Standard Bank Group and an approximately 80% stake in ICBC (Macau). In 2010 the company bought a 70% stake in Bank of East Asia's Canadian unit —now ICBC (Canada); it upped its stake to 80% the following year. The bank also opened a Malaysian subsidiary indicative of growing trade between China and Malaysia.

ICBC ventured into the US broker-dealer business in 2010 when it acquired the Prime Dealer Services unit of Fortis Securities from BNP Paribas. The company again hooked up with Bank of East Asia in 2012 when it bought a majority of that company's US operations including more than a dozen bank branches in New York and California. The deal marked the first time that a US retail bank was acquired by a Chinese company.

ICBC also has plans to establish operations in Peru and Brazil. In 2011 it arranged to buy 80%

of Standard Bank's three Argentinean businesses further boosting its presence in the Americas. (South America has a growing Chinese population which the bank hopes to take advantage of.)

EXECUTIVES

VP and Director, Li Xiaopeng, age 55
Chairman and Executive Director, Jiang Jianqing, age 61
President and the vice chairman of ICBC, Yang Kaisheng, age 65
VP and Director, Zhang Furong, age 62
VP and Director, Zhang Qu, age 67
VP and Director, Wang Lili, age 63
President ICBC Beijing, Yi Huiman, age 50
Secretary, Pan Gongsheng, age 52
Chief Risk Officer, Wei Guoxiong, age 59
SEVP, Zhang Hongli
VP and Director, Li Xiaopeng, age 55
Vice Chairman and President, Yang Kaisheng, age 64
VP and Director, Zhang Furong, age 62
VP and Director, Zhang Qu, age 67
VP and Director, Wang Lili, age 63
Director, Song Zhigang, age 63
Auditors: Ernst&YoungHuaMing

LOCATIONS

HQ: Industrial and Commercial Bank of China Ltd
No. 55 Fuxingmennei Avenue, Xicheng District, Beijing 100140
Phone: (86) 10 66108608   **Fax:** (86) 10 66107571
Web: www.icbc-ltd.com

PRODUCTS/OPERATIONS

Sales

	% of total
Interest	
Loans & Financial	59
Other	17
Noninterest	7
Fees & Other	16
	1
Total	**100**

Sales by Segment

	% of total
Corporate	53
Personal	31
Treasury	15
Other	1
Total	**100**

COMPETITORS

Agricultural Bank of China	China Construction Bank
Bank of China	China Merchants Bank
Bank of Communications	HSBC
CITIC International Financial	Hua Xia Bank

HISTORICAL FINANCIALS

Company Type: Public

Income Statement

FYE: December 31

	ASSETS ($ mil.)	NET INCOME ($ mil.)	INCOME AS % OF ASSETS	EMPLOYEES
12/13	3,124,889	43,385	1.4%	441,902
12/12	2,813,847	38,261	1.4%	427,356
12/11	2,458,831	33,087	1.3%	408,859
12/10	2,041,783	25,055	1.2%	397,339
12/09	1,725,989	18,840	1.1%	389,827
Annual Growth	**16.0%**	**23.2%**	**—**	**3.2%**

2013 Year-End Financials

Return on assets: 1.4%	Dividends
Return on equity: 21.9%	Yield: 0.0%
Long-term debt ($ mil.): —	Payout: 14.2%
No. of shares (mil.): —	Market value ($ mil.): —
Sales ($ mil): 151,472	

	STOCK PRICE ($) FY Close	P/E High/Low		PER SHARE ($) Earnings	Dividends	Book Value
12/13	13.58	1	0	0.12	0.02	0.60
12/12	14.48	1	0	0.11	0.01	0.52
12/11	11.92	1	0	0.09	0.01	0.44
12/10	15.65	2	1	0.07	0.02	0.36
12/09	41.68	3	1	0.06	0.01	0.30
Annual Growth	**(24.4%)**	—	—	**20.9%**	**17.5%**	**19.3%**

Industrial Bank Co., Ltd.

There's nothing average about Industrial Bank. Founded in 1988 Industrial Bank is one of China's first joint stock commercial banks. Through some 95 branches and more than 815 sub-branches across China Industrial Bank offers standard deposit loan wealth management credit card and e-banking products and services to personal and commercial banking customers. Fujian Finance Department a government institution controls nearly a fifth of Industrial Bank while Hong Kong's Hang Seng Bank owns more than 10%.

EXECUTIVES

President, Li Renjie, age 59
VP, Kang Yukun, age 60
VP, Chen Dekang, age 60
Secretary of the Board; Director, Bin Tang
Head of Bank; Director, Renjie Li
Vice President Industrial Bank Co. Ltd, Jiang Yunming
Independent Director, Bin Xu
Independent Director, Bingkun Lin
Independent Director, Qinye Zhou
Independent Director, Ruoshan Li
Independent Director, Shusong Ba

LOCATIONS

HQ: Industrial Bank Co., Ltd.
154 Hudong Road, Fuzhou, Fujian Province 350003
Phone: (86) 591 87824863   **Fax:** (86) 591 87842633
Web: www.cib.com.cn

COMPETITORS

Bank of China	China Merchants Bank
Bank of East Asia	China Minsheng Banking
Bank of Shanghai	Shanghai Pudong
China Construction Bank	Development Bank

HISTORICAL FINANCIALS

Company Type: Public

Income Statement

FYE: December 31

	ASSETS ($ mil.)	NET INCOME ($ mil.)	INCOME AS % OF ASSETS	EMPLOYEES
12/13	607,449	6,807	1.1%	0
12/12	521,470	5,568	1.1%	0
12/11	382,689	4,052	1.1%	0
12/10	280,610	2,809	1.0%	0
12/09	195,102	1,945	1.0%	0
Annual Growth	32.8%	36.8%	—	—

2013 Year-End Financials

Return on assets: 1.1%
Return on equity: 22.3%
Long-term debt ($ mil.): —
No. of shares (mil.): —
Sales ($ mil): 18,032

Dividends
  Yield: —
  Payout: —
Market value ($ mil.): —

ING Bank N.V. (Netherlands)

LOCATIONS

HQ: ING Bank N.V. (Netherlands)
Bijlmerplein 888, Amsterdam 1102 MG
Phone: (31) 20 5639111   **Fax:** (31) 20 5760950
Web: www.ing.com

HISTORICAL FINANCIALS

Company Type: Public

Income Statement

FYE: December 31

	REVENUE ($ mil.)	NET INCOME ($ mil.)	NET PROFIT MARGIN	EMPLOYEES
12/13	77,155	4,216	5.5%	64,373
12/12	86,064	4,105	4.8%	66,879
12/11	90,271	5,180	5.7%	71,175
12/10	99,292	6,015	6.1%	71,287
12/95	5,884	672	11.4%	0
Annual Growth	15.4%	10.7%	—	—

2013 Year-End Financials

Debt ratio: —
Return on equity: 8.8%
Cash ($ mil.): 16,410
Current ratio: —
Long-term debt ($ mil.): —

No. of shares (mil.): 465
Dividends
  Yield: —
  Payout: —
Market value ($ mil.): —

ING Groep N.V.

ING Groep is a Dutch hybrid of banking insuring and asset-managing services. One of the world's largest banking and financial services companies its operations are focused on its home Benelux market as well as the rest of Europe and in the Americas and Asia. The company's banking operations include wholesale and retail banking mortgage lending and online retail banking (ING Direct). Key insurance products include life insurance pensions and retirement services. ING provides asset management for individuals and institutions through both its insurance and banking units. The firm is selling off insurance operations as well as some banking and investment businesses to repay government bailout loans.

Geographic Reach

ING operates in about 40 countries in Europe North America South America Asia and the Asia/Pacific region. North America is the largest segment accounting for 38% of revenues in 2012 with the Netherlands accounting for about one-third of sales.

Operations

Amid the global financial crisis of 2008 ING accepted a Â10 billion (about $13 billion) bailout loan from the Dutch government to shore up its capital position and reassure wary investors. Since then ING has been focused on repaying the loan and enacting strategic measures to further offset losses including layoffs and asset sales. Under requirements for the bailout funds ING is also working to separate its banking and insurance operations through the sale of the insurance assets (as well as some banking assets). Through its restructuring measures and stock rights issuances the company was able to repay half of the funds received through the Dutch government bailout at the end of 2009. By the end of 2012 it had reduced the funds owed to about Â2 billion.

The company is focused on its European banking operations –including divisions in the Netherlands Belgium and Germany –which provide a full range of services including savings and investment products. Due to the restructuring efforts banking operations now account for 70% of revenues (insurance was previously the core business). Remaining insurance operations are primarily located in the Benelux region and in the US.

Sales and Marketing

ING uses a multi-channel distribution model to reach customers including individuals families small business entities large corporations government agencies and institutions. Marketing and sales methods include Internet banking mobile banking call centers mailings and branch and outbound sales representative efforts.

Financial Performance

ING's revenues fell 7% in 2012 to Â91.1 billion largely due to asset disposal efforts. Net income also fell by 31% to Â3.3 billion on lower revenues and increased restructuring costs and banking operational expenses.

Strategy

ING's restructuring plan encompasses the sale or spinoff of all of its insurance operations which have included life insurance and non-life insurance businesses in Europe the Americas and the Asia/Pacific. In early 2014 the company raised $1.18 billion by selling off a majority stake in its US insurance unit. The plan also includes the divestiture of the company's insurance-related investment management operations as well as select noncore banking operations. Through its restructuring measures ING aims to improve finances streamline its portfolio and repay state aid. The company is focusing its business efforts on building strong domestic retail and commercial banking units as well as strong banking positions in other Central and Eastern European markets.

The company is focused on selling insurance operations in Asia. In late 2013 ING sold its investment management business in South Korea to Macquarie Group an Australian global financial services provider. It sold its Malaysian insurance operations to AIA Group for Â1.3 billion in 2012. It also sold its insurance assets in Hong Kong Macau and Thailand to Pacific Century Group for Â1.6 billion ($2.1 billion) as well as its 33% stake in China Merchants Fund (investment management venture) to partner China Merchants Bank for Â100 million. From 2009 to 2011 the company sold off a number of insurance and investment management businesses in North America Latin America the Asia/Pacific region and Europe.

To narrow the focus of its banking operations in early 2012 the group sold its ING Direct USA banking business to Capital One for $6 billion in cash and a 10% ownership stake in Capital One; ING sold the Capital One shares for some $3 billion later that year. The ING Direct Canada unit was sold to Scotiabank for some Â2.4 billion in 2012 and in 2013 ING completed the sale of its ING Direct UK division to Barclays. In 2014 ING exited its equity investment management business in the Middle East and North Africa.

Some of ING's divestitures will be conducted through public offerings. In late 2012 ING U.S. filed a registration statement to complete an IPO; the offering was completed in May 2013 to raise some $1.3 billion. ING retained a 75% stake in ING U.S. which holds ING's remaining US-based life insurance retirement and investment management operations. The company plans to reduce its stake through future share offerings; it also plans to rename ING U.S. as Voya Financial. ING also plans to conduct an IPO of its European life insurance and investment management operations.

Company Background

Prior to the economic meltdown ING took aim at becoming a financial services player in all four corners of the world and made acquisitions accordingly. Along with much of the insurance industry it shifted its base from traditional life insurance products to investment-backed products which favor companies that can sell through banks. ING utilized its owns banks to distribute such products. The company also targeted expansion in growing economies such as South Korea Turkey and Thailand to meet anticipated consumer demand for new banking and retirement options. In more mature markets like North America and Europe the company had the aging population in its sights and placed retirement planning and pensions as sources of future growth.

HISTORY

HCING Groep's roots go back to 1845 when its earliest predecessor the Netherlands Insurance Co. was founded. The firm began expanding geographically; in 1903 it added life insurance. In 1963 it merged with the century-old Nationale Life Insurance Bank to form Nationale-Nederland (NN). Over the next three decades the company grew primarily through acquisitions in Europe North America and Australia. In 1986 NN became the first European life insurance company to be licensed in Japan.

Another predecessor the Rijkspostspaarbank was founded in 1881 to provide Dutch citizens with simple post office savings accounts. In 1918 the Postcheque-en Girondienst (giro) system was established to allow people to use vouchers drawn on their savings accounts to pay bills. This system became the main method of settling accounts (instead of bank checking accounts).

Rijkspostspaarbank and Postcheque merged in 1986 to become Postbank. Postbank merged in 1989 with the Nederlandse Middenstandsbank (founded 1927) to become NMB Postbank. The vast amounts of cash tied up in the post office savings and giro systems fueled NMB's business.

In 1991 as the European economic union became a reality and barriers between banking and insurance began to fall NN merged with NMB Postbank to form Internationale Nederland Groep (ING). ING began cutting costs shedding redundant offices and unprofitable operations in both its segments. In the US where insurance and banking were legally divided the company "debanked" itself in order to keep its more lucrative insurance operations (but retained the right to provide banking services to those operations).

ING sought to increase its investment banking and finance operations in the 1990s. In 1995 it took over UK-based Barings Bank (personal banker to the Queen of England) after Nicholas Leeson a trader in Barings' Singapore office lost huge sums of money in derivatives trading. The acquisition gave the firm a higher profile but cost more than anticipated and left it embroiled in lingering legal actions.

In 1996 ING bought Poland's Bank Slaski (the company had first entered Poland in 1994). The next year it expanded its securities business by acquiring investment bank Furman Selz doubled its US life insurance operations by purchasing Equitable of Iowa and listed on the NYSE. In 1998 ING's acquisition strategy again involved Europe and North America: It bought Belgium's Banque Bruxelles Lambert and Canadian life insurer Guardian Insurance Co. (from Guardian Royal Exchange now part of AXA UK).

ING turned eastward in 1999 kicking off asset management operations in India and buying a minority stake in South Korea's HC&B (formerly Housing & Commercial Bank). In 2000 the company bulked up its North American operations with the purchase of 40% of Savia SA a Mexican insurance concern. It also bought US firm ReliaStar Financial in a $6 billion deal and Charterhouse Securities from CCF (then called Credit Commercial de France).

In 2004 ING realigned its management structure dividing the company's operations into six business lines: Insurance Americas Insurance Europe Insurance Asia-Pacific Wholesale Banking Retail Banking and ING Direct. ING boosted its North American insurance operations with the acquisition of Allianz's Canadian property and casualty operations.

The company struggled with investment banking arm ING Barings. The unit was reorganized and streamlined for cost-savings purposes but ultimately was put on the block. Its Asian equities operations were sold to Macquarie Bank in 2004. Barings Private Equity Partners unit was sold to its management. The Barings investment management operations were sold to MassMutual in 2005 while Northern Trust bought up its fund administration trust and custody operations.

ING sold most of ING BHF-Bank to Sal. Oppenheim during 2004. The next year ING turned over its US life reinsurance operations to Scottish Re and sold subsidiary Life Insurance Company of Georgia to Jackson National Life.

During 2005 ING acquired a 20% stake in the Bank of Beijing as part of a strategic alliance. In 2006 the company sold off its UK brokerage business Williams de Broe to The Evolution Group.

In 2008 the company acquired CitiStreet a leading US administrator of defined-contribution retirement savings pension health and other plans; it paid about $900 million for the firm.

After the global financial crisis hit in 2008 ING accepted a Â10 billion (more than $13 billion) bailout loan from the Dutch government. The bailout was intended to shore up the company's capital position and reassure wary investors. Strategic measures to further offset losses and repay debt were enacted in 2009 including layoffs and asset sales. CEO Michael Tilmant stepped down and was replaced by former chairman Jan Hommen. By the end of 2009 job cuts totaled about 10% of its workforce. The company also outlined plans to split the company in half by separating its insurance and banking operations.

Prior to the bailout ING has already been working to simplify and streamline its operations through a "Back to Basics" strategy. Restructuring measures under the strategy include the refocusing of ING's banking operations on (mostly Central) Europe and the reduction of the company's US financial product offerings.

In early 2009 the company sold its ING Canada property/casualty business which was then renamed Intact Financial. ING sold its life insurance joint venture stake in Australia and New Zealand to partner ANZ and offloaded its noncore annuity and mortgage businesses in Chile to life insurer Corp Group Vida Chile in late 2009. The company also sold its Taiwanese life insurance business to Fubon Financial Holding in a deal worth Â447 million ($600 million) in mid-2009. ING gained a 5% stake in Fubon through the deal which it sold the following year for another Â395 million ($522 million).

In early 2010 ING completed sales of the company's Swiss Private Banking unit to Julius Baer for $506 million and its Asian Private Banking unit (operating in Hong Kong the Philippines and Singapore) to OCBC Bank for nearly $1.5 billion. In addition the company sold its North American reinsurance operations to RGA and most of its US insurance brokerage operations to Lightyear Capital in early 2010. ING has also agreed to sell its stake in one of its Chinese life insurance ventures (Pacific Antai with China Pacific Insurance) to China Construction Bank.

In 2011 ING sold its Asian and European real estate investment management (REIM) operations as well as select US REIM assets for about $940 million to broker CBRE Group (formerly CB Richard Ellis Group). The firm sold its remaining US REIM assets to Lightyear Capital for some $100 million. Also that year the firm agreed to sell its Australian investment management business to UBS for an undisclosed sum.

Farther south in 2011 the company sold its Latin American insurance operations to Columbian insurer GrupoSura for $3.7 billion. The sale included insurance savings and investment management operations in Chile Colombia Mexico Uruguay and Peru. It also sold ING Car Least to BMW.

EXECUTIVES

Chairman Executive Board, Jan H. M. Hommen, age 72

Vice Chairman Supervisory Board, Peter A. F. W. Elverding, age 67

CEO ING Investment Management, Gilbert Van Hassel

COO Insurance; Management Board Insurance, Thomas J. (Tom) McInerney, age 58, $579,013 total compensation

CEO Retail Banking Direct and International, Eli P. Leenaars, age 53, $396,996 total compensation

CEO Commercial Banking; Vice Chairman Management Board Banking, Eric Boyer de la Giroday, age 62, $1,278,414 total compensation

Head of Operations and Information Technology Banking, Steve Van Wyk

CEO Retail Banking Benelux, Hans van der Noordaa, age 53, $396,996 total compensation

CEO ING Insurance U.S., Robert G. (Rob) Leary

Vice Chairman Management Board Banking, J. V. (Koos) Timmermans, age 55, $978,813 total compensation

Head Media Relations, Peter Jong

Head Group Investor Relations, Dorothy Hillenius, age 45

CEO Nationale-Nederlanden, Lard Friese, age 51

Member Executive Board and CFO, Patrick G. Flynn, age 53, $650,673 total compensation

Chief Administrative Officer, Matthew J. Rider

CEO ING Bank Slaski, Malgorzata Kolakowska

Chief Risk Officer, Wilfred F. Nagel, age 59

Head of Media Relations, Raymond Vermeulen

Chairman of the Supervisory Board, Jeroen Veer

Member Supervisory Board, Aman Mehta, age 69

Vice Chairman Supervisory Board, Peter A. F. W. Elverding, age 67

Member Supervisory Board, Piet C. Klaver, age 70

Member Supervisory Board, Henk W. Breukink, age 65

Member Supervisory Board, Lodewijk J. de Waal, age 65

Member Supervisory Board, Tineke J.P. Bahlmann, age 65

Member of the Supervisory Board, Jan Holsboer

Member of the Supervisory Board, Joost Kuiper

Member of the Supervisory Board, Lodewijk Waal

Member of the Supervisory Board, Robert Reibestein

Member of the Supervisory Board, Sjoerd Keulen

Member of the Supervisory Board, Yvonne Rooy

Auditors: Ernst&YoungAccountants

LOCATIONS

HQ: ING Groep N.V.
Bijlmerplein 888, Amsterdam 1102 MG
Phone: (31) 20 563 6710
Web: www.ing.com

Sales

	% of total
Europe	
The	33
Belgium	10
Other	16
North	38
Asia	2
Australia	1
Total	**100**

PRODUCTS/OPERATIONS

Sales

	% of total
Banking	
Commercial	22
Retail	20
Retail	11
Retail other & corporate line	17
Insurance	30
Total	**100**

COMPETITORS

ABN AMRO Group	KBC
AEGON	Legal & General
AIG	Group
AXA	Lincoln Financial
Achmea	Group
Ageas Insurance	MetLife
International	Nationwide
Allianz	Principal Financial
Aviva	Prudential
Barclays	Prudential plc
CNP Assurances	RSA Insurance
Citigroup	Rabobank
Credit Suisse	Swiss Life
Delta Lloyd	The Hartford
Deutsche Bank	UBS
Deutsche Bundesbank	Zurich Financial
Generali	Services
HSBC	

HISTORICAL FINANCIALS

Company Type: Public

Income Statement

FYE: December 31

	ASSETS ($ mil.)	NET INCOME ($ mil.)	INCOME AS % OF ASSETS	EMPLOYEES
12/13	1,482,196	6,301	0.4%	83,690
12/12	1,531,742	4,295	0.3%	92,572
12/11	1,647,314	6,130	0.4%	104,419
12/10	1,663,388	3,716	0.2%	106,139
12/09	1,671,020	(2,049)	—	110,325
Annual Growth	(3.0%)	—	—	(6.7%)

2013 Year-End Financials

Return on assets: 0.4%
Return on equity: 9.5%
Long-term debt ($ mil.): —
No. of shares (mil.): —
Sales ($ mil): 95,252

Dividends
Yield: 0.0%
Payout: —
Market value ($ mil.): —

	STOCK PRICE ($) FY Close	P/E High/Low	PER SHARE ($) Earnings	Dividends	Book Value
12/13	14.01	25 12	1.46	0.00	15.77
12/12	9.49	25 13	0.91	0.00	17.95
12/11	7.17	30 12	1.10	0.00	15.18
12/10	9.79	35 19	0.83	0.00	15.35
12/09	9.81	— —	(1.08)	0.00	13.58
Annual Growth	9.3%	— —	—	—	3.8%

Intesa Sanpaolo S.P.A.

Ciao money! Intesa Sanpaolo provides retail and commercial banking services in Italy through its Banca dei Territori division. The company serves 11.1 million customers from 4500 branches throughout Italy and an additional 1400 locations in Central and Eastern Europe as well as the Mediterranean basin. Intesa Sanpaolo also performs investment banking public and infrastructure finance factoring and trade financing services. The company offers life property and casualty insurance through EurizonVita and other insurance subsidiaries. Asset management is handled by Eurizon Capital and its Banca Fideuram arm provides financial planning services.

Strategy

Intesa Sanpaolo is working to strengthen its retail banking operations and maintain a diversified presence in international markets. For now its focus is on the Banca dei Territori division which handles domestic commercial banking and is responsible for retail customers individual customers and small businesses.

Company Background

Intesa Sanpaolo is the result of the 2007 megamerger between Banca Intesa and Sanpaolo IMI. After the merger the company reshuffled its assets and sold off some branches in order to comply with antitrust orders and raise capital.

HISTORY

In Italy charity begins at home and often heads to the financial institutions. In 1563 Turin citizens founded Compagnia di San Paolo a foundation that provided education and dowries to orphaned girls and aid to impoverished nobility. In 1579 the organization began a pawn shop the Monte di Pieta or Mountain of Mercy (founded in 1519 and reopened by the Compagnia). The foundation grew over the next 200 years fattened by bequests and inheritances from wealthy Piedmontese families.

The French Republican government in Piedmonte gradually took control of the foundation's operations and closed it in 1802. The Monte di Pieta was reopened in 1804 and under the French influence became more bank-like. In 1848 the charitable and financial operations were formally divided.

Industrialization came slowly to Italy after its unification in the 1860s (the country remained largely agricultural until after WWII) and the organization survived a banking crisis from 1887 to 1894 by operating conservatively. It contributed to the WWI effort by purchasing government bonds. In 1928 the foundation separated Monte di Pieta's credit and pawn operations and adopted the name Istituto di San Paolo di Torino - Beneficenza e Credito (San Paolo).

Specialized institutions were founded in the 1920s to finance utilities and transportation; one of them La Centrale Societa per il Finanziamento di Imprese Elettriche e Telefoniche was formed in 1925 to help finance Italy's energy and telecommunications industries. In 1965 this entity enlarged its focus and changed its name to La Centrale Finanziaria Generale a forerunner of Banca Intesa.

La Centrale's interests in energy were transferred to ENEL the state holding company in 1985 leaving it with banking finance and insurance holdings. That year the bank merged with Nuovo Banco Ambrosiano formerly Banco Ambrosiano.

Banco Ambrosiano was founded in 1896 by Guiseppi Tovino whose good works and sturdy faith made him a saint (he was beatified in 1998). Betraying his legacy in 1981 chairman Roberto Calvi was found hanging under the Blackfriars Bridge in London. Calvi called "God's Banker" for his connections to the Vatican left behind a tangle of debt phony holding companies and fraud that implicated the Catholic Church brought down an archbishop and involved a secretive Masonic lodge. Banco Ambrosiano was taken over by a group of creditor banks and its name was changed to Nuovo Banco Ambrosiano.

In 1989 Nuovo Banco Ambrosiano merged with its subsidiary Banco Cattolica del Veneto and became known as Banco Ambroveneto. It bought La Cassa di Risparmio delle Provincie Lombarde (Cariplo) Italy's biggest savings bank in 1997; they merged to form Banca Intesa the following year. Cariplo was founded by the Austro-Hungarian government in 1823 when the region was still recovering from Napoleon's depredations. Count Giovanni Pietro Porro wanted to allow artisans and day laborers to set aside money and the company remained true to that mission throughout Italy's unification and two world wars.

Italy began its race toward privatization in 1990 to counter the growing interest of foreign banks in the Italian market and help the nation meet the criteria for joining the European Union. In 1992 San Paolo was one of the first banks to sell a 20% stake in itself (it sold another 20% in 1997). The bank bought several regional and national banks over the next few years and in 1998 merged with investment bank Istituto Mobiliare Italiano or IMI (founded 1931) to form Sanpaolo IMI.

Banca Intesa was the product of a combination of the staid Cassa di Risparmio delle Provincie Lombarde (Cariplo) and the somewhat more colorful Banco Ambroveneto whose history helped inspire the plot of "The Godfather Part III". It took over Banca Commerciale Italiana (BCI or Comit) in 2000 creating one of Italy's largest banks. Banca Intesa integrated BCI to form IntesaBci the following year and then in late 2002 rebranded as Banca Intesa.

Banca Intesa and Sanpaolo IMI merged in 2007. After the deal antitrust authorities ordred the company to sell some 200 branches to France-based Credit Agricole. In late 2008 the Italian banking group sold 36 branches to Veneto Banca for Â274 million ($401 million).

A good portion of its branches were acquired in 2007 when Intesa Sanpaolo increased its stake in Banca CR Firenze to some 60% in preparation for taking over the bank outright. Banca CR Firenze added about 550 locations in Tuscany and surrounding regions to Intesa Sanpaolo's network.

The next year the bank upped its stake in Cassa dei Risparmi di Forli e della Romagna to about 70% increasing its influence in northern Italy. During more reshuffling of assets Intesa Sanpaolo sold a 30% stake in Cassa di Risparmio di Fano to Credito Valtellinese in 2009.

EXECUTIVES

Chairman, Giovanni Bazoli, age 82
Chief Risk Officer, Bruno Picca, age 65
Deputy Chairman Management Board, Orazio Rossi, age 82
Chairman Management Board, Enrico Salza, age 77
CEO, Enrico T. Cucchiani, age 64
Head Corporate Affairs, Piero Luongo, age 59
Head Retail Marketing Banca dei Territori Division, Marina Tabacco, age 59
Head of Administration and Tax, Ernesto Riva
CFO, Carlo Messina, age 53
Managing Director and General Manager Finance Banca Infrastrutture Innovazione e Sviluppo, Mario Ciaccia, age 68
Head of Internal Auditing, Renato Dalla Riva
Head Legal Affairs, Elisabetta Lunati
Head International Subsidiary Banks Divisions, Giovanni Boccolini, age 61
Head of Research, Gregorio de Felice
Head Operations Intesa Sanpaolo Group Services, Maurizio Manzotti
Manager Banca dei Territori Division Milano and Province, Franco Ceruti
Manager Banca dei Territori Division Lazio Sardegna and Sicilia, Franco Gallia
Head of Corporate Relationship Management and International Network, Giuseppe Castagna
Head of Merchant Banking Corporate Division, Marco Cerrina Feroni
Deputy CEO and General Manager; Head of the Banca dei Territori Division, Marco Morelli
Manager Banca dei Territori Division Toscana and Umbria, Luciano Nebbia
Managing Director and General Manager Banca Fideuram, Matteo Colafrancesco, age 64
COO, Pier Luigi Curcuruto, age 64
Chief Lending Officer, Eugenio Rossetti, age 59
Head ICT Systems Intesa Sanpaolo Group Services, Silvio Fraternali
Head Real Estate and Procurement Intesa Sanpaolo Group Services, Luca Tedesi
Head Media Relations, Matteo Fabiani
Corporate and Investment Banking Media Relations, Simone Blasi
Head Human Resources, Marco Vernieri
Head External Relations, Vittorio Meloni
Treasurer, Stefano Del Punta
Head Planning and Control, Lucia Ariano
Head Compliance, Piero Boccassino
Head Risk Management, Davide Alfonsi
Head Organization and Security Intesa Sanpaolo Group Services, Marco Cesareo
Head Loan Recovery, Stefano Marchetti
Head Investor Relations, Andrea Tamagnini
Head Rating Agencies, Marco Delfrate
Head SME Marketing Banca dei Territori Division, Carlo Berselli
Manager Banca dei Territori Division Piemont Valle d'Aosta and Liguria, Adriano Maestri

Manager Banca dei Territori Division Lombardia,
Bruno Bossina
Manager Banca dei Territori Division Veneto
Friuli-Venezia Giulia and Trentino-Alto Adige,
Fabio Innocenzi
Manager Banca dei Territori Division Emilia-
Romagna Marche Abruzzo and Molise, Giuseppe
Feliziani
Manager Banca dei Territori Division Campania
Basilicata Calabria and Puglia, Antonio Nucci
Deputy Chairman, Mario Bertolissi, age 66
Deputy Chairwoman, Elsa Fornero, age 66
Chief Risk Officer of Intesa Sanpaolo, Bruno
Paesana
Chief Operating Officer of Intesa Sanpaolo,
Francesco Roma
Chief Executive Officer of Intesa Sanpaolo, Enrico
Milano
Chief Lending Officer of Intesa Sanpaolo, Eugenio
Roma
Board Member, Marco Mangiagalli, age 65
Board Member, Jean-Paul Fitoussi, age 72
Board Member, Rosalba Casiraghi
Board Member, Franco Dalla Sega, age 55
Board Member, Gianluca Ferrero, age 52
Board Member, Pietro Garibaldi, age 46
Board Member, Giulio Lubatti, age 67
Board Member, Gianluca Ponzellini, age 68
Board Member, Gian Guido Sacchi Morsiani, age 79
Board Member, Ferdinando Targetti, age 69
Board Member, Livio Torio, age 71
Board Member, Riccardo Varaldo, age 79
Deputy Chairman, Mario Bertolissi, age 66
Deputy Chairwoman, Elsa Fornero, age 66
Board Member, Gianni Marchesini, age 55
Board Member, Fabio Pasquini, age 61
Board Member, Marco Spadacini, age 76
Board Member, Luigi A. Bianchi, age 56
Auditors: RecontaErnst&YoungS.p.A.

LOCATIONS

HQ: Intesa Sanpaolo S.P.A.
Piazza San Carlo, 156, Torino 10121
Phone: (39) 11 5551
Web: www.intesasanpaolo.com

Sales

	% of total
Italy	77
Other	22
Total	**100**

PRODUCTS/OPERATIONS

Sales

	% of total
Banca dei	58
Corporate & Investment	20
International Subsidiary	13
Banca	4
Public	2
Eurizon	1
Total	**100**

COMPETITORS

BBVA	Dexia
BNL bc	Mediobanca
Banca Popolare di Milano	Monte dei Paschi di Siena
Banco Popolare	UniCredit

HISTORICAL FINANCIALS
Company Type: Public

Income Statement
FYE: December 31

	ASSETS ($ mil.)	NET INCOME ($ mil.)	INCOME AS % OF ASSETS	EMPLOYEES
12/13	862,226	(6,264)	—	93,845
12/12	887,669	2,115	0.2%	96,170
12/11	826,801	(10,593)	—	100,118
12/10	881,662	3,620	0.4%	102,501
12/09	900,131	4,040	0.4%	103,718
Annual Growth	(1.1%)	—	—	(2.5%)

2013 Year-End Financials
Return on assets: (-0.7%)
Return on equity: (-9.6%)
Long-term debt ($ mil.): —
No. of shares (mil.): —
Sales ($ mil): 56,637
Dividends
Yield: 3.8%
Payout: —
Market value ($ mil.): —

	STOCK PRICE ($) FY Close	P/E High/Low	PER SHARE ($) Earnings	Dividends	Book Value
12/13	14.95	— —	(0.39)	0.57	3.96
12/12	10.64	223 99	0.13	0.28	4.22
12/11	9.94	— —	(0.72)	2.19	3.93
12/10	16.22	258 106	0.28	0.41	6.05
12/09	27.10	279 85	0.32	0.00	6.40
Annual Growth	(13.8%)	— —	—	—	(11.3%)

Israel Discount Bank Ltd.

Who doesn't love a discount? Israel Discount Bank the third-largest bank in Israel has about 150 locations across the country. The bank offers standard consumer services like deposits loans and credit cards in addition to private banking international trade and commercial banking activities. Israel Discount Bank oversees five subsidiaries –Discount Mortgage Bank Mercantile Discount Bank (which has about 75 branches) Israel Discount Bank of New York Discount Bank Latin America (headquartered in Uruguay) and IDB (Swiss) Bank Ltd. It also owns a 26% stake in First International Bank of Israel the country's fifth-largest bank.

In 2010 Israel Discount Bank announced it was selling off Tachlit Investment House its portfolio management subsidiary that has about $3 billion in assets under management.

The bank's largest shareholders are US-Canadian businessman Matthew Bronfman and New York real estate investor Rubin Schron who control 26%. The government of Israel owns 20% of the bank.

LOCATIONS

HQ: Israel Discount Bank Ltd.
23 Yehuda Halevi Street, Tel-Aviv 65136
Phone: (972) 3 514 5555   **Fax:** (972) 3 514 5346
Web: www.discountbank.net

PRODUCTS/OPERATIONS

Sales

	% of total
Retail - household	25
Corporate - corporate	23
Retail - small business	17
Corporate - middle	14
Financial	14
Private	7
Total	**100**

HISTORICAL FINANCIALS
Company Type: Public

Income Statement
FYE: December 31

	ASSETS ($ mil.)	NET INCOME ($ mil.)	INCOME AS % OF ASSETS	EMPLOYEES
12/13	57,783	251	0.4%	9,877
12/12	53,893	215	0.4%	9,942
12/11	52,966	244	0.5%	10,211
12/10	52,437	204	0.4%	10,221
12/09	49,712	244	0.5%	10,290
Annual Growth	3.8%	0.8%	—	(1.0%)

2013 Year-End Financials
Return on assets: 0.4%
Return on equity: 7.2%
Long-term debt ($ mil.): —
No. of shares (mil.): 105
Sales ($ mil): 2,980
Dividends
Yield: —
Payout: —
Market value ($ mil.): 158

	STOCK PRICE ($) FY Close	P/E High/Low	PER SHARE ($) Earnings	Dividends	Book Value
12/13	1.50	0 0	0.24	0.00	33.45
12/12	0.96	0 0	0.20	0.00	30.14
12/11	1.42	0 0	0.21	0.00	26.67
12/10	2.02	0 0	0.21	0.00	30.10
12/09	0.74	0 0	0.25	0.00	26.97
Annual Growth	19.5%	— —	(1.0%)	—	5.5%

Itau Unibanco Holding S.A.

Itau Unibanco is one way of saying "really big bank." The Brazilian bank offers a variety of standard retail and commercial banking services as well as consumer credit financial management leasing foreign exchange and trade financing. It is one of Brazil's largest credit card issuers. It also provides investment banking securities brokerage and insurance services. Besides its network of more than 3900 Brazilian branches the firm boasts operations in other South America countries and in North America the Caribbean Asia and Europe. It leverages acquisitions such as its 2013 Credicard purchase to boost its presence. Banco Itau merged with Unibanco in 2009 to become Itau Unibanco.

The deal to combine the two Brazilian megabanks established the largest private financial conglomerate in South America. Itau Unibanco is now better equipped to compete on an international level as it expands its global presence. The merger also allowed the bank to expand credit and increase its range of products and services. Since joining forces the group has more than doubled its earnings.

In 2012 the bank agreed to buy the 49.99% it doesn't already own in card payment processing firm Redecard for some R11.8 billion (approximately $6.8 billion). The deal will help boost earnings from credit and debit card usage; it should also help Redecard compete in the growing payment-processing sector.

Itau Unibanco is controlled by holding company IUPAR itself controlled by the Egydio de Souza Aranha family. The Moreira Salles family which previously controlled Unibanco holds a stake of about 25% of the bank. Together the families have board representation with five company directors (including president and CEO Egydio Setubal).

EXECUTIVES

Vice Chairman President and CEO, Roberto Egydio Setubal, age 59
Investor Relations Officer and Director, Alfredo Egydio Setubal, age 55
Director, Henri Penchas, age 67
EVP and Director, Candido Botelho Bracher, age 54
Director, Alcides Lopes Tapias, age 71
Director, Ricardo Villela Marino, age 37
Director, Gustavo Jorge Laboissiere Loyola, age 60
Vice Chairman and EVP, Alfredo Egydio Arruda Villela Jr.
Director, Fernando Roberto Moreira Salles, age 67
Director, Francisco Eduardo de Almeida Pinto
Director, Israel Vainboim, age 69
Director, Pedro Luiz Bodin de Moraes, age 57
Auditors:
PricewaterhouseCoopersAuditoresIndependentes

LOCATIONS

HQ: Itau Unibanco Holding S.A.
Praca Alfredo Egydio de Souza Aranha, 100, Sao Paulo 04344-902
Phone: (55) 11 5019 1267
Web: www.itau-unibanco.com

PRODUCTS/OPERATIONS

Sales

	% of total
Interest	
Loans &	47
Trading	7
Other	17
Noninterest	
Fees &	15
Insurance premiums &	6
Other	8
Total	**100**

COMPETITORS

Banco Bradesco	Banco do Brasil
Banco Frances	Caixa Economica
Banco Santander	Federal

HISTORICAL FINANCIALS

Company Type: Public

Income Statement

FYE: December 31

	ASSETS ($ mil.)	NET INCOME ($ mil.)	INCOME AS % OF ASSETS	EMPLOYEES
12/13	434,889	6,952	1.6%	95,696
12/12	468,153	6,179	1.3%	96,977
12/11	438,678	7,419	1.7%	104,542
12/10	438,241	7,053	1.6%	0
12/09	343,415	8,073	2.4%	101,640
Annual Growth	**6.1%**	**(3.7%)**	**—**	**(1.5%)**

2013 Year-End Financials

Return on assets: 1.6%	Dividends
Return on equity: 20.6%	Yield: 3.0%
Long-term debt ($ mil.): —	Payout: 29.3%
No. of shares (mil.): —	Market value ($ mil.): —
Sales ($ mil): 62,247	

	STOCK PRICE ($) FY Close	P/E High/Low		PER SHARE ($) Earnings	Dividends	Book Value
12/13	13.57	1	1	1.40	0.37	13.99
12/12	16.46	2	1	1.36	0.46	16.22
12/11	18.56	3	1	1.64	0.17	17.32
12/10	24.01	4	2	1.55	0.41	17.44
12/09	22.84	2	1	1.86	0.22	8.77
Annual Growth	**(12.2%)**	**—**	**—**	**(6.9%)**	**14.4%**	**12.4%**

ITOCHU Corp. (Japan)

If you drive it eat it fly it or wear it there's a good chance this company is involved with it. ITOCHU Corporation is a leading Japanese "sogo shosha" (general trading company) along with Mitsui & Co. and Mitsubishi and has business interests in such diverse areas as aerospace equipment manufacturing food distribution and clothing production. It also has interests and operations in chemicals energy and mining financial services and retailing. The conglomerate has approximately 130 offices in 67 countries and operates through some 500 subsidiaries and affiliated companies around the world.

In 2011 ITOCHU began rebounding from a flat fiscal 2010 caused by sagging prices for raw materials and energy and a downturn in the economy. It saw its revenues jump to $43.9 billion in 2011 nearly 7% over the previous year despite the effects of the earthquake that hit Japan in 2011. Driving the hike was higher sales in several divisions higher prices for mineral resources and oil and gas operations returns from its strategic investments and higher volumes of transactions in its chemicals businesses. It also saw net income increase nearly 26% to about $2 billion following ITOCHU's jettisoning of inefficient assets and the tidying up of pending problems on its balance sheet by March 2011.

In what it calls its "Brand-new Deal 2012" ITOCHU believes it is financially ready to seek new opportunities and expand the scale of its operations. Among targets it has set for 2012 are to increase its net income by 49% over 2011 expand operations in China increase assets in the machinery-related sector and expand its natural resources operations. It also will seek acquisitions in regions besides China based on the strategies of its individual divisions.

ITOCHU has invested the past few years in streamlining its business divisions and focusing on growth industries. It is looking to expand its involvement in new energy resources pharmaceutical marketing and environmental services as well as communications logistics and technology services. Geographically the company continues to increase its presence in China and North America; however its domestic operations still account for some three-quarters of its revenue.

Following its strategy ITOCHU formed a joint venture in 2011 in China with Toho Holdings and Jointown Pharmaceutical Group to distribute Japanese-made wholesale drugs and medical equipment in China. Based in Wuhan in Hubei province the venture will sell over-the-counter medicines and daily goods —such as disposable pocket warmers —to local drugstores. It will also market prescription drugs and medical equipment such as X-ray machines to hospitals. Toho holds 41% of the venture with ITOCHU holding 10% and Jointown the balance.

In another move to expand its overseas operations in 2011 ITOCHU acquired UK auto repair business Kwik-Fit (GB) Ltd. from European private equity firm PAI Partners for about $1 billion. The purchase which boosts ITOCHU's presence in Europe's auto services market was something of a bargain —PAI Partners paid about $1.5 billion in 2005 after a bidding war for the company.

ITOCHU also agreed to acquire a 20% stake in a Colombian coal mine in a joint venture with US miner Drummond Co. The $1.5 billion deal will tie up the two companies in a mine with about 2 billion tons of provable and probable coal reserves. The deal fits ITOCHU's strategy of raising its equity share in coal mining operations to about 20 million tons per year by 2015.

To raise cash in 2011 the company sold US-based diesel engine marketer and distributor EMDSI - Hunt Power to Stewart & Stevenson for an undisclosed price. That year it also unloaded subsidiary Cieco Energy Ventures which held oil and gas properties in the Gulf of Mexico to Houston-based Tammany Oil & Gas for an undisclosed price.

HISTORY

Chubei Itoh was only 18 when he organized his own wholesale linen business C. Itoh & Co. in 1858. As Japan opened to foreign trade in the 1860s the company prospered and was one of Osaka's largest textile wholesalers by the 1870s. C. Itoh established a trade office in San Francisco in 1889.

By 1919 C. Itoh had trading offices in New York Calcutta Manila and four cities in China. Although it was not one of the "zaibatsu" (industrial groups) that flourished in Japan during the period between the world wars C. Itoh benefited from the general increase in trade.

C. Itoh merged in 1941 with two other trading operations Marubeni and Kishimoto into a new company Sanko Kabushiki Kaisha. C. Itoh and Marubeni were separated in 1949. C. Itoh supplied UN troops with provisions during the Korean War; profits were used to diversify into petroleum machinery aircraft and automobiles.

After the oil crisis of 1973 demonstrated Japan's vulnerability to oil import disruptions C. Itoh actively participated in the development of petroleum production technology. To prevent the failure of Japan's 10th-largest trading company Ataka the Japanese government arranged a merger in 1977 making C. Itoh the third-largest "sogo shosha."

The company established Japan Communications Satellite (JCSAT) with Mitsui and Hughes Communications in 1985. JCSAT launched its first two satellites in 1989 and 1990. The following year C. Itoh and Toshiba joined Time Warner in a limited partnership Time Warner Entertainment Company to produce and distribute movies and television programs and to operate cable TV systems in the US. C. Itoh Time Warner and Toshiba formed another joint venture to distribute Warner Bros. films and develop amusements parks in Japan.

C. Itoh changed its name to ITOCHU a transliteration of its Japanese name in 1992. After sales dropped the next year ITOCHU began selling poorly performing subsidiaries reducing its investment portfolio by more than one-third.

In 1996 the company formed an alliance with US oil company Atlantic Richfield to buy Coastal Corp.'s western US coal operations and it took a stake in a massive project led by Amoco and British Petroleum to develop oil and gas deposits in the Caspian Sea. That year PerfecTV! (a joint venture with Sumitomo and other Japanese companies) began satellite broadcasting. Also in 1996 ITOCHU bought stakes in the Asia Broadcasting and Communications Network a satellite communications company.

To help cover its losses from the Asian currency crisis the company sold 40% of its stake in Time Warner in 1998; in 1999 ITOCHU sold its remaining stake. ITOCHU also sold low-performing real estate investments and laid plans to divest about one-third of its subsidiaries.

Two of ITOCHU's agricultural subsidiaries were liquidated in 2000. The company also sought out partnerships in order to offset costs incurred in new ventures: it joined with Japan's other top trading companies and Brazil's Petrobras to develop oil fields in South America. And in response to the rapid consolidation of Japan's steel industry ITOCHU and Marubeni agreed to integrate their steel operations in 2001 to better compete.

In 2002 ITOCHU formed a partnership with Bally International to expand the European fashion brand's presence in Japan. In 2004 the company sold its interest in Utah-based Canyon Fuel Co. to Arch Coal Inc. for $112 million and dissolved its subsidiary ITOCHU Coal International Inc. Also that year the company formed a joint venture with Ishimori Shotaro Pro Inc. to establish Ishimori Entertainment which produces movies television programs and publications based on Shotaro Ishimori titles including the popular MASKED RIDER.

ITOCHU established a fund with Turner Broadcasting to finance Japanese animation in 2005. It also acquired two US medical-device-distribution companies Products for Surgery and Flanagan Instruments marking ITOCHU's first step into that market.

In 2008 the company partnered with BayCorp Holdings and Energy Management to form American Renewables to develop build and operate biomass-fueled power-generation facilities in the US. Also that year it acquired 41% of Medical Collective a Japanese company that provides marketing assistance to pharmaceutical companies.

In 2010 ITOCHU bought China-based daily goods wholesaler Hangzhou New Huahai Business & Trading boosting its presence in that market. That same year ITOCHU agreed to acquire a 15% stake in Kalahari Minerals PLC which holds uranium gold copper and other base metal interests in Namibia.

Also that year ITOCHU made deals to move into the US energy market joining Chubu Electric Power in a joint venture to buy five natural-gas fired power plants from Tenaska and acquire a 25% interest in the Niobrara shale oil mining project in southeastern Wyoming. With the latter transaction ITOCHU became the first Japanese company to participate in a US shale oil project. The company had acquired 85% of US-based solar power systems maker Solar Net LLC in 2009.

Masahiro Okafuji was named president of ITOCHU in 2010. He replaced Eizo Kobayashi who was named the company's chairman. Okafuji was previously ITOCHU's EVP.

EXECUTIVES

EVP, Yoichi Kobayashi
Chairman, Eizo Kobayashi, age 65
President and CEO, Masahiro Okafuji, age 64
President and CEO ITOCHU International, Eiichi Yonekura
President Machinery, Takao Shiomi
Senior Managing Executive Officer; President Food, Yoshihisa Aoki
CEO ITOCHU East Asia Bloc, Shuichi Koseki
President Metals and Minerals, Ichiro Nakamura
President General Products and Realty, Tomofumi Yoshida
Senior Managing Executive Officer, Koji Takayanagi

EVP and CFO, Tadayuki Seki
President Textile, Hitoshi Okamoto
President Energy and Chemicals, Yuji Fukuda
CEO Oceania ASEAN and South West Asia Bloc, Junichi Sasaki
CEO ITOCHU Europe, Masahiro Imai
Director, Uichiro Niwa, age 74
Senior Managing Director; President Energy Metals and Minerals Company and Director, Yoichi Kobayashi
EVP and Director, Toshihito Tamba
Chief Officer Human Resources General Affairs Legal and Chief Compliance Officer and Director, Yoshio Akamatsu
Director, Tohru Matsushima
Director, Takanobu Furuta
President Food Company and Director, Yoshihisa Aoki
President ICT Aerospace and Electronics Company and Director, Hiroo Inoue
Managing Executive Officer and Director, Kenji Okada
Chief Corporate Planning Officer CIO and Director, Koji Takayanagi
President Chemicals Forest Products and General Merchandise Company and Director, Satoshi Kikuchi
CFO and Director, Tadayuki Seki
Director, Hitoshi Okamoto
Auditors: DeloitteToucheTohmatsu

LOCATIONS

HQ: ITOCHU Corp. (Japan)
3-1-3 Umeda, Kita-ku, Osaka 530-8448
Phone: (81) 6 7638 2121
Web: www.itochu.co.jp

Sales

	% of total
Japan	74
Australia	6
Total	**100**

COMPETITORS

Altria
Balli
Dow Chemical
Exxon Mobil
Fluor
Ito-Yokado
JX Nippon Mining & Metals
Kanematsu
LG Group
Marubeni
Marui Group
Mitsubishi Corp.
Mitsui
NTT
Nippon Steel & Sumitomo Metal Corporation
Nippon Television
Panasonic Corp
Rio Tinto plc
Samsung Group
Sharp Corp.
Sojitz
Sumitomo
Sumitomo Metal Mining
Tokyo Broadcasting System
Yahoo Japan

HISTORICAL FINANCIALS

Company Type: Public

Income Statement

FYE: March 31

	REVENUE ($ mil.)	NET INCOME ($ mil.)	NET PROFIT MARGIN	EMPLOYEES
03/14	54,132	2,376	4.4%	104,310
03/13	48,673	2,978	6.1%	98,272
03/12	52,066	3,663	7.0%	94,366
03/11	44,074	1,943	4.4%	84,589
03/10	36,577	1,371	3.8%	84,695
Annual Growth	10.3%	14.7%	—	5.3%

2014 Year-End Financials

Debt ratio: 0.3%
Return on equity: 12.8%
Cash ($ mil.): 6,333
Current ratio: 1.47
Long-term debt ($ mil.): 23,452
No. of shares (mil.): 1,577
Dividends
Yield: 3.4%
Payout: 0.0%
Market value ($ mil.): 36,884

	STOCK PRICE ($) FY Close	P/E High/Low		PER SHARE ($) Earnings	Dividends	Book Value
03/14	23.38	0	0	1.50	0.81	12.56
03/13	24.49	0	0	1.88	0.00	11.89
03/12	21.85	0	0	2.32	0.00	10.54
03/11	20.90	0	0	1.23	1.24	8.84
03/10	87.15	0	0	0.87	0.34	7.45
Annual Growth	(28.0%)	—	—	14.7%	24.6%	13.9%

Iyo Bank, Ltd. (Japan)

With 15-plus branches and about a dozen subsidiaries The Iyo Bank targets customers across the four prefectures of Shikoku and the seven prefectures surrounding the Seto Inland Sea. The institution which has grown to become Japan's #1 regional bank offers retail products including deposits leasing services trusts and pension products and mergers and acquisitions support services. The Iyo Bank also operates a securities brokerage business arm. Its Corporate Consulting Division helps companies galvanize their operations and capital. Established in 1941 the bank owns and operates branch offices in Hong Kong Shanghai and New York. It boasts alliances with banks in China Thailand Indonesia and India.

Auditors: KPMGAZSA&Co.

LOCATIONS

HQ: Iyo Bank, Ltd. (Japan)
1 Minami-Horibata-cho, Matsuyama, Ehime 790-8514
Phone: (81) 89 941 1141   **Fax:** 212 688-6420
Web: www.iyobank.co.jp

COMPETITORS

Aozora Bank
Joyo Bank
Miyazaki Bank
Shizuoka Bank
Toho Bank

Income Statement

FYE: March 31

	ASSETS ($ mil.)	NET INCOME ($ mil.)	INCOME AS % OF ASSETS	EMPLOYEES
03/14	59,337	253	0.4%	2,937
03/13	63,817	195	0.3%	2,872
03/12	69,151	224	0.3%	2,857
03/11	64,794	182	0.3%	2,888
03/10	55,781	142	0.3%	2,897
Annual Growth	1.6%	15.5%	—	0.3%

2014 Year-End Financials

Return on assets: 0.4%
Return on equity: 5.5%
Long-term debt ($ mil.): —
No. of shares (mil.): 316
Sales ($ mil): 1,224

Dividends
Yield: —
Payout: —
Market value ($ mil.): 2,504

	STOCK PRICE ($) FY Close	P/E High/Low	PER SHARE ($) Earnings	Dividends	Book Value
03/14	7.92	— —	0.80	0.00	15.56
03/13	7.92	— —	0.61	0.00	16.02
03/12	11.57	— —	0.70	0.00	15.84
03/11	11.57	— —	0.57	0.00	14.31
03/10	11.57	— —	0.45	0.00	12.59
Annual Growth	(9.0%)	— —	15.8%	—	5.4%

J. Sainsbury PLC

J Sainsbury's trolley is filled with more than groceries. The UK's third-largest food retailer (after Tesco and ASDA) operates the Sainsbury's Supermarkets chain of some 570 stores throughout the UK. Its Sainsbury's online home delivery shopping service covers more than 90% of the UK population. In addition to supermarkets it operates a fast-growing convenience store business with 440 shops under the Sainsbury's Local banner. The firm also owns half of Sainsbury's Bank (in a 50-50 joint venture with Lloyds Banking Group) and a pair of property joint ventures. Sainsbury also sells apparel and home goods including cookware and bedding in its supermarkets and online. In 2011 it acquired Global Media Vault.

Sainsbury bought the online entertainment company from MBL Group plcfor Â1 billion ($1.57 billion) in October. The grocery chain which launched its own entertainment Web site in late 2010 said the acquisition will support its drive into the growing online and digital entertainment market. Global Media Vault's digital database includes more than three million music film and game assets for the UK market.

After losing the #2 slot in the UK grocery market years ago to Wal-Mart-owned ASDA Sainsbury has made a strong comeback battling back and forth with ASDA for second place. Currently with a market share of more than 16% Sainsbury trails ASDA by about a percentage point. The two rivals are enmeshed in an ongoing price war with market leader Tesco and other domestic and foreign food retailers including deep-discounters such as ALDI and Lidl. (Sainsbury enjoys an even stronger position in populous London with about 25% of the market.)

Despite pricing pressures Sainsbury has seen its total sales grow by about 40% over the past five years with nonfood sales growing three times as fast as food sales. In fiscal 2012 (ends March) Sainsbury's retails sales and profit both rose nearly 7% vs. the previous year. Sales got a boost from the addition of more than 75 new stores in fiscal 2012 most of which were convenience stores. The company expects to open one to two convenience stores per week throughout the coming year.

Sainsbury also attributes its recent strong performance to growing demand for fresh food and its own private-label brand products which now number more than 5000 items. The grocery chain has also cut prices and stepped up promotions in a bid to lure cash-strapped shoppers from more upscale rivals such as Marks & Spencer and Waitrose. The company's TU clothing brand for women and children has been a big success. Launched in 2004 TU has grown into the seventh-largest apparel retailer in the UK market by volume where it competes with ASDA's George line of apparel Marks & Spencer and others.

Qatar Holdings LLC controls about a 26% of Sainsbury's voting shares.

HISTORY

Newlyweds John James and Mary Ann Sainsbury established a small dairy shop in their London home in 1869. Customers flocked to the clean and efficient store a far cry from most cluttered and dirty London shops. They opened a second store in 1876. By 1914 115 stores had been opened and the couple's sons had entered the business.

During WWI the company's stores established grocery departments to meet demand for preserved products such as meat and jams which were sold under the Sainsbury's label.

Mary Ann died in 1927 and John James the next year. Son John Benjamin wholly devoted to the family business took charge. (He is reported to have said on his deathbed "Keep the stores well lit.") In the 1930s he engineered the company's first acquisition the Thoroughgood stores.

Sales dropped by 50% during WWII and some shops were destroyed by German bombing. Under third-generation leader Alan John Sainsbury the company opened its first self-service store in 1950 in Croydon. The 75000-sq.-ft. store opened in 1955 in Lewisham was considered to be the largest supermarket in Europe.

J Sainsbury went public in 1973. It established a joint venture with British Home Stores in 1975 forming the Savacentre hypermarkets (the company bought out its partner in 1989).

Sainsbury partnered with Grand Bazaar Innovation Bon Marche of Belgium in 1979 to establish Homebase a do-it-yourself chain. (It bought the remaining 25% in 1996 and then sold the company in 2001 retaining only 18%.)

By 1983 most of Sainsbury's 229 stores were clustered in the south of England. A mature market and stiff competition forced the company to look elsewhere —both overseas and close to home. It began buying out US-based Shaw's Supermarkets in New England and in 1984 opened its first Scottish hypermarket. By 1987 the grocer owned 100% of Shaw's which had 60 stores in Massachusetts Maine and New Hampshire.

In 1991 Sainsbury came under competitive pressure from Tesco and the Argyll Group (later renamed Safeway plc) which also began building superstores. It responded with an expansion drive of its own including opening its first Scottish supermarket (in Glasgow) the next year.

In 1994 the company purchased a $325 million stake in Maryland-based Giant Food. Sainsbury bought home improvement retailer Texas Homecare from UK leisure concern Ladbroke in 1995 and integrated it into its Homebase unit. The following year it bought 12 supermarkets in Connecticut from Dutch retailer Royal Ahold (the purchase lowered its profits for the year) and entered Northern Ireland.

A year later the company opened Sainsbury's Bank. Royal Ahold bought Giant Food including Sainsbury's 20% stake in 1998. David Sainsbury —a great-grandson of the founders —retired as chairman in 1998 to pursue politics marking the first time a Sainsbury had not headed up the company in its more-than-a-century history.

As a cost-cutting effort in 1999 Sainsbury cut 2200 jobs more than half in management. It also launched its convenience store concept called Sainsbury's Local. Also that year Sainsbury bought the 53-store Star Markets chain of Massachusetts merging it into its Shaw's operations. In March 2000 Sir Peter Davis took over as CEO of Sainsbury's Supermarkets replacing David Bremner.

In 2001 Sainsbury acquired 19 Grand Union stores in the US (17 of which were converted to the Shaw's banner) and opened 25 new stores in the UK. The company also exited the Egyptian market and sold its home-and-garden chain Homebase to private equity firm Permira.

In 2002 Shaw's Supermarkets bought control of 18 stores in New England from bankrupt discounter Ames.

In November 2003 Sainsbury reached a Â2 million out-of-court settlement with designer Jeff Banks over termination of his contract to revamp its clothing line in a bid to emulate rival ASDA's success with its George line of apparel.

In January 2004 the grocery chain acquired Swan Infrastructure (an Accenture affiliate) the company that ran its information technology systems for about $1 billion. The move brought the grocers information technology operations which were outsourced in 2000 back in-house.

In February 2004 Sainsbury acquired 54 Bells convenience stores. (Bells Stores was founded in 1968 by Les Bell and was owned by the Bell family until its acquisition.) Justin King (formerly of Marks & Spencer) joined Sainsbury as its CEO in March 2004 succeeding Sir Peter Davis who became chairman of the board. In April Sainsbury sold JS USA Holdings which operated 203 Shaw's and Star Markets stores in New England to US grocery chain Albertson's in a deal worth about $2.4 billion. The retailer also disposed of JS Developments its property development operation in fiscal 2004. Davis stepped down as chairman of Sainsbury on July 1 2004 one year ahead of schedule and following a prolonged dispute with investors that culminated in a fight over his compensation.

Philip Hampton (former finance director of Lloyds TSB (now Lloyds Banking Group) BT Group and BG Group) joined Sainsbury as its new chairman on July 19 2004. Hampton's appointment and experience with mergers and acquisitions fueled speculation that the struggling grocery chain may become a takeover target. In August Sainsbury acquired Jacksons Stores Ltd. and its wholly owned subsidiary Jacksons Stores 2002 Ltd. for about Â100 million. In September Sainsbury agreed to pay ex-chairman Davis Â2.6 million despite shareholder protests in July that forced the grocery retailer to withdraw a similar offer. At that time Lord Levene of Portsoken and Keith Butler-Wheelhouse both non-executive directors of the company and members of the remuneration committee resigned from the board.

In October 2004 Sainsbury said it was writing off Â140 million against information technology systems and an another Â120 million linked to ineffective supply chain equipment as a result of a huge infrastructure investment program instituted by ex-chairman Davis that failed. In November the company acquired JB Beaumont a convenience store chain with six stores in the East Midlands. In 2005 the grocery chain acquired the five-store SL

Shaw chain in southeastern England. Sainsbury renamed the shops Sainsbury's Local. The acquisitions pushed Sainsbury's convenience store count to nearly 300 outlets throughout the UK giving the company a 2% share of the convenience market.

The company sold 5% of its majority stake in Sainsbury's Bank in February 2007 to its joint venture partner HBOS for about Â21 million ($40 million). As a result the bank became a 50-50 joint venture between the two firms. Also in 2007 the company shutdown its online entertainment division Sainsbury's Entertain You which offered books CDs DVDs videos computer games and a DVD rental service citing stiff competition in the online arena. The company removed hydrogenated fats from its branded products in 2007.

In mid-2008 Qatar Holding-backed real estate investment group Delta Two increased its stake in Sainsbury to about 25% fueling speculation that it may attempt to take over the British grocer. (In 2007 Delta Two made a bid to buy the remainder of the company but withdrew the offering in November amid turmoil in the credit markets.) Delta Two was the second suitor to leave the grocery chain at the altar. The company and key shareholders from the founding Sainsbury family rebuffed a group of private equity investors led by CVC Capital earlier in the year.

In mid-2009 the grocery chain launched online sales of some 8000 non-food items such as kitchenware and furniture. It also extended its online home grocery delivery service to an additional 200 stores. The company welcomed David Tyler formerly chairman of Logica as its new chairman in November 2009. Tyler succeeded Sir Philip Hampton.

In November 2010 the company launched Sainsbury's Entertainment a digital download service that provides customers with access to more than 150000 books DVDs Blu-rays CDs and games to purchase online.

EXECUTIVES

Chairman, David A. Tyler, age 61
MD of General Merchandise Clothing & Logistics, Roger Burnley
Chief Executive Officer, Justin King, age 52, $700,000 total compensation
Human Resources Director, Imelda Walsh
Group Development Director, Darren Shapland, age 46, $261,000 total compensation
Executive Chef, John Wood
Company Secretary, Tim Fallowfield
Customer Director, Gwyn Burr
Retail Director, Helen Buck
Manager Agriculture, Annie Graham
Managing Director Non-Food, Luke Jensen
Director Commercial Services, Neil Sachdev
Chief Financial Officer, John Rogers
Head - Investor Relations, Adam Adam Katsibas Katsibas
IT Director, Rob Fraser
Marketing Director, Sarah Warby
Group Commercial Director, Mike Coupe
Director, Robert J. (Bob) Stack, age 62
Director, John D. G. McAdam, age 66
Director, Gary Hughes, age 52
Director, Valerie F. (Val) Gooding, age 62
Commercial Director, Michael (Mike) Coupe, age 52
CEO and Director, Justin King, age 51
Group Development Director, Darren Shapland, age 46
Director, Anna Ford, age 70
Director, Mary E. Harris, age 48
CFO and Director, John Rogers
Director, Matthew (Matt) Brittin
Auditors: PricewaterhouseCoopersLLP

LOCATIONS

HQ: J. Sainsbury PLC
33 Holborn, London EC1N 2HT
Phone: (44) 20 7921 6000
Web: www.j-sainsbury.co.uk

PRODUCTS/OPERATIONS

2012 Stores

	No.
Sainsbury's	572
Convenience	440
Total	**1,012**

COMPETITORS

ALDI	Musgrave Retail
ASDA	Partners
Alliance Boots	One Stop Stores
Co-operative Group	SNAX 24
Costcutter	SPAR (UK)
Supermarkets	Tesco
Iceland Foods	Waitrose
Lidl	Wm Morrison
METRO AG	Supermarkets
Marks & Spencer	

HISTORICAL FINANCIALS

Company Type: Public

Income Statement

FYE: March 15

	REVENUE ($ mil.)	NET INCOME ($ mil.)	NET PROFIT MARGIN	EMPLOYEES
03/14	39,747	1,188	3.0%	160,500
03/13	35,322	930	2.6%	105,000
03/12	35,079	940	2.7%	101,900
03/11	34,073	1,033	3.0%	99,300
03/10	30,247	886	2.9%	97,300
Annual Growth	**7.1%**	**7.6%**	**—**	**13.3%**

2014 Year-End Financials

Debt ratio: 27.9%
Return on equity: 12.2%
Cash ($ mil.): 2,642
Current ratio: 0.65
Long-term debt ($ mil.): 3,734

No. of shares (mil.): 1,907
Dividends
Yield: 0.0%
Payout: 440.3%
Market value ($ mil.): 40,318

	STOCK PRICE ($) FY Close	P/E High/Low		PER SHARE ($) Earnings	Dividends	Book Value
03/14	21.14	192	146	0.61	2.70	5.22
03/13	21.84	173	125	0.49	2.46	4.59
03/12	19.10	193	121	0.50	2.46	4.70
03/11	22.60	190	121	0.55	2.13	4.68
03/10	19.94	184	116	0.48	2.16	4.04
Annual Growth	**1.5%**	**—**	**—**	**6.3%**	**5.7%**	**6.6%**

Jardine Matheson Holdings Ltd.

LOCATIONS

HQ: Jardine Matheson Holdings Ltd.
4th Floor, Jardine House, 33-35 Reid Street, Hamilton HM 12
Phone: (441) 292 0515   **Fax:** (441) 292 4072
Web: www.jardines.com

HISTORICAL FINANCIALS

Company Type: Public

Income Statement

FYE: December 31

	REVENUE ($ mil.)	NET INCOME ($ mil.)	NET PROFIT MARGIN	EMPLOYEES
12/13	39,465	1,566	4.0%	390,000
12/12	39,593	1,688	4.3%	0
12/11	37,967	3,449	9.1%	0
12/10	30,053	3,084	10.3%	0
12/09	22,501	1,604	7.1%	0
Annual Growth	**15.1%**	**(0.6%)**	**—**	**—**

2013 Year-End Financials

Debt ratio: 17.6%
Return on equity: 8.6%
Cash ($ mil.): 5,214
Current ratio: 1.29
Long-term debt ($ mil.): 6,473

No. of shares (mil.): 303
Dividends
Yield: 2.4%
Payout: 30.2%
Market value ($ mil.): 16,001

	STOCK PRICE ($) FY Close	P/E High/Low		PER SHARE ($) Earnings	Dividends	Book Value
12/13	52.81	16	12	4.25	1.29	60.68
12/12	62.23	14	10	4.62	1.19	59.34
12/11	47.51	6	5	9.46	1.10	54.89
12/10	44.26	6	3	8.34	0.91	46.32
12/09	30.45	7	4	4.44	0.72	33.83
Annual Growth	**14.8%**	**—**	**—**	**(1.1%)**	**15.6%**	**15.7%**

Jardine Strategic Holdings Ltd (Bermuda)

Jardine Strategic Holdings (JSH) has a garden of multinationals. Primary interests include Dairy Farm International with 5800 locations hotel group Mandarin Oriental with 45 hotels holding company Jardine Cycle & Carriage (the largest engine manufacturer in Indonesia) financial services firm Rothchilds Continuation and real estate developer Hongkong Land. JSH and its Hong Kong-based affiliate Jardine Matheson Holdings share these interests and are operated together in a complex ownership structure. Jardine Matheson provides services to JSH owns about 80% of its stock. Formed after the breakup of the East India Company's tea monopoly in 1832 JSH was instrumental in the formation of Hong Kong.

The company was originally formed in the wake of the breakup of the East India Company's tea trade monopoly in 1832. Following Jardines' founding it was a key company that promoted the founding of Hong Kong.

EXECUTIVES

Managing Director and Director, Anthony J. L. Nightingale
Chairman, Henry Keswick
CFO, James Riley
Company Secretary, C. H. Wilken
Director, Simon L. Keswick, age 71
Managing Director and Director, Anthony J. L. Nightingale
Director, Percy Weatherall
Director, Lord C. G. Rodney Leach, age 79
Director, Jenkin Hui
Director, George C.G. Koo
Director, P.L.A. Jamieson
Auditors: PricewaterhouseCoopersLLP

LOCATIONS

HQ: Jardine Strategic Holdings Ltd (Bermuda)
Jardine House, 33-35 Reid Street, Hamilton
Phone:
Web: www.jardines.com

COMPETITORS

Accor	Hutchison Whampoa
China Resources	Hyatt
Enterprise	ITOCHU
Continental Automotive	Marriott
Group	Marubeni
Daiei	McDonald' s
HSBC	Royal Ahold
Hopewell Holdings	Swire Pacific

HISTORICAL FINANCIALS

Company Type: Public

Income Statement
FYE: December 31

	REVENUE ($ mil.)	NET INCOME ($ mil.)	NET PROFIT MARGIN	EMPLOYEES
12/13	32,666	1,700	5.2%	0
12/12	33,098	1,839	5.6%	0
12/11	31,049	3,943	12.7%	0
12/10	25,498	3,535	13.9%	0
12/09	18,905	1,844	9.8%	0
Annual Growth	14.7%	(2.0%)	—	—

2013 Year-End Financials

Debt ratio: 17.2%	No. of shares (mil.): 196
Return on equity: 7.8%	Dividends
Cash ($ mil.): 4,901	Yield: 0.6%
Current ratio: 1.34	Payout: 3.8%
Long-term debt ($ mil.): 6,226	Market value ($ mil.): 3,138

	STOCK PRICE ($) FY Close	P/E High/Low		PER SHARE ($) Earnings	Dividends	Book Value
12/13	16.01	7	5	2.79	0.11	112.39
12/12	17.76	23	5	2.99	0.42	106.72
12/11	54.92	11	8	6.34	0.10	98.26
12/10	55.20	10	6	5.54	0.37	78.99
12/09	36.00	12	6	2.93	0.09	56.73
Annual Growth	(18.3%)	—	—	(1.2%)	5.3%	18.6%

JBS SA

Carnivores have a friend in JBS. With a daily slaughter capacity of 86000 head of cattle JBS is the world's biggest beef (and pork poultry and lamb) processor and exporter. In addition to fresh and processed beef and pork (it is the #3 pork producer in the US) JBS offers cooked and canned meats ready-to-eat meals as well as hides and dairy products. JBS sells beef domestically under the Friboi brand. It also owns about 75% of US poultry giant Pilgrim's Pride. JBS exports products worldwide; top markets include Japan the Middle East and Africa and Mexico. Positioned as an integrated food company JBS is expanding in the US and Australia. The Batista family through FB Participaces owns 47% of JBS.

Managing its growth strategy is challenging the company's already full plate of activities. JBS posted almost a 60% increase in year-over-year revenues in 2010 fueled in part by its business acquisitions and marking it as Brazil's third largest company by revenue. Earnings before interest and taxes soared too. Nonetheless net earnings plummeted to roughly a $180 million loss eroded by

debt which swelled by more than 20% and other costs. Among them the cost to restructure its US operations (including consolidation of Pilgrim's Pride) simultaneous with incorporating Bertin (a Brazilian meatpacker taken over in late 2009) with the JBS Mercosul food division has taken a toll on working capital resulting in higher financial expenses.

Adding to its frustration after two unsuccessful runs at Sara Lee in 2011 and late 2010 JBS ended its attempt to buy the iconic cheesecake maker. A takeover of Sara Lee's packaged meat business (Ball Park Jimmy Dean) would have consolidated JBS's power as a global integrated meat producer rivaling US-based Tyson Foods and Smithfield Foods. Following JBS's second failed bid Wesley Batista succeeded his brother Joesley as company CEO. Wesley formerly head of JBS USA Holdings has more than two decades of experience in the company.

Under Joesley Batista JBS undertook an aggressive international expansion strategy culminating in alliances and acquisitions in Argentina Australia Europe and the US. Late 2010 JBS entered a 50/50 joint venture with Jack Link's Beef Jerky a maker of the top US meat snack brand. Concurrently Jack Link's purchased a beef jerky manufacturing plant from JBS and JBS agreed to supply raw meat to Jack Link's for processing packaging and distribution.

Significant acquisitions have included taking over the ailing Pilgrim's Pride (2009). The deal marked JBS's entry into the US poultry industry and rank as the #2 poultry producer in the world with a daily slaughtering capacity of 7.9 million birds. After acquiring its initial stake in Pilgrim's Pride JBS upped its holding to more than 67% in late 2010 and later to 75% in 2012.

JBS also bought out US beef producer Swift Foods (2007) now JBS USA. To diversify its funding resources and raise money for acquisitions the company in 2009 filed to take JBS USA public. It delayed the IPO and paid an approximately $315 million penalty for its inaction (which added to the company's loss in 2010). In early 2011 JBS withdrew the IPO.

HISTORY

After nearly two decades in operation JBS began to expand its business significantly and steadily during the 1970s by purchasing independent slaughterhouses and cattle processing facilities throughout Brazil. These acquisitions continued through the end of the century at which point JBS also began to turn an acquisitive eye toward Argentina.

In 2005 the Brazilian meat giant took its first step abroad buying 85% of Swift Armour Argentina's largest beef processor for $200 million. In 2007 the company acquired US-based Swift Foods for $225 million and assumed its heavy debt load estimated at more than $1 billion a few months after going public on the Sao Paulo Stock Exchange.

In 2008 JBS acquired Australian-based beef producer Tasman Group for $107 million in cash. Also that year it bought US processor Smithfield Beef from Smithfield Foods for $565 million. In Europe it formed a 50:50 joint venture with Italy's Cremonini and subsidiary Inalca with plants in Italy Russia and Africa for $328 million.

In 2009 JBS filed with US regulators to hold a $2 billion initial public offering for JBS USA Holdings (It withdrew the proposed IPO in 2011.) Also in 2009 JBS acquired a 64% stake in restructured US poultry producer Pilgrim's Pride for $800 million. Prior to declaring bankruptcy in 2008 Pilgrim was the #1 US chicken producer and despite selling off some of its operations was still a huge poul-

try operation. Other than saying it hoped to increase Pilgrim's competitiveness both domestically and internationally JBS made no other statement as to Pilgrim's future. In late 2009 JBS acquired Australia's Tatiara Meat Company from the Dutch company VION Food Group for $28 million. Tatiara is Australia's largest exporter of fresh lamb meat; it also offers value-added lamb products. It was integrated into JBS's Swift Australia operations. At home JBS bought #2 Brazilian beef producer Bertin with 38 plants at home and abroad in an all-stock deal in 2009.

Eyeing acquisitions on the other side of the globe JBS in September 2010 bought Australia's Rockdale Beef from joint owners Itoham Foods and Mitsubishi Corporation. The deal valued at about $38 million boosted the firm's processing capacity by some 550 cattle per day and secured its foothold in the country. In February 2011 Wesley Batista succeeded his brother Joesley Batista as CEO of the company. Wesley formerly head of the company's US subsidiary is a 22-year veteran of JBS. Joesley Batista continued as chairman. In March JBS terminated its joint venture with Italy's Cremonini after a protracted dispute by selling its 50% stake in Inalca back to Cremonini for $304 million.

In March 2012 JBS through its subsidiary JBS USA Holdings increased its stake in Pilgrim's Pride to more than 75% through the purchase of nearly 19 million shares owned by Lonnie Bo Pilgrim for about $107 million.

EXECUTIVES

Chairman, Joesley Mendonca Batista, age 37
President CEO and Director, Wesley Mendonca Batista, age 42
Director Legal, Franciso de Assis
Investor Relations Officer, Jeremiah A. (Jerry) O'Callaghan, age 59
President CEO and Director, Wesley Mendonca Batista, age 42
Director, Jose Batista Sobrinho
Director, Jose Batista Jr.
Director, Marcus Vinicius Pratini de Moraes
Director, Wagner Pinheiro de Oliveira
Auditors: GrantThornton

LOCATIONS

HQ: JBS SA
Avenida Marginal Direita do Tiete, 500, Sao Paulo, SP 05118-100
Phone: (55) 11 3144 4000   **Fax:** (55) 11 3144 4279
Web: www.jbs.com.br

Sales

	% of total
Domestic	70
Export	30
Total	**100**

2010 Export Sales

	% of total
Africa & Middle	18
Mexico	14
Japan	12
Russia	10
EU	8
Hong	7
South	5
Canada	4
China	4
USA	3
Taiwan	2
Indonesia	1
Other	12
Total	**100**

PRODUCTS/OPERATIONS

Sales

	% of total
Beef	64
Chicken	22
Pork	9
Other	5
Total	**100**

Selected Products and Brands

Agricultural inputs (animal nutrition sanitation and
   management)
Beef jerky
Biodiesel
   JBS Biodiesel
   Bertin
Biolins (thermoelectric plant)
Cans
   JBS Latas
Casings (for sausage salamis hotdogs)
Collagen
   Novaprom
Confinements (livestock fencing structures)
Dairy products
   Amelia
   Bertin
   Carmelita
   Danubio
   Faixa Azul
   Franciscano
   Leco
   Mesa
   Serrabella
   Vigor
Leather
   JBS Couros
Oleochemicals
Pet feed
   Bertin
Protein (beef pork chicken sheep)
   Anglo
   Apeti
   Bertin
   Bordon
   Caba?a Las Lilas
   Friboi
   Maturatta
   Organic Beef
   Pilgrim's Pride
   Swift
Recycling (HDPE LDPE LDLPE and PP resins)
Shipping
   JBS Transportadora
Trade (vegetal oils chemicals animal fat)
Vegetables
   Anglo
   Bordon
   Swift

COMPETITORS

Agri Beef	Lykes Bros.
AzTx Cattle	Marfrig
Bachoco	Minerva sa
Birchwood Meat &	Moksel
Provision	National Beef Packing
Brasil Foods	Perdue Incorporated
Cactus Feeders	Pilgrim' s Pride
Campofrio Foopd	Rosen' s Diversified
Cargill Meat Solutions	Sam Kane Beef
Danish Crown	Processors
Eleva	Sanderson Farms
Ellison Meat Company	Seara Alimentos
Golden Belt Feeders	Smithfield Foods
Greater Omaha Packing	Tejon Ranch
HKScan	Tyson Foods
Hormel	U.S. Premium Beef
Kepak Group	VION N.V.
King Ranch	

HISTORICAL FINANCIALS

Company Type: Public

Income Statement

FYE: December 31

	REVENUE ($ mil.)	NET INCOME ($ mil.)	NET PROFIT MARGIN	EMPLOYEES
12/13	39,328	392	1.0%	185,000
12/12	37,024	351	0.9%	0
12/11	33,134	(40)	—	0
12/10	33,166	(182)	—	0
12/09	19,668	74	0.4%	0
Annual Growth	**18.9%**	**51.7%**	**—**	**—**

2013 Year-End Financials

Debt ratio: 20.2%
Return on equity: 4.3%
Cash ($ mil.): 3,815
Current ratio: 1.63
Long-term debt ($ mil.): 9,876
No. of shares (mil.): —
Dividends
Yield: 0.7%
Payout: 0.0%
Market value ($ mil.): —

	STOCK PRICE ($) FY Close	P/E High/Low		PER SHARE ($) Earnings	Dividends	Book Value
12/13	7.34	0	0	136.87	0.05	3.24
12/12	6.00	0	0	121.22	0.00	3.54
12/11	6.31	—	—	(14.89)	0.00	3.74
12/10	8.67	—	—	(73.16)	0.02	4.25
12/09	11.11	—	—	(0.00)	0.00	4.13
Annual Growth	**(9.8%)**	**—**	**—**	**—**	**(127.0%)**	**(5.9%)**

JFE Holdings Inc

JFE Holdings has an iron will unmatched in Japan and much of the rest of the world. The "J" in JFE stands for Japan; "F" is for Fe the chemical symbol for iron; and "E" stands for engineering. JFE Holdings' steel business unit JFE Steel accounts for about 85% of total sales and manufactures steel products such as bars pipes steel frames tubes and stainless steel for the automotive construction and petroleum industries. JFE is among the world's largest steel companies ranking behind ArcelorMittal Japan's Nippon Steel & Sumitomo Metal and China's Hebei Iron and Steel and Baosteel.

Geographic Reach

While most of its steel production facilities are in Japan JFE's reach is global and it has offices in 12 other countries.

Operations

JFE's engineering unit makes designs and builds facilities such as gasifying and melting furnaces water purification plants steelworks plants and equipment and steel structures used in the energy environmental and steel structural sectors. Its shipbuilding unit constructs both merchant and military vessels in several Japanese ports including Kyoto and Yokahama. JFE's urban development unit develops large-scale condominium complexes using large plots of undeveloped land while its microelectronics (LSI) division includes Kawasaki Microelectronics which produces integrated circuits for digital cameras.

Financial Performance

The company's revenues decreased by a marginal 1% (in local currency) in fiscal year 2012 to a decrease in sales in the steel urban development and LSI segments due to a decline in demand which was partially offset by an increase in sales in the engineering and shipbuilding segments.

However its net income decreased by 163% in local currency in fiscal year 2012 due to a drop in operating income and ordinary income and a loss on the valuation of overseas investments.

Strategy

The company buys and sell steel companies and other assets as it seeks to deliver the best returns for its shareholders.

In 2012 JFE Steel agreed to acquire threading business and related assets of US-based Benoit Machine LLC through holding company Benoit Holding jointly owned by JFE Steel and Kanematsu USA a subsidiary of Kanematsu. The deal will enable JFE Steel and Kanematsu to establish a total supply chain for the manufacture threading and distribution of oilfield tubing and downhole accessories and thereby meet diversified needs in the oil and gas industry and capture growing demand for oilfield tubing going

On the other side of the ledger in 2012 JFE Steel sold part of its stake in South Korean steelmaker Hyundai Hysco to the Hyundai Group for an undisclosed amont. The stake was cut to below 8%. JFE Steel supplies hot-rolled steel sheet to Hyundai Hysco for the construction and automobile industries but Hyundai has stepped up its steel production and reduced the need for imports.

In 2010 JFE Steel acquired all shares of Toyohira Steel it did not already own taking full control of the company. Toyohira a Sapporo-based electronic furnace steelmaker is a wholly-owned subsidiary of JFE Steel.

That same year JFE Steel acquired a 24% stake in Pancheng Yihong Pipe Co. a China-based maker of seamless pipes for oilfields in a stock-purchase deal. Following the investment JFE jointly owns the company along with China's Chengdu Steel & Vanadium Co. (51%) and another Japanese company Marubeni-Itochu Steel (25%).

EXECUTIVES

CEO and Board Member, Fumio Sudo, age 72
Director and EVP, Toshikuni Yamazaki
President JFE Engineering, Sumiyuki Kishimoto
President JFE Steel Corporation, Eiji Hayashida
President and CEO JFE Shoji Trade Corporation, Tsutomu Yajima
EVP Finance Investor Relations and Corporate Planning, Shinichi Okada
SVP General Administration, Sakio Sasamoto
Director; President JFE Steel, hajime Yamazaki
President and CEO, Hajime Bada, age 65
CEO and Board Member, Fumio Sudo, age 72
Director and EVP, Toshikuni Yamazaki
Director; President JFE Engineering, Sumiyuki Kishimoto
Director and SVP Corporate Planning and Controller, Eiji Hayashida
Director; President JFE Steel, hajime Yamazaki
Director, Shigeo Asai
Auditors: Ernst&YoungShinNihon

LOCATIONS

HQ: JFE Holdings Inc
2-2-3 Uchisaiwai-cho, Chiyoda-ku, Tokyo 100-0011
Phone: (81) 3 3597 4321
Web: www.jfe-holdings.co.jp

PRODUCTS/OPERATIONS

Sales

	% of total
Steel	85
Engineering	8
Shipbuilding	6
LSI	1
Total	**100**

COMPETITORS

ArcelorMittal
Baosteel
BlueScope Steel
Kobe Steel
Nippon Steel & Sumitomo Metal Corporation
Nippon Yakin
Nisshin Steel
Severstal
Shougang Corp.
Sumitomo Metal Industries
United States Steel

HISTORICAL FINANCIALS

Company Type: Public

Income Statement

FYE: March 31

	REVENUE ($ mil.)	NET INCOME ($ mil.)	NET PROFIT MARGIN	EMPLOYEES
03/14	35,524	991	2.8%	57,210
03/13	33,894	420	1.2%	57,044
03/12	38,601	(446)	—	54,133
03/11	38,590	707	1.8%	54,400
03/10	30,451	488	1.6%	53,892
Annual Growth	3.9%	19.4%	—	1.5%

2014 Year-End Financials

Debt ratio: 0.3%
Return on equity: 6.2%
Cash ($ mil.): 609
Current ratio: 1.50
Long-term debt ($ mil.): 11,121

No. of shares (mil.): 576
Dividends
 Yield: —
 Payout: —
Market value ($ mil.): 11,390

	STOCK PRICE ($) FY Close	P/E High/Low	PER SHARE ($) Earnings	Dividends	Book Value
03/14	19.75	— —	1.72	0.00	29.33
03/13	20.15	— —	0.76	0.00	29.41
03/12	22.05	— —	(0.84)	0.00	32.97
03/11	29.60	— —	1.32	0.00	33.62
03/10	39.25	— —	0.92	0.00	29.67
Annual Growth	(15.8%)	— —	16.8%	—	(0.3%)

Jiangxi Copper Co., Ltd.

Jiangxi Copper Company is China's largest copper producer. The company makes about 800000 tons of copper products annually and holds more than 10 million tons of proved and probable reserves. It owns a handful of copper mines another seven processing plants and three sulfuric acid refineries; majority-owned (38%) Jiangxi Copper Products makes copper rods and wires. Jiangxi also turns out nearly 5 million tons of sulfuric products per year. Other operations include gold and silver production with proved reserves of 340 tons of gold 9664 tons of silver and 246000 tons of molybdenum. Jiangxi Copper Company was formed by parent Jiangxi Copper Corporation which is owned by the Chinese government in 1997.

EXECUTIVES

Chairman and President, Li Yihuang
VP, Wang Chiwei
Chief Accountant, Gan Chengjiu
Secretary, Li Baomin
VP, Long Ziping
Auditors: DeloitteToucheTohmatsu

LOCATIONS

HQ: Jiangxi Copper Co., Ltd.
 15 Yejin Avenue, Guixi City, Jiangxi Province 335424
Phone: (86) 701 3777011 **Fax:** (86) 701 3777013
Web: www.jxcc.com

COMPETITORS

Codelco
Tongling Nonferrous Metals
Xstrata

HISTORICAL FINANCIALS

Company Type: Public

Income Statement

FYE: December 31

	REVENUE ($ mil.)	NET INCOME ($ mil.)	NET PROFIT MARGIN	EMPLOYEES
12/13	28,955	587	2.0%	22,425
12/12	25,344	829	3.3%	22,596
12/11	18,606	1,046	5.6%	22,500
12/10	11,550	756	6.6%	27,879
12/09	7,532	349	4.6%	22,917
Annual Growth	40.0%	13.9%	—	(0.5%)

2013 Year-End Financials

Debt ratio: 4.0%
Return on equity: 8.1%
Cash ($ mil.): 3,248
Current ratio: 1.67
Long-term debt ($ mil.): 998

No. of shares (mil.): —
Dividends
 Yield: 0.0%
 Payout: 45.8%
Market value ($ mil.): —

	STOCK PRICE ($) FY Close	P/E High/Low	PER SHARE ($) Earnings	Dividends	Book Value
12/13	70.71	3 2	0.17	0.08	2.12
12/12	108.25	2 1	0.24	3.95	1.98
12/11	86.01	2 1	0.30	0.05	1.80
12/10	124.17	2 1	0.23	0.01	1.50
12/09	94.00	3 1	0.11	0.40	1.11
Annual Growth	(6.9%)	— —	12.3%	(33.6%)	17.7%

Joyo Bank, Ltd.

Tracing its roots back to 1938 The Joyo Bank offers regional banking services for Japan's Ibaraki Prefecture and its surrounding regions. Backed by more than 170 branches Joyo offers deposits loans investment portfolios international business and other traditional retail banking products. Subsidiaries and affiliated companies include Joyo Computer Service Co. (calculation software) Joyo Lease Co. (machinery and equipment leasing) Joyo Credit Guarantee Co. (housing loans credit) and Joyo Cash Service Co. (ATM and CD management and maintenance).

EXECUTIVES

President, Kazuyoshi Terakado
Auditors: Ernst&YoungShinNihon

LOCATIONS

HQ: Joyo Bank, Ltd.
 2-5-5 Minami-machi, Mito, Ibaraki 310-0021
Phone: (81) 29 231 2151 **Fax:** (81) 29 231 2193
Web: www.joyobank.co.jp

COMPETITORS

Aozora Bank
Miyazaki Bank

Iyo Bank
Mitsubishi UFJ Financial Group
Norinchukin Bank
Shizuoka Bank
Towa Bank

HISTORICAL FINANCIALS

Company Type: Public

Income Statement

FYE: March 31

	ASSETS ($ mil.)	NET INCOME ($ mil.)	INCOME AS % OF ASSETS	EMPLOYEES
03/14	82,703	242	0.3%	3,713
03/13	87,871	241	0.3%	3,766
03/12	97,589	221	0.2%	3,783
03/11	89,827	168	0.2%	3,793
03/10	79,401	150	0.2%	3,863
Annual Growth	1.0%	12.7%	—	(1.0%)

2014 Year-End Financials

Return on assets: 0.3%
Return on equity: 4.9%
Long-term debt ($ mil.): —
No. of shares (mil.): 745
Sales ($ mil): 1,542

Dividends
 Yield: —
 Payout: —
Market value ($ mil.): 3,804

	STOCK PRICE ($) FY Close	P/E High/Low	PER SHARE ($) Earnings	Dividends	Book Value
03/14	5.10	— —	0.32	0.00	6.72
03/13	4.97	— —	0.32	0.00	7.17
03/12	6.05	— —	0.29	0.00	7.16
03/11	6.05	— —	0.22	0.00	6.69
03/10	6.05	— —	0.19	0.00	5.93
Annual Growth	(4.2%)	— —	13.7%	—	3.2%

Juroku Bank, Ltd.

The Juroku Bank is industriously working to serve its customers in the prefectures of Gifu and Aichi both part of the industrial region of Chubu. The regional bank has about 150 offices in its primary service areas as well as offices in Osaka and Tokyo and overseas offices in Hong Kong and Shanghai. In addition to traditional deposit banking products and services The Juroku Bank and its subsidiaries do business in such areas as credit cards credit guarantees investments and leasing. The bank joined with five other regional banks to form the Tokai-Kinki PFI Financial Network which is intended to help its member strengthen their abilities related to private finance initiatives.

In 2005 the bank fell prey to an ATM scam in 2005 the same year Juroku Bank signed on to use Hitachi's finger-vein authentication system to verify identification at its cash machines.

Auditors: DeloitteToucheTohmatsu

LOCATIONS

HQ: Juroku Bank, Ltd.
 8-26 Kanda-machi, Gifu 500-8516
Phone: (81) 58 265 2111
Web: www.juroku.co.jp

COMPETITORS

Mie Bank
Mitsubishi UFJ Financial Group
Mizuho Financial
Resona
Sumitomo Mitsui

Income Statement

FYE: March 31

	ASSETS ($ mil.)	NET INCOME ($ mil.)	INCOME AS % OF ASSETS	EMPLOYEES
03/14	55,667	163	0.3%	3,497
03/13	60,236	246	0.4%	3,565
03/12	66,902	145	0.2%	3,689
03/11	64,124	112	0.2%	3,704
03/10	46,735	96	0.2%	3,048
Annual Growth	4.5%	14.1%	—	3.5%

2014 Year-End Financials

Return on assets: 0.3%
Return on equity: 5.6%
Long-term debt ($ mil.): —
No. of shares (mil.): 373
Sales ($ mil): 1,123
Dividends
  Yield: —
  Payout: —
Market value ($ mil.): —

JX Holdings, Inc.

LOCATIONS

HQ: JX Holdings, Inc.
  2-6-3 Otemachi, Chiyoda-ku, Tokyo 100-8161
Phone: (81) 3 6275 5009
Web: www.hd.jx-group.co.jp

HISTORICAL FINANCIALS

Company Type: Public

Income Statement

FYE: March 31

	REVENUE ($ mil.)	NET INCOME ($ mil.)	NET PROFIT MARGIN	EMPLOYEES
03/14	120,248	1,037	0.9%	26,616
03/13	119,239	1,694	1.4%	25,569
03/12	130,730	2,079	1.6%	24,236
03/11	116,348	3,764	3.2%	24,691
Annual Growth	1.1%	(34.9%)	—	2.5%

2014 Year-End Financials

Debt ratio: 0.3%
Return on equity: 5.2%
Cash ($ mil.): 2,729
Current ratio: 1.09
Long-term debt ($ mil.): 12,027
No. of shares (mil.): —
Dividends
  Yield: —
  Payout: —
Market value ($ mil.): —

	STOCK PRICE ($) FY Close	P/E High/Low	PER SHARE ($) Earnings	Dividends	Book Value
03/14	9.50	— —	0.42	0.00	10.26
03/13	11.39	— —	0.68	0.00	9.93
03/12	11.80	— —	0.84	0.00	10.02
03/11	13.75	— —	1.51	0.00	9.16
/0.00	—	—(0.00)	0.00	(0.00)	
Annual Growth	—	— —	—	—	—

Kansai Electric Power Co., Inc. (Kansai Denryoku K. K.) (Japan)

LOCATIONS

HQ: Kansai Electric Power Co., Inc. (Kansai Denryoku K. K.) (Japan)
  3-6-16 Nakanoshima, Kita-ku, Osaka 530-8270
Phone: (81) 6 6441 8821
Web: www.kepco.co.jp

HISTORICAL FINANCIALS

Company Type: Public

Income Statement

FYE: March 31

	REVENUE ($ mil.)	NET INCOME ($ mil.)	NET PROFIT MARGIN	EMPLOYEES
03/14	32,237	(943)	—	33,657
03/13	30,385	(2,587)	—	33,537
03/12	34,273	(2,953)	—	32,961
03/11	33,448	1,487	4.4%	32,418
03/10	27,905	1,361	4.9%	32,083
Annual Growth	3.7%	—	—	1.2%

2014 Year-End Financials

Debt ratio: 0.5%
Return on equity: (-7.9%)
Cash ($ mil.): 1,060
Current ratio: 0.80
Long-term debt ($ mil.): 36,384
No. of shares (mil.): 893
Dividends
  Yield: —
  Payout: —
Market value ($ mil.): 4,796

	STOCK PRICE ($) FY Close	P/E High/Low	PER SHARE ($) Earnings	Dividends	Book Value
03/14	5.37	— —	(1.06)	0.00	13.16
03/13	4.55	— —	(2.90)	0.00	15.21
03/12	7.65	— —	(3.31)	0.00	20.88
03/11	12.66	— —	1.66	0.00	24.78
03/10	45.60	— —	1.50	0.00	21.26
Annual Growth (11.3%)	(41.4%)	— —	—	—	—

KB Financial Group, Inc.

KB Financial Group holding company for Kookmin Bank provides commercial and consumer banking services in South Korea. It offers asset management and life insurance through alliances with Netherlands-based ING Groep. The bank's lending activities mainly entail residential mortgages home equity loans consumer loans and corporate loans. Kookmin Bank has more than 1200 branches in its home country where it claims some 26 million customers or about half of the population of South Korea. The bank provides corporate services such as foreign exchange and securities trading from offices at home and abroad in New York London Hong Kong Tokyo and Auckland New Zealand.

KB Financial became a bank holding company in 2008 and made no bones about its ambitions to stretch its wings with acquisitions. It has been eyeing brokerage firms as well as other financial services companies.

It is reportedly interested in acquiring troubled Korea Exchange Bank. This is the second time KB Financial has wanted to buy KEB; in 2006 its $7 billion offer was stymied by KEB's parent US-based private equity firm Lone Star Funds. In 2008 the South Korean government blocked HSBC's acquisition of KEB putting the bank in play once more.

A proposed KEB acquisition is just one part of KB Financial's strategy. Seeking strategic opportunities in emerging markets the bank has opened representative offices in Kazakhstan the Ukraine and Vietnam and is mulling moves into other Central and Southeast Asian nations. In 2008 it bought a 30% stake in Kazakhstan bank JSC Bank CenterCredit; it eventually intends to build up to a controlling stake of that bank.

In the meantime the company sold its nearly 14% stake in PT Bank International Indonesia to Malayan Banking Berhad for some $309 million.

Kookmin Bank spun off its credit card business in 2011 and KB Financial took it over. The new company KB Kookmin Card Co. will focus on credit card/telecommunications services and include a mobile credit card. Other services include consumer financing and insurance.

In 2006 erstwhile Kookmin Bank CEO Kim Jung-tae resigned in the face of disciplinary sanctions imposed by financial regulators after he was accused of accounting irregularities. Some South Korean newspapers speculated that a disciplinary warning issued by the Financial Supervisory Commission was retaliation for Kim's opposition to government-led bailouts of financially troubled companies.

Citigroup owns around 17% of KB Financial.

EXECUTIVES

SEVP Capital Markets and Treasury Group, Young Han Choi, age 56
Chairman and CEO, Yoon-Dae Euh, age 69
Director, Jacques P.M. Kemp, age 64
Director, Dam Cho, age 61
SEVP Strategy Planning Group and Director, Ki Hong Kim, age 56
Director, Bo Kyung Byun, age 60
SEVP Strategy Group and Director, In Gyu Choi, age 57
Director, Suk Sig Lim, age 60
Director, Sang Moon Hahm, age 61
Director, Han Kim, age 60
Director, Chan Soo Kang, age 52
Chief Audit Executive and Director, Yong Hwa Cheong, age 60
Director, Chee Joong Kim, age 58
Auditors: SamilPricewaterhousecoopers

LOCATIONS

HQ: KB Financial Group, Inc.
  84 Namdaemun-ro Jung-gu, Seoul 100-845
Phone: (82) 2 2073 2844   Fax: (82) 2 2073 2848
Web: www.kbfng.com

PRODUCTS/OPERATIONS

Selected Subsidiaries

KB Asset Management Co. Ltd. (80%)
KB Credit Information Co. Ltd. (99.7%)
KB Data Systems Co. Ltd. (99.99%)
KB Futures Co. Ltd. (99.98%)
KB Investment Co. Ltd. (99.99%)
KB Real Estate Trust Co. Ltd. (99.99%)
Kookmin Bank
Kookmin Bank Hong Kong Ltd.
Kookmin Bank International Ltd.

Busan Bank
Citigroup
Daegu Bank
Hana Bank
Industrial Bank of
Korea

Korea Exchange Bank
SHC Management
Samsung Life Insurance
Shinhan Financial
Woori

HISTORICAL FINANCIALS

Company Type: Public

Income Statement

FYE: December 31

	ASSETS ($ mil.)	NET INCOME ($ mil.)	INCOME AS % OF ASSETS	EMPLOYEES
12/13	277,505	1,198	0.4%	151
12/12	264,124	1,594	0.6%	157
12/11	239,580	2,048	0.9%	148
12/10	230,781	130	0.1%	155
12/09	226,584	466	0.2%	100
Annual Growth	5.2%	26.6%	—	10.9%

2013 Year-End Financials

Return on assets: 0.4%
Return on equity: 5.0%
Long-term debt ($ mil.): —
No. of shares (mil.): 386
Sales ($ mil): 14,807

Dividends
Yield: 1.3%
Payout: 20.6%
Market value ($ mil.): 15,651

	STOCK PRICE ($) FY Close	P/E High/Low	PER SHARE ($) Earnings	Dividends	Book Value
12/13	40.51	— —	3.09	0.53	63.14
12/12	35.90	— —	4.12	0.64	59.42
12/11	31.34	— —	5.56	0.00	51.19
12/10	52.89	— —	0.38	0.21	42.70
12/09	50.85	— —	1.43	0.00	39.93
Annual Growth	(5.5%)	— —	21.2%	—	12.1%

KBC Group NV

Neither a purveyor of fried chicken nor an ominous Russian spy shop KBC Groep (or KBC Group as its known in the US) is actually one of Belgium's largest financial services firms. The company operates 845 bank branches in Belgium and more than 1100 in Central and Eastern Europe. It has other operations in Western Europe the US and Southeast Asia although much of the company's international operations are being scaled back. KBC caters to individuals small and mid-sized businesses and private banking clients. It also offers insurance and asset management. The group is organized into four business units: Belgium; Central and Eastern Europe banking; merchant banking; and shared services and operations.

HISTORY

KBC Group traces its roots back to 1931 when a commercial bank named Algemeene Bankvereeniging responded to the global financial crisis by restructuring. The bank decided to re-group its assets in Belgium and Hungary and create a new holding company Algemene Maatschappij voor Nijverheidskrediet —or Almanij for short.

In 1935 Almanij helped organize a new bank Kredietbank in exchange for a majority stake in the company. Within the next few years Almanij managed to accrue a large debt to Kredietbank; in order to pay it back the company was forced to sell its shares in other firms. The debt was finally cleared by 1945.

Kredietbank quickly grew to be one of Belgium's leading banks. In 1949 it set up private bank KB Luxembourg which would later operate as an independent company majority-controlled by Almanij. In the ensuing years Almanij benefited from Belgium's ability to bounce back after WWII relative to the rest of Europe.

Fears that the Belgian government would like the French nationalize the country's banks led Almanij to make some changes in 1978. The company sliced Kredietbank and KB Luxembourg into two firms and refocused its investments into three major branches: Kredietbank KB Luxembourg and insurance and leasing entities such as the insurer Fidelitas. Though the 1980s were a shaky time for Belgian banks Almanij endured and industry conditions improved toward the end of the decade.

In 1991 the Banking and Finance Commission in Brussels announced changes in the regulations for Belgian banks; these changes included the stipulation that the main shareholders of banks make up the majority on their boards. The new regulations allowed holding companies like Almanij to have more influence over banks' strategies while also forcing them to drum up more capital for the banks.

Almanij acquired a majority stake in investment firm Gevaert in 1997. The following year it hit the big time with the creation of KBC Bank and Insurance Holding Company which went on to become one of the top financial services firms in Belgium. In 1999 Almanij formed Almafin a wholly owned consulting services subsidiary.

Almanij ran into some trouble in 2000 when the government began investigating Kredietbank and KBC Bank and Insurance for possible tax fraud. That year Cera Holding spun off most of its stake in Almanij in the form of a new holding company called Almancora.

Late in 2004 KBC Bank and Almanij announced that KBC would acquire Almanij to streamline operations; the deal which created KBC Group was completed early in 2005.

The company then expanded through a variety of deals. It acquired the Czech-based Ceskoslovenska Obchodni Banka (CSOB Bank) which it later split into two entities separately serving the Czech Republic and Slovakia. KBC also acquired complete ownership of Hungary-based K&H Bank. Other deals included acquisitions in Romania and Bulgaria. In 2008 the group bought Slovakia's eighth largest bank Istrobanka which it merged into CSOB Bank.

EXECUTIVES

President CEO and Director, Jan Vanhevel, age 65
Director, Jo Cornu, age 69
Director, Philippe Naert, age 70
Director, Paul Bostoen, age 74
Director, Luc Debaillie, age 73
Director, Noel Devisch, age 70
Director, Dirk Heremans, age 70
Director, Alain Tytgadt, age 57
CEO European Private Banking and Director, Etienne Verwilghen, age 66
Vice Chairman, Philippe Vlerick, age 58
Director, Frank Donck, age 48
Director, Paul Borghgraef, age 59
Director, Germain Vantieghem, age 68
Director, Franky Depickere, age 54
Director, Theodoros Roussis, age 59
Director, Hendrik Soete, age 63
Director, Marc Wittemans, age 56
Director, Charles Van Wymeersch
Director, Lode Morlion, age 53
Director, Ghislaine Van Kerckhove, age 50
Auditors: Ernst&YoungReviseursd'EntreprisesSCC

LOCATIONS

HQ: KBC Group NV
Havenlaan 2, Brussels 1080
Phone: (32) 2 429 49 16   **Fax:** (32) 2 429 44 16
Web: www.kbc.com

PRODUCTS/OPERATIONS

Selected Subsidiaries

KBC Bank NV
Antwerp Diamond Bank NV (Belgium)
CBC Banque SA (universal bank serving French-speaking region of Belgium)
CIBANK (Bulgaria)
CSOB (Slovakia)
CSOB (Czech Republic)
K&H Bank Rt. (Hungary)
KBC Asset Management NV
KBC Bank Nederland NV
KBC Finance Ireland
Kredyt Bank (Poland)
KBC Insurance
A. Banka A.D. (Russia)
Assurisk SA (Luxembourg)
CSOB Poist' ovna (Slovakia)
CSOB Pojist' ovna (Czech Republic)
DZI Insurance (Bulgaria)
Fidea NV (Belgium)
K&H Insurance (Hungary)
TUiR WARTA SA (Poland)
VAB Group (Belgium)
KBL EPB
Brown Shipley & Co. Limited (UK)
KBL Richelieu Banque Privee (France)
KBL European Private Bankers (Luxembourg)
KBL (Switzerland) Ltd.
Merck Fink & Co. (Germany)
Puilaetco Dewaay Private Bankers SA (Belgium)
Theodoor Gilissen Bankiers NV (99.9% Netherlands)
VITIS Life SA (Luxembourg)

COMPETITORS

BNP Paribas
Commerzbank
Credit Suisse
Deutsche Bank
Dexia

ING
Natixis
Rabobank
SEB AB

HISTORICAL FINANCIALS

Company Type: Public

Income Statement

FYE: December 31

	ASSETS ($ mil.)	NET INCOME ($ mil.)	INCOME AS % OF ASSETS	EMPLOYEES
12/13	332,214	1,397	0.4%	36,177
12/12	338,588	806	0.2%	37,083
12/11	369,127	16	0.0%	47,530
12/10	429,380	2,489	0.6%	50,494
12/09	467,077	(3,552)	—	54,185
Annual Growth	(8.2%)	—	—	(9.6%)

2013 Year-End Financials

Return on assets: 0.4%
Return on equity: 6.8%
Long-term debt ($ mil.): —
No. of shares (mil.): 417
Sales ($ mil): 17,426

Dividends
Yield: 1.5%
Payout: 54.6%
Market value ($ mil.): 11,841

	STOCK PRICE ($) FY Close	P/E High/Low	PER SHARE ($) Earnings	Dividends	Book Value
12/13	28.37	53 29	1.42	0.43	46.71
12/12	17.83	— —	(1.44)	0.00	49.31
12/11	6.10	— —	(2.50)	0.69	61.01
12/10	17.39	11 8	4.98	0.00	70.49
Annual Growth	17.7%	—	(26.9%)	—	(9.8%)

KDDI Corp

LOCATIONS

HQ: KDDI Corp
3-10-10 Iidabashi, Chiyoda-ku, Tokyo 102-8460
Phone: (81) 3 6678 0712
Web: www.kddi.com

HISTORICAL FINANCIALS

Company Type: Public

Income Statement

	REVENUE ($ mil.)	NET INCOME ($ mil.)	NET PROFIT MARGIN	EMPLOYEES
				FYE: March 31
03/14	41,984	3,119	7.4%	27,073
03/13	38,922	2,566	6.6%	20,238
03/12	43,546	2,908	6.7%	19,680
03/11	41,476	3,080	7.4%	18,418
03/10	36,850	2,277	6.2%	18,301
Annual Growth	3.3%	8.2%	—	10.3%

2014 Year-End Financials

Debt ratio: 0.2%
Return on equity: 12.9%
Cash ($ mil.): 2,151
Current ratio: 1.47
Long-term debt ($ mil.): 7,011

No. of shares (mil.): 834
Dividends
  Yield: 2.6%
  Payout: —
Market value ($ mil.): 12,124

	STOCK PRICE ($) FY Close	P/E High/Low	PER SHARE ($) Earnings	Dividends	Book Value
03/14	14.52	— —	3.86	0.39	33.85
03/13	20.80	— —	3.07	0.00	32.30
03/12	16.24	— —	3.45	0.00	33.95
03/11	62.18	— —	3.51	0.37	30.89
03/10	51.80	— —	2.56	0.32	24.98
Annual Growth	(27.2%)	— —	10.9%	4.7%	7.9%

Kia Motors Corp. (South Korea)

South Korea's #2 carmaker (behind Hyundai Motor) Kia Motors produces about 3 million vehicles a year at 10 manufacturing and assembly plants in five countries which are then sold through a network of distributors and dealers covering 150 countries. Its compact Kia picanto is the second-best selling car in South Korea. Other popular models include the Forte the Sorento and the Soul. Kia also makes a number of commercial vehicles. Its high-capacity plants outside Korea are in the US Slovakia and China. After Korea Kia's second-largest market is the US. Part of the Hyundai Kia Automotive Group Kia operates as an affiliate of Hyundai Motor.

Geographic Reach

Kia has established manufacturing plants in key regions two in China (set up as joint partnerships with Yueda and Dongfeng Motor) a Slovakia assembly plant in Eastern Europe (that also produces Hyundai vehicles) and one in the US (in Georgia). In 2014 it invested $1 billion to launch a new manufacturing plant in Monterrey Mexico.

Strategy

Kia is focused on edging out the competition with its stylish design that doesn't come with a European price tag. By strengthening its platform to smaller lighter cars Kia aims to rapidly respond to changes in consumer demand. The company markets its value in design esthetics and fuel efficiency. None of its vehicles are gas guzzlers and its Optima sedan came with a hybrid engine option. Most of its vehicles have a gasoline direct injection (GDI) engine that results in better fuel economy.

HISTORY

Kia's conglomerate ownership is also fundamental to its operation. Favoring its founding family former president of Kia Hyundai Motors vice chairman Chung Eui-sun is the son of Hyundai Kia Automotive Group chairman Chung Mong-koo. The elder Chung is the son of Hyundai's founder and controls the car company through a series of cross-holdings involving auto-parts maker Hyundai Mobis and steelmaker Hyundai Steel. In 2010 he stepped down from Kia Motors' board. To fill his vacancy the role of CEO was jointly held by Kia vice chairman Chung Sung-eun and Kia president Seo Young-jong until late 2010 when Chung Sung-eun resigned amidst the recall of some 100000 automobiles. President and COO Lee Hyoung-keun was named as Chung's replacement.

Leadership has had other rough patches as well. A court found then-chairman Chung guilty of embezzlement and fraud in a slush fund scandal that passed corporate control and wealth from father to son hurting shareholders' value. An appeals court suspended the chairman's prison sentence to community service citing the executive's irreplaceable role in the company and country's economic well-being. He was subsequently pardoned by the South Korean president.

EXECUTIVES

Chairman and CEO, Chung Mong-Koo, age 65
Chief Designer Kia Europe Design Center, Gregory Guillaume
Chief Design Officer, Peter Schreyer, age 60
Chairman and Group CEO Kia Motors America and Kia Motors Manufacturing Georgia; President and CEO Kia Motors America Inc., Byung Mo Ahn
Vice Chairman, Hyoung-Keun (Hank) Lee
President and Director, Chung Euisun
Deputy General Manager International Public Relations Overseas Communications Team, Michael Choo
Senior Executive Vice President COO, Thomas Oh
Director, Shin Keon-Soo
Director, Hong Hyun-Kook
Head Finance Division and Director, Lee Jae-Rok
Vice Chairman, Hyoung-Keun (Hank) Lee
CEO President and Director, Seo Young-Jong
President and Director, Chung Euisun
Director, Park Young-Soo
Vice Chairman, Jeong Seung-Eun
Auditors: KPMGSamjongAccountingCorp.

LOCATIONS

HQ: Kia Motors Corp. (South Korea)
12 Heolleung-ro Seocho-gu, Seoul 137-130
Phone: (82) 2 3464 1114   **Fax:** (82) 2 3464 6813
Web: www.kia.co.kr

Sales

	% of total
South	23
Europe	19
US	17
China	16
Rest of	25
Total	**100**

PRODUCTS/OPERATIONS

Selected Models

Commercial vehicles
  K2700/Strong/3000s/2500TCI
  K4000G
Passenger cars
  Cadenza
  cee'd
  cee'd_sw
  Cerato/Forte
  Cerato/Forte Koup
  Optima
  Picanto
  pro_cee'd
  Rio
  Soul
SUV & MPV
  Borrego/Mohave
  Carens/Rondo
  Carnival/Sedona
  Sorento
  Sportage
  Venga

COMPETITORS

BYD	Isuzu
Chery Automobile	Mazda
China FAW	Nissan
Chrysler	Peugeot
Daimler	Renault
Fiat	Shanghai Automotive
Ford Motor	Ssangyong Motor
Fuji Heavy Industries	Suzuki Motor
GM Korea	Toyota
General Motors	Volkswagen
Honda	

HISTORICAL FINANCIALS

Company Type: Public

Income Statement

	REVENUE ($ mil.)	NET INCOME ($ mil.)	NET PROFIT MARGIN	EMPLOYEES
				FYE: December 31
12/13	45,260	3,629	8.0%	33,255
12/12	44,247	3,619	8.2%	32,756
12/11	37,275	2,947	7.9%	32,411
12/10	31,951	2,392	7.5%	32,599
12/09	25,448	846	3.3%	32,616
Annual Growth	15.5%	43.9%	—	0.5%

2013 Year-End Financials

Debt ratio: 0.0%
Return on equity: 20.5%
Cash ($ mil.): 2,197
Current ratio: 1.25
Long-term debt ($ mil.): 1,603

No. of shares (mil.): 404
Dividends
  Yield: —
  Payout: —
Market value ($ mil.): —

Koc Holdings AS

In Turkey Koc (pronounced "coach") class equals first class. Led by its energy businesses Koc Holding is Turkey's dominant industrial conglomerate. The company's Tofas unit an alliance with Fiat is Turkey's champion carmaker; Koc's joint venture with Ford Motor sells imported Ford models. Other businesses include consumer goods such as large household appliances (Arcelik teaming up with LG Electronics) and energy (distribution of liquefied petroleum gas). Subsidiaries engage in food production construction international trading and hospitality and tourism. Koc also operates banking securities brokerage and insurance businesses. The Koc family one of the wealthiest in Turkey controls the company.

Operations

Koc's business activities include the acquisition disposal and exchanging of shares of domestic and foreign corporations and limited liability companies for all types of commercial industrial agricultural and financial activities.

Koc and Royal Dutch Shell together continue to drive a 51% stake in oil refiner T PRAS. T PRAS the 8th largest refining company in Europe controls 40% ownership in the fuel distribution company Opet Petrolcolok.

The company's finance segment includes three main groups; banking insurance and consumer finance. Leasing factoring portfolio management custody and brokerage services are included in the banking sector.

Financial Performance

Koc's revenues increased by 41% in 2011 thanks to a growth in revenues from all of its segments. Higher revenues fueled the company's net income growth of 23% that year.

Strategy

Koc is reaching far across the Bosporus while simultaneously refocusing its efforts in consumer goods automotive finance and energy markets. The company's strategy is to buy and sell assets to achieve portfolio diversification to minimize sector and regional risks. It is also focusing on expanding its operations in developing markets through acquisitions and joint ventures.

In 2011 its Arcelik subsidiary acquired the South Africa-based Defy which is engaged in the production of refrigerators freezers dryers ovens cooking appliances and the selling and marketing of all kinds of durable home appliances across Southern Africa.

That year Koc established a shipping subsidiary Sariyer Tankercilik. To raise cash it also agreed to sell Koc.Net Haberlesme Teknolojileri ve Iletisim Hizmetleri A.S. (Kocnet) to Vodafone.

Expanding its role in power production and responding to the Turkish government's plan to privatize power generation in Turkey in 2010 Koc formed a joint venture with energy powerhouse AES to develop new power plants. AES-Entek aims to become one of the top five independent power producers in Turkey by 2015.

Ownership

With a combined stake of more than 69% members of the Koc family direct the operations of Koc Holding.

HISTORY

In 1917 16-year-old Vehbi Koc and his father opened a small grocery store in Ankara Turkey. With the fall of the Ottoman Empire after WWI Turkey's capital was moved to Ankara which was then only a village. The Kocs recognized an opportunity and expanded into construction and building supplies winning a contract to repair the roof of the Turkish parliament building. By age 26 Koc was a millionaire.

Ford Motor made Koc its Turkish agent in 1928. In 1931 Mobil Oil and Koc entered an exclusive agreement to search for oil in Turkey. The company incorporated in 1938 as Koc Ticaret Corporation the first Turkish joint stock company with an employee stock-ownership program.

Despite Turkey's neutrality in WWII the fighting disrupted Koc's business. The nation became isolationist after the war and restricted foreign concerns to selling through local agents; Koc benefited by importing foreign products.

General Electric and Koc entered a joint venture in 1946 to build Turkey's first lightbulb factory. In 1955 Koc set up Arcelik the first Turkish producer of refrigerators washing machines and water

heaters; Tork Demir Dokom the first Turkish producer of radiators and later auto castings; and Turkay the country's first private producer of matches. In 1959 Koc constructed Turkey's first truck assembly plant (Otosan).

Other firsts followed in the 1960s as the company leveraged its size and government influence to attract more ventures. These included a tire factory (with Uniroyal) a cable factory (with Siemens) production of electric motors and compressors (with GE) and the production of Anadol the first car to be made entirely in Turkey (by Otosan under license from Ford). In 1974 Koc expanded into retailing with the purchase of Migros Turkey's largest chain of supermarkets.

The Turkish military imposed martial law in 1980 and restricted foreign exchange payments forcing Koc to limit its operations. In 1986 a year after foreign companies were allowed to export products directly to Turkey Koc and American Express started Koc-Amerikan Bank (which Koc bought out and renamed Kocbank in 1992). In the late 1980s Vehbi's only son Rahmi took over the company's leadership. Vehbi Koc died in 1996.

Auto sales fell sharply in 1996 as buyers awaited the country's entry into the European Union's customs union. In an effort to offset market risks Koc forged a number of alliances in 1997. It participated in a British-Canadian-Turkish consortium that was building a large power plant in central Turkey.

Reflecting a greater willingness to open the company to foreign investors Koc announced plans to offer $250 million in shares in a public offering in 1998 but it soon canceled the offering because of market volatility. A year later the company completed an auto plant in Samarkand Uzbekistan to build Otoyol-Iveco buses and trucks.

Koc entered into a joint venture –Koc Finansal Hizmetler –with Unicredito Italiano in 2002 in an effort to further consolidate its financial holdings.

Significant company moves in 2008 included selling its Otomotiv Lastikleri Tevzi (Oltas) to Germany's Continental AG. Oltas had distributed Continental tires and related products since 2003. The company's interest in supermarkets dwindled to less than 50% with the sale of its stake in Migros. Its sway however in the IT data processing business of KocNet Haberlesme Teknolojileri ve Iletisim Hizmetleri A.S. increased to almost 100%. The company picked up military aero and marine tech simulator Kaletron an arm of Kale Group too.

In 2009 the global recession curtailed industrial output and demand and hurt the company's revenues. However its diversified portfolio and cost saving measures enabled it to post a modest improvement in net income.

LOCATIONS

HQ: Koc Holdings AS
Nakkastepe, Azizbey Sok No. 1, Istanbul, Kuzguncuk 34674
Phone: (90) 216 531 0000   **Fax:** (90) 216 531 0099
Web: www.koc.com.tr

PRODUCTS/OPERATIONS

Sales

	% of total
Energy	63
Automotive	13
Consumer	11
Finance	8
Other	5
Total	**100**

Core Businesses
Automotive
Construction mining
Durable goods
Food/Beverage/Tobacco

Energy
Financial services
Information technology
International trade
Marinas
New developmen
Tourism services

HISTORICAL FINANCIALS

Company Type: Public

Income Statement

FYE: December 31

	REVENUE ($ mil.)	NET INCOME ($ mil.)	NET PROFIT MARGIN	EMPLOYEES
12/13	30,940	1,252	4.0%	80,996
12/12	47,364	1,292	2.7%	82,158
12/11	40,127	1,125	2.8%	80,987
12/10	34,861	1,123	3.2%	73,063
12/09	29,931	1,762	5.9%	71,221
Annual Growth	**0.8%**	**(8.2%)**	**—**	**3.3%**

2013 Year-End Financials

Debt ratio: 13.5%
Return on equity: 15.6%
Cash ($ mil.): 4,159
Current ratio: 1.35
Long-term debt ($ mil.): 5,791

No. of shares (mil.): —
Dividends
  Yield: 2.0%
  Payout: 21.7%
Market value ($ mil.): —

	STOCK PRICE ($) FY Close	P/E High/Low		PER SHARE ($) Earnings	Dividends	Book Value
12/13	20.61	8	4	0.49	0.41	0.03
12/12	26.16	9	5	0.51	0.27	0.04
12/11	14.88	11	5	0.47	0.22	0.03
12/10	24.45	17	8	0.47	0.38	(0.00)
12/09	15.25	11	8	0.38	0.00	0.05
Annual Growth	**7.8%**	**—**	**—**	**7.0%**	**—**	**(9.4%)**

Kommunalbanken A/S (Norway)

LOCATIONS

HQ: Kommunalbanken A/S (Norway)
Munkedamsveien 45, Oslo N-0110
Phone: (47) 21 50 20 00   **Fax:** (47) 21 50 20 01
Web: www.kbn.org

HISTORICAL FINANCIALS

Company Type: Public

Income Statement

FYE: December 31

	ASSETS ($ mil.)	NET INCOME ($ mil.)	INCOME AS % OF ASSETS	EMPLOYEES
12/13	59,561	178	0.3%	56
12/12	62,385	335	0.5%	54
12/11	61,022	120	0.2%	50
12/10	52,725	126	0.2%	48
12/09	40,257	242	0.6%	44
Annual Growth	**10.3%**	**(7.4%)**	**—**	**6.2%**

2013 Year-End Financials

Return on assets: 0.3%
Return on equity: 13.8%
Long-term debt ($ mil.): —
No. of shares (mil.): 2
Sales ($ mil): 945

Dividends
  Yield: —
  Payout: —
Market value ($ mil.): —

Koninklijke Ahold NV

A tattered prince of global food retailing Royal Ahold owns or has an interest in more than 5600 supermarkets and specialty stores in Europe and the US. While its status as one of the world's largest grocery retailers has been greatly diminished it still ranks as a leading supermarket operator along the East Coast of the US under names including Giant Food and Stop & Shop which account for about 60% of its total sales. Royal Ahold also operates Albert Heijn (the #1 food retailer in The Netherlands) as well as stores in Portugal the Baltic states the Czech Republic and Slovakia. Other interests include the US online grocery ordering and delivery service Peapod and Gall & Gall liquor stores.

HISTORY

Albert Heijn and his wife took over his father's grocery store in Ootzaan Netherlands in 1887. By the end of WWI the company had 50 Albert Heijn grocery stores in Holland and at WWII's end it had almost 250 stores. In 1948 the company went public.

It opened its first self-service store in 1952 and its first supermarket in 1955. Growing into the #1 grocer in the Netherlands Albert Heijn opened liquor and cosmetic stores in 1973. (It changed its name to Ahold that year to better reflect its range of businesses.) Ahold expanded outside the Netherlands in 1976 when it founded supermarket chain Cadadia in Spain (sold 1985).

Ahold entered the US in 1977 by purchasing BI-LO and furthered its expansion in 1981 by adding Pennsylvania-based Giant Food Stores. In 1987 in honor of its 100th anniversary Ahold was granted the title Koninklijke (Dutch for "royal"). In 1988 it bought a majority stake in Dutch food wholesaler Schuitema.

The company added New York-based TOPS Markets in 1991. That year Royal Ahold founded food retailer and distributor Euronova (now called Ahold Czech Republic) and in 1992 it acquired 49% of Portuguese food retailer Jeronimo Martins Retail. In 1993 Cees van der Hoeven was promoted to chief executive and Royal Ahold was listed on the NYSE.

Other acquisitions included New England grocery giant The Stop & Shop Companies in 1996. That year saw the beginning of several Asian joint ventures that gave Royal Ahold stores in Singapore Malaysia and Thailand. It also formed a joint venture in 1998 with Argentina's Velox Retail Holdings (owner of about 90% of supermarket operators DISCO and Santa Isabel) and Royal Ahold added Maryland-based grocer Giant Food Inc. (unrelated to Royal Ahold's Giant Food Stores).

Royal Ahold's moves in 1999 included the acquisition of several Spanish supermarket chains (with a total of about 200 stores) the purchase of Dutch institutional food wholesaler Gastronoom and the acquisition of 50% of Sweden's top food seller ICA AB. In Central America it acquired half of La Fragua an operator of supermarkets and discount stores. However North American expansion plans hit a snag when Royal Ahold backed out of a deal to buy Pathmark Stores.

In 2000 Royal Ahold acquired Spanish food retailer Kampio+ #2 and #4 foodservice distributors U.S. Foodservice and PYA/Monarch US convenience store chains Sugar Creek and Golden Gallon and all of the voting stock of Brazilian retailer Bompreco. In June the firm bought a 51% stake in online grocer Peapod. Royal Ahold took over food retailer Superdiplo which runs more than 300 stores in Spain (including the Canary Islands) in late 2000.

In March 2001 Royal Ahold began buying the remaining outstanding shares of Bompreco with the intention of delisting the company from the Brazilian Luxembourg and New York stock exchanges (which it did in late December). Chicago-based Peapod became a wholly owned Royal Ahold subsidiary in 2001. The retailer also expanded its bricks-and-mortar US presence in 2001 by purchasing Alliant Exchange parent of Alliant Foodservice which distributes food to more than 100000 customers and Bruno's Supermarkets which operates more than 180 stores in the Southeast. In December Ahold also agreed to buy the 32-store G. Barbosa supermarket chain which would add to its holdings in Brazil.

Royal Ahold reported its first net loss in nearly 30 years in the second quarter of 2002. In August 2002 Royal Ahold assumed full control of Disco Ahold International Holdings its former joint venture company with Velox Retail Holdings. Soon after the company increased its ownership stake in Chilean grocery chain Santa Isabel from 70% to 97% in a tender offer. In October the company integrated its Polish Czech and Slovak operations under the umbrella of Ahold Central Europe (ACE). ACE will manage more than 400 Albert supermarkets and Hypernova hypermarkets in Central Europe. In late 2002 subsidiary U.S. Foodservice agreed to buy Allen Foods a major independent foodservice distributor in the Central Plains region.

In February 2003 CEO Cees van der Hoeven and CFO Michiel Meurs resigned following an announcement that the grocery giant would restate its financial results by at least $500 million because of accounting irregularities at U.S. Foodservice. (van der Hoeven is facing charges by Dutch prosecutors in connection with the scandal at U.S. Foodservice.) Chairman Henny de Ruiter became acting CEO of the company and Dudley Eustace a British national who serves as a director of several Dutch companies was named interim CFO in March. In May 2003 IKEA veteran Anders Moberg became acting CEO; de Ruiter remained chairman. Soon after Ahold said it would restate earnings downward by $880 million (much more than the original $500 million projection) because of the accounting scandal at U.S. Foodservice. Further accounting investigations uncovered about $29 million in irregularities at the company's TOPS Markets US subsidiary.

In May Ahold completed the sale of its De Tuinen natural product stores to NBTY's British subsidiary Holland & Barrett Europe. In June it sold its Jamin chain of candy stores to Jamin management. The Santa Isabel chain in Chile was sold in July to Cencosud for about $95 million far less than the $150 million originally discussed. Adding to its woes in July the public prosecutor in Amsterdam launched a criminal investigation into possible falsification of accounts by the company. Soon after Ahold completed the sale of 22 stores in Indonesia to PT Hero Supermarket as well as its Malaysian retail business. In September the board of directors of Royal Ahold approved the appointment of Moberg and Ryopponen as CEO and CFO respectively. Later in the month the global grocer sold its operations in Paraguay (Supermercados Stock S.A.) to A.J. Vierci for about $4 million.

In October 2003 Royal Ahold published its long-awaited 2002 results revealing a $1.27 billion loss which the retailer attributed to special charges related to overstated profits at U.S. Foodservice. That month the company completed the sale of its 138-store Golden Gallon convenience chain to The Pantry for about $187 million and de Ruiter resigned and was succeeded by Karel Vuursteen previously a board member. In November Royal Ahold sold two hypermarkets in Poland to Carrefour Poland as part of its overall strategy to restructure its retail portfolio. In December the Peruvian operations of its Santa Isabel chain were sold to Grupo Interbank and other investors led by Nexus Group.

In March 2004 Royal Ahold sold its 118-store Bompreco chain in Brazil to Wal-Mart Stores and its credit card business (Hipercard) there to Unibanco S.A. for a combined price of about $500 million. Also in March the Dutch chain sold its stake in CRC Ahold operating in Thailand to its partner the Central Food Retail Co. completing the company's withdrawal from Asia. At a shareholders meeting in March Ahold placed the blame for the accounting scandal which nearly bankrupted the company in 2003 squarely on the shoulders of Jim Miller the former CEO of U.S. Foodservice. (Later Miller and Ahold agreed in late 2007 to settle litigation related to the matter with Miller paying Ahold $8 million.) In August Karel Vuursteen resigned as chairman of the supervisory board for personal reasons as was succeeded by Rene Dahan. In September Ahold reached a settlement with the Dutch public prosecutor in which the company agreed to pay Â8 million. In return the Dutch prosecutor agreed not to undertake proceedings against Royal Ahold. In October the company reached a settlement with the US Securities and Exchange Commission that imposed no fines on Royal Ahold due in part to its "extensive co-operation" with the investigation. The company also finalized a deal to increase its stake in its Scandinavian retail joint venture ICA AB. It paid its Â811 million for a 20% stake in the partnership sold by Canica. In December Ahold completed the sale of its retail activities in Spain and the Canary Islands (nearly 600 stores) to the Permira Funds.

In January 2005 the grocery giant sold its BI-LO and Bruno's chains in the southeastern US to an affiliate of Lone Star Funds for some $660 million. In February the Dutch retailer completed the sale of a dozen Hypernova hypermarkets in Poland to rival Carrefour followed by the sale of a single large hypermarket to a local Polish firm two months later. Also in April Royal Ahold completed its exit from Brazil with the sale of 32 G. Barbosa hypermarkets there to ACON Investments a US-based investment firm. In May the company announced completion of the sale of its 50% stake in Spanish winery Bodegas Williams & Humbert (formerly known as Luis Paez) to its joint venture partner Jose Medina y Cia SA for an undisclosed sum. In June Ahold completed the sale of its chain of 198 Wilson Farms and Sugarcreek convenience stores part of its TOPS Markets subsidiary in the US to WFI Acquisition for an undisclosed sum. In September Ahold sold its Deli XL foodservice operation in Belgium and the Netherlands to a subsidiary of South Africa-based The Bidvest Group for about Â140 million.

CFO Hannu Ryopponen resigned at the end of August 2005 to join Stora Enso an integrated paper packaging and forest products company. In October Royal Ahold completed the acquisition of 56 stores in the Czech Republic from Julius Meinl a.s. In November the company settled a US class action lawsuit by paying $1.1 billion to shareholders who purchased stock between July 3 1999 and February 23 2003; just before the 2003 accounting scandal broke. Concurrently the company reached an agreement to settle litigation with the Dutch Shareholders' Association.

The grocery chain also sold 13 large Hypernova hypermarkets in Poland to Carrefour and a local operator in early 2005. The company also moved its corporate headquarters from Zaandam to Amsterdam later in the year.

In 2006 the company sold three shopping centers in Poland and the Czech Republic for about Â108 million. In April Jose Alvarez was named president and CEO of the combined Stop & Shop/Giant-Landover organization succeeding Marc Smith who retired. In September Royal Ahold was reported to be in talks with its Belgian counterpart Delhaize regarding a possible merger. However negotiations were later suspended. In November the Dutch grocer completed the acquisition of 27 Konmar stores in the Netherlands from Laurus B.V. for about $130 million.

More than three years after teetering on the brink of bankruptcy as a result of one of Europe's largest financial scandals a Dutch court found former CEO Cees van der Hoeven and former CFO Michael Meurs guilty of fraud. Van der Hoeven and Meurs were accused of improperly booking sales from four subsidiaries in Scandinavia Argentina and Brazil. Both men were fined and given suspended sentences. Former executive board member Jan Andreae who headed Ahold's European operations was sentenced to four months in jail suspended for two years and fined.

CEO Anders Moberg left the company in July 2007. Also in July U.S. Foodservice was finally sold to a consortium of Clayton Dubilier & Rice and Kohlberg Kravis Roberts & Co. for about $7.1 billion. In November John Rishton Ahold's CFO who had been serving as interim chief executive since Moberg's departure was named to the post permanently. In December Royal Ahold sold its underperforming TOPS Markets chain to Morgan Stanley Private Equity for about $310 million.

In June 2008 the company completed sold its 73% stake in Schuitema N.V. to private equity firm CVC Capital Partners in return for cash and the transfer of 50-plus Schuitema stores to Ahold.

In 2009 Royal Ahold's Albert/Hypernova business in the Czech Republic and Slovakia closed 23 underperforming stores and downsized a dozen hypermarkets. It also finished converting its Hypernova stores to the Albert brand in the Czech Republic.

In February 2010 Ahold acquired 25 Ukrop's Super Market stores inventory equipment and leases in a $140 million transaction. The Ukrop's chain became part of Ahold USA's Giant-Carlisle division.

In March 2013 the company sold its 60% stake in the Sweden's largest food retailer ICA AB to Sweden's Hakon Invest for SEK 21.2 billion ($3.3 billion) in cash to better stick to its strategy of focusing on businesses it controls.

EXECUTIVES

Vice Chairman, Tom de Swaan, age 68
Chairman, Rene Dahan, age 73
CEO, A. Dick Boer, age 57, $828,250 total compensation
COO Europe, Sander van der Laan, age 45
Division President Giant Food Stores, Rick Herring
CFO, Jeff Carr, age 53
COO Ahold USA, James McCann, age 45
President and CEO Albert and Hypernova, Jan Van Dam, age 42
EVP and Chief Corporate Governance Counsel, Lodewijk Hijmans van den Bergh, age 50
General Manager Gall & Gall, Marit van Egmond
Vice Chairman, Tom de Swaan, age 68
Director, Derk C. Doijer, age 64
Director, Judith A. (Judy) Sprieser, age 60
Director, Ben J. Noteboom, age 56
Director, Stephanie M. Shern, age 66
Director, Rob F. van den Bergh
Director, Mark G. McGrath, age 67
Auditors: DeloitteAccountantsB.V.

LOCATIONS

HQ: Koninklijke Ahold NV
  Provincialeweg 11, Zaandam 1506 MA
Phone: (31) 88 659 5100
Web: www.ahold.com

2012 Stores

	No.
Europe	2,302
US	772
Total	**3,074**

Sales

	% of total
US	61
Europe	
The	34
Other	5
Total	**100**

PRODUCTS/OPERATIONS

2012 Stores

	No.
Albert Heijn Etos Gall &	1,996
Stop & Shop New England & Metro	403
Giant-Carlisle &	369
Albert/Hypernova	306
Total	**3,074**

Selected Operations

Retail
  Europe
    Albert (supermarkets Czech Republic and Slovakia)
    Albert Heijn (supermarkets convenience stores)
    bol.com (e-commerce nonfood)
    Etos (drugstores online shopping)
    Feira Nova (hypermarkets Portugal)
    Gall & Gall (liquor stores)
    Hypernova (hypermarkets Slovakia)
    Pingo Doce (supermarkets Portugal)
  US
    Giant-Carlisle (supermarkets & superstores)
    Giant-Landover (supermarkets)
    Stop & Shop (supermarkets)
    Peapod (online grocery shopping)

COMPETITORS

A&P	Lidl
ALDI	METRO AG
BJ's Wholesale Club	NorgesGruppen
Big Y Foods	Safeway
Carrefour	Shaw's
Costco Wholesale	Target Corporation
Delhaize	Tesco
Golub	Wal-Mart
Kooperativa Forbundet	Wegmans
Kroger	Whole Foods

HISTORICAL FINANCIALS

Company Type: Public

Income Statement

FYE: December 29

	REVENUE ($ mil.)	NET INCOME ($ mil.)	NET PROFIT MARGIN	EMPLOYEES
12/13	45,217	3,517	7.8%	222,000
12/12*	43,286	1,090	2.5%	225,000
01/12	39,154	1,315	3.4%	218,000
01/11	39,475	1,140	2.9%	213,000
01/10	40,136	1,284	3.2%	206,000
Annual Growth	**3.0%**	**28.6%**	**—**	**1.9%**

*Fiscal year change

2013 Year-End Financials

Debt ratio: 27.6%	No. of shares (mil.): 982
Return on equity: 40.6%	Dividends
Cash ($ mil.): 3,460	Yield: 0.0%
Current ratio: 1.51	Payout: 19.6%
Long-term debt ($ mil.): 3,983	Market value ($ mil.): 17,891

	STOCK PRICE ($) FY Close	P/E High/Low		PER SHARE ($) Earnings	Dividends	Book Value
12/13	18.21	15	10	3.31	0.65	9.20
12/12*	13.33	32	23	1.03	0.00	7.61
01/12	13.45	29	21	1.15	0.00	7.17
01/11	13.19	36	27	0.96	0.00	6.90
01/10	13.25	40	24	1.06	0.00	6.62
Annual Growth	**8.3%**	**—**		**32.9%**	**—**	**8.6%**

*Fiscal year change

Koninklijke Philips N.V.

In the beginning Koninklijke Philips (Royal Philips in English) created light. Now it makes light bulbs (#1 worldwide) LED lighting and lamps as well as audio/multimedia entertainment electronics electric shavers and toothbrushes coffee makers and other kitchen appliances. It also makes a slew of medical equipment for disease diagnosis treatment and management. Amid a down economy and weak markets Philips has dumped noncore businesses such as its stakes in TSMC LG Display and music giant PolyGram as it acquires and forms JVs in its fast-growing businesses: healthcare consumer lifestyle and lighting. The company's presence in developing markets generates about one-third of its sales.

HISTORY

Gerard Philips (later joined by brother Anton) founded Philips & Co. in the Dutch city of Eindhoven in 1891. Surviving an industry shakeout Philips prospered as a result of Gerard's engineering and Anton's foreign sales efforts. The company had become Europe's #3 light bulb maker by 1900. It adopted the name Philips Gloeilampenfabrieken (light bulb factory) in 1912.

The Netherlands' neutrality during WWI allowed Philips to expand and integrate into glass manufacturing (1915) and X-ray and radio tubes (1918). The company set up its first foreign sales office in Belgium in 1919; it started building plants abroad in the 1930s to avoid trade barriers and tariffs.

During WWII Philips created US and British trusts to hold majority interests in North American Philips (NAP) and in Philips' British operations. Following the war the company established hundreds of subsidiaries worldwide. It repurchased its British businesses in 1955; NAP operated independently until it was reacquired in 1987.

The company started marketing televisions and appliances in the 1950s. Philips introduced audiocassette VCR and laser disc technology in the 1960s but had limited success with computers and office equipment. Despite its development of new technologies in the 1970s Philips was unable to maintain market share against an onslaught of inexpensive goods from Japan. Meanwhile NAP acquired Magnavox (consumer electronics) in 1974. NAP also purchased GTE Television in 1981 and Westinghouse's lighting business in 1983. In 1986 it provided $60 million in seed money to start Taiwan Semiconductor Manufacturing with the Taiwanese government.

Philips' successful PolyGram unit (formed in 1972) went public in 1989 and bought record companies Island (UK) that year and A&M (US) the next. In 1991 the company changed its name to Royal Philips Electronics.

Ill-timed product introductions contributed to huge losses in the early 1990s. Philips cut some 60000 jobs and sold money-losing businesses including its computer business. Cor Boonstra a former Sara Lee executive was named chairman and president in 1996. The company sold its cellular communications business in 1996 to AT&T and merged its systems integration unit with BSO/Origin to form Origin B.V. Continuing to focus on core businesses it sold its 75% stake in PolyGram to Seagram and bought US-based medical instruments maker ATL Ultrasound in 1998. Also that year Philips sold its optoelectronics unit to Uniphase Corp.

The company formed an alliance with Sun Microsystems and Sony in 1999 to develop appliances that use the Internet. Philips then launched a hostile takeover of microchip maker VLSI Technology and after negotiations bought VLSI for nearly $1 billion. It also bought a 50% stake in LG LCD a subsidiary of LG Group for $1.6 billion. It was renamed LG.Philips LCD Co. soon thereafter. Since then Philips has begun to slowly reduced its stake in LG.Philips LCD to some 20%. In one move Philips in October 2007 sold the equivalent of $2.2 billion in LG.Philips LCD (some 46.4 million shares) or a 13% stake.

In 2000 the company formed TriMedia Technologies with Sony to create embedded processor core designs and software. Also that year Philips divested its 24% stake ($3.8 billion) in semiconductor equipment maker ASML Holding. In late 2000 Philips bought 60% of top medical transcription service MedQuist and agreed to buy Adac Laboratories (nuclear imaging technology) for $426 million.

In 2001 amid a large decline in profits Philips announced plans to trim its semiconductor spending by up to 50%. Also that month Boonstra retired and COO Gerard Kleisterlee became chairman and president. In August 2001 Philips completed its acquisition of the Healthcare Solutions Group of Agilent Technologies for $1.7 billion and in October the firm acquired Marconi Medical Systems a distributor of medical imaging systems.

Since 2001 Philips has cut more than 35000 jobs; the reductions are the result of support staff job eliminations and the sale of noncore businesses (Communication Security and Imaging unit to Robert Bosch GmbH; contract manufacturing services to Jabil Circuit; healthcare products group to Platinum Equity Holdings). The company also dissolved its components division (maker of screens for mobile phones and optical storage products) and transferred Mexican production of computer monitors to China.

In 2003 Fidelio Acquisition Company (an investor firm led by Philips along with Sony Corporation of America) acquired InterTrust Technologies a manufacturer of digital copy-protection software for $450 million.

The company sold 80% of its aerospace division to Italian firm the Avio Group who renamed it DutchAero.

In a transaction valued at $2 billion Philips in 2005 sold its computer-monitor manufacturing operations and a portion of its flat screen TV business to Hong Kong-based TPV Technology making that company the world's largest manufacturer of PC monitors.

Also that year Frits Philips son of founder Anton Philips and the last member of the Philips family to manage the company (he retired in 1977) and who helped develop audio cassettes and the compact disc died at the age of 100.

The company focused on strengthening its presence in its core lighting industry during 2005. It extended its reach into LEDs with the purchase of Agilent Technologies that year.

It also focused on developing its presence in health care. Philips purchased personal emergency response service Lifeline Systems in 2006 and rolled the Lifeline operations into its medical systems unit. Also that year it acquired Intermagnetics General Corporation a US manufacturer of magnetic resonance imaging (MRI) scanners for about $1.3 billion in cash. The deal allows Philips to flex its muscle in the MRI niche of the medical imaging and equipment industry and gives the company a leg up in fast-growing radio frequency coils which are sold to hospitals and imaging centers. (Intermagnetics was folded into the company's medical systems division; its headquarters in Latham New York became the worldwide base for Philips' MRI business.)

Philips Electronics sold 80% of its semiconductor division in 2006 to a group of private equity firms including Kohlberg Kravis Roberts & Co. Silver Lake Partners and AlpInvest Partners for about $4.3 billion. The deal created a stand-alone company called NXP (for Next Experience) based in Eindhoven the Netherlands. NXP supplies chips to improve the performance of next generation consumer devices including digital TVs and cell phones rather than personal computers. Philips also sold its Philips Sound Solutions (PSS) business to Japan's D&M Holdings. PSS supplied speaker systems primarily to the automotive industry.

In 2007 the company announced a reorganization of its top units in order to simplify structure. The company established three core units: Philips Lighting Philips Consumer Lifestyle and Philips Healthcare.

Extending its reach into the home health and baby care arenas in 2007 the company acquired personal emergency-response service Health Watch Holdings for $130 million and UK baby care products maker Avent for about $860 million. The move was part of a Philips strategy to solidify its baby products presence in Europe with an eye toward expansion of Avent into Asia.

Philips and China Electronics Corporation (CEC) inked a deal in 2007 that transferred Philips' remaining mobile phone activities to CEC. As a result of the deal CEC took over the responsibility for Philips' mobile phone business.

In order to gain its own share in growing light-emitting diode (LED) sector Philips in 2007 acquired Color Kinetics which caters to the professional LED niche for some $690 million as well as Canada's TIR Systems for about $70 million. (Following the acquisition of Color Kinetics Philips changed the unit's name to Philips Solid-State Lighting Solutions.)

In 2008 Philips purchased Respironics a leading medical alert system in North America for $4.9 billion. Respironics also develops medical devices for treating sleep apnea and other respiratory disorders a growing healthcare issue. The deal gained a foothold in the home health care solutions market a new line of business for the Dutch conglomerate. Philips' other significant acquisition in 2008 was Genlyte Group bought for nearly $3 billion. The addition later renamed Philips Lighting Business Unit Professional Luminaires North America boosted Philips' place in the lighting industry which accounts for approximately one-third of its sales.

Building on its health care information technology holdings Philips in 2008 also acquired VISICU which develops remote patient-monitoring systems for about Â300 million (about $430 million) and cardiac data monitoring company TOMCAT Systems. Concurrently Philips unloaded the final shares in Taiwan Semiconductor Manufacturing Company one of the largest contract semiconductor manufacturers in the world. The company

recorded a profit of Â260 million (nearly $400 million) from the sale.

To better focus on its core businessesPhilips in 2009 sold its nearly 15% stake in LG Display for about Â630 million (about $900 million). LG Display originally a joint venture with LG Electronics was formed when the two firms merged their LCD businesses. The company built on its emergency care offerings in 2009 through the purchase of InnerCool Therapies a developer of temperature management products from Cardium Therapeutics. The deal was worth about $10 million and included the transfer of some $1.5 million in trade payables.

Philips paid Â170 million ($241.5 million) to acquire the Italian espresso machine maker Saeco International Group in 2009. Following the purchase Saeco became part of the domestic appliances unit of the Philips Consumer Lifestyle business.

Among its 11 acquisitions in 2010 Philips purchased specialized lighting company Burton Medical Products Corporation. Burton's lineup is mainly used in healthcare facility lighting. It also acquired China-based Shanghai Apex Electronics Technology (Apex). Supporting Philips' lead in the medical equipment market Apex manufactures ultrasound equipment. The Consumer Lifestyle arm of Phillips gained Discus Holdings a maker of professional tooth-whitening products.

Frans van Houten was named president/CEO and chairman of the company's management board in April 2011.

EXECUTIVES

VP Member of Management Board and Chief Exec, Stephen H. (Steve) Rusckowski, age 58

EVP; CEO Philips Lighting, Rudy S. Provoost, age 55

President; Chief Executive Officer; Chairman of the Board of Management and Executive Committee, Frans van Houten, age 55

EVP and CFO, Ron H. Wirahadiraksa

EVP; CEO Philips Consumer Lifestyle, Pieter Nota, age 50

EVP; CEO Greater China, Patrick S. Kung

EVP; CEO Philips Healthcare, Deborah DiSanzo

Member Group Management Committee Chief Strategy Officer and Group Controller, Gerard Ruizendaal, age 56

Member Group Management Committee and CTO, Rick Harwig, age 65

Head External Communications, Gerd Gotz

SVP and General Manager Global Business Unit Hospitality, Paul Peeters, age 51

EVP and Chief Legal Officer, Eric Coutinho, age 63

Member Group Management Committee and Global Head Human Resources Management, Hayko Kroese, age 59

Member Group Management Committee CIO and Global Head Purchasing, Maarten de Vries

Director Corporate Communications, David L. Wolf

Head Investor Relations, Stewart McCrone

Chief Press Officer, Arent Jan Hesselink

Senior Press Officer, Shai Dewan

Vice Chairman Supervisory Board, John M. Thompson, age 71

Manager Investor Relations, Pim Preesman

Communications Manager Healthcare, Andre Manning

Communications Manager Philips Design, Ange Dunselman

Communications Manager Consumer Lifestyle, Jurn Hageman

Communications Manager Philips Corporate Technologies, Ellen de Vries

Communications Manager Lighting, Marike Westra

Communications Manager Philips Intellectual Property and Standards, Bjorn Teuwsen

Communications Manager Asia Pacific, Donough
  Foley
Communications Manager Latin America, Fabiano
  Lima
EVP Chief Strategy Officer and Chief Innovation
  Officer, Jim Andrew, age 53
EVP and Chief Human Resources Officer, Carole
  Wainaina, age 49
Executive Vice President & Chief Market Leader;
  Member of Executive Committee, Ronald Jong
CEO of Philips Healthcare, DiSanzo Deborah
Member of the Management Board and Chief
  Executive Officer Philips Lighting Division, Eric
  Rondolat
Chairman of the Supervisory Board, Jeroen Veer
Director, James J. (Jim) Schiro, age 68
Director, Cornelis J. A. (Cees) van Lede, age 72
Director, Ewald Kist, age 70
Director, Heino von Prondzynski, age 64
Director, Jackson P. Tai, age 63
Member of the Supervisory Board, Christine A.
  (Chris) Poon, age 61
Vice Chairman Supervisory Board, John M.
  Thompson, age 71
Member of the Supervisory Board, Cornelis Lede
Member of the Supervisory Board, Heino
  Prondzynski
Member of the Supervisory Board, Neelam Dhawan
Auditors: KPMGAccountantsN.V.

LOCATIONS

HQ: Koninklijke Philips N.V.
  Breitner Center, Amstelplein 2, Amsterdam 1096 BC
Phone: (31) 20 59 77 777
Web: www.philips.com

Sales

	% of total
US	28
China	9
Germany	6
France	5
Japan	4
Brazil	3
Netherlands	3
Other	41
Total	**100**

PRODUCTS/OPERATIONS

Sales

	% of total
Healthcare	39
Lighting	34
Consumer	26
Group management & services	1
Total	**100**

Sales

	% of total
Goods	85
Services	13
Licenses and	2
Total	**100**

Selected Business Areas
Consumer
  Audio video multimedia and accessories
  Coffee
  Domestic appliances
  Health and wellness
  Personal care
Healthcare
  Home healthcare
  Imaging systems
  Patient care and clinical informatics
  Customer services
Lighting
  Automotive
  Home luminaries and systems
  Lamps
  Lighting systems and controls
  Lumileds

Professional luminaries and systems
  Special lighting applications
Philips Group
  Healthcare Incubators
  Philips Design
  Philips Innovation Campus
  Philips Innovation Services
  Philips Intellectual Property and Standards
  Philips Research

COMPETITORS

BSH Bosch und Siemens Hausgerate	Pioneer Corporation
	ResMed
Covidien	SANYO
De' Longhi	Samsung Group
Fujitsu	Sharp Corp.
GE	Siemens AG
GE India	Siemens Corp.
Harman International	Sony
Invacare	Spectrum Brands
LG Electronics	Technicolor
Mitsubishi Electric	Texas Instruments
OSRAM	Toshiba
Panasonic Corp	

HISTORICAL FINANCIALS
Company Type: Public

Income Statement

FYE: December 31

	REVENUE ($ mil.)	NET INCOME ($ mil.)	NET PROFIT MARGIN	EMPLOYEES
12/13	32,117	1,609	5.0%	116,681
12/12	32,671	297	0.9%	118,087
12/11	29,204	(1,675)	—	125,241
12/10	34,020	1,935	5.7%	119,001
12/09	33,405	590	1.8%	115,924
Annual Growth	**(1.0%)**	**28.5%**	**—**	**0.2%**

2013 Year-End Financials

Debt ratio: 20.2%	No. of shares (mil.): 913
Return on equity: 10.4%	Dividends
Cash ($ mil.): 3,393	Yield: 2.2%
Current ratio: 1.35	Payout: 202.2%
Long-term debt ($ mil.): 4,555	Market value ($ mil.): 33,766

	STOCK PRICE ($) FY Close	P/E High/Low	PER SHARE ($) Earnings	Dividends	Book Value
12/13	36.97	55 37	1.75	0.83	16.90
12/12	26.54	187 113	0.32	0.80	16.05
12/11	20.95	— —	(1.76)	0.00	17.26
12/10	30.70	42 29	2.05	0.79	21.28
12/09	29.44	138 55	0.66	0.80	22.67
Annual Growth	**5.9%**	**— —**	**27.5%**	**1.0%**	**(7.1%)**

Korea Electric Power Corp

Korea Electric Power (KEPCO) is slowly relinquishing its status as South Korea's electric utility monopoly. The company is still the country's primary power distributor serving 12 million households. It generates 87% of Korea's power supply with an installed capacity of more than 65380 MW (primarily from thermal and nuclear plants). KEPCO also buys capacity from independent power producers. Industrial demand accounts for more than 50% of the company's annual output. In response to deregulation the company plans to divest more than half of its Korean-based gen-

eration assets while it builds an extensive power plant portfolio in other countries. The Korean government controls 51% of KEPCO.

In a government effort to restructure the power industry KEPCO is required to spin off all of its fossil-fueled power generation operations which have been split up into five new subsidiaries; the utility will retain its nuclear and hydroelectric plants. However due to market conditions the privatization plans have been delayed. The government looked at options to allow competition in the country's power distribution market but these plans have also been suspended.

KEPCO is looking to become both a leader in the use of green technology (pushing "smart" grid deployment and cleaner burning power plants and wind farms). With power use beginning to plateau in Korea KEPCO is looking to become a global power player (a "Global Top Five Energy and Engineering Company by 2020"). In 2010 the company was engaged in power plant and related projects in a wide range of countries including Australia China Egypt Nigeria the Philippines Russia and the US and had more than 5420 MW of installed capacity outside of Korea. All told it was involved in 84 international projects in nuclear hydro and thermal power plants transmission and distribution projects and energy resources development initiatives.

To improve its coal self-sufficiency in 2010 KEPCO acquired the Bylong coal mine in Australia from Anglo American PLC for $340 million.

The reviving economy higher commodity prices and increased energy demand helped to lift sales and net income in 2010.

In 2011 the company agreed to set up a 66%-owned joint venture with Germany's Uhde GmbH. Kepco-Uhde Inc. will work on joint projects in Korea relating to integrated gasification combined cycle and synthetic natural gas.

EXECUTIVES

President CEO and Director, Ssang-Su Kim, age 68
EVP Chief Nuclear Project Officer and Director,
  Jun-Yeon Byun, age 57
EVP COO and Director, Woo-Kyum Kim, age 59
Controller Auditor General and Director, Dae-Soo
  Han
EVP CFO and Director, In-Kook Cho, age 58
EVP Chief Human Resources Officer and
  Director, Jong-Ho Kim
EVP CTO and Director, Chong-Young Kim
President CEO and Director, Ssang-Su Kim, age 68
EVP Chief Nuclear Project Officer and Director,
  Jun-Yeon Byun, age 57
Director, Tae-Sik Lee, age 67
Director, Seog-Hoon Kang, age 48
Director, Jung-Kook Kim, age 66
Director, Kyung-Min Kim, age 57
Director, Il-Soon Shin, age 64
Director, Dong-Rack Chung
Director, Gi-Pyo Lee
EVP COO and Director, Woo-Kyum Kim, age 59
Controller Auditor General and Director, Dae-Soo
  Han
EVP CFO and Director, In-Kook Cho, age 58
EVP Chief Human Resources Officer and
  Director, Jong-Ho Kim
EVP CTO and Director, Chong-Young Kim
Director, Hae-Joo Chung
Auditors: DeloitteAnjinLLC

LOCATIONS

HQ: Korea Electric Power Corp
  512 Yeongdong-daero Gangnam-gu, Seoul 135-882
Phone: (82) 2 3456 3114   Fax: (82) 2 3456 4298
Web: www.kepco.co.kr

PRODUCTS/OPERATIONS

Sales

	% of total
Electricity	97
Other	3
Total	**100**

Selected Subsidiaries

Korea-based companies
  Korea East-West Power Co. Ltd. (EWP power generation)
  Korea Hydro & Nuclear Power Co. Ltd. (KHNP power generation)
  Korea Midland Power Co. Ltd. (KOMIPO power generation)
  Korea South-East Power Co. Ltd. (KOSEP power generation)
  Korea Southern Power Co. Ltd. (KOSPO power generation)
  Korea Western Power Co. Ltd. (KOWEPO power generation)
KEPCO Austrailia Pty. Ltd.
KEPCO International Hong Kong Ltd.
KEPCO Middle East Holding Company
KEPCO Philippines Corporation

COMPETITORS

AES	National Power
CLP Holdings	Power Assets
EGAT	Taiwan Power
Huaneng Power	Tokyo Electric
International Power	Tractebel Engineering

HISTORICAL FINANCIALS

Company Type: Public

Income Statement

FYE: December 31

	REVENUE ($ mil.)	NET INCOME ($ mil.)	NET PROFIT MARGIN	EMPLOYEES
12/13	51,384	57	0.1%	20,000
12/12	46,287	(2,965)	—	19,568
12/11	37,570	(2,908)	—	19,579
12/10	35,233	(106)	—	19,927
12/09	29,379	(83)	—	20,170
Annual Growth	**15.0%**	**—**		**(0.2%)**

2013 Year-End Financials

Debt ratio: 0.0%	No. of shares (mil.): 623
Return on equity: 0.1%	Dividends
Cash ($ mil.): 2,122	Yield: —
Current ratio: 0.76	Payout: —
Long-term debt ($ mil.): 50,552	Market value ($ mil.): 10,349

	STOCK PRICE ($) FY Close	P/E High/Low	PER SHARE ($) Earnings	Dividends	Book Value
12/13	16.61	— —	0.09	0.00	76.71
12/12	13.97	— —	(4.76)	0.00	75.00
12/11	10.98	— —	(4.67)	0.00	73.79
12/10	13.51	— —	(0.17)	0.00	81.38
12/09	14.54	— —	(0.13)	0.00	56.95
Annual Growth	**3.4%**	— —	—	—	**7.7%**

Korea Gas Corp. (South Korea)

As the world's largest importer of liquefied natural gas (LNG) KOGAS single-handedly helps South Koreans stay warm and chill out. The company is the sole provider of LNG to the country (about 25 million tons imported annually) operating three terminals and a nationwide pipeline network. KOGAS supplies LNG to power plants and utility companies throughout South Korea and produces and supplies LNG products to domestic and overseas markets. It imports come around the world including from Indonesia Malaysia Myanmar Oman Qatar and Russia. KOGAS development initiatives include natural gas vehicles LNG chiller/heater systems for homes and fuel cells.

Operations
KOGAS operates three LNG terminals and a nationwide pipeline network spanning over 3022 km. The company imports LNG and distributes it to consumers across South Korea. Ten power generation companies (17 power generation plants) supply the gas to their end users within their respective regions.

It major business lines include: Construction and Operation of LNG Terminals and Natural Gas Distribution Network; Exploration and Import/Export of Natural Gas and LNG; Production and Distribution of Natural Gas (including Purification and Sales of By-products); and Research and Technical Development.

Financial Performance
In 2011 KOGAS' revenues increased by 25% and its net income by 134%.

Strategy
It has expanded its research and development's core competencies in upstream businesses new energy and future growth engines and is expanding its network by adding domestic and overseas energy research and development institutes.

Seeking future LNG supply it is also active in global gas supply and LNG projects. In 2011 KOGAS signed on to an LNG joint development project in Indonesia and in 2010 it secured development and production rights in the oil and gas fields in Zubair and Badra in Iraq and an equity partnership in Australia's Gladstone LNG project.

Ownership
The Korean government owns about 27% of the company KEPCO 24.5%.

Company Background
KOGAS was incorporated by the Korean government in 1983.

In 2006 KOGAS acquired an 8% interest in China Gas Holdings as a strategic partner. The deal paved the way for further expansion in China's gas distribution market. KOGAS additionally acquired four LNG tankers in a joint venture with three other South Korean companies. The move pointed to a broadening of its overall LNG business.

EXECUTIVES

CEO, Kangsoo Choo

LOCATIONS

HQ: Korea Gas Corp. (South Korea)
  171, Dolma-ro Bundang-gu, Seongnam-si, Gyeonggi-do 463-754
Phone: (82) 31 710 0114   **Fax:** (82) 31 710 0399
Web: www.kogas.or.kr

COMPETITORS

BP	JX Nippon Oil &
Exxon Mobil	Energy
GS Caltex	SK Innovation

HISTORICAL FINANCIALS

Company Type: Public

Income Statement

FYE: December 31

	REVENUE ($ mil.)	NET INCOME ($ mil.)	NET PROFIT MARGIN	EMPLOYEES
12/13	36,193	(190)	—	3,202
12/12	32,809	343	1.0%	2,999
12/11	24,591	156	0.6%	2,815
12/10	20,280	246	1.2%	2,797
12/09	16,889	206	1.2%	2,790
Annual Growth	**21.0%**	**—**		**3.5%**

2013 Year-End Financials

Debt ratio: 0.0%	No. of shares (mil.): 87
Return on equity: (-2.3%)	Dividends
Cash ($ mil.): 211	Yield: —
Current ratio: 1.47	Payout: —
Long-term debt ($ mil.): 20,276	Market value ($ mil.): —

Kreditanstalt Fuer Wiederaufbau (Germany, Fed. Rep.)

KfW Bankengruppe is a state-owned development bank designed to assist developing countries and the German economy. The bank lends to small and midsized enterprises (SMEs) and buys securitized SME loan portfolios from German banks to keep that area of lending robust. It also provides funds for housing infrastructure environmental protection and venture capital. Additionally KfW finances telecommunications transportation energy infrastructure and industrial projects worldwide. The bank receives funds from the federal budget as well as through investments in the domestic and international capital markets. The German government owns 80% of KfW; the Lander or German states own the rest.

Geographic Reach
KfW maintains offices in Frankfurt Bonn and Berlin but it relies on a network of commercial banks throughout the nation to process applications and to service loans.

Operations
KfW Mittelstandsbank is KfW's lending business lending and investment arm while KfW Privatkundenbank and KfW Kommunalbank provide housing environmental education and infrastructure funding. The group's main operating subsidiaries include KfW IPEX-Bank which provides project and export financing and DEG a unit focused on promoting the private sector in developing and industrializing countries where the company's KfW Entwicklungsbank is funding projects to fight hunger and poverty.

Financial Performance
Revenues for KfW Bankengruppe rose 9% in fiscal 2011 as compared to 2010. Net income for the same reporting period dropped 21% as net cash inflow rose by E126 million in 2011 vs. 2010.

Company Ownership
The German government owns 80% of the company while the Lander or German states hold the remaining stake.

HISTORY

The Kreditanstalt for Wiederaufbau (KfW) began operations in 1948 to distribute Marshall Plan funds from the Allies. Formed by the British and American military governments that occupied West Germany following WWII the Frankfurt-based company (whose name translates as "reconstruction loan corporation") spent its first five years channeling about half of its financing directly to West German firms and the rest to banks that doled out loans. Concentrating on the highly industrialized Ruhr Valley it mainly funded rebuilding projects and industries relating to raw materials energy generation steel farming and food.

By 1954 the bank had largely achieved its original goals. But the West German government to which the company reported realized the political advantages of an entity with expertise in economic development and set up the European Recovery Program an extension of Marshall Plan funds. KfW shifted its focus to financing projects in such weak regions of West Germany as areas bordering East Germany and Saarland which joined the republic after French occupation ended in 1957.

During the second half of the 1950s the bank began its metamorphosis from a distribution agency for postwar reconstruction aid to a financial institution that had a role in driving the West German economy. It entered into export financing providing funds for middle- and long-term West German export risks like power plants and machinery. The company also began to offer loans to West German firms that contracted with domestic suppliers.

As the Berlin Wall was being constructed in 1961 the bank started providing financing to foreign countries with an emphasis on development aid projects. Among its initial programs was a partnership with the International Development Organization to finance the construction of the Rosieres Dam in Sudan. Also that year spurred by a meeting between West German chancellor Konrad Adenauer and Israeli Prime Minister David Ben-Gurion the company began to surreptitiously provide loans to Israel in a project known as "Operation Business Partner" which continued until 1965 when Israel began to officially receive aid.

In the 1970s KfW started floating bonds on the domestic capital market to raise funds. Using this money it initiated programs that granted low-interest loans to small to midsized domestic businesses that traditionally did not have access to international capital markets. The bank also financed major West German companies that were involved in such prominent international projects as the Channel Tunnel which would connect the UK to continental Europe.

In 1975 the company subsidized the migration of ethnic Germans from Poland into West Germany.

The bank received permission from the US Securities and Exchange Commission to become the first German financial institution to issue bonds on the US capital markets in 1986. Two years later it formed US-based subsidiary KfW International Finance.

After the fall of the Berlin Wall in 1989 KfW concentrated its efforts on reconstruction efforts in East Germany. By 1990 approximately two-thirds of its loans were being funneled into the eastern Lander (German states). Its largest deal though was a program to construct some 45000 homes in the USSR for Russian soldiers being transferred from East Germany. The company merged with Staatsbank Berlin the central bank of the former East Germany in 1994.

On behalf of the German government KfW spun off interests in Deutsche Telekom and Deutsche Post in 2000. The next year the company acquired a 33% stake in IKB Deutsche Industriebank.

In the following years KfW increasingly focused on international development. It formed its KfW IPEX-Bank unit in 2006. Also that year KfW began offering domestic student loans.

LOCATIONS

HQ: Kreditanstalt Fuer Wiederaufbau (Germany, Fed. Rep.)
Palmengartenstrasse 5-9, Frankfurt am Main D-60325
Phone: (49) 69 7431 0   **Fax:** (49) 69 7431 2944
Web: www.kfw.de

Selected Subsidiaries

KfW IPEX-Bank GmbH Frankfurt am Main (KfW IPEX-Bank)
DEG Deutsche Investitions- und Entwicklungsgesellschaft mbH Cologne (DEG)
KfW IPEX-Beteiligungsholding GmbH Frankfurt am Main
KfW Beteiligungsholding GmbH Bonn
tbg Technologie-Beteiligungs-Gesellschaft mbH Bonn (tbg)
Finanzierungs- und Beratungsgesellschaft mbH Berlin (FuB)

PRODUCTS/OPERATIONS

Selected Markets

Energy infrastructure
Industrial projects
Telecommunications
Transportation

HISTORICAL FINANCIALS

Company Type: Public

Income Statement

FYE: December 31

	ASSETS ($ mil.)	NET INCOME ($ mil.)	INCOME AS % OF ASSETS	EMPLOYEES
12/13	639,844	1,752	0.3%	5,374
12/12	674,343	3,142	0.5%	5,190
12/11	640,023	2,674	0.4%	4,765
12/10	591,235	3,521	0.6%	4,531
12/09	576,348	1,623	0.3%	4,265
Annual Growth	2.6%	1.9%	—	5.9%

2013 Year-End Financials

Return on assets: 0.2%
Return on equity: 6.1%
Long-term debt ($ mil.): —
No. of shares (mil.): —
Sales ($ mil): 16,451

Dividends
  Yield: —
  Payout: —
Market value ($ mil.): —

L'Oreal S.A. (France)

LOCATIONS

HQ: L' Oreal S.A. (France)
41, rue Martre, Clichy, Cedex 92117
Phone: (33) 1 47 56 70 00   **Fax:** (33) 1 47 56 86 42
Web: www.loreal.com

HISTORICAL FINANCIALS

Company Type: Public

Income Statement

FYE: December 31

	REVENUE ($ mil.)	NET INCOME ($ mil.)	NET PROFIT MARGIN	EMPLOYEES
12/13	31,632	4,072	12.9%	77,452
12/12	29,606	3,779	12.8%	72,637
12/11	26,312	3,153	12.0%	68,886
12/10	26,092	2,997	11.5%	66,619
12/09	25,170	2,581	10.3%	64,643
Annual Growth	5.9%	12.1%	—	4.6%

2013 Year-End Financials

Debt ratio: 1.7%
Return on equity: 13.5%
Cash ($ mil.): 3,589
Current ratio: 1.42
Long-term debt ($ mil.): 129

No. of shares (mil.): 599
Dividends
  Yield: 1.7%
  Payout: 16.1%
Market value ($ mil.): 21,083

	STOCK PRICE ($) FY Close	P/E High/Low		PER SHARE ($) Earnings	Dividends	Book Value
12/13	35.15	14	10	6.70	0.60	51.96
12/12	27.98	10	7	6.25	0.52	46.11
12/11	20.83	12	8	5.28	1.01	38.37
12/10	22.46	12	7	5.07	0.40	33.74
12/09	22.30	16	7	4.42	0.39	33.49
Annual Growth	12.0%		—	— 11.0%	11.1%	11.6%

Landesbank Baden-Wurttemberg

Landesbank Baden-Worttemberg (LBBW) acts as the central bank to savings banks in the German states of Baden-Worttemberg Rhineland Palatinate and Saxony. The bank handles large transactions (wholesale banking financial securities foreign exchange) too costly for the smaller state savings banks. Through its regional banks Baden Worttembergische Bank and Sachsen Bank and Rheinland-Pfalz Bank LBBW also provides traditional retail banking services such as real estate and commercial loans and portfolio management at more than 200 branches. Other subsidiaries provide leasing factoring venture capital and equity financing services.

LBBW operates offices worldwide that assist export-oriented companies and other German-based customers. LBBW has offices in New York London Singapore Seoul and Mexico City. Those operations are supplemented by four German Centres of Industry in Beijing Mexico City Singapore and India.

Banks all over the world felt the impacts of the global financial crisis and LBBW was not immune. Solid income from its corporate financial markets and private customer segments was not enough to protect the bank from overall losses due to a slowdown in the banking sector and exposure to toxic assets in 2008 and 2009.

In order to strengthen its capital base and provide LBBW with enough liquidity for it to continue functioning as a financing partner the company's government owners pumped in about E5 billion ($6.5 billion) to the bank in 2009. The state of Baden-Worttemberg also provided a E13 billion ($16.5 billion) protection guarantee against risks.

As a condition of the bailout the European Commission ordered LBBW to undergo restructuring.

Under the plan the bank was forced to scale back its credit substitute business and cut costs by selling equity investments and eliminating 2500 jobs. At the end of the restructuring LBBW will be smaller and more focused on its core business with corporations private customers and savings banks. It also plans to grow its financial markets and real estate financing business.

As part of the restructuring LBBW agreed to sell its LBBW Securities to Guggenheim Partners in 2010. LBBW Securities is the US broker/dealer for LBBW and handles repurchase agreements securities lending and other financing transactions.

The Savings Banks Association of Baden-Worttemberg owns about 40% of LBBW. The state of Baden-Worttemberg its capital of Stuttgart and Landesbeteilgungen Baden-Worttemberg each controls about 20%.

HISTORY

Landesbank Baden-Worttemberg traces its roots to three German institutions. The oldest Landesgirokasse - Offentliche Bank und Landessparkasse was founded in 1818 in Stuttgart Germany and eventually grew to be a medium-sized regional savings bank.

Landeskreditbank Baden-Worttemberg was formed in 1924 and throughout the rest of the 20th century Landeskreditbank operated as a public-sector bank serving the western German state of Baden-Worttemberg.

Sodwestdeutsche Landesbank Girozentraler (SodwestLB) was formed in 1988 by the merger of Badische Kommunale Landesbank Girozentrale (Bakola) and Landesbank Stuttgart Girozentrale (formerly Worttembergische Kommunale Landesbank Girozentrale).

SodwestLB established itself as the first Landesbank to be wholly owned by the state's savings banks. In 1990 SodwestLB became the first regional bank to take a stake in WestDeutsche Landesbank at the time Germany's largest public-sector financial institution; the move was intended to increase SodwestLB's presence abroad. SodwestLB then joined with WestDeutsche Landesbank Girozentrale in 1992 to purchase Chartered WestLB a pan-European corporate finance company.

In 1998 SodwestLB agreed to merge with Landesgirokasse and the commercial banking unit of Landeskreditbank. The merger which took effect on January 1 1999 resulted in the formation of Landesbank Baden-Worttemberg (LBBW). LBBW immediately became one of the top public-sector banks in Germany.

In 2005 LBBW focused on growing its retail banking business. It acquired Baden Worttembergische Bank (BW Bank) in Landesbank Rheinland-Pfalz (renamed Rheinland-Pfalz Bank). Three years later LBBW looked to broaden its retail banking reach in Central Germany. It acquired Sachsen LB in 2008 which was integrated under the name Sachsen Bank.

EXECUTIVES

Chairman Board of Managing Directors, Siegfried Jaschinski

Deputy Chairman Board of Managing Directors, Michael Horn

Member Board of Managing Directors, Joachim E. Schielke

Member Board of Managing Directors, Bernhard Walter

Head of Capital Markets Trading and Sales, Ralf Winkelmann

Member Board of Managing Directors and Head of International Funding and Investor Relations, Peter A. Kaemmerer

Head of Strategic Debt Distribution, Karl Haeling

Head of Group Communications and Marketing, Michael Pfister

Head of Press Office, Christian Potthoff

Auditors:
PricewaterhouseCoopersAGWirtschaftsprufungsgesellschaft

LOCATIONS

HQ: Landesbank Baden-Wurttemberg
Am Hauptbahnhof 2, Stuttgart D-70173
Phone: (49) 7 11 127 0   **Fax:** (49) 7 11 127 43544
Web: www.LBBW.de

PRODUCTS/OPERATIONS

Select Subsidiaries and Affiliates

Baden-Wurttembergische Equity Gesellschaft mit beschrankter Haftung
Baden-Wurttembergische L-Finance
BW Capital Markets Inc.
BWK GmbH
Cellent AG
Cellent Finance Solutions AG
Deutsche Mittelstandsinformatik GmbH
Landesbank Baden-Wurttembergische Capital Markets plc
LBBW Asset Management Investmentgesellschaft mbH
LBBW Bank CZ a.s.
LBBW Dublin Management GmbH
LBBW Equity Partners GmbH & Co. KG
LBBW Immobilien GmbH
LBBW Leasing GmbH
LBBW Pensionsmanagement GmbH
LBBW Structured Investment LLC
LBBW (Schweiz) AG
LBBW Venture Capitala GmbH
LHI Leasing GmbH
MKB Mittelrheinische Bank GmbH
SudFactoring GmbH
Sud Beteiligungen GmbH
SudWERT Wohnungsprivatisierungsgesellschaft mbH
Vorarlberger Landes- und Hypothekendbank AG

COMPETITORS

BayernLB	Deutsche Bank
Commerzbank	UniCredit Bank AG
DZ BANK	

HISTORICAL FINANCIALS

Company Type: Public

Income Statement

FYE: December 31

	ASSETS ($ mil.)	NET INCOME ($ mil.)	INCOME AS % OF ASSETS	EMPLOYEES
12/13	376,568	472	0.1%	11,308
12/12	443,294	525	0.1%	11,642
12/11	482,533	113	0.0%	12,231
12/10	501,103	(464)	—	13,906
12/09	593,073	(2,136)	—	14,292
Annual Growth	(10.7%)	—	—	(5.7%)

2013 Year-End Financials

Return on assets: 0.1%	Dividends
Return on equity: 2.9%	Yield: —
Long-term debt ($ mil.): —	Payout: —
No. of shares (mil.): —	Market value ($ mil.): —
Sales ($ mil): 32,561	

Landesbank Berlin Holding AG (Berlin)

Landesbank Berlin Holding (LBB Holding) provides comprehensive banking services to its core market of Berlin and adjoining areas. Formerly Bankgesellschaft Berlin LBB Holding operates through several subsidiaries namely Berliner Sparkasse a leading German savings bank for retail customers with about 150 branches and Landesbank Berlin AG a regional corporate banking center for small and medium-sized businesses. LBB Holding also offers services in capital markets which help private investors with trading and sales and commercial real estate financing which support institutional investors and residential developers. Erwerbsgesellschaft der S-Finanzgruppe mbH & Co. KG owns 88% of LBB Holding.

Erwerbsgesellschaft der S-Finanzgruppe mbH & Co. KG became a majority shareholder when the state of Berlin finalized the sale of its 81% interest in mid-2007.

LBB Holding holds about 40% of Berlin's market share. It continues to solidify that standing by increasing sales activities in consumer loans and securities and by cross-selling certain products to acquire new customers.

HISTORY

Landesbank Berlin Holding predecessor Berliner Bank was formed in 1950 by the city of West Berlin. Although the bank was legally a private institution it was owned by the city. After more than 30 years of keeping Berliner Bank funded (in the early 1980s it was hit hard by bad loans to Polish and German companies that failed) in 1984 the city floated a portion of the bank on the West German stock market cutting its stake to about 75%. Two years later West Germany's Gothaer insurance group claimed a 17% share. Before the insurer could raise its stake the Berlin Wall came tumbling down.

After buying Berliner Stadtbank its East Berlin counterpart in 1991 Berliner Bank was in talks with other Berlin banking institutions to form a financial services group in the city. By the end of 1992 a deal had been arranged: Berliner Bank would merge with Berliner Hypotheken und Pfandbriefbank (Berlin Hyp) a property financing specialist and Landesbank Berlin the central bank for the region's "sparkassen" (savings banks). The banks would be managed by a public company BGB. Both Berlin Hyp and Landesbank Berlin were state-owned and the new group was the first blending of private and public entities.

BGB began operations in 1994. The city of Berlin claimed a 68% stake in the bank Gothaer owned 10% and private investors owned the rest. To win the growing mortgage sector in eastern and northern Germany the group partnered with Norddeutche Landesbank Girozentrale (Nord LB) and sold it a 10% stake that year.

BGB stumbled early when its bottom line was hit hard by loans to businesses many located in the former East Germany that went bankrupt. In 1996 it cut some 1000 jobs to reduce costs and its struggle to remain competitive in overbanked Germany led to merger talks with Nord LB. Discussions resulted not in a merger (BGB's bad loans made it too risky) but in an agreement to become closer allies.

In 1997 BGB opened its Berliner Bank (Polska) subsidiary in Poland. At home the group was still struggling with losses; it reorganized along business lines and trimmed 10% of its employees. BGB continued to grow outside Germany buying a majority stake in Zivnostenska banka a leading Czech bank and entering a project finance deal with Bank of Moscow. Merger talks with Nord LB began again and in early 1998 they announced plans of a union.

The engagement was short-lived. BGB once again found itself in loan trouble (bad property loans in Berlin and eastern Germany made by Berliner Bank were largely to blame) and when its stock tumbled in late 1998 Nord LB split. Jilted in 1999 the group consoled itself with yet another reorganization to try to stem its losses. It closed a number of branches in eastern Germany with banking giant Deutsche Bank taking over the accounts and sold its direct banking unit. The next year BGB announced plans to expand in Eastern Europe; as part of this move it increased its stake in Zivnostenska banka to about 80% and considered upping its 5% stake in Poland's BIG Bank Gdanski.

In 2001 the EU approved a state-sponsored bailout plan for Bankgesellschaft Berlin mandating that the government sell its stake in the bank by the end of 2007 (the deal with Deutscher Sparkassen- und Giroverband was completed in August 2007). In 2006 BGB changed its name to Landesbank Berlin Holding AG.

As one of Germany's top credit card issuers the company boosted its consumer credit operations in early 2008 with the acquisition of Deutsche Postbank subsidiary BHW's loan business.

EXECUTIVES

Chairman of the Supervisory Board, Heinrich Haasis
Managing Director Retail Banking Landesbank Berlin, Johannes Evers
Managing Director Regional Corporate Banking Landesbank Berlin, Hans Jurgen Kulartz
Deputy Chairwoman Supervisory Board, Barbel Wulff
Managing Director Risk Controlling Controlling Compliance Lending Business Risk Management and BankenService Landesbank Berlin, Martin K. Mueller
Member of the Management Board, Jan Bettink
Member of the Management Board, Patrick Tessmann
Member of the Management Board, Serge Demoliere
Deputy Chairwoman Supervisory Board, Barbel Wulff
Director, Dietmar P. Binkowska
Director, Gregor Bohmer
Director, Dagmar Brose
Director, Hans Jorg Duppre
Director, Christina Forster
Director, Artur Grzesiek
Director, Jurgen Hilse
Director, Claus Friedrich Holtmann
Director, Thomas Mang
Director, Peter Schneider
Director, Friedrich Schubring-Giese
Director, Harald Vogelsang
Member of the Supervisory Board; Employee Representative, Christina Foerster
Member of the Supervisory Board; Employee Representative, Daniel Kasteel
Member of the Supervisory Board; Employee Representative, Frank Meysel
Member of the Supervisory Board; Employee Representative, Frank Wolf
Member of the Supervisory Board; Employee Representative, Gerald Herrmann
Member of the Supervisory Board, Gerhard Grandke

Member of the Supervisory Board; Employee Representative, Gerhard Henschel
Member of the Supervisory Board, Hans Duppre
Member of the Supervisory Board; Employee Representative, Heiko Barten
Member of the Supervisory Board, Helmut Schleweis
Member of the Supervisory Board; Employee Representative, Michael Dutschke
Member of the Supervisory Board; Employee Representative, Michael Jaenichen
Member of the Supervisory Board; Employee Representative, Peter Mohr
Member of the Supervisory Board; Employee Representative, Sabine Garzon
Member of the Supervisory Board; Employee Representative, Sascha Haendler
Member of the Supervisory Board; Employee Representative, Wolfgang Pansegrau
Auditors: PwCDeutscheRevisionAG

LOCATIONS

HQ: Landesbank Berlin Holding AG (Berlin)
Alexanderplatz 2, Berlin D-10178
Phone: (49) 30 86 95 00   **Fax:** (49) 30 86 98 30 74
Web: www.llb-holding.de

PRODUCTS/OPERATIONS

Sales

	% of total
Retail	39
Regional corporate	13
Capital	17
Real estate	31
Total	**100**

COMPETITORS

BayernLB   Nordea Bank
Commerzbank   UniCredit Bank AG
DZ BANK   WestLB
Deutsche Bank
Landesbank
  Baden-Wurttemberg

HISTORICAL FINANCIALS

Company Type: Public

Income Statement   FYE: December 31

	ASSETS ($ mil.)	NET INCOME ($ mil.)	INCOME AS % OF ASSETS	EMPLOYEES
12/13	141,028	(374)	—	5,516
12/12	155,922	130	0.1%	5,802
12/11	169,668	(107)	—	5,931
12/10	175,965	357	0.2%	5,985
12/09	207,204	370	0.2%	6,009
Annual Growth	**(9.2%)**	**—**	**—**	**(2.1%)**

2013 Year-End Financials

Return on assets: (-0.2%)   Dividends
Return on equity: (-10.8%)   Yield: —
Long-term debt ($ mil.): —   Payout: —
No. of shares (mil.): —   Market value ($ mil.): —
Sales ($ mil): 5,389

Landesbank Hessen-Thueringen Girozentrale (Helaba) (Germany, Fed. Rep.)

LOCATIONS

HQ: Landesbank Hessen-Thueringen Girozentrale (Helaba) (Germany, Fed. Rep.)
Neue Mainzer Strasse 52-58, Frankfurt am Main D-60311
Phone: (49) 69 91 32 01   **Fax:** (49) 69 29 15 17
Web: www.helaba.de

HISTORICAL FINANCIALS

Company Type: Public

Income Statement   FYE: December 31

	ASSETS ($ mil.)	NET INCOME ($ mil.)	INCOME AS % OF ASSETS	EMPLOYEES
12/13	245,173	484	0.2%	6,293
12/12	262,688	417	0.2%	6,284
12/11	212,106	513	0.2%	5,748
12/10	222,496	400	0.2%	6,180
12/09	244,754	466	0.2%	5,890
Annual Growth	**0.0%**	**0.9%**	**—**	**1.7%**

2013 Year-End Financials

Return on assets: 0.1%   Dividends
Return on equity: 5.0%   Yield: —
Long-term debt ($ mil.): —   Payout: —
No. of shares (mil.): —   Market value ($ mil.): —
Sales ($ mil): 8,552

Landwirtschaftliche Rentenbank (Germany, Fed. Rep.)

LOCATIONS

HQ: Landwirtschaftliche Rentenbank (Germany, Fed. Rep.)
Hochstrasse 2, Frankfurt am Main D-60313
Phone: (49) 69 2107 0   **Fax:** (49) 69 2107 6444
Web: www.rentenbank.de

HISTORICAL FINANCIALS

Company Type: Public

Income Statement

FYE: December 31

	ASSETS ($ mil.)	NET INCOME ($ mil.)	INCOME AS % OF ASSETS	EMPLOYEES
12/13	112,799	633	0.6%	257
12/12	116,512	321	0.3%	256
12/11	114,958	(89)	—	239
12/10	112,132	203	0.2%	227
12/09	112,145	(110)	—	218
Annual Growth	**0.1%**	**—**	**—**	**4.2%**

2013 Year-End Financials

Return on assets: 0.5%
Return on equity: 16.1%
Long-term debt ($ mil.): —
No. of shares (mil.): —
Sales ($ mil): 5,363

Dividends
Yield: —
Payout: —
Market value ($ mil.): —

Legal & General Group PLC (United Kingdom)

Legal & General Group is one of the UK's biggest life insurers. The holding company operates four main divisions: investment management risk savings and international. Its investment management arm generates more than 50% of revenues as the UK's largest pension fund manager serving institutional and retail investors. Its risk businesses provide groups and individuals with life insurance annuities and homeowners insurance. Personal savings products include unit trusts investment bonds and savings accounts. International offers life insurance group benefits and wealth management products. The firm operates in the US as Banner Life Insurance Company and William Penn Life Insurance Company of New York.

As part of its distribution network Legal & General's Mortgage Club serves as a marketplace for mortgage advisors to shop for lenders and other services.

The company serves more than 7 million individual corporate and institutional customers. It mainly distributes its insurance products in the UK through retail independent financial advisers (IFAs) and employee benefit consultants which make up more than 70% of its distribution mix. Banks and building societies including Sainsbury's Bank and Barclays also distribute its products.

Strategically Legal & General is focused on broadening its core product offerings finding new markets building its brand recognition and widening its distribution network to provide a variety of ways to access its products. Additionally the company is pursuing growth opportunities both domestically and overseas to expand its global reach in response to customer demand particularly in North America the Gulf and Asia. Other key strategic goals include improving customer engagement by 2014 increasing cash generation and delivering strong return on equity results through capital management and improving organizational production responsiveness and diversity. Achieving positive results toward its objectives has put the company in a postion of strength in the midst of economic uncertainties and regulatory changes.

Legal & General managed to serve up positive results in 2011 with across-the-board increases in its sales operational cash generation and operating profits in each of its divisions even though its revenues of Â18.3 million ($28.5 million) for the year represented a decrease of more than 50% from 2010 and its net income fell nearly 12% to Â0.7 million ($1.1 million) mainly due to a 63% drop in investment returns.

HISTORY

The Legal in Legal & General's name comes from its founding mission —to provide life insurance to members of the legal profession. The company was started in 1836 by six lawyers as the Legal & General Life Assurance Society; its first customer solicitor Thomas Smith ill-manneredly died four years later after paying less than 200 pounds on a 1000-pound policy.

Throughout that century and into the next the company made loans to individuals and corporations; it also moved into real estate. After struggling under claims during WWI and the 1918 flu pandemic it moved into fire and accident coverage in 1920. It opened membership to nonlawyers in 1929. The company took over the UK operations of the US firm Metropolitan Life (MetLife) in 1933.

In 1934 Legal & General bought Gresham Life Assurance and Gresham Fire and Accident to gain a presence in Australia. During WWII the company was hit hard by German air attacks both physically (it had to relocate away from London for a time) and at the bottom line.

The postwar years were a time of expansion as the company moved into South Africa and also broadened its operations at home. In 1949 it moved into marine insurance and in 1956 inaugurated life insurance in Australia.

The company began expanding its product offerings in the 1970s with managed pension funds and retail unit trusts. It established a direct sales force for life and pensions in 1977. The company also formed alliances with several European insurance companies and sold its Gresham life subsidiary. In 1979 it formed Legal & General Group Limited as a holding company for its now-separate insurance international and investment management operations.

In 1981 Legal & General bought US auto insurer GEICO's two-thirds interest in Government Employees Life Insurance Company changing the subsidiary's name to Banner Life. Three years later it bought the Dutch operations of Unilife Assurance and created a subsidiary in the Netherlands. Despite all this activity however the company's performance during the 1980s was poor and it brought in David Prosser (who became CEO in 1991) to goose its asset management operations.

In 1989 the company bought William Penn Life Insurance from Continental Corp. and opened its first real estate agency —just in time for the real estate market crash. Legal & General and other mortgage guarantee insurers were also squeezed by the resulting increase in mortgage default rates as homebuyers were caught between high interest rates and high unemployment.

The company formed a joint venture with Woolwich Building Society to provide Woolwich customers with insurance products in 1995. The next year it followed the insurance industry trend by establishing a bank of its own.

With each succeeding merger of its rivals Legal & General became the target of rumors about its own fate. The company has remained adamantly independent with Prosser claiming that Legal & General could instead benefit by picking up business left behind by the new entities.

In 1998 the British insurance industry was stung by scandalous revelations regarding improper pension sales in the late 1980s and early 1990s. Legal & General set aside about $1 billion to compensate victims; it also sold its Australian operations. In 1999 banking company National Westminster and Legal & General talked takeover but the deal fell through. (NatWest was eventually bought by Royal Bank of Scotland.)

In 2001 Legal & General announced a deal with UK-based Barclays to provide the bank's customers with life insurance and pension products. In 2002 Legal & General extended its marketing agreement with UK financial services company Alliance & Leicester.

The company then discontinued its health insurance offerings and reduced its venture capital investment operations. In 2005 the company sold its Gresham Insurance subsidiary to Barclays Bank.

EXECUTIVES

Vice Chairman, Henry E. Staunton, age 65
Chief Executive and Director, Nigel Wilson, age 58
Chairman, John M. Stewart, age 65
Group Executive Director Risk and Director, John Pollock, age 55, $738,631 total compensation
Executive Director Savings and Director, Mark Gregory, age 50
Group M&A and Strategy Director and Interim Group CFO, Wadham Downing
Group Executive Director LGIM, Mark Zinkula
Director, Nicholas E. T. (Nick) Prettejohn, age 53
Director, Rudy H. P. Markham, age 67
Director, Michael E. (Mike) Fairey, age 64
Director, Dame Clara H. F. Furse, age 55
Vice Chairman, Henry E. Staunton, age 65
Chief Executive and Director, Nigel Wilson, age 58
Group Executive Director Risk and Director, John Pollock, age 55
Director, Julia Wilson
Executive Director Savings and Director, Mark Gregory, age 50
Director, Stuart Popham
Auditors: PricewaterhouseCoopersLLP

LOCATIONS

HQ: Legal & General Group PLC (United Kingdom)
One Coleman Street, London EC2R 5AA
Phone: (44) 20 3124 2000   **Fax:** (44) 20 3124 2500
Web: www.legalandgeneralgroup.com

PRODUCTS/OPERATIONS

2011 Revenues by Segment

	% of total
Investment	52
Risk (life & property	33
Savings	9
International	6
Group capital &	-
Total	**100**

2011 Distribution Channels

	% of total
Retail independent financial advisers	37
Employee benefit	35
Bancassurance	23
Direct	3
Tied	2
Total	**100**

Selected Acquisitions

2012
  Bechtel House ($66.7 million; London; office building - Investment management)

Selected Subsidiaries

Banner Life Insurance Company Inc - long-term business; US
First British American Reinsurance Company II - reinsurance; US
First British Bermudan Reinsurance Company II Limited - reinsurance; Bermuda
First British Vermont Reinsurance Company II - reinsurance; US

First British Vermont Reinsurance Company - reinsurance; US
Legal & General (France) SA - long-term business
Legal & General (Portfolio Management Services) Limited - institutional fund management
Legal & General (Unit Trust Managers) Limited - unit trust management
Legal & General Assurance (Pensions Management) Limited - long-term business
Legal & General Assurance Society Limited - long-term and general insurance
Legal & General Bank (France) SA - financial services
Legal & General Finance PLC1 - treasury operations
Legal & General Insurance Limited - general insurance
Legal & General International (Ireland) Limited - long-term business
Legal & General Investment Management America Inc - institutional fund management
Legal & General Investment Management Limited - institutional fund management
Legal & General Nederland Levensverzekering Maatschappij NV - long-term business; Netherlands
Legal & General Partnership Services Limited - provision of services
Legal & General Pensions Limited - reinsurance
Legal & General Property Limited - property management
Legal & General Resources Limited1 - provision of services
Legal & General Risques Divers (France) SA - insurance company
LGV Capital Limited - private equity
Nationwide Life Limited - long-term business
Suffolk Life Annuities Limited - long-term business
Suffolk Life Pensions Limited - long-term business
William Penn Life Insurance Company of New York Inc - long-term business; US

COMPETITORS

AEGON	MetLife
AXA	Prudential
Allianz	Prudential plc
Aviva	Royal London Mutual
Friends Provident	Standard Life
ING	Zurich Insurance Group
Lloyds Banking Group	

HISTORICAL FINANCIALS

Company Type: Public

Income Statement

FYE: December 31

	ASSETS ($ mil.)	NET INCOME ($ mil.)	INCOME AS % OF ASSETS	EMPLOYEES
12/13	600,157	1,475	0.2%	11,163
12/12	558,191	1,310	0.2%	9,864
12/11	504,733	1,121	0.2%	9,138
12/10	502,858	1,273	0.3%	8,662
12/09	481,086	1,397	0.3%	9,324
Annual Growth	5.7%	1.4%	—	4.6%

2013 Year-End Financials

Return on assets: 0.2%
Return on equity: 16.1%
Long-term debt ($ mil.): —
No. of shares (mil.): —
Sales ($ mil): 64,865

Dividends
Yield: 3.1%
Payout: 601.6%
Market value ($ mil.): —

	STOCK PRICE ($) FY Close	P/E High/Low		PER SHARE ($) Earnings	Dividends	Book Value
12/13	18.45	332	198	0.25	0.59	1.58
12/12	12.42	227	144	0.22	0.49	1.49
12/11	7.95	211	129	0.19	0.95	1.37
12/10	7.67	153	82	0.22	0.27	1.28
12/09	6.50	137	25	0.24	0.23	1.16
Annual Growth	29.8%	—		1.0%	27.1%	8.1%

Lenovo Group Ltd

Workhorse Lenovo Group has risen to the top of the worldwide PC market ahead of #2 HP and #3 Dell. The China-based group is a global supplier of Think-branded commercial PCs and Idea-branded consumer PCs holding a dominant position in China. The company makes tablets smartphones laptops desktops workstations servers software and accessories and it is developing and launching mini ultrabooks and ideapads. Lenovo offers services for enterprise small business and home office markets. Certain products and services are geared specifically at the growing education government and health care verticals. Lenovo formed out of the acquisition of IBM's Personal Computing division in 2005.

Geographic Reach

Hong Kong-based Lenovo serves customers in more than 160 countries. The company generates more than 40% of its sales in China where it holds more than 30% market share in PCs. Elsewhere it generates about 20% of its sales in both Europe the Middle East and Africa and in the Asia-Pacific and Latin America regions. Lenovo is also increasing sales in other emerging markets.

Operations

Lenovo has operations in more than 60 countries across the globe. It has operations hubs in Beijing Paris and North Carolina and a marketing hub in Bangalore India. It also has major research centers in Yokohama Japan and in China in Beijing Shanghai and Shenzhen. Aiming to boost sales growth Lenovo in 2013 began producing PCs in Raleigh North Carolina at a new assembly plant. As part of this effort the company is devoting more investment dollars to domestic manufacturing.

Financial Performance

Lenovo's sales jumped 15% in fiscal 2013 (ended March) versus the prior year to an all-time high of $33.9 billion. Indeed the company's sales have more than doubled over the past four years while profits have risen steadily. Driving the strong performance in fiscal 2013 was a 7% year-over-year increase in notebook computer sales and a 6% jump in sales of desktop computers. Sales of mobile Internet and digital home products more than doubled to $3.1 billion driven largely by brisk smartphone sales in China. The company saw growth in all of its geographic markets with China and Europe the Middle East and Africa posting the strongest results. Buoyed by rising sales net income rose 33% to $631.3 million.

Strategy

Lenovo has invested heavily in acquisitions and infrastructure over the past several years to bolster its PC business with stellar results. Between 2011 and 2013 Lenovo jumped from being the world's fourth-largest PC vendor to the largest surpassing HP in worldwide PC shipments and market share in the second quarter of 2013. More impressively while the global PC industry is in a slump (down 5.6% in 2013) Lenovo is the only PC vendor that is growing. Indeed Lenovo shipped almost 54 million PCs in 2013 up slightly from just over 52 million in 2012. Dell and HP both posted declines in shipments in 2013. With demand for PCs declining worldwide Lenovo has diversified into smartphones tablets and other mobile devices as well as into the enterprise sector such as servers.

In addition to being the #1 PC company in the world Lenovo is also the top PC company for large enterprises and the public sector. Lenovo used a different growth strategy than most of its big competitors to reach this market spot expanding East to West. New products are introduced in China then spread across the globe.

Although it has long been the leader in China Lenovo does not rest on its laurels when it comes to increasing additional share in the Asia/Pacific region. To maintain supremacy in this market Lenovo's Hefei China-based joint venture with Compal Electronics began mass producing notebooks in 2013. Lenovo which holds a 51% stake and Compal which owns the remaining 49% will invest a total of $300 million in the JV's expansion.

In Japan Lenovo leverages the strength of that country's #1 PC company NEC through a joint venture called NEC Lenovo Japan Group. That JV of which Lenovo holds a majority stake is the dominant PC maker in Japan with about a 25% share of the market. Prior to the JV's formation in 2011 NEC had been the market leader in Japan but was not turning a profit when it made the deal. The JV helps give NEC access to cheaper Chinese supplies and manufacturing.

Mergers and Acquisitions

In the last two years Lenovo has made acquisitions to beef up its hardware offerings and support expansion in select markets. In January 2014 it agreed to pay more than $5 billion to acquire two new major product lines. First it announced plans to buy IBM's low-end x86 server business for $2.3 billion. The business includes System x BladeCenter and Flex System blade servers and switches x86-based Flex integrated systems NeXtScale and iDataPlex servers and associated software blade networking and customer service operations. The 7500 employees who work for IBM are expected to be transferred to Lenovo. The acquisition frees up IBM to focus on its cloud computing business.

A few weeks later it agreed to pay $2.9 billion for Motorola Mobility. Google bought Motorola's smartphone business in 2012 with big plans for its Android phones. However the division continued to suffer losses in the highly competitive smartphone market and Motorola Mobility was forced to cut staff and close locations. As part of the deal Lenovo will own the brands Moto X Moto G and the DROID Ultra series while Google will own the patent portfolio.

In 2012 the company acquired US-based Stoneware to expand its secure cloud computing portfolio. The deal add new technologies and added capabilities for both commercial and consumer cloud offerings particularly the ability to provide secure content across multiple devices in education and government. Also in September of that year Lenovo made strides in Latin America by acquiring Brazil's CCE a regional leader in PCs and consumer electronics. It added manufacturing facilities; an extensive selection of consumer products such as PCs tablets smartphones and televisions; and a robust supply chain.

Across the Atlantic Lenovo's growth in Europe was supported by a majority stake acquisition in mid-2011 of Germany-based computer and electronics reseller MEDION. The MEDION buy doubled Lenovo's market share in Germany and made it the third-largest PC company in Europe's largest PC market.

HISTORY

Liu Chuanzhi an engineer at the Chinese Academy of Sciences who wrote industry research reports established Legend Group Holdings Co. in 1984 in Beijing. Backed by a modest investment from the academy Liu who went on to become something of an entrepreneurial hero in China and 10 other engineers were given a green light to form a retail business. They first bought and sold items ranging from TVs to roller skates but later focused on distributing computer products and eventually moved into manufacturing PCs for AST

Research. Legend introduced its first proprietary product a Chinese character system for PCs in 1985.

In 1988 the company formed Legend Holdings Limited which was originally a Hong Kong-based PC distributor. The following year the parent company began designing and manufacturing motherboards and added systems integration services to its offerings. In 1990 China reduced import tariffs a move that opened the trade door for companies such as IBM and Compaq. That year Legend Group Holdings began making its own brand of PCs.

Legend Holdings went public in 1994 and the following year began absorbing operations from its parent company which retained approximately 60% ownership in the subsidiary. By 1996 it was tied with IBM for PC market share in China; it became the country's top brand the following year.

In 1998 parent company Legend Group Holdings transferred Beijing Legend Group to its Hong Kong-based subsidiary. The following year Microsoft looking to extend its operating system dominance into China teamed up with Legend Holdings to create set-top boxes. In 2000 the company partnered with Pacific Century CyberWorks to provide broadband Internet services. The following year Legend spun off its distribution business Digital China as a separate public company. In 2001 Yang Yuanqing was named CEO of the company.

In 2002 Legend Holdings changed its English company name to Legend Group Limited. The company launched a corporate brand Lenovo the following year and in 2004 it officially adopted Lenovo as its English name. It also sold its non-telecom IT services business to AsiaInfo Holdings renamed AsiaInfo-Linkage in 2004.

Lenovo acquired IBM's worldwide PC operations for approximately $1.75 billion in 2005. IBM executive Stephen Ward was named CEO of Lenovo at the time of the merger but he was replaced by William Amelio before year's end. Amelio headed Dell's Asia/Pacific operations before joining Lenovo. In 2006 Lenovo launched a unit called Lenovo Services.

In 2007 Lenovo stopped using the IBM PC brand to which it still held the rights and began offering only Lenovo-branded machines. The following year it sponsored and supported the Olympic Summer Games in Beijing providing more than 30000 pieces of equipment and 600 engineers.

Looking to focus on its core PC operations Lenovo sold its mobile phone business Lenovo Mobile Communications to Hony Capital in 2008. Hony the private equity arm of Legend Holdings paid $100 million for the unit.

A year later Lenovo bought back the mobile communications business for about $200 million in cash and stock. The company cited the growth of the mobile Internet market and the increasing convergence between the PC and wireless handset sectors for the about-face in product strategy. Lenovo's move came as Dell introduced a mobile phone for the Chinese market.

Citing a flagging economy Lenovo announced a restructuring plan in 2009 that included a workforce reduction of 11% executive pay cuts and the consolidation of its China and the Asia/Pacific units. The company also initiated a management shakeup including its chairman taking over as CEO. The change may in part have reflected a strategy shift for Lenovo. With corporate spending flagging particularly in the US the company planned to focus on China and other emerging markets with an emphasis on consumers.

EXECUTIVES

SVP and Chief Marketing Officer, David A. Roman

Vice Chairman, Ma Xuezheng, age 61, $114,000 total compensation
Chairman, Liu Chuanzhi, age 70
Chairman and CEO, Yuanqing Yang, age 51, $894,000 total compensation
SVP and CTO, George Z. Q. He, age 52
SVP WW Services and CIO, Xiaoyan Wang, age 53
SVP; President Consumer Business Group, Jun Liu, age 46
SVP and Chief Procurement Officer, Qiao Song, age 46
SVP; Acting CEO and President Lenovo Mobile, Lu Yan
senior Vice President Emerging Markets, Chen Shaopeng, age 45
VP Corporate Strategy and Planning, Qiao Jian
SVP; Group President Lenovo China, Xudong Chen
SVP E-Commerce and Chief Marketing Officer, Deepak Advani, age 50
General Manager Large Customer, Tong Fuyao
senior Vice President Human Resources, Kenneth A. (Ken) DiPietro, age 55
General Manager China, Xia Li
SVP EMEA President, Gianfranco Lanci, age 59
Senior Vice President ; THINK Product, Francis K. (Fran) O'Sullivan, age 55
SVP Think Business Group, Peter D. Hortensius, age 54
Managing Director Lenovo India, Amar Babu
SVP and CFO, Wai Ming Wong, age 56
VP Investor Relations, Gary Ng
SVP Operations Mature Markets, David Schmoock, age 45
SVP; President Asia Pacific, Milko Van Duijl, age 52
President and COO; Acting President Latin America Group, Rory Read, age 52
SVP; President Americas, Gerry P. Smith, age 51
VP Diversity, Yolanda Conyers
SVP and General Counsel, Michael J. O'Neill, age 57
Executive Director External Communications, Raymond (Ray) Gorman
Managing Director Lenovo Ireland, Fiona O'Brien
VP Worldwide Notebook Product Marketing, Sam Dusi
Regional Director Transactional Business, Ali Al Amine
VP Corporate Identity and Design, David Hill
SVP Global Services, Peter Bartolotta
Senior Manager Investor relations, William Li
General Manager Hong Kong and Macau Operationso, Alice N. L. Ong
senior Vice President Human Resources, Jian Gina
Senior Vice President General Counsel, Michael Oneill
Senior Vice President Legal, Jay Clemens
Vice Chairman, Ma Xuezheng, age 61
Director, James G. (Jim) Coulter, age 54
Director, William O. Grabe, age 76
Director, Prof Woo Chia-Wei, age 77
Director, Tian Suning, age 50
Director, Zhu Linan, age 52
Director, Ting Lee Sen, age 71
Director, Nicholas C. Allen, age 59
Director, Wu Yibing, age 46
Auditors: PricewaterhouseCoopers

LOCATIONS

HQ: Lenovo Group Ltd
23rd Floor, Lincoln House, Taikoo Place, 979 King' s Road, Quarry Bay,
Phone: (852) 2590 0228   **Fax:** (852) 2516 5384
Web: www.lenovo.com

Sales

	$ mil.	% of total
Emerging markets		
China	10,015	46
Other	3,859	18
Mature markets	7,719	36
Total	**21,594**	**100**

PRODUCTS/OPERATIONS

Sales

	$ mil.	% of total
Personal computer		
Notebook	12,990	60
Desktop	7,307	34
Mobile phone	804	4
Others	492	2
Total	**21,594**	**100**

COMPETITORS

ASUSTeK	IBM
Acer	LG Electronics
Apple Inc.	Microsoft
BlackBerry	NEC
Dell	Nokia
Digital China	Panasonic Corp
Founder Holdings	Positivo Informatica
Fujitsu	Samsung Electronics
Great Wall Technology	Siemens AG
HTC Corporation	Sony
Hedy Holding	Toshiba
Hewlett-Packard	Wipro
Hitachi	

HISTORICAL FINANCIALS

Company Type: Public

Income Statement

FYE: March 31

	REVENUE ($ mil.)	NET INCOME ($ mil.)	NET PROFIT MARGIN	EMPLOYEES
03/14	38,707	817	2.1%	54,000
03/13	33,873	635	1.9%	35,026
03/12	29,574	472	1.6%	27,000
03/11	21,594	273	1.3%	27,039
03/10	16,604	129	0.8%	22,205
Annual Growth	**23.6%**	**58.5%**	**—**	**24.9%**

2014 Year-End Financials

Debt ratio: 2.4%	No. of shares (mil.): —
Return on equity: 31.1%	Dividends
Cash ($ mil.): 3,858	Yield: 2.1%
Current ratio: 1.00	Payout: —
Long-term debt ($ mil.): 10	Market value ($ mil.): —

	STOCK PRICE ($) FY Close	P/E High/Low	PER SHARE ($) Earnings	Dividends	Book Value
03/14	1.10	18 11	0.08	0.48	0.27
03/13	1.01	19 11	0.06	0.00	0.24
03/12	0.90	20 11	0.05	0.00	0.23
03/11	0.56	28 18	0.03	0.15	0.18
03/10	0.68	54 14	0.01	0.02	0.16
Annual Growth	**12.8%**	**— —**	**55.5%**	**119.0%**	**13.1%**

LG Electronics Inc

LG Electronics (LGE) makes the products that have tech-savvy consumers chomping at the bit in the kitchen in the media room and on the go. A leader in consumer electronics mobile communications and home appliances LGE operates through more than 100 subsidiaries worldwide that design and make flat panel TVs audio and video products mobile handsets air conditioners washing machines refrigerators and more. Asia and North America are its two largest markets each contributing about a quarter of LGE's sales. LGE owns Zenith Electronics (acquired in 1995) and LG Display. Founded in 1958 as Goldstar LGE established a North American headquarters in 2004. South Korea's LG Corp. owns about one-third of LGE.

Geographic Reach

Seoul-based LG Electronics (LGE) rings up nearly 15% of its sales at home in South Korea. North America accounts for nearly a quarter of its total sales. Other important markets for geographically-diversified LGE include Central and South America (15%) and Europe. About 15% of the company's sales come from emerging markets including India China and Russia. The Middle East and Africa accounts for about 10%. The company controls 114 local subsidiaries across the globe.

Operations

Home entertainment including OLED and Ultra HD TVs and other video and audio products is LGE's largest business accounting for a 45% of sales. Home appliances and mobile communications products each represent about 20% of sales.

Financial Performance

The consumer electronics giant rang up $53.1 billion in sales and a net profit of $203.7 million in 2013 marking an improvement over 2012 results. LGE's operating profit increased modestly in 2013 to nearly $1.2 billion up from $1.1 billion in 2012. The company's mobile communications business posted a 29% jump in annual sales with help from stronger smartphone sales including its G2 and Nexus 5 models. Smartphone shipments rose 54% year over year. LGE's air conditioning and home appliance businesses also posted annual sales gains of 8% and 5% respectively. The laggard was home entertainment which suffered a 5% decline in annual sales despite higher demand for LCD TVs in North America Asia and the CIS countries.

Strategy

LGE is focusing on boosting its mobile communication handset business and enhancing its share of the LCD TV market. Indeed the company is looking to sell about 20% more cell phones. To that end LGE will enter the world's largest 4G mobile market —China —with the introduction of its LG-E985T smartphone through China Mobile (the world's largest mobile operator with nearly 750 million subscribers). The company is also going after the premium kitchen appliance market with the establishment in 2013 of a new division focused exclusively on high-end kitchen packages. The new division will initially focus on the US and Korean markets. The Korean company has formed a strategic relationship with GE to share patents on kitchenware and refrigerators. LGE also has alliances with other companies including Prada (phones) Siemens (air conditioners) and Hitachi (optical storage).

LGE is continuing to invest heavily in marketing to boost its position as one of the world's top consumer electronics brands up there with rivals Sony Samsung and Panasonic. The company is also focused on boosting sales of its commercial air conditioners drum washing machines and side-by-side (aka French door) refrigerators. LGE and US rival Whirlpool have been trading patent infringement claims over refrigerator technology.

Mergers and Acquisitions

In February 2013 LGE acquired the webOS operating system technology from Hewlett-Packard to support its next-generation Smart TV technology. LGE acquired the source code and other assets associated with webOS. The purchase will allow LGE to offer an intuitive user experience and Internet services across a range of consumer electronics devices.

To bolster production of large-scale air conditioning systems both in South Korea and abroad LGE acquired the A/C business of industrial machinery manufacturer LS Mtron for $134 million in early 2011. The deal included a factory in Jeonju

South Korea as well as a research and development team. LS Mtron operated as part of LG Group until 2003 when its operations were spun off.

EXECUTIVES

CEO, Bon Joon Koo, age 62
EVP and CEO Home Appliance, Moon-Bum Shin
CEO LG Corp.; Vice Chairman, Yu-Sig Kang
Public Relations and Corporate Communications, Judy Pae
EVP CFO and Director, David Jung
President and CEO Mobile Communications Company, Skott Ahn
President and CEO Air Conditioning & Energy Solution Company, Hwan Yong Nho, age 59
President Home Entertainment, Havis Kwon
EVP and CEO Mobile Communications, Jong-Seok Park
CEO LG Corp.; Vice Chairman, Yu-Sig Kang
EVP CFO and Director, David Jung
Director, In Ki Joo
Director, Kyu Min Lee
Director, Jong Nam Joo
Auditors: SamilPricewaterhousecoopers

LOCATIONS

HQ: LG Electronics Inc
LG Twin Towers, 128 Yeouido-dong, Yeongdeungpo-gu, Seoul 150-721
Phone: (82) 2 3777 1114 **Fax:** (82) 2 3777 3428
Web: www.lge.com

Sales

	% of total
North	28
Europe	20
China & Asia-	19
South & Central	9
Korea	8
Middle East &	7
Other	9
Total	**100**

PRODUCTS/OPERATIONS

Sales

	% of total
Home	35
Mobile	32
Home	17
Air	8
Business	8
Total	**100**

Selected Major Products & Services

Home Entertainment (LCD TVs plasma TVs audio video & optical storage)
Mobile Communication (mobile handsets mobile accessory)
Home Appliance (washing machines refrigerators cooking appliances vacuum cleaners built-in appliances)
Air Conditioning (residential air conditioners commercial air conditioners home solution compressors)
Business Solutions (monitors commercial displays car infotainment security business)

COMPETITORS

BSH Home Appliances	Philips Electronics
Electrolux	SANYO
GE Appliances & Lighting	Samsung Electronics
Haier Group	Sony
Motorola Solutions	Technicolor
Panasonic Corp	Whirlpool

HISTORICAL FINANCIALS

Company Type: Public

Income Statement

FYE: December 31

	REVENUE ($ mil.)	NET INCOME ($ mil.)	NET PROFIT MARGIN	EMPLOYEES
12/13	55,285	168	0.3%	38,363
12/12	47,728	62	0.1%	36,376
12/11	46,825	(405)	—	35,286
12/10	49,723	1,094	2.2%	32,972
12/09	47,959	1,977	4.1%	29,554
Annual Growth	3.6%	(46.0%)	—	6.7%

2013 Year-End Financials

Debt ratio: 0.0%	No. of shares (mil.): 162
Return on equity: 1.4%	Dividends
Cash ($ mil.): 2,579	Yield: —
Current ratio: 1.09	Payout: —
Long-term debt ($ mil.): 5,884	Market value ($ mil.): —

Lloyds Banking Group Plc

Don't confuse Lloyds Banking Group with that "other" Lloyds. Unrelated to Lloyd's of London Lloyds Banking Group was formed by the 2009 merger of UK banks Lloyds TSB and HBOS. Its retail banking services include deposit accounts credit cards loans and wealth management. Lloyds Banking Group is also one of the nation's top home mortgage lenders. Other products include insurance and investment services through Scottish Widows and wholesale and international banking for UK corporate clients and multinationals. Lloyds Banking Group which operates under the brands Lloyds TSB Halifax and Bank of Scotland has some 2900 branches with representative offices in the Middle East Asia and the Americas.

The UK government owns slightly less than 40% of Lloyds after bailing it out in 2008. After the bailout the company embarked on one of the largest-ever capital raisings in Europe. Although the merger with HBOS nearly destroyed Lloyds — HBOS had a much higher risk tolerance than Lloyds and the company has faced billions in losses since the deal —the combined company controls some 30% of the UK's mortgage market and half of the savings market.

The company has been compelled by European authorities to sell the 600 retail banking branches associated with the Lloyds TSB brand along with a large part of its Cheltenham & Gloucester network. It has received some interest from Virgin Money; another option would be spinning them off to the public. Lloyds Banking Group has divested some noncore businesses such as its fund management arm Insight which was sold to Bank of New York Mellon for Â235 million ($386 million); its Irish retail unit which lost billions in toxic loans and its Australian and New Zealand property and corporate loans for $684 million. The company also may spin off its private equity unit Lloyds TSB Development Capital. In late 2013 the company sold its remaining stake in St. James's Place Plc for about 680 pounds ($1.1 billion) to focus on its primary retail and commercial businesses.

As part of its strategic review and after some layoffs related to the ill-fated HBOS acquisition the company announced another round of job cuts in 2011 (mostly back-office and middle management positions). Lloyds has already shed 27500 jobs and will cut another 15000 in the process. The group's strategy for growth include simplifying operations (it completed the integration of HBOS in 2011) while investing in core areas and strengthening its balance sheet and liquidity position.

The restructuring efforts have helped to cut the company's losses. In 2011 Lloyds lost Â342 million before taxes a large improvement over the 2010 losses of Â2.9 billion. Net interest grew 1% to Â12.7 million a modest increase as retail lending markets remained pressured. However revenues declined that year 32% to Â17.2 billion largely due to the ongoing economic challenges in the UK and Ireland. Fees and commissions as well as net trading income declined in 2011. The wholesale business' profits decreased by 67% that year as a result of lower asset balances and losses on asset disposals. Earnings were also affected by some Â3.6 billion in provisions including a Â375 million provision for the mis-selling of payment protection insurance to customers from 2007 to 2011.

HISTORY

In 1765 John Taylor and Sampson Lloyd II founded Taylors and Lloyds bank in Birmingham England; five years later their sons opened a London agency. In 1852 the last Taylor involved with the bank died. In 1865 the bank converted to joint stock form and became Lloyds Banking Company Ltd. Over the next half century it grew by merging with some 50 banks becoming one of England's largest banks by the turn of the century.

Despite the post-WWI roller-coaster economy the bank acquired Capital and Counties Bank (1918 bringing foreign connections); Fox Fowler & Company (1921); and Cox & Company (1923). During both wars deposits grew while lending dropped. After WWII growth was hampered by high inflation.

Lloyds added branches and products in the 1960s. By 1971 it had branches in 43 countries. It moved into insurance (1972) home mortgages (1979) real estate agency services (1982) and merchant banking (1986).

In 1987 Latin American bank defaults pummeled Lloyds. Refocusing on domestic operations the bank sold overseas subsidiaries (including Lloyds Bank Canada in 1990) and acquired 58% of life insurer Abbey Life (1988) and Cheltenham & Gloucester Building Society (1994). HSBC outbid Lloyds for Midland Bank in 1992; Lloyds bought TSB Group in 1995.

TSB Group evolved from the trustee savings banks (TSBs) formed in the 1800s. By 1860 there were 600 such banks mainly in northern England and Scotland. During WWI many TSBs consolidated or closed. By WWII about 100 remained and the mergers continued.

In the 1960s TSBs began offering checking accounts and trust services. Loans credit cards and other services came in 1973. In 1986 the four remaining TSBs (TSB Channel Islands TSB England and Wales TSB Northern Ireland and TSB Scotland) agreed to merge and go public in order to gain equal footing with stock banks. TSB Group was born.

Flush with cash from its offering TSB group defied the late 1980s recession to buy Target Group (life insurance sold 1993) Hill Samuel (merchant banking) and other units; the purchases sent TSB sprawling.

As debt rose in the 1990s TSB Group refocused on banking and insurance. TSB and Lloyds merged in 1995 linking their geographically complementary branch networks to fend off competition.

After the merger Lloyds TSB focused on loans and insurance and dabbled in consumer finance including the sale and delivery of big-ticket items (cars large appliances). Returning overseas it bought the consumer finance unit of Brazil's Banco Multiplic.

In late 1997 and 1998 the bank overhauled its operations to eliminate redundancies and began rebranding under one green and blue banner. In 1999 Lloyds TSB bailed out Abbey Life which had nearly been bankrupted by the cost of settling pension mis-selling claims.

The bank in 2000 bought Scottish Widows to boost its fund management services. It sold the Abbey Life name and its new business to Zurich Financial Services' Allied Dunbar; Abbey Life continued to service existing business for Lloyds. Also that year Lloyds TSB bought consumer and auto finance unit Chartered Trust from Standard Chartered. After a yearlong battle to buy London-based mortgage lender Abbey National the UK government in 2001 blocked the merger attempt because of concerns for the consumer.

Earlier in 2001 Lloyds TSB closed Bahamas-based subsidiary British Bank of Latin America because of alleged money-laundering links revealed in a US Senate report.

Lloyds TSB's asset finance operations bought First National Vehicle Holdings and Abbey National Vehicle Finance from Abbey National plc in 2002. The division also acquired Chartered Trust and Dutton-Forshaw Group a car dealership. Lloyds TSB sold National Bank of New Zealand to Australia and New Zealand Bank Group in 2003. Commerzbank unit Comdirect Bank sold its UK subsidiary Comdirect Ltd to Lloyds TSB unit Executive Services Group in 2004.

The company sold its Abbey Life unit to Deutsche Bank for nearly $2 billion in 2007. (The life insurer had been closed to new business since 2000.) The group also sold Lloyds TSB Registrars and car dealership The Dutton-Forshaw Group which were noncore units of its wholesale and international business.

The global economic crisis was a difficult time for Lloyds. The UK government took a 40% stake in the company after bailing it out along with seven other top banks in 2008. Lloyds accepted some Â17 billion ($25 billion) in taxpayer money. The government hoped the infusion of cash would loosen up credit markets and restore confidence in the financial system. As part of a restructuring plan (and to repay the UK government) Lloyds Banking Group launched one of the largest-ever capital raisings in Europe which included a Â9 billion ($13 billion) debt exchange and a nearly Â14 billion ($20 billion) rights issue.

Around the same time of the government bailout Lloyds TSB agreed to take over struggling HBOS the UK's top mortgage lender. The controversial Â12 billion ($22 billion) deal was announced after HBOS shares fell dramatically amid rising concerns surrounding the vitality of financial services companies worldwide. The combined bank served about one of every three UK consumers and controlled more than a quarter of the UK residential mortgage market. The UK government further capitalized the deal to ensure its viability.

Within weeks though Lloyds Banking Group revealed that HBOS had incurred some Â11 billion ($18 billion) in losses and shareholder unrest grew concerning the billions of pounds in toxic assets gained with the acquisition. The merger meant drastic cost cuts and job losses as the company announced more than 42000 job cuts.

Needless to say not everyone was happy with the HBOS merger. At Lloyds Banking Group's annual meeting in 2009 a large group of shareholders loudly criticized the company's board for the HBOS deal demanding resignations and threatening lawsuits over the merger. In 2010 one group of disgruntled shareholders launched legal action in order to recoup up to Â14 billion ($20 billion) that they claim they lost as a result of the merger.

Lloyds Banking Group defended the merger though saying it helped improve the company's strategic position by improving its market position (it controlled about half of the savings market) brand recognition and expanding its customer base. Although the deal brought short-term costs company leaders were convinced that it was better positioned for future growth.

EXECUTIVES

Chairman, Sir Winfried F. W. (Win) Bischoff, age 73
Vice Chairman, David L. Roberts, age 51
Group Director Finance and Director, George Culmer, age 51
Group Chief Executive and Director, Antonio Horta-Osorio, age 50
Director, Anita M. Frew, age 55
Vice Chairman, David L. Roberts, age 51
Group Director Finance and Director, George Culmer, age 51
Director, Martin A. Scicluna, age 62
Director, Anthony (Tony) Watson, age 68
Director, T. Timothy Ryan Jr., age 68
Group Chief Executive and Director, Antonio Horta-Osorio, age 50
Auditors: PricewaterhouseCoopersLLP

LOCATIONS

HQ: Lloyds Banking Group Plc
25 Gresham Street, 5th Floor, London EC2V 7HN
Phone: (44) 20 7626 1500
Web: www.lloydsbankinggroup.com

PRODUCTS/OPERATIONS

Sales

	% of total
Interest	64
Insurance	20
Net fees &	9
Other	7
Total	**100**

Sales by Division

	% of total
Retail	47
Wholesale	21
Insurance	13
Wealth &	10
Commercial	9
Total	**100**

Selected Brands

Bank of Scotland
Cheltenham & Gloucester
Clerical Medical
Halifax
Lloyds TSB
Scottish Widows

COMPETITORS

Barclays	Northern Rock plc
Grupo Santander	Royal Bank of Scotland
HSBC	Standard Life Bank
Invesco	Woolwich
Northern Rock (Asset Management)	

HISTORICAL FINANCIALS
Company Type: Public

Income Statement
FYE: December 31

	ASSETS ($ mil.)	NET INCOME ($ mil.)	INCOME AS % OF ASSETS	EMPLOYEES
12/13	1,399,784	(1,384)	—	88,977
12/12	1,490,254	(2,300)	—	92,788
12/11	1,499,351	(696)	—	98,538
12/10	1,539,557	(496)	—	104,230
12/09	1,663,722	4,578	0.3%	107,144
Annual Growth	(4.2%)	—	—	(4.5%)

2013 Year-End Financials

Return on assets: (-0.0%)	Dividends
Return on equity: (-2.0%)	Yield: 0.0%
Long-term debt ($ mil.): —	Payout: —
No. of shares (mil.): —	Market value ($ mil.): —
Sales ($ mil): 87,908	

	STOCK PRICE ($) FY Close	P/E High/Low		PER SHARE ($) Earnings	Dividends	Book Value
12/13	5.32	—	—	(0.02)	0.16	0.90
12/12	3.20	—	—	(0.03)	0.16	1.01
12/11	1.57	—	—	(0.01)	0.00	1.03
12/10	4.11	—	—	(0.01)	0.00	1.05
12/09	3.27	272	68	0.12	2.28	1.10
Annual Growth	12.9%	—	—		(48.2%)	(4.8%)

Loblaw Cos. Ltd.

LOCATIONS
HQ: Loblaw Cos. Ltd.
1 President's Choice Circle, Brampton, Ontario L6Y 5S5
Phone: 905 459-2500　　**Fax:** 905 861-2206
Web: www.loblaw.ca

HISTORICAL FINANCIALS
Company Type: Public

Income Statement
FYE: December 28

	REVENUE ($ mil.)	NET INCOME ($ mil.)	NET PROFIT MARGIN	EMPLOYEES
12/13	30,394	591	1.9%	138,000
12/12	31,776	653	2.1%	134,000
12/11*	30,634	753	2.5%	135,000
01/11	30,916	676	2.2%	136,000
01/10	29,224	623	2.1%	138,000
Annual Growth	1.0%	(1.3%)	—	0.0%

*Fiscal year change

2013 Year-End Financials

Debt ratio: 37.4%	No. of shares (mil.): 282
Return on equity: 9.4%	Dividends
Cash ($ mil.): 2,122	Yield: 0.0%
Current ratio: 1.43	Payout: 42.3%
Long-term debt ($ mil.): 6,264	Market value ($ mil.): 11,132

	STOCK PRICE ($) FY Close	P/E High/Low		PER SHARE ($) Earnings	Dividends	Book Value
12/13	39.43	20	15	2.08	0.88	23.34
12/12	41.20	19	13	2.29	0.85	22.91
12/11*	37.82	17	12	2.66	0.82	20.93
01/11	40.50	18	13	2.39	0.84	20.02
01/10	32.10	12	7	2.26	0.80	21.60
Annual Growth	5.3%	—	—	(2.0%)	2.5%	2.0%

*Fiscal year change

London Life Insurance Co.

LOCATIONS
HQ: London Life Insurance Co.
255 Dufferin Avenue, London, Ontario N6A 4K1
Phone: 519 432-5281　　**Fax:** 519 435-4445
Web: www.londonlife.com

HISTORICAL FINANCIALS
Company Type: Public

Income Statement
FYE: December 31

	ASSETS ($ mil.)	NET INCOME ($ mil.)	INCOME AS % OF ASSETS	EMPLOYEES
12/13	72,948	(145)	—	0
12/12	70,581	208	0.3%	0
12/11	64,535	65	0.1%	0
12/10	64,641	(33)	—	0
12/09	25,045	372	1.5%	0
Annual Growth	30.6%	—	—	—

2013 Year-End Financials

Return on assets: (-0.2%)	Dividends
Return on equity: (-4.5%)	Yield: —
Long-term debt ($ mil.): —	Payout: —
No. of shares (mil.): 0	Market value ($ mil.): —
Sales ($ mil): 8,655	

LVMH Moet Hennessy Louis Vuitton

LVMH Moet Hennessy Louis Vuitton is the world's largest luxury goods company with brands that are bywords for the good life and everything showy. LVMH makes wines and spirits (Dom Perignon Moet & Chandon Veuve Clicquot and Hennessy) perfumes (Christian Dior Guerlain and Givenchy) cosmetics (Bliss Fresh and BeneFit) fashion and leather goods (Donna Karan Givenchy Kenzo and Louis Vuitton) and watches and jewelry (TAG Heuer Bulgari). LVMH's selective retail division includes Sephora cosmetics stores Le Bon Marche Paris department stores and 61% of DFS Group (duty-free shops). Chairman Bernard Arnault and his family through Groupe Arnault own about 46% of LVMH.

Geographic Reach

The Paris-based luxury powerhouse operates some 3385 stores across Asia (including China and Japan) Europe and North America. While more than a third of its stores are in Europe Asia is the company's single largest market accounting for more than 35% of sales. LVMH rings up about 30% of its sales in Europe (including France with 11%). The US represents more than 20%.

Financial Performance

After a period of relatively flat sales during the global financial crisis LVMH has experience four consecutive years of accelerating revenue growth. Indeed sales topped Â29.1 billion ($40 billion) in 2013 an 8% increase in organic revenue versus 2012 and an all-time record for the luxury goods company. Profits have risen as well with net income topping $4.7 billion in 2013 up 5% over 2012. Like its customers the company is cash rich reporting more than $4 billion in cash flow from operations in 2013.

Driving revenue growth in 2013 were the company's Selective Retailing business which reported a double-digit increase in sales and to a lesser extent Wines & Spirits and Perfumes & Cosmetics. Fashion & Leather Goods and Watches & Jewelry posted year-over-year declines in sales. On a regional basis Asia (excluding Japan) contributed a growing share (30%) of the group's revenue in 2013 while Japan and Europe (excluding France) accounted for less. Challenging economic conditions kept a lid on growth in Europe and France.

Strategy

With the market for luxury goods on a tear —especially in fast-growing markets in Asia —LVMH is flush with cash for acquisitions and organic growth. Indeed the company is growing its stores base in all of its markets except for Japan where it held steady at 370 shops in 2013. LVMH added 180 stores in 2013 after adding about 165 in 2012. China is a huge emerging market for luxury goods including wines & spirits and a pillar of growth for the French company.

The company has been focusing on controlling as much of its distribution across its 60 brands as possible. LVMH has more than 3380 retail outlets (87% are outside France). Nearly half belong to its Selective Retailing business which consists primarily of Sephora cosmetics stores. About 40% are fashion and leather goods shops led by Louis Vuitton and also include Fendi boutiques and hundreds of other shops under the Celine Givenchy Donna Karan Thomas Pink Pucci and Marc Jacobs brands among others. LVMH's namesake Louis Vuitton brand as well as Fendi and Marc Jacobs are proving resilient in Europe despite the economic slowdown there and posting strong revenue gains in Asia.

Striking out in a new direction the luxury goods firm has entered the hotel business via a partnership with Egypt's Orascom Development Holding. Together the two are developing upmarket resorts in Egypt and Oman with LVMH overseeing the design and running of the hotels.

Mergers and Acquisitions

LVMH expanded its products portfolio in mid-2013 when it purchased an 80% stake in Italian cashmere company Loro Piana for $2.57 billion more than three times the $900 million in sales the company had expected to post in 2013. LVMH values Loro Piana for its products' unique quality and craftsmanship and its six generations of leadership. As part of the transaction the cashmere company's owners will retain a stake in the business.

Putting its ample cash to good use in late 2011 the French luxury goods firm completed a Â3.7 billion ($5 billion) tender offer for the shares of Rome-based jeweler Bulgari. Bulgari is the smallest of the major luxury jewelry and watch makers and the deal doubles LVMH's watch and jewelry business. The Bulgari deal was announced soon after LVMH acquired a pair of niche brands: Ole Henriksen and Nude skin care. In late 2010 LVMH bought more than 20% of the shares of its rival Hermes International. While LVMH described the move as friendly and said it would not launch a takeover bid for Hermes it nevertheless led to speculation regarding further consolidation in the luxury goods industry as LVMH is known for its predatory nature.

HISTORY

Woodworker Louis Vuitton started his Paris career packing dresses for French Empress Eugenie. He later designed new types of luggage and in

1854 he opened a store to sell his designs. In 1896 Vuitton introduced the LV monogram fabric that the company still uses. By 1900 Louis Vuitton had stores in the US and England and by WWI Louis' son Georges had the world's largest retail store for travel goods.

Henry Racamier a former steel executive who had married into the Vuitton family took charge in 1977 repositioning the company's goods from esoteric status symbols to designer must-haves. Sales soared from $20 million to nearly $2.5 billion within a decade. Concerned about being a takeover target Racamier merged Louis Vuitton in 1987 with Moet Hennessy (which made wines spirits and fragrances) and adopted the name LVMH Moet Hennessy Louis Vuitton.

Moet Hennessy had been formed through the 1971 merger of Moet et Chandon (the world's #1 champagne maker) and the Hennessy Cognac company (founded by Irish mercenary Richard Hennessy in 1765). Moet Hennessy acquired rights to Christian Dior fragrances in 1971.

Racamier tried to reverse the merger when disagreements with chairman Alain Chevalier arose. Racamier invited outside investor Bernard Arnault to increase his interest in the company. Arnault gained control of 43% of LVMH and became chairman in 1989. Chevalier stepped down but Racamier fought for control for another 18 months and then set up Orcofi a partner of cosmetics rival L'Oreal.

LVMH increased its fashion holdings with the purchases of the Givenchy Couture Group (1988) Christian Lacroix (1993) and Kenzo (1993). The company also acquired 55% of French media firm Desfosses International (1993) Celine fashions (1996) the Chateau d'Yquem winery (1996) and duty-free retailer DFS Group (1996). Next LVMH bought perfume chains Sephora (1997) and Marie-Jeanne Godard (1998). In 1998 LVMH integrated the Paris department store Le Bon Marche which was controlled by Arnault.

LVMH accumulated a 34% stake in Italian luxury goods maker Gucci in early 1999 and planned to buy all of it. Fellow French conglomerate Pinault-Printemps-Redoute (PPR) later thwarted LVMH by purchasing 42% of Gucci.

Through its LV Capital unit in 1999 LVMH began acquiring stakes in a host of luxury companies including a joint venture with fashion company Prada to buy 51% of design house Fendi (LVMH bought Prada's 25.5% stake for $265 million in November 2001). It has since upped its Fendi stake to about 70%. LVMH later added the Ebel Chaumet and TAG Heuer brands to its new watch division.

In early 2000 LVMH bought Miami Cruiseline Services which operates duty-free shops on cruise ships auction house L'Etude Tajan and 67% of Italian fashion house Emilio Pucci. The company later purchased 35% of French video game retailer Micromania and 51% of department store Samaritaine. In late 2000 LVMH acquired Gabrielle Studio which owns all Donna Karan licenses. In 2001 the company bought Donna Karan International.

LVMH bought in 2001 the Newton and MountAdam vineyards for about $45 million. It then began marketing De Beers diamond jewelry in a 50-50 joint venture with the diamond powerhouse. In March LVMH prompted the investigation of a Dutch court into the PPR-Gucci alliance. The company sold its stake in Gucci to PPR for $806.5 million in October.

In October 2002 LVMH ceased trading on the Brussels and Nasdaq exchanges to concentrate on its Euronext investors. In October 2003 the company sold Canard-Duchene to the Alain Thienot Group. LVMH shed several of the less productive of its 50 brands in 2003 including auction house

Phillips de Pury & Luxemborg and fashion brand Michael Kors.

LVMH opened its biggest store —a four-story emporium on New York's Fifth Avenue —in February 2004. A few months later the company added whisky-maker Glenmorangie PLC to its subsidiary roster. LVMH also made its debut in the South African market in October 2004 opening its first sub-Saharan boutique in Johannesburg. Also during the year Bliss spas was sold off.

In early 2004 LVMH won a landmark lawsuit against Morgan Stanley alleging that the firm had used biased research in misstatements about the financial health of LVMH that caused damage to the company's image. The presiding Parisian court ordered Morgan Stanley to pay 100 million euros (about $38 million) in damages. Morgan Stanley appealed the ruling later that year.

In late 2005 LVMH opened its largest store to date on the Champs-Elysees in Paris and the De Beers brand was introduced in the US with stores in New York and Los Angeles. Also that year LVMH was the winning bidder for whisky maker Glenmorangie PLC for which it paid Â300 million. On the sell side LVMH divested fashion design house Christian Lacroix SNC.

In May 2007 LVMH acquired a 55% stake in Chinese distillery Wenjun for an undisclosed amount. (Jiannanchun the distillery's previous owner retained a 45% stake in Wenjun.) In December 2007 the luxury goods firm acquired the French newspaper Les Echos from publisher Pearson. LVMH controls Les Echos' rival the financial daily La Tribune but has agreed to sell it. Group Les Echos deal includes the newspaper Web site business magazine Enjeux and other financial information services.

In late 2008 Sephora SA acquired a 45% stake in the Russian perfume and cosmetics chain Ile de Beaute. (The agreement which gave Sephora the option to become a majority shareholder allowed LVMH to up its share to 65% in mid-2011.) The firm acquired the luxury yacht-maker Royal Van Lent.

In August 2009 LVMH acquired 50% stakes in two French wine makers: privately-held Cheval Blanc; and La Tour du Pin owner of the Chateau Quinault l'Enclose estate.

In early 2010 LVMH acquired a 40% stake in Dondup an Italian apparel and denim brand for more than $43 million (or 30 million euros). Its plans are to expand Dondup's business internationally. Later in 2010 the company purchased a 70% stake in the Brazilian fragrance and cosmetics retailer Sack's. The acquisition estimated to be worth R$250 million is a move on LVMH's part to expand its Sephora beauty chain in Brazil one of the fastest-growing beauty markets in the world.

Adding to its vast portfolio of luxury brands in February 2011 LVMH acquired Ole Henriksen a leading luxury botanical skincare company founded and owned by its namesake. Later that same week LVMH bought a 70% stake in Nude Brands skin care as the company continues to acquire niche brands. The four-year-old line - described as "biocompatible luxury skin care" - was founded by Bryan Meehan and Ali Hewson wife of U2 front man Bono. In March LVMH fired Dior star designer John Galliano amid charges of anti-Semitism. In September LVMH completed its tender offer from Rome-based Bulgari acquiring about 98% of the shares.

EXECUTIVES

Chief Executive Officer, Bernard Arnault, age 65
President Watches & Jewelry, Francesco Trapani, age 57
Group Managing Director and Board Member, Antonio (Toni) Belloni

CEO Bulgari, Jean-Christophe Babin, age 55
Member Executive Committee Human Resources, Chantal Gaemperle
Board Member, Nicholas C. Worms
Executive Committee Member Development and Acquisitions and Board Member, Nicolas Bazire, age 56
Board Member, Yves-Thibault de Silguy, age 64
Board Member, Charles F. W. de Croisset, age 70
Group Managing Director and Board Member, Antonio (Toni) Belloni
Board Member, Baron Albert Frere, age 87
Board Member, Felix G. Rohatyn, age 85
Vice Chairman, Antoine Bernheim, age 89
Board Member, Gilles Hennessy
Board Member, Patrick Houel
Board Member, Antoine Arnault
Vice Chairman, Pierre Gode, age 69
Board Member, Hubert Vedrine
Board Member, Lord Powell of Bayswater
Board Member, Delphine Arnault
Board Member, Bernadette Chirac
Auditors: Deloitte&Associes

LOCATIONS

HQ: LVMH Moet Hennessy Louis Vuitton
22, avenue Montaigne, Paris 75008
Phone: (33) 1 44 13 22 22   **Fax:** (33) 1 44 13 22 23
Web: www.lvmh.com

2012 Stores

	No.
Europe	
France	412
Other	910
Asia	
Japan	370
Other	670
US	644
Other	198
Total	**3,204**

Sales

	% of total
Europe	
France	11
Other	20
Asia	
Japan	8
Other	28
US	23
Other	10
Total	**100**

PRODUCTS/OPERATIONS

Sales

	% of total
Fashion & leather	35
Selective retailing	28
Wines & spirits	15
Perfumes & cosmetics	13
Watches & jewelry	10
Adjustment	(1)
Total	**100**

Selected Brands and Operations

Fashion and leather goods
  Berluti
  Celine
  Donna Karan
  Emilio Pucci
  Fendi
  Gabrielle Studio (Donna Karan label)
  Givenchy
  Kenzo
  Loewe
  Loro Piana
  Louis Vuitton
  Marc Jacobs
  Thomas Pink
Retailing
  DFS Group
  La Samaritaine

Le Bon Marche
Miami Cruiseline Services (duty-free shops)
Sephora
Fragrances and cosmetics
  Aqua di Parma
  BeneFit
  Bliss
  Fresh
  Guerlain
  Kenzo Parfums
  Make Up For Ever
  Marc Jacobs Fragrances
  Nude skin care
  Ole Henriksen
  Parfums Christian Dior
  Parfums Givenchy
Spirits and wines
  10 Cane
  Belvedere
  Canard-Duchene
  Chandon Estates
  Chateau d' Yquem
  Dom Perignon
  Hennessy
  Krug
  Mercier
  Moet & Chandon
  MountAdam
  Newton
  Ruinart
  Veuve Clicquot
Watches and jewelry
  Bulgari
  Chaumet
  De Beers
  Ebel
  Fred
  Omas
  TAG Heuer
  Zenith
Media (Desfosses International Group)
  Investir
  La Tribune
  Les Echos
  Radio Classique
Other
  Royal van Lent (luxury yachts)

COMPETITORS

Armani	Kirin Holdings Company
Asprey	L' Oreal
Avon	MacAndrews &
Bacardi	Forbes
Brown-Forman	Oscar de la Renta
Calvin Klein	Patek Philippe
Chanel	Prada
Douglas Holding	Puig
E. & J. Gallo	Ralph Lauren
Escada	Remy Cointreau
Estee Lauder	Richemont
Galeries Lafayette	Rolex
Gianni Versace	Shiseido
Harry Winston	Swatch
Hermes	Taittinger
Hugo Boss	Tiffany & Co.
Inditex	Unilever
Kering	Vera Wang

HISTORICAL FINANCIALS
Company Type: Public

Income Statement
FYE: December 31

	REVENUE ($ mil.)	NET INCOME ($ mil.)	NET PROFIT MARGIN	EMPLOYEES
12/13	40,130	4,730	11.8%	114,635
12/12	37,041	4,513	12.2%	106,348
12/11	30,601	3,964	13.0%	97,559
12/10	27,195	4,057	14.9%	83,542
12/09	24,566	2,528	10.3%	77,302
Annual Growth	13.1%	17.0%	—	10.4%

Debt ratio: 21.8%
Return on equity: 13.4%
Cash ($ mil.): 4,434
Current ratio: 1.37
Long-term debt ($ mil.): 5,725

No. of shares (mil.): 500
Dividends
  Yield: 2.1%
  Payout: 15.4%
Market value ($ mil.): 18,315

	STOCK PRICE ($) FY Close	P/E High/Low		PER SHARE ($) Earnings	Dividends	Book Value
12/13	36.60	11	8	9.40	0.79	73.44
12/12	37.69	9	7	8.99	0.76	64.75
12/11	28.10	11	7	8.06	1.11	58.29
12/10	33.15	10	5	8.46	0.50	48.08
12/09	22.45	13	5	5.33	0.45	41.90
Annual Growth	13.0%	—	—	15.2%	15.1%	15.1%

LyondellBasell Industries NV

LOCATIONS

HQ: LyondellBasell Industries NV
  Stationsplein 45, Rotterdam 3013 AK
Phone: (31) 10 275 5500
Web: www.lyondellbasell.com

HISTORICAL FINANCIALS
Company Type: Public

Income Statement
FYE: December 31

	REVENUE ($ mil.)	NET INCOME ($ mil.)	NET PROFIT MARGIN	EMPLOYEES
12/14	45,608	4,174	9.2%	13,100
12/13	44,062	3,857	8.8%	13,300
12/12	45,352	2,848	6.3%	13,500
12/11	51,035	2,147	4.2%	14,000
12/10	27,684	1,587	5.7%	14,000
Annual Growth	13.3%	27.3%	—	(1.6%)

2014 Year-End Financials

Debt ratio: 29.2%
Return on equity: 40.1%
Cash ($ mil.): 1,031
Current ratio: 2.14
Long-term debt ($ mil.): 6,757

No. of shares (mil.): 486
Dividends
  Yield: 3.4%
  Payout: 31.8%
Market value ($ mil.): 38,661

	STOCK PRICE ($) FY Close	P/E High/Low		PER SHARE ($) Earnings	Dividends	Book Value
12/14	79.39	14	9	7.99	2.70	17.07
12/13	80.28	12	8	6.75	2.00	22.74
12/12	57.09	11	7	4.92	4.20	19.47
12/11	32.49	12	6	3.74	5.05	18.61
12/10	34.40	12	5	2.78	0.00	20.43
Annual Growth	23.3%	—	—	30.2%	—	(4.4%)

Macquarie Group Ltd

One of the few domestically owned investment banks in the Land Down Under Macquarie Group does business at home in Australia and beyond.

The holding company for Macquarie Bank and other subsidiaries it operates an investment banking practice that performs financing trading strategic advisory equities research and other services for corporate and government clients. Other operations include fund management retail banking and lending and wealth management. Macquarie has jumped headfirst into the international private-equity market as well focusing on the energy sector through its Macquarie Energy arm. Founded in 1969 Macquarie has more than 70 offices around the world.

Macquarie's business activities are divided into six operating groups: Banking and Financial Services; Corporate and Asset Finance; Fixed Income Currencies and Commodities; Macquarie Capital; Macquarie Funds; and Macquarie Securities.

The company aims to be a global organization and its strategy is to not only build upon assets in Australia but to also enter markets abroad (mostly in the US and Europe). Most of its focus is on the energy renewables resources financial services and infrastructure sectors. The company's main strategy is to build diversity and expand its global platform.

Most recently Macquarie has been acquiring several North America-based financial services companies including investment bank Fox-Pitt Kelton Cochran Caronia Waller. In 2010 Macquarie expanded upon its individual and institutional asset management business when it acquired US-based Delaware Investments. It also bought the Canadian investment dealing business of Blackmont Capital and rebranded it as Macquarie Private Wealth.

Two more US acquisitions were designed to enhance Macquarie Capital's advisory business. In 2010 Macquarie bought US-based specialist Presidio Partners which performs real estate advisory and capital raising advisory services. Macquarie also bought Los Angeles-based investment bank Regal Capital Advisors a specialist in strategic and financial advice for the gaming lodging and leisure industries. Macquarie's recent US shopping spree has helped boost revenues brought in from the US. That market now contributes about 30% of the company's revenues.

Next on the acquisition radar is Europe. Macquarie acquired the cash equities sales and research business of German private bank Sal. Oppenheim Jr. & Cie. in 2010. The acquisition broadened Macquarie's European business bolstering its presence in several key markets. Macquarie is looking to buy trading and investment banking businesses in Europe.

Macquarie is known as a specialist in the Asia/Pacific market. The firm has expanded in that sector and worked on some of the largest transactions in the region such as the IPO of Agricultural Bank of China. The company also manages several funds in Asia most of them focused on infrastructure.

Macquarie also has been focusing on the energy market. Intrigued by the steady long-term returns of regulated power assets Macquarie in 2014 inked a deal to buy Louisiana utility Cleco Corporation for $3.4 billion in cash.

In 2009 it acquired Canadian boutique investment bank Tristone Capital which serves the oil and gas industry. Macquarie also acquired the downstream natural gas trading operations of Constellation Energy. The company then combined that business with its Macquarie Cook Energy business to form Macquarie Energy a larger North American wholesale gas company. In 2010 Macquarie Energy acquired the wholesale electric marketing and trading portfolio of Integrys Energy Services in a deal that more than doubled Macquarie Energy's customer base and strengthened its position in key North American power markets. Also that year subsidiary Macquarie Aerospace agreed to purchase a portfolio of 53 aircraft from AIG unit International Lease Finance Corporation.

But acquisitions aren't the only tricks up Macquarie's sleeves. The company has created investment funds and management companies out of acquired assets ranging from tollways to office buildings to water treatment systems and unleashed them on public markets around the globe. These include Macquarie Infrastructure Company in the US and Macquarie Infrastructure Group in Australia.

In 2012 a fund managed by Macquarie Group acquired WCA Waste Corp. The deal will expand and diversity Macquarie's North American portfolio.

While the energy and financial services sectors seem to be Macquarie's main focus other parts of the company's business are being reshuffled as a result of the global financial crisis. The group restructured several of its property-related subsidiaries in 2008 merging its property advisory division with the investment bank's real estate group which covers funds management and development finance. The company also scaled back its mortgage business. In 2010 Macquarie sold the majority of its Australian real estate management platform to the Charter Hall property group.

David Clarke resigned as chairman of Macquarie Group and Macquarie Bank in 2011. After 40 years with the company Clarke stepped down due to health issues. He died shortly afterwards. Former director Kevin McCann was appointed the new chairman.

EXECUTIVES

Head Risk Management Group, Stephen Allen
Head Banking and Financial Services Group, Peter J. Maher, $455,273 total compensation
Managing Director Chief Executive Officer, Nicholas W. Moore, age 55, $474,459 total compensation
Head Fixed Income Currencies and Commodities, Andrew J. Downe, $479,234 total compensation
Head Corporate Affairs Group, Greg C. Ward
Chairman, H. Kevin McCann, age 73
Executive Chairman Macquarie Capital, Michael Carapiet, $383,387 total compensation
Head Macquarie Funds Group, Shemara Wikramanayake
Head Macquarie Securities Group and Macquarie Capital, Roy Laidlaw
CEO Macquarie Capital (USA), Tim Bishop
Head Corporate and Asset Finance Group, Garry Farrell
Head Cash Equities Macquarie Securities Group, Stevan Vrcelj
Country Head - United States of America, M. McLaughlin
Assistant Company Secretary, Nigel Donnelly
Assistant Company Secretary, Paula Walsh
Deputy Head - Global Oil and Gas; Executive Director, Sandy Edmonstone
Chief Operating Officer, Nicole Sorbara
Director, Michael J. (Mike) Hawker, age 54
Director, Peter M. Kirby, age 66
Managing Director Chief Executive Officer, Nicholas W. Moore, age 55
Director, John R. Niland, age 73
Director, Helen M. Nugent, age 63
Director, Catherine B. Livingstone, age 58
Director, Peter H. Warne, age 58
Independent Non-Executive Director, Diane Grady
Independent Non-Executive Director, Michael Coleman
Auditors: PricewaterhouseCoopers

LOCATIONS

HQ: Macquarie Group Ltd
No. 1 Martin Place, Sydney, New South Wales 2000
Phone: (61) 2 8232 3333   **Fax:** (61) 2 8232 4330
Web: www.macquarie.com.au

Sales

	% of total
Australia	54
Americas	23
Europe Middle East	16
Asia/Pacific	7
Total	**100**

PRODUCTS/OPERATIONS

Sales

	% of total
Banking & financial	21
Fixed income currencies &	17
Macquarie Funds	14
Corporate & asset	13
Macquarie Securities	12
Corporate	12
Macquarie	11
Total	**100**

Sales

	% of total
Lending	30
Financial	29
Capital	21
Asset & wealth	20
Total	**100**

COMPETITORS

Citigroup	Merrill Lynch
Deutsche Bank	Morgan Stanley
Goldman Sachs	UBS Investment Bank
HSBC	

HISTORICAL FINANCIALS

Company Type: Public

Income Statement

FYE: March 31

	ASSETS ($ mil.)	NET INCOME ($ mil.)	INCOME AS % OF ASSETS	EMPLOYEES
03/14	142,035	1,167	0.8%	13,913
03/13	157,029	886	0.6%	13,663
03/12	159,857	759	0.5%	14,202
03/11	163,063	989	0.6%	15,556
03/10	133,547	960	0.7%	14,657
Annual Growth	**1.6%**	**5.0%**	**—**	**(1.3%)**

	STOCK PRICE ($) FY Close	P/E High/Low		PER SHARE ($) Earnings	Dividends	Book Value
03/14	53.40	12	8	3.41	0.00	32.82
03/13	38.72	18	10	2.56	0.00	34.96
03/12	30.22	21	9	2.11	0.00	33.44
03/11	38.04	16	9	2.86	0.00	34.03
03/10	43.10	14	4	2.90	0.00	29.86
Annual Growth	**5.5%**	**—**	**—**	**4.1%**	**—**	**2.4%**

Magna International Inc.

Through its various subsidiaries and divisions Magna International makes just about everything needed to put together a motor vehicle. Magna Steyr its largest division offers vehicle engineering and assembly. Magna's interior and exterior systems division makes trim lighting sealing systems instrument and door panels and sound insulation. Cosma International makes body and chassis systems. Magna Powertrain offers transaxles transmission systems and engine parts while Magna Mirrors makes mirrors and driver assistance products. Other Magna operations include Seating E-Car Systems Electronics Roof and Closures. Its geographic markets include North America Europe Africa and Asia.

Geographic Reach

The company operates through almost 310 manufacturing operations and roughly 90 product development engineering and sales centers in nearly 30 countries. Magna follows a decentralized mode of operation meaning its businesses operate independently.

The company has restructured itself along geographic lines to be more responsive to customers' needs and is paying particular attention to the "Rest of World" market that encompasses developing regions such as Africa Asia Eastern Europe and South America.

Sales and Marketing

BMW Daimler Fiat/Chrysler Ford GM and VW accounted for approximately 83% of Magna's total sales in 2012.

Financial Performance

Magna has enjoyed sizable growth over the years as the global automotive sector recovers. Its total sales were up by 7% from $28.8 billion to $30.8 billion during 2011 to 2012. Profits also skyrocketed by 41% from $1 billion to $1.4 billion during that same time period. Both these revenue and profit totals represented historical milestones for the company.

The company attributes the growth in 2012 to an increase in light vehicle production in North America (18%) and western Europe (7%). It also was helped by a 33% increase in Rest of World production sales and by acquisitions it made in 2012.

Strategy

Magna International seeks expansion opportunities in the Eastern European and Russian markets by strengthening its ties to the GAZ Group Russia's largest auto maker. Magna has several facilities in Russia including a plant in Kaluga that makes parts for Volkswagen (VW) Skoda Renault and Peugeot. It also has facilities in the St. Petersburg area.

Farther East Magna's Cosma International formed a joint venture in 2011 with China-based Guangzhou Automobile Group Component Co. (GACC). The business entity Changsha Cosma Automotive manufactures major body and chassis components and structural assemblies from a new facility in Changsha City in the Hunan Province. The company also opened new facilities in India and South Korea.

Looking to the Western Hemisphere Magna Seating acquired Germany-based Vogelsitze GmbH in early 2011. Vogelsitze makes seats for buses and passenger trains. A year later Magna obtained Verwaltungs GmbH a maker of automotive vacuum engine and transmission pumps with two facilities in Germany and one in each of China and

Bulgaria.

Strengthening its automotive pump operations even further in 2012 Magna purchased the remaining 50% interest it didn't already own of STT Technologies. STT makes transmission and engine related pumps and caters to the North American market.

HISTORY

Magna International is rooted in a tool and die shop founded by Frank Stronach and friend Tony Czapka in Ontario Canada in 1957. Austrian-born Stronach immigrated to Canada in 1954. By the end of 1957 the business called Multimatic had 10 employees. Multimatic delved into car parts when it landed a contract in 1960 to make sun visor brackets for a General Motors division in Canada.

To go public Multimatic underwent a reverse merger in 1969 with Magna Electronics a publicly traded maker of components for aerospace defense and industrial markets. (Stronach retained control of the company.) Annual sales reached $10 million that year. The company expanded its automotive operations during the early 1970s by adding more stamped and electronic components. Magna was renamed Magna International in 1973.

With sales increasing steadily among its auto parts businesses Magna sold its aerospace and defense business (now part of Heroux-Devtek) in 1981. The new Magna consisted of five distinct automotive divisions that made seat tracks door latches electronic components and other auto parts. During the 1980s the company expanded by adding factories and product lines. It also capitalized on car makers' penchant for outsourcing labor and bypassing unions. By 1987 when sales reached $1 billion the company was producing systems for every area of the automobile. Stronach didn't spend all his time on cars however; he owned race horses and restaurants. He had opened restaurants tried various publishing ventures (which failed) and even made an unsuccessful run for a Canadian parliament seat in 1988.

Aggressive expansion during the 1980s eventually caught up with the company and in 1989 Magna began to restructure selling assets to pay off its debt. The company also was bailed out in part by two of its principal customers –General Motors and Chrysler. Having recovered somewhat Magna began acquiring small auto parts companies in Europe in 1992.

Magna expanded its European presence with the purchase of Austria-based Steyr-Daimler-Puch in 1998 adding about $1 billion in annual sales. The deal steered Magna into the auto assembly business. Stronach also added Santa Anita Park to his holdings that year. In late 1999 the company's racetrack interests were spun off as Magna Entertainment with Magna retaining a 78% stake. Stronach's horse Red Bullet won the 2000 Preakness. Later that year Magna sold its 50% stake in Webasto Sunroofs to privately-owned German auto parts maker Webasto.

Early in 2001 Stronach's daughter Belinda was named vice chairman and CEO. The company then prepared to spin off Magna Steyr and Intier (now Magna's interiors and seating divisions) as public companies; Intier was spun off later in 2001.

Magna acquired rival automotive mirror maker Donnelly in 2002 in a stock-and-debt deal worth $320 million. The company divested its stake in Magna Entertainment in 2003.

Belinda Stronach stepped down as president CEO and director in order to make a bid for the leadership of Canada's new Conservative Party. Her father assumed the role of interim president in early 2004. Ms. Stronach's bid for the leadership of the Conservative Party was not successful. Mr. Stronach ran the company until 2005 when Magna adopted a co-CEO management structure with Donald Walker and Siegfried Wolf at the helm.

Magna and Daimler announced in 2004 that Magna would buy Daimler's drivetrain manufacturing subsidiary New Venture Gear for about $435 million. After approval by the European Commission New Venture Gear was acquired by a newly created joint venture called New Process Gear with Magna holding an 80% interest; Daimler held 20% until 2007 when Magna bought out its stake.

Russian conglomerate Basic Element led by Russian aluminum magnate Oleg Deripaska spent about $1.5 billion to purchase 20% of Magna in 2007. The transaction gave Magna entry to the Russian market but late in 2008 Deripaska's bank BNP Paribas made a margin call that forced the businessman to give up his shares. In 2008 Magna International acquired Technoplast a Russia-based manufacturer of plastic automotive interior and exterior parts which bolstered its capacity in Eastern Europe and Russia.

On the heels of the General Motors bankruptcy filing in 2009 the German government selected Magna International as a partner for Adam Opel and agreed to provide about Â1.5 billion (around $2 billion) in bridge loans while GM and Magna finalized the contract. A trusteeship for Opel was arranged to keep European operations separate from the Chapter 11 proceedings of GM.

Magna teamed up with Russian banking firm Sberbank to purchase a 55% interest in Opel and its UK-based Vauxhall unit. While GM initially agreed to the sale in September 2009 it backed out in November. The GM board decided to restructure Opel and its European operations instead because business conditions were improving and the Opel brand was important to its global strategy. In Europe the decision was met with demands by the German government that its Â1.5 billion in bridge loans be returned as well as protests and planned work stoppages by the German labor union.

The GM bankruptcy was brought on by the economic crisis of 2008 and 2009. Magna responded by implementing cost cutting measures which included reducing its headcount by approximately 11500 representing a 14% cutback between 2007 and 2009. It also sold off some of its non-core assets.

Founder and chairman Frank Stronach stepped down in 2010 citing the trend toward more regulatory limitations on company management as one of the reasons. He gave up his controlling share in the company and with it his voting control. The company purchased and cancelled all of its Class B shares held by the Stronach Group and issued Class A Common shares. This capital transaction ended the company's dual class stock structure. The former premier of Ontario Mike Harris took Stronach's place. Co-CEO Siegfried ("Sigi") Wolf also resigned which made co-CEO Donald Walker the sole CEO of Magna International as of mid-2011.

EXECUTIVES

Chief Executive Officer; Director, Donald J. Walker, age 58

Executive Vice-President and Chief Financial Officer, Vincent J. Galifi, $110,500 total compensation

Executive Vice President; Chief Legal Officer, Jeffrey O. Palmer

Executive Vice President - Global Human Resources, Marc J. Neeb

Chief Operating Officer, Tom Skudutis, $110,500 total compensation

EVP and Chief Strategy Officer, Herbert Demel, age 61

Executive Vice President, Alon Ossip

Chairman of the Board, William L. Young, age 58

President Magna Europe, Guenther Apfalter

VP and Secretary, Bassem A. Shakeel

Chief Marketing Officer and President Magna Asia, James J. (Jim) Tobin Sr.

CTO, Burkhard Goeschel, age 67

Director Corporate Communications and Media Relations, Tracy Fuerst

Executive Vice-President Corporate Engineering & R&D, Seetarama Kotagiri

Vice President Sales & Marketing, Hubert H?dl

CEO and Director, Donald J. Walker, age 57

Director, Lady Barbara T. Judge, age 68

Director, Donald Resnick, age 85

Director, Rt. Hon. Franz Vranitzky, age 75

Director, Lawrence D. Worrall, age 72

Director, Michael D. (Mike) Harris, age 68

Independent Director, Kurt Lauk

Independent Director, Trevor Eyton

Auditors: Ernst&YoungLLP

LOCATIONS

HQ: Magna International Inc.
337 Magna Drive, Aurora, Ontario L4G 7K1
Phone: 905 726-7070   **Fax:** 905 726-7173
Web: www.magna.com

Sales

North America	53
Other regions	6

PRODUCTS/OPERATIONS

Sales

	$ mil.	% of total
Exterior & interior systems	11,673	38
Body systems & chassis systems	7,123	23
Powertrain systems	3,825	12
Complete vehicle assembly	2,561	8
Tooling engineering & other	2,317	8
Vision & electronic systems	2,132	7
Closure systems	1,206	4
Total	**30,837**	**100**

Sales by Customer

General Motors	19
Fiat/Chrysler	13
Volkswagen	12
Other	17

Selected Operations Products and Services

Cosma International Inc. - body and chassis systems
   Body systems
   Chassis systems
   Design and engineering
   Finishing
   Metal forming technologies
   Stampings
Decoma International - exterior and interior systems
   Body side systems
   Bumper systems (front and rear)
   Cargo management
   Carpet and loadspace
   Cockpit systems
   Engineered glass
   Exterior trim
   Greenhouse systems
   Lighting systems
   Plastic body panels
   Polymeric glazing systems
   Sealing systems
   Vehicle enhancement packages
Magna Car Top Systems - roof systems
   Soft tops
   Removable roof systems
   Retractable hard tops
   Sliding roof systems
Magna Closures - closure systems
   Door modules
   Driver controls
   Handle assemblies
   Power closures and latching systems
   Window systems
Magna E-Car Systems

Battery cells and packs
Hybrid and electric vehicle development and
  production
Magna Electronics - electronic systems
  Body electronics
  Driver assistance and safety systems
  Engine electronics
  Intelligent power systems
  Lighting systems
  Liquid sensors
Magna Mirrors - vision systems
  Actuators
  Electronic vision systems
  Exterior and interior mirrors
Magna Powertrain - powertrain systems
  Automatic overdrives
  Die castings
  Differentials
  Engine systems
  Fluid pressure and controls
  Power take-offs
  Stampings
  Transaxles
  Transfer cases
  Transmission systems
Magna Seating - seating systems
  Seat mechanism systems
  Seating systems
Magna Steyr - complete vehicle manufacturing and OEM
  engineering
  Energy storing systems
  Fuel systems

COMPETITORS

A.G. Simpson	Hella
Aisin Seiki	Johnson Controls
American Axle &	KUO
Manufacturing	Lacks Enterprises
Benteler Automotive	Lear Corp
BorgWarner	Linamar Corp.
Calsonic Kansei	Meritor
Commercial Vehicle	Plastic Omnium
DENSO	Prodrive
DURA Automotive	Robert Bosch
Dana Holding	Tenneco
Delphi Automotive	Textron
Systems	Torotrak
Eaton	Tower International
Faurecia	Toyota Auto Body
Ficosa	Valeo
GKN	Visteon
Gentex	ZF Friedrichshafen
Haldex	

HISTORICAL FINANCIALS
Company Type: Public

Income Statement
FYE: December 31

	REVENUE ($ mil.)	NET INCOME ($ mil.)	NET PROFIT MARGIN	EMPLOYEES
12/13	34,835	1,561	4.5%	125,000
12/12	30,837	1,433	4.6%	119,000
12/11	28,748	1,018	3.5%	108,275
12/10	24,102	973	4.0%	96,600
12/09	17,367	(493)	—	72,500
Annual Growth	19.0%	—	—	14.6%

2013 Year-End Financials

Debt ratio: 2.0%
Return on equity: 16.3%
Cash ($ mil.): 1,554
Current ratio: 1.36
Long-term debt ($ mil.): 102
No. of shares (mil.): 221
Dividends
  Yield: 1.5%
  Payout: 18.9%
Market value ($ mil.): 18,148

	STOCK PRICE ($) FY Close	P/E High/Low		PER SHARE ($) Earnings	Dividends	Book Value
12/13	82.06	13	7	6.76	1.28	43.51
12/12	50.02	8	5	6.09	1.10	40.44
12/11	33.31	14	7	4.20	1.00	35.04
12/10	52.00	24	11	4.18	0.42	33.25
12/09	50.58	—	—	(2.21)	0.36	32.66
Annual Growth	12.9%			—	37.3%	7.4%

Malayan Banking Berhad

Malaysia's largest bank Malayan Banking Berhad (better known as Maybank) and its subsidiaries operate some 500 branches mostly in Malaysia but also in Singapore Indonesia Thailand the Philippines Pakistan and elsewhere throughout Southeast Asia. Its core services consist of deposits mortgages and other loans and credit cards to individuals and businesses. Other offerings include investment banking asset management online banking brokerage insurance unit trusts and other investments and corporate finance. Overall Maybank has more than 2200 offices in 20 countries. Amanah Raya a trust company controlled by the Malaysian government owns more than 45% of Maybank.

Strategy

One of Maybank's fastest growing segments is banking services and Takaful (insurance) that adhere to Islamic law which prohibits the collection of interest but allows profit-sharing and the sale and buy-back of homes (instead of the origination of mortgages). Serving Muslim individuals organizations and businesses the company is opening branches at home and abroad that offer such services.

Maybank has also targeted Indonesia as a growth market. The bank completed its acquisition of the 250-branch Bank Internasional Indonesia (BII) in 2008. The deal had stalled when banking regulator Bank Negara Malaysia prohibited the transaction but that decision was reversed and the acquisition was ultimately allowed. Maybank plans to add 200 new branches to BII's network by 2013.

The company has made other moves to expand its international presence. It acquired minority stakes in Pakistan's MCB Bank and Vietnam's An Binh Bank (ABBank) in 2008; it also bought Kookmin Bank's minority stake in PT Bank International Indonesia. In 2011 the company acquired 100% of Singapore brokerage Kim Eng Holdings. The addition boosts Maybank's international profile and expands its distribution capabilities.

EXECUTIVES

President Chief Executive Officer, George Martirez
President & CEO, Abdul Farid Alias
President; Chief Executive Officer; Non-Independent Executive Director, Abdul Abdul Wahid bin Omar Omar
Acting President Director - PT Bank Internasional Indonesia Tbk, Bapak Bapak Alimhamzah Alimhamzah
Head - Enterprise Transformation Services, Geoffrey Geoffrey Stecyk Stecyk

Head - Insurance & Takaful; Chief Executive Officer - Mayban Ageas Holdings Berhad, Hans Hans De Cuyper Cuyper
Group Chief Risk Officer, Hin Hin Hock Lee Lee
Independent & Non-Executive Director, Johan Johan bin Ariffin Ariffin
Chairman, Megat Zaharuddin Megat Mohd Nor
General Counsel; Company Secretary; Head of Corporate & Legal Services, Mohd Mohd Nazlan bin Mohd Ghazali Ghazali
Independent Non-Executive Vice Chairman of the Board, Mohd Mohd Salleh bin Harun Harun
Head Islamic Banking; Chief Executive Officer Maybank Islamic Berhad, Muzaffar Hisham
Head - Group Human Capital, Nora Nora Abd Manaf Manaf
Chief Strategy & Transformation Officer, Seong Seong Yew Foong Foong
Chief Executive Officer - Maybank Singapore, Sim Sio Hoong
Head - Investment Banking; Chief Executive Officer - Maybank Investment Bank Bhd, Zafrul Zafrul Abd Aziz Aziz
CFO, Mohamed Merican
Deputy President & Head Community Financial Services, Lim Hong Tat
Chief Executive Officer Etiqa, Kamaludin Ahmad
Director, Spencer Lee Tien Chye
Director, Datuk Syed Tamin Syed Mohamed
President CEO and Director, Abdul Wahid bin Omar, age 49
Director, Wai Tan Tat, age 67
Director, Ismail Shahudin, age 63
Director, Hadenan Jalil, age 68
Director, Abidin Jamal Zainal
Independent Non-Executive Director, Alister Alister Maitland Maitland
Independent Non-Executive Director, Erry Erry Riyana Hardjapamekas Hardjapamekas
Independent Non-Executive Director, Mohaiyani Mohaiyani binti Shamsudin Shamsudin
Independent Non-Executive Director, Tat Tat Wai Tan Tan
Independent Non-Executive Director, Teik Teik Seng Cheah Cheah
Non-Independent Non-Executive Director, Zainal Zainal Abidin bin Jamal Jamal
Auditors: Ernst&Young

LOCATIONS

HQ: Malayan Banking Berhad
14th Floor, Menara Maybank, 100, Jalan Tun Perak, Kuala Lumpur 50050
Phone: (60) 3 2070 8833   **Fax:** (60) 3 2032 4775
Web: www.maybank.com

COMPETITORS

AmBank Group	Malaysian Industrial
Bank Muamalat	Development Finance
Bank of China	OCBC Bank
Bank of East Asia	Public Bank
Hang Seng Bank	RHB Capital
Hong Leong Bank	Standard Chartered

HISTORICAL FINANCIALS
Company Type: Public

Income Statement
FYE: December 31

	ASSETS ($ mil.)	NET INCOME ($ mil.)	INCOME AS % OF ASSETS	EMPLOYEES
12/13	171,082	2,000	1.2%	47,771
12/12	161,627	1,876	1.2%	47,233
12/11*	142,407	815	0.6%	45,000
06/11	136,387	1,473	1.1%	42,000
06/10	103,108	1,169	1.1%	40,000
Annual Growth	13.5%	14.4%	—	4.5%

*Fiscal year change

Return on assets: 1.2%	Dividends
Return on equity: 14.8%	Yield: 5.1%
Long-term debt ($ mil.): —	Payout: 13.1%
No. of shares (mil.): —	Market value ($ mil.): —
Sales ($ mil) 7,753	

	STOCK PRICE ($) FY Close	P/E High/Low		PER SHARE ($) Earnings	Dividends	Book Value
12/13	6.00	1	1	0.23	0.31	1.58
12/12	6.11	1	1	0.24	0.42	1.63
12/11*	5.65	2	1	0.11	0.03	1.38
06/11	5.60	1	1	0.20	0.31	1.39
06/10	4.00	2	0	0.17	0.01	1.21
Annual Growth 10.7%		—	—	8.8%	160.0%	7.1%

*Fiscal year change

Manulife Financial Corp.

Manulife the holding company for The Manufacturers Life Insurance Company and John Hancock Financial Services has gone mano a mano with its competitors. Manulife provides individual life insurance group life and health group pension products variable annuities wealth management and financial products in nearly two dozen countries and territories worldwide. North America and Asia make up its largest operations. Manulife's reinsurance division provides life health and accident reinsurance and was one of North America's top life retrocessionaires (firms that reinsure reinsurers) until it sold that division in 2011. The company also provides investment management real estate and lending services.

Geographic Reach

Sales in the US still make up about a third of Manulife's annual revenue (though the market there has shrunk in response to the flagging economy); Canada and Asia each account for about 30% of Manulife's premium income. Its efforts to grow in China through partnerships have paid off with the company's sales there challenging those in Canada (formerly its second-largest market after the US).

Operations

Along with its John Hancock subsidiary Manulife is one of the top five life insurers in North America and is a top 10 global life insurer based on market capitalization. North American financial products are offered primarily under the John Hancock brand while life insurance is offered through Manufacturers Life. Other brands and subsidiaries include Portland Investment Counsel (mutual funds retail investment funds) and Pottruff & Smith (travel insurance).

Strategy

Besides building up its more successful offerings and divesting those with higher risks Manulife's strategy for growth includes maintaining a diversified mix and hedging its in-force public equity and interest rate risks over time. The company's objective is to increase its earnings to $4 billion by 2015.

Manulife also grows through collaborations such as its partnership with Edward Jones which helped the company expand its sales network in the US and add agents to increase its distribution presence in Asia. Its Manulife-Sinochem (MSL) partnership with Sinochem has also allowed the company to deepen its reach in China. With operations in 50 Chinese cities MSL has the broadest geographic footprint of any foreign invested joint venture firm in that country. Manulife also has a 49% interest in ABN AMRO TEDA Fund Management in China. The Manulife-TEDA partnership allows the company to expand in China's wealth management market.

Further expansion in China is in the company's plans as is increasing sales of wealth management products. In 2012 for example Manulife Asset Management procured licensure to provide institutional asset management services in Korea's fast-growing market.

Mergers and Acquisitions

Manulife continues to invest in acquisitions in the near-term specifically as they relate to bolstering its mutual fund business as that is an area Manulife is making great effort to grow. To that end it purchased Wellington West Financial Services from National Bank Financial Group in 2012 for an undisclosed price adding about 40 advisors and some $900 in assets under management to its Canadian investment unit (Manulife Securities) in the deal.

In 2013 Manulife expanded in Canada's mortgage creditor insurance market through the purchase of Benesure Canada. Benesure provides distribution and third-party administration of life and disability creditor policies to mortgage brokerage entities.

In 2011 Manulife continued to diversify and grow different arms of its business. Its global real estate arm Manulife Real Estate made acquisitions valued at $555 million in the key markets of metropolitan New York San Diego and Toronto bringing its total real estate assets to C$7.5 billion ($7.3 billion). This unit is also expanding its multi-family residential holdings having recently acquired properties in New Brunswick New Jersey and Alexandria Virginia.

Manulife sold its life retrocession business to Pacific Life Insurance in 2011 because it didn't align with the firm's future growth strategy of focusing on its other insurance offerings: individual and group life health and group pension. Additionally Manulife wanted to avoid the more restrictive Canadian regulatory requirements for the life retrocession business.

Company Background

Manulife acquired US financial services giant John Hancock in a $10 billion deal in 2004 bringing Manulife into the top ranks of US and global life insurers. Manulife subsequently rebranded its US financial products with the more-recognizable John Hancock name and logo. Manulife also consolidated John Hancock's Canadian subsidiary Maritime Life Assurance Company into its flagship subsidiary The Manufacturers Life Insurance Company.

EXECUTIVES

Vice Chairman, Richard B. DeWolfe, age 70
President; Chief Executive Officer; Director, Donald A. Guloien, $738,340 total compensation
Senior Executive Vice President and General Manager; Asia, Robert A. (Bob) Cook
EVP Individual Wealth Management Canadian Division; Chairman and CEO Elliott and Page Limited, J. Roy Firth
EVP and Chief Strategy Officer, Beverly S. Margolian
Chairman, Gail C. A. Cook-Bennett, age 73
President and CEO Manulife Canada, Paul L. Rooney
SEVP and Chief Investment Officer; Chairman Manulife Asset Management, Warren A. Thomson, age 59

SEVP Corporate Development and General Counsel, Jean-Paul (J.-P.) Bisnaire
SEVP and General Manager Canadian Division, Marianne Harrison
President and CEO Indonesia, Alan Merten
Media Relations Canada, Tom Nunn
Public Affairs Corporate, Laurie Lupton
President John Hancock Financial Services, Craig Bromley
EVP General Account Investments, Scott Hartz
Public Affairs Corporate, David Paterson
Media Relations Canada, Jasmine Mangalaseril
Corporate Communications John Hancock Financial, Roy Anderson
Corporate Communications John Hancock Financial, Leslie Uyeda
Media Relations Asia, Juliana Gittler
Media Relations Manulife-Sinochem Life Insurance Co. Ltd. (China), Lillian Li
Director Marketing and Communications PT Asuransi Jiwa Manulife Indonesia, Kumala D. Ruslie
Media Relations Hong Kong, Helena Lee
Media Relations Hong Kong, Lily Chan
Media Relations Manulife Insurance (Malaysia) Berhad, Susan Ong
Media Relations The Manufacturers Life Insurance Co. (Philippines), Lils Liwanag
Media Relations Manulife (Singapore) Pte Ltd., Cindy Cheng
Media Relations Manulife (International) Limited Taiwan Branch, Suzanne Lee
Media Relations Manulife (Vietnam) Limited, Hang Luu
Communications Japan, Minoru Shimizu
Media Relations Real Estate Division Canada, Tina Acranis
Media Relations MFC Global Investment Management, Brian Carmichael
VP and Head Agency Sales Hong Kong, Kareen Chow
VP and CFO Hong Kong, Nigel Ke
Senior Vice President, Paul Lorentz
President CEO, Doug Conick
Manager Sales Midwest John Hancock Retirement Plan Services (RPS), Cheney L. Hunt III
Head Fixed Income Manulife Asset Management (Singapore), Pang Cheng Duan
President and CEO Singapore, Annette King
Head Institutional Sales North Asia, Edwina Ho
EVP Human Resources and Communications, Stephani E. Kingsmill
Chief Actuary; Executive Vice President, Cindy Forbes
Assistant VP and Head Sales and Marketing Employee Benefits Sales Manulife (International) Limited, Doris Chan
EVP and Chief Risk Officer, Rahim Hirji
SEVP and CFO, Steve Roder
COO, Paul L. Rooney
Director, Thomas E. (Tom) Kierans, age 73
Director, Scott M. Hand, age 72
Vice Chairman, Richard B. DeWolfe, age 70
President CEO and Director, Donald A. Guloien
Director, Lino J. Celeste, age 75
Director, John M. Cassaday, age 61
Director, Pierre Y. Ducros, age 73
Director, Hugh W. Sloan Jr., age 73
Director, Lorna R. Marsden, age 72
Director, Robert J. (Bob) Harding, age 56
Director, Donald R. (Don) Lindsay, age 56
Director, Linda B. Bammann
Director, Robert E. Dineen Jr., age 73
Director, Gordon G. Thiessen, age 74
Director, Thomas P. d'Aquino, age 73
Director, Luther S. Helms
Director, John R. V. Palmer
Director, Joseph P. Caron
Director, Tsun-yan Hsieh
Director, Andrea Rosen

Director, Sheila Fraser
Auditors: Ernst&YoungLLP

LOCATIONS

HQ: Manulife Financial Corp.
200 Bloor Street East, North Tower 10, Toronto, Ontario M4W 1E5
Phone: 416 926-3427   **Fax:** 416 926-5657
Web: www.manulife.com

Revenues

US	32
Canada	30
Total	**100**

PRODUCTS/OPERATIONS

Revenues

Premiums	
Annuities & pensions	12
Other	17

Selected Subsidiaries & Affiliates

Elliott & Page Limited
FNA Financial Inc.
John Hancock Financial Network Inc. (US)
John Hancock Financial Services Inc, (US)
John Hancock Investment Management Services LLC (US)
John Hancock Life Insurance Company (U.S.A.)
John Hancock Life Insurance Company of New York
Manulife International Holdings Limited (Bermuda)
Manulife (Singapore) Pte. Ltd.
Manulife (Vietnam) Limited
Manulife Bank of Canada
Manulife Life Insurance Company (Japan)
Manulife Sinochem Life Insurance Co. Ltd. (China)
NAL Resources Management Limited
P.T. Asuransi Jiwa Manulife Indonesia
The Manufacturers Investment Corporation (US)
The Manufacturers Life Insurance Co. (Philippines) Inc.
The Manufacturers Life Insurance Company

COMPETITORS

AEGON
AIG
Allianz
Canada Life
China Life Insurance
Dai-ichi Life
Fairfax Financial Holdings
Generali
Great-West Lifeco
ING
Industrial Alliance Insurance and Financial Servic
Liberty Mutual
Meiji Yasuda Life
MetLife
Nationwide
New York Life
Nippon Life Insurance
Power Financial
Principal Financial
Prudential
Sun Life
Swiss Re
T&D Holdings
The Hartford
Tokio Marine

HISTORICAL FINANCIALS
Company Type: Public

Income Statement

	ASSETS ($ mil.)	NET INCOME ($ mil.)	INCOME AS % OF ASSETS	EMPLOYEES
12/13	483,036	2,943	0.6%	0
12/12	488,707	1,745	0.4%	28,000
12/11	452,995	126	0.0%	26,000
12/10	425,672	(1,666)	—	25,000
12/09	195,669	1,354	0.7%	24,000
Annual Growth	**25.3%**	**21.4%**	—	—

FYE: December 31

	STOCK PRICE ($) FY Close	P/E High/Low		PER SHARE ($) Earnings	Dividends	Book Value
12/13	19.73	11	8	1.52	0.51	14.58
12/12	13.59	16	11	0.88	0.52	14.08
12/11	10.62	962467		0.02	0.51	13.32
12/10	17.18	—	—	(0.99)	0.51	13.68
12/09	18.34	27	6	0.78	0.67	15.68
Annual Growth	**1.8%**	—	—	**18.1%**	**(6.8%)**	**(1.8%)**

Mapfre SA

To whom do you turn when your vehicle intersects with the "Running of the Bulls?" Through its subsidiaries MAPFRE provides customers with property/casualty (especially auto) coverage life insurance and reinsurance. The firm does business primarily in its home country of Spain where it is a top insurer and in about 45 other nations including many in North and South America. Individual and group offerings include funeral home medical and agricultural insurance. It additionally provides financial services such as investment and pension funds. MAPFRE also maintains a very successful alliance with Spanish banking company Caja Madrid through which the companies cross-market each other's products.

Geographic Reach
MAPFRE operates a network of 15000 branches half of which are located in Spain. Of the international locations about 2000 offices are located in Latin American countries. International operations account for about 60% of MAPFRE's annual revenues.

Operations
MAPFRE conducts its operations through about 240 subsidiaries. The group's activities are divided into four segments: life direct motor direct other non-life direct and reinsurance and other activities.

Sales and Marketing
MAPFRE's products are primarily marketed through distribution agreements with third parties especially banks; it also has direct sales operations in Spain. The company has relationships with some 9700 bank branches and other retail outlets. MAPFRE and Caja Madrid run CCM Vida Y Pensiones a 50/50 joint venture to develop and sell life and pension insurance at the bank and banking products through insurance agents. The company also markets products through a network of 70000 agents and brokers in the Americas.

Financial Performance
MAPFRE achieved 15% revenue growth and doubled net income in 2011. Progress was attributed to its diversification activities and strong returns from the international direct insurance and reinsurance operations. Efforts to strengthen the distribution network in Spain also led to stabilization of sales in the domestic auto life and homeowner's insurance markets. The company has also attributed growth to its prudent financing and investment strategies. MAPFRE has reported increased revenues each year since 2007.

Strategy
MAPFRE is focused on expanding its operations through geographic diversification and continued acquisitions in high-growth markets are key to MAPFRE's expansion plans as domestic markets contract. In South America it has moved to become one of the largest non-life insurers in countries including Brazil and Argentina. The company has a partnership with Banco do Brazil to collaborate on the marketing of property insurance in the Brazilian market. Other areas of expansion have included the emerging markets of India Panama and Ecuador.

North America has been another area of focus for MAPFRE's international expansion strategy. Its MAPFRE U.S.A. unit sells car insurance in Massachusetts and more than a dozen other states.

To increase efficiencies and streamline operations in 2011 the company reorganized its domestic distribution network to focus on retail and corporate customers. It is also revamping its international sales networks to maximize returns.

To increase direct sales in Spain the company launched its VERTI internet and phone sales organization in 2011 for home and auto insurance products. MAPFRE also formed a joint venture with Euler Hermes to market credit and surety products in Spain Portugal and Latin America in 2011.

EXECUTIVES

Secretary, Jose Manuel Gonzalez Porro
Vice Chairman, Filomeno Mira Candel
Chairman and CEO, Jose Manuel Martinez Martinez
Secretary, Jose Manuel Gonzalez Porro
Vice Chairman, Filomeno Mira Candel
Auditors: Ernst&YoungS.L.

LOCATIONS

HQ: Mapfre SA
Paseo de Recoletos, 25, Madrid 28004
Phone: (34) 91 581 1100   **Fax:** (34) 91 581 1143
Web: www.mapfre.es

PRODUCTS/OPERATIONS

Sales

	% of total
International	60
Spain	
Life	19
Non-life	18
Commercial	3
Total	**100**

COMPETITORS

AEGON	Generali
AXA	Grupo Santander
Allianz	ING
Allstate	Markel International
Arbella Insurance	Munich Re Group
BUPA	Progressive
Banco Popular Espa?ol	Corporation
Catalana Occidente	Safety Insurance
El Corte Ingles	Triple-S Management
GEICO	

Income Statement

	ASSETS ($ mil.)	NET INCOME ($ mil.)	INCOME AS % OF ASSETS	EMPLOYEES
12/13	78,234	1,088	1.4%	36,280
12/12	75,106	877	1.2%	34,962
12/11	70,953	1,245	1.8%	32,798
12/10	65,141	1,249	1.9%	35,704
12/09	62,096	1,335	2.2%	34,326
Annual Growth	5.9%	(5.0%)	—	1.4%

Marubeni Corp.

Marubeni's name combines the Japanese words for "circle" and "red" and Marubeni hopes the comprehensive range of products manufactured and traded by its circle of operating units will keep the company out of the red. One of Japan's largest "sogo shosha" (general trading companies) Marubeni has a broad range of operating segments: Chemicals; Energy; Finance Logistics & IT Business; Food; Forest Products; Lifestyle; Metals & Mineral Resources; Real Estate Development; Plant & Industrial Machinery; Power Projects & Infrastructure; and Transportation Machinery.

In 2011 the trading company simplified its reporting structure into four broad segments: Machinery (Plant & Industrial Machinery Power Projects & Infrastructure and Transportation Machinery); Resources (Energy and Metals & Mineral Resources); Materials (Chemicals Forest Products and General Merchandise); and Consumer Products (Finance Logistics & IT Business Food Lifestyle and Real Estate Development.)

Marubeni has hundreds of operating companies in 70 countries.

A recovering economy and a robust growth in commodity prices lifted Marubeni's revenues and income in 2012. In fiscal 2012 the company reported a 19% increase in revenues driven by a 17% jump in the volume of Marubeni's trading transactions especially from higher oil prices. Energy accounted for 29% of total trading volume in 2012 and was 22% greater in actual volume than in 2011. Marubeni's higher overall revenues in 2012 outpaced increased expenses enabling the trading house to post a 26% jump in net income.

The group has been particularly active in Asia where its diversity has enabled it to develop local industries and to help build utility and industrial infrastructures such as telephone systems power plants and water systems. The company has championed international expansion since the mid-1990s but Japan's credit crunch and the Asian economic crisis have hurt the company's production and processing operations across Southeast Asia. Marubeni has been reducing debt controlling operating costs and investing in commodity trading natural resources projects and international power generation schemes.

Growing its commodity business in 2012 the company agreed to acquire US-based grain fertilizer and energy commodities distribution and natural gas network Gavilon for $3.6 billion.

Taking advantage of BP's need to raise cash in the wake of its Gulf of Mexico oil disaster in 2011 Marubeni bought four mature producing deepwater oil and gas fields in Gulf from BP for $650 million. In 2013 it also agreed to acquire a 49% stake in Williams Partners' floating production platform project for Tubular Bells Field in the Gulf of Mexico.

In 2011 Marubeni formed a joint venture with Supreme Energy and International Power to develop the Rantau Dedap geothermal project located in Sumatra. The 220 MW geothermal plant is part of the Indonesian government's long-term plan meet its country's needs with renewable power.

It also entered a new market that year airplane leasing with a deal with Deucalion Limited to set up a company in Singapore to invest into aircraft assets.

In 2011 the company announced a medium-term growth plan focusing on natural resources (primarily copper) infrastructure environmental products (especially water businesses) and essential living commodities (building up its grain position in China).

HISTORY

Marubeni's origins are closely linked to those of another leading Japanese trading company. ITOCHU founder Chubei Itoh set up Marubeni Shoten K. K. in 1858 as an outlet in Osaka for his textile trading business (originally C. Itoh & Co.). The symbol for the store was a circle ("maru") drawn around the Japanese word for red ("beni"). As C. Itoh's global operations expanded the Marubeni store served as headquarters.

Marubeni was split off from C. Itoh in 1921 to trade textiles although it soon expanded its operations to include industrial and consumer goods. To mobilize for WWII the Japanese government reunited Marubeni and C. Itoh in 1941 merging them with another trading company Kishimoto into a new entity Sanko Kabushiki Kaisha. In 1944 Sanko Daido Boeki and Kureha Spinning were ordered to consolidate into a larger entity to be called the Daiken Co. but the war ended before all operations were fully integrated.

Spun off from Daiken in 1949 Marubeni began trading internationally. It opened a New York office in 1951 and diversified into food metals and machinery. During the Korean War Marubeni benefited from the UN's use of Japan as a supply base.

In 1955 Marubeni merged with Iida & Company and changed its name to Marubeni-Iida. It received a government concession to supply silicon steel and iron sheets critical to the growing Japanese auto and appliance industries. The company expanded into engineering —building factories aircraft and a nuclear reactor for the Japan Atomic Energy Research Institute —and into petrochemicals fertilizers and rubber products.

Marubeni-Iida was behind the Fuyo "keiretsu" formed in the early 1960s. Fuyo (another word for Mt. Fuji) is a powerful assemblage of some 150 companies including Canon Hitachi and Nissan that form joint ventures and develop think tanks.

The firm became Marubeni Corp. in 1972 and a year later it bought Nanyo Bussan another trading company. In 1973 Marubeni's image was tarnished by allegations that it had hoarded rice for sale on the Japanese black market.

In the 1990s Marubeni won several major construction contracts. Among them Marubeni formed a venture in 1998 with John Laing and Turkey's Alarko Alsim to rebuild three airports in Uzbekistan.

Marubeni had begun offering Internet access in 1995 and two years later it launched an Internet-based long-distance telephone service. In 1999 the trading house formed two ventures with US firm Global Crossing one to start operating Pacific Crossing One (the Japan-US cable) and another to lay a cable network in Japan.

That year Marubeni tied up with fellow trading company ITOCHU to integrate their steel processing subsidiaries in China to try to keep their Chinese businesses afloat. In 2000 ITOCHU and Marubeni formed an online steel trading joint venture with US-based e-commerce company MetalSite. The two companies also integrated their entire steel divisions in 2001 forming the Marubeni-Itochu Steel joint venture among the largest steel companies in Japan.

Taking responsibility for the sharp downturn in Marubeni's financial performance chairman Iwao Toriumi announced in 2001 that he would step down. The company launched a major restructuring effort the next year that was designed to give more autonomy to the managers of individual business units.

In 2005 Marubeni launched a large power and water project in Abu Dhabi.

In 2007 Marubeni entered into the finance leasing industry in the US launching subsidiary CoActiv Capital Partners.

In 2008 Marubeni acquired US-based The PIC Group Inc. an independent global provider of services and programs focused on power generation and other industrial facilities and services. In 2009 it acquired 49% of Invenergy Thermal Financing LLC which owns three natural-gas fired power plants (with 1014 MW of generating capcity) in the US.

In 2009 the company completed the Laffan Refinery in Qatar which began commercial operations that year. It also signed a $2 billion deal to build the Shuweihat S2 Independent Water and Power Producer project in the United Arab Emirates.

EXECUTIVES

Chairman, Nobuo Katsumata
Chairman, Teruo Asada
Corporate Auditor, Hideyuki Yasue
President and CEO, Fumiya Kokubu
Managing Executive Officer and Director, Takafumi Sakishima
Managing Executive Officer and Director, Michihiko Ota
Regional CEO Chairman, Shinji Kawai
Corporate Auditor, Hiroshi Kudo
Senior Managing Executive Officer, Shigeru Yamazoe
Senior Managing Executive Officer, Mitsuru Akiyoshi
Executive Officer, Chihiro Shikama
Executive Officer, Masahiro Enoki
Senior Managing Executive Officer, Yutaka Nomura
Executive Officer, Naoya Iwashita
Executive Officer, Shoichi Ikuta
Managing Executive Officer, Shoji Kuwayama
Managing Executive Officer, Daisuke Okada
Executive Officer, Shingo Tsuda
Executive Officer, Keizo Torii
Managing Executive Officer, Kazuaki Tanaka
Managing Executive Officer, Yukihiko Matsumura
Executive Officer, Hiroshi Ikuno
Executive Officer, Kaoru Iwasa
General Manager Human Resources Dept, Kaoru Kuzume
General Manager Finance Dept, Nobuhiro Yabe
Regional COO for North & Central America, Yoshiaki Mizumoto
Managing Executive Officer, Masumi Kakinoki
President CEO and Director, Teruo Asada
Managing Executive Officer and Director, Toshinori Umezawa
Managing Executive Officer and Director, Takafumi Sakishima
Managing Executive Officer and Director, Michihiko Ota

Managing Executive Officer and Director, Hisashi Sunaoshi
Managing Executive Officer and Director, Shinji Kawai
Director, Toshiyuki Ogura
Director, Shigeaki Ishikawa
Auditors: Ernst&Young

LOCATIONS

HQ: Marubeni Corp.
1-4-2 Ohtemachi, Chiyoda-ku, Tokyo 100-8088
Phone: (81) 3 3282 2111   **Fax:** (81) 3 3282 4241
Web: www.marubeni.co.jp

Sales

	% of total
Japan	68
US	17
Singapore	6
Other	9
Total	**100**

PRODUCTS/OPERATIONS

Sales

	% of total
Consumer	44
Materials	22
Resources	21
Machinery	13
Total	**100**

COMPETITORS

ITOCHU	Samsung Group
Jardine Matheson	Seika
Kanematsu	Showa Denko
LG Group	Sime Darby
Largo Vista	Sojitz
Mitsubishi Corp.	Sojitz Corporation of
Mitsubishi	America
International	Sumikin Bussan
Mitsui	Sumitomo
Nissan Chemical	Sumitomo Heavy
Rio Tinto plc	Industries

HISTORICAL FINANCIALS

Company Type: Public

Income Statement

FYE: March 31

	REVENUE ($ mil.)	NET INCOME ($ mil.)	NET PROFIT MARGIN	EMPLOYEES
03/14	68,356	2,043	3.0%	39,465
03/13	51,665	2,186	4.2%	42,937
03/12	53,521	2,098	3.9%	41,503
03/11	44,487	1,648	3.7%	38,700
03/10	35,114	1,020	2.9%	29,604
Annual Growth	18.1%	19.0%	—	7.5%

2014 Year-End Financials

Debt ratio: 0.0%
Return on equity: 16.7%
Cash ($ mil.): 6,447
Current ratio: 1.25
Long-term debt ($ mil.): —
No. of shares (mil.): 1,735
Dividends
  Yield: 3.5%
  Payout: 0.0%
Market value ($ mil.): 117,661

	STOCK PRICE ($) FY Close	P/E High/Low	PER SHARE ($) Earnings	Dividends	Book Value
03/14	67.80	0 0	1.18	2.40	7.73
03/13	76.48	0 0	1.26	0.00	6.93
03/12	72.50	0 0	1.21	0.00	5.98
03/11	72.43	0 0	0.95	0.00	5.38
03/10	62.55	0 0	0.59	0.70	4.60
Annual Growth	2.0%	— —	19.0%	36.2%	13.9%

Mediobanca Banca Di Credito Finanziario SpA

There's not much room for mediocrity at Mediobanca. A leading Italian investment bank the firm offers underwriting M&A support wholesale banking and financial advisory to corporate clients. It also offers private banking factoring credit management and leasing services. CheBanca! (formerly Micos Banca) operates about 40 retail banking branches mostly in Italy. Mediobanca has expanded domestically and internationally: It opened some 20 new branches in Italy Germany Spain and the UK in 2008. The bitter fights that plagued Mediobanca in the early part of the decade have simmered down and the bank is less-often called secretive and Machiavellian following the 2003 departure of CEO Vincenzo Maranghi.

The firm has been strengthening its position as the primo Italian corporate underwriter a reputation shaken in recent years amid shareholder disputes that would have had the late CEO Enrico Cuccia spinning in his grave. Vincenzo Maranghi who replaced Cuccia in 2000 was forced out of the company after shareholders questioned his operating methods.

Mediobanca has holdings in some of Italy's most powerful companies including broadband provider Telecom Italia and insurer Assicurazioni Generali.

HISTORY

In 1946 the three Italian "banks of national interest" Banca Commerciale Italiana (Comit) Credito Italiano (now Unicredito Italiano) and Banco di Roma (now part of Banca di Roma) founded Mediobanca to offer medium-term credit a market they were barred from.

Enrico Cuccia was with Comit at the time Mediobanca was formed and moved over to head the new institution. In 1955 he created the shareholder structure that later caused a twin uproar in Italian banking and politics: Although the state owned well more than half of the bank's shares a group of wealthy shareholders who together owned less than 10% of the bank wielded the power.

Over the next several decades Cuccia and Mediobanca operated on the behalf of these powerful shareholders and their family businesses devising deals on terms that other companies could not get. Mediobanca also created a web of crossholdings in other banks which made money for the bank by selling its funds and other services.

In the 1960s and 1970s the bank was at the center of a number of deals not all of which were stellar successes. The bank engineered a merger between Pirelli and Dunlop which fizzled and also pushed the merger of chemical companies Montecatini and Edison into Montedison which took a beating in the marketplace.

In 1982 Cuccia ostensibly retired taking the title of honorary chairman. However his influence never waned and the 1980s brought a war for the soul of Italian business. In 1985 Romano Prodi head of IRI the state-run organization (liquidated in 2000) that owned nearly 60% of the bank planned to privatize the bank. Instead the noble wing came up with its own privatization plan: The private shareholders requested that the state bring its stake in Mediobanca to below 50% by selling some of its shares to the Mediobanca cabal. In 1988 the privatization went through but as part of the pact it was stipulated that the new shareholders would

share decision-making powers with the "Ala Nobile."

If the 1980s were wild the 1990s were out of control. Italy's banking industry hampered by red tape and old alliances was left behind the rest of Europe. Many of Italy's banks became stock companies when banking laws changed and many merged to compete in the European Union. Many of those deals threatened Mediobanca's hegemony so it tried to block them. The bank nixed Unicredito's 1998 bid for Comit (which instead merged with Banca Intesa) as well as Sanpaolo IMI's 1999 offer for Banca di Roma.

In 2000 the bank still keeping a grip on the wheels of finance orchestrated investment firm Compart's buyout of Montedison (the merged entity took the Montedison name). That year the company launched an online private banking joint venture with Mediolanum.

Also in 2000 its 46-year relationship with Lazard ended when the international investment banker announced plans to sell back to Mediobanca its 4% stake in the company along with its nearly 5% stake in Assicurazioni Generali.

After Cuccia's death in 2000 successor Vincenzo Maranghi battled such controlling shareholders as the Agnelli and Pirelli families and Deutsche Bank over the bank's future. These shareholders wanted to bring Mediobanca into the modern world by possibly merging it with another top Italian bank or even separating its investment management operations from its investment banking which generates a large majority of Mediobanca's profits.

However in a bid to stick to the old ways Maranghi arranged for backing (in exchange for a small stake in Mediobanca) from Swiss Life. Maranghi was blamed in part for the bank's decline: He forced out some of the investment banking division's top talent in the late 1990s and eventually resigned in 2003

Despite efforts to become more open some of the mystery surrounding Mediobanca remains. The shareholder dispute erupted after the death of Cuccia (whose body was subsequently robbed from its grave and later found).

Maranghi's replacement Gabriele Galateri di Genola had his work cut out for him repairing cracks in Mediobanca's image but he saw profits rise considerably. Under his watch the group has made its first foray into operations abroad opening an office in Paris. By 2004 the company posted improved financial results for a second consecutive year including a 20% increase in investment banking fees.

Galateri di Genola resigned from Mediobanca in 2007 after he lost the support of the supervisory board. He was succeeded by Alberto Nagel the company's general manager.

EXECUTIVES

Managing Director, Alberto N. Nagel, age 49
Manager Investor Relations, Jessica Spina
Media Relations, Lorenza Pigozzi
Head Financial Reporting, Massimo Bertolini
Chairman, Marco T. Provera
Management Board Member, Maurizio Cereda
Management Board Member, Massimo Di Carlo
Management Board Member, Francesco Saverio Vinci
Deputy Chairman and Interim Chairman, Dieter Rampl, age 66
Board Member, Ennio Doris, age 74
Board Member, Gilberto Benetton, age 73
Board Member, Vincent Bollore, age 62
Board Member, Pietro Ferrero, age 50
Board Member, Jonella Ligresti, age 46
Board Member, Fabrizio Palenzona, age 61
Board Member, Roberto Bertazzoni, age 72

Board Member, Carlo Pesenti, age 51
Board Member, Antoine Bernheim, age 90
Board Member, Eric Strutz, age 48
Board Member, Luigi Zunino, age 54
Board Member, Jean Azema, age 60
Board Member, Francesco Denozza, age 67
Board Member, Giancarlo Cerutti, age 60
Board Member, Tarak Ben Ammar, age 65
Board Member, Angelo Caso'
Board Member, Eugenio Pinto
Chairman, Marco T. Provera
Board Member, Gabriele Villa
Auditors: RecontaErnst&YoungS.p.A.

LOCATIONS

HQ: Mediobanca Banca Di Credito Finanziario SpA
Piazzetta Enrico Cuccia 1, Milan 20121
Phone: (39) 02 8829 1   Fax: (39) 02 882 9367
Web: www.mediobanca.it

Sales

	% of total
Italy	92
Other	8
Total	**100**

COMPETITORS

Banca Carige	Goldman Sachs
Banca Popolare di Milano	Interbanca
	Intesa Sanpaolo
Banco di Desio	Lazard
CREDEM	Morgan Stanley
Credit Suisse	UBS Investment Bank
Deutsche Bank	UniCredit
Gemina	Vontobel

HISTORICAL FINANCIALS
Company Type: Public

Income Statement
FYE: June 30

	ASSETS ($ mil.)	NET INCOME ($ mil.)	INCOME AS % OF ASSETS	EMPLOYEES
06/13	95,201	(235)	—	3,673
06/12	99,026	101	0.1%	3,652
06/11	109,031	533	0.5%	3,452
06/10	93,870	491	0.5%	3,242
06/09	104,444	3	0.0%	3,105
Annual Growth	**(2.3%)**	**—**	**—**	**4.3%**

2013 Year-End Financials

Return on assets: (-0.2%)
Return on equity: (-2.6%)
Long-term debt ($ mil.): —
No. of shares (mil.): 844
Sales ($ mil): 4,047
Dividends
  Yield: 0.0%
  Payout: —
Market value ($ mil.): —

	STOCK PRICE ($) FY Close	P/E High/Low	Earnings	PER SHARE ($) Dividends	Book Value
06/13	0.00	— —	(0.26)	0.07	10.76
Annual Growth	—	— —	—	—	—

Medipal Holdings Corp.

In Japan Medipal Holdings keeps drug and household products retailers well-stocked. Its primary business is the wholesale distribution of prescription and OTC pharmaceuticals medical supplies cosmetics and personal sundries. In addition to supplying some 300000 Japanese pharmacies and retail stores Medipal distributes to hospitals and provides information technology support to its customers through its numerous subsidiaries and affiliates including Mediceo Everlth Atol and Paltac. Its MP Agro subsidiary distributes animal health products.

Strategy

Medipal is focused on marketing of new prescription products as well as niche prescription offerings including subsidized vaccines and lifestyle disease drugs. In addition it is investing in R&D firms to contribute to the development of new pharmaceuticals with the condition that it receives an option to exclusively market the drugs if they gain regulatory approval. The company is also adding new services for retail cosmetic and OTC outlets such as point-of-sale marketing tools.

Financial Performance

Medipal has experienced rising revenues over the last five years including a 3% increase in fiscal 2012 due to increased product sales. Growth is attributed to aggressive marketing of new and niche market products and expanded service offerings for retailers.

Ownership

Takeda Pharmaceutical owns a 10% stake in Medipal.

Company Background

Medipal was formed when Mediceo Holdings took over household products distributor Paltac in 2005. Paltac brought with it a distribution network and logistical prowess which allowed the new firm to move further into the OTC and non-drugs business. Previously Mediceo Holdings become Japan's largest drug wholesaler in 2004 when it was formed through the merger of three smaller drug wholesalers (Kuraya Pharmaceuticals Sanseido and Tokyo Iyakuhin).

EXECUTIVES

EVP and Representative Director, Shuichi Watanabe
Senior Executive Officer, Kikuo Miki
Senior Executive Officer, Kazuo Misaki
Managing Executive Officer, Fuminari Hikita
Managing Executive Officer, Toshio Hirasawa
Senior Executive Officer; Manager of General Affairs in Main Administration Unit, Yuji Taniguchi
Executive Officer; Deputy Chief Director of Pharmaceutical Sales, Hideaki Takemura
Executive Officer; Director of Sales Planning in Main Pharmaceutical Sales Unit, Masao Shibamiya
Director, Toshihide Yoda
Director, Yasuhiro Choufuku
Director, Takuro Hasegawa
Director, Kazushi Takao
Executive Officer, Masaaki Shimizu
Executive Officer, Kenichi Takase
Executive Officer; Deputy Chief Director of System, Kazuki Kazuki Kakutani Kakutani
President of Subsidiary; Director, Koji Koji Orime Orime
Executive Officer; Deputy Chief Director of Business Development, Kuniaki Kuniaki Imagawa Imagawa
Executive Officer, Masanori Masanori Kawara Kawara
President of Subsidiary; Director, Yasuhiro Yasuhiro Chofuku Chofuku
EVP and Representative Director, Shuichi Watanabe
Director, Yasuhiro Choufuku
Director, Takuro Hasegawa
Director, Kazushi Takao
Independent Director, Michiko Michiko Kawanobe Kawanobe
Auditors: KPMGAZSA&Co.

LOCATIONS

HQ: Medipal Holdings Corp.
2-7-15 Yaesu, Chuo-ku, Tokyo 104-8461
Phone: (81) 3 3517 5800   Fax: (81) 3 3517 5811
Web: www.medipal.co.jp

PRODUCTS/OPERATIONS

Selected Divisions and Brands

Atol Co.
Butsuryu 24
Everlth Co.
Kuraya (USA)
Mediceo
M.I.C. (Medical Information College)
MM Corporation
MP Agro
Paltac
Tokimo Co.
Trim Co.

COMPETITORS

Alfresa	Takeda Pharmaceutical
Shionogi & Co.	Toho Pharmaceutical
Suzuken	

HISTORICAL FINANCIALS
Company Type: Public

Income Statement
FYE: March 31

	REVENUE ($ mil.)	NET INCOME ($ mil.)	NET PROFIT MARGIN	EMPLOYEES
03/14	28,558	246	0.9%	10,930
03/13	29,874	198	0.7%	11,115
03/12	33,527	142	0.4%	11,194
03/11	32,157	20	0.1%	11,661
03/10	27,257	20	0.1%	11,363
Annual Growth	**1.2%**	**85.3%**	**—**	**(1.0%)**

2014 Year-End Financials

Debt ratio: 0.0%
Return on equity: 7.6%
Cash ($ mil.): 1,286
Current ratio: 1.14
Long-term debt ($ mil.): 85
No. of shares (mil.): 225
Dividends
  Yield: —
  Payout: —
Market value ($ mil.): 3,376

	STOCK PRICE ($) FY Close	P/E High/Low	Earnings	PER SHARE ($) Dividends	Book Value
03/14	14.94	— —	1.09	0.00	17.47
03/13	12.21	— —	0.87	0.00	18.01
03/12	12.43	— —	0.60	0.00	18.51
03/11	8.60	— —	0.09	0.00	17.56
03/10	12.30	— —	0.09	0.00	15.11
Annual Growth	**5.0%**	**— —**	**87.2%**	**—**	**3.7%**

Meiji Yasuda Life Insurance Co.

Meiji Yasuda Life Insurance knows the value of life. The company one of Japan's largest life insurers offers individual life and annuities group life and pensions and investment products. It also has some general insurance health care and investment and financial services operations. Meiji Yasuda provides its products to a range of customers including individuals small businesses and corporations. The company has about ¥211 billion ($2.6 billion) of life insurance policies in force. While most of its operations are in Japan Meiji Yasuda operates in Asia Europe and North America.

Geographic Reach

Meiji Yasuda is headquartered in Tokyo. It also has about 75 regional offices 20 marketing centers and some 1000 agency locations. It has international affiliate locations in nine global cities: Beijing Frankfurt Hong Kong Honolulu London Los Angeles New York Seoul and Shanghai.

Sales and Marketing

The company sells its products through an internal sales force of about 29000 personnel. It makes some sales to banks and other financial institutions through general agents.

Financial Performance

Meiji Yasuda reported a 27% revenue increase to Â6116 billion (about $79 billion) in 2011 due to higher premium income and investment income as well as higher interest and dividend payouts on securities. Higher premiums have contributed to revenue growth for the past five years. Net income also increased by 32% to Â173 billion (about $2 billion) in 2011 as a result of the higher earnings.

Strategy

Meiji Yasuda is especially focused on growth in international markets. Through a partnership with Talanx for instance the company is investing in the German insurance market. It has also expanded its operations in countries including Poland Indonesia and China through partnerships and by investing in minority ownership of global insurance entities.

In addition Meiji Yasuda works to expand its domestic life insurance business as well as on entering other health related markets in Japan such as the nursing home business. Other strategies include increasing risk management efforts across the company's operations to strengthen its finances and its capital base.

Mergers and Acquisitions

Meiji Yasuda entered the nursing care market in 2012 through the acquisition of Sunvenus Tachikawa an operator of nursing homes.

Company Background

Tracing its roots back to 1881 Meiji Yasuda in its current incarnation was formed through the merger of Meiji Life Insurance and Yasuda Mutual Life in 2004. Prior to their merger Meiji Life and Yasuda Mutual Life were part of the Mitsubishi Group and Mizuho Financial Group respectively.

LOCATIONS

HQ: Meiji Yasuda Life Insurance Co.
2-1-1 Marunouchi, Chiyoda-ku, Tokyo 100-0005
Phone: (81) 3 3283 8293   **Fax:** (81) 3 3215 8123
Web: www.meijiyasuda.co.jp

PRODUCTS/OPERATIONS

HISTORICAL FINANCIALS

Company Type: Public

Income Statement

	REVENUE ($ mil.)	NET INCOME ($ mil.)	NET PROFIT MARGIN	EMPLOYEES
03/13	48,296	2,515	5.2%	0
03/12	71,958	2,105	2.9%	0
03/11	55,968	1,586	2.8%	0
03/10	42,715	1,528	3.6%	40,280
03/09	33,091	1,264	3.8%	40,000
Annual Growth	9.9%	18.8%	—	—

FYE: March 31

Metallurgical Corp China Ltd

LOCATIONS

HQ: Metallurgical Corp China Ltd
MCC Tower, 28 Shuguang Xili, Chaoyang District, Beijing 100028
Phone: (86) 10 59868666   **Fax:** (86) 10 59868999
Web: www.mccchina.com

HISTORICAL FINANCIALS

Company Type: Public

Income Statement

FYE: December 31

	REVENUE ($ mil.)	NET INCOME ($ mil.)	NET PROFIT MARGIN	EMPLOYEES
12/13	33,480	492	1.5%	0
12/12	35,468	(1,115)	—	0
12/11	36,496	674	1.8%	127,746
12/10	31,312	807	2.6%	126,987
12/09	24,167	653	2.7%	120,385
Annual Growth	8.5%	(6.8%)	—	—

2013 Year-End Financials

Debt ratio: 5.0%
Return on equity: 6.9%
Cash ($ mil.): 5,547
Current ratio: 1.10
Long-term debt ($ mil.): 6,974

No. of shares (mil.): —
Dividends
Yield: —
Payout: —
Market value ($ mil.): —

	STOCK PRICE ($) FY Close	P/E High/Low		PER SHARE ($) Earnings	Dividends	Book Value
12/13	3.36	—	—	0.03	0.00	(0.00)
12/12	3.36	—	—	(0.06)	0.00	(0.00)
12/11	4.79	1	1	0.03	0.00	0.40
12/10	9.25	1	1	0.04	0.00	0.36
Annual Growth	(28.6%)	—	—	(11.2%)	—	—

Metro AG

A ride on this METRO could be a shopper's delight. Germany's ober retailer the company ranks fourth in the world (behind Wal-Mart Carrefour and Tesco). METRO owns and operates more than 2200 wholesale stores supermarkets hypermarkets department stores and the fast-growing Media Markt and Saturn consumer electronics chains. More than 930 of its shops are in Germany but METRO also has stores in more than 30 other countries including China Egypt France India Russia and Vietnam. Store banners include METRO and Makro Cash & Carry wholesale outlets Real hypermarkets and Galeria Kaufhof department

---

2013 Year-End Financials

Debt ratio: —
Return on equity: 10.8%
Cash ($ mil.): 2,692
Current ratio: 629.38
Long-term debt ($ mil.): —

No. of shares (mil.): —
Dividends
Yield: —
Payout: —
Market value ($ mil.): —

---

stores. METRO is also launching e-commerce platforms for each of its retail businesses.

The German retail group comprises five units: Metro Cash & Carry self-service wholesale stores; Media Markt and Saturn consumer electronics stores; Real hypermarkets; Galeria Kaufhof department stores in Germany and Belgium; and METRO Properties the group's international real estate arm with properties in 33 countries. METRO Cash & Carry and Makro wholesale outlets which sell food and other grocery and non-grocery items to businesses and institutional customers account for 47% of group sales while Media-Saturn is Europe's #1 seller of consumer electronics with about 900 locations in 16 countries. With about 140 department stores Galeria Kaufhof is a leading Germany department store chains. Real operates about 425 hypermarkets mostly in Germany but also in Eastern Europe including Poland Romania and Russia.

Germany is METRO AG's largest market accounting for 39% of sales in 2011. About 25 other countries in Western and Eastern Europe account for 56% of sales while Asia and Africa make up the rest.

The debt crisis in the euro zone negatively impacted METRO AG's operations in 2011. Against a backdrop of high unemployment and weak consumer confidence group sales totaled E66.7 billion in 2011 vs. E67.3 billion in 2010. Western Europe suffered a 3% decline in sales in 2011 vs. the prior year while Germany (Europe's strongest economy) saw sales fall 1%. Asia and Africa were bright spots with sales in the region posting an 11% gain. The group's core Metro Cash & Carry business saw its sales eke up 0.2% while department store chain Galeria Kaufhof's sales fell nearly 4% and METRO's consumer electronics chains Media Markt and Saturn saw sales decline 1%.

Economic uncertainty has slowed METRO's historically rapid store development plans. But while the company has trimmed its store count at home it continues to grow abroad. Its focus is on Eastern Europe (especially Poland and Russia) and Asia. China is METRO's most promising new market. Media Markt which opened six locations in Shanghai in 2011 after entering the market in 2010 saw its sales in China increase to E92 million from E 9 million in 2010.

METRO AG's largest shareholders are German conglomerate Franz Haniel and the Schmidt-Ruthenbeck and Beisheim families which together control METRO with about 60% of the voting rights and are actively involved in the management of the company.

HISTORY

Otto Beisheim founded METRO SB-Grossmarkte in the German town of Mulheim in 1964. A wholesale business serving commercial customers it operated under the name METRO Cash & Carry. Three years later Beisheim received backing from the owners of Franz Haniel & Cie (an industrial company founded in 1756) and members of the Schmidt-Ruthenbeck family (also in wholesaling). This allowed METRO to expand rapidly in Germany and in 1968 into the Netherlands under the name Makro Cash & Carry via a partnership with Steenkolen Handelsvereeniging (SHV). During the 1970s the company expanded its wholesaling operations within Europe and moved into retailing.

METRO's foray into retailing was aided during the next decade by the acquisition of department store chain Kaufhof AG. By the 1980s the rise of specialty stores had many department stores on the defensive and Kaufhof's owners sold it to METRO and its investment partner Union Bank of Switzerland.

As METRO's ownership interest in Kaufhof rose above 50% the chain began converting some of its stores from department stores into fashion and sporting goods sellers. Kaufhof began acquiring a stake in computer manufacturer and retailer Vobis in 1989. In 1993 METRO now operating as METRO Holding AG acquired a majority interest in supermarket company Asko Deutsche Kaufhaus which owned the Praktiker building materials chain. The reclusive Beisheim retired from active management the following year.

To cut costs and prepare for expansion into Asia in 1996 METRO Holding merged its German retail holdings –Kaufhof; Asko; another grocery operation Deutsche SB Kauf; and its German cash-and-carry operations –into one holding company METRO AG. The new subsidiary purchased 58 Wirichs home improvement centers in Germany that year to complement its Praktiker chain.

In 1998 METRO bought the 196-store Makro self-service wholesale chain from Dutch-based SHV. METRO also added to its German food operations by acquiring the 94-store German Allkauf hypermarket chain and then by purchasing the 20-store Kriegbaum hypermarket chain.

Later that year METRO transferred its interests in non-core businesses including office supply stores footwear stores discount stores computer operations (including Vobis) and 25 unprofitable Kaufhof department stores to its Divaco (formerly Divag) unit. Divaco then sold 165 German Tip discount stores to Tengelmann Group.

Hans-Joachim Korber became METRO's CEO in 1999. In 2000 the company transferred 290 hypermarkets and department stores in Germany Greece Hungary Luxembourg and Turkey to a joint venture company (51% owned by Westdeutsche Landesbank) to raise cash for the expansion and remodeling of its wholesale outlets. Expanding on the Internet METRO acquired control of German e-commerce business Primus Online.

In 2001 METRO AG redistributed all of its shares held by METRO Holding AG to its top three shareholders for tax purposes. At the end of the year the first two Cash & Carry stores in Russia and one in Croatia opened.

In August 2002 METRO sold its entire stake in Primus Online to Beisheim Holding Schweiz AG. Overall in 2002 METRO opened 61 stores –53 of which were Metro Cash & Carry outlets –including new stores in China Bulgaria and Russia (one each) and Vietnam (two outlets). In April 2003 the company opened its first store in St. Petersburg (its fourth in Russia). In July a third METRO Cash and Carry store opened in Vietnam. The German retailer opened a global sourcing headquarters in Hong Kong in September that covers all markets outside the European Union.

As part of its international expansion plan in October 2003 METRO opened the first of two cash-and-carry distribution centers in Bangalore India. In December 2003 METRO sold its 49% stake in Divaco in a buyout led by Divaco's management. Divaco was originally founded together with financial investors as a joint venture with the objective of optimally divesting noncore METRO Group activities.

Gunther Hulse stepped down as chairman of METRO's supervisory board for personal reasons in June 2004. Hulse was succeeded by Theo Siegert a member of the management board of Franz Haniel & Cie a German wholesale drug distribution company. The German retailer added two new nations to its roster in 2004: Russia and Moldova. On the technology front METRO began using radio frequency identification (RFID) tags throughout the supply chain in November 2004.

METRO closed three of its Kaufhof stores in Germany in early 2005 amid slumping sales in its department store business. In late 2005 METRO

took its DIY home improvement chain Praktiker Bau- und Heimwerkermarkte public. Following the IPO METRO retained a 40% stake in its former subsidiary. (It sold the remainder of its shares less 5% in April 2006.)

In February 2006 Theo Siegert stepped down as chairman of the supervisory board and was succeeded by Eckhard Cordes. In the first half of the year METRO completed the conversion of 85 stores acquired from Wal-Mart Germany and 20 stores purchased from France's Casino Guichard-Perrachon to the Real banner. In a follow-up deal METRO agreed to buy express-delivery provider DHL's SCM logistics unit which supplied the stores acquired from Wal-Mart for an undisclosed sum.

In 2007 the retailer opened more than 130 new stores including 84 Media Markt and Saturn consumer electronics shops and a single Galeria Kaufhof department store.

Continuing its global tour METRO entered Kazakhstan and Egypt with Makro stores in those markets in 2009 and 2010 respectively.

In July 2012 METRO sold its UK wholesale business Makro Self Service Wholesalers Ltd. (aka Makro UK) to Booker Group. Under the terms of the deal Booker acquired all 30 of Makro UK's wholesale stores and METRO received 10% of Booker's shares plus Â15.8 million (~25 million).

EXECUTIVES

CEO Metro Cash and Carry (Asia/New Markets) Advertising, Frans W.H. Muller, age 53
Head Human Resources, Heiko Hutmacher, age 57
Chairman Management Board, Olaf Koch, age 44
CEO METRO Cash & Carry Germany, John Rix
Sales Director METRO Cash & Carry Germany, Arnd Riehl
Managing Director Food Division METRO Cash & Carry Germany, Jorg Ossenberg-Engels
CFO, Mark Frese, age 50
CEO of Booker, Charles Wilson
Chairman of the Supervisory Board, Franz Haniel
Director, Klaus J. Mangold, age 68
Director, Hans-Jurgen Schinzler, age 73
Director, Wulf H. Bernotat, age 64
Director, Marie-Christine Lombard, age 54
Director, M. P. M. (Theo) de Raad, age 68
Director, Ulrich Dalibor
Director, Erich Greipl
Director, Bernd Pischetsrieder
Director, Werner Klockhaus
Director, Peter Kupfer
Director, Rainer Kuschewski
Director, Peter Stieger
Director, Hubert Frieling
Director, Andreas Herwarth
Director, Xaver Schiller
Director, Angelika Will
Director, Uwe Hoepfel
Auditors: KPMGDeutscheTreuhand-GesellschaftAG

LOCATIONS

HQ: Metro AG
Schluterstrasse 1, Duesseldorf 40235
Phone: (49) 211 6886 0   **Fax:** (49) 211 68 86 20 00
Web: www.metrogroup.de

Sales

	% of total
Western Europe	
Germany	39
Other	31
Eastern	25
Africa &	5
Total	**100**

2011 Stores

	No.
Western Europe	

Germany	937
Other	619
Eastern	531
Asia &	100
Total	**2,187**

PRODUCTS/OPERATIONS

Sales

	% of total
Cash &	47
Consumer	31
Food	17
Department	5
Other	-
Total	**100**

2011 Stores

	No.
Media Markt &	893
METRO Cash &	728
Real	426
Galeria	140
Total	**2,187**

Selected Operations

Wholesale Stores
    Makro
    Metro Cash & Carry (wholesale stores)
Food
    Extra (supermarkets)
    Real (hypermarkets)
Nonfood Specialty Stores
    Media Markt (consumer electronics)
    Saturn (consumer electronics)
Department Store
    Galeria Kaufhof
Other Operations
Dinea Gastronomie (restaurants/catering)
METRO MGE Einkauf (purchasing)
METRO MGI Informatik (IT services)
METRO Real Estate Management (construction services)
METRO Werbegesellschaft (advertising)
METRO Online AG (Internet retailer)
MGB METRO Buying Group Hong Kong Ltd.
    (purchasing Asia and Non-European Union countries)

COMPETITORS

ALDI	Lidl
Best Buy	Marktkauf
Carrefour	Maxeda
Casino Guichard	REWE
Darty	Royal Ahold
Delhaize	Tengelmann
Dixons Retail	Tesco
Edeka Zentrale	Wal-Mart

HISTORICAL FINANCIALS

Company Type: Public

Income Statement

FYE: September 30

	REVENUE ($ mil.)	NET INCOME ($ mil.)	NET PROFIT MARGIN	EMPLOYEES
09/13*	62,520	(95)	—	278,594
12/12	87,965	3	0.0%	536,744
12/11	86,275	816	0.9%	533,233
12/10	90,016	1,137	1.3%	283,280
12/09	94,399	551	0.6%	286,091
Annual Growth	**(9.8%)**	**—**	**—**	**(0.7%)**

*Fiscal year change

2013 Year-End Financials

Debt ratio: 37.3%	No. of shares (mil.): 324
Return on equity: (-1.6%)	Dividends
Cash ($ mil.): 3,460	Yield: 2.1%
Current ratio: 0.78	Payout: 61.6%
Long-term debt ($ mil.): 7,778	Market value ($ mil.): 2,586

	STOCK PRICE ($) FY Close	P/E High/Low	Earnings	PER SHARE ($) Dividends	Book Value
09/13*	7.98	— —	(0.30)	0.17	21.57
12/12	5.60	1444832	0.01	0.38	24.50
12/11	7.81	15 7	2.50	0.49	25.40
Annual Growth	1.1%	— —	—	(23.0%)	(4.0%)

*Fiscal year change

Minmetals Development Co Ltd

Minmetals Development does the maximum to help China develop. The company works in raw materials and steel trading as well as distribution and logistics. It imports steel iron ore and hulks and exports coal coke billet ferrosilicon ferrosilicomanganese fluorite magnesium ferromolybdenum and carborundum. Through its logistics subsidiaries it is also engaged in international shipping and forwarding storage and warehousing international tendering and bidding. Minmetals also has its hands in luxury hotels high and new technology financing and industrial manufacturing. Minmetals Development is owned by minerals company China Minmetals.

EXECUTIVES

CFO and Finance Manager, Ren Jianhua
Vice Chairman, Feng Guiquan
General Manager, He Jianzeng

LOCATIONS

HQ: Minmetals Development Co Ltd
Block B, No. 5, Sanlihe Road, Haidian District, Beijing 100044
Phone: (86) 10 68494205   **Fax:** (86) 10 68494207
Web: www.minlist.com.cn

PRODUCTS/OPERATIONS

HISTORICAL FINANCIALS

Company Type: Public

Income Statement

FYE: December 31

	REVENUE ($ mil.)	NET INCOME ($ mil.)	NET PROFIT MARGIN	EMPLOYEES
12/13	33,574	46	0.1%	0
12/12	23,962	(61)	—	0
12/11	25,745	85	0.3%	8,492
12/10	19,944	58	0.3%	7,861
12/09	13,811	39	0.3%	7,365
Annual Growth	24.9%	4.3%		

2013 Year-End Financials

Debt ratio: 5.4%	No. of shares (mil.): —
Return on equity: 3.3%	Dividends
Cash ($ mil.): 290	Yield: —
Current ratio: 0.99	Payout: —
Long-term debt ($ mil.): 485	Market value ($ mil.): —

Mitsubishi Chemical Holdings Corp

Mitsubishi Chemical Holdings is the largest chemical manufacturer in Japan. Subsidiary Mitsubishi Chemical Corporation produces a wide variety of petrochemicals specialty chemicals and the like. Another unit Mitsubishi Plastics manufactures plastics and films data storage devices such as CDs and DVDs as well as chemicals for semiconductor manufacturing. Mitsubishi Tanabe Pharma makes pharmaceutical products for central nervous system cardiovascular and gastrointestinal disorders in addition to OTC and anti-inflammatory drugs. Mitsubishi Rayon as its fourth business unit.

Mitsubishi Chemical Holdings serves customers in the performance products health care and industrial material markets. Its major products include optical recording media polymer films plastics pharmaceuticals purified terephthalic acid synthetic fibers and a range of polymers. It has more than 340 consolidated subsidiaries and more than 60 affiliated companies.

The company has major operations in Australia India North Asia Southeast Asia Europe and the US.

In Fiscal 2012 Mitsubishi Chemical Holdings reported a 1% drop in revenues (in local currency) as the company's growth in production was offset by weak economic conditions in Japan (still recovering from the major earthquake in 2011) the appreciation of the yen Europe's economic slowdown and the industrial disruption caused by floods in Thailand. However it posted a 36% drop in net income (in local currency) largely due to higher current and deferred taxes.

In 2010 Mitsubishi Chemical Holdings spent $2.4 billion to purchase Mitsubishi Rayon a manufacturer of monomers and polymers which became the holding company's fourth line of business. It is also the world's #1 maker of methyl methacrylate (a common and versatile plastic also known as MMA) through its 2008 acquisition of Lucite.

Earlier the company merged the former Mitsubishi Pharma with the former Tanabe Seiyaku to form Mitsubishi Tanabe of which it owns about half. In 2008 the company split off its Performance Products segment into a separate operating subsidiary.

Mitsubishi Chemical Holdings was formed in 2005 as the parent of Mitsubishi Chemical Corporation. The company is a subsidiary of Mitsubishi Corporation.

EXECUTIVES

President and CEO, Yoshimitsu Kobayashi
Deputy CEO, Shotaro Yoshimura
Senior Managing Executive Officer, Noboru Tsuda
Managing Executive Officer, Noriyoshi Ohira
Managing Executive Officer, Masanori Karatsu
Auditors: Ernst&YoungShinNihon

LOCATIONS

HQ: Mitsubishi Chemical Holdings Corp
1-1-1 Marunouchi, Chiyoda-ku, Tokyo 100-8251
Phone: (81) 3 6748 7115
Web: www.mitsubishichem-hd.co.jp

Sales

	% of total
Japan	73
Other	27
Total	**100**

PRODUCTS/OPERATIONS

Sales

	% of total
Chemicals	31
Polymers	22
Designed	21
Health	16
Electronics	4
Other	6
Total	**100**

COMPETITORS

Asahi Kasei	Hitachi Chemical
Astellas	Kyowa Hakko Kirin
BASF SE	Mitsui Chemicals
Bayer AG	Nissan Chemical
Chugai	SABIC Innovative
Daicel Chemical	Plastics
Daiichi Sankyo	Sinopec Group
Dainippon Sumitomo	Sumitomo Chemical
Pharma	Takeda Pharmaceutical
DuPont	Tokai Carbon
Evonik Degussa	Tokuyama

HISTORICAL FINANCIALS

Company Type: Public

Income Statement

FYE: March 31

	REVENUE ($ mil.)	NET INCOME ($ mil.)	NET PROFIT MARGIN	EMPLOYEES
03/14	33,897	312	0.9%	56,031
03/13	32,825	197	0.6%	55,131
03/12	39,109	432	1.1%	53,979
03/11	38,243	1,009	2.6%	53,882
03/10	26,925	137	0.5%	53,907
Annual Growth	5.9%	22.8%	—	1.0%

2014 Year-End Financials

Debt ratio: 0.3%	No. of shares (mil.): 1,464
Return on equity: 3.7%	Dividends
Cash ($ mil.): 1,333	Yield: —
Current ratio: 1.24	Payout: —
Long-term debt ($ mil.): 6,711	Market value ($ mil.): 30,474

	STOCK PRICE ($) FY Close	P/E High/Low	Earnings	PER SHARE ($) Dividends	Book Value
03/14	20.81	— —	0.21	0.00	8.70
03/13	23.85	— —	0.13	0.00	8.67
03/12	26.99	— —	0.28	0.00	9.46
03/11	31.81	— —	0.65	0.52	9.12
03/10	24.30	— —	0.09	0.00	8.06
Annual Growth	(3.8%)	— —	22.7%	—	1.9%

Mitsubishi Corp

In Japanese "mitsubishi" means "three diamonds" and Mitsubishi Corporation is one of Japan's crown jewels. The "sogo shosha" or trading company operates through six main business groups: living essentials (agricultural products food and beverages textiles and construction materials); metals; machinery (power generation equipment electrical systems automobiles); energy (liquefied natural gas crude oil); and chemicals (petrochemicals fertilizers plastics). Its other main business group is industrial finance which handles banking asset management construction and logistics. The company generated most of its fiscal 2012 gross profit from living essentials (42%) metals (24%) and machinery (16%).

Mitsubishi Corporation is part of the Mitsubishi "keiretsu" a network of affiliated companies that has no official status as a group but within which there is some cross-ownership and considerable business activity. Other affiliates include Mitsubishi Heavy Industries The Bank of Tokyo-Mitsubishi Mitsubishi Electric Mitsubishi Motors and Nikon.

Mitsubishi operates a network of more than 500 group companies in about 90 countries.

Buoyed by higher energy commodity prices and earlier investments in its chemicals segment the company posted an 8% rise in revenues in fiscal 2012. However lower metals income (due in part to a strike which disrupted coal operations in Australia) and lower automobile manufacturing production (due to flooding in Thailand) dragged down Mitsubishi's net income by 2%.

The Sendai earthquake and tsunami in 2011 severely disrupted the Japanese economy and affected Mitsubishi's operations and domestic revenues and net income that year (limited as it occurred late in the fiscal year). Nevertheless Mitsubishi was able to post an overall growth in revenues and net income thanks to a stronger global economy and an increase in demand for steel products and higher oil prices among other factors.

Mitsubishi has set about strengthening its financial position and devised a strategic growth plan that involves focusing on new operational initiatives including new energy sources and on environment and financial services.

Energy plans include the development of biofuels solar and wind energy technologies as industrial emissions-reducing technologies. It is also looking to ramp up its holdings in the global water business to meet growing water infrastructure demand from emerging economies.

On the financial front Mitsubishi is leveraging the group's financial assets and sheer size to facilitate the financing of its own as well as other companies' growth efforts. With its financial services operations the group is targeting real estate development aircraft and other industrial leasing services and it is considering strategic acquisitions of additional financial services assets.

Growing its metals assets in 2011 Mitsubishi acquired nearly 25% of Anglo American Sur a Chile-based copper mining and smelting company owned by Anglo American plc. Anglo American Sur's copper assets include the Los Bronces mine El Soldado mine and Chagres smelter. The purchase is expected to boost Mitsubishi's attributable copper production to 250000 metric tons per year.

To further expand its metals operations Mitsubishi agreed in 2012 to invest about $95 million to acquire a 25% stake in Stillwater Mining's Marathon PGM (platinum group metals) project in Ontario Canada. The project is expected to produce about 200000 ounces of PGMs and 17000 metric tons of copper per year for about 11 1/2 years. Mitsubishi also has the option to purchase up to 100% of the PGM production. PGMs are used in applications such as automobile catalysts electronic devices and fuel cells.

In 2012 Mitsubishi along with Indian fertilizer company Zuari Industries acquired a 30% stake in Fasfatos del Pacifico (FOSPAC) from a Peruvian cement manufacturer Cementos Pacasmayo. Pacasmayo explores for and produces rock phosphate in Peru and the investment will allow the companies to acquire FOSPAC's rock phosphate production (after fulfillment of local demand) for 20 years. The initial production capacity is expected to be about 2.5 million metric tons per year.

That year the company entered the Indonesian geothermal power market through the acquisition of 20% of Star Energy Geothermal Pte Ltd. Mit-

subishi is looking to become further involved in geothermal power generation in countries that possess promising geothermal resources including Japan.

Growing another segment in 2013 the company agreed to buy Kirin's Food Science Business.

To raise cash in 2011 Mitsubishi sold its subsidiary Jicoux Datasystems Inc. to NEC Corp. Jicoux offers a fleet management service for commercial vehicles that includes automatic creation of daily reports based on speed route and distance data collected from in-vehicle devices over the internet. NEC plans to absorb the Jicoux's employees and operations and liquidate the company.

Along with the rest of the Mitsubishi companies Mitsubishi Corporation has been hurt by Japan's persistent economic stagnation. The company has restructured and reduced its workforce in the past decade and it has divided the operations of its former information technology and electronics business among its other groups.

HISTORY

Yataro Iwasaki's close ties to the Japanese government (along with subsidies and monopoly rights) ensured the success of his shipping and trading company Mitsubishi. Founded in 1870 Mitsubishi diversified into mining (1873) banking (1885) and shipbuilding (1887); it began to withdraw from shipping in the 1880s. During the next decade it invested in Japanese railroads and property.

In 1918 the Mitsubishi "zaibatsu" (conglomerate) spun off its central management arm Mitsubishi Trading (the forerunner of Mitsubishi Corporation). By WWII the group was a huge amalgam of divisions and public companies. During the war it made warplanes ships explosives and beer.

The "zaibatsu" were dissolved by US occupation forces and Mitsubishi was split into 139 entities. After the occupation the Japanese government encouraged many of the former business groups to reunite around the old "zaibatsu" banks. In 1954 Mitsubishi Trading became the leader of the Mitsubishi Group and established Mitsubishi International (US) which became a leading exporter of US goods.

The 1964 merger of three Mitsubishi companies created Mitsubishi Heavy Industries a top Japanese maker of ships aircraft plants and heavy machinery. Mitsubishi Kasei separated from Asahi Glass and Mitsubishi Rayon by a US fiat became Japan's #1 chemical concern. Mitsubishi Electric emerged as one of the country's leading electrical equipment and electronics manufacturers. In 1971 Chrysler invested in Mitsubishi Motors which began making cars for the US automaker. That year Mitsubishi Trading was renamed Mitsubishi Corporation.

Through the 1980s Japan seemed economically invincible. Then its "bubble economy" burst. The group fell behind in electronics and autos in the US consumer demand dried up at home and Mitsubishi Bank was left with a heavy burden of bad loans. Group members which traditionally provided materials supplies and sales outlets for each other began loosening old "keiretsu" ties during Japan's recession of the 1990s.

In 1993 Chrysler sold its stock in Mitsubishi Motors and two years later the companies severed production ties. This loss and declining demand in the US for Mitsubishi cars hurt auto sales.

Mitsubishi Bank merged with Bank of Tokyo in 1996 to form the biggest bank in the world The Bank of Tokyo-Mitsubishi (BTM). In 1997 several Mitsubishi companies admitted paying off a corporate racketeer setting off a wave of executive resignations.

By 1999 BTM had tumbled from the top spot and was unable to keep the money freely flowing to fellow Mitsubishi members.

Hit hard by the Asian economic crisis all the struggling Mitsubishi companies had to look outside of the "keiretsu" for help. In 1999 Mitsubishi Motors found a foreign partner Volvo for its truck making operations. Mitsubishi Oil merged with an outsider Nippon Oil to form Nippon Mitsubishi Oil (later renamed Nippon Oil). In 2000 DaimlerChrysler (now Chrysler and Daimler) acquired a controlling stake in Mitsubishi Motors for $2.1 billion.

Executives at Mitsubishi Motors were charged in 2001 after they allegedly kept the lid on thousands of reported defects in Mitsubishi cars instead of issuing recalls. Stung by this and the after-effects of scandals from the previous decade Mitsubishi unveiled a new corporate philosophy as part of a strategy to revive the group's reputation.

In 2003 Mitsubishi disbanded its information technology and electronics business unit. The unit's operations were divided between the new business and machinery groups. In 2004 the company formed an alliance with GE Yokogawa Medical Systems (GEYMS) to provide GEYMS with help in developing its presence in the Japanese diagnostic imaging market.

In 2004 the company formed a food distribution joint venture with five Japanese food wholesalers comprising national wholesaler Meidi-ya and four regional companies. The joint venture called Alliance Network became one of Japan's largest food wholesalers. Mitsubishi had a 51% stake in Alliance Network. Later in 2004 Mitsubishi acquired the food beverage additive and pharmaceutical active and excipient businesses of Ashland Distribution.

In 2006 Mitsubishi bolstered its automotive operations when it acquired shares in Isuzu from General Motors; Mitsubishi ended up with a 10% stake in Isuzu. Mitsubishi and Isuzu soon after formed a European joint venture to market light-duty trucks throughout the continent. Later that year Mitsubishi bought the Avon Automotive subsidiary of Avon Rubber in a deal worth $120 million.

The following year Mitsubishi bought majority control of Nosan Corporation a manufacturer of livestock feed. In late 2007 the company acquired the majority interest in Kentucky Fried Chicken Japan.

On the medical health care front Mitsubishi shifted the focus of certain of its subsidiaries to providing services to hospitals and nursing care facilities. It established the Trinity Healthcare Fund in 2007 to provide management support for the restructuring of hospitals and other medical institutions. Other Mitsubishi subsidiaries focused on medical services include ProCure which is a medical equipment wholesale distributor and Apprecia which provides hospital construction consulting services.

During 2007 the group began investing in energy-related assets as part of this strategy. It acquired nearly 40% of Encore Energy Pte. which in turn owns 51% of Medco Energy an Indonesian oil and gas concern. The deal was valued at about $350 million and gave Mitsubishi a 20% stake in Medco. Mitsubishi was already working with Medco on an Indonesian gas plant and the two companies plan to pursue further international energy partnerships.

In 2009 it entered the solar energy business buying 34% of a subsidiary of Spanish renewable energy firm Acciona SA

Mitsubishi in 2010 it merged subsidiaries Mitsubishi Corporation Unimetals and Mitsubishi Shoji Light Metal Sales Corporation. The resulting company was named Mitsubishi Corporation

Unimetals and remained a subsidiary of Mitsubishi. The merger was made to concentrate the company's management expertise in the non-ferrous metals industry.

EXECUTIVES

Chairman, Yorihiko Kojima
EVP; Group CEO Industrial Finance Logistics and Development Group, Eiichi Tanabe
EVP; General Manager Nagoya Branch, Ichiro Ando
Executive Vice President; Representative Director, Ryoichi Ueda
SEVP, Hideto Nakahara
EVP; Regional CEO Asia and Oceania, Toru Moriyama
SVP; Division COO Isuzu Business Division, Morikazu Chokki
EVP; Regional CEO Latin America, Seiji Shiraki
EVP; Group CEO Energy Business Group, Seiji Kato
President and CEO, Ken Kobayashi
SEVP and CIO, Hideyuki Nabeshima
SEVP, Jun Yanai
EVP; General Manager Nagoya Branch, Shosuke Yasuda
SEVP, Jun Kinukawa
EVP; Group CEO Global Environment and Infrastructure Business Group, Nobuaki Kojima
SEVP, Takahisa Miyauchi
EVP; Regional CEO Middle East and Central Asia, Shigeaki Yoshikawa
SVP; Chairman and Managing Director Mitsubishi Corporation India, Keiichi Nakagaki
SVP; Division COO Development and Construction Project Division, Ichiro Miyahara
EVP, Yasuo Nagai
EVP; Group CEO Machinery Group, Kozo Shiraji
EVP; President Americas, Yasuyuki Sugiura
EVP and CFO, Shuma Uchino
EVP; Group CEO Business Service Group, Toshimitsu Urabe
EVP; Regional CEO East Asia, Shunichi Matsui
SVP; Division COO Non-Ferrous Metals Division, Kenji Tani
EVP; Group CEO Living Essentials Group, Takehiko Kakiuchi
SVP; Division COO Infrastructure Project Division, Kazushi Okawa
SVP; Division COO Petroleum Business Division, Hajime Hirano
SVP; Division COO Asset Finance and Business Development Division, Yuichi Hiromoto
SVP; Division COO Commodity Chemicals Division A, Tatsuya Kiyoshi
Vice President Treasurer, Yuzo Nouchi
Vice President Secretary, Jason Stevens
Senior Vice President Chief Technology Officer, Jeffrey W. Daley
Vice President Director of Human Resources, Jil Galloway
Senior Vice President, Makoto Okawara
Vice President, Masakazu Horikawa
Senior Vice President Energy, Masatsugu Kurahashi
Senior Vice President Chemicals, Nobuhiko Otomo
Vice President, Ryugo Izumida
Vice President, Ryuji Watanabe
Senior Vice President, Tsunehiko Yanagihara
Vice President, Gosuke Nakae
Senior Vice President, Shinichiro Kawazoe
Vice President, Tadashi Takasugi
Senior Vice President Machinery, George Takahashi
General Manager Finance Department, Yoichi Shimoyama
Senior Vice President Metals, Daiju Mita
EVP, Kazuyuki Mori
Senior Vice President Metals Group, Hideki Nakagawa
Senior Vice President Corporate Staff Group, Katsuhiro Ito

EVP Audits and Internal Control and Director, Kiyoshi Fujimura
Director, Tamotsu Nomakuchi
Director, Mikio Sasaki
SEVP Resources and Energy Strategies and Director, Hisanori Yoshimura
SEVP Food Agricultural Resources and Consumer Market Strategies Customer Relations Management Regional Strategy (Japan) and Director, Takeshi Inoue, age 67
Director, Kazuo Tsukuda
SEVP CFO and Director, Ryoichi Ueda
EVP Corporate Administration Legal and Human Resources and Director, Tsuneo Iyobe
EVP Global Strategy Regional Development and Director, Hideto Nakahara
Director, Tomio Tsutsumi
SEVP; Group CEO Living Essentials Group and Director, Masahide Yano
Director, Kunio Ito
President CEO and Director, Ken Kobayashi
SEVP; Group CEO Business Service Group and Director, Hideyuki Nabeshima
EVP; Regional Strategy Japan and Director, Yasuo Nagai
Director, Ryozo Kato
Director, Hidehiro Konno
Auditors: DeloitteToucheTohmatsu

LOCATIONS

HQ: Mitsubishi Corp
2-3-1 Marunouchi, Chiyoda-ku, Tokyo 100-8086
Phone: (81) 3 3210 2121
Web: www.mitsubishicorp.com

Sales

	% of total
Japan	73
Australia	10
Thailand	7
Other	10
Total	**100**

PRODUCTS/OPERATIONS

Selected Products and Services
Metals
  Bullion and metals futures
  Fabricated steel structures
  Metallurgical and thermal coal
  Nonferrous metal products
  Nonferrous metals
  Nuclear fuel and components
  Precious metals
  Raw materials for steel
  Semifinished products
  Steel materials
  Specialty steel
Living Essentials
  Apparel
  Canned foods
  Ceramic materials
  Cigarettes
  Coffee beans coffee and beverages
  Confections and snacks
  Contract food services
  Dairy foods and processed foods
  Fabrics
  Feedstuffs
  Fresh and frozen foods
  Grains and agricultural products
  Marine products
  Meat and livestock
  Mineral water
  Oils and fats
  Photosensitized materials
  Pulp paper and packaging materials
  Soft drinks
  Sweeteners
  Textile raw materials
  Textiles for industrial use
  Tires
  Wood wood products and construction materials
Machinery

  Automobiles
  Commercial aviation
  Defense systems and equipment
  Electronics products
  Industrial agricultural construction and other general machinery
  Plant and machinery for power generation electricity oil/gas/chemicals steel/cement and environmental protection
  Project development and construction
  Satellite communications
  Ships
  Space systems
  Transportation systems
Energy
  Carbon materials and products
  Crude oil
  LNG
  LPG
  Orimulsion
  Petroleum products
Industrial Finance Logistics and Development
  Commerce services
  Consumer services
  Financial services
  Logistics
Chemicals
  Fertilizers
  Fine and specialty chemicals
  Inorganic chemicals
  Petrochemicals
  Plastics

COMPETITORS

ITOCHU	Samsung Group
Marubeni	Sime Darby
Mitsui	Sumitomo

HISTORICAL FINANCIALS
Company Type: Public

Income Statement

FYE: March 31

	REVENUE ($ mil.)	NET INCOME ($ mil.)	NET PROFIT MARGIN	EMPLOYEES
03/14	73,970	3,500	4.7%	68,383
03/13	63,435	3,826	6.0%	83,891
03/12	67,851	5,532	8.2%	82,792
03/11	62,879	5,593	8.9%	77,494
03/10	48,620	2,924	6.0%	78,146
Annual Growth	**11.1%**	**4.6%**	**—**	**(3.3%)**

2014 Year-End Financials

Debt ratio: 0.3%
Return on equity: 7.8%
Cash ($ mil.): 12,904
Current ratio: 1.50
Long-term debt ($ mil.): 45,474
No. of shares (mil.): 1,648
Dividends
  Yield: 3.2%
  Payout: 0.0%
Market value ($ mil.): 61,193

	STOCK PRICE ($) FY Close	P/E High/Low		Earnings	PER SHARE ($) Dividends	Book Value
03/14	37.12	0	0	2.12	1.19	29.78
03/13	37.53	0	0	2.32	0.00	26.97
03/12	46.76	0	0	3.36	0.00	25.99
03/11	55.33	0	0	3.39	1.08	24.12
03/10	52.60	0	0	1.78	0.72	19.29
Annual Growth	**(8.3%)**	**—**	**—**	**4.5%**	**13.4%**	**11.5%**

Mitsubishi Electric Corp.

If it has an "on" switch chances are Mitsubishi Electric makes it or makes a part for it. The company part of the Mitsubishi Corporation operates across five primary sectors: Energy and Electric Systems (power generation plants supervisory systems and escalators); Industrial Automation Systems (programmable controllers measurement and control systems); Home Appliances (air-conditioning systems TVs and Blu-ray disc recorders); Information and Communication Systems (satellites wireless systems and network systems); and Electronic Devices (power devices LCD displays). Mitsubishi Electric has operations in about 40 countries but it earns the majority of its sales from Japan.

Energy and Electric Systems representing 25% of sales which the company terms its social infrastructure business includes building systems with elevators and escalators. The AXIEZ elevator features LED lighting and speed-adjustment technology that reduces waiting time. The segment also installs power plants for operations that range from utility companies to the individual sites of companies seeking in-house power generation.

Industrial Automation Systems making up 23% of sales provides such products as programmable logic controllers under the MELSEC brand; the MELSERVO-J4 used for the manufacturing of semiconductors flat panel display equipment and industrial machinery; no-fuse circuit breakers and earth leakage circuit breakers for wiring protection and short-circuit protection; and electrical discharge machines for the manufacturing of automobiles home electronics and IT-related devices. Home Appliances accounting for 20% of sales includes KIRIGAMINE air conditioners photovoltaic generation heat pumps LED lighting RakuRaku-UD technology that enhances the performance of appliances as well as products that go beyond the domestic market such as digital signage and other visual equipment.

Information and Communication Systems 12% of sales offers services that include information systems monitoring server integration and such products as satellite platforms vehicle-mounted satellite communication equipment broadband optical access systems and digital closed-circuit TV systems. Electronic Devices 5% include products for cutting power losses and power consumption integrated circuits for electric vehicles high-electron mobility transistor amplifiers and LCD modules for high brightness and contrast. The company's Other segment 15% of sales mainly comprises materials procurement and engineering.

Mitsubishi Electric has more than 20 manufacturing plants in Japan as well as factories in other countreis that include China Malaysia Thailand the US and the UK.

Consolidated net sales were flat year-over-year from 2011 to fiscal 2012 falling a fraction of a percentage point. By segment Energy and Electric Systems' net sales were also flat falling likewise a fraction of a percentage point. The segment struggled with falling orders in the Japanese public utility and rolling-stock equipment markets.

Supported by demand in the Asian smartphone and tablet markets as well as the automotive equipment markets in the developing world and North America Industrial Automation Systems' sales headed up about 6% in fiscal 2012 compared with 2011. Home Appliances was down 8% in fiscal 2012 versus 2011 as a result in part of lower demand for photovoltaic systems in Europe and weak demand for hot water supply and induction heating cooking systems.

Thanks in part to large orders for submarine line terminal equipment and demand for communications infrastructure systems integration network and system operations and electronics Information and Communication Systems increased 6% over the period between 2011 and fiscal 2012. Electronic Devices rose 14% in fiscal 2012 versus 2011 to meet a strong demand for power modules in the industrial commercial automotive and railcar markets. The Other segment headed up just a fraction of a percentage point in 2012 versus 2011. During that period the company's net income declined about 10% mainly due to a tax adjustment.

Looking ahead each segment has specific goals for product development. The Energy and Electric Systems segment is focused on research and development to improve rotating machines for generators electric motors switches and transformers transportation systems and elevators and escalators. The segment is also concentrating its R&D efforts on IT for supervision and control power information systems and building management systems.

Industrial Automation Systems is focused on improving motors mechatronics equipment automotive components electric power steering and auto multimedia systems. Information and Communication Systems is emphasizing network systems for telecommunication operators and space systems.

Electronic Devices is tasked with product development in semiconductors while Home Appliances is focused on energy saving recycling universal design and digital imaging systems. The Other segment is focused on work that helps the entire group. This segment's accomplishments include a robot system for bulk components and a multi-band power amplifier.

Each segment has also enjoyed some significant capital expenditures. Energy and Electric Systems received investments for more production capacity. Factory automation systems and automotive equipment operations were the focus for Industrial Automation. Home Appliance spending favored increasing production capacity for air-conditioning equipment. Improving research and development received the most capital expenditure focus in Information and Communication Systems and the Other segment. Electronic Devices concentrated on improvements for its power device operations.

In 2012 Mitsubishi Electric acquired the Messung Group which makes programmable logic controllers and human machine interfaces and had served as a sales and distribution partner in India.

HISTORY

Mitsubishi Electric was among 10 companies fined in 2007 by the European Commission (EC) for allegedly conspiring to fix prices for gas-insulated switchgear industrial equipment used by electric utilities. Along with Fuji Electric Hitachi Toshiba and other Japanese manufacturers the company was accused of colluding with ALSTOM AREVA Schneider Electric and Siemens to reserve European markets for Europe-based manufacturers while European companies generally stayed out of the Japanese market. Mitsubishi Electric was fined a mere E118.5 million ($1 million) for its part in the price-fixing cartel.

EXECUTIVES

Executive Officer Accounting and Finance; Director, Hiroki Yoshimatsu
Chairman, Setsuhiro Shimomura, age 70
Executive Officer Energy & Industrial Systems, Yoshiaki Nakatani
EVP, Mitsuo Muneyuki
Executive Officer Living Environment & Digital Media Equipment, Hiroyuki Umemura
Executive Officer Auditing Government & External Relations Legal Affairs Export Control and Intellectual Property, Tsuyoshi Nakamura
President and CEO, Kenichiro Yamanishi, age 64
SVP Global Strategic Planning & Marketing, Takashi Sasakawa
SVP Factory Automation Systems, Hideyasu Nonaka
Executive Officer Communication Systems, Yasuyuki Nakanishi
Executive Office Public Utility Systems, Susumu Shikata
Executive Officer Total Productivity Management and Environmental Programs, Masaharu Moriyasu
EVP, Masaki Sakuyama
Senior Vice President, Noritomo Hashimoto
Executive Officer Purchasing, Shoichi Sakata
Executive Officer, Kazuhiko Tsutsumi
Managing Executive Officer, Hideyuki Ohkubo
Section Chief of Accounting Unit, Homare Ikeda
Managing Executive Officer, Isao Iguchi
Managing Executive Officer, Masayuki Ichige
Managing Executive Officer; Director, Nobuyuki Ohkuma
Executive Officer, Takayuki Sueki
Managing Executive Officer, Toru Yoshinaga
Managing Executive Officer, Yutaka Ohashi
Executive Officer, Akihiro Matsuyama
Director, Mikio Sasaki
Director, Shigemitsu Miki, age 79
Executive Officer Accounting and Finance; Director, Hiroki Yoshimatsu
Director, Kazuo Sawamoto
Executive Officer General Affairs Human Resources and Public Relations; Director, Noritomo Hashimoto
Director, Hiroyoshi Murayama
Director, Shunji Yanai
Director, Osamu Shigeta
Independent Director, Fujiatsu Makino
Independent Director, Mitoji Yabunaka
Auditors: KPMGAZSA&Co.

LOCATIONS

HQ: Mitsubishi Electric Corp.
2-7-3 Marunouchi, Chiyoda-ku, Tokyo 100-8310
Phone: (81) 3 3218 2272
Web: www.mitsubishielectric.co.jp

Sales

	$ mil.	% of total
Asia		
Japan	38,862	74
Other Asia	7,108	13
Europe	3,780	7
North America	2,714	5
Rest of the World	490	1
Eliminations	(8571)	-
Total	**44,383**	**100**

PRODUCTS/OPERATIONS

Sales

	$ mil.	% of total
Energy & electric systems	12,526	25
Industrial automation systems	11,931	23
Home appliances	10,357	20
Information & communication systems	6,297	12
Electronic devices	2,449	5
Other	7,458	15
Eliminations	(6635)	-
Total	**44,383**	**100**

Selected Products

Energy and Electric Systems
　Elevators

Nuclear power plant equipment
Power distribution systems
Power generation systems
Propulsion control systems
Smart grids

Substation systems
Train information systems
Train vision systems
Visual information systems
Home Appliances
Air-conditioning systems
Blu-ray disc players
Televisions
Industrial Automation Systems
Automotive equipment
Circuit breakers
Factory automation systems
Industrial robots
Power meters
Information and Communication Systems
Antenna technology
Closed-circuit television systems
Radar system technology
Space systems
Wireless systems
Electronic Devices
High frequency & optical devices
LCD displays
Power devices

COMPETITORS

Autoliv	Raytheon
Continental AG	Robert Bosch
DENSO	Rockwell Collins
Delphi Automotive	SANYO
Systems	Samsung Electronics
Ericsson	Sanken Electric
Fujitsu	Schindler Holding
Hella	Schneider Electric
Hitachi	Sharp Corp.
Intel	Siemens AG
Johnson Controls	Sony
KONE	Spirit AeroSystems
Lear Corp	Sumitomo Electric
Magneti Marelli	TRW Automotive
Meritor	ThyssenKrupp
Motorola Solutions	Toshiba
NEC	United Technologies
Oki Electric	Valeo
Panasonic Corp	Visteon
Philips Electronics	Yokogawa Electric

HISTORICAL FINANCIALS

Company Type: Public

Income Statement

FYE: March 31

	REVENUE ($ mil.)	NET INCOME ($ mil.)	NET PROFIT MARGIN	EMPLOYEES
03/14	39,279	1,486	3.8%	124,305
03/13	37,911	738	1.9%	120,958
03/12	44,367	1,366	3.1%	117,314
03/11	44,022	1,503	3.4%	114,443
03/10	35,899	302	0.8%	109,565
Annual Growth	2.3%	48.9%	—	3.2%

2014 Year-End Financials

Debt ratio: 0.1%
Return on equity: 10.8%
Cash ($ mil.): 4,050
Current ratio: 1.53
Long-term debt ($ mil.): 2,048

No. of shares (mil.): 2,143
Dividends
Yield: 1.0%
Payout: 67.3%
Market value ($ mil.): 48,493

	STOCK PRICE ($) FY Close	P/E High/Low		PER SHARE ($) Earnings	Dividends	Book Value
03/14	22.62	0	0	0.69	0.24	6.89
03/13	16.40	0	0	0.34	0.00	6.45
03/12	17.78	0	0	0.64	0.00	6.44
03/11	23.85	0	0	0.70	0.00	5.92
03/10	93.50	0	0	0.14	0.04	4.82
Annual Growth	(29.9%)	—	—	48.8%	53.2%	9.3%

Mitsubishi Heavy Industries Ltd.

Japanese industrial behemoth Mitsubishi Heavy Industries (MHI) is heavy into machinery manufacturing for a myriad of markets. A member of the Mitsubishi keiretsu the group builds and supplies everything from nuclear power plants bridges and aircraft to engines ships and air conditioners to various industries and customers around the world. MHI operates through six business segments: Power Systems Machinery & Steel Structures Aerospace General Machinery & Special Vehicles Shipbuilding & Ocean Development and Others. The company's core market is Japan but it also does business in other parts of Asia North America Europe Central and South America Africa and the Middle East.

As the world continues to transition to a low-carbon society MHI is focused on four key areas for growth. It is trying to meet growing demand for gas turbines especially as industrialized nations work to replace aging facilities in line with tougher environmental regulations. To this end it is trying to commercialize its J-series gas turbines which offer the highest level of heat efficiency in the world. Second it reached an agreement with UK-based utility Scottish and Southern Energy to develop low-carbon energy. Third it took a capital stake in Italy's ATLA to strengthen its gas turbine service network in Europe. Overall service business sales are projected to account for 35% of sales by fiscal 2014. And fourth the company seeks to expand into fast-growing emerging markets such as India and China.

MHI is specifically pushing for greater localization in these emerging markets. Through two joint ventures with Mumbai-based Larsen & Toubro MHI completed two plants in India to manufacture supercritical-pressure boilers as well as steam turbines and generators in response to India's strong electricity demand. In 2010 it launched a Shanghai subsidiary to oversee its air conditioning and refrigeration business. The subsidiary will manufacture commercial air conditioners and truck refrigeration systems with the goal of doubling sales within the first two years.

In more developed countries like the US MHI is building gas and wind turbine assembly plants to expand its network of overseas production sites. In Japan the group's largest market by sales MHI continues to receive orders for gas turbine combined-cycle thermal power plants to replace aging facilities. In the wake of the catastrophic earthquake that struck eastern Japan in early 2011 the company's efforts are focused on trying to improve the safety of its pressurized water reactor plants and collaborating with Hitachi Ltd. to support recovery and stabilize operations at the Fukushima Daiichi Nuclear Power Plant.

In fiscal 2011 MHI's consolidated net sales remained around the same level as in 2010. Sales in 2010 fell nearly 13% from their record high in 2009 as a result of the global economic crisis. Net sales for 2011 rose in the Shipbuilding & Ocean Development segment on increased deliveries of new vessels and in General Machinery & Special Vehicles on increased orders for engines in China turbochargers in Europe and forklifts in Asia and the Middle East. The Others segment consisting of air conditioning and refrigeration systems also reported both in an increase in orders and higher sales of automotive thermal systems and residential and commercial air conditioners. However net sales decreased in the Power Systems Aerospace

and Machinery & Steel Structures segments. Lackluster sales of wind turbines commercial aircraft and defense- and space-related products as well as customer postponement of steel and transportation projects contributed to the decrease in sales in these segments.

EXECUTIVES

Chairman, Kazuo Tsukuda
SVP and Deputy General Manager Power Systems Headquarters, Noriaki Fuseya
President and CEO, Shunichi Miyanaga, age 66
EVP General Manager Power Systems Headquarters and Director, Yoshiaki Tsukuda
EVP, Takashi Abe, age 65
EVP, Akira Hishikawa, age 63
EVP; President and CEO Integrated Defense and Space Systems, Hisashi Hara, age 64
EVP, Takato Nishizawa, age 67
EVP, Masafumi Wani, age 65
SEVP; President and CEO Energy and Environment, Atsushi Maekawa, age 64
Vice President Mitsubishi Heavey Industries, Kiyoshi Yamauchi
EVP, Shigero Masamori, age 64
SVP and General Manager Nagoya Aerospace Systems Works, Shinichi Yoshida
EVP; Chairman PW Power Systems, Koji Hiramoto
SVP and Deputy General Manager Aerospace Headquarters, Takashi Kobayashi
EVP, Toshio Kodama, age 63
SVP and General Manager Global Strategic Planning and Operations Headquarters, Yukinori Horiguchi
EVP, Masahiko Arihara, age 62
SVP; President Mitsubishi-Hitachi Metals Machinery, Yasukuni Yamasaki
SVP and General Manager Machine Tool Division, Akihiko Fujiwara
EVP; President and CEO Commercial Aviation and Transportation Systems, Yoichi Kujirai, age 63
EVP, Hisakazu Mizutani, age 63
Executive Officer; Deputy Chief Director Nuclear Energy Business; Manager of Kobe Shipbuilding Center, Ei Kadokami
Chairman, Hideaki Omiya, age 68
Executive Officer; Deputy Chief Director of Motor Business, Kazuo Soma
Executive Officer; Deputy Chief Director of Aerospace Business, Keiichiro Iwasaki
Executive Officer; Deputy Chief Director of Motor Business; Manager of Takasago Factory, Kenji Ando
President Mitsubishi Power Systems Americas, Koji Hasegawa
Executive Officer; Deputy Chief Director of Ship & Ocean Business; Senior Director of Ship & Ocean Technology; Manager of Nagasaki Shipbuilding Center, Kunifumi Hashimoto
Vice President Commercial Aviation & Transportation Systems, Mutsuo Hiroe
Executive Officer; Deputy Chief Director of Engineering; Deputy Chief Director of Machinery & Steel Infrastructure Business, Naohito Hoshino
EVP, Takashi Funato, age 62
Executive Officer; Deputy Chief Director of Engineering; Manager of Yokohama Management Center, Takio Nishizuma
EVP, Tatsuhiko Nojima, age 62
Executive Officer; Deputy Chief Director of Ship & Ocean Business, Terufumi Kajiwara
Executive Officer; Deputy Chief Director of Nuclear Energy Business, Terumasa Ohnaka
Executive Officer; Deputy Chief Director of Ship & Ocean Business; Manager of Shimonoseki Shipbuilding Center, Tsuyoshi Kabata
SVP; President Mitsubishi Heavy Industries America, Yoshiyuki Ishii

Executive Officer; Deputy Chief Director of Motor Business; Manager of India JV Business Promotion Office, Yozaburo Mabuchi

Executive Officer; Chief Director of Work Machinery Business; Manager of Ritto Manufacturing Center, Yukio Kodama

SVP; President MHI Plant Engineering, Masao Ishikawa

Director, Yorihiko Kojima

Director, Akihiro Wada, age 79

EVP General Manager Nuclear Energy Systems Headquarters and Director, Akira Sawa

EVP General Manager Machinery and Steel Structures Headquarters and Director, Shunichi Miyanaga

EVP General Manager Power Systems Headquarters and Director, Yoshiaki Tsukuda

EVP and Director Accounting Finance and Material, Yujiro Kawamoto

SVP and Director, Makoto Shintani

SVP and Director, Takashi Abe

SVP and Director, Akira Hishikawa

Director, Yoshihiro Sakamoto

EVP and Director Internal Audit Corporate Social Responsibility General Affairs Legal and Personnel, Katsuhiko Yasuda

Independent Director, Christina Ahmadjian

Auditors: Ernst&YoungShinNihon

LOCATIONS

HQ: Mitsubishi Heavy Industries Ltd.
2-16-5 Konan, Minato-ku, Tokyo 108-8215
Phone: (81) 3 6716 3111   Fax: (81) 3 6716 5800
Web: www.mhi.co.jp

Sales

	% of total
Asia/Pacific	
Japan	51
Other	13
North	10
Europe	7
Central & South	7
Africa	6
Middle	4
Other	2
Total	**100**

PRODUCTS/OPERATIONS

Sales

	% of total
Power	34
Machinery & Steel	19
Aerospace	16
General Machinery & Special	12
Shipbuilding & Ocean	10
Others	9
Total	**100**

Selected Products

Aerospace
  Aeroengines
  Civil aircraft
  Defense aircraft
  Guided weapon systems
  Laser radar surveillance system
  Launch vehicles
  Rocket engines
  Space stations
General Machinery & Special Vehicles
  Agricultural machinery
  Construction machinery
  Forklift trucks
  Medium- and small-sized engines
  Tractors
  Turbochargers
Machinery & Steel Structures
  Air brakes
  Automated people movers
  Chemical plants
  CO2 recovery plants
  Crane and material handling systems
  Flue gas desulphurization plants

Injection molding machines
Monorails
Production robots
Rail transit systems
Sludge treatment systems
Testing equipment
Power Systems
  Boilers
  Desalination plants
  Fans and blowers
  Diesel engines
  Gas turbines
  Hydraulic equipment (actuators generators motors pumps and water pressure systems)
  Instrumentation and control systems
  Lithium-ion secondary batteries
  Solid oxide fuel cells
  Steam turbines
  Thin-film photovoltaic module
  Wind turbines
Shipbuilding & Ocean Development
  Cargo ships
  Floating facilities
  Marine engines
  Marine machinery
  Passenger ships
  Pure car carriers
  Special-purpose ships
  Tankers
Others
  Air conditioning and refrigeration systems
  Automotive thermal systems
  Centrifugal chillers
  Machine tools

COMPETITORS

ALSTOM
Aker Solutions
Babcock & Wilcox
Baltija Shipbuilding
Bharat Heavy Electricals
Caterpillar
Chiyoda Corp.
DSME
Doosan Heavy Industries
Foster Wheeler
GE
Hanjin Heavy Industries & Construction
Hitachi
Hyundai Heavy Industries
IHI Corp.
Kajima
Kawasaki Heavy Industries
Komatsu
Kubota
MAN
Marubeni
Mitsui Engineering & Shipbuilding
Nippon Sharyo
Nishimatsu Construction
Obayashi
Samsung Heavy Industries
Siemens AG
Sumitomo Heavy Industries
Suzlon Energy Limited
Taisei

HISTORICAL FINANCIALS

Company Type: Public

Income Statement

FYE: March 31

	REVENUE ($ mil.)	NET INCOME ($ mil.)	NET PROFIT MARGIN	EMPLOYEES
03/14	32,451	1,554	4.8%	80,583
03/13	29,948	1,034	3.5%	68,213
03/12	34,388	299	0.9%	68,887
03/11	35,066	363	1.0%	68,816
03/10	31,484	151	0.5%	67,669
Annual Growth	**0.8%**	**78.9%**	**—**	**4.5%**

2014 Year-End Financials

Debt ratio: 0.1%
Return on equity: 10.9%
Cash ($ mil.): 3,691
Current ratio: 1.39
Long-term debt ($ mil.): 5,182

No. of shares (mil.): —
Dividends
  Yield: —
  Payout: —
Market value ($ mil.): —

	STOCK PRICE ($) FY Close	P/E High/Low	Earnings	PER SHARE ($) Dividends	Book Value
03/14	5.54	— —	0.46	0.00	5.12
03/13	5.61	— —	0.31	0.00	4.53
03/12	4.71	— —	0.09	0.00	4.75
03/11	4.73	— —	0.11	0.00	4.73
03/10	4.25	— —	0.05	0.00	4.24
Annual Growth	**6.9%**	**— —**	**78.8%**	**—**	**4.9%**

Mitsubishi UFJ Financial Group Inc

Mitsubishi UFJ Financial Group (MUFG) is the largest banking group in Japan (ahead of Mizuho Financial and Sumitomo Mitsui Financial) and one of the largest in the world. The group provides retail banking corporate banking and trust services in more than 40 countries. Subsidiary The Bank of Tokyo-Mitsubishi UFJ operates about 500 branches across Japan and another 80 overseas. Mitsubishi UFJ Trust and Banking oversees some Â27 trillion ($343 billion) in assets under management. Other holdings include investment bank Mitsubishi UFJ Securities California-based MUFG Union Bank and a more than 20% stake in Morgan Stanley. MUFG was formed in the 2005 merger of Mitsubishi Tokyo Financial Group and UFJ Holdings

The group also includes credit card company Mitsubishi UFJ NICOS and Mitsubishi UFJ Lease & Finance. The company is targeting the latter unit for growth; it also plans to expand its corporate investment banking practice in North America Japan and the rest of Asia.

Japan's weakened economy in which loan demand remains soft and consumer spending is down has negatively impacted MUFG's earnings. Its NICOS consumer loan portfolio has contracted recently due to regulatory reforms in Japan thereby lowering the bank's interest income. In fiscal 2012 the bank's revenues fell 5% while profits fell 8%. Although overall interest earnings grew (largely due to the conversion rate related to the conversion of Morgan Stanley's preferred stock into common stock) noninterest earnings including fees and commissions declined that year. That decline could be primarily attributed to the securities business as well as a reduction of business volume all of which reflects the slowly recovering economy.

With the stagnant Japanese economy the company has increasingly looked to emerging markets in Asia Latin America and Central and Eastern Europe (among its most recent targets: Turkey) for growth. In the US subsidiary MUFG Union Bank has been expanding through the acquisition of other community banks.

MUFG is also looking towards its alliance with Morgan Stanley to grow its global investment banking operations. The two companies combined their Japanese brokerage operations in 2010; to help fund that deal MUFG raised more than $10 billion through a stock offering. The company then got approval from the US Federal Reserve to up its stake in Morgan Stanley to nearly 25% in 2011. The partnership could ultimately prove very lucrative for MUFG although the bank does not have any control over Morgan Stanley's business operations.

On a much smaller scale MUFG has been expanding its reach by acquiring stakes in firms in other parts of the world. In 2010 it became the first Japanese bank to acquire an interest in a Chinese asset manager when it bought out BNP Paribas Asset Management's 33% stake in a joint venture with Shenyin & Wanguo Securities. The following year it acquired some 15% of AMP Limited in Australia. The moves should allow it to expand its investment services to pension funds and other institutional investors as part of a plan to expand its trust operations.

MUFG is a member of the Mitsubishi group a melange of about 30 different companies —active in manufacturing transportation insurance and other industries —that shared common ownership before WWII but have been operated autonomously since.

HISTORY

Mitsubishi Bank emerged from the exchange office of the original Mitsubishi "zaibatsu" (industrial group) in 1885. It evolved into a full-service bank by 1895 and became independent in 1919 though its primary customers were Mitsubishi group companies. The bank survived WWII but a US fiat dismantled the "zaibatsu" after the war. Mitsubishi Bank reopened as Chiyoda Bank in 1948. After reopening offices in London and New York the bank readopted the Mitsubishi name.

In the 1950s Mitsubishi Bank became the lead lender for the reconstituted Mitsubishi group ("keiretsu"). In the 1960s it followed its Mitsubishi partners overseas helping finance Japan's growing international trade. In 1972 it acquired the Bank of California and began doing more business outside the group.

Japan's overinflated real estate market of the 1980s devastated many of the country's banks including Nippon Trust Bank of which Mitsubishi owned 5%. Japan's Ministry of Finance (MoF) urged Mitsubishi to bail Nippon out; as a reward for raising its stake in Nippon to 69% and assuming a mountain of unrecoverable loans the MoF allowed Mitsubishi to begin issuing debt before other Japanese banks. In 1995 Mitsubishi Bank and Bank of Tokyo agreed to merge.

Bank of Tokyo (BOT) was established in 1880 as the Yokohama Specie Bank; the Iwasaki family founders of the Mitsubishi group served on its board. With links to the Imperial family the bank was heavily influenced by government policy. With Japan isolated after the Sino-Japanese War its international operations suffered greatly even before WWII. Completely dismantled after WWII the bank was re-established in 1946 as the Bank of Tokyo a commercial city bank bereft of its foreign exchange business. During the 1950s the government restored it as a foreign exchange specialist but regulations limited its domestic business.

BOT evolved into an investment bank in the 1970s; its reputation as the leading foreign exchange bank brought in international clients and successful derivatives trading and overseas banking. By the time BOT and Mitsubishi Bank agreed to merge BOT had 363 foreign offices (only 37 in Japan) with more foreign than Japanese employees.

The two banks merged in 1996 to form The Bank of Tokyo-Mitsubishi (BTM); Mitsubishi was the surviving entity. Their California banks merged to create Union Bank of California (UnionBanCal). The next year BTM reorganized its operations but

had problems assimilating its disparate corporate cultures.

In 1998 Japanese banking regulators doled out nearly $240 billion to the industry to prop up failing banks and to strengthen healthier ones. Also that year BTM was fined for bribing MoF officials with entertainment gifts and posted a huge loss after writing off $8.4 billion in bad debt. Losses continued in 1999 and the bank responded by reorganizing operationally cutting jobs and offices and selling stock in UnionBanCal.

In 2000 BTM announced plans to form a financial group with Mitsubishi Trust Bank and Nippon Trust Bank. The following year the three banks unified and formed Mitsubishi Tokyo Financial Group. Before rolling into Mitsubishi Trust Financial Group BTM paid back the money showered upon it by the Japanese government in 1998.

In 2004 MTFG introduced a new organizational structure that focused on its three core markets — retail corporate and trust asset businesses. The company planned to unify business within each division and to improve decision-making companywide. The group also introduced a new executive officer system with the idea of separating company oversight and business execution. A mechanism for credit risk control was also added.

It was all to change in 2005 however. During this time Mitsubishi Tokyo Financial Group merged with UFJ Holdings emerging (at that time) as the world's largest bank by assets. As a result of the merger the group was renamed Mitsubishi UFJ Financial Group (MUFG).

As with most of its peers MUFG was not immune to the global credit crisis that began in 2007. Its NICOS consumer lending subsidiary had a disappointing year due to the credit crunch. The unit sold its installment credit car loan and car leasing businesses to JACCS in 2008. In 2009 MUFG announced plans to close 50 branches and cut nearly 1000 jobs as a part of a long-term restructuring plan. In addition the bank shut down some 200 ATMs and relocated another 1000 employees.

In 2008 the group bought the rest of UnionBanCal and Mitsubishi UFJ NICOS it didn't already own and acquired a stake in bulge-bracket firm Morgan Stanley. MUFG also bought a 10% stake in UK-based Aberdeen Asset Management that year. (It later upped its interest to around 17%.)

EXECUTIVES

President CEO and Representative Director, Katsunori Nagayasu, age 67
Chairman, Takamune Okihara, age 63
Deputy Chairman, Kinya Okauchi, age 62
President and CEO, Nobuyuki Hirano, age 63
Managing Officer, Takehiko Nemoto, age 60
Senior Managing Director, Taihei Yuki, age 62
Deputy President, Masaaki (Masa) Tanaka, age 61
Executive Officer, Muneaki Tokunari
Executive Officer, Saburo Araki
Deputy President and Representative Director, Tatsuo Tanaka
Deputy Chairman, Tatsuo Wakabayashi
Managing Director, Akihiko Kagawa
Director, Ryuji Araki, age 75
President CEO and Representative Director, Katsunori Nagayasu, age 67
Director, Takuma Otoshi, age 66
Managing Director and Representative Director, Ichiro Hamakawa
Director, Takashi Oyamada, age 58
Deputy Chairman, Kinya Okauchi, age 62
Deputy President and Representative Director, Nobuyuki Hirano, age 62
Senior Managing Director and Representative Director, Taihei Yuki, age 61
Managing Director and Representative Director, Masao Hasegawa

Deputy President and Representative Director, Tatsuo Tanaka
Deputy Chairman, Tatsuo Wakabayashi
Auditors: DeloitteToucheTohmatsu

LOCATIONS

HQ: Mitsubishi UFJ Financial Group Inc
7-1, Marunouchi 2-chome, Chiyoda-ku, Tokyo 100-8330
Phone: (81) 3 3240 8111   **Fax:** (81) 3 3240 7073
Web: www.mufg.jp

Sales

	% of total
Asia/Oceania	
Japan	69
Other	9
US	12
Europe	7
Other	3
Total	**100**

PRODUCTS/OPERATIONS

Sales

	% of total
Interest	
Loans including	36
Investment	9
Trading account	6
Other	1
Noninterest	
Fees &	22
Net trading account	14
Other	12
Total	**100**

COMPETITORS

Aozora Bank	Mizuho Trust &
BNP Paribas Bangkok	Banking Ltd
Chuo Mitsui Trust	ORIX
Citigroup	Resona
HSBC	Shinsei Bank
Ito-Yokado	Sony
Japan Post	Sumitomo Mitsui
Mizuho Financial	

HISTORICAL FINANCIALS

Company Type: Public

Income Statement

FYE: March 31

	ASSETS ($ mil.)	NET INCOME ($ mil.)	INCOME AS % OF ASSETS	EMPLOYEES
03/14	2,457,493	9,837	0.4%	135,300
03/13	2,450,358	11,362	0.5%	112,100
03/12	2,623,454	5,074	0.2%	110,500
03/11	2,449,821	5,576	0.2%	113,000
03/10	2,142,061	9,205	0.4%	115,300
Annual Growth	**3.5%**	**1.7%**	**—**	**4.1%**

2014 Year-End Financials

Return on assets: 0.4%	Dividends
Return on equity: 8.9%	Yield: 2.5%
Long-term debt ($ mil.): —	Payout: 0.0%
No. of shares (mil.): —	Market value ($ mil.): —
Sales ($ mil): 38,822	

	STOCK PRICE ($) FY Close	P/E High/Low		PER SHARE ($) Earnings	Dividends	Book Value
03/14	5.54	0	0	0.68	0.14	8.35
03/13	6.00	0	0	0.79	0.00	7.97
03/12	4.98	0	0	0.34	0.00	7.40
03/11	4.60	0	0	0.38	0.14	7.13
03/10	5.23	0	0	0.73	0.12	6.72
Annual Growth	**1.5%**	**—**	**—**	**(1.7%)**	**3.8%**	**5.6%**

Mitsui & Co., Ltd.

Part of a network of companies that was founded by a samurai centuries ago Mitsui & Co. now does battle in the marketplace. Mitsui & Co. spearheads the Mitsui Group one of Japan's largest "keiretsu" (companies loosely connected through cross-ownership). A leading Japanese general trading firm (sogo shosha) Mitsui & Co. has about 320 subsidiaries in a wide range of industries. Its major business units are engaged in the production and sale of chemicals electronics and information energy foods iron and steel nonferrous metals textiles and machinery. The company's largest revenue generators are its trading activities in the energy and chemical sectors.

Geographic Reach

The company maintains a global network of 151 offices in 67 countries as well as about 320 subsidiaries in a wide range of industries and associated companies worldwide.

Operations

Mitsui & Co.'s operating units include Americas; Asia Pacific; Basic Chemicals; Consumer Service; Energy; Europe the Middle East and Africa; Financial & New; Food Products & Services; Food Resources; Infrastructure Projects; Iron & Steel Products; IT; Marine & Aerospace; Mineral & Metal Resources; Motor Vehicles & Construction Machinery; Performance Chemicals; and Transportation Logistics.

Financial Performance

After a decline in its revenues in fiscal years 2010 over 2009 due to the impact of the recession and the major tsunami Mitsui & Co. experienced significant growths in revenues in both fiscal years 2011 and 2012. In fiscal year 2012 the company's revenues increased by 12% and profits grew by 42%. The increase in the revenues was due to the positive impact of the recovering global economy. The growth in profits was due to the increases in commodity prices including crude oil gas iron ore and coal as well as the reversal effect of the previous year's settlement payment related to the Deepwater Horizon oil spill incident in the Gulf of Mexico. (Mitsui & Co. had a minority interest in the doomed rig. Mitsui's energy sector through its MOEX Offshore 2007 subsidiary saw impairment losses on property equipment and mineral rights from its involvement with the massive oil rig fire and subsequent oil spill in the Gulf of Mexico during the summer of 2010).

Strategy

Mitsui & Co.'s strategic role as a sogo shosha brings together marketing financing logistics risk management and IT and process development functions on behalf of its many subsidiaries. It grows through acquisitions and by forming joint ventures and strategic partnerships.

In 2013 Mitsui & Co. agreed to acquire Total E&P Energia Italia S.r.l which owns a 25% stake in the Tempa Rossa onshore oil field in the Gorgoglione concession in Italy. That year the company also formed a joint venture with JGC Corporation and Chongqing Liangjiang New Area Development & Investment Group Co. Ltd. The joint venture company will produce an urban development master plan for the Yulin Business Park to be developed in the Chongqing Liangjiang New Area and will also be involved in promotional activities for inward investment for the Business Park. Liangjiang New Area Development & Investment will hold a 50% stake in the joint venture company and Mitsui and JGC will own 25% respectively.

Mitsui & Co. entered a 50-50 joint venture with Dow Chemical in 2010 to build and operate a membrane chlor-alkali facility located at Dow's Freeport Texas complex. The new facility is expected to begin operations in mid-2013. Mitsui formed yet another joint venture with Dow in 2011 to develop biofuels and biopolymers or organic plastics in Brazil. The 50-50 operation will use Dow's sugar cane production to develop ethanol and packaging materials offering a "green alternative" and replacement product for the flexible packaging hygiene and medical markets.

In 2011 Mitsui & Co. raised its stake in Brazilian grain broker Multigrain SA to almost 90% by buying a 44% stake from US grain company CHS Inc. for $480 million. Mitsui which hopes to improve its competitiveness on the global grain market previously owned about half of the company.

Also that year Mitsui & Co. entered a joint venture with Russian automaker Sollers to construct Toyota vehicles in a production facility in Vladivostok. The venture would be the first Japanese auto assembly operation in Russia's Far East region. The deal calls for the the Mitsui/Sollers JV to manufacture about 30000 vehicles a year and distribute them throughout the Russian Federation via the Trans-Siberian Railway.

Mitsui & Co. also acquired Mercian Corporation's pharmaceutical and chemical businesses in 2011. Mercian's drug and chemical businesses known as MBS Company utilize fermentation technology. Mitsui aims to boost its business in substances such as anti-cancer bioagents and will position MBS as part of its core group.

HISTORY

In the 17th century unemployed samurai (warrior nobleman) Sokubei Mitsui opened a sake and soy sauce brewery at the urging of his wife Shuho. After parental encouragement their youngest son Hachirobei went to Edo (now Tokyo) and opened a dry goods store in 1673. Breaking with Japanese retailing tradition the store offered merchandise at fixed prices on a cash-and-carry basis.

Hachirobei in 1683 opened a currency exchange that evolved into Mitsui Bank. The bank became the Osaka government's official money changer in 1691 and was the first bank to offer money orders in Japan. Before his death in 1694 Hachirobei drafted a unique succession plan to hand down control of the company to every related family not just the eldest son's side.

The shogun's government called upon Mitsui in the mid-1800s to help finance its war against rebels. The family hired Rizaemon Minomura an outsider with influence in the government to protect the company from increasing demands for money. Mitsui became the bank of the Meiji government after Minomura astutely switched support to the winning rebels. Government industrialization pushed Mitsui into textiles paper goods and machinery. Minomura emphasized foreign trade and banking creating Mitsui Bussan (now Mitsui & Co.) and Mitsui Bank in 1876. In the late 1800s Mitsui Bussan profited from a Japanese military buildup formed a shipping line to take on Mitsubishi's monopoly and bought coal mines. The Mitsui family withdrew from Mitsui Bussan management in 1936 following attacks by right-wing terrorists who opposed its democratic leanings.

Mitsui prospered during the 1930s as Japan's military prepared for war. After the defeat occupation forces disbanded Japan's "zaibatsu" industrial groups slicing Mitsui into more than 200 separate entities. By 1950 more than two dozen leaders of the former Mitsui companies began gathering the Mitsui Group back together. Trading firm Mitsui & Co. was established in 1959. The oil crises of the 1970s stalled the oil-dependent Japanese economy prompting Mitsui companies to expand operations overseas and move into industries such as technology and aluminum.

The mammoth Sakura Bank was formed in 1990 with the merger of Mitsui Bank and Taiyo Kobe Bank. Other major ventures were to follow: In 1992 Mitsui & Co. joined with Marathon and Royal Dutch Shell and others to search for oil and gas off Russia's Sakhalin Island; and Mitsui & Co. and other Japanese traders were enlisted by Oman in 1993 for a $9 billion liquefied natural gas transport venture. As cable TV emerged in Japan Mitsui & Co. teamed up the next year with National Media Corp. to launch a home-shopping network.

In anticipation of deregulation in Japan's financial markets four Mitsui Group firms' pension funds —Sakura Bank Mitsui Marine & Fire Insurance Mitsui Mutual Life Insurance and Mitsui Trust and Banking —were linked in 1998. The next year Sakura Bank set aside old loyalties and agreed to merge with Sumitomo Bank the Sumitomo "keiretsu's" main bank; the deal closed in 2001. The group's Mitsui Trust and Banking merged with Chuo Trust and Banking to form Chuo Mitsui Trust and Banking part of Mitsui Trust Holdings.

Mitsui & Co. was implicated in bid-rigging and bribery scandals in 2002 and the company's chairman and CEO resigned. In 2003 the company moved into the German pesticide market by acquiring an 80% stake in Spiess-Urania Chemical a subsidiary of Norddeutsche Affinerie. Later that year it entered the biotechnology market by creating TM Cell Research a 35%-owned joint venture created with Toyobo. The company also entered the telecommunications market by acquiring a 30% stake in Shineedotcom from Shin Corp.

In 2003 Mitsui turned its focus back to the expansion of its current operations. The company acquired a 15% stake in Valepar a holding company of Brazilian-based iron ore producer Companhia Vale do Rio Doce. Mitsui and International Power completed the acquisition of the 1200 MW gasfired Saltend Power plant in the UK from Calpine Corporation. In 2005 Mitsui acquired a stake in Gas Participacqes (Gaspart) a Brazil-based gas distribution company.

To help pay down debt related to its purchase of Union Fenosa in 2009 Gas Natural sold power assets in Mexico to Mitsui and Tokyo Gas for $1.2 billion.

Mitsui sold its share of the TAMCO steel mini-mill joint venture to Gerdau Ameristeel in 2010 for about $40 million. Its other partners Ameron and Tokyo Steel also sold their shares in the project to Gerdau.

Eyeing opportunities in the North American gas market Mitsui in 2010 announced plans to invest $1.4 billion to develop a shale gas project in Pennsylvania with Anadarko Petroleum. It also teamed up with Penn West Energy Trust to form an $850-million natural-gas joint venture to develop an oil shale play in British Columbia.

Also in 2010 Mitsui teamed up with US fertilizer company Mosaic for a joint venture in a phosphorus ore development project in Peru. Mitsui will spend $275 million to acquire a 25% stake and voting rights in a subsidiary of Vale while Mosaic will hold a 24% stake. Mitsui is seeking to obtain a steady supply of phosphate which is used in its fertilizer production operations.

Mitsui entered the water infrastructure business in China in 2010 through a 50-50 joint venture with Singapore's Hyflux Ltd. a major provider of integrated water management services. Mitsui plans to do business with local governments and in areas with many industrial complexes by leveraging Hyflux's technological expertise and its own business network.

EXECUTIVES

Chairman, Shoei Utsuda, age 71
Corporate Auditor, Satoru Miura, age 67
Representative Director; EVP, Ken Abe, age 65
EVP CFO and Representative Director, Junichi Matsumoto, age 66
EVP; COO Asia/Pacific Business Unit, Toshimasa Furukawa, age 65
Corporate Auditor, Motonori Murakami, age 65
Senior Executive Managing Officer; COO EMEA Business Unit, Koji Nakamura, age 66
Managing Officer; President Mitsui & Co. (Canada), Terukazu Okahashi
President and CEO, Masami Iijima, age 64
EVP, Seiichi Tanaka, age 62
Senior Executive Managing Officer; COO Americas Business Unit; President and CEO Mitsui USA, Masaaki Fujita
Managing Officer; Deputy COO Americas Business Unit, Katsumi Ogawa
Representative Director; Senior Executive Managing Officer Energy Business Unit I; Energy Business Unit II; Financial Markets Business Unit; Domestic Offices and Branches; Chairman of Environment and New Energy Committee, Norinao Iio, age 63
Senior Executive Managing Officer and CFO, Joji Okada, age 76
Managing Officer; COO Foods & Retail Business Unit, Takashi Fukunaga
Senior Managing Executive Officer, Takashi Yamauchi
Managing Officer; COO IT Business Unit, Shuji Nakura
Managing Executive Officer; Chief Director of America, Mitsuhiko Kawai
Senior Executive Managing Officer, Daisuke Saiga, age 59
Senior Executive Managing Officer CIO and Chief Privacy Officer, Masayuki Kinoshita
Executive Managing Officer; Chief Representative Mitsui & Co. Ltd. China, Atsushi Oi
Representative Director; Senior Executive Managing Officer Infrastructure Projects Business Unit; Motor Vehicles Business Unit; Consumer Service Business Unit; IT Business Unit, Takao Omae, age 64
Representative Director; Senior Executive Managing Officer Iron & Steel Products Business Unit; Marine & Aerospace Business Unit; and Foods & Retail Business Unit, Masayoshi Komai, age 65
Executive Managing Officer; Deputy COO EMEA Business Unit, Noriaki Sakamoto
EVP, Fuminobu Kawashima
Executive Officer; Vice President of Kansai Office, Katsunori Aikyo
Managing Executive Officer; President of Subsidiary, Makoto Suzuki
Senior Executive Managing Officer, Shintaro Ambe
Representative Director; EVP, Ken Abe, age 65
EVP CFO and Representative Director, Junichi Matsumoto, age 66
Director, Toshiro Muto, age 71
President CEO and Representative Director, Masami Iijima, age 63
EVP CIO Chief Privacy Officer and Representative Director, Seiichi Tanaka, age 61
Director, Ikujiro Nonaka, age 79
Director, Hiroshi Hirabayashi, age 74
Director, Nobuko Matsubara, age 74
Representative Director; Senior Executive Managing Officer Energy Business Unit I; Energy Business Unit II; Financial Markets Business Unit; Domestic Offices and Branches; Chairman of Environment and New Energy Committee, Norinao Iio, age 63

Representative Director; Executive Managing Officer and Chief Compliance Officer, Daisuke Saiga, age 59
Representative Director; Senior Executive Managing Officer Infrastructure Projects Business Unit; Motor Vehicles Business Unit; Consumer Service Business Unit; IT Business Unit, Takao Omae, age 64
Representative Director; Senior Executive Managing Officer Iron & Steel Products Business Unit; Marine & Aerospace Business Unit; and Foods & Retail Business Unit, Masayoshi Komai, age 65
Auditors: DeloitteToucheTohmatsu

LOCATIONS

HQ: Mitsui & Co., Ltd.
2-1 Ohtemachi 1-chome, Chiyoda-ku, Tokyo 100-0004
Phone: (81) 3 3285 1111   **Fax:** (81) 3 3285 9821
Web: www.mitsui.com

COMPETITORS

ITOCHU	Mitsubishi Corp.
Kanematsu	Samsung Group
Komatsu	Sojitz
Marubeni	Sumitomo

HISTORICAL FINANCIALS
Company Type: Public

Income Statement
FYE: March 31

	REVENUE ($ mil.)	NET INCOME ($ mil.)	NET PROFIT MARGIN	EMPLOYEES
03/14	55,531	3,391	6.1%	48,090
03/13	52,200	3,272	6.3%	61,898
03/12	64,020	5,296	8.3%	64,218
03/11	56,510	3,703	6.6%	59,404
03/10	43,855	1,602	3.7%	60,961
Annual Growth	6.1%	20.6%	—	(5.8%)

2014 Year-End Financials

Debt ratio: 0.3%	No. of shares (mil.): 1,792
Return on equity: 10.0%	Dividends
Cash ($ mil.): 11,880	Yield: 3.2%
Current ratio: 1.50	Payout: 0.0%
Long-term debt ($ mil.): 33,601	Market value ($ mil.): 505,656

	STOCK PRICE ($) FY Close	P/E High/Low		PER SHARE ($) Earnings	Dividends	Book Value
03/14	282.07	0	0	1.86	9.11	20.62
03/13	279.00	0	0	1.79	0.00	18.53
03/12	330.63	0	0	2.90	0.00	17.64
03/11	359.10	0	0	2.03	7.20	15.66
03/10	335.71	0	0	0.88	1.58	13.08
Annual Growth	(4.3%)	—	—	20.6%	54.9%	12.0%

Mitsui Life Insurance Co., Ltd.

LOCATIONS

HQ: Mitsui Life Insurance Co., Ltd.
1-1-20 Aomi, Koto-ku, Tokyo 135-8222
Phone: (81) 3 6831 8000
Web: www.mitsui-seimei.co.jp

HISTORICAL FINANCIALS
Company Type: Public

Income Statement
FYE: March 31

	ASSETS ($ mil.)	NET INCOME ($ mil.)	INCOME AS % OF ASSETS	EMPLOYEES
03/14	69,986	125	0.2%	10,259
03/13	76,823	81	0.1%	11,552
03/12	87,382	167	0.2%	12,118
03/11	87,242	171	0.2%	12,610
03/10	80,300	49	0.1%	13,868
Annual Growth	(3.4%)	26.3%	—	(7.3%)

2014 Year-End Financials

Return on assets: 0.1%	Dividends
Return on equity: 3.9%	Yield: —
Long-term debt ($ mil.): —	Payout: —
No. of shares (mil.): 278	Market value ($ mil.): —
Sales ($ mil): 8,558	

Mizrahi Tefahot Bank Ltd

Mizrahi Tefahot Bank one of Israel's largest banks offers a variety of international commercial domestic and personal banking services. It also commands more than 40% of the country's mortgage market. Subsidiaries provide financial services including portfolio and fund management and capital market advice. The bank has more than 125 domestic branches and representative offices in the US Switzerland Germany the UK Mexico and the Cayman Islands. The bank was created in 2004 after the merger of United Mizrahi Bank and subsidiary Tefahot Israel Mortgage Bank. The Ofer and Wertheim families control approximately 46% of Mizrahi Tefahot's shares.

Mizrahi Tefahot has been working to grow its customer base. It improved its position in the retail market and expanded its branch network when it bought a 50% stake in Bank Yahav from Bank Hapoalim in 2008. The remaining shares of the Bank Yahav which caters to government employees is held by the government and the Culture & Economic Projects for State Workers. Also in 2008 Mizrahi Tefahot received an option to buy 10% of Israel Credit Cards-Cal. As part of the deal ICC-Cal will begin issuing Mizrahi-Tefahot brand credit cards.

LOCATIONS

HQ: Mizrahi Tefahot Bank Ltd
7 Jabotinsky Street, P.O. Box 3450, Ramat Gan 5252007
Phone: (972) 3 7559000   **Fax:** (972) 3 7559210
Web: www.mizrahi-tefahot.co.il

PRODUCTS/OPERATIONS

Sales by Segment

	% of total
Retail (mortgages small business and private	67
Corporate (commercial and business	25
Financial (financial	8
Total	**100**

Income Statement

FYE: December 31

	ASSETS ($ mil.)	NET INCOME ($ mil.)	INCOME AS % OF ASSETS	EMPLOYEES
12/13	51,761	310	0.6%	5,827
12/12	43,527	288	0.7%	5,670
12/11	39,300	273	0.7%	5,518
12/10	37,608	226	0.6%	5,252
12/09	31,348	140	0.4%	5,156
Annual Growth	13.4%	22.0%	—	3.1%

2013 Year-End Financials

Return on assets: 0.6%
Return on equity: 11.5%
Long-term debt ($ mil.): —
No. of shares (mil.): 23
Sales ($ mil): 2,288

Dividends
  Yield: —
  Payout: 6.6%
Market value ($ mil.): —

Monte dei Paschi di Siena (Italy)

The city of Siena knows its way around a horse race –and also the world of banking. It's the home to one of Italy's largest banks Banca Monte dei Paschi di Siena (BMPS) which provides consumer business and other banking services to 6 million clients through more than 3000 branches throughout the country. BMPS also has limited operations in several other nations. The bank which claims to be the oldest in the world was founded in 1472 to help the poor. It is split into a public institution (chiefly active in benevolent works grants and public assistance) and the incorporated banking arm (focused on profits). The Fondazione Monte dei Paschi owns about 49% of the bank but controls some 60% of it.

BMPS in 2008 announced restructuring plans under which banking subsidiaries Banca Agricola Mantovana Banca Antonveneta and Banca Toscana would be integrated into the group. Banca Agricola Mantovana which operated some 300 branches in northeastern Italy was absorbed in September 2008. The integration of Banca Antonveneta acquired from Banco Santander in 2008 followed shortly after. Finally the group absorbed Banca Toscana which operated more than 400 branches (mostly in Tuscany and Umbria) in early 2009.

Other bank holdings include shares in Banca Monte Parma and Banca Popolare di Spoleto. In 2007 BMPS bought a majority stake in Cassa di Risparmio di Biella e Varcelli (Biverbanca) which operates about 100 branches. BMPS opened more than 100 new branches and offices in 2007 and 2008 and plans to open more over the next several years.

While the company has expanded its retail and banking business it has streamlined its foreign network and by simplifying its structure reduced administrative costs. It spun off two-thirds of its asset management subsidiaries (now jointly owned by Italian fund manager Clessidra) to further emphasize its focus on commercial banking; the move also allows the group to minimize conflicts of interest from being both distributor and producer. In 2007 it sold most of its 25% stake in Finsoe the holding company for insurer Unipol .

BMPS itself is frequently touted as a potential acquisition target in Italy's consolidating banking industry.

International growth targets include China where the bank has several representative offices –one of which it is converting to a branch office. Other focus areas include southeastern Europe northern Africa and India.

HISTORY

And the Rockefellers think they come from old money!

In 1472 Monte di Pieta was founded by the courts of the State of Siena with the mission of offering banking services to people hard hit by local economic conditions. Soon after the bank increased its array of services. In 1624 the bank's nature was transformed through legal and political developments. The State of Siena was absorbed into the Grand Duchy of Tuscany and Grand Duke Ferdinando II of Tuscany stepped forward to guarantee the bank's deposits. The bank took the name Banca Monte dei Paschi di Siena (BMPS) the same year.

Following the unification of Italy in 1861 the bank continued its geographical and financial expansion offering more services along the way. After WWI BMPS helped merge Credito Toscano with Banca di Firenze to create Banca Toscana.

In 1936 BMPS through a new law was declared a public credit institute. Such an arrangement endured until 1995 when the Treasury Ministry split BMPS into two entities: BMPS a public lending institution and BMPS S.p.A. The former retained the original mission of providing public assistance as well as funding for scientific research and artistic educational and health projects with an emphasis on Siena and its surrounding region. The latter inherited the for-profit operations which by 1995 included finance and insurance divisions. The move also positioned BMPS to survive the free trade zone created among EU member nations allowing the sizable BMPS to take advantage of the provincial and fragmented state of Italian banking.

Given the license to increase its for-profit activities BMPS wasted no time in restructuring its brittle operations and snapping up shares of other Italian banks. Between 1995 and 1999 BMPS sold off its control of MPS Australia and Spain-based Sindibank integrated its information systems and incorporated its once-separate leasing and factoring operations. At the same time BMPS took minority shares in Banca Popolare di Spoleto Banca Monte Parma and Cassa di Risparmio di San Miniato. Its 1999 acquisition of Banca Agricola Mantovana helped reinforce its presence in northern Italy.

In 2000 BMPS bought the majority of Banca del Salento changed its name to Banca 121 and expanded its telephone-based banking services. The buying spree continued the following year with the acquisition of Florence-based Banca Steinhauslin and a stake in Finsoe the holding company for insurer Unipol.

LOCATIONS

HQ: Monte dei Paschi di Siena (Italy)
Piazza Salimbeni 3, Siena I-53100
Phone: (39) 0577 294111   **Fax:** (39) 0577 294313

PRODUCTS/OPERATIONS

Sales

	% of total
Commercial	56
Corporate banking & capital	28
Corporate	10
Private banking & wealth	6
Total	**100**

Income Statement

FYE: December 31

	ASSETS ($ mil.)	NET INCOME ($ mil.)	INCOME AS % OF ASSETS	EMPLOYEES
12/13	274,116	(1,981)	—	28,417
12/12	288,497	(4,178)	—	30,265
12/11	311,336	(6,060)	—	31,170
12/10	326,936	1,318	0.4%	31,495
12/09	323,861	317	0.1%	32,003
Annual Growth	(4.1%)	—	—	(2.9%)

2013 Year-End Financials

Return on assets: (-0.6%)
Return on equity: (-22.8%)
Long-term debt ($ mil.): —
No. of shares (mil.): —
Sales ($ mil): 11,286

Dividends
  Yield: —
  Payout: —
Market value ($ mil.): —

Morrison (Wm.) Supermarkets Plc

Wm Morrison Supermarkets moved up the UK food chain with the acquisition of its larger rival Safeway plc. The UK's fourth-largest grocery chain Morrison runs about 475 stores throughout England and Scotland up from just 125 when it beat out UK supermarket giants Tesco (the UK's #1 food retailer) and Wal-Mart-owned ASDA in a highly-contested takeover battle. Morrison's supermarkets offer a variety of food and nonfood items most notably through its Market Street specialty departments. About 300 of the locations sell gas. The Safeway purchase transformed Wm Morrison into a national chain with about a 13% share of the UK grocery market. Wm Morrison was founded by its namesake in 1899.

Morrison has been a good steady performer in recent years despite the recession government austerity measures and continued fierce price competition among grocery chains in the UK. In fiscal 2012 (ends January) its sales increased by 7% helped by the addition of 37 new stores including the company's first three convenience stores. The 7% rise followed a similar 7% increase and 6% increase in fiscal years 2011 and 2010 respectively. The launch of its new M savers brand for budget conscious shoppers helped drive sales despite a tough economic backdrop.

As England's fourth-largest chain Morrison feels it has plenty of room to grow. With shops ranging in size from 11000 to more than 40000 sq. ft. it can be flexible when selecting sites. It is also growing by making acquisitions. To that end in early 2011 Morrison acquired 16 former Netto UK stores from rival ASDA which recently bought the Netto chain. Morrison paid some Â28 million ($44 million) for the stores the first of which began trading under the Morrison banner in May. The 16 Netto conversions accounted for nearly half the new stores opened in fiscal 2012. To boost the flower offering in its supermarkets the grocer in mid-2011 acquired flower importer and distributor Flower World.

Under CEO Dalton Philips who joined the business from Loblaw in Canada in 2010 Morrison has made some interesting moves. It opened its first convenience stores –under the M local banner –in 2011 and is finally set to launch an online offering in 2012. (Morrison is the only major UK supermarket without an online business.) To this end in February 2011 it acquired Kiddicare a multichannel online retailer of baby products for GBP70 million ($112 million). Morrison plans to run the company separately and leverage Kiddicare's technology platform and management team. Soon after Morrison bought a 10% stake in the US online grocer Fresh Direct. The Å35 million ($56 million) investment will give Morrison access to Fresh Direct's profitable model and help the UK grocer develop its own online food offering which is slated to debut shortly and will target Londoners. Morrison will take on Ocado and Waitrose in the online space.

Morrison has steadily increased its share of the UK grocery market from just under 12% in 2007 to 12.8% in fiscal 2012. The chain is strongest in Yorkshire with a 22% share of the market in the North and in Scotland where is claims in excess of 16% of the market. Morrison's focus on its instore specialty shops known as Market Street has boosted meat bakery pre-packed fresh food and convenience food sales. To compete with discounters including rival ASDA and limited assortment ALDI and appeal to cash-strapped shoppers the firm has been cutting thousands of prices despite its own rising costs. While nonfood items account for a small percentage of overall sales Morrison is looking to expand its general merchandise offering by adding clothing and other goods. To that end it has begun adding Peacocks concessions to some of its larger stores.

The chain is known as the master of small to medium-sized supermarkets as most of the company's stores fall into the 25000-to-40000 sq. ft. range. The shops are noted for their Market Street departments a collection of in-store specialty shops that ring the perimeter of the store. They include a bakery butcher shop and deli. Market Street departments also offer pizza pies and curry. Outlets also have in-store cafes. Morrison is vertically integrated including operating facilities for processing packing and distributing meat and produce. Its Farmers Boy unit supplies its stores with fresh food including pizzas cooked meats and other prepared foods. It also operates three bakeries. Morrison is one of the UK's top food producers.

HISTORY

A former grocer's apprentice William Morrison founded his company in Bradford UK in 1899 as a wholesale seller of eggs and butter. Named William Morrison (Provisions) the business eventually expanded into retail by opening grocery stalls and by the 1920s was operating counter service shops as well.

Self-service stores became popular in the UK during the late 1940s and 1950s and the company began opening self-service outlets during that time. William's son Ken (born when William was 57 years of age) joined the company in 1950 and became chairman in 1956. The chain opened its first supermarket in Bradford in 1962 by converting an abandoned cinema. Wm Morrison Supermarkets went public five years later.

In 1979 Wm Morrison moved into Lancashire by purchasing the 10-store grocery chain Whelans Discount founded by Dave Whelan an ex-football star who also founded JJB Sports. Two years later it bought the Mainstop chain. The company's sales grew by a factor of 10 during the 1980s and 1990; it added about 50 stores in the 1990s. In 1993 Wm Morrison began opening stores on Sundays and in 1997 it teamed up with Midland Bank to offer in-store banking.

The company had operated mostly in northeastern England but a new distribution center that opened in 1996 in Cheshire allowed it to handle

more distribution duties and gave it the base to expand west. Wm Morrison also turned south opening superstores in three southern regions (Oxford Essex and Kent) in 1998. The retailer also acquired two stores from Food Giant and three superstores (one near London) from Co-operative Retail Services that year. Wm Morrison expanded its Farmers Boy food processing operations by opening a new 180000-sq.-ft. facility in 1999. It opened four new stores in 2000 and bought three others.

The company's highly regarded Managing Director John Dowd resigned in March 2002 because of ill health. Soon after Marie Melnyk and Robert Stott were promoted to the positions of joint managing director. Morrison added six stores in fiscal year 2003 (ended January 2003).

On January 9 2003 Morrison made an offer of 1.32 Morrison shares for each share of Safeway plc. In March the company's bid for its rival lapsed after the Office of Fair Trading referred the bid to the Competition Commission.

Following clearance from Britain's High Court the company's acquisition of Safeway closed on March 8 2004. (Morrison shareholders own 60% of the enlarged company with Safeway shareholders left with 40%.)

In June 2006 the company named Marc Bolland formerly COO of brewer Heineken as CEO succeeding Bob Stott who retired. Stott became CEO in 2005.

Sir Kenneth Morrison retired as chairman in March 2008 after 55 years with the company. Morrison who was named honorary president was succeeded by former deputy chairman Sir Ian Gibson. The grocery chain opened eight new supermarkets in fiscal 2008.

In 2009 Morrisons acquired about 40 Co-operative Group and former Somerfield stores for about Å220 million (about $330 million). In November Bolland resigned to join Marks and Spencer. He was succeeded by Dalton Philips who joined the business in March 2010.

In 2011 Morrisons acquired about 18 Netto UK stores from ASDA. In June it bought Flower World an importer and wholesaler of flowers in the UK in a bid to improve the flower offering at its supermarkets.

EXECUTIVES

Manufacturing Director, M. Fletcher
Corporate Services Director, Martyn Jones, age 55, $679,235 total compensation
Retail Projects Director, P. J. Pleasance
Trades Specialist Director, T. Robinson
Regional Director, A. Downey
Public Relations Director, G. Hall
Group Retail Director, Mark D. Harrison
Security Director, A. Hudson
Construction Director, D. N. Wade
Chairman, Sir Ian Gibson, age 67, $596,880 total compensation
Group Finance Director and Director, Richard Pennycook, age 50, $1,076,374 total compensation
Marketing Director, M. Bates
Regional Director, S. Eastwood
Regional Director, David Gardner
Regional Director, I. Grace
Purchasing Director, K. L. Johnson
Stores Director (South), C. Taylor
MIS Director, G. Barr
Managing Director Morrisons.com, Simon Thompson
Chief Executive; Executive Director, Dalton T. Philips, age 46
Logistics Director, Neal Austin
Corporate Affairs Director, Richard Taylor
Licensed Trades Director, Grant Eastwood

Director Investor Relations and Financial Planning, Niall Addison
Secretary, Greg McMahon
Human Resources Director, Norman Pickavance
Group Property Director, Terry Hartwell
Corporate Services Director, Martyn Jones, age 55
Director, Philip G. Cox, age 63
Director, Penelope L. (Penny) Hughes, age 55
Group Finance Director and Director, Richard Pennycook, age 50
Director, Nigel Robertson, age 54
Director, Brian Flanagan, age 61
Director, Johanna Waterous, age 56
Auditors: KPMGAuditPlc

LOCATIONS

HQ: Morrison (Wm.) Supermarkets Plc
  Hilmore House, Gain Lane, Bradford BD3 7DL
Phone: (44) 845 611 5000
Web: www.morrisons.co.uk

PRODUCTS/OPERATIONS

Sales

	% of total
Food & general	76
Fuel	23
Total	**100**

COMPETITORS

ALDI	John Lewis
ASDA	Marks & Spencer
Alliance Boots	Musgrave Retail
BP	Partners
Co-operative Group	Royal Dutch Shell
Exxon Mobil	SPAR (UK)
J Sainsbury	Tesco

HISTORICAL FINANCIALS

Company Type: Public

Income Statement

FYE: February 2

	REVENUE ($ mil.)	NET INCOME ($ mil.)	NET PROFIT MARGIN	EMPLOYEES
02/14	29,105	(391)	—	127,403
02/13*	28,681	1,024	3.6%	128,705
01/12	27,743	1,083	3.9%	131,207
01/11	26,247	1,006	3.8%	132,074
01/10	24,629	955	3.9%	133,744
Annual Growth	**4.3%**	—	—	**(1.2%)**

*Fiscal year change

2014 Year-End Financials

Debt ratio: 46.5%
Return on equity: (-4.8%)
Cash ($ mil.): 429
Current ratio: 0.50
Long-term debt ($ mil.): 4,082

No. of shares (mil.): —
Dividends
  Yield: 0.0%
  Payout: —
Market value ($ mil.): —

	STOCK PRICE ($) FY Close	P/E High/Low		PER SHARE ($) Earnings	Dividends	Book Value
02/14	19.81	—	—	(0.17)	2.24	3.31
02/13*	19.74	231	186	0.42	2.02	3.53
01/12	22.89	244	194	0.41	2.20	3.35
01/11	20.97	257	178	0.37	1.42	3.25
01/10	23.59	293	158	0.36	1.14	2.98
Annual Growth	**(4.3%)**	—	—	—	**18.4%**	**2.6%**

*Fiscal year change

MS&AD Insurance Group Holdings

LOCATIONS

HQ: MS&AD Insurance Group Holdings
1-3-7 Yaesu, Chuo-ku, Tokyo 103-0028
Phone: (81) 3 6202 5270
Web: www.ms-ad-hd.com

HISTORICAL FINANCIALS

Company Type: Public

Income Statement

FYE: March 31

	REVENUE ($ mil.)	NET INCOME ($ mil.)	NET PROFIT MARGIN	EMPLOYEES
03/14	42,171	905	2.1%	37,055
03/13	45,785	888	1.9%	36,643
03/12	45,775	(2,065)	—	36,929
03/11	40,878	65	0.2%	36,538
03/10	20,903	402	1.9%	21,908
Annual Growth	**19.2%**	**22.4%**	**—**	**14.0%**

2014 Year-End Financials

Debt ratio: 0.0%
Return on equity: 4.3%
Cash ($ mil.): 14,393
Current ratio: 0.19
Long-term debt ($ mil.): 2,191

No. of shares (mil.): 619
Dividends
Yield: 2.4%
Payout: —
Market value ($ mil.): 7,055

	STOCK PRICE ($) FY Close	P/E High/Low	PER SHARE ($) Earnings	Dividends	Book Value
03/14	11.38	— —	1.46	0.27	35.72
03/13	11.02	— —	1.43	0.00	34.55
03/12	10.26	— —	(3.32)	0.00	29.64
03/11	11.27	— —	0.10	0.31	31.72
03/10	13.77	— —	0.96	0.29	33.83
Annual Growth	**(4.7%)**	**— —**	**11.0%**	**(1.8%)**	**1.4%**

Muenchener Rueckversicherungs-Gesellschaft AG (Germany)

Some companies live with risk... Monchener Rockversicherungs-Gesellschaft (Munich Re) on the other hand "thrives" on risk. Reinsurance coverage (insurance for insurers) includes fire life motor and liability policies on both a facultative (individual risk) and treaty (categorized risk) basis. The company also provides direct insurance including life health and property coverage through Germany-based ERGO and other subsidiaries and it provides asset management services through MEAG MUNICH ERGO. Through Munich Re America Munich Re enjoys greater access to the US market. As one of the world's largest reinsurance and risk management firms the company operates in some 160 countries.

Geographic Reach

Europe is Munich Re's biggest market (accounting for about 55% of premiums in 2011) and the company has expanded its European presence over the years through acquisitions and internal growth programs. North America is the second-largest market accounting for about 30% of premiums (up from 25% in 2010 due to acquisitions and organic growth in the US).

Operations

Munich Re's reinsurance and primary insurance segments respectively account for about 50% and 40% of annual premiums. After focused growth efforts in the primary insurance segment the ERGO division has grown to insure clients in 30 countries in Europe and Asia.

The company's health insurance operations are handled through the company's Deutsche Krankenversicherung unit (DKV a subsidiary of ERGO) in Germany and through the Munich Health division (which also holds Munich Re's health reinsurance operations) in international countries. The MEAG asset management unit holds some E200 billion ($260 billion) in investments.

Financial Performance

Munich Re reported E61 billion ($79 billion) in revenues in 2011 down 7% from results in 2010. Net income was E712 million ($922 million) down 71%.

Munich Re suffered a significant natural catastrophe loss (estimated at some E1.5 billion or $2.1 billion) in the first quarter of 2011 due to the earthquake and tsunami that struck Japan in March. The subsequent damage to the Japanese infrastructure led to one of the largest levels of commercial coverage claims for Munich Re. The firm also experienced high catastrophe losses in 2010; however such losses are part and parcel for reinsurance companies who rely on the less-disastrous years to even out those creating heavy burdens.

Strategy

Though reinsurance is its largest operating segment the company hopes to continue the growth of its traditional insurance segment in the core German market and other European markets focusing on personal lines. As part of this strategy the company is widening the presence of the ERGO brand across its insurance operations in its European markets (especially in Germany).

Additionally Munich Re is working to extend the ERGO brand into new markets especially in emerging markets in Eastern Europe and parts of Asia. In 2011 ERGO formed a joint venture with Assets Investment Holding to sell life insurance in China; it also entered the Vietnamese market that year. However ERGO has also been selling off select international operations in noncore markets; it exited operations in Portugal and South Korea in 2011 and 2012.

In the North American market Munich Re is expanding in the specialty property/casualty and health insurance markets primarily through acquisitions. It is also working to expand its presence in the growing health care insurance arena in emerging markets like India.

Mergers and Acquisitions

To expand its global health insurance operations in 2011 Munich Re's Munich Health North America division acquired Windsor Health Group a US provider of Medicare services for some $131 million.

Ownership

Billionaire investment mogul Warren Buffett who controls a number of insurance and reinsurance players through Berkshire Hathaway has taken notice of Munich Re. Buffett increased his stake in the company to 10% in 2010.

HISTORY

Investors Carl Thieme and Theodor Cramer-Klett founded Munich Re in 1880. Within a month Munich Re opened offices in Hamburg Berlin Vienna and St. Petersburg establishing treaties with German and Danish insurers. In 1888 Munich Re went public; two years later it opened an office in London and helped finance the creation of Allianz which would soon come to dominate the German insurance industry. In 1892 the firm opened a branch in the US (it incurred severe losses from the 1906 San Francisco earthquake).

WWI interrupted Munich Re's UK and US operations. The company recovered after 1918 only to be hobbled again by the Great Depression. In 1933 Munich Re executive Kurt Schmitt became minister of economic affairs for the Nazis. Objecting to the evolving policies of National Socialism he left after a year returning to Munich Re where he became chief executive in 1938.

Hitler's ignition of WWII wasn't quite the boom Munich Re needed; its international business was again disrupted. After the war the Allies further limited overseas operations. Because of his involvement with the Nazi government Schmitt was replaced by Eberhard von Reininghaus in 1945. The division of Germany further hampered the company's recovery.

Jump-started by the Marshall Plan in 1950 the West German "Wirtschaftswunder" (economic miracle) kicked into high gear as the devastated country rebuilt. Relaxation of occupation-era trading limits also helped as the company rebuilt its foreign business. By 1969 Munich Re's sales topped DM 2 billion. Amid the global oil crisis and a rash of terrorist acts in Germany the firm reported its first-ever reinsurance loss in 1977.

German reunification in 1990 provided new markets for Munich Re but advantages from new business in the East were wiped out by claims arising from that year's harsh winter.

In 1992 an investigation by the German Federal Cartel Office prompted a realignment in the insurance business —Allianz ceded its controlling interests in three life insurers (Hamburg-Mannheimer Versicherungs Karlsruher Lebensversicherung and Berlinische Lebensversicherung) to Munich Re bringing it into direct insurance. Munich Re took over Deutsche Krankenversicherung (DKV) in 1996. Also that year Munich Re acquired American Re.

During the 1990s reinsurance sales dwindled as competition increased forcing lower premiums and alternatives to insurance and reinsurance became more common. Munich Re looked to direct insurance particularly individual property/casualty and life insurance to compensate. In 1997 it merged Hamburg-Mannheimer and DKV with another insurer Victoria AG to form ERGO Versicherungsgruppe. Within a year ERGO's insurance income accounted for half of all revenues.

Munich Re and ERGO launched asset management firm MEAG Munich ERGO AssetManagement in 1999. That year Munich Re experienced its worst year ever after natural disasters hit its reinsurance business hard. To recoup its losses the next year the firm expanded both its reinsurance and primary insurance operations into key markets in Europe North and South America and Asia. Also in 2000 Munich Re bought CNA Financial's life reinsurance operations. Together with Swiss Re the company launched Inreon an online reinsurance exchange in 2001.

As one of the companies hit hardest financially by the World Trade Center tragedy Munich Re paid out some $2 billion in claims. In 2003 Allianz and Munich Re terminated their cooperation agreement as their shareholdings in each other fell to under 15%. (The two companies gradually sold off nearly all of their ownership interests in following years.)

In 2004 Munich Re entered its first Asian market by forming a joint venture in China.

In 2005 Munich Re took a nearly 75% hit on its profit margin due to re-investment in its American Re subsidiary whose internal reserves required a $1.6 billion injection for expected claims related to asbestos and environmental claims on policies mostly written between 1997 and 2002. The firm also suffered a large natural catastrophe loss that year due to Hurricane Katrina's devastating effects on the US Gulf Coast; Munich Re paid some $1.6 billion in claims as a result of the disaster.

The company expanded in the European market in 2007 when it bought British underwriting management group Bell & Clements Group in an effort to bolster its bottom line with profit-making basic services. It also purchased MSP Underwriting UK parent of Lloyd's Syndicate 318 manager Beaufort Underwriting Agency.

To further its US property/casualty operations in 2008 the company acquired US specialty insurance provider The Midland Company for $1.3 billion; Midland's American Modern Insurance Group subsidiaries became part of the Munich Re America organization. Munich Re also bought Aon subsidiary Sterling Life Insurance for $352 million to expand its life and health insurance provisions in the US. Sterling Life became part of the newly formed Munich Health unit in 2009.

In 2009 Munich Re America expanded again by purchasing specialty insurance and reinsurance provider HSB Group from American International Group for $739 million in cash (plus $76 million in debt assumptions). The acquisition expanded Munich Re's niche insurance and risk management offerings in North America.

The company launched a re-branding program in 2009 to increase the presence of its ERGO brand across its insurance operations included the retiring of some older German monikers and in 2010 a widespread marketing program was launched to make the ERGO brand more familiar to German consumers.

EXECUTIVES

Member Board of Management Chairman Reinsurance Committee, Torsten Jeworrek, age 53, $791,580 total compensation

Member Board of Management Europe and Latin America, Georg Daschner, age 65, $699,152 total compensation

Head Group Communications, Christian Lawrence

Member Board of Management Services Germany Asia/Pacific and Africa, Ludger Arnoldussen, age 52, $588,760 total compensation

Member Board of Management Special and Financial Risks Reinsurance Investments and Central Procurement, Thomas Blunck, $571,678 total compensation

Member Board of Management Health and Human Resources and Labor Relations Director, Wolfgang Strassl, age 57, $571,678 total compensation

Spokesperson US; VP and Head Marketing Communications Munich Reinsurance America, Terese Rosenthal

Member Board of Management Global Clients and North America, Peter Roder, age 54, $462,630 total compensation

Member Board of Management Life, Joachim Wenning, age 49, $300,000 total compensation

Head Media Relations, Johanna Weber
Deputy Head Media Relations, Michael Able
Media Relations Solvency II and Human Resources, Irmgard Joas

Media Relations Reinsurance Life Munich Health Primary Insurance Issues Munich Re (Group), Regine Kaiser
Media Relations Reinsurance Property, Anke Rosumek
Spokesperson Asia, Nikola Kemper
Chief Financial Officer, Greg Guelfand
Chief Risk Officer, Joachim Oechslin
President Chief Executive Officer, Kenneth B. Irvin
President Chief Executive Officer, Mary Forrest
Chief Executive Officer, Peter Goschl
Executive Director Chairman, Tony Medniuk
Head of Investor & Rating Agency Relations, Christian Christian Becker-Hussong Becker-Hussong
Deputy Chairman of the Supervisory Board; Employee Representative, Hans Hans Claussen Claussen
Chairman of the Management Board; Chief Investment Officer, Nikolaus Nikolaus von Bomhard Bomhard
Member of the Management Board, Peter Peter Roeder Roeder
Chief Financial Officer, Jorg Schneider
Member Supervisory Board, Wolfgang Mayrhuber, age 67
Member Supervisory Board, Thomas Wellauer, age 58
Member Supervisory Board, Ron Sommer, age 65
Member Supervisory Board, Herbert Bach
Member Supervisory Board, Henning Kagermann, age 67
Member Supervisory Board, Anton van Rossum, age 69
Member Supervisory Board, Bernd Pischetsrieder
Member Supervisory Board, Peter Loscher, age 56
Deputy Chairman Supervisory Board, Hans-Peter Clau?en
Member Supervisory Board, Frank Fassin
Member Supervisory Board, Reinhard Pasch
Member Supervisory Board, Richard Sommer
Member Supervisory Board, Peter Gruss, age 65
Member Supervisory Board, Dina Bosch
Member Supervisory Board, Christian Fuhrmann
Member Supervisory Board, Silvia Muller
Member Supervisory Board, Marco Norenberg
Member Supervisory Board, Andres Ruiz Feger
Supervisory Board Member, Benita Ferrero-Waldner, age 66
Member of the Supervisory Board; Employee Representative, Andres Andres Ruiz Feger Feger
Member of the Supervisory Board, Annika Annika Falkengren Falkengren
Member of the Supervisory Board, Anton Anton van Rossum Rossum
Member of the Supervisory Board; Employee Representative, Dina Dina Boesch Boesch
Member of the Supervisory Board; Employee Representative, Marco Marco Noerenberg Noerenberg
Member of the Supervisory Board, Peter Peter Loescher Loescher
Member of the Supervisory Board; Employee Representative, Silvia Silvia Mueller Mueller
Auditors: KPMGBayerischeTreuhandgesellschaftAG

LOCATIONS

HQ: Muenchener Rueckversicherungs-Gesellschaft AG (Germany)
Koeniginstrasse 107, Munich D-80802
Phone: (49) 89 38 91 0   **Fax:** (49) 89 39 90 56
Web: www.munichre.com

2011 Premiums

	% of total
Europe	55
North	30
Asia &	10
Latin	3
Africa Near & Middle	2
Total	**100**

PRODUCTS/OPERATIONS

Sales

	% of total
Reinsurance	
Property/casualty	31
Life	17
Primary insurance	
Life	18
Health	13
Property/casualty	10
Munich	10
Asset	1
Total	**100**

Selected Brands

ERGO (primary insurance)
  Deutscher Automobil Schutz (D.A.S. auto insurance)
  Deutsche Krankenversicherung (DKV)
  ERV
ERGO Direkt (commercial customer consulting)
DKV (domestic health insurance)
Munich Health (international health insurance domestic and international health reinsurance)
Munich Re
Munich Re America
  American Modern Insurance (specialty property/casualty insurance life insurance reinsurance)
  Hartford Steam Boiler (HSB specialty property/casualty insurance and reinsurance)

COMPETITORS

ACE Limited	Manulife Financial
AEGON	MetLife
AIG	Nippon Life Insurance
AXA	OdysseyRe
Allianz	PartnerRe
Allstate	Prudential plc
Baloise-Holding	Reinsurance Group of
Berkshire Hathaway	America
Everest Re	RenaissanceRe
General Re	Swiss Re
Hannover Re	Transatlantic Holdings
Helvetia Group	XL Group plc
ING	

HISTORICAL FINANCIALS

Company Type: Public

Income Statement

	ASSETS ($ mil.)	NET INCOME ($ mil.)	INCOME AS % OF ASSETS	FYE: December 31 EMPLOYEES
12/13	350,087	4,561	1.3%	44,665
12/12	340,531	4,211	1.2%	45,437
12/11	320,232	908	0.3%	47,206
12/10	316,335	3,241	1.0%	46,915
12/09	321,840	3,631	1.1%	47,429
Annual Growth	**2.1%**	**5.9%**	**—**	**(1.5%)**

2013 Year-End Financials

Return on assets: 1.2%
Return on equity: 12.4%
Long-term debt ($ mil.): —
No. of shares (mil.): 179
Sales ($ mil): 88,627
Dividends
  Yield: 2.7%
  Payout: —
Market value ($ mil.): 3,988

	STOCK PRICE ($) FY Close	P/E High/Low		PER SHARE ($) Earnings	Dividends	Book Value
12/13	22.24	2	2	25.47	0.62	199.46
12/12	18.03	2	1	23.70	0.55	199.76
12/11	12.28	8	5	5.10	1.14	166.33
12/10	15.11	2	1	17.48	0.54	161.79
12/09	15.50	3	1	18.66	0.51	165.51
Annual Growth	**9.4%**	**—**	**—**	**8.1%**	**4.9%**	**4.8%**

Nanto Bank, Ltd.

The Nanto Bank primarily serves the Nara region of Japan. The bank operates from about 135 offices branches and other facilities located in the Hyogo Kyoto Mie Nara Osaka Tokyo and Wakayama areas of the country. Nanto Bank provides a selection of financial services including consumer banking credit card services securities leasing and lending. The bank traces its historical roots back to 1934. Major subsidiaries include Nanto Credit Guarantee Co. Nanto Lease co. Nanto Estate Co. Nanto Staff Service Co. and Nanto Investment Management Co.

Strategy

The Nanto Bank aims to increase its balance of loans deposits and assets by expanding its branch net work mainly through the establishment of new branches. In Osaka Prefecture identified as an important strategic area two new branches –the Eiwa branch and the Wakaeiwata branch –were built and opened in Higashiosaka City in September 2012. The company also opened in 2013 its Joto corporate business office and the Hokusetsu corporate business office with a plan to eventually developing these into branches.

EXECUTIVES

Chairman, Hiromune Nishiguchi
President, Yasuo Ueno
Senior Managing Director, Yasuo Shimakawa
Managing Director, Masaaki Hashimoto
Managing Director, Hiroki Matsuoka
Managing Director, Takashi Hashimoto
Managing Director, Kohsaku Yoshida
Managing Director, Yoshihiko Kita
Auditors: KPMGAZSA&Co.

LOCATIONS

HQ: Nanto Bank, Ltd.
16 Hashimoto-cho, Nara 630-8677
Phone: (81) 742 22 1131
Web: www.nantobank.co.jp

COMPETITORS

Aozora Bank	Shizuoka Bank
Kiyo Bank	Towa Bank
Mitsubishi UFJ	
Financial Group	

HISTORICAL FINANCIALS

Company Type: Public

Income Statement

FYE: March 31

	ASSETS ($ mil.)	NET INCOME ($ mil.)	INCOME AS % OF ASSETS	EMPLOYEES
03/14	50,254	87	0.2%	2,866
03/13	53,405	81	0.2%	2,889
03/12	58,631	42	0.1%	2,928
03/11	55,654	79	0.1%	2,882
03/10	48,912	78	0.2%	2,836
Annual Growth	0.7%	3.0%	—	0.3%

2014 Year-End Financials

Return on assets: 0.1%	Dividends
Return on equity: 4.3%	Yield: —
Long-term debt ($ mil.): —	Payout: —
No. of shares (mil.): 268	Market value ($ mil.): —
Sales ($ mil): 801	

National Australia Bank Ltd.

National Australia Bank (NAB) is one of Australia's Big Four banks (along with ANZ Westpac and Commonwealth Bank of Australia). It operates in Australia New Zealand Asia the UK and the US through subsidiaries that provide banking wealth management and investment banking services. NAB also offers debt risk management and investment products for institutional clients. The company and its subsidiaries have more than 1800 branches and service centers. Subsidiaries Clydesdale Bank and Yorkshire Bank operate offices in the UK. In New Zealand NAB operates as Bank of New Zealand and in the US the company's Great Western Bank includes 200 branches.

NAB's main strategy is to develop a diverse business portfolio. The company often looks to expand its geographic reach in addition to its service offerings through acquisitions and organic growth.

Australia is at the core of NAB and the company works to improve its business banking personal banking and wealth businesses as well as drive mortgage and deposit growth at home. In 2011 the company's net profits were up 24% from the previous year. The increase was largely due to strong growth in its Australian business and personal banking segments (which saw net operating growth of 7% and 10% respectively.)

In 2011 NAB acquired Challenger Financial Service's mortgage management business (rebranded as Advantage). NAB also launched UBank a branchless direct bank that specializes in home loans. Both deals expanded the company's retail banking business.

While NAB works to develop its portfolio in Australia expansion abroad (including its branch network in the US and in Asia) is a main focus. In 2009 NAB expanded its asset management business in Asia when it acquired Hong Kong-based Calibre Asset Management. In 2010 Great Western further established its presence in the US Midwest (and increased agriculture lending) when it acquired F&M Bank with its 10 Iowa branches and TierOne Bank in Nebraska.

The company also is building up its offerings for high-net-worth customers. In 2009 it bought the Australian life and pensions business of British insurance giant Aviva for $A825 million ($650 million) increasing its position in the life insurance market. It also acquired a majority stake in Goldman Sachs' Australia and New Zealand wealth management operations. Goldman Sachs retained ownership of about 20% of the unit which operates under the JBWere brand.

NAB is reviewing its UK operations and it is expected to retool the structure of its Clydesdale and Yorkshire bank brands which represent 330 retail branches and 70 service centers. The economic recession and slow recovery in the UK banking sector lowered profits for NAB. Poor performance in business lending was mostly to blame. NAB saw net operating income drop 7% in the UK in 2011.

HISTORY

Formed in 1858 in Melbourne National Bank of Australasia (NBA) just missed the peak of the Victoria gold rush. The bank expanded across the territory and was one of the first to lend to farmers and ranchers using land deeds as security. In the late 1870s drought imperiled Victoria. Seeking greener pastures NBA entered New South Wales in 1885 then headed into Western Australia. Eco-

nomic instability continued; in 1893 the bank experienced its first panic and was shuttered for eight weeks. NBA reopened only to close a quarter of its branches between 1893 and 1896.

During the Australian commonwealth's early years Western Australia was the bank's salvation as the economies in Victoria and South Australia stagnated. NBA helped fund Australia's WWI efforts through public loans. A postwar consolidation wave in banking swept up NBA which made acquisitions in 1918 and 1922.

Overdue farm and ranch loans weakened the bank during the Depression. As WWII raged the Commonwealth Bank (established in 1912) took greater control of Australia's banks. With competition among banks primarily limited to branch growth NBA acquired Queensland National Bank in 1948 and Ballarat Banking Co. in 1955. The bank diversified into consumer finance through acquisition. In the 1960s Australia experienced an economic boom as immigration and industrialization grew. The boom went bust in the 1970s as the world sunk into recession. Still under the Commonwealth Bank's tight control the banks watched business that had once been theirs lost to building societies merchant banks and credit unions.

The 1980s brought banking deregulation. To vie with foreign banks entering Australia NBA in 1981 merged with Commercial Banking Co. of Sydney and became the National Commercial Banking Corp. of Australia in 1982. (It took its present name in 1984.) Throughout the 1980s the bank diversified and moved into the US and Japan. It invested in property and made loans to foreign countries. All too quickly though property values sank and countries defaulted on loans.

To fight recession NAB looked abroad for opportunities. In 1987 it bought Clydesdale Bank Northern Bank and National Irish Bank from Midland Bank Group (now part of HSBC Holdings). Three years later NAB bought Yorkshire Bank then turned the four banks around by linking them and tightening loan operations. In 1992 it bought the troubled Bank of New Zealand again tightening loan operations. Three years later NAB claimed Michigan National in the US.

After the mid-1990s economic recovery NAB bought HomeSide to try to adapt the US mortgage firm's efficient operations for all its banks.

NAB in 2000 bought Lend Lease's MLC fund management group. It also announced plans to launch a separate stock for its European businesses fueling speculation it might be on the prowl to buy or merge with a large UK bank. The Australian Competition and Consumer Commission (ACCC) that year accused NAB of credit card transaction price-fixing; the bank faced a possible fine of nearly $6 million but the ACCC dropped litigation against the group the following year.

Also in 2001 NAB sold US-based Michigan National Bank to ABN AMRO and sold mortgage lender HomeSide International to Washington Mutual the following year. In fiscal year 2002 the bank cut some 2000 jobs mostly in back-office operations.

During fiscal year 2003 the company booked pre-tax losses of some $360 million due to unauthorized trading in the company's foreign currency options department. By the end of March 2004 chairman Charles Allen chief executive Frank Cicutto and the heads of global markets and foreign exchange had resigned. Three more executives and at least five traders were fired. The fallout continued the next year as the company struggled to regroup.

NAB sold its Irish banks –National Irish Bank and Northern Bank –to Danske Bank in 2005. It retained its UK banks Yorkshire Bank (England) and Clydesdale Bank (Scotland).

In 2006 NAB sold its Custom Fleet vehicle leasing division to GE Capital as well as its Asian life insurance and wealth management operations. The downsizing was part of the company's move to streamline operations.

To establish a foothold in the US NAB acquired Great Western Bancorporation for $A836 million (nearly US$800 million) in 2008.

Also that year NAB took a 20% stake in Chinese property trust Union Trust and Investment. The deal made NAB the first foreign bank to buy into a Chinese trust firm.

EXECUTIVES

Group Executive People Communications & Governance, Michaela J. Healey, age 46
Group Executive Product & Markets, Rick Sawers
Chairman, Michael A. Chaney, age 64
Managing Director & CEO Bank of New Zealand, Andrew Thorburn
CEO and Director, Cameron A. Clyne, $903,998 total compensation
Group Executive Personal Banking, Gavin R. Slater
Group Chief Risk Officer, Bruce Munro
Group Executive Business Banking, Joseph Healy
Executive Director Finance, Mark A. Joiner, $823,837 total compensation
Group Executive Enterprise Services and Transformation, Lisa Gray
Group Executive NAB Wealth, Andrew Hagger
General Manager China Banking, Danny Armstrong
Group Executive Finance & Strategy, Craig Drummond
Director, Sir Malcolm Williamson, age 74
Director, Paul J. Rizzo, age 67
Director, Geoffrey A. (Geoff) Tomlinson, age 66
CEO and Director, Cameron A. Clyne
Director, John G. Thorn, age 65
Director, Patricia Cross, age 54
Director, Daniel T. (Danny) Gilbert, age 61
Director, Jillian S. Segal, age 56
Executive Director Finance, Mark A. Joiner
Director, John Waller
Director, Anthony K. T. Yuen
Auditors: Ernst&Young

LOCATIONS

HQ: National Australia Bank Ltd.
 Level 1, 800 Bourke Street, Docklands, Melbourne, Victoria 3008
Phone: (61) 3 8872 2461
Web: www.nabgroup.com

PRODUCTS/OPERATIONS

2011 Cash Earnings

	% of total
Business	44
Personal	17
wholesale	12
New Zealand	11
MLC & NAB	10
UK	3
Great Western	3
Total	**100**

Selected Subsidiaries

Calibre Asset Management
Great Western Bancorporation
nabCapital (formerly Institutional Markets & Services)
National Australia Group Europe Limited
 Clydesdale Bank PLC
  Yorkshire Bank Home Loans Limited
  Yorkshire Bank Investments Limited
 National Australia Group Europe Services Limited
National Australia Group (NZ) Limited
 Bank of New Zealand
  BNZ International Funding Limited
National Australia Trustees Limited

National Wealth Management Holdings Limited
MLC Limited
 National Wealth Management International Holdings Limited

COMPETITORS

Australia and New Zealand Banking	Lloyds Banking Group
Barclays	Northern Rock (Asset Management)
Commonwealth Bank of Australia	Royal Bank of Scotland
HSBC	Westpac Banking

HISTORICAL FINANCIALS

Company Type: Public

Income Statement

FYE: September 30

	ASSETS ($ mil.)	NET INCOME ($ mil.)	INCOME AS % OF ASSETS	EMPLOYEES
09/14	769,692	4,613	0.6%	42,853
09/13	753,097	5,078	0.7%	42,000
09/12	796,373	4,260	0.5%	0
09/11	732,251	5,070	0.7%	0
09/10	664,069	4,089	0.6%	0
Annual Growth	**3.8%**	**3.1%**	**—**	**—**

2014 Year-End Financials

Return on assets: 0.6%
Return on equity: 11.2%
Long-term debt ($ mil.): —
No. of shares (mil.): —
Sales ($ mil): 39,006
Dividends
 Yield: 9.1%
 Payout: 37.9%
 Market value ($ mil.): —

	STOCK PRICE ($) FY Close	P/E High/Low		PER SHARE ($) Earnings	Dividends	Book Value
09/14	14.18	13	5	1.90	1.30	18.06
09/13	32.19	15	10	2.12	1.78	18.90
09/12	26.43	18	12	1.82	0.92	20.35
09/11	21.15	14	8	2.25	1.65	19.03
09/10	24.54	14	8	1.85	1.27	18.07
Annual Growth	**(12.8%)**	**—**	**—**	**0.8%**	**0.6%**	**(0.0%)**

National Bank of Abu Dhabi

LOCATIONS

HQ: National Bank of Abu Dhabi
 P.O. Box 4, Abu Dhabi
Phone:
Web: www.nbad.com

HISTORICAL FINANCIALS

Company Type: Public

Income Statement

FYE: December 31

	ASSETS ($ mil.)	NET INCOME ($ mil.)	INCOME AS % OF ASSETS	EMPLOYEES
12/14	102,401	1,518	1.5%	0
12/13	88,500	1,288	1.5%	0
12/12	81,833	1,179	1.4%	0
12/11	69,606	1,009	1.5%	0
12/10	57,560	1,002	1.7%	4,216
Annual Growth	**15.5%**	**10.9%**	**—**	**—**

2014 Year-End Financials

Return on assets: 1.5%
Return on equity: 15.3%
Long-term debt ($ mil.): —
No. of shares (mil.): —
Sales ($ mil): 3,555
Dividends
 Yield: —
 Payout: —
 Market value ($ mil.): —

National Bank of Canada

What's the bank for the Quebecois? The National Bank of Canada says "C'est moi!" Also known as National Bank Financial Group the company offers personal and commercial banking services through about 450 branches in Canada primarily in Quebec. The bank's offerings include deposits mortgages loans and credit cards. Through subsidiaries it also provides insurance trust services wealth management online brokerage and private banking. The company with $185 billion in assets manages more than 50 proprietary mutual funds under the National Bank Omega and Altamira banners. Its Natbank unit has two branches in Florida for snowbirds.

Through some 85 locations the company's National Bank Financial subsidiary offers investments portfolio management and group insurance plans. The unit manages more than $50 billion of client assets. It also performs investment banking and brokerage services such as mergers and acquisitions advice institutional trading securities clearing and corporate finance.

To boost its institutional services business National Bank of Canada agreed in late 2013 to acquire The Toronto-Dominion Bank's TD Waterhouse Institutional Services business for $250 million.

In 2012 National Bank of Canada sold its Natcan Investment Management arm to Fiera Sceptre (since renamed Fiera Capital) for more than $309 million. As part of the deal the bank received voting shares representing about 35% of Fiera. National Bank of Canada's strategy is to develop partnerships to grow in the wealth management business. In years prior the bank had been growing its wealth management segment hoping to capitalize on an aging Canadian populace investing toward retirement.

National Bank of Canada has benefited from a relatively strong Canadian economy and a rebound in employment in Quebec in particular. It reported more than $1 billion in net income in 2010 and enjoys one of the lowest loan loss ratios among financial institutions in the country. The company is focusing on referrals between its banking and financial markets segments to foment growth.

EXECUTIVES

President CEO and Director, Louis Vachon, age 52, $838,000 total compensation
EVP Finance Risk and Treasury and CFO, Patricia Curadeau-Grou, $330,800 total compensation
SVP Finance Taxation and Investor Relations, Jean Dagenais, age 56, $174,311 total compensation
Chairman, Jean Douville, age 71
EVP Human Resources and Corporate Affairs, Lynn Jeanniot
VP and Corporate Secretary, Linda Caty
EVP Finance and Treasury and CFO, Ghislain Parent

EVP Wealth Management; Co-President and Co-CEO National Bank Financial, Luc Paiement, $279,750 total compensation

VP Corporate Marketing and Communications, Sylvie Roy

SVP Information Technology Sourcing and Organizational Performance, John B. Cieslak

EVP Financial Markets; Co-President and Co-CEO National Bank Financial, Ricardo Pascoe, $279,750 total compensation

President and CEO Natcan Investment Management, Pascal Duquette

President National Bank Direct Brokerage, Nicolas Milette

EVP Risk Management, William Bonnell

Senior Advisor Public Relations, Joan Beauchamp

Manager Branding and Advertising, Alison Marks

Senior Manager Branding and Advertising, Lise-Anne Amyot

VP Operations National Bank General Insurance, Denis Blackburn

President and CEO Natbank, Marie-Claude Lebel

Senior Manager Public Affairs, Claude Breton

Vice Chairman, Luc Bertrand

EVP Personal and Commercial Banking, Diane Giard

Executive Vice President - Operations, France Maffe

Executive Vice President - Personal and Commercial Banking, Rejean Levesque

EVP Marketing, Karen Leggett

EVP Information Technology and Organizational Performance, Dominique Fagnoule

EVP Operations, Stephane Bilodeau

President CEO and Director, Louis Vachon, age 52

Director, Jean R. Gaulin, age 70

Director, Paul Gobeil, age 71

Director, Pierre Bourgie, age 56

Director, Andre Caille, age 69

Director, Lawrence S. Bloomberg, age 71

Director, Marcel Dutil, age 70

Director, Shirley A. Dawe, age 66

Director, Marc P. Tellier, age 44

Director, Gerard Coulombe, age 66

Director, Roseann Runte, age 66

Director, Bernard Cyr, age 66

Director, Nicole Diamond-Gelinas, age 68

Director, Louise Laflamme, age 61

Director, Gillian H. (Jill) Denham, age 53

Vice Chairman, Luc Bertrand

Independent Director, Andre Caille

Independent Director, Pierre Thabet

Auditors: SamsonBelair/Deloitte&Touchesencrl

LOCATIONS

HQ: National Bank of Canada
600 De La Gauchetiere Street West, 4th Floor, Montreal, Quebec H3B 4L2
Phone: 514 394-5000   **Fax:** 514 394-8434
Web: www.nbc.ca

PRODUCTS/OPERATIONS

Sales

	% of total
Interest	
Loans	37
Securities &	18
Noninterest	
Trust services & mutual	7
Securities brokerage	6
Securitization	5
Underwriting & advisory	5
Deposit & payment service	4
Lending	3
Other	15
Total	**100**

Selected Subsidiaries

Natbank (banking US)

NATCAN (75% portfolio management and investments)
National Bank Direct Brokerage (online brokerage)
National Bank Financial (investment banking)
National Bank General Insurance (home and auto coverage)
National Bank Insurance Firm (insurance brokerage)
National Bank Life Insurance Company
National Bank Securities (mutual funds)
National Bank Trust (trust services)

COMPETITORS

BMO Financial Group	Laurentian Bank
CIBC	RBC Financial Group
Caisses centrale Desjardins	Scotiabank
	TD Bank

HISTORICAL FINANCIALS

Company Type: Public

Income Statement

FYE: October 31

	ASSETS ($ mil.)	NET INCOME ($ mil.)	INCOME AS % OF ASSETS	EMPLOYEES
10/14	183,589	1,277	0.7%	19,955
10/13	179,938	1,375	0.8%	19,691
10/12	178,387	1,522	0.9%	19,920
10/11*	167,519	1,141	0.7%	19,431
11/10	151,807	0	—	0
Annual Growth	**4.9%**	**—**	**—**	**—**

*Fiscal year change

2014 Year-End Financials

Return on assets: 0.7%	Dividends
Return on equity: 16.0%	Yield: 3.5%
Long-term debt ($ mil.): —	Payout: 47.2%
No. of shares (mil.): 329	Market value ($ mil.): 15,434
Sales ($ mil): 6,716	

	STOCK PRICE ($) FY Close	P/E High/Low		PER SHARE ($) Earnings	Dividends	Book Value
10/14	46.87	18	7	3.86	1.73	26.34
10/13	86.95	18	14	4.21	3.35	23.88
10/12	77.36	18	12	4.67	3.06	22.44
10/11*	72.47	25	17	3.47	2.77	20.27
11/10	65.26	—	—	(0.00)	2.40	(0.00)
Annual Growth	**(7.9%)**	—	—	**—**	**(7.9%)**	**—**

*Fiscal year change

National Bank Of Greece S A

Like the ancient ruins that dominate the landscape of Greece National Bank of Greece (NBG) dominates the banking landscape of the Mediterranean. In addition to holding the top position at home NBG has taken a leading position in the Balkans by acquiring controlling stakes in banks throughout the region. The bank offers such services as commercial and consumer banking asset management investment banking financing and insurance. It has more than 500 domestic branches and another 1200 in a dozen outside countries. NBG once served as the Greek central bank but the government sold its stake in the company in 2004.

Geographic Reach

In addition to Greece NBG operates banks in Albania Bulgaria Cyprus Egypt Macedonia Romania Serbia South Africa and Turkey.

HISTORY

The National Bank of Greece (NBG) can trace its banking heritage back to Pasion a metic (non-Greek) former slave living in Athens in the fourth century BC. To help his former master rebuild after one of Greece's many wars he obtained a small private bank that had been formed a few decades earlier and became one of Athens' greatest bankers.

The bank as it exists today though was established in 1841 and for most of its existence served as Greece's central bank. It listed on the Athens Stock Exchange in 1880. NBG survived WWI and Germany's occupation of Greece during WWII. It weathered the civil war in the late 1940s the military coup that overthrew the constitutional monarchy in the 1960s and democratic reformation in the 1970s.

As the 1980s dawned and Andreas Papandreou's socialist government came to power in Greece the bank launched a joint venture in Paris with Credit Lyonnais and other investors. NBG caused plenty of problems for its privately owned competitors during the early part of the decade — as deposits declined profits shrank and labor costs rose the bank was able to undercut competitors thanks to its government backing.

A banking scandal involving NBG and Papandreou helped topple the socialist government in the late 1980s. The bank's US subsidiary Atlantic Bank of New York was one of two Greek banks charged with money laundering to the tune of $700 million. Rival political parties called for Papandreou already ailing to resign. (In 1992 the former leader was acquitted of corruption charges stemming from the scandal.)

Under the leadership of a different government in the early 1990s the bank looked to shake up its holdings to improve profits. It sold off a number of subsidiaries including a chain of luxury hotels an insurance unit and Traders Credit Bank a small commercial bank. These divestitures were just the beginning as the Greek government looked to privatize a number of its holdings. Turmoil in the Greek economy in the mid-1990s forced the bank to limit withdrawals hike interest rates and take other conservative measures as the government tried to prevent a devaluation of the native currency.

In the late 1990s Greece looked to join the Euro zone and its institutions began shaping up. Doing its part NBG took measures to clean up its balance sheet writing off a number of bad loans it had been pressured to make by the government. The bank focused on retail operations absorbed the National Mortgage Bank and transformed its ETEVA development banking subsidiary into a full-fledged investment bank. It began shoring up flagging overseas operations listed on the NYSE (1999) and looked to expand in the Balkans.

In 1997 the bank opened offices in Albania and three years later bought controlling interests in Macedonia's Skopanska Banka and United Bulgarian Bank. As the 20th century drew to a close NGB won more freedom from the Greek government when the finance ministry announced it would no longer appoint the bank's executive officers instead allowing NGB's board of directors and shareholders to make the decisions.

In 2000 the company launched subsidiary NBG Venture Capital which concentrates on Greece southeast Europe and the eastern Mediterranean. The government sold 10% of its stake in the bank in 2003 as part of its privatization program. Although the move dropped its holdings to 30% the government retained management control. The state divested its interest in the company in 2004.

EXECUTIVES

Head of Human Resources, Andreas Vranas

Deputy CEO, Petros Christodoulou, age 54, $405,545 total compensation

General Manager Risk Management, Michael Oratis, age 57, $405,994 total compensation

CEO; Chairman of the Executive Committee, Alexandros G. Tourkolias, age 68, $514,114 total compensation

Deputy CEO and Member of the Executive Committee, Anthimos C. Thomopoulos, age 53, $529,985 total compensation

General Manager of Strategy & International Activities Chief Economist of the Group, Paul Mylonas, age 56, $367,008 total compensation

Chairman, Prof Vassilios T. Rapanos, age 67

General Manager International Activities, Agis Leopoulos, age 46, $311,960 total compensation

Chief Risk Officer, Demetrios Lefakis, age 54, $482,980 total compensation

CEO and Director, Apostolos S. Tamvakakis, age 57

General Manager of Corporate Banking Chairman of the Board of Directors at Ethniki Insurance Co, Dimitrios G. Dimopoulos, age 68, $305,636 total compensation

General Manager of Retail Banking, Nelly Tzakou-Lambropoulou, age 53, $294,213 total compensation

General Manager Investment Banking, Lambros Papakonstantinou, age 49

General Manager Real Estate, Aristotelis Karytinos, age 59, $494,215 total compensation

General Manager Treasury and Global Markets, Leonidas Fragkiadakis, age 49, $346,367 total compensation

Chief Financial Officer, Paula N. Hadjisotiriou, age 57

Chairman, George P. Zanias, age 59

Manager Investor Relations, Gregory Papagrigoris

Assistant General Manager and Supervisor Operational Procedures Ethnodata S.A., Demetrios Vrailas, age 63, $176,103 total compensation

Assistant General Manager Retail Banking, Ioanna Katzilieri-Zour, age 53, $212,286 total compensation

Deputy CFO, Ioannis Kyriakopoulos, age 55, $169,249 total compensation

Assistant General Manager Corporate Banking, Theofanis Panagiotopoulos, age 59, $96,248 total compensation

Assistant General Manager Financial and Operations, Garyfallia Spyriouni, age 51, $346,019 total compensation

Deputy CEO and Member of the Executive Committee, Leonidas Theoklitos

Assistant General Manager and Chief Audit Officer, Petros Fourtounis

General Manager, Maria-Ioanna Politopoulou

General Manager Retail Banking, Antreas Athanassopoulos

General Manager Corporate Banking, Dimitrios G. Dimopoulos

CFO, Babis Mazarakis

General Manager Group Retail Collections, Marianna Politopoulou

General Counsel, Miltiadis Stathopoulos

Assistant General Manager Branch Network, Spyros Asimopoulos

Chief of Operations, Damianos Charalampidis

Chief Credit Officer, Dimitris Frangetis

Group CIO, Nikos Christodoulou

Head of Human Resources, Andreas Vranas

Non-Executive Director, Petros K. Sabatacakis, age 68

Deputy CEO and Member of the Executive Committee, Alexandros Tourkolias, age 68

Deputy CEO and Member of the Executive Committee, Anthimos C. Thomopoulos, age 53

Non-Executive Director, Alexandra Papalexopoulou-Benopoulou, age 48

Non-Executive Director, H. E. the Metropolitan of Ioannina Theoklitos

Non-Executive Director, Stefanos C. Vavalidis, age 68

Director, Ioannis C. Giannidis, age 64

CEO and Director, Apostolos S. Tamvakakis, age 57

Director, Ioannis P. Panagopoulos, age 59

Non-Executive Director, Alexandros Makridis, age 52

Non-Executive Director, George P. Zanias, age 59

Non-Executive Director, Vassilios Konstantakopoulos, age 79

Director, Avraam Triandafyllidis

Deputy CEO and Member of the Executive Committee, Leonidas Theoklitos

Director, Maria (Marily) Frangista

LOCATIONS

HQ: National Bank Of Greece S A
86 Eolou St., Athens 10232
Phone: (30) 210 334 1000   **Fax:** (30) 210 334 2235
Web: www.nbg.gr

COMPETITORS

Agricultural Bank of Greece	EFG Eurobank Ergasias
Alpha Bank	Emporiki Bank
Bank of Cyprus	HSBC
Citibank	Piraeus Bank S.A.
	Royal Bank of Scotland

HISTORICAL FINANCIALS
Company Type: Public

Income Statement
FYE: December 31

	ASSETS ($ mil.)	NET INCOME ($ mil.)	INCOME AS % OF ASSETS	EMPLOYEES
12/13	147,091	50	0.0%	37,591
12/12	133,328	(3,344)	—	35,577
12/11	133,829	(18,806)	—	34,530
12/10	158,907	(474)	—	36,866
12/09	0	563	***************%	36,314
Annual Growth	—	(45.2%)		0.9%

2013 Year-End Financials
Return on assets: 0.0%
Return on equity: ***,***.*%
Long-term debt ($ mil.): —
No. of shares (mil.): —
Sales ($ mil): 9,707

Dividends
Yield: —
Payout: —
Market value ($ mil.): —

	STOCK PRICE ($) FY Close	P/E High/Low	PER SHARE ($) Earnings	Dividends	Book Value
12/13	5.60	430 38	0.04	0.00	1.34
12/12	1.79	— —	(34.93)	0.00	(84.14)
12/11	1.98	— —	(196.86)	0.00	(57.60)
12/10	1.68	— —	(7.49)	0.00	107.21
12/09	5.21	3 1	7.64	0.00	(0.00)
Annual Growth	1.8%	— —	(72.9%)	—	—

National Bank of Hungary

LOCATIONS

HQ: National Bank of Hungary
1054 Szabadsag ter 8-9, Budapest, V. H-1850
Phone: (36) 1 302 30 00   **Fax:** (36) 1 332 39 13
Web: www.mnb.hu

HISTORICAL FINANCIALS
Company Type: Public

Income Statement
FYE: December 31

	ASSETS ($ mil.)	NET INCOME ($ mil.)	INCOME AS % OF ASSETS	EMPLOYEES
12/13	52,990	121	0.2%	727
12/12	48,370	(180)	—	581
12/11	51,750	56	0.1%	590
12/10	48,989	(200)	—	591
12/09	48,287	349	0.7%	605
Annual Growth	2.4%	(23.2%)	—	4.7%

2013 Year-End Financials
Return on assets: 0.2%
Return on equity: 5.1%
Long-term debt ($ mil.): —
No. of shares (mil.): 0
Sales ($ mil): 2,459

Dividends
Yield: —
Payout: —
Market value ($ mil.): —

National Westminster Bank Plc

One of the retail banking arms of The Royal Bank of Scotland (RBS) National Westminster Bank (NatWest) provides banking and financial services to individual and small business clients in the UK. The bank offers deposits mortgages credit cards and personal loans through a network of 1500 bank branches. It also offers phone and Internet banking as well as a network of cash machines and mobile banking units. Subsidiary Ulster Bank has some 240 branches across the island of Ireland. Other offerings include life insurance pensions private banking services carbon offsets and other more prosaic business services as well as investment and retirement management.

NatWest was formed by the 1968 merger of National Provincial Bank (established in 1833) and Westminster Bank (1836). RBS acquired the company in 2000 in the UK's largest bank takeover to date.

The bank has struggled through the global financial crisis which deeply crippled parent RBS. RBS became 84% owned by the UK government after it received a series of bailouts in 2008 and 2009. NatWest reported a loss in 2010 as the result of lower gains on redemption of own debt higher costs and higher impairment losses.

As part of RBS' agreement with the European Commission the company is selling more than 300 of its branches and locations including seven NatWest branches in Scotland to Spanish bank Santander. The transaction (aimed at cutting costs) is expected to close in 2012.

EXECUTIVES

Chief Executive, Stephen A. M. Hester, age 53
Chairman, Sir Philip Hampton, age 61
Auditors: Deloitte&Touche

LOCATIONS

HQ: National Westminster Bank Plc
135 Bishopsgate, London EC2M 3UR
Phone: (44) 131 626 4099   **Fax:** (44) 131 626 3081
Web: www.natwest.com

PRODUCTS/OPERATIONS

Sales

	% of total
Net interest	39
Non interest	61
Total	**100**

COMPETITORS

AIB	HSBC
Barclays	Lloyds Banking Group
Clydesdale Bank	Yorkshire Bank
Grupo Santander	

HISTORICAL FINANCIALS

Company Type: Public

Income Statement

FYE: December 31

	ASSETS ($ mil.)	NET INCOME ($ mil.)	INCOME AS % OF ASSETS	EMPLOYEES
12/13	584,120	(9,854)	—	25,600
12/12	612,451	(5,280)	—	24,100
12/11	567,814	(5,950)	—	26,900
12/10	569,092	(3,502)	—	27,300
12/09	568,032	1,836	0.3%	29,700
Annual Growth	**0.7%**	**—**		**(3.6%)**

2013 Year-End Financials

Return on assets: (-1.6%)	Dividends
Return on equity: (-35.5%)	Yield: 7.7%
Long-term debt ($ mil.): —	Payout: —
No. of shares (mil.): 1,678	Market value ($ mil.): 42,257
Sales ($ mil): 18,700	

	STOCK PRICE ($) FY Close	P/E High/Low		PER SHARE ($) Earnings	Dividends	Book Value
12/13	25.18	— —		(0.00)	1.94	12.68
12/12	24.78	— —		(0.00)	1.94	19.88
12/11	16.78	— —		(0.00)	4.81	14.85
12/10	21.73	— —		(0.00)	1.94	13.93
12/09	17.35	— —		(0.00)	1.94	13.70
Annual Growth	**9.8%**	**— —**		**—**	**(0.0%)**	**(1.9%)**

NATIXIS SA

Natixis operates in the nexus of the money movers and the money shakers. The company is the corporate banking asset management and specialized financial services arm of French banking giant Groupe BPCE. Natixis serves commercial and financial institutions and wealthy individuals in some 70 countries worldwide. It has some E540 billion (some $790 billion) of assets under management. Other activities include real estate finance brokerage employee benefits planning and payment processing services. Subsidiary Coface provides credit insurance and credit management

services. BPCE which was formed in 2009 through the merger of Banques Populaires and Caisses d'Epargne controls some 70% of Natixis.

Natixis has been working to recover from steep revenue declines in 2008 and 2009 some of the toughest years on the global financial sector in several decades. It has restructured itself to streamline operations consolidating units and selling others. The company is also increasingly taking advantage of its connection to BPCE and the cross-selling opportunities that offers as well as investing in new business lines such as exchange-traded funds. Although revenues continued to sink in 2010 the company returned to profitability that year.

The company is looking abroad for future growth. It recently established new offices in Asia where it hopes to build its asset management business. Natixis is beefing up its operations in the US as well.

In 2011 Natixis Global Asset Management (NGAM) acquired Darius Capital Partners an investment advisory and consulting firm with offices in Paris and New York. The addition will help the firm address a growing demand from institutional investors for for transparency liquidity and risk management. NGAM has been gaining momentum in Europe. It also acquired French-based OS-SIAM and London-based H2O Asset Management.

HISTORY

Natexis Banques Populaires traces its roots back to end of both world wars. Credit National was formed in 1919 at the end of WWI to oversee reconstruction grants. The bank specialized in long-term loans for industry and energy companies.

Banque Francaise du Commerce Exterieur (BFCE) was formed in 1946 to provide loans for France's postwar foreign trade. BFCE made commercial loans and offered credits for importers and exporters. Both Credit National and BFCE were "quasi state-controlled" and fulfilled institutional roles set up by the French government.

In the 1980s stagnation in international trade the end of subsidized interest rates and deregulation in the French banking industry meant French banks would have to become more competitive. Unfortunately for Credit National and BFCE the limited structure of their state-mandated business left them woefully unprepared to do other sorts of business. Rather than redirect their business aim Credit National and BFCE looked for partners who would complement them.

In 1996 Credit National and BFCE merged to become Natexis Group. The new entity linked Credit National's domestic client base with BFCE's international operations. The name "Natexis" was chosen because it was easy to pronounce and inoffensive to clients in any of dozens of countries where the company was active.

In 1997 Groupe Banques Populaires (GBP) in an effort to develop more international business and widen its range of services acquired a 23% interest in Natexis Group. Natexis benefited from the financial stability and depth of its new shareholder. The next year GBP upped its stake in Natexis to 71%. The acquisition rounded out GBP's mostly retail products with large and midsized corporate banking lines.

In 1999 GBP merged its main subsidiary Caisse Centrale des Banques Populaires (France's fifth-largest retail banker) with Natexis to form Natexis Banques Populaires. This regrouping paired Natexis with Banques Populaires' regional business to create a single full-service European bank.

In 2000 Natexis bought an 80% share of London Metals Exchange trader Sogemin Metals.

Natixis was formed in 2006 when Natexis Banques Populaires merged with CNCE's investment

divisions including Ixis Corporate and Investment Bank and Ixis Asset Management.

In 2007 Natixis sold its bond insurance business CIFG Holding to parents CNCE and GPB for E1.1 billion ($1.5 billion). The move was intended to preserve CIFG's AAA debt rating which is integral to its business.

The following year the company restructured its corporate and investment banking businesses. It announced plans to stop offering credit and structured credit proprietary investments as well as complex capital investments such as complex fixed-income derivates. It also dropped plans to develop in India and Korea and closed an office in South America. The firm opened an office in Taiwan in 2009.

Also in 2009 the firm named Laurent Mignon as its CEO replacing Dominique Ferrero who was not renewed to the post by the board of directors.

LOCATIONS

HQ: NATIXIS SA
30, avenue Pierre Mendes France, Paris 75013
Phone: (33) 1 58 32 30 00
Web: www.natixis.com

PRODUCTS/OPERATIONS

2010 Net Revenues

	% of total
Corporate & investment	46
Investment	27
Specializes financial	14
Financial	13
Total	**100**

HISTORICAL FINANCIALS

Company Type: Public

Income Statement

FYE: December 31

	ASSETS ($ mil.)	NET INCOME ($ mil.)	INCOME AS % OF ASSETS	EMPLOYEES
12/13	702,315	1,217	0.2%	19,632
12/12	696,417	1,187	0.2%	20,198
12/11	656,701	2,020	0.3%	20,451
12/10	612,986	2,318	0.4%	19,576
12/09	647,129	(2,459)	—	19,439
Annual Growth	**2.1%**	**—**		**0.2%**

2013 Year-End Financials

Return on assets: 0.1%	Dividends
Return on equity: 4.7%	Yield: 0.1%
Long-term debt ($ mil.): —	Payout: 3,984.0%
No. of shares (mil.): —	Market value ($ mil.): —
Sales ($ mil): 23,123	

	STOCK PRICE ($) FY Close	P/E High/Low		PER SHARE ($) Earnings	Dividends	Book Value
12/13	53.50	369250		0.37	14.81	7.96
12/12	32.50	229206		0.36	1.36	8.34
12/11	31.20	246128		0.56	6.12	8.69
12/10	58.50	213213		0.62	0.00	9.65
Annual Growth	**(2.9%)**	**—**		**(11.9%)**	**—**	**(4.7%)**

NEC Corp

NEC knows a little something about Networking Electronics and Computers. The Japanese tech giant provides a broad range of IT products and services through five business groups. IT Services offers consulting integration and support services. Personal Solutions oversees personal computers monitors mobile handsets and Internet service. Carrier Network supplies network infrastructure equipment for telecom carriers. The Platform business supplies network systems such as servers supercomputers storage equipment and IP telephony systems while the Social Infrastructure segment provides broadcasting systems satellites CCTV surveillance and other security systems. NEC does most of its business domestically.

NEC has suffered declining revenues since the onset of the global economic recession that began in late 2008. Sales dropped again in fiscal 2011 by about 13% which was less severe than the 15% decline of the previous year. Unlike 2010 when the company was able to earn a profit by cutting Å320 billion ($3.4 billion) in operating costs mostly by reducing headcount of outsourced engineers and administrative expenses NEC lost money in 2011.

In addition to a slow recovery in the Japanese IT market and the catastrophic 2011 earthquake in eastern Japan the company cited the 2010 spin off of its Electron Devices semiconductor business segment as the key contributor to lower sales in 2011. It divested NEC Electronics which was combined with Renesas Technology to form Renesas Electronics a specialist in semiconductor systems for mobile phones and automotive appications. The merging of NEC Electronics and Renesas created one of the largest chip makers in Japan rivaling Toshiba Semiconductor. The move was prompted by intense competition in the mobile handset sector particularly outside Japan; NEC decided that getting out of the global chip business would enable it to better concentrate on its core domestic sales efforts.

NEC continues to pursue a strategy that includes efforts to address the growing market for products and services that support corporate cloud computing and attempts to expand its global business. To further its cloud computing strategy the company's IT Services division has revamped its core IT system into a hosted service platform and developed systems to enable customers to provide their own cloud computing services from its data centers. As part of this NEC announced in 2011 that it would form a joint venture with ST Electronics the electronics unit of Singapore Technologies Engineering to offer Software-as-a-Service (SaaS) capabilities from a new data center to clients in Asia. NEC will own a 60% stake in the business which will be known as NEC STEE Cloud Services.

In 2012 NEC bought the IT services (managed services enterprise services and consulting) business of CSG Limited extending its reach in Australia. The acquired business will be an independent business unit within NEC Australia.

NEC enlisted even more help on its business support and cloud expansion hopes in 2012 when its NetCracker subsidiary bought Massachusetts-based Convergys' information management business for about $450 million. The unit made business support systems software designed for the communications utilities and logistics industries among others. The products were integrated into NetCracker's operations.

The IT Services unit's other core services are systems integration consulting and maintenance. It supports public sector and health care IT and digital records systems; banking and broadcast systems for financial services telecom carriers and media companies; production and sales management systems for manufacturers; and inventory and distribution systems for retail and consumer services companies.

NEC restructured its Personal Solutions division in 2011 by breaking out its domestic PC business to become part of a new joint venture with

Hong Kong-based PC maker Lenovo. Known as NEC Lenovo Japan Group the business markets personal computers in Japan. Lenovo contributed its Tokyo-based Lenovo Japan subsidiary and $175 million in stock to the new enterprise which is the largest PC seller in Japan giving it 51% ownership. NEC Lenovo Japan Group competes with other Japanese companies (Fujitsu and Toshiba) as well as US-based vendors (Dell and HP). Personal Solutions continues to handle international PC sales as well as peripherals mobile devices and BIGLOBE one of Japan's top Internet service providers.

NEC's Carrier Network unit provides enterprise and carrier-grade communications infrastructure and access networking equipment including optical systems switching gear wireless base stations satellite systems broadcasting transmitters studio equipment and IP telephony systems. It also provides operational and systems support services. Telecom companies make up a large segment of the division's customers.

Together NEC's IT Services Personal Solutions and Carrier Network divisions accounted for 70% of sales in 2011 (up from nearly two-thirds the previous year).

Formerly the company's largest segment (representing almost a quarter of sales in 2009) NEC's Network business was renamed as the Platform unit in 2010 when the company reorganized and disbanded Electron Devices. Platform sells enterprise computing products such as workstations servers thin clients mainframes enterprise software supercomputers storage systems and networking equipment. Due to decreased demand for hardware the segment accounted for only 12% of sales in 2011.

To diversify its business in 2011 NEC bought Jicoux Datasystems a unit of Mitsubishi that offers fleet management services for commercial vehicles. NEC wants to develop information services that automatically exchange information between commercial and privately owned vehicles. Vehicle-to-vehicle communications systems —also called automotive telematics —are hoped to help ease traffic congestion.

As for its global business sales outside Japan make up 15% of revenues. In recent years NEC has consolidated a number of its hundreds of international subsidiaries across Asia and in the US including the merger of NEC Infrontia and NEC Unified Solutions into NEC America. In 2011 the company established a Latin American headquarters in Sao Paulo Brazil to act as the hub for all of its business in the region; it also has operations in Argentina Chile Colombia and Mexico. NEC also has partnerships with Alcatel-Lucent EMC and Philips to develop products specifically aimed at markets outside Japan.

With Fujitsu Fujitsu Semiconductor Panasonic Mobile Communications and Samsung Electronics the company attempted to establish a joint venture that would develop and market semiconductor products for mobile devices but it was abandoned after being unable to come to an agreement over details by the deadline in 2012.

HISTORY

A group of Japanese investors led by Kunihiko Iwadare formed Nippon Electric Company (NEC) in a joint venture with Western Electric (US) in 1899. Starting as an importer of telephone equipment NEC soon became a maker and a major supplier to Japan's Communications Ministry. Western Electric sold its stake in NEC in 1925. The company became affiliated with the Sumitomo "keiretsu" (industrial group) in the 1930s and went public in 1949.

After Nippon Telegraph and Telephone (NTT) was formed in 1952 NEC became one of its four leading suppliers. The post-WWII need to repair Japan's telephone systems and the country's continuing economic recovery resulted in strong demand from NTT for NEC's products. In the 1950s and 1960s NTT business represented more than half of sales even though NEC expanded overseas diversified into home appliances and formed a computer alliance with Honeywell. NTT which began acquiring shares in the company decades earlier and owned as much as 59% of NEC sold its stake in the 1960s.

In the 1970s Honeywell's lagging position in computers hurt NEC; the company recovered through in-house development efforts and a mainframe venture with Toshiba. In 1977 CEO Koji Kobayashi articulated his revolutionary vision of NEC's future as an integrator of computers and communications through semiconductor technology.

NEC invested heavily in R&D and expansion becoming the world's largest semiconductor maker in 1985. Despite its proprietary operating system NEC garnered more than 50% of the Japanese computer market in the 1980s. NEC entered into a mainframe computer partnership with Honeywell and France's Groupe Bull in 1987.

By the early 1990s NEC lost its status as the world's largest semiconductor maker to Intel. NEC bought 20% of US computer maker Packard Bell in 1995 and merged most of its PC business outside Japan with that company creating Packard Bell NEC in 1996. Also in 1996 NEC created US subsidiary Holon Net Corp. to make hardware and software for Internet and intranet markets.

NEC took control of Packard Bell NEC in 1998 upping its stake to 53%. A sluggish Japanese economy and slumping memory prices contributed to NEC's drop in income for fiscal 1998. A defense contract scandal involving overbilling and improper hiring by an NEC unit forced the resignation of chairman Tadahiro Sekimoto and later president Hisashi Kaneko.

President Koji Nishigaki the first at NEC without an engineering background led a sweeping reorganization to cut 10% of the company's workforce —15000 employees —over three years. He revamped NEC operations around Internet application hardware software and services. In 1998 NEC formed a rare pact with a Japanese rival allying with Hitachi to consolidate memory chip operations. The restructuring of Packard Bell NEC (NEC by then owned 88%) helped cause a $1.3 billion loss for fiscal 1999 NEC's worst-ever drop. NEC folded up its Packard Bell NEC division later that year imposing layoffs of about 80% of its staff divesting it from the US retail market and excising the historic Packard Bell brand name in that region.

NEC restructured again in 2000 splitting into more autonomous units and streamlining its PC operations. That year the company launched an aggressive spending program in a move to lead the broadband mobile networking market. In 2001 NEC ended a long-running dispute with Cray investing $25 million in the company and granting distribution rights to its vector supercomputers in North America —a deal contingent upon Cray's dropping an antidumping suit that led to heavy import taxes being placed on NEC supercomputers sold in the US.

Nishigaki became vice chairman in 2004 and Akinobu Kanasugi was named president. Kanasugi held the post just two years until poor health forced him to turn the reins over to SVP Kaoru Yano. Yano stepped down as president in April 2010 but retained his position as chairman. SVP Nobuhiro Endo who has been with the company since 1981 was promoted to president.

In 2004 NEC took public its DRAM joint venture Elpida Memory thereby reducing its stake in the company and the volatile memory sector. NEC also sold its plasma display business to Pioneer that same year. In 2005 the company dissolved its monitor joint venture with Mitsubishi and took full ownership of the unit (NEC Display Solutions). The next year it sold its European PC operations Packard Bell to Lap Shun "John" Hui a co-founder of eMachines.

The company joined with Sumitomo Electric Industries in 2008 to acquire fiber-optic submarine cable manufacturer OCC Holdings; NEC and Sumitomo acquired 75% and 25% stakes respectively.

Kaoru Yano stepped down as president of NEC in 2010 but retained his position as chairman. SVP Nobuhiro Endo who has been with the company since 1981 was promoted to president.

EXECUTIVES

Chairman, Kaoru Yano, age 70
SEVP Chief Supply Chain Officer and Director, Junji Yasui, age 64
President and Director, Nobuhiro Endo, age 61
Associate SVP, Masaki Kidowaki
Associate SVP, Takayuki Morita
Executive Vice President Chief Marketing Officer, Toshiyuki Mineno, age 63
Associate SVP, Naoki Yoshimura
SVP and Director, Manabu Kinoshita, age 60
Senior Executive Vice President CSO Chief Strategy Officer CIO Chief Information Officer, Takashi Niino
SVP and Associate SVP, Tomonori Nishimura
SVP, Takayuki Okada
Senior Executive Vice President and Member of the Board Re, Yukihiro Fujiyoshi, age 65
SVP, Masaki Fukui
SVP, Kuniaki Okada
Associate SVP, Takashige Mouri
SVP, Masato Yamamoto
SVP, Fujio Okada
Associate SVP, Masamichi Imai
Associate SVP, Nobuyuki Yanaginuma
Associate SVP, Masahiro Annaka
Associate SVP, Shunichiro Tejima
Associate SVP, Masao Wada
Associate SVP, Hirokazu Takahara
Associate SVP, Takaaki Shimizu
Associate SVP, Masanobu Yamaguchi
Associate SVP, Takemi Hosaka
Associate SVP, Takao Maruyama
Associate SVP, Yasushi Abe
Associate SVP, Kunio Kondo
Associate SVP, Katsumi Emura
Associate SVP, Yasuyuki Nakae
SVP and Director, Takemitsu Kunio, age 60
Associate SVP and CFO, Isamu Kawashima
Associate Senior Vice President, Shinya Oda
Director, Kenji Miyahara, age 79
Director, Yoshinari Hara, age 71
Director, Hideaki Takahashi, age 66
Director, Toshio Morikawa, age 79
SEVP Chief Marketing Officer and Director, Toshimitsu Iwanami, age 64
SEVP Chief Supply Chain Officer and Director, Junji Yasui, age 64
Director, Sawako Nohara, age 57
President and Director, Nobuhiro Endo, age 61
SVP and Director, Toshiyuki Mineno, age 62
SVP and Director, Manabu Kinoshita, age 60
SEVP CIO and Director, Yukihiro Fujiyoshi, age 65
SVP and Director, Takemitsu Kunio, age 60
Auditors: Ernst&YoungShinNihon

LOCATIONS

HQ: NEC Corp
5-7-1 SHiba, Minato-ku, Tokyo 108-8001
Phone: (81) 3 3454 1111
Web: www.nec.co.jp

Sales

	% of total
Asia	
Japan	85
Other	5
Europe	3
Other	7
Total	**100**

PRODUCTS/OPERATIONS

Sales

	% of total
IT	26
Personal	25
Carrier	19
Platform	12
Social	10
Other	8
Total	**100**

Selected Products

IT Services
  Consulting
  Maintenance
  Outsourcing
  Support
  Systems integration
Personal Solutions
  Internet service (NEC BIGLOBE)
  Mobile handsets
  Peripherals (floppy and optical drives monitors printers projectors)
  Personal computers
Carrier Network
  Access Networking systems (broadband and mobile microwave communication systems)
  Backbone networking systems (SDH systems WDM systems routers/switching systems)
  Network control platform systems
  Network infrastructure (fixed-line and mobile communication systems)
  Network service delivery platform systems
Platform Business Systems
  Enterprise computing (workstations servers storage systems mainframes supercomputers)
  Enterprise network systems (IP telephony routers/switching systems wireless LAN)
  Networking equipment (enterprise carrier)
  Software (application middleware operating systems)
  Storage products
Social Infrastructure
  Aerospace and defense systems
  Broadcasting systems and video equipment
  Control systems
  Fire and disaster prevention systems
  Transportation and public systems

COMPETITORS

AMD	Lexmark
Acer	Micron Technology
Alcatel-Lucent	Microsoft
Apple Inc.	Mitsubishi Electric
Avaya	Motorola Solutions
BlackBerry	NTT DATA
CASIO COMPUTER	Nokia
Canon	Nortel Networks
Cisco Systems	Oki Electric
Citizen	Panasonic Corp
Dell	Philips Electronics
Emerson Electric	Ricoh Company
Epson	SCSK
Ericsson	STMicroelectronics
FUJIFILM	Samsung Electronics
Fujitsu	Sharp Corp.
Harris Corp.	Siemens AG
Hewlett-Packard	Sony
Hitachi	Sony Mobile
Huawei Technologies	Texas Instruments
IBM	Toshiba
Intel	UTStarcom
Kyocera	Unisys
Lenovo	ZTE

HISTORICAL FINANCIALS

Company Type: Public

Income Statement
FYE: March 31

	REVENUE ($ mil.)	NET INCOME ($ mil.)	NET PROFIT MARGIN	EMPLOYEES
03/14	29,481	326	1.1%	100,914
03/13	32,644	323	1.0%	102,375
03/12	37,020	(1,344)	—	109,102
03/11	37,622	(151)	—	115,840
03/10	38,360	122	0.3%	142,358
Annual Growth	(6.4%)	27.9%	—	(8.2%)

2014 Year-End Financials

Debt ratio: 0.2%
Return on equity: 4.8%
Cash ($ mil.): 1,866
Current ratio: 1.52
Long-term debt ($ mil.): 4,587
No. of shares (mil.): —
Dividends
  Yield: —
  Payout: —
Market value ($ mil.): —

	STOCK PRICE ($) FY Close	P/E High/Low		PER SHARE ($) Earnings	Dividends	Book Value
03/14	2.75	—	—	0.13	0.00	2.86
03/13	2.55	—	—	0.12	0.00	3.42
03/12	1.95	—	—	(0.52)	0.00	3.65
03/11	2.12	—	—	(0.06)	0.04	4.07
03/10	2.40	—	—	0.05	0.00	3.84
Annual Growth	3.5%	—	—	24.4%	—	(7.1%)

Nedbank Group Ltd

LOCATIONS

HQ: Nedbank Group Ltd
Nedbank 135 Rivonia Campus, 135 Rivonia Road, Sandown, Johannesburg 2196
Phone: (27) 11 294 4444   **Fax:** (27) 11 294 6540
Web: www.nedbankgroup.co.za

HISTORICAL FINANCIALS

Company Type: Public

Income Statement
FYE: December 31

	ASSETS ($ mil.)	NET INCOME ($ mil.)	INCOME AS % OF ASSETS	EMPLOYEES
12/13	71,165	819	1.2%	29,513
12/12	80,221	878	1.1%	28,748
12/11	80,032	764	1.0%	28,494
12/10	91,622	724	0.8%	27,525
12/09	77,113	652	0.8%	27,037
Annual Growth	(2.0%)	5.9%	—	2.2%

2013 Year-End Financials

Return on assets: 1.2%
Return on equity: 15.0%
Long-term debt ($ mil.): —
No. of shares (mil.): 461
Sales ($ mil.): 6,211
Dividends
  Yield: 3.3%
  Payout: 0.3%
Market value ($ mil.): 9,256

	STOCK PRICE ($)	P/E		PER SHARE ($)		
	FY Close	High/Low	Earnings	Dividends	Book Value
12/13	20.07	0 0	1.73	0.68	12.48
12/12	22.54	0 0	1.87	0.73	13.86
12/11	17.66	0 0	1.66	0.01	13.28
12/10	40.34	0 0	1.58	1.18	14.80
12/09	34.05	0 0	1.50	1.20	12.30
Annual Growth	(12.4%)	— —		3.7% (13.2%)	0.4%

Nestle S.A.

With instant coffee baby food and bottled water in the mix Nestle crunches more than just chocolate. The world's #1 food and drinks company in terms of sales Nestle is also the world leader in coffee (Nescafe). It also makes coffee for the home-brewing system Nespresso. Nestle is one of the world's top bottled water makers (Nestle Waters) one of the biggest frozen pizza makers (DiGiorno) and a big player in the pet food business (Friskies Purina). Its most well-known global food brands include Buitoni Dreyer's Maggi Milkmaid Carnation and Kit Kat. The company also owns Gerber Products. North America is Nestle's most important market.

HISTORY

Henri Nestle purchased a factory in Vevey Switzerland in 1843 that made products ranging from nut oils to rum. In 1867 he developed a powder made from cow's milk and wheat flour as a substitute for mother's milk. A year earlier Americans Charles and George Page had founded the Anglo-Swiss Condensed Milk Company in Cham Switzerland using Gail Borden's milk-canning technology. In 1875 Nestle sold his eponymous company then doing business in 16 countries. When Anglo-Swiss launched a milk-based infant food in 1878 Nestle's new owners responded by introducing a condensed-milk product. In 1905 a year after Nestle began selling chocolate the companies ended their rivalry by merging under the Nestle name. Hampered by limited milk supplies during WWI the company expanded into regions less affected by the war such as the US. In 1929 it acquired Cailler the first company to mass-produce chocolate bars and Swiss General inventor of milk chocolate. An investment in a Brazilian condensed-milk factory during the 1920s paid an unexpected dividend when Brazilian coffee growers suggested the company develop a water-soluble "coffee cube." Released in 1938 Nescafe instant coffee quickly became popular. Other new products included Nestle's Crunch bar (1938) Quik drink mix (1948) and Taster's Choice instant coffee (1966). Nestle expanded during the 1970s with acquisitions such as Beringer Brothers wines (sold in 1995) Stouffer's and Libby's. Moving beyond foods in 1974 Nestle acquired a 49% stake in Gesparal a holding company that controls the French cosmetics company L'Oreal. It acquired pharmaceutical firm Alcon Laboratories three years later. Helmut Maucher was named chairman and CEO in 1981. He began beefing up Nestle's global presence. Boycotters had long accused Nestle of harming children in developing countries through the unethical promotion of infant formula and Maucher acknowledged the ongoing boycott by meeting with the critics and setting up a commission to police adherence to World Health Organi-

zation guidelines. Nestle bought Carnation in 1985. Maucher doubled the company's chocolate business in 1988 with the purchase of UK chocolate maker Rowntree (Kit Kat). Also in the 1980s Nestle acquired Buitoni pastas. The company expanded in the 1990s with the purchases of Butterfinger and Baby Ruth candies Source Perrier water Alpo pet food and Ortega Mexican foods. Company veteran Peter Brabeck-Letmathe succeeded Maucher as CEO in 1997. He cleaned out Nestle's pantry by selling non-core businesses (Contadina tomato products Libby's canned meat products) but restocked with San Pellegrino (mineral water) and Dalgety's Spillers (pet food) in 1998. By 1999 the company started rolling out its Nestle Pure Life bottled water. It also sold its Findus brand (fish vegetables) and its non-instant US coffee brands. That year Nestle merged its US novelty ice-cream unit with operations of Pillsbury's Haagen-Dazs to form Ice Cream Partners USA. In 2000 Nestle purchased snack maker PowerBar. In 2001 it bought Ralston Purina for $10.3 billion making it the world's largest pet food maker. To win FTC approval the companies agreed to sell Meow Mix and Alley Cat dry cat food brands to Hartz Mountain. In a deal that gives Nestle a 99-year license to use the Haagen-Dazs brand in the US the company agreed to pay $641 million to General Mills (which has bought Pillsbury from Britain's Diageo) for the other half of Ice Cream Partners. In 2002 Nestle acquired German ice-cream maker Schoeller Holding Group as well as US food company Chef America maker of Hot Pockets and Lean Pockets. That same year Nestle also spun off eyecare subsidiary Alcon Laboratories but retained about 75% ownership of it. The company renamed its water unit from Perrier Vittel SA to Nestle Waters and bought Russian bottled water company Saint Springs. The company sold its savory flavor business Food Ingredients Specialties (FIS) to Swiss flavoring company Givaudan and its UK and Ireland ambient foods business to HM Capital Partners (then named Hicks Muse Tate & Furst). It also formed a joint venture with New Zealand dairy co-op Fonterra to produce and distribute dairy products in the Americas. Nestle and Cadbury Schweppes (now Cadbury) made a joint $10.5 billion bid for The Hershey Company in 2002 but Hershey called the sale off later that year. While Nestle already owned 30% of US ice cream powerhouse Dreyer's in 2002 it proposed a merger of its US ice cream businesses. After months of antitrust scrutiny the final deal gave Nestle 67% of Dreyer's. Seeking to further strengthen its position in the worldwide ice cream market Nestle acquired the ice cream and related products of Movenpick a Swiss food company 2003. The acquisition brought Nestle licensing agreements with companies in Egypt Finland Germany Norway Sweden and Saudi Arabia. Other transactions in 2003 included the Nestle USA unit selling its Ortega brand Mexican food products to B&G Foods and the parent company selling Mont Blanc France's leading dessert brand to French investment firm Activa Capital. Also that year the company added to its bottled-water business by acquiring Hutchison Whampoa's Powwow which operates in Denmark France Germany Italy the Netherlands Portugal and the UK. In addition it acquired Clear Water a bottled-water home-and-office delivery company located in Russia. In line with its strategy to concentrate on value-added products in 2004 Nestle sold its cocoa-processing facilities in Germany and the UK to Cargill. Also in 2004 the company acquired Finnish dairy company Valid's Valiojaatelo ice cream business and increased its stake in Israeli bakery company Osem to 53%. In addition Nestle sold its German frozen food distributor Eastman that year and Nestle Espana bought Nestle Portugal for about $682 mil-

lion. Nestle was ordered by the Brazilian government to sell its Chocolates Garoto in 2004 on the grounds that ownership of Garoto presented unfair market competition. Later that same year CEO Peter Brabeck-Letmathe announced he was considering reducing the number of outside directorships that he held because of increased demands as the leader of Nestle. At the time Brabeck-Letmathe sat on the boards of Alcon Credit Suisse Dreyer's Grand Ice Cream L'Oreal Roche Holding and "Winterthur" Swiss Insurance Company. (He has since left the "Winterthur" board.) And that year in a tangle with a French union over retirement benefits Nestle threatened to sell Perrier or produce its popular water from another source. However the company reached a settlement with the union and the production of Perrier continued. Long-time chairman Rainer Gut retired in 2005 and Brabeck-Letmathe replaced him. In 2005 it became a 90% owner of Dreyer's Grand Ice Cream. The next year Nestle became the owner of more than 90% of Dreyer's as the result of an exercise of a Put Right whereby Nestle was required to purchase certain shareholders' Class A Callable Puttable Common Stock (or Class A shares). As a result of this "short form merger" Dreyer's ceased trading on the Nasdaq stock exchange. In keeping with its strategy to concentrate on value-added products during 2006 Nestle sold its cocoa processing facilities in Germany and the UK to Cargill. Adding to its dominance in the European ice cream sector the company acquired Finnish dairy company Valid's Valiojaatelo's ice cream business and Greece's Delta Ice cream which has operations in Bulgaria Greece Macedonia Montenegro Romania and Serbia. Later that year Nestle bought the Australian breakfast cereal snack and soup operations of Uncle Tobys from Burns Philp for $670 million. The cereal portion was integrated into Cereal Partners Worldwide. In another streamlining move the company agreed to sell its canned liquid milk businesses in Southeast Asia to Singapore-based Fraser and Neave. Hedging its bets considering its food products (candy bars ice cream) are on the opposite end of the waistline wars Nestle acquired Jenny Craig for $600 million in 2006. In 2007 the company purchased the medical-nutrition business of Novartis for Â1.88 billion ($2.5 billion). The business which has operations in 40 countries worldwide makes food for hospital patients. The purchase was seen as a move by Nestle to concentrate on higher-margin products. Brands in the acquisition included Boost and Resource nutritional supplements and Optifast dieting products. Nestle divested some operations in France and Spain in order to settle competitive concerns surrounding the deal voiced by the European Commission. On the food front Nestle subsidiary Dreyer's purchased the Eskimo Pie and Chipwich brands from Canadian ice cream maker CoolBrands in 2007 for almost $19 million. Nestle spooned out $5.5 billion in cash to purchase Gerber Products from Novartis in 2007. The deal made Nestle the world's largest baby food company.

Due to the increased workload as chairman Peter Brabeck-Letmathe stepped down as CEO in 2008; he remained in an active role as board chairman. Paul Bulcke former head of Zone Americas for Nestle replaced Brabeck-Letmathe as CEO.

The company it added to its "out of home food and beverage" operations (i.e. foodservice) in 2009 with the purchase of Tampa-based Vitality Foodservice. Vitality provides commercial and non-commercial beverage services worldwide.

In August 2010 Nestle acquired Liverpool-based Vitaflo a maker of clinical nutrition products for people with metabolic disorders. Also in August it completed the sale of Alcon to Novartis. The pharmaceutical maker acquired Nestle's stake in Alcon in two steps beginning with the sale of a 25% stake for $11 billion in July 2008. Novartis exercised its option to buy Nestle's remaining percentage of Alcon for $28 billion in 2010.

In November 2011 Nestle acquired the Oscar stocks and sauces business from Paulig Group building Nestle Professional's presence in the culinary flavors sector.

In July 2014 Nestle acquired L'Oreal's 50% stake in Galderma a joint venture formed by the two companies in 1981. Going forward Galderma will operate as the pharmaceutical arm of Nestle Skin Health S.A. established in June 2014 as a fully-owned Nestle subsidiary.

EXECUTIVES

Chairman, Peter Brabeck-Letmathe, age 70, $1,514,880 total compensation

SVP Corporate Governance Compliance and Corporate Services, David P. Frick, age 49

EVP Zone Americas, Chris Johnson, age 53

EVP; Chairman and CEO NestlT Waters, John J. Harris, age 64

EVP CTO and Head Innovation Technology and Research and Development, Werner J. Bauer, age 64

Deputy EVP Nestle Professional, Marc Caira, age 60

Head of Investor Relations, Roddy Child-Villiers

Member of the Executive Board; Deputy Executive Vice President Nestle Nutrition, Kurt T. Schmidt, age 57

CEO, Paul Bulcke, age 60, $1,893,600 total compensation

Member of the Executive Board; Executive Vice President Strategic Business Units; Marketing; Sales and Nespresso, Patrice Bula

EVP and CFO, Wan Ling Martello

Member of the Management Board; Chief Financial Officer; Executive Vice President, James Singh, age 68

EVP Europe, Laurent Freixe

Executive Vice President, Martial C. Rolland

Deputy EVP Human Resources and Centre Administration, Jean-Marc Duvoisin, age 55

Member of the Executive Board; Deputy Executive Vice President Nestle S.A.; Head of Nestle Nutrition, Nandu Nandkishore

Second Vice Chairman of the Board, Rolf Haenggi

Second Vice Chairman, Rolf Hanggi, age 69

Board Member, Jean-Pierre Meyers, age 66

Board Member, Jean-Rene Fourtou, age 74

Board Member, Daniel V. Borel, age 64

Board Member, Jean-Pierre Roth, age 68

Board Member, Andre Kudelski, age 53

First Vice Chairman, Andreas N. Koopmann, age 62

Board Member, Beat W. Hess, age 65

Board Member, Carolina Muller-Mohl, age 44

Board Member, Steven G. Hoch, age 60

Board Member, Naina L. Kidwai, age 56

Board Member, Titia de Lange

Second Vice Chairman of the Board, Rolf Haenggi

Auditors: KPMGS.A.

LOCATIONS

HQ: Nestle S.A.
Avenue Nestle 55, Vevey CH-1800
Phone: (41) 21 924 2111   **Fax:** (41) 21 924 4800
Web: www.nestle.com

2012 Factories

	No.
Americas	171
Europe	153
Asia Oceania &	144
Total	**468**

Sales

	% of total
Americas	44
Europe	29
Asia Oceania &	27
Total	**100**

PRODUCTS/OPERATIONS

2012 Product Sales

	% of total
Powdered & liquid	22
Milk products & ice	20
Prepared dishes & cooking	15
Pet	12
Nutrition & health	12
Confectionery	11
Water	8
Total	**100**

Selected Products and Brands

Bouillons soups seasonings pasta and sauces
Buitoni
Maggi
Thomy
Winiary

Chilled Nestle
Chiquitin
La Laitiere
La Lechera
LC1
Molico
Ski
Sveltesse
Svelty
Yoco

Chocolate confectionery and biscuits
Aero
Baci
Butterfinger
Cailler
Crunch
Galak/Milkybar
Kit Kat
Nestle
Polo
Smarties

Coffee
Bonka
Loumidis
Nescafe
Nespresso
Ricore Ricoffy
Taster' s Choice
Zoegas

Foodservice and professional products
Chef
Davigel
Minor' s
Santa Rica

Frozen foods (prepared dishes pizzas)
Buitoni
California Pizza Kitchen (licensed)
Delissio (Canada only)
Hot Pockets
Jack' s Pizza
Lean Cuisine
Maggi
Stouffer' s
Tombstone

Healthcare and nutrition
Clinutren
Modulen
Nutren
Peptamen

Ice cream
Antica Gelateria del Corso
Chipwich
Dreyer' s
Drumstick/Extreme
Edy' s
Eskimo Pie
Haagen-Dazs
Maxibon/Tandem
Mega
Movenpick
Parar
Sin Parar/Sem

Infant food and nutrition
Beba
Cerelac
Gerber

Good Start
Guigoz
Lactogen
Nan
Neslac
Nestle
Nestogen
Nestum

Other beverages
Carnation
Caro
Libby' s
Milo
Nescau
Nesquik
Nestea

Performance nutrition
PowerBar
Pria

Pet care
Alpo
Beneful
Cat Chow
Dog Chow
Fancy Feast
Felix
Gourmet
Pro Plan
Purina Friskies
Purina ONE
Tidy Cats

Refrigerated products (cold meat products dough pasta pizzas sauces)
Buitoni
Herta
Nestle
Toll House

Shelf-stable products
Bear Brand
Carnation
Coffee-Mate
Gloria
Klim
La Lechera
Milkmaid
Moca
Molico
Nestle Omega
Nido
Ninho
Svelty

Water
Acqua Panna
Al Manhal
Arrowhead
Contrex
Deer Park
Hepar
Ice Mountain
Levissima
Nestle Aquarel
Nestle Pure Life
Nestle Vera
Ozarka
Perrier
Poland Spring
Quezac
S.Pellegrino
San Bernardo
Vittel
Zephyrhills

Selected Subsidiaries Joint Ventures and Affiliates

Beverage Partners Worldwide (50% with The Coca-Cola Company US)
Cereal Partners Worldwide (50% with General Mills US)
Galderma and Laboratoires inneov (29% with L' Oreal cosmetic and nutritional supplement products)
Gerber Products Company (infant nutrition US)
Jenny Craig Inc. (weight-loss centers and foods US)
Uncle Tobys (soups breakfast cereal snacks Australia)

COMPETITORS

Abbott Labs	Kerry Group
Associated British Foods	Lindt & Sprungli
Atkins Nutritionals	Mars Incorporated
Bally Total Fitness	Medifast
	Mondelez International

Barilla
Beech-Nut
Campbell Soup
Coca-Cola
ConAgra
Danone
Danone Water
Dean Foods
Dreyer's
Ferrara Pan Candy
Fit America
GNC
General Mills
Goya
HMG
Heinz
Hershey
Indofood
Kellogg
Kent Gida

Nutrisystem
PepsiCo
Procter & Gamble
Revlon
Russell Stover
Sara Lee
Slim-Fast
Smucker
Starbucks
Suntory Holdings
Tata Global Beverages
United Biscuits
Weight Watchers
International
Wimm-Bill-Dann
World's Finest
Chocolate
eDiets.com
maxingvest

HISTORICAL FINANCIALS

Company Type: Public

Income Statement

FYE: December 31

	REVENUE ($ mil.)	NET INCOME ($ mil.)	NET PROFIT MARGIN	EMPLOYEES
12/13	103,667	11,239	10.8%	333,000
12/12	100,713	11,575	11.5%	339,000
12/11	89,041	10,084	11.3%	328,000
12/10	117,250	36,581	31.2%	281,005
12/09	104,483	10,124	9.7%	278,165
Annual Growth	(0.2%)	2.6%	—	4.6%

2013 Year-End Financials

Debt ratio: 20.2%
Return on equity: 16.2%
Cash ($ mil.): 7,915
Current ratio: 0.91
Long-term debt ($ mil.): 11,630

No. of shares (mil.): —
Dividends
  Yield: 2.9%
  Payout: 74.4%
Market value ($ mil.): —

	STOCK PRICE ($) FY Close	P/E High/Low		PER SHARE ($) Earnings	Dividends	Book Value
12/13	73.59	30	24	3.51	2.16	22.02
12/12	65.17	24	19	3.62	2.11	20.85
12/11	57.71	31	20	3.15	2.47	19.03
12/10	58.82	7	4	10.81	1.38	20.30
12/09	48.35	17	8	2.83	1.24	13.68
Annual Growth	11.1%	—		5.6%	15.0%	12.6%

Nippon Life Insurance Co. (Japan)

Nippon Life Insurance also known as Nissay is a top life insurer in Japan. The company which has some 10 million policyholders uses a door-to-door sales corps and other representatives to peddle its traditional insurance products including individual and group life and annuity policies to Japanese consumers. In addition to its life insurance products the company administers pension plans and medical coverage plans and provides asset management services. Through its affiliates and subsidiaries the company also sells auto and other property/casualty insurance in Japan and it has some international life insurance operations as well as select real estate and financial service assets.

Geographic Reach

Nippon Life operates about 50 subsidiaries and affiliates and has some 120 branch locations. It operates in China India Japan Continental Europe the UK and the US.

Operations

In addition to the core insurance operations other Nippon Life subsidiaries and affiliates are involved in real estate investment mortgage lending and investment advisory among other financial services activities. Its operating group includes subsidiaries NLI Insurance Tokyo Agency of Nippon NLI Properties Nissay Asset Management and Nissay Capital.

Sales and Marketing

Nippon Life primarily sells policies through its dedicated field sales force as well as through retail store locations call centers and online. It also sells through select insurance brokerages and via partnerships with financial services firms including banks.

Financial Performance

Nippon Life increased revenues by 7% to ¥7.2 trillion ($87 billion) in 2012 due to higher insurance and reinsurance premiums and lower than expected policy payouts (related to the massive tsunami/earthquake events in 2011) despite reporting lower investment income levels that year. Net income decreased slightly due to decreased gains on asset disposals and change in security investment prices. Nippon Life has increased revenues steadily over the past few years.

Strategy

Nippon Life along with its competitors in Japan is faced with several market challenges including a declining population (meaning a smaller customer pool) an aging population (meaning more payouts on claims) and an uneven economic recovery (which translates to cutbacks in personal expenditures).

To combat some of these problems Nippon Life has been broadening its sales channels to include an agency network and partnerships with financial services firms. (Deregulation has allowed sales of some insurance products at banks.)

Nippon Life has also been adding more medical coverage products to appeal to older consumers and is working to offer more comprehensive and flexible life insurance coverage options. Nippon Life is also investing in information technology system improvements to enhance customer service and it is expanding its international operations particularly in China India and the US.

In response to a decline in policies in force the company launched an new integration strategy in 2012. The project focuses on combining innovative insurance policies with stronger IT infrastructure and sales force resources.

Mergers and Acquisitions

Nippon Life acquired minority stakes in two affiliates Reliance Life Insurance Company Limited and Reliance Capital Asset Management Limited during 2011 and 2012. The purchases were part of a strategic collaboration with Reliance Capital formed in 2011 through which Nippon Life aims to increase its operations in India.

HISTORY

Nippon Life known as Nissay was a product of the modernization that began after US Commodore Matthew Perry opened Japan's ports to foreigners in 1854. Industry and trade were Japan's first focus but financial infrastructure soon followed. The country's first insurer (Meiji Mutual) opened in 1881. In 1889 Osaka banker Sukesaburo Hirose founded Nippon Life as a stock company. It grew and opened branches in Tokyo (1890) and Kyushu (1895).

In the 20th century the company developed a direct sales force and began lending directly to businesses. Lending remained the backbone of its asset strategy through most of the century. The insurance market in Japan grew quickly until the late 1920s but had already slowed by the eve of the Depression.

After WWII the company reorganized as a mutual and began mobilizing an army of women to build its sales of installment-premium basic life policies. In 1962 the company began automating its systems and established operations in the US (1972) and the UK (1981).

As interest rates rose in the wake of oil price hikes in the 1970s the company began offering term life and annuities and slowly moved to diversify its asset holdings from mostly government bonds (whose yields declined as rates rose) to stocks. This movement accelerated in the 1980s as the businesses that traditionally borrowed from Nippon Life turned directly to capital markets to raise money through debt issues. Seeking to replace its shrinking lending business the company began investing in US real estate and businesses whose values rose in the mid-1980s. The company reached its zenith in 1987; it owned about 3% of all the stocks on the Tokyo Exchange held more real estate than Mitsubishi's real estate units and had bought 13% of US brokerage Shearson Lehman from American Express.

By the end of the year thanks to the US stock market crash the value of the Shearson investment had fallen 40%. But the company felt confident enough of its importance as the world's largest insurance company (by assets) to crow its intentions to strong-arm Japan's Ministry of Finance into letting it diversify into trust and securities operations.

Then its bubble burst. In 1989 real estate crashed and the stock market lost more than half its value. Japan's economy failed to improve and Nippon Life was left struggling with nonperforming loans and assets whose value had declined. The company suffered further from policy cancellations and from the Ministry of Finance's focus on buoying banks. In 1997 the ministry asked Nippon Life to convert its subordinated debt from Nippon Credit Bank (now Aozora Bank) to stock. That year Nippon Life formed an alliance with Marsh & McLennan's Putnam Investments subsidiary to help manage its assets; the relationship deepened in 1998 when they began developing investment trust products.

The next year Nippon Life faced a shareholder lawsuit over its involvement in the collapse of Nippon Credit Bank; the company claims the Ministry of Finance tricked it into bailing out the bank even though it was beyond rescue. In 2001 the company merged its Nissay General subsidiary with Dowa Fire & Marine creating nonlife insurer Nissay Dowa.

In 2003 joint venture Nissay-SVA Life Insurance was formed with consumer electronics manufacturer SVA (Group) Ltd.

The company made a $1.2 billion real estate investment in 2009 when it purchased the Japan headquarters of ailing US insurer AIG.

EXECUTIVES

Chairman, Kunie Okamoto, age 70
Vice Chairman, Sadao Kato, age 66
Senior Managing Executive Officer, Kazuo Kobayashi
President, Yoshinobu Tsutsui
EVP, Takeshi Furuichi
EVP, Kenichi Kobayashi
Senior Managing Executive Officer, Koji Aiba
Senior Managing Executive Officer, Yasuomi Matsuyama
Senior Managing Executive Officer, Masami Kuroda

President and CEO Nippon Life Benefits, Toshihiro Nakashima

SVP; CFO Nippon Life Benefits, Bruce Walker

Executive Vice President Chief Operating Officer, Francine Young

Vice President Chief Business Development Officer, Joe McLaughlin

Vice President General Counsel Secretary, Tess Leopold

President Chief Executive Officer, Takayuki Murai

Vice Chairman, Sadao Kato, age 64

Managing Executive Officer and Director, Kazuo Kobayashi

Senior Managing Executive Officer and Director, Hiroshi Manabe

EVP and Director, Kiyoshi Ujihara

President and Director, Yoshinobu Tsutsui

Senior Managing Executive Officer and Director, Takeshi Furuichi

EVP and Director, Kenichi Kobayashi

Senior Managing Executive Officer and Director, Yasuomi Matsuyama

Managing Executive Officer and Director, Masami Kuroda

Managing Executive Officer and Director, Yoshinori Terajima

Executive Officer and Director, Nobusuke Matsui

Executive Officer and Director, Shohei Miki

Executive Officer and Director, Hiroyuki Nishi

Auditors: Tohmatsu&Co.

LOCATIONS

HQ: Nippon Life Insurance Co. (Japan)
3-5-12, Imabashi, Chuo-ku, Osaka 541-8501
Phone: (81) 6 6209 4500 **Fax:** 212 906-1933
Web: www.nissay.co.jp

PRODUCTS/OPERATIONS

Selected Products and Services

Products for Individuals
  Annuities
  Asset management
  Cancer Medical Insurance
  Dread Disease Insurance
  Endowment Insurance
  General Medical Insurance
  Limited Injury Insurance
  Non-life Insurance Products
  Nursing Care Insurance
  Physical Disability Insurance
  Products for Children
  Single-payment Products
  Term Life Insurance
  Term Life Insurance with Survival Benefits
  Whole Life Insurance
Products for Businesses
  Disability coverage
  Home buying preparation
  Medical coverage
  Retirement coverage
  Survivor coverage
  Various life plans

COMPETITORS

AIG	ING
AXA	Meiji Yasuda Life
AXA Life Insurance	MetLife
Allianz	Mitsui Life
American Life	Sompo Japan Insurance
Insurance	Sumitomo Life
Asahi Mutual Life	Taiyo Life
Dai-ichi Life	The Hartford
Daido Life	Tokio Marine
Fukoku Mutual	
Gibraltar Life	
Insurance	

HISTORICAL FINANCIALS

Company Type: Public

Income Statement

FYE: March 31

	ASSETS ($ mil.)	NET INCOME ($ mil.)	INCOME AS % OF ASSETS	EMPLOYEES
03/13	586,294	2,635	0.4%	70,004
03/12	623,756	2,741	0.4%	69,620
03/11	603,214	2,721	0.5%	70,002
03/10	522,981	2,608	0.5%	67,438
03/09	467,097	1,544	0.3%	66,074
Annual Growth	5.8%	14.3%	—	1.5%

2013 Year-End Financials

Return on assets: 0.4%
Return on equity: 7.6%
Long-term debt ($ mil.): —
No. of shares (mil.): —
Sales ($ mil): 77,167

Dividends
  Yield: —
  Payout: —
  Market value ($ mil.): —

Nippon Steel & Sumitomo Metal Corp

When it comes to steel Nippon Steel & Sumitomo Metal rates as Japan's heavy lifter. The company the world's second-largest steelmaker after ArcelorMittal manufactures pig iron and ingots steel bars plates sheets pipes and tubes as well as specialty processed and fabricated steel products. Nippon Steel & Sumitomo Metal's annual crude steel output is 48 million tons. The company's operations include engineering construction chemicals nonferrous metals ceramics electricity supply information and communications and urban development (theme parks and condominiums). In 2012 Nippon Steel acquired fellow Japanese steel maker Sumitomo Metal Industries to form a global metals giant.

The $24 billion acquisition of Sumitomo Metal Industries mating Japan's #1 and #3 steelmakers boosted the expended company's market share against ArcelorMittal and other Asian rivals in an increasingly competitive marketplace. Similar consolidation has been happening in other countries —particularly China and Russia —aimed at elevating their steel industries to compete in the international market.

Nippon Steel & Sumitomo Metal makes a range of products including pig iron and ingots steel bars plates sheets pipes and tubes and specialty processed and fabricated steel items. Other operations include engineering construction chemicals nonferrous metals ceramics electricity supply information and communications and urban development. It also provides energy finance and insurance services.

Nippon Steel & Sumitomo Metal's primary operations are in Japan but it also has major subsidiaries in Australia Brazil China Indonesia Thailand and the US.

Prior to the acquisition in fiscal 2012 (FYE March 31 2012) Nippon Steel reported flat revenues (in local currency). Increased demand from industrial machinery and carmakers in Japan was offset by a slump in demand from flood-ravaged Thailand and the slowing of other Asian economies. Nippon Steel reported a 37% drop in net income (in local currency) that year as higher selling general and administrative expenses and steeper losses on securities significantly outpaced revenues.

The company has experienced steady growth in its overall business over the past several years due to an increase in exports primarily to East Asia and more specifically China. The rising demand for steel has brought its own challenges such as bottlenecked production.

Part of its strategy to meet demand calls for alliances with other major steelmakers including one with POSCO where Nippon Steel & Sumitomo Metal has transferred its direct-melting gasification technology. Nippon Steel & Sumitomo Metal has also formed an alliance with Kobe Steel to acquire equity stakes in East Asia United Steel which will share semi-finished products. The then Nippon Steel and Sumitomo Metal Industries integrated their building products units (structural steel sheet) and civil engineering materials operations creating two new joint ventures.

In 2013 ArcelorMittal formed a joint venture with Nippon Steel & Sumitomo Metal to buy ThyssenKrupp Steel USA from ThyssenKrupp for $1.5 billion. The deal is expected to deliver $60 million in annual savings.

The company set up a joint venture in 2011 with China's Wuhan Iron & Steel Co. to make and sell tin plate in China. Nippon and Wuhan China's third-largest steelmaker will each take a 50% stake in the $293 million venture. When operational in 2013 the Hubei province-based plant will have a 400000-ton-per-year annealing and processing line and a 200000-ton-per-year electrolytic tinning line. It also increased its holding in a joint venture with Baosteel to make steel sheets for China's booming automotive market. ArcelorMittal agreed to sell its 12% stake in Baosteel-NSC/Arcelor Automotive Steel Sheets Co. (known as BNA) to Nippon Steel in 2011 making the then Nippon Steel a 50% owner.

Nippon Steel and Ternium agreed to form a joint venture in Monterrey Mexico in 2010 to manufacture and sell hot-dip galvanized and galvannealed steel sheets to serve the Mexican automobile market. Production at the $350 million Tenigal SRL de CV facility is set to begin in 2013.

HISTORY

As Japan prepared for war the government in 1934 merged Yawata Works its largest steel producer and other Japanese steelmakers into one giant company —Japan Iron & Steel. During postwar occupation Japan Iron & Steel was ordered to dissolve. Yawata Iron & Steel and Fuji Iron & Steel emerged from the dissolution and with Western assistance the Japanese steel industry recovered from the war years. In the late 1960s Fuji Steel bought Tokai Iron & Steel (1967) and Yawata Steel took over Yawata Steel Tube Company (1968).

Yawata and Fuji merged in 1970 and became Nippon Steel the world's largest steelmaker. In the 1970s the Japanese steel industry was criticized in the US; American competitors complained that Japan was "dumping" low-cost exports. Meanwhile Nippon Steel aggressively courted China.

The company diversified in the mid-1980s to wean itself from dependence on steel. It created a New Materials unit in 1984 retraining "redundant" steelworkers to make silicon wafers and forming an Electronics Division in 1986. Nippon Steel began joint ventures with IBM Japan (small computers and software) Hitachi (office workstations) and C. Itoh (information systems for small and midsized companies) in 1988 as increased steel demand for construction and cars in Japan's "bubble economy" took the company to new heights.

In an atmosphere of economic optimism the company spent more than four times the expected expense to build an amusement park capable of competing with Tokyo Disneyland. The company plowed ahead spending some $230 million on the park. Space World amusement park opened on the island of Kyushu in 1990. The company's bubble burst that year. (The theme park declared bankruptcy in May 2005 and was sold to Kamori Kanko later that year.)

In response Nippon Steel cut costs and intensified its diversification efforts by targeting electronics information and telecommunications new materials and chemicals markets. Seeking to remake its steel operations the company began a drastic phased restructuring in 1993 that included a step most Japanese companies try to avoid —cutting personnel. A semiconductor division was organized that year as part of the company's diversification strategy.

Upgrading its steel operations Nippon Steel and partner Mitsubishi in 1996 introduced the world's first mass-production method for making hot-rolled steel sheet directly from smelted stainless steel. Profits were hurt that year by a loss-making project in the information and communications segment and by a steep decline in computer memory-chip prices.

The company began operation of a Chinese steelmaking joint venture Guangzhou Pacific Tinplate in 1997. The next year its Singapore-based joint venture with Hitachi Ltd. began mass-producing computer memory chips in hopes of stemming semiconductor losses. But falling prices convinced Nippon Steel to get out of the memory chip business and in 1999 it sold its semiconductor subsidiary to South Korea's United Microelectronics.

That year the US imposed antidumping duties on the company's steel products. The next year Nippon Steel agreed to form a strategic alliance with South Korea-based Pohang Iron and Steel (POSCO) at that time the world's #1 steel maker. The deal called for the exploration of joint ventures shared research and joint procurement as well as increased equity stakes in each other (at 2%-3%). Also in 2000 Nippon Steel agreed to provide Sumitomo Metal Industries and Nisshin Steel Co. with stainless steel products.

Early in 2001 Nippon Steel formed a cooperative alliance —focused on automotive sheet products —with French steel giant Usinor (now a part of ArcelorMittal). At the end of the year Nippon Steel decided to form an alliance with Kobe Steel to pare down costs and share in distribution and production facilities. In 2002 the company continued its series of comprehensive alliances by forming alliances with Japanese steelmaker Nippon Metal Industry to exchange its semi-finished stainless steel technologies and with POSCO to build environment-related businesses.

The company reported a loss of Â51.69 billion ($430 million) for fiscal 2003 due to securities valuation losses and group restructuring charges. In 2004 Nippon Steel formed a joint venture with Baoshan Iron & Steel and Arcelor to manufacture high-grade automotive steel sheets.

Nippon Steel moved into the South American market in 2006 forming alliances with steelmaker Usiminas and iron miner CVRD. And the next year it created a JV with Baosteel and ArcelorMittal that produces automotive steel sheets.

The company joined up with Sumitomo Metal Industries in 2009 when the two companies agreed to form a joint venture that will combine their arc-welded stainless steel pipe and tube operations. Sumitomo will own 60% of the JV. The operations that make up the new company which will be called Sumikin & Nippon Steel Stainless Steel Pipe Co. achieved sales of more than $250 million in 2008.

EXECUTIVES

President and COO, Hiroshi Tomono, age 69
Chairman and CEO, Shoji Muneoka, age 68
EVP, Syuichiro Kozuka, age 66
EVP and Representative Director, Shinichi Taniguchi, age 64
EVP, Masakazu Iwaki, age 65
EVP Director Technical Development and Representative Director, Norio Katsuyama
EVP, Kosei Shindo
EVP, Shinya Higuchi
EVP, Katsuhiko Ota
EVP, Akihiro Miyasaka
President and Board Member, Shoji Muneoka, age 66
Managing Director General Manager Personnel and Labor Relations and Board Member, Kizo Hirayama, age 64
EVP and Representative Director, Kozo Uchida, age 64
EVP and Representative Director, Shinichi Taniguchi, age 64
EVP and Representative Director, Masakazu Iwaki, age 64
Managing Director and Board Member, Yasuo Hamamoto, age 62
EVP Director Technical Development and Representative Director, Norio Katsuyama
EVP and Representative Director, Kosei Shindo
Auditors: KPMGAZSA&Co.

LOCATIONS

HQ: Nippon Steel & Sumitomo Metal Corp
2-6-1 Marunouchi, Chiyoda-ku, Tokyo 100-8071
Phone: (81) 3 6867 4111   **Fax:** (81) 3 6867 5607
Web: www.nssmc.com

Sales

	% of total
Asia	
Japan	67
Other	24
Other	9
Total	**100**

PRODUCTS/OPERATIONS

Sales

	% of total
Steelmaking & Steel Fabrication	84
Chemicals	4
Urban Development	2
Total	**100**

Selected Products and Services
Steelmaking and Steel Fabrication
  Fabricated and processed steels
  Pig iron and ingots
  Pipes and tubes
  Plates and sheets
  Sections
  Specialty sheets
Engineering and Construction
  Building construction
  Civil engineering
  Marine construction
  Plant and machinery
  Technical cooperation
Chemicals
  Aluminum products
  Ammonium sulfate
  Cement
  Ceramic products
  Coal tar
  Coke
  Ferrite
  Metallic foils
  Slag products
System Solutions
  Communications services
  Computers and equipment
  Data processing
  Systems development and integration

Urban Development
  Condominiums
  Theme parks
New Materials
  Semiconductor bonding wire
  Silicon wafers
  Titanium products
  Transformers
Other operations
  Services
    Energy services
    Financial services
    Insurance services
  Transportation
    Loading and unloading
    Marine and land transportation
    Warehousing

Selected Subsidiaries and Affiliates
Subsidiaries
Nippon Steel & Sumikin Coated Sheet Corporation
Nippon Steel & Sumikin Metal Products Co. Ltd.
Nippon Steel & Sumikin Stainless Steel Corporation
Nippon Steel & Sumikin Welding Co. Ltd.
Nippon Steel Australia Pty. Limited
Nippon Steel Blast Furnace Slag Cement Co. Ltd.
Nippon Steel Drum Co. Ltd. 1654
Nippon Steel Logistics Co. Ltd.
Nippon Steel Shipping Co. Ltd.
Nippon Steel Transportation Co. Ltd.
Nippon Steel U.S.A. Inc.
Nittetsu Cement Co. Ltd.
Nittetsu Elex Co. Ltd.
Nittetsu Finance Co. Ltd.
Nittetsu Steel Pipe Co. Ltd. 4832
Nittetsu Tokai Steel Wire Co. Ltd.
NS Preferred Capital Limited
Osaka Steel Co. Ltd.
Siam Nippon Steel Pipe Co. Ltd.
The Siam United Steel (1995) Co. Ltd.
Affiliates
Daiwa Can Company
Geostr Corporation
Godo Steel Ltd.
Japan Casting & Forging Corporation
Krosaki Harima Corporation
Mitsui Mining Co. Ltd.
Nichia Steel Works Ltd.
Nippon Steel Trading Co. Ltd.
Sanko Metal Industrial Co. Ltd.
Sanyo Special Steel Co. Ltd.
Sanyu Co. Ltd.
Suzuki Metal Industry Co. Ltd.
Taihei Kogyo Co. Ltd.
Topy Industries Ltd.

COMPETITORS

ArcelorMittal	POSCO
BlueScope Steel	Tata Europe
JFE Holdings	ThyssenKrupp Steel
Kobe Steel	United States Steel
Marubeni	Vale
Mitsubishi Corp.	Yamato Kogyo

HISTORICAL FINANCIALS
Company Type: Public

Income Statement

	REVENUE ($ mil.)	NET INCOME ($ mil.)	NET PROFIT MARGIN	EMPLOYEES
03/14	53,441	2,351	4.4%	84,361
03/13	46,655	(1,323)	—	83,187
03/12	49,871	712	1.4%	60,508
03/11	49,631	1,125	2.3%	59,183
03/10	37,338	(123)	—	52,205
Annual Growth	**9.4%**	**—**	**—**	**12.7%**

FYE: March 31

2014 Year-End Financials
Debt ratio: 0.3%
Return on equity: 9.5%
Cash ($ mil.): 1,020
Current ratio: 1.26
Long-term debt ($ mil.): 16,988
No. of shares (mil.): —
Dividends
  Yield: 2.1%
  Payout: —
Market value ($ mil.): —

	STOCK PRICE ($) FY Close	P/E High/Low	PER SHARE ($) Earnings	Dividends	Book Value
03/14	27.38	— —	0.26	0.59	3.44
03/13	25.42	— —	(0.17)	0.00	3.44
03/12	27.50	— —	0.11	0.00	4.55
03/11	32.10	— —	0.18	0.00	4.58
03/10	39.02	— —	(0.02)	0.00	3.98
Annual Growth	(8.5%)	— —	—	—	(3.6%)

Nippon Telegraph & Telephone Corp. (Japan)

Nippon Telegraph and Telephone (NTT) executed an AT&T-style breakup but unlike Ma Bell's gang the family stuck together. One of the world's largest telecom companies NTT owns a controlling stake in Japan's dominant cellular carrier NTT DoCoMo (60 million subscribers) and it is a holding company for regional phone companies NTT East and NTT West which enjoy de facto monopolies in their respective markets. NTT provides long-distance international and data networking services through subsidiary NTT Communications. The company also operates an ISP and provides IT services through majority-owned NTT DATA. NTT has foreign holdings in Europe the Pacific Rim and the US. The Japanese state owns 34% of the company.

Geographic Reach

NTT does business principally in Japan although the company has investments and operations throughout the Pacific Rim –including holdings in Australia Hong Kong Malaysia the Philippines Singapore –as well as in Europe Latin America and the US. The company is investing in its international operations particularly in the areas of data networking and IT services through strategic partnerships and acquisitions primarily to address the needs of its globalized corporate clientele.

Operations

NTT's key Asian holdings include minority stakes in Philippine Long Distance Telephone and Mumbai-based Tata Teleservices. The company operates in the US through enterprise communications services subsidiary NTT America and it owns Colorado-based Web-hosting and data services provider Verio. NTT also operates a submarine communications system known as Pacific Crossing which directly links NTT's network in Japan with carriers in the US. The company does business in Europe through UK-based NTT Europe and Germany-based itelligence Cirquent and Integralis.

Financial Performance

The company brings in billions every year but its revenue has been declining year-over-year. NTT's net income has remained relatively stable in recent fiscal years despite the decreased revenue during the past two fiscal periods. The company's cash flow increased slightly in fiscal 2014 compared to fiscal 2013 levels.

Strategy

Like most large carriers NTT is investing in upgrades to its landline and mobile networks to improve and expand existing services and enable new functionality. The company has extended the reach of its domestic broadband Internet network and fiber optic video services as landline voice subscriptions continue to decline. While sales from NTT's wireless business have slipped due to decreased voice revenue the company has added mobile subscribers and improved profits by offering more robust data services and improving customer retention.

HISTORY

In 1889 the Japanese Ministry of Communications began telephone service operated as a monopoly after 1900. In 1952 the ministry formed Nippon Telegraph and Telephone Public Corporation (NTT). Regulated by the Ministry of Posts and Telecommunications NTT was charged with rebuilding Japan's war-ravaged phone system. Another company Kokusai Denshin Denwa (now KDD) was created in 1953 to handle international phone service.

Japanese authorities cast NTT in the image of AT&T but prohibited it from manufacturing to encourage competition among equipment suppliers. Nonetheless NTT bought most equipment from favored Japanese vendors. By the late 1970s NTT was a large bureaucracy perceived as inefficient and corrupt. NTT's president quipped that the only equipment the firm would buy overseas was telephone poles and mops but in 1981 NTT was forced to allow US companies to bid. The phone firm spent heavily in the 1980s installing a nationwide fiber-optic network and high-speed ISDN lines.

In 1985 Japan privatized NTT as a precursor to deregulation. At its IPO NTT became the world's most valuable public company. NTT International was established to provide overseas telecom engineering and NTT Data Communications Systems Japan's largest systems integrator was formed in 1988.

As Japan's stock market bubble burst in 1990 NTT chose AT&T Motorola and Ericsson to develop a digital mobile phone system and the next year formed NTT Mobile Communications Network (NTT DoCoMo) as its mobile carrier. Following the deregulation of Japan's cellular market NTT launched its Personal Handyphone Service (PHS) in 1995.

The Japanese government unveiled a plan to break up NTT in 1996 a year before the World Trade Organization spearheaded a historic agreement to open international telecom markets. Meanwhile the government forced NTT to allow rivals to connect to its new all-digital systems. Overseas NTT made its first significant investment in the US by buying a 12.5% stake in local carrier Teligent (later reduced).

In 1998 tiny Tokyo Telecommunications Net (a Tokyo Electric Power affiliate) offered discount phone rates spurring NTT to do the same. NTT spun off DoCoMo in the world's largest IPO at the time.

NTT lost its 1999 bidding war with the UK's Cable and Wireless for International Digital Communications. That year NTT split into three carriers two near-monopoly regional local phone providers –NTT East and NTT West –and a long-distance and international carrier called NTT Communications. Unlike AT&T's breakup in 1984 this split featured a holding company –the new NTT — that owns the three carriers. Criticized for continuing to promote last-generation ISDN as the key to high-speed Internet access NTT in 1999 began to test higher-speed digital subscriber line (DSL) service and planned to cut 21000 jobs at NTT West and NTT East over three years.

The company pressed forward with international investments taking a 49% stake in HKNet of Hong Kong and a 49% stake in Davnet Telecommunications a subsidiary of Australia's Davnet Limited (both were later increased to 100%). In 2000 the Japanese government said it would sell another 6% of NTT. That year NTT paid $5.5 billion for the 90% of US Web-hosting firm Verio that it didn't already own.

NTT purchased mobile phone application developer Panasonic Mobile Communications from parent Panasonic Corporation (formerly Matsushita Electric) in 2008.

In 2010 the company acquired a 70% stake in Singapore-based Emerio GlobeSoft in a further effort to boost its international technology services business. Active primarily in the Asia/Pacific region Emerio specialized in custom software development and support IT network support and business process outsourcing services such as account processing. Additionally NTT established a wireless subsidiary in China through NTT DoCoMo to tap into the booming market there.

EXECUTIVES

Chairman, Norio Wada, age 74
SEVP CTO CIO and Board Member, Noritaka Uji, age 65
President and CEO, Hiroo Unoura, age 66
Chairman, Satoshi Miura, age 70
President NTT DoCoMo, Ryuji Yamada, age 66
President and CEO America, Kazuhiro Gomi
President and CEO Verio, Kiyoshi Maeda
SEVP Risk Management and International Standardization Chief Compliance Officer and Board Member, Kaoru Kanazawa, age 69
SVP Director Finance and Accounting Department and Board Member; President NTT Capital UK, Toshio Kobayashi, age 62
SEVP CIO and CTO, Yasuyoshi Katayama, age 63
SEVP and CFO, Hiroki Watanabe, age 61
EVP, Hiromichi Shinohara, age 60
Board Member, Takashi Imai, age 84
Board Member, Yotaro Kobayashi, age 81
SEVP CTO CIO and Board Member, Noritaka Uji, age 65
SEVP Business Strategy CFO Director Strategic Business Development Division and Board Member, Hiroo Unoura, age 65
President CEO and Board Member, Satoshi Miura, age 70
SEVP Risk Management and International Standardization Chief Compliance Officer and Board Member, Kaoru Kanazawa, age 69
SVP Director Finance and Accounting Department and Board Member; President NTT Capital UK, Toshio Kobayashi, age 62
EVP Director Technology Planning Department and Next Generation Network Office and Board Member, Yasuyoshi Katayama, age 62
EVP Director Corporate Strategy Planning Department and Board Member, Hiroki Watanabe, age 61
SVP Director General Affairs Department and Internal Control Office and Board Member, Tetsuya Shouji
SVP Director Research and Development Planning Department and Board Member, Hiromichi Shinohara
Auditors: KPMGAZSA&Co.

LOCATIONS

HQ: Nippon Telegraph & Telephone Corp. (Japan)
Otemachi First Square, East Tower, 5-1 Otemachi, 1-Chome, Chiyoda-Ku, Tokyo 100-8116
Phone: (81) 3 6838 5481   **Fax:** (81) 3 6838 5499
Web: www.ntt.co.jp

PRODUCTS/OPERATIONS

Sales

	% of total
IP/packet	32
Fixed-line	21
Mobile	20
Systems	13
Telecom	8
Other	6
Total	**100**

COMPETITORS

AT&T	Jupiter
BT	Telecommunications
Cable & Wireless	KDDI
Deutsche Telekom	KEPCO
EMOBILE	Pacnet
Fujitsu	SOFTBANK MOBILE
Hikari Tsushin	Telstra
Internet Initiative	Tokyo Electric
Japan	

HISTORICAL FINANCIALS
Company Type: Public

Income Statement
FYE: March 31

	REVENUE ($ mil.)	NET INCOME ($ mil.)	NET PROFIT MARGIN	EMPLOYEES
03/14	105,844	5,672	5.4%	340,211
03/13	113,726	5,569	4.9%	324,713
03/12	128,091	5,701	4.5%	313,586
03/11	124,446	6,154	4.9%	302,226
03/10	108,999	5,270	4.8%	271,253
Annual Growth	(0.7%)	1.9%	—	5.8%

2014 Year-End Financials

Debt ratio: 0.2%
Return on equity: 6.9%
Cash ($ mil.): 9,537
Current ratio: 1.32
Long-term debt ($ mil.): 34,098

No. of shares (mil.): 1,110
Dividends
　Yield: 2.9%
　Payout: 16.5%
Market value ($ mil.): 30,238

	STOCK PRICE ($) FY Close	P/E High/Low		PER SHARE ($) Earnings	Dividends	Book Value
03/14	27.24	—	—	4.93	0.80	74.51
03/13	21.74	0	0	4.60	0.00	74.59
03/12	22.62	0	0	4.47	0.00	78.52
03/11	22.49	0	0	4.65	0.69	73.21
03/10	21.02	0	0	3.98	0.62	63.01
Annual Growth	6.7%	—	—	5.5%	6.3%	4.3%

Nishi-Nippon City Bank Ltd.

The Nishi-Nippon City Bank is more of a community bank. It operates about 200 branches in the Kyushu region of southern Japan (poplation 14.5 million) for a customer base of mainly individuals and small and midsized businesses. Nishi-Nippon City Bank offers traditional banking services such as checking and savings accounts as well as securities credit guarantees credit cards and credit management and business consulting services. In addition to the parent bank it operates through eight subsidiaries. It also maintains representative offices in Hong Kong Seoul and Shanghai. Tracing its roots back to 1944 the bank took its current form in 2004 when Nishi-Nippon Bank acquired Fukuoka City Bank.

EXECUTIVES

Chairman, Masahiro Honda
President and Director, Isao Kubota
Deputy President and Director, Kazushige Higuchi
Executive Director, Seiji Isoyama
Executive Director, Hiromichi Tanigawa
Executive Director, Shigeru Urayama
Managing Director, Sadamasa Okamura
Managing Director, Kiyota Takata
Executive Director, Soichi Kawamoto
Managing Director, Yasuyuki Ishida
Managing Director, Hiroyuki Irie
Managing Director, Michiharu Kitazaki
President and Director, Isao Kubota
Deputy President and Director, Kazushige Higuchi
Executive Director, Seiji Isoyama
Executive Director, Hiromichi Tanigawa
Executive Director, Shigeru Urayama
Managing Director, Sadamasa Okamura
Managing Director, Kiyota Takata
Executive Director, Soichi Kawamoto
Managing Director, Yasuyuki Ishida
Managing Director, Hiroyuki Irie
Managing Director, Michiharu Kitazaki

LOCATIONS

HQ: Nishi-Nippon City Bank Ltd.
　3-1-1 Hakata-ekimae, Hakata-ku, Fukuoka 812-0011
Phone: (81) 92 476 1111
Web: www.ncbank.co.jp

COMPETITORS

Aozora Bank	Mitsubishi UFJ
Awa Bank	Financial Group
Bank of Kyoto	Nanto Bank
Bank of Yokohama	Norinchukin Bank
Chiba Bank	Shiga Bank
Chugoku Bank	Shinsei Bank
Chuo Mitsui Trust	Shizuoka Bank
Eighteenth Bank Ltd.	Sumitomo Mitsui
Fukuoka Financial	Suruga Bank
Group	Tokyo Tomin Bank
Hokkoku Bank	Towa Bank
Hokuhoku Financial	
Group	

HISTORICAL FINANCIALS
Company Type: Public

Income Statement
FYE: March 31

	ASSETS ($ mil.)	NET INCOME ($ mil.)	INCOME AS % OF ASSETS	EMPLOYEES
03/14	77,767	232	0.3%	4,259
03/13	82,627	195	0.2%	4,392
03/12	93,513	219	0.2%	4,534
03/11	89,386	644	0.7%	4,677
03/10	78,022	233	0.3%	4,688
Annual Growth	(0.1%)	(0.1%)	—	(2.4%)

2014 Year-End Financials

Return on assets: 0.3%
Return on equity: 6.1%
Long-term debt ($ mil.): —
No. of shares (mil.): 794
Sales ($ mil): 1,513

Dividends
　Yield: —
　Payout: —
Market value ($ mil.): —

Nissan Motor Co., Ltd.

Nissan Motor one of Japan's leading automakers wants to get big by going small. Through its small-car initiative the company primarily produces low-cost and fuel-efficient small cars with standard comfort safety style and performance. Nissan's models include Maxima and Sentra cars and Altima and Infiniti upscale sedans as well as pickups SUVs and sports cars. It is also one of the world's largest manufacturers of forklifts. Renault holds a 43% stake in Nissan Motor and Nissan has a 15% stake in Renault constituting the Renault-Nissan Alliance.

Nissan manufactures in about 20 countries and sells and services products in more than 160 countries.

Revenue rose around 7% in fiscal 2012 compared with 2011. Despite such challenges as the Great East Japan Earthquake Nissan enjoyed record sales in fiscal 2012. It sold more than 4.8 billion units in 2012 which was about a 16% increase from the previous year. It also grew its market share by 0.6 points to more than 6%. The company's strong sales were supported by demand for the Serena and Juke in Japan; the Sunny Teana Sylphy Qashqai and Tiida in China; and the Altima Rogue and Versa in North America. The company expects to enjoy double-digit sales growth in fiscal 2013 as a result in part of demand in China the company's largest market.

The Nissan Power 88 plan calls for attaining 8% global market share and an 8% operating profit margin by 2017. A major element of Power 88 is the development of about 90 new technologies including a next-generation XTRONIC continuously variable transmission technology. The plan additionally includes investing 70% of research and development expenses into green technology.

Nissan responded to the 2008 financial crisis by initiating what it calls a localization strategy that stresses a balance of manufacturing and sourcing with sales operations. As a result of the strategy Nissan has implemented local manufacturing and sales of the V-platform car in China India Mexico and Thailand. China is not only Nissan's largest market but also the location of its biggest manufacturing site the Huada facility —where the Tiida hatchback is made —with the ability to produce some 600000 units a year. Nissan spearheads its business development efforts in China through a joint venture with Dongfeng Motor.

Nissan also has set a goal of increasing the percentage of fully built units that are locally made in the Americas to 85% by 2015. New plants in Brazil and Mexico are tasked with increasing production in the Americas from 1.2 million units a year in 2011 to 2 million units annually by 2014. The Great East Japan of Earthquake of 2011 and other contingencies also lead the company to create more efficient business continuity procedures for parts purchasing.

HISTORY

In 1911 US-trained Masujiro Hashimoto established Tokyo-based Kwaishinsha Motor Car Works to repair import and manufacture cars. Kwaishinsha made its first car sporting its DAT ("fast rabbit" in Japanese) logo in 1913. Renamed DAT Motors in 1925 and suffering from a strong domestic preference for American cars the company consolidated with ailing Jitsuyo Motors in 1926. DAT introduced the son of DAT in 1931 —the Datsun minicar ("son" means "damage or loss" in Japanese hence the spelling change).

Tobata Casting (cast iron and auto parts) bought Datsun's production facilities in 1933. Tobata's Yoshisuke Aikawa believed there was a niche for small cars and the car operations were spun off as Nissan Motors that year.

During WWII the Japanese government limited Nissan's production to trucks and airplane engines; Nissan survived postwar occupation in part due to business with the US Army. The company went public in 1951 and signed a licensing agreement the next year with Austin Motor (UK) which put it back in the car business. A 40% import tax allowed Nissan to compete in Japan even though it had higher costs than those of foreign carmakers.

Nissan entered the US market in 1958 with the model 211 using the Datsun name; it established Nissan Motor Corporation in Los Angeles in 1960. Exports rose as factory automation led to higher quality and lower costs. In the 1970s Nissan expanded exports of fuel-efficient cars such as the Datsun B210. The company became the leading US car importer in 1975.

The company's name change in the US from Datsun to Nissan during the 1980s confused customers and took six years to complete. In 1986 Nissan became the first major Japanese carmaker to build its products in Europe. It launched its high-end Infiniti line in the US in 1989.

Nissan and Japanese telecom firm KDDI Corporation set up cellular phone operations in 1992. Japan's recession resulted in a $450 million loss the next year. The company cut costs in 1993 and sold $200 million in real-estate holdings in 1994.

Nissan suffered its fourth straight year of losses posting an $834 million loss for 1996. Fiscal 1997 brought profits for Nissan —its first since 1992 —in part the result of cost-cutting moves sales to countries with currencies stronger than the yen and the launching of new models. In 1998 Nissan received an $827 million loan from the government-owned Japan Development Bank to restructure its debt.

Suffering under an estimated $30 billion in debt in 1999 Nissan invited major carmakers to buy into the company. Renault took a 37% stake and a 15% stake in affiliate Nissan Diesel Motor for $5.4 billion. The stake gave Renault veto power and enabled it to install its chief cost-cutter Carlos Ghosn (nicknamed "Le Cost Killer" based on his talent for turning red ink black) as COO. Ghosn began plans to slash the number of suppliers close five plants and cut its workforce by 14% by 2002.

Under the watchful eye of Ghosn Nissan went from a doubtful future to a corporate success story in just a few years. The company announced its Nissan Revival Plan (NRP) in 1999. The plan called for the closing of inefficient factories workforce reductions curbing purchasing costs sharing operations with Renault and introducing new products. By 2001 Nissan was again making a profit —one year earlier than the NRP predicted.

Not satisfied with this Nissan then launched a three-year business scheme called Nissan 180 aiming to grow annual sales by 1 million units generate an 8% operating profit margin and eliminate automotive debt. Nissan made good on all these goals. In fact the company's operating margin exceeded 10% every year since the plan was initiated (making it the envy of most of the world's carmakers). Nissan not only managed to erase automotive debt it piled up cash reserves of about $1.65 billion. Meanwhile Nissan sold its interests in nine mobile-phone companies and its powder metallurgy business.

In 2000 Nissan sold its stake in Fuji Heavy Industries. That year Ghosn became president of Nissan; Nissan's former president Yoshikazu Hanawa remained as CEO and chairman. Nissan also announced that it was developing a full-sized truck for the US market and that it and Renault were combining their European sales and marketing operations. Late in the year the company announced plans to build a $930 million manufacturing plant in the US.

Ghosn was named CEO (in addition to president) in 2001. Later in 2001 Nissan announced it would take a 15% stake in Renault while the French carmaker would increase its stake in Nissan to 44%. These steps along with the French government's decision to reduce its interest in Renault from 44% to 25% were aimed at further strengthening the bond between the two companies. In 2002 Nissan and Renault completed their planned equity swap.

The following year Nissan rolled out the most dramatic new lineup of vehicles it had introduced in years. The company debuted the Murano urban SUV the full-size Titan pickup and the full-size Armada SUV.

In mid-2005 Nissan announced that it had selected its assembly plant in Tennessee for production of its first hybrid vehicle. The following year Nissan began talks with AB Volvo and the Chinese authorities for the sale of Nissan's 50% stake in Dongfeng Motor —China's largest maker of commercial trucks.

Later in 2006 billionaire General Motors investor Kirk Kerkorian (who owned about a 10% stake in GM at the time) proposed that the beleaguered US automaker should form a three-way alliance with Nissan and Renault. The three companies' boards subsequently held hasty meetings to ponder the idea. The companies later announced they'd decided there would be no alliance. Also in 2006 Nissan sold its remaining 6% stake in Nissan Diesel Motor to AB Volvo for about $69 million.

Nissan hit its first series of speed bumps in 2006 after a long stretch of smooth road. Sales hiccups in Japan the US and Europe prompted a few tweaks. After a surge of new products in 2005 Nissan rode out the product in-between time in the US until freshened versions of the Altima and Sentra were unveiled in late 2006. Nissan also made production adjustments at its plants in the US and Japan.

Just as some observers began to suggest a dearth of hybrids might also be causing sales doldrums at Nissan the company devised an ambitious hybrid scheme. Late in 2006 Nissan announced plans to introduce a hybrid based on Nissan-developed technology in fiscal 2010. The move was part of the self-described "Nissan Green Program 2010." The plan also called for bringing clean diesel engines to Europe in fiscal 2007 with the US China and Japan getting them sometime after April 2010.

The company also planned to expand the availability of flex-fuel vehicles (capable of burning gasoline and ethanol-derived E85) in 2007 with the debut of a flex-fuel Armada (the flex-fuel Titan was introduced in 2004). The Nissan Green plan also called for reducing CO_2 plant emissions to 7% less than 2005 levels by 2010 the vague launching of an electric car sometime in the next decade the introduction of a three-liter car that will go more than 60 miles on less than a gallon of gas and entering the lithium-ion battery market.

In a deal completed in 2008 Nissan agreed to build a small car for Chrysler; in return a Chrysler manufacturing facility in Mexico would make the replacement for the Nissan Titan truck scheduled to debut in 2011. However in 2009 both parties decided to freeze the project and reassess the profitability of the venture. Chrysler admitted that having Fiat on board (Fiat had invested in Chrysler in 2009) to develop small cars had a bearing in the decision.

EXECUTIVES

Chairman President and CEO, Carlos Ghosn, age 60

Vice Chairman, Toshiyuki Shiga

EVP Manufacturing and SCM, Hidetoshi Imazu

EVP and CFO, Joseph G. (Joe) Peter, age 51

EVP, Mitsuhiko (Mike) Yamashita

EVP and Chief Competitive Officer, Hiroto Saikawa, age 61

Corporate VP Infiniti Product Development Vehicle Test Technology Development, Tsuyoshi Yamaguchi

EVP, Kimiyasu Nakamura

SVP; President Infiniti Global, Johan de Nysschen, age 49

SVP External and Government Affairs and Intellectual Asset Management, Hitoshi Kawaguchi

SVP Technology Development Division, Minoru Shinohara

SVP Office of CEO, Greg Kelly

Corporate VP, Toshifumi Hirai

Corporate VP, Atsushi Hirose

EVP, Takao Katagiri

Executive Vice President; Chairman & President of Subsidiaries; Director, Colin Dodge

Corporate VP, Asako Hoshino

Corporate VP and CIO, Celso Guiotoko

SVP Production Engineering Division, Shigeaki Kato

Fellow, Haruyoshi Kumura

EVP and Chief Planning Officer, Andy Palmer

Corporate VP, Gilles Normand

SVP Product Development Division Nissan PV Product Development Division No.2 and Nissan LCV Product Development Division, Atsushi Shizuta

Corporate VP, Joji Tagawa

SVP Purchasing, Yasuhiro Yamauchi

SVP Japan Marketing and Sales, Massaaki Nishizawa

Fellow, Kimio Tomita

Corporate VP, Shohei Kimura

Corporate VP, Shunichi Toyomasu

Corporate VP, Yusuke Takahashi

Corporate VP, John Martin

Corporate VP, Vincent Cobee

Corporate VP, Takao Asami

Corporate VP, Makoto Yoshimoto

Corporate VP, Hideyuki Sakamoto

Corporate VP, Hideto Murakami

Corporate VP Global Control Budget and Accounting, Hiroshi Karube

Corporate VP, Shuichi Nishimura

Auditor, Toshiyuki Nakamura

EVP, Jose Munoz

SVP Manufacturing and Industrial Engineering, Akira Sakurai

Director Customer and Sales Satisfaction, William (Billy) Hayes

IR Contact Officer, Minoru Tagami

Executive Officer, Rakesh Kochhar

Managing Executive Officer, Toshiaki Ohtani

EVP and Chief Performance Officer, Trevor Mann

SVP; President Dongfend Motor, Jun Seki

Corporate VP, Roel De Vries

Director, Jean-Baptiste Duzan, age 68

SVP Design and Brands Champion, Shiro Nakamura

Vice Chairman, Toshiyuki Shiga

EVP Manufacturing and SCM and Director, Hidetoshi Imazu

EVP Research and Development and Total Customer Satisfaction Function and Director, Mitsuhiko (Mike) Yamashita

EVP Japan Asia/Pacific Industrial Machinery Marine Administration for Affiliates Purchasing and Director, Hiroto Saikawa, age 60

EVP Americas Operations and Director; Chairman Americas, Carlos Tavares, age 54

EVP Europe Africa Middle East India and New
 Project and Director, Colin Dodge
Auditors: Ernst&YoungShinNihon

LOCATIONS

HQ: Nissan Motor Co., Ltd.
 1-1-1 Takashima, Nishi-ku, Yokohama 220-8686
Phone: (81) 45 523 5523
Web: www.nissan-global.com

PRODUCTS/OPERATIONS

Selected Products

Forklifts
  Engine-powerd forklifts
  Electric-powered forklifts
  Warehouse products
    Order pickers
    Pallet stackers
    Pallet transporters
    Reach trucks
Infiniti
  Infiniti G
  Infiniti G convertible
  Infiniti G coupe
  Infiniti M
  Infiniti EX
  Infiniti FX
  Infiniti JX
  Infiniti QX
Nissan
  Altima
  Altima coupe
  Altima hybrid
  Armada
  Cube
  Frontier
  GT-R
  Maxima
  Murano
  Pathfinder
  Rogue
  Sentra
  Titan
  Versa
  Xterra
Nissan Marine outboard motors

COMPETITORS

BMW	Isuzu
CLARK Material	Kia Motors
Handling	Mazda
Chrysler	Mitsubishi Motors
Crown Equipment	NACCO Industries
Daihatsu	Peugeot
Daimler	Saab Automobile
Deere	Suzuki Motor
Fiat	Tata Motors
Ford Motor	Toyota
Fuji Heavy Industries	Volkswagen
General Motors	Volvo
Honda	Volvo Car Corp.
Hyundai Motor	

HISTORICAL FINANCIALS

Company Type: Public

Income Statement

FYE: March 31

	REVENUE ($ mil.)	NET INCOME ($ mil.)	NET PROFIT MARGIN	EMPLOYEES
03/14	101,555	3,769	3.7%	147,939
03/13	102,342	3,639	3.6%	160,530
03/12	114,701	4,162	3.6%	157,365
03/11	105,946	3,855	3.6%	155,098
03/10	80,478	453	0.6%	151,698
Annual Growth	6.0%	69.8%	—	(0.6%)

2014 Year-End Financials

Debt ratio: 0.3%
Return on equity: 9.6%
Cash ($ mil.): 7,971
Current ratio: 1.66
Long-term debt ($ mil.): 35,116
No. of shares (mil.): —
Dividends
 Yield: 4.7%
 Payout: —
Market value ($ mil.): —

	STOCK PRICE ($) FY Close	P/E High/Low	PER SHARE ($) Earnings	Dividends	Book Value
03/14	17.87	— —	0.90	0.84	10.08
03/13	19.20	— —	0.87	0.00	9.64
03/12	21.47	— —	1.00	0.00	9.37
03/11	17.65	— —	0.92	0.12	8.82
03/10	17.20	— —	0.11	0.00	7.36
Annual Growth	1.0%	— —	68.6%	—	8.2%

Noble Group Ltd

LOCATIONS

HQ: Noble Group Ltd
 18th Floor, MassMutual Tower, 38 Gloucester Road,
Phone: (852) 2861 3511   **Fax:** (852) 2527 0282
Web: www.thisisnoble.com

HISTORICAL FINANCIALS

Company Type: Public

Income Statement

FYE: December 31

	REVENUE ($ mil.)	NET INCOME ($ mil.)	NET PROFIT MARGIN	EMPLOYEES
12/13	97,878	243	0.2%	15,649
12/12	94,045	471	0.5%	15,000
12/11	80,732	431	0.5%	14,000
12/10	56,696	605	1.1%	8,000
12/09	31,183	556	1.8%	4,900
Annual Growth	33.1%	(18.7%)	—	33.7%

2013 Year-End Financials

Debt ratio: 31.1%
Return on equity: 4.7%
Cash ($ mil.): 1,055
Current ratio: 1.32
Long-term debt ($ mil.): 4,091
No. of shares (mil.): —
Dividends
 Yield: 1.9%
 Payout: 947.6%
Market value ($ mil.): —

	STOCK PRICE ($) FY Close	P/E High/Low	PER SHARE ($) Earnings	Dividends	Book Value
12/13	16.68	600361	0.03	0.32	0.78
12/12	18.81	351237	0.07	0.30	0.79
12/11	17.55	543235	0.07	0.46	0.72
12/10	33.35	340309	0.10	0.70	0.66
Annual Growth	(20.6%)	— —	(23.8%)	(18.0%)	4.2%

Nomura Holdings Inc

Nomura Holdings is the parent company of Nomura Securities Japan's leading investment bank and brokerage house. The company performs trading equity and bond underwriting research and mergers and acquisitions (M&A) advisory services. It also makes private equity and venture capital investments. Subsidiary Nomura Asset Management

is Japan's largest asset management company in terms of assets under management in investment trusts which it offers to retail investors and through institutional funds. It oversees some Å71 trillion in retail client assets. Nomura Holdings has operations in more than 30 countries; Nomura Securities International is the company's US trading and investment banking unit.

Nomura operates through three business divisions: retail (investment consultation services) asset management (investment trusts and investment advisory services) and wholesale (corporate and institutional products and services). On the retail side Nomura Securities serves individuals and businesses from nearly 200 locations in Japan. The group controls about 20% of Japan's public mutual fund market. Additional units include Nomura Trust & Banking big-ticket financing firm Nomura Babcock & Brown and the Nomura Institute of Capital Markets Research.

Nomura's earnings have improved significantly since fiscal 2009 when the group lost more than $7 billion. Revenues grew 37% in 2012 from the prior year despite challenges that faced the financial sector. During that fiscal year Japan was recovering from a major earthquake and tsunami which caused disruptions to industry in the country and led to a reduction in the nation's real gross domestic product. Nomura's retail profits slipped that year by 11% primarily because of a decline in brokerage and investment trust commissions. Although the company saw declines in earnings it saw increases in client accounts and client asset inflows. Wholesale profits also slipped in 2012 by 12% to Å555.9 billion. Those declines were largely attributed to market weaknesses related to the sovereign debt crisis in Europe.

The group's strategy for growth in its retail business includes providing a variety of delivery channels for services including online and telephone centers. Nomura continues to open new retail branches and in 2011 launched Nomura Net & Call to provide non-face-to-face services. Nomura is also focused on providing a diverse product offering.

Internationally Nomura is well-positioned to take advantage of expected growth in other Asian nations. It manages funds that invest in several countries including Thailand India Taiwan and Korea.

In the wake of 2011's record earthquake and tsunami disaster Nomura marketed stock-based loans to consumers. The niche product generally provides customers with access to cash more quickly than they would be able to get via traditional bank loans. As a result of the marketing push and the demand for liquid capital Nomura's retail lending jumped by 50% within weeks.

HISTORY

Tokushichi Nomura started a currency exchange Nomura Shoten in Osaka in 1872 and began trading stock. His son Tokushichi II took over and in 1910 formed Nomura's first syndicate to underwrite part of a government bond issue. It established the Osaka Nomura Bank in 1918. The bond department became independent in 1925 and became Nomura Securities. The company opened a New York office in 1927 entering stock brokerage in 1938.

The firm rebuilt and expanded retail operations after WWII. It encouraged stock market investing by promoting "million ryo savings chests" —small boxes in which people saved cash (ryo was an old form of currency). When savings reached 5000 yen savers could buy into investment trusts. Nomura distributed more than a million chests in 10 years.

Nomura followed clients overseas in the 1960s helped underwrite a US issue of Sony stock and opened a London office. It became Japan's leading securities firm after a 1965 stock market crash decimated rival Yamaichi Securities. The firm grew rapidly in the 1970s ushering investment capital in and out of Japan and competing with banks by issuing corporate debt securities.

As the Japanese economy soared in the 1980s the company opened Nomura Bank International in London (1986) and bought 20% of US mergers and acquisitions advisor Wasserstein Perella (1988 sold 2001).

Then the Japanese economic bubble burst. Nomura's stock toppled 70% from its 1987 peak and underwriting plummeted. In 1991 and 1992 amid revelations that Nomura and other brokerages had reimbursed favored clients' trading losses the firm was accused of manipulating stock in companies owned by Japanese racketeers. Nomura's chairman and president --both named Tabuchi --resigned admitting no wrongdoing.

The firm trimmed staff and offices and focused on its most efficient operations. From 1993 to 2000 it seesawed from red to black and back again.

Junichi Ujiie became president after the payoff scandal; he restructured operations to prepare for Japan's financial deregulation. Nomura invested in pub chain Inntrepreneur and William Hill a UK betting chain. It also created an entertainment lending unit to lend against future royalties or syndication fees and spun off a minority stake in its high-risk US real estate business which ceased lending altogether the next year.

In 1998 Nomura was dealt a double blow when Asian economies collapsed and Russia defaulted on its debts. Incurring substantial losses the firm refocused on its domestic market and reduced overseas operations. That year it teamed with Industrial Bank of Japan for derivatives sales in the UK and pension plan consulting in Japan.

In 1999 Nomura bailed out ailing property subsidiary Nomura Finance which had been crippled by the sinking Japanese real estate market. It also invested heavily in UK real estate and bought 40% of the Czech beer market with South African Breweries.

The next year the firm agreed to buy the business services arm of Welsh utilities firm Hyder; it also bought 114000 flats in Germany with local government authorities its first European deal outside the UK. Also in 2000 Nomura sold its assets in pachinko parlors and "love" hotels Japanese cultural traditions with less-than-sparkling reputations. British authorities that year fined Nomura traders in relation to charges of trying to rig Australia's stock market in 1996.

The company converted to a holding company structure in 2001 and months later made its debut on the NYSE. It made two big deals in the UK that year buying hotel chain Le Meridien and becoming the nation's largest pub owner via the purchase of some 1000 locations from Bass. The company also bought a stake in Thomas Weisel Partners to increase its participation in M&A action between US and Japanese firms. In 2002 the company decided to sell the network of more than 4100 pubs to a consortium of private investors for some $3 billion.

In 2007 Nomura acquired global agency brokerage Instinet. The deal allowed the company to begin offering electronic trading services.

In 2008 Japanese regulators chose a consortium led by Nomura to take control of troubled Ashikaga Bank from the government; Nomura's private equity arm took a stake of about 45% in Ashikaga. The deal marked Nomura's first foray into retail banking.

The global financial crisis heavily impacted Nomura which reported steep declines in 2008 and 2009. The company lost some Â208 billion ($2 billion) in 2009 alone on trading and equity invest-

ments. The US subprime mortgage bust further hurt the group which lost money on mortgage-backed securities.

In response Nomura cut operating costs and fine-tuned its offerings. The following year the company boosted its global investment banking capabilities by acquiring parts of the fallen bulge-bracket firm Lehman Brothers including operations in Asia Europe and the Middle East as well as the India-based back office operations. (In its post-acquisition transition the company laid off some 11% of its UK workforce or about 1000 employees in its London office.) In an effort to boost its domestic asset management business Nomura bought NikkoCiti Trust and Banking from Citigroup in 2009. The company also exited the US residential mortgage-backed securities business entirely.

The Lehman Brothers acquisition helped boost Nomura's profile in European equities and fixed-income trading. Adding on to that purchase Nomura bought London-based Tricorn Partners --a move that further complements its UK corporate finance advisory business.

Nomura Asset Management also bought a 35% stake in LIC Mutual Fund Asset Management Company of India. The deal gave Nomura a larger foothold in the Indian market and strengthened its credentials as an international asset manager.

EXECUTIVES

President and COO, Atsushi Yoshikawa, age 60
Senior Managing Director, Paul Spanswick
Senior Managing Director; Regional Co-CEO Europe Middle East and Africa, Yasuo Kashiwagi
CFO, Shigesuke Kashiwagi, age 55
Senior Managing Director, Akihito Watanabe, age 57
Senior Managing Director, Hiromasa Yamazaki
Senior Managing Director, Naoki Matsuba
Executive Managing Director, Shoichi Nagamatsu, age 63
Senior Managing Director, Noriaki Nagai, age 57
Senior Managing Director, Yuji Nakata
CEO; President Nomura Securities, Koji Nagai
Senior Managing Director; Regional CEO Asia except Japan, Minoru Shinohara
Joint Head Global Investment Banking, William Vereker
Chief Risk Officer and Senior Managing Director, David Benson
Senior Managing Director Advisory Fund Management Nomura Asset Management, Kunio Watanabe
Senior Managing Director, Kentaro Okuda
Senior Managing Director, Junko Nakagawa
Head of Regional Property Research, Paul Louie
Senior Partner Chairman, Edward Tse
Senior Managing Director; Regional CEO Americas, David Findlay
Senior Managing Director, Steven Ashley
Senior Managing Director; Regional CEO Europe Middle East and Africa, Jeremy Bennett
Senior Managing Director; Regional Co-CEO Americas, Toshiya Hasegawa
Senior Managing Director, Masaru Konno
Senior Managing Director, Eiji Miura
Senior Managing Director, Hisato Miyashita
Executive Managing Director, Toshio Morita
Senior Managing Director, Lewis O'Donald
Senior Managing Director and CIO, Naohiro Sako
Senior Managing Director, Chie Toriumi
Deputy President COO and Director Nomura Holdings and Nomura Securities; Chairman Wholesale, Takumi Shibata, age 60
President CEO and Director; President CEO and Director Nomura Securities, Kenichi Watanabe, age 60
Director, Masahiro Sakane, age 72

Director, Masaharu Shibata, age 76
Director, Masanori Itatani
Director, Hideaki Kubori, age 69
Director, Haruo Tsuji, age 81
Director, Fumihide Nomura, age 79
Director, Yoshifumi Kawabata, age 61
Executive Managing Director and Merchant Banking CEO; Director and President Nomura Principal Finance; Senior Managing Director Nomura Securities, Soichi Nagamatsu, age 62
Executive Managing Director Group Compliance Head Head Global Operations and CIO; Senior Corporate Managing Director Nomura Securities, Hiroshi Tanaka, age 57
Director, Tsuguoki Fujinuma
Auditors: Ernst&YoungShinNihon

LOCATIONS

HQ: Nomura Holdings Inc
9-1 Nihonbashi 1-chome, Chuo-Ku, Tokyo 103-8645
Phone: (81) 3 5255 1000
Web: www.nomuraholdings.com

PRODUCTS/OPERATIONS

Sales

	% of total
Interest &	24
Commissions	19
Net gain on	15
Asset management & portfolio service	8
Fees from investment	3
Gain on private equity	1
Gain on investments in equity	-
Other	30
Total	**100**

COMPETITORS

Bank of America	Goldman Sachs
Barclays	HSBC
Boom Securities	SMBC Nikko Securities
Daiwa Securities Group	UBS Investment Bank
Deutsche Bank	

HISTORICAL FINANCIALS

Company Type: Public

Income Statement

FYE: March 31

	ASSETS ($ mil.)	NET INCOME ($ mil.)	INCOME AS % OF ASSETS	EMPLOYEES
03/14	421,629	2,069	0.5%	27,670
03/13	403,248	1,139	0.3%	27,956
03/12	435,172	141	0.0%	34,395
03/11	443,117	346	0.1%	26,871
03/10	345,052	725	0.2%	26,374
Annual Growth	5.1%	29.9%	—	1.2%

2014 Year-End Financials

Return on assets: 0.5%	Dividends
Return on equity: 8.8%	Yield: 2.1%
Long-term debt ($ mil.): —	Payout: 0.0%
No. of shares (mil.): —	Market value ($ mil.): —
Sales ($ mil): 8,905	

	STOCK PRICE ($) FY Close	P/E High/Low		PER SHARE ($) Earnings	Dividends	Book Value
03/14	6.43	0	0	0.54	0.14	6.55
03/13	6.17	0	0	0.30	0.00	6.57
03/12	4.41	0	0	0.04	0.00	7.01
03/11	5.20	0	0	0.09	0.09	6.98
03/10	7.33	0	0	0.23	0.13	6.21
Annual Growth	(3.2%)	—	—	23.7%	1.0%	1.4%

Nordea Bank AB

Nordea Bank is one of the largest financial services groups in the Nordic and Baltic Sea regions. Sweden is its home but Nordea also is active in Denmark Finland Norway Estonia Latvia Lithuania Poland and Russia. The bank splits its operations into three main divisions: retail banking wholesale banking and wealth management. The bank also provides life and pension products. It operates through a network of about 1400 branches and serves some 11 million customers including about 700000 corporate clients —a key customer segment for Nordea. About 60% of its lending activity is to corporations. Its Internet bank claims nearly 6 million users.

Nordea Bank also has an international network present in some 20 countries around the world. Additional offices are located in major cities such as New York London and Frankfurt. In addition Nordea has various agreements with banks in places such as Asia and Latin America where customers are able to be served through representative offices.

Growth in new European markets has been a focus for Nordea. The company purchased a 75% stake in Russian bank JSB Orgresbank. It bought the remaining stake in 2009 and the bank was rebranded OJSC Nordea Bank. Nordea also bought the Polish life insurance operations of Finnish banking group Sampo doubling Nordea's customer base in Poland. However Nordea put the breaks on aggressive growth and completely halted branch expansion in Russia and the Baltic countries in light of the global financial crisis.

The worldwide economic slowdown began affecting Nordea in 2008 as the bank saw an increase in loan losses. Nordea announced a "middle-of-the-road approach" in 2009 and slowed acquisition growth to focus on doing more business with existing customers and attracting new customers with good credit.

By 2010 Nordea emerged from the financial crisis and started looking to grow again. The company is mostly focused on organic growth in order to attract new customers. It launched several initiatives to increase customer activity income and profit. That year Nordea also opened 45 new branches in Poland which is one of the most important growth markets for the company. Other growth strategies include expanding the company's corporate merchant banking business in Sweden in addition to investing in technical infrastructure.

In 2011 Nordea reorganized itself in order to focus on capital and cost efficiency. The reshuffling was done in effort to adapt to new government regulations that require banks to hold more capital. That year company chairman Hans Dalborg stepped down from the post. He was replaced by Bjorn Wahlroos.

Sampo owns more than 20% of Nordea. The Swedish government held a nearly 20% stake in the bank but reduced that to 13% in 2011 as part of its plan to raise capital. It plans to sell more and possibly all of its Nordea stake over time.

HISTORY

Nordea traces its roots to 1974 when two Swedish government-owned banks Postbanken and Sveriges Kreditbank merged to form the country's largest bank Post-och Kreditbanken (PKbanken) in order to compete with S-E-Banken and Svenska Handelsbanken.

PKbanken didn't hold on to the top spot long. By the early 1980s a recession and languid prof-

its sank the company to third. However the firm did expand teaming with Norway's Christiana Bank og Kreditkasse to open joint offices in Hong Kong Houston London So Paolo and Singapore.

As regulatory restrictions in Sweden eased the government spun off 15% of its interest in the company on the Stockholm Stock Exchange in 1984.

PKbanken pulled out of its deal in London with Christiana Bank in 1986 but it bought a stake in London-based English Trust Group to expand its merchant banking services. In 1988 PKbanken acquired government-owned Carnegie Fondkommission Sweden's largest brokerage and in 1989 purchased the state-controlled Swedish Investment Bank a provider of funding to small and midsized businesses.

A year later PKbanken acquired regional Swedish bank Nordbanken and assumed the smaller firm's name. Soon after the government axed the combined firm's top officers and installed new management. The purging didn't help as another recession and a real estate market crash hammered the company's bottom line. In 1992 the Swedish government intervened again acquiring all of the outstanding shares of Nordbanken that it did not already own. The company rebounded quickly after selling bad loans to the state and cutting staff by a fifth.

In 1994 the Swedish government transferred its ownership of Gota Bank to Nordbanken. The company resumed trading on the Stockholm Stock Exchange the following year.

Across the border in Finland rivals Union Bank of Finland and Kansallis-Osake-Pankki merged in 1995 to create Merita Bank the country's largest.

In 1997 Nordbanken and Merita Bank combined to form MeritaNordbanken but their parents Nordbanken Holdings and Merita Ab remained separate. In 2000 the company bought Danish bank Unidanmark. MeritaNordbanken's holding companies united and assumed the name Nordic Baltic Holding. Later the company changed its name to Nordea an amalgamation of "Nordic" and "idea."

In 2001 Nordea bought Christiania Bank og Kreditkasse and later that year attached the Nordea Bank name to its banking subsidiaries in Denmark Finland Norway and Sweden.

By 2003 the company composed primarily of the four national banking groups —Nordea Bank Denmark Nordea Bank Finland Nordea Bank Norway and Nordea Bank Sweden —decided to change its complex legal structure and create one European company under the Nordea Bank banner.

Nordea acquired Denmark's Fionia Bank in 2009 including the bank's staff and its 29 branches but excluding some 2000 troubled corporate customers. The Denmark government had taken control of the failing bank earlier in the year.

EXECUTIVES

Vice Chairman, Timo Peltola, age 68, $167,377 total compensation
President and CEO, Christian Clausen, age 59, $1,408,087 total compensation
Chairman, Bjorn Wahlroos, age 62
EVP and CFO; Head Group Corporate Centre; Country Senior Executive Sweden, Fredrik Rystedt, age 50
Head Banking Sweden, Hans Jacobson
Head Planning and Control and Investor Relations, Johan Ekwall
Executive Vice President Chief Risk Officer Head Group Risk Management Country Senior Executive Finland, Ari Kaperi, age 54
Head of Banking Products and Group Operations, Michael Rasmussen, age 50
Head of Banking Denmark, Anders Jensen
Chief Press Officer Denmark, Claus Christensen

Chief Press Officer Finland, Kati Tommiska
Chief Press Officer Norway, Thomas Sevang
Press Officer Poland Russia Baltic Region and International, Anders Edlund
Head of Household Management Denmark, Ken Adrian
Chief Economist Denmark, Helge J. Pedersen
Head of Nordea Finance Denmark, Lars Bang
Head of Legal Denmark, Niels B. J?rgensen
Director Marketing Denmark, Kim Grue
Head of Corporate Merchant Banking Finland, Olli-Petteri Lehtinen
Managing Director Nordea Investment Fund Company Finland; Head of Asset Management Products Finland, Jari Kivihuhta
Head European Affairs, Leena Morttinen
Deputy Head of Banking Norway, Jon Brenden
Chief Economist Norway, Steinar Juel
Head of Global Sales and Research Norway, Jan Pollestad
Director Marketing Norway, Arne Lambech
Head of Household Management Sweden, Petra Eklund
Chief Economist Sweden, Annika Winsth
Head of Global Sales and Research Sweden, Mads Jakobsen
Head of Investment Funds Sweden, Erik Feldt
Head of Life and Pensions Sweden, Britta Burreau
Head of Private Banking Sweden, Inga-Lill Carlberg
Head of New European Markets Sweden, Thomas Neckmar
Investor Relations Officer, Andreas Larsson
Head Group Identity and Communications, Jan Larsson
Chief Economist Finland, Martti Nyberg, age 48
Deputy Chairman, Marie Ehrling, age 60
Head of Strategic Customer Events Sweden, Tomas Bjorklund
Head Private Banking Nordic, Niklas Ekvall
Executive Vice President Head of Wholesale Banking, Casper von Koskull
Executive Vice President Head of Wealth Management Country Senior Executive in Norway, Gunn W?rsted, age 59
Executive Vice President Head of Retail Banking Country Senior Executive in Sweden, Lennart Jacobsen, age 48
Head of Group Corporate Centre and Group CFO, Torsten Hagen J?rgensen
Executive Vice President Chief Operating Officer of Wholesale Banking Country Senior Executive in Denmark, Peter Nyegaard, age 51
Director, Svein S. Jacobsen, age 63
Director, Lars G. Nordstrom
Vice Chairman, Timo Peltola, age 68
Director, Tom Knutzen, age 52
Director, Bjorn Saven, age 63
Director, Christine (Stine) Bosse, age 54
Director, Heidi M. Petersen, age 55
Director, Marie Ehrling, age 59
Auditors: KPMGAB

LOCATIONS

HQ: Nordea Bank AB
   Smalandsgatan 17, Stockholm SE-105 71
Phone: (46) 8 614 78 00   **Fax:** (46) 8 10 50 69
Web: www.nordea.com

Sales

	% of total
Denmark	26
Sweden	22
Finland	17
Norway	14
New European	7
Other	14
Total	**100**

PRODUCTS/OPERATIONS

Sales

	% of total
Banking	55
Capital markets	22
Savings products and asset	7
Life and	4
Other	12
Total	**100**

COMPETITORS

BNP Paribas	KBC
Citigroup	SEB AB
Danske Bank	Schroders
Deutsche Bank	Skandia
HSBC	Svenska Handelsbanken
JPMorgan Asset Management	

HISTORICAL FINANCIALS

Company Type: Public

Income Statement

FYE: December 31

	ASSETS ($ mil.)	NET INCOME ($ mil.)	INCOME AS % OF ASSETS	EMPLOYEES
12/13	867,940	4,289	0.5%	29,429
12/12	892,873	4,111	0.5%	31,466
12/11	926,375	3,397	0.4%	33,068
12/10	777,378	3,556	0.5%	33,809
12/09	731,152	3,333	0.5%	0
Annual Growth	**4.4%**	**6.5%**		

2013 Year-End Financials

Return on assets: 0.4%
Return on equity: 10.8%
Long-term debt ($ mil.): —
No. of shares (mil.): —
Sales ($ mil): 21,892

Dividends
Yield: 3.2%
Payout: 74.6%
Market value ($ mil.): —

	STOCK PRICE ($) FY Close	P/E High/Low		Earnings	Dividends	Book Value
12/13	13.51	33	23	1.06	0.44	9.97
12/12	9.61	22	15	1.03	0.35	9.23
12/11	7.82	34	18	0.84	0.75	8.32
Annual Growth	**31.4%**	—	—	**6.0%**	**(12.6%)**	**4.6%**

Nordea Bank Denmark A/S

LOCATIONS

HQ: Nordea Bank Denmark A/S
Strandgade 3, PO Box 850, Copenhagen C DK-0900
Phone: (45) 33 33 33 33   **Fax:** (45) 33 33 63 63
Web: www.nordea.com

HISTORICAL FINANCIALS

Company Type: Public

Income Statement

FYE: December 31

	ASSETS ($ mil.)	NET INCOME ($ mil.)	INCOME AS % OF ASSETS	EMPLOYEES
12/13	867,940	4,289	0.5%	29,429
12/12	892,873	4,111	0.5%	31,466
12/11	926,375	3,397	0.4%	33,068
12/10	777,378	3,556	0.5%	33,809
12/09	731,152	3,333	0.5%	33,347
Annual Growth	**4.4%**	**6.5%**		**(3.1%)**

2013 Year-End Financials

Return on assets: 0.4%
Return on equity: 10.8%
Long-term debt ($ mil.): —
No. of shares (mil.): —
Sales ($ mil): 21,892

Dividends
Yield: —
Payout: —
Market value ($ mil.): —

North Pacific Bank, Ltd.

Sapporo Hokuyo Holdings supposes it has what customers need in the way of banking and financial services. The company was formed in 2001 to serve as the holding company for North Pacific Bank and The Sapporo Bank; together the regional banks have some 230 offices in Hokkaido as well as an office in Tokyo and two offices in China. North Pacific Bank which is the largest bank in Hokkaido accounts for most of the holding company's sales; the bank traces its roots to 1917. The company also has subsidiaries active in credit cards and leasing; bank subsidiaries engage in such activities as financing.

LOCATIONS

HQ: North Pacific Bank, Ltd.
3-7 Odori Nishi, Chuo-ku, Sapporo, Hokkaido 060-0042
Phone: (81) 11 261 1311   **Fax:** (81) 11 261 2280
Web: www.hokuyobank.co.jp

COMPETITORS

Hokkoku Bank	Mizuho Financial
Hokuhoku Financial Group	Resona
Hyakujushi Bank	Sumitomo Mitsui
Mitsubishi UFJ Financial Group	

HISTORICAL FINANCIALS

Company Type: Public

Income Statement

FYE: March 31

	ASSETS ($ mil.)	NET INCOME ($ mil.)	INCOME AS % OF ASSETS	EMPLOYEES
03/14	76,415	842	1.1%	3,744
03/13	83,029	206	0.2%	3,808
03/12	93,947	294	0.3%	3,886
03/11	89,384	148	0.2%	3,941
03/10	79,164	339	0.4%	4,107
Annual Growth	**(0.9%)**	**25.5%**		**(2.3%)**

2014 Year-End Financials

Return on assets: 1.1%
Return on equity: 24.1%
Long-term debt ($ mil.): —
No. of shares (mil.): 398
Sales ($ mil): 2,215

Dividends
Yield: —
Payout: —
Market value ($ mil.): —

	STOCK PRICE ($) FY Close	P/E High/Low		Earnings	Dividends	Book Value
03/14	0.00	—	—	1.35	0.00	7.93
03/13	0.00	—	—	0.29	0.00	10.69
03/12	2.99	—	—	0.48	0.00	10.53
Annual Growth	—			**29.8%**	—	**(6.8%)**

Novartis AG Basel

Although it's based in neutral Switzerland Novartis has been aggressive in attacking illnesses on multiple fronts including pharmaceuticals vaccines and consumer health. Its largest division Pharmaceuticals develops and manufactures prescription drugs for blood pressure cancer and other ailments. Novartis' Sandoz subsidiary produces generic drugs and active pharmaceutical ingredients while the Vaccine and Diagnostics segment makes immune health and blood-screening tools. Its Alcon division makes ophthalmic drugs surgery systems and contact lenses. The Consumer Health unit includes OTC medications such as Excedrin and Theraflu as well as agricultural animal and pet care products.

Geographic Reach

Novartis has operations in 140 countries around the world including sales administrative research and manufacturing locations. The US is the company's largest geographic market accounting for about one-third of revenues followed by Japan Germany and France (each accounting for less than 10% of sales).

Operations

Prescription drugs account for more than half of Novartis' annual revenues. Its blockbusters include high blood pressure treatment Diovan leukemia drug Gleevec/Glivec age-related macular degeneration drug Lucentis and Zometa an intravenous treatment for bone tumors caused by prostate lung and breast cancers. Other strong products include hormone balancing drug Sandostatin Exelon for Alzheimer's disease and Femara which is used to treat postmenopausal women with early and advanced breast cancer.

The company's Sandoz and Alcon units each account for nearly 20% of sales. Sandoz is currently among the largest manufacturers of generic drugs in the world while Alcon is a leader in cataract and vision correction surgical equipment.

Financial Analysis

Novartis' steady growth pace has produced rising revenues over the past decade including a 15% increase to some $59 billion in 2011. The annual sales increase was largely attributed to the acquisition of Alcon as well as to positive currency impacts and sales of newly launched products. However net income dropped 7% to $9.1 billion in 2011 due to acquisition and restructuring costs as well as increased sales marketing manufacturing and other operational expenses.

Like most large drugmakers Novartis is facing increasing pressure to keep its operations lean and develop new blockbusters in the face of patent expiration and rising levels of generic competition. Several of the company's former best sellers including Famvir (antiviral) Lotrel (high blood pressure) and Trileptal (epilepsy treatment) are experiencing dwindling sales due to launches of generic versions in recent years. The company is especially hurting as top seller Diovan which previously accounted for more than $6 billion in sales (or 20%

of the firm's annual pharmaceutical revenues) lost patent protection in the US market in 2012 and in Europe in 2011.

To balance out the reduced sales from off-patent products Novartis is conducting cost-cutting programs including a number of workforce reduction plant closure divestiture and outsourcing measures announced in 2011 and 2012.

Strategy

To ward off competitive pressures and support its prescription drug business Novartis maintains a healthy drug pipeline with about 140 candidates in clinical development stages. Novartis relies upon a steady regimen of internal development partnerships and acquisitions to keep its pipeline up and running. R&D programs are focused on core therapeutic areas including cardiology metabolism oncology neurology respiratory ophthalmic and infectious disease. The company is especially focused on increasing its development of biologic (protein and gene-based) drugs. Recently launched products in the US market include chronic obstructive pulmonary disease (COPD) treatment Arcapta in 2011. In addition oncology drug Afinitor gained FDA approval to treat pancreatic tumors and breast cancer in 2012.

In addition Novartis is counting on its new drug for multiple sclerosis Gilenya (licensed from Mitsubishi Tanabe) to be a big revenue earner in the coming years. Gilenya was launched in the US market in 2010 and is the first oral treatment for MS. It is also among the most expensive drugs for the disease. The drug was approved in the European Union market in 2011.

Though the Alcon Sandoz consumer health and vaccines and diagnostics units are smaller than the core pharmaceuticals business Novartis maintains strong acquisition and internal research programs in those divisions as well. For instance to further its goals in personalized medicine Novartis is working to develop more sensitive molecular diagnostics that can be used to monitor patients and determine which medicines will most effectively treat their ailments.

Mergers Acquisitions & Divestitures

Along with new drugs the company's other pharma growth efforts are conducted through numerous acquisitions. Making a bold move in the eye-care market Novartis made ocular drug and vision care company Alcon a wholly owned subsidiary in 2011 after a drawn-out series of share purchases: Novartis first acquired about 77% of Alcon from Nestle for some $39 billion (through two transactions in 2008 and 2010). Then in early 2011 Novartis acquired the remaining shares in Alcon through a public tender offer worth nearly $13 billion. Novartis then combined its existing CIBA Vision eye care unit into Alcon which became Novartis' fifth operating segment.

To expand its Sandoz division Novartis completed a $1.5 billion deal to acquire generic drugmaker Fougera Pharmaceuticals in 2012. The purchase strengthened Sandoz's position in the global dermatology medication market.

Additionally the company periodically divests underperforming or noncore assets to focus on its key areas of growth. For instance in 2011 the company sold global rights to eczema treatment Elidel to Meda for some $420 million.

In 2014 the company announced it would spend up to $16 billion depending on milestones to purchase GlaxoSmithKline's oncology unit. At the same time it will sell its vaccine business to GSK for about $7 billion and the two will combine their consumer products. The deal brings Tafinlar and Mekinist two recently approved skin cancer drugs into the Novartis camp. Annual revenue will drop slightly but profits will rise as it picks up higher margin products.

HISTORY

Johann Geigy began selling spices and natural dyes in Basel Switzerland in 1758. A century later the Geigy family began producing synthetic dyes. About that time Alexander Clavel also entered the synthetic dye trade in Basel forming the Gesellschaft fur Chemische Industrie Basel (Ciba). Ciba was Switzerland's #1 chemical firm at century's end.

After WWI Ciba Geigy and Sandoz (a Basel synthetic dye maker founded in 1886) formed the Basel AG cartel to compete with German rival I.G. Farben. Basel used its profits to diversify into pharmaceuticals and other chemicals and to gain a foothold in the US. In 1929 Basel merged with its German and later French and British counterparts but WWII shattered the so-called Quadrapartite Cartel in 1939 leaving only Basel AG intact.

Basel scientist Paul Muller won a Nobel Prize in 1948 for inventing DDT. Basel AG voluntarily dissolved itself back into its component parts in 1951.

Ciba Geigy and Sandoz continued to diversify. Finding new markets in agricultural chemicals Geigy had passed Ciba in sales by 1967. That year Sandoz bought the Wander group of companies (dietetic products). Ciba and Geigy merged in 1970 and began a series of US acquisitions including Funk Seeds in 1974. Sandoz bought Minneapolis-based Northrup King & Co. (1976) and Dutch seed company Zaadunie (1980).

Ciba-Geigy and US biotech company Chiron started a joint venture in 1986 to produce and market genetically engineered vaccines (Ciba-Geigy acquired 50% of Chiron in 1994). Sandoz also bought shares in US biotechnology companies including Genetic Therapy and SyStemix in 1991. It bought Gerber (founded 1927) in 1994.

Ciba-Geigy and Sandoz rejoined to form Novartis in 1996. To win approval for the merger Sandoz (whose Daniel Vasella became CEO of the new company) sold its corn herbicide and US animal health businesses. Novartis spun off its specialty chemicals unit in 1997 and bought Merck's insecticide and fungicide operations.

In 1998 the company merged its OTC health and nutrition businesses into a new consumer health division and in the following year sold several units including cracker maker Wasa to focus the new division's operations. Chairman Alex Krauer who had overseen the formation of Novartis stepped down that year leaving the post to Vasella.

To boost its market share CIBA Vision bought colored contact lens maker Wesley Jessen VisionCare in 2000. Novartis spun off its crop protection and seed units merging them with AstraZeneca's Agrochemicals unit to create Syngenta.

Novartis Ophthalmics split off from the CIBA Vision division to become a separate eye health care unit under the Pharmaceutical Division of Novartis in 2001. The firm's joint venture with BioTransplant successfully cloned genetically altered pigs whose organs would be more suitable for human transplants. Attempting to refine the company's focus on pharmaceuticals Novartis made several acquisitions in 2002 including two animal vaccine companies Grand Laboratories and Immtech Biologies and generic manufacturer Lek Pharmaceuticals while divesting its food and beverage division to Associated British Foods. The remaining assets including sports nutrition health and weight loss products were grouped under the Nutrition & Sante banner and were sold to management in 2004.

Novartis engineered one of the largest deals in European pharma in 2004 when it acquired the rights to a prospective inhaled chronic obstructive pulmonary disease (COPD) treatment from UK drug concerns Arakis and Vectura Group.

Novartis' consumer health business got a Boost literally when it purchased Mead Johnson's adult nutrition business in 2004. The buy included brands such as Boost nutritional drinks and feeding tube products Isocal and Ultracal. In a move to further bolster its consumer offerings that same year the company purchased the US and Canadian consumer products division of Bristol-Myers Squibb which brought headache remedy Excedrin cold and flu treatment Comtrex and Keri moisturizers into the company's consumer products stable.

To bulk up Sandoz (which had refocused strictly on generic pharmaceuticals over the years) in 2004 Novartis bought a Canadian maker of generic injectable drugs and a Danish generics maker to increase market share in key regional markets. In 2005 the firm acquired Hexal AG one of Germany's top generics makers and a controlling stake in Hexal's sister firm Eon Labs a US generics manufacturer.

The constant appetite of its drug pipeline was briefly sated in mid-2006 when Novartis acquired NeuTec Pharma a UK-based biopharmaceutical company with two drug candidates that target otherwise drug-resistant "superbugs." That year Novartis spent $5.1 billion to acquire struggling vaccine and biopharmaceuticals products maker Chiron despite Chiron's board rebuffing an earlier offer. Novartis then created a Vaccine and Diagnostics division composed of its existing vaccine operations and Chiron's diagnostics.

Putting its focus entirely on health care Novartis sold off the last of its non-health care businesses in 2007 when Nestle purchased Novartis' medical nutrition business for $2.5 billion and its Gerber baby products business for $5.5 billion. Also in 2007 Novartis formed a new unit to focus on biologic drug development which already made up 25% of its preclinical research pipeline.

In 2008 Novartis purchased Speedel the Swiss biotech drugmaker with which it developed blood pressure medication Rasilez (known as Tekturna in the US) for $888 million. It also completed a $400 million acquisition of US biopharmaceutical development company Protez Pharmaceuticals which added a late-stage candidate for drug-resistant Staphylococcus infections. Later that year the company also acquired the pulmonary drug delivery R&D business of Nektar Therapeutics for $115 million. The two companies had already collaborated on the development of an inhaled powder therapy for lung infections and the deal brought that treatment fully under Novartis' roof.

Also in 2008 Novartis struck a deal with Nestle to acquire its majority stake (about 77%) in eye care firm Alcon. The deal took place over the course of two years and included a $10.4 billion purchase in mid-2008 and a $28.3 billion transaction in mid-2010.

In 2009 it completed a $1.3 billion acquisition of the specialty generic injectables arm of Austrian-based Ebewe Pharma. The buy gave Sandoz a line of oncology drugs that are widely considered to be essential to adhering to standard-of-care guidelines for treating a range of cancers.

To increase the capacity of its Vaccine and Diagnostics division Novartis opened a new vaccine plant in North Carolina in 2009 and in 2010 the company launched Menveo a new meningitis vaccine.

Novartis conducted an executive management shift in early 2010 when Daniel Vasella stepped down as CEO after holding the job for 14 years but remained chairman. Joe Jimenez moved from his position as head of the company's pharmaceutical division to become CEO.

Schizophrenia treatment Fanapt was approved by the FDA in early 2010. Novartis added some late-stage heart failure drugs to its pipeline that year by acquiring privately held drug developer Corthera for $120 million plus up to $500 million in potential milestones. The firm also sold the US rights to overactive bladder treatment Enablex to Warner Chilcott for $400 million in 2010.

EXECUTIVES

Vice Chairman, Ulrich Lehner, age 68
Chairman, Daniel L. Vasella, age 60, $3,188,700 total compensation
General Counsel, Felix R. Ehrat
Chief Executive Officer; Member of the Executive Committee, Joseph (Joe) Jimenez Jr., age 55, $1,054,050 total compensation
President Novartis Institutes for BioMedical Research, Mark C. Fishman, age 63, $963,333 total compensation
CEO Novartis Pharmaceuticals, David R. Epstein, age 53
Public Relations US, Pamela (Pam) McKinlay
Head Human Resources, Juergen Brokatzky-Geiger, age 62, $534,459 total compensation
CEO Consumer Health Division; Head Novartis Animal Health Business Unit, George Gunn, age 64
Division Head Alcon, Kevin J. Buehler, age 56
Head Corporate Communications, Sheldon Jones
Chief Financial Officer; Member of the Executive Committee, Jonathan R. (Jon) Symonds, age 54
Director Global Media Relations, Eric Althoff
CEO Sandoz Division, Jeffrey (Jeff) George, age 37
CEO Vaccines and Diagnostics Division, Andrin Oswald
Head Public Relations Switzerland, Michael Schiendorfer
Head Novartis Group Quality, Juan Andres
Head Group Country Management and External Affairs, Kim Stratton
President Novartis Corporation, Andre (Andy) Wyss
Head OTC Division, Naomi Kelman
Chief Compliance Officer of Novartis, Peter Kornicker
Corporate Secretary, Charlotte Pamer-Wieser
Vice President Internal Audit, Yves Teirlynck
Vice President Ethics & Compliance, Julie Kane
Chief Procurement Officer, Phillip Duncan
Vice Chairman, Ulrich Lehner, age 68
Director, Alexandre F. Jetzer-Chung, age 73
Director, Ann M. Fudge, age 62
Director, Wendelin Wiedeking, age 62
Director, Pierre Landolt, age 67
Director, Rolf M. Zinkernagel, age 70
Director, Srikant M. Datar, age 61
Director, Andreas von Planta, age 60
Director, Marjorie M. T. Yang, age 62
Director, William Brody, age 69
Director, Enrico Vanni
Auditors: PricewaterhouseCoopersAG

LOCATIONS

HQ: Novartis AG Basel
Lichtstrasse 35, Basel CH-4056
Phone: (41) 61 324 1111   **Fax:** (41) 61 324 7826
Web: www.novartis.com

Sales

	% of total
US	33
Japan	9
Germany	7
France	5
Switzerland	1
Other	45
Total	**100**

PRODUCTS/OPERATIONS

Sales

	% of total
Pharmaceuticals	56
Alcon	17
Sandoz	16
Consumer	8
Vaccines &	3
Total	**100**

Selected Acquisitions

2012
Fougera Pharmaceuticals ($1.5 billion; Melville New York; generic dermatology medications)
2011
Alcon ($52 billion over three years; contact lenses vision pharmaceuticals surgery equipment)
Genoptix ($470 million; Carlsbad California; laboratory services and molecular diagnostics)
Zhejiang Tianyuan ($194 million; China; vaccines)
2010
Corthera ($120 million; late-stage heart failure candidate)
Oriel Therapeutics (respiratory drug development)

Selected Products

Pharmaceuticals
Afinitor/Votubia (breast cancer pancreatic tumors brain tumors)
Arcapta/Onbrez (pulmonary inhalation medicine)
Clozaril/Leponex (schizophrenia)
Comtan/Stalevo (Parkinson's disease)
Diovan/Co-Diovan (hypertension)
Estraderm/Estragest (menopause and osteoporosis)
Exelon/Exelon Patch (Alzheimer's disease)
Exforge (hypertension)
Exjade (iron chelator)
Extavia (multiple sclerosis)
Famvir (antiviral for herpes)
Fanapt (schizophrenia)
Femara (advanced breast cancer)
Foradil (asthma chronic obstructive pulmonary disease)
Galvus (diabetes)
Gilenya (multiple sclerosis)
Gleevec/Glivec (chronic myeloid leukemia and gastrointestinal tumor treatment)
Lescol (cholesterol)
Lotrel (hypertension)
Lucentis (age-related macular degeneration)
Miacalcin/Miacalcic (osteoporosis)
Myfortic (transplant)
Neoral/Sandimmun (transplant rejection preventative)
Ritalin/Focalin (attention deficit hyperactivity disorder)
Reclast/Aclasta (osteoporosis)
Sandostatin (acromegaly)
Tasigna (chronic myeloid leukemia)
Tekturna/Rasilez (blood pressure)
Tegretol (epilepsy acute mania and bipolar affective disorders)
Trileptal (epilepsy)
Visudyne (wet age-related macular degeneration pathological myopia)
Voltaren (antirheumatic for inflammation and pain)
Xolair (asthma)
Zaditor/Zaditen (allergic conjunctivitis)
Zometa (cancer complications)
Sandoz generic pharmaceuticals
Acetylcysteine (respiratory)
Amlodipine/Benazepril (hypertension)
Amoxicillin (antibiotic)
Enoxaparin sodium (anti-coagulant)
Fentanyl (pain)
Lansoprazole (proton pump inhibitor)
Losartan (hypertension)
Omeprazole (heartburn and ulcer)
Paclitaxel (cancer)
Simvastatin (cholesterol)
Tacrolimus (transplant)
Tiamulin (statin)
Vancomycin (antibiotic)
Zarzio/Filgrastim Hexal (cancer)
Consumer Health
Animal health
Atopica (atopic dermatitis management)
Denaguard (antimicrobial for pigs)
Deramaxx (pain relief for dogs and cats)
Sentinel/Milbemax/Interceptor (intestinal parasite and

heart worm control)
OTC
Benefiber (fiber supplements)
Excedrin (systemic analgesic)
Lamisil AT Cream (athlete's foot treatment)
Nicotinell (or Habitrol smoking cessation patch)
Prevacid/Pantoloc (heartburn)
Theraflu/NeoCitran (flu treatment)
Triaminic/Otrivin (cough and cold remedies)
Voltaren Emulgel (topical analgesic)
Vaccines and Diagnostics
Flu vaccines (Agrippal AgriFlu Fluad Fluvirin Optaflu)
HIV hepatitis and West Nile tests (Procleix)
Meningitis vaccines (Menveo Menjugate)
Pediatric vaccines (Polioral Quinvaxem)
Traveling vaccines (Encepur Ixiaro Rabipur)
Alcon
Ophthalmic drugs
Azopt/Azarga (glaucoma)
Ciprodex Otic (anti-infective)
Patanase/Pantanol (allergy)
TobraDex (ophthalmic suspension)
Travatan/DuoTrav (glaucoma)
Vigamox (antibiotic)
Surgical
Allegretto (laser surgery system)
AcrySof (intraocular lenses for cataract surgery)
Infiniti (cataract lens removal system)
WaveLight (refractive laser)
Vision Care
Air Optix (monthly contact lenses)
Aquify (contact lens cleaning solution)
Cibasoft (contact lenses)
Clear Care (aka Aosept contact lens cleaning system)
Dailies (disposable contact lenses)
FreshLook (tinted contact lenses)
ICAPS (vitamins)
Opti-Free (cleaning solution)
Systane (eye drops)

COMPETITORS

Abbott Labs	Essilor International
Allergan	GlaxoSmithKline
Amgen	Johnson & Johnson
AstraZeneca	Merck
Bausch & Lomb	Novo Nordisk
Baxter International	Perrigo
Bayer AG	Pfizer
Biogen Idec	Ranbaxy Laboratories
Bristol-Myers Squibb	Roche Holding
Carl Zeiss Meditec	Sanofi
Dr. Reddy' s	Teva
Eli Lilly	

HISTORICAL FINANCIALS

Company Type: Public

Income Statement

FYE: December 31

	REVENUE ($ mil.)	NET INCOME ($ mil.)	NET PROFIT MARGIN	EMPLOYEES
12/14	53,634	10,210	19.0%	133,413
12/13	58,831	9,175	15.6%	135,696
12/12	57,561	9,505	16.5%	127,724
12/11	59,375	9,113	15.3%	123,686
12/10	51,561	9,794	19.0%	119,418
Annual Growth	1.0%	1.0%	—	2.8%

2014 Year-End Financials

Debt ratio: 16.2%	No. of shares (mil.): —
Return on equity: 14.0%	Dividends
Cash ($ mil.): 13,023	Yield: 2.9%
Current ratio: 1.39	Payout: 66.8%
Long-term debt ($ mil.): 13,799	Market value ($ mil.): —

NTT DOCOMO, Inc.

Mobile phone carrier NTT DoCoMo is one of the world's largest wireless network operators in terms of subscribers behind global leader Vodafone. NTT DoCoMo (which means "anywhere") boasts about 65 million subscribers to its FOMA-branded wireless voice network in Japan (giving it about half of market share) while about 49 million customers subscribe to its i-mode mobile Internet services. The company also sells wireless telephone handsets under the DoCoMo brand and it provides emergency satellite services primarily for maritime use. NTT DoCoMo is the wireless spinoff of Japan's leading telecommunications carrier Nippon Telegraph and Telephone (NTT); NTT owns two-thirds of NTT DoCoMo.

The company saw sales slip in 2010 mainly due to the decline of its core voice segment. Meanwhile NTT DoCoMo improved its profits for the year due to decreased costs of equipment and reduced network costs. The company has said that it expects profits to increase in 2011 due to ongoing efforts to further bring down costs as well as initiatives to drive customer usage of data services by offering reduced pricing options and expanded mobile services such as original content delivery and wireless Internet tethering between wireless devices and portable computers.

DoCoMo means "anywhere" and NTT DoCoMo is everywhere in the Japanese market for mobile communication services. However faced with a mature market and stiff competition at home NTT DoCoMo has renewed its efforts to tap into growth markets abroad particularly in the Asia/Pacific region.

In 2011 the company agreed to a deal with JG Summit that gives it the option to buy additional shares in Philippine Long Distance Telephone (PLDT) for around $263 million. NTTDoCoMo already owns about 10% of PLDT.

Its largest purchase in this overseas push was the 2009 acquisition of about one-quarter of India-based Tata Teleservices for about $2.7 billion. The company hopes to tap into the burgeoning Indian market through this alliance with the telecommunications arm of the Tata Group. Also that year NTT DoCoMo bought a 35% stake in US multimedia software maker PacketVideo to bolster its internal efforts to develop applications for mobile video services. It acquired the rest of the company from parent NextWave Wireless for about $115 million in 2010.

NTT DoCoMo's efforts to garner higher subscription fees from its existing customer base in Japan and improve retention have included an increase in the variety of mobile services it offers the introduction of cell phones offering a broader set of features (email music playback and gaming) and ongoing investments in its network infrastructure to enable bandwidth-hungry streaming content such as video programming. The company is counting on increased data usage to fuel profits as sales of voice services decline.

HISTORY

Formed in 1952 by the Japanese Ministry of Communications to rebuild Japan's war-ravaged phone system Nippon Telegraph and Telephone (NTT) enjoyed a monopoly on phone services for more than four decades.

NTT first went into mobile communications with a maritime phone service in 1959 and in 1968 the company began offering paging services. Other telecommunications services followed: car phone service (1979) in-flight phone service (1986) and mobile phone service (1987).

In 1991 NTT established a subsidiary to adopt these wireless segments; it launched operations in 1992 as NTT Mobile Communications Network under the leadership of NTT executive Kouji Ohboshi. The firm quickly took on the DoCoMo nickname. The year closed with slightly more than a million analog mobile phone users in Japan —a market DoCoMo shared with upstart telecom companies DDI and IDO (later bought by DDI). Paging service was more popular and DoCoMo won more than 3 million customers.

DoCoMo in 1993 launched digital mobile phone service based on a scheme called PDC (personal digital cellular) —a system incompatible with the digital standards that would take root in Europe and the US. Liberalization of the cellular phone market in 1994 triggered unexpected growth: Customers who previously had to lease mobile phones from the network operators could now buy them at retail stores. Further competition emerged in 1995 with the launch of personal handyphone services or PHS (parent company NTT was among the companies providing PHS) but DoCoMo's subscriber count passed 3.5 million mobile phone users —about half the market.

DoCoMo's pager business peaked in 1996 before commencing a long-term decline; the mobile phone market where DoCoMo had more than 8 million subscribers overtook it. The company launched a satellite-based mobile phone system that year to serve customers beyond the range of cell sites reaching ships and mountainous regions.

Financial crises rocked the Pacific Rim in 1997 and Japan's Fair Trade Commission rocked NTT by ordering it to cut its 95% ownership of DoCoMo. Customers continued to flock to mobile phones despite economic turmoil and DoCoMo passed the 15-million-subscriber mark. In 1998 DoCoMo gave hope to Japan's low-flying market when it left the nest: Its mammoth IPO raised more than $18 billion.

Meanwhile DDI (now KDDI) had become the first Japanese carrier to launch a digital mobile phone network based on CDMA (code division multiple access) technology. Though DoCoMo still used PDC it redoubled its efforts to help develop and standardize a next-generation wideband version of CDMA.

In 1999 DoCoMo took over NTT's unprofitable PHS unit and rolled out a high-speed data service over the PHS network. That year it acquired a 19% stake in the telecom unit of Hong Kong's Hutchison Whampoa but failed expectations led the company to sell its stake in Hutchison 3G UK to Hutchison Whampoa in 2005 for Â120 million.

In 2000 the company adopted NTT DoCoMo as its corporate name. To promote its new data services NTT DoCoMo launched a joint venture in Japan with Microsoft (Mobimagic). It took the i-mode service international in 2001 when the company teamed up with Telecom Italia Mobile to introduce the 3G service in Europe. The next year NTT DoCoMo became the largest shareholder in America Online Japan but it sold the more than 40% stake to America Online in 2003.

The company staked its claim in the US too by paying $9.8 billion for a 16% stake in AT&T Wireless in 2001. NTT DoCoMo sold its stake following the 2004 takeover of AT&T Wireless by rival Cingular Wireless (now AT&T Mobility) in a deal valued at $41 billion.

The company in 2002 took full ownership of its eight majority-owned regional operating subsidiaries and began consolidating operations. The company also has liquidated several other subsidiaries including an operating unit in Brazil and it has reorganized its European holdings under a single subsidiary DoCoMo Europe Ltd.

It also continued to advance digital wireless technologies through partnerships that include an alliance (formed in 2000) with Hutchison Whampoa and Dutch mobile phone company KPN Mobile to bid on European operating licenses. It also paid $4.5 billion for a 15% stake in KPN Mobile. (The stake was reduced to 2% then sold back to parent firm KPN. An i-mode affiliation continues however.)

After the number of paging service subscribers fell to less than 300000 from a high of 6.5 million (in 1996) NTT DoCoMo ended the service in early 2007. It additionally dissolved allucher a marketing and consulting services provider to mobile phone users and its animation-related Web portal management and marketing business known as Hive. NTT DoCoMo also discontinued its Personal Handyphone Service (PHS) and its CITYPHONE digital mobile service in 2008.

NTT DoCoMo in 2008 bought stakes in operators in Bangladesh (TM International 30%) and the Philippines (PLDT 20%). Additionally the company has i-mode network technology licensing agreements with about a dozen GSM network operators in Europe including Russia and Greece as well as in the Asia/Pacific region.

EXECUTIVES

President and CEO PacketVideo, Mark Tapling
SEVP Multimedia Services and Technology and Board Member, Kiyoyuki Tsujimura, age 64
EVP Consumer Sales, Takashi Tanaka, age 59
EVP Consumer Sales and Director, Bunya Kumagai, age 61
SEVP Global Business and Board Member, Masatoshi Suzuki, age 62
SVP and Managing Director Hokkaido Regional Office, Hiroaki Nishioka, age 65
SEVP Chief Privacy Officer and Chief Information Security Officer, Fumio Iwasaki, age 61
President CEO and Board Member, Ryuji Yamada, age 65
EVP Managing Director Research and Development and Board Member, Mitsunobu Komori, age 61
EVP and Managing Director Tokai Regional Office, Toru Kobayashi
SEVP and CFO, Kazuto Tsubouchi, age 62
SVP and Managing Director Credit Card Business, Masaki Yoshikawa
SVP and Managing Director Chugoku Regional Office, Akiko Ide
SVP and Managing Director Advertising and Promotion, Yuji Araki
EVP and Managing Director Network, Kiyoshi Tokuhiro
EVP and CIO, Seiji Nishikawa
SVP Managing Director General Affairs and Corporate Citizenship and Board Member, Katsuhiro Nakamura, age 61
SVP and Managing Director Global Business, Toshinari Kunieda
EVP Marketing, Tsutomu Shindou

EVP and Managing Director of Corporate Strategy & Planning Department, Kazuhiro Yoshizawa
SVP and Managing Director Product, Kiyohito Nagata
SEVP and Board Member, Hiroshi Matsui, age 67
President and CEO, Kaoru Kato, age 63
EVP and Managing Director Corporate Marketing, Akio Oshima
EVP and Deputy Managing Director Corporate Marketing, Haruhide Nakayama
EVP and Managing Director Kansai Regional Office, Shozo Nishimura
SVP and Managing Director Business Process Improvement Office, Tooru Azumi
SVP and Managing Director Shikoku Regional Office, Masaaki Sado
SVP and General Manager Kanagawa Branch, Yasuhiro Taguchi
EVP and CTO, Seizo Onoe
SVP and Managing Director Hokuriku Regional Office, Tadashi Kitamura
SVP and Managing Director Tohoku Regional Office, Tetsuya Suzuki
SVP and Deputy Managing Director Research and Development, Yoshiyuki Takeda
EVP Multimedia Services, Hiroyasu Asami
SVP Managing Director Public Relations and Deputy Managing Director Mobile Society Research Institute, Yoshikiyo Sakai
SVP and Managing Director Communication Device Support, Tomohiro Kurosawa
CEO, Isao Moriyasu
President CEO Director Oricon Inc, Koh Koike
Executive Vice President, Masaaki Shintaku
SEVP Multimedia Services and Technology and Board Member, Kiyoyuki Tsujimura, age 64
SVP Managing Director Human Resources Management and Board Member, Takashi Tanaka, age 59
EVP Consumer Sales and Director, Bunya Kumagai, age 61
SEVP Global Business and Board Member, Masatoshi Suzuki, age 62
SVP Managing Director Kyushu Regional Division and Board Member, Fumio Iwasaki, age 61
President CEO and Board Member, Ryuji Yamada, age 65
EVP Managing Director Research and Development and Board Member, Mitsunobu Komori, age 61
EVP CFO Managing Director Accounts and Finance and Board Member, Kazuto Tsubouchi, age 62
SVP Managing Director General Affairs and Corporate Citizenship and Board Member, Katsuhiro Nakamura, age 60
SEVP and Board Member, Hiroshi Matsui, age 67
President CEO, Kaoru Kato, age 63
Board Member, Hiroshi Tsujigami, age 55
Board Member, Akio Oshima
Auditors: KPMGAZSA&Co.

LOCATIONS

HQ: NTT DOCOMO, Inc.
Sanno Park Tower, 2-11-1 Nagata-cho, Chiyoda-ku, Tokyo 100-6150
Phone: (81) 3 5156 1111   **Fax:** (81) 3 5156 0271
Web: www.nttdocomo.co.jp

PRODUCTS/OPERATIONS

Sales

	% of total
Wireless services	
Cellular	
Voice	44
Packet	37
Other	6
Equipment	13
Total	**100**

Selected Services
Cellular
i-mode (wireless Internet access)
In-flight telephone
Mobile multimedia
Satellite mobile communications
Third-generation (3G) wireless (W-CDMA)
World Call (direct international calling)

Selected Regional Operating Subsidiaries
DOCOMO Business Net Inc.
DOCOMO Engineering Chugoku Inc.
DOCOMO Engineering Hokkaido Inc.
DOCOMO Engineering Hokuriku Inc.
DOCOMO Engineering Inc.
DOCOMO Engineering Kansai Inc.
DOCOMO Engineering Kyushu Inc.
DOCOMO Engineering Shikoku Inc.
DOCOMO Engineering Tohoku Inc.
DOCOMO Engineering Tokai Inc.
DOCOMO I Kyushu Inc.
DOCOMO Mobile Inc.
DOCOMO Mobile Tokai Inc.
DOCOMO Mobile Media Kansai Inc.
DOCOMO Service Chugoku Inc.
DOCOMO Service Hokkaido Inc.
DOCOMO Service Hokuriku Inc.
DOCOMO Service Inc.
DOCOMO Service Kansai Inc.
DOCOMO Service Kyushu Inc.
DOCOMO Service Shikoku Inc.
DOCOMO Service Tohoku Inc.
DOCOMO Service Tokai Inc.
DOCOMO Support Inc.
DOCOMO Systems Inc.
DOCOMO Technology Inc.

COMPETITORS

BT	Optus
China Mobile	SK Telecom
EMOBILE	SOFTBANK MOBILE
Hutchison	Telstra
Telecommunications	Vodafone
KDDI	

HISTORICAL FINANCIALS
Company Type: Public

Income Statement
FYE: March 31

	REVENUE ($ mil.)	NET INCOME ($ mil.)	NET PROFIT MARGIN	EMPLOYEES
03/14	43,220	4,502	10.4%	36,253
03/13	47,507	5,267	11.1%	35,426
03/12	51,688	5,655	10.9%	32,244
03/11	51,013	5,923	11.6%	31,157
03/10	45,867	5,297	11.5%	29,266
Annual Growth	(1.5%)	(4.0%)	—	5.5%

2014 Year-End Financials

Debt ratio: 0.0%	No. of shares (mil.): —
Return on equity: 8.4%	Dividends
Cash ($ mil.): 5,104	Yield: 3.8%
Current ratio: 2.10	Payout: 0.3%
Long-term debt ($ mil.): 2,137	Market value ($ mil.): —

	STOCK PRICE ($) FY Close	P/E High/Low		PER SHARE ($) Earnings	Dividends	Book Value
03/14	15.77	0	0	1.09	0.61	13.22
03/13	14.87	0	0	1.27	0.62	13.91
03/12	16.67	0	0	1.36	0.66	14.88
03/11	17.59	0	0	1.42	0.59	14.13
03/10	15.20	0	0	1.27	0.54	11.93
Annual Growth	0.9%	—	—	(3.8%)	3.2%	2.6%

Oesterreichische Nationalbank

LOCATIONS

HQ: Oesterreichische Nationalbank
Otto-Wagner-Platz-3, Vienna 1090
Phone: (43) 1 40420 6666   **Fax:** (43) 1 40420 046698
Web: www.oenb.at

HISTORICAL FINANCIALS
Company Type: Public

Income Statement
FYE: December 31

	ASSETS ($ mil.)	NET INCOME ($ mil.)	INCOME AS % OF ASSETS	EMPLOYEES
12/13	134,211	27	0.0%	1,233
12/12	144,154	37	0.0%	1,222
12/11	128,502	24	0.0%	1,146
12/10	106,757	29	0.0%	1,145
12/09	103,165	30	0.0%	1,152
Annual Growth	6.8%	(2.7%)	—	1.7%

Oil and Natural Gas Corp. Ltd.

The crown jewel of India's oil and gas assets state-owned Oil & Natural Gas Corporation (ONGC) is India's largest exploration and production company. It is also the country's largest multinational corporation. In a country reliant on imported fuels ONGC which has estimated proved and probable reserves of 6.4 billion metric tonnes of oil equivalent accounts for the 78% of India's oil and gas production. ONGC operates a more than 15000-km. pipeline network and owns nearly 72% of Mangalore Refinery & Petrochemicals Ltd. (MRPL). International exploration and production subsidiary ONGC Videsh has established exploration activities in 17 countries. India's government owns 74% of ONGC.

ONGC has been searching for ways to expand its stakes in oil patches around the world.

Through its ONGC Videsh subsidiary the company joined rival China National Petroleum Corporation (CNPC) to acquire a 38% stake in Syria's largest oil company from Petro-Canada. The Syrian company Al Furat Petroleum is 62%-owned by Royal Dutch Shell. ONGC had lost out to CNPC in an earlier bid in 2005 for PetroKazakhstan.

In 2006 ONGC acquired Exxon Mobil's 30% stake in a field in the Campos Basin of Brazil for $1.4 billion. Other partners in the field are the state-owned Petrobras and Royal Dutch Shell which each own 35%. ONGC had lost out to Chinese rivals in previous bids for assets in South America.

In 2008 ONCG Videsh announced plans to acquire Imperial Energy for $2.6 billion giving it a foothold in the Siberian oil market.

EXECUTIVES

Chairman and Managing Director, R. S. Sharma

Director Human Resources, A. K. Balyan
Director Onshore, A. K. Hazarika
Director Offshore, N. K. Mitra
Director Exploration, N. K. Pande
Director Technology and Field Services, U N Bose
Director Finance, D. K. Sarraf
Director Operations, Shyamal Bhattacharya
Director Human Resources, A. K. Balyan
Director Onshore, A. K. Hazarika
Director Offshore, N. K. Mitra
Director Exploration, N. K. Pande
Director Technology and Field Services, U N Bose
Director Finance, D. K. Sarraf

LOCATIONS

HQ: Oil and Natural Gas Corp. Ltd.
Tel Bhavan, Dehradun, Uttaranchal 248 003
Phone: (91) 135 275 9561   **Fax:** (91) 11 2331 6413
Web: www.ongcindia.com

COMPETITORS

BP	Royal Dutch Shell
Cairn Energy	TOTAL
Exxon Mobil	Talisman Energy
Occidental Petroleum	

HISTORICAL FINANCIALS

Company Type: Public

Income Statement

FYE: March 31

	REVENUE ($ mil.)	NET INCOME ($ mil.)	NET PROFIT MARGIN	EMPLOYEES
03/13	309,278	44,615	14.4%	32,923
03/12	298,969	55,319	18.5%	32,909
03/11	277,788	50,366	18.1%	33,273
03/10	23,838	4,394	18.4%	32,826
03/09	21,486	3,962	18.4%	33,035
Annual Growth	94.8%	83.2%	—	(0.1%)

2013 Year-End Financials

Debt ratio: 0.1%	No. of shares (mil.): —
Return on equity: 16.7%	Dividends
Cash ($ mil.): 36,140	Yield: —
Current ratio: 1.15	Payout: —
Long-term debt ($ mil.): 16,289	Market value ($ mil.): —

Oil Co Lukoil

Russians look to LUKOIL for their energy needs. Russia's #1 integrated oil company produces refines and sells oil and oil products; it accounts for 16% of Russia's crude oil production. In 2012 LUKOIL reported proved reserves of 17.3 billion barrels of oil equivalent the majority of which is located in Russia. The company explores for oil and gas in Russia and in about a dozen other countries in Eastern Europe the Middle East Asia and South America. It owns refineries in five countries and marketing and distribution assets in nearly 30 including about 6000 gas stations. In addition LUKOIL has power generation assets in Russia Bulgaria Romania and the Ukraine.

Operations

It operates five refineries in Russia one each in Ukraine Bulgaria Romania the Netherlands and Italy; LUKOIL's gas stations are located in Russia the Baltic states Central and Eastern Europe and the US.

LUKOIL Russia's second-largest company behind natural gas monopoly Gazprom is steadily transforming itself from a top-heavy bureaucratic enterprise into a decentralized entrepreneurial company competing in free markets through joint ventures and strategic relationships.

Financial Performance

The company has seen a few years of robust growth in revenues and net income due in part to the expansion of its activities (including increased hydrocarbon production and the growth of its gas station network) but largely because of the recovering global economy's effect on increasing demand and lifting commodity prices.

Ownership

LUKOIL president Vagit Alekperov controls about 20% of the company. ING Bank Eurasia holds about 70% of LUKOIL's shares on behalf of other investors.

HISTORY

LUKOIL was formed from the combination of three major state-owned oil and gas exploration companies —Langepasneftegaz Uraineftegaz and Kogalymneftegaz —that traced their origins to the discovery of oil in western Siberia in 1964. More than 25 years later after the Soviet Union broke up the oil and gas sector was one of the first industries marked for privatization.

In 1992 the government called for Langepasneftegaz Uraineftegaz and Kogalymneftegaz to merge and LUKOIL was created the next year. (The LUK of LUKOIL comes from the initials of the three companies.) Russian president Boris Yeltsin appointed Siberian oil veteran Vagit Alekperov as the company's first president. The Russian government also formed several other large integrated oil companies including Yukos Surgutneftegaz Sidanco and Sibneft.

LUKOIL went public on the fledgling Russian Trading System in 1994. The next year the company absorbed nine other enterprises including oil exploration companies Astrakhanneft Kaliningradmorneftegaz and Permneft. That year LUKOIL became the first Russian oil company to set up an exploration and production trading arm. In 1996 LUKOIL acquired a 41% stake in "Izvestia" Russia's major independent newspaper.

Chevron and LUKOIL with seven other oil and gas companies and three governments agreed in 1996 to build a 1500-kilometer pipeline to link the Kazakhstan oil fields to world markets.

In 1997 LUKOIL became the first Russian corporation to sell bonds to international investors and the government sold 15% of its stake in the company. That year LUKOIL's 50%-owned Nexus Fuels unit opened its first gas stations located in the parking lots of US grocery stores (the partnership dissolved and Nexus went bankrupt in 2000).

LUKOIL began a partnership with Conoco (later ConocoPhillips) in 1998 to develop oil and natural gas reserves in Russia's northern territories. LUKOIL also acquired 51% of Romania's Petrorel refinery. In 1999 it acquired control of refineries in Bulgaria and Ukraine and in a petrochemical firm in Saratov. It also acquired oil company KomiTEK in one of Russia's largest mergers.

The government sold a 9% stake in LUKOIL to a Cyprus-based unit Reforma Investments held in part by LUKOIL's "boss of bosses" Vagit Alekperov (gained at the bargain price of $200 million). Critics cited the sale as Yeltsin's bid to gain Alekperov's political support.

The company announced the first major oil find in the Russian part of the Caspian Sea in 2000 and formed a joint venture (Caspian Oil Company) with fellow Russian energy giants Gazprom and Yukos to exploit resources in the Caspian. The next year LUKOIL acquired more than 1300 gas stations on the East Coast of the US when it bought Getty Petroleum Marketing.

That year LUKOIL also acquired Bitech a Canadian oil exploration and production firm with operations in the Republic of Komi in the Russian Federation. In 2002 the company sold its oil service business a move that cut its overall workforce by some 20000 and resulted in savings of $500 million annually.

With an appetite for expansion the company upped its production with refinery acquisitions and invested heavily in new oil patches such as the Caspian Sea. In 2005 LUKOIL acquired Finland-based Oy Teboil AB and Suomen Petrooli Oy affiliated refined oil products companies for an undisclosed amount. LUKOIL also acquired Nelson Resources which had oil and gas interests in Western Kazakhstan for about $2 billion.

The next year the company acquired Marathon Oil's assets in Khanty-Mansiysk Autonomous Region —Yugra of Western Siberia —for $787 million. LUKOIL also acquired 376 European gas stations from ConocoPhillips in 2006.

In 2007 LUKOIL signed a strategic exploration and production agreement with Qatar Petroleum.

In 2008 the company diversified its operations further creating a power generation segment which encompasses its own generators at well sites and a number of generating units in Bulgaria Romania and Ukraine.

In 2008 it began to re-engage in Iraq where it had held oil concessions prior to the US-led invasion in 2003. It also acquired a retail network in Turkey in 2008 for $500 million.

EXECUTIVES

First VP Economics and Finance, Sergei P. Kukura, age 61
First EVP Exploration and Production, Ravil U. Maganov, age 60
President; Chairman of the Management Board; Director, Vagit Y. Alekperov, age 63
VP General Affairs Corporate Security and Communications, Anatoly A. Barkov, age 65
VP Strategic Development, Leonid A. Fedun, age 57
SVP Finance, Alexander K. Matytsyn, age 53
First VP Refining Marketing and Distribution, Vladimir I. Nekrasov, age 57
Chairman, Valery Grayfer, age 85
Vice-President Chief Accountant, Lyubov Khoba, age 57
VP HR Corporate Structure Development, Anatoly Moskalenko, age 54
Secretary and Head of the Board's Office, Evgueni Havkin, age 49
VP Technologies Oil and Gas Fields Development, Vladimir Mulyak, age 58
VP Sales and Supplies, Valery Subbotin, age 37
SVP Oil and Gas Production, Azat Shamsuarov, age 51
Vice-President OAO ?LUKOIL? Chief of Staff, Evgeny Khavkin
Head of Business Development, Graham Marshall
VP Petroleum Products Sales Coordination, Vadim Vorobyev
Vice-President General Counsel, Ivan Maslyaev
First EVP Exploration and Production and Director, Ravil U. Maganov, age 59
President and Director, Vagit Y. Alekperov, age 63
Director, Alexander Shokhin, age 62
Director, Sergei Mikhailov, age 56
Director, Donald E. (Don) Wallette Jr., age 54
Director, Herman Gref, age 50
Director, Igor Belikov, age 58
Director, Igor Ivanov, age 69
Director, Victor Blazheev, age 53
Director, Mark Mobius
Auditors: ZAOKPMG

LOCATIONS

HQ: Oil Co Lukoil
11 Sretensky Boulevard, Moscow 101000
Phone: (7) 495 627 4444   **Fax:** (7) 495 625 7016
Web: www.lukoil.com

Sales

	$ mil.	% of total
Russia	64,725	36
Other countries	114,001	64
Adjustments	(39555)	—
Total	**139,171**	**100**

PRODUCTS/OPERATIONS

Sales

	$ mil.	% of total
Refined products	103,407	95
Crude oil 27	670	3
Gas & gas products	3,477	2
Petrochemicals	1,410	—
Sales of energy & related services	1,394	—
Other	1,813	—
Total	**139,171**	**100**

COMPETITORS

Ashland Inc.	PETROBRAS
BP	Petroleos de Venezuela
Exxon Mobil	Rosneft
Gazprom Neft	Royal Dutch Shell
Imperial Oil	Surgutneftegas
Norsk Hydro ASA	TOTAL
Occidental Petroleum	Tatneft
PEMEX	

HISTORICAL FINANCIALS

Company Type: Public

Income Statement

FYE: December 31

	REVENUE ($ mil.)	NET INCOME ($ mil.)	NET PROFIT MARGIN	EMPLOYEES
12/13	141,452	7,832	5.5%	0
12/12	139,171	11,004	7.9%	0
12/11	133,650	10,357	7.7%	0
12/10	104,956	9,006	8.6%	0
12/09	81,083	7,011	8.6%	0
Annual Growth	14.9%	2.8%	—	—

2013 Year-End Financials

Debt ratio: 9.8%
Return on equity: 10.3%
Cash ($ mil.): 1,712
Current ratio: 1.79
Long-term debt ($ mil.): 9,483

No. of shares (mil.): 754
Dividends
Yield: 5.7%
Payout: 25.2%
Market value ($ mil.): 47,647

	STOCK PRICE ($) FY Close	P/E High	P/E Low	Earnings	Dividends	Book Value
12/13	63.12	7	5	10.18	3.66	104.10
12/12	67.50	5	4	14.17	3.05	96.98
12/11	53.20	6	4	13.04	1.71	87.34
12/10	57.22	6	4	10.94	1.39	75.76
12/09	56.40	8	4	8.28	1.38	66.13
Annual Growth	2.9%	—	—	5.3%	27.7%	12.0%

Old Mutual Plc

The name belies its demutualized status: Financial services group Old Mutual provides banking insurance and asset management services in about 30 nations in southern Africa Europe Asia and the Americas. Founded in 1845 Old Mutual owns a majority stake of South Africa's Nedbank Group which provides commercial banking finance investment banking and other services. It also owns Old Mutual (US) Holdings also known as Old Mutual Asset Management (US) or OMAM (US). Skandia Insurance offers insurance products and mutual funds primarily in the UK and Sweden. Old Mutual has some Â262 billion (some $357 billion) in funds under management.

Geographic Reach

London-based Old Mutual generated more than 40% of its fiscal 2012 revenue from emerging markets. This includes business in Africa operations in Colombia and Mexico and joint ventures in India and China.

Operations

Old Mutual operates through several business lines: long-term savings and investments US asset management banking and short-term insurance. Long-term savings and investments accounted for 70% of the company's fiscal 2012 revenue.

Old Mutual's Asset Management arm offers clients access to more than 115 investment strategies through its affiliated investment firms.

Sales and Marketing

The financial firm boasts more than 14 million customers worldwide. Clients buy products directly from Old Mutual or indirectly through an intermediary such as an independent financial advisor. Old Mutual reaches out to customers through a combined strategy of tied agents and independent financial advisors as well as via the Internet and call center functionality.

Strategy

Old Mutual aims to expand in South Africa Africa and other selected emerging markets. In 2013 the firm purchased a majority stake in Ghana-based Provident Life Assurance Company Limited and entered a strategic partnership with Faulu Kenya DTM LTD by buying a controlling stake in its emerging marketing business. To boot Old Mutual acquired Oceanic Life the life assurance operations of the former Oceanic Bank of Nigeria to extend its reach into the Nigerian market. Focused on strengthening its distribution capabilities in Latin America Old Mutual in 2012 acquired AIVA Business Platforms (AVIA) one of the largest financial groups globally.

It's also working to develop and grow its Old Mutual Wealth and US Asset Management businesses even including a partial IPO of its US Asset Management unit when economic conditions are favorable. For its Nedbank business Old Mutual is focused on boosting non-interest revenue growing the retail business via client-centered strategies and effective risk management and shifting the focus of its portfolio on profit-enhancing products and services.

Stung in the US Old Mutual has been restructuring its operations to recover from the financial crisis. To this end it exited several underperforming markets and sold noncore businesses. The group sold its US life insurance operations to Harbinger Group for $350 million in 2011. Old Mutual also sold its Skandia's business in the Nordic region and rebranded its remaining Skandia units Old Mutual Wealth to unify its brand. By divesting certain businesses Old Mutual can concentrate on its core long-term savings and investments operations. Proceeds from the sales are being used to reduce debt.

Not content with just making divestitures Old Mutual remains as aggressive as practical in target areas such as developing new investment products for distribution in emerging markets. The company has also seen marked improvements in returns due to an upswing in the economy. By streamlining its expansive structure while investing in growth Old Mutual is positioning itself to take advantage of the expected economic recovery.

HISTORY

Old Mutual was founded in 1845 as the Mutual Life Assurance Society of the Cape of Good Hope to sell life insurance in the Cape Colony. When South Africa gained self-governance from the UK in 1910 Old Mutual chairman John Merriman became the colony's first premier. In 1927 the company made its first international expansion into Zimbabwe (then called Rhodesia).

Life insurance remained the firm's sole line of business until 1948 when it acquired a controlling stake in what would become Mutual & Federal a general insurer. To better administer its mutual fund and trust businesses the firm formed the South African Mutual Unit Trust Company in 1966.

Old Mutual diversified in 1986 buying a controlling stake in the Nedcor banking group. Also that year the firm made its first major acquisition outside Africa buying UK life insurer Providence Capitol. In 1995 the firm expanded into Hong Kong and the US where it opened Old Mutual Investment Advisers in Boston. Seeking a way into the UK financial services market the company acquired asset managers Capel-Cure Myers and Albert E Sharp in 1997 and 1998 respectively merging them into Capel-Cure Sharp.

The firm further globalized its asset management operations in 1999 establishing an alliance with Japanese insurer Sumitomo Life to cross-market trust and investment services. Also that year its Nedcor banking subsidiary launched a hostile takeover bid for Standard Bank Investment Corporation (of which Old Mutual already owned 20%); the merger would have created South Africa's largest bank but government regulators nixed the deal.

Old Mutual demutualized in 1999 listing on both the London and Johannesburg stock exchanges. In 2000 the company sold its UK insurance operations to XL Mid Ocean Reinsurance and Century Group then acquired UK brokerage Gerrard Group and started an infrastructure investment joint venture with Australia's Macquarie Bank. Old Mutual also bought US-based United Asset Management (selling its Murray Johnstone Holdings subsidiary to Aberdeen Asset Management). Meanwhile Nedcor (now Nedbank) bought 50.1% of Imperial Bank a South African bank with a large vehicle finance business.

While the firm's Old Mutual (US) operations proved successful other areas of growth were less salutary. Three years after forming Gerrard Limited in 2000 as part of a bid to boost the UK business the asset manager was sold to Barclays.

Old Mutual gained control of insurer and mutual fund manager Skandia Insurance in 2006 through a nearly Â4 billion ($7 billion) hostile takeover bid. The acquisition brought more life insurance asset management and banking to Old Mutual and gave it deeper access into Asia Europe Latin America and the UK.

Satisfied with the results of its asset management operations in the US the company began expanding its asset management services in South Africa and the UK. In a shift from operating its businesses regionally the company took to grouping them by their primary operations.

EXECUTIVES

Group Company Secretary, Martin C. Murray
Group Finance Director, Philip Broadley, age 54, $796,015 total compensation
President Asia Pacific, Steffen Gilbert, age 52

CEO Nedbank Group, Michael W. T. (Mike) Brown, age 46

Regional Director Old Mutual Europe, Robert M. (Bob) Head, age 55

Interim CEO and COO Old Mutual Asset Management, Linda T. Gibson

CEO Long-Term Savings; Chairman Old Mutual South Africa, Paul Hanratty, age 53

Managing Director Mutual & Federal, Keith N. Kennedy

CEO Skandia Nordic, Bertil Hult, age 58

CEO South Africa, Kuseni Dlamini, age 46

CEO US Life Business, Christopher (Chris) Chapman

CEO Skandia UK, Peter Mann

Director Group Risk and Actuarial, Andrew Birrell, age 44

Head Strategy Development, Donald I. (Don) Hope, age 57

Head Strategic Implementation, Paul Maddox, age 53

Group Human Resources Director, Don Schneider, age 57

Manager Corporate Communications, Julie Hutchins

Head Corporate Responsibility, Helen Wilson

Group Investor Relations Manager, Aleida White

Director External Communications, Patrick Bowes

Managing Director Customer Solutions South Africa, Mike Harper, age 59

Managing Director Retail (Mass Market) South Africa, Marshall Rapiya, age 62

Director Corporate Affairs Media and Marketing South Africa, Crispin Sonn

Managing Director African Operations South Africa, Johannes Gawaxab, age 58

Group Finance Director South Africa, Diane Radley

Managing Director Old Mutual Service Technology and Administration South Africa, Rose Keanly

Managing Director Fairbairn Private Bank, Greg J. Horton

Executive General Manager Human Resources Mutual & Federal, Basetsana Magano

CEO Old Mutual Bermuda, Andrew Darfoor

CEO Namibia, Gregg MacIntyre

Group CEO Zimbabwe, Luke Ngwerume

CEO Skandia Retail Europe, Jonas Jonsson

Chief Executive and Chief Investment Officer Old Mutual Asset Management UK, Peter Baxter

Director Investor Relations, Deward Serfontein

Media Contact Finsbury, Don Hunter

Treasurer, James Simpson

Chief Executive Officer, Ralph Mupita

Group Strategy Director, Ian Gladman

Chairman of the Board, Patrick OSullivan

President and Chief Executive Officer - US Asset Management, Peter Bain

Chief Risk Officer, Sue Kean

Director, Richard A. Pym, age 65

Chief Executive and Director, Julian V. F. Roberts, age 55

Director, Nigel D. T. Andrews, age 67

Director, Alan R. Gillespie, age 63

Director, Russell P. Edey, age 72

Director, Reuel Khoza, age 64

Director, Michael (Mike) Arnold, age 66

Director, Lars Otterbeck, age 72

Director, Bongani Nqwababa, age 48

Independent Non-Executive Director, Eva Castillo

Independent Non-Executive Director, Nonkululeko Nyembezi-Heita

Independent Non-Executive Director, Roger Marshall

Auditors: KPMGAuditPlc

LOCATIONS

HQ: Old Mutual Plc
5th Floor, Millennium Bridge House, 2 Lambeth Hill, London EC4V 4GG
Phone:
Web: www.oldmutual.com

Selected Subsidiaries

Old Mutual (South Africa) Ltd
Old Mutual Africa Holdings (Pty) Ltd
Old Mutual Life Assurance Company (South Africa) Ltd
Old Mutual Investment Group (South Africa) (Pty) Ltd
Nedbank Group Ltd
Nedbank Ltd
Mutual & Federal Insurance Company Ltd
Old Mutual Life Assurance Company (Namibia) Ltd
Old Mutual (US) Holdings Inc
Old Mutual (Bermuda) Ltd
Acadian Asset Management LLC
Barrow Hanley Mewhinney & Strauss LLC
Rogge Global Partners plc
OM Group (UK) Ltd
Old Mutual Wealth Management Limited

PRODUCTS/OPERATIONS

2012 Revenue

	% of total
Long-term savings	
Emerging	43
Old mutual	27
NedBank	25
M&F	3
US Asset	2
Total	**100**

COMPETITORS

Absa	FirstRand
Alliance Trust	Investec
Allianz	PineBridge Investments
Aviva	Russell
Fidelity Worldwide Investment	Sanlam
	Standard Bank Group

HISTORICAL FINANCIALS

Company Type: Public

Income Statement

FYE: December 31

	ASSETS ($ mil.)	NET INCOME ($ mil.)	INCOME AS % OF ASSETS	EMPLOYEES
12/13	231,908	1,165	0.5%	56,812
12/12	231,298	1,890	0.8%	54,368
12/11	250,861	1,030	0.4%	57,430
12/10	300,516	(437)	—	55,730
12/09	265,297	(550)	—	53,706
Annual Growth	(3.3%)	—	—	1.4%

2013 Year-End Financials

Return on assets: 0.5%
Return on equity: 9.3%
Long-term debt ($ mil.): —
No. of shares (mil.): —
Sales ($ mil): 32,772

Dividends
Yield: 4.0%
Payout: 935.3%
Market value ($ mil.): —

	STOCK PRICE ($) FY Close	P/E High/Low	PER SHARE ($) Earnings	Dividends	Book Value
12/13	25.40	482358	0.23	1.02	2.45
12/12	23.00	244141	0.37	0.47	2.58
12/11	16.88	372221	0.18	0.00	2.26
12/10	15.25	— —	(0.09)	0.00	2.44
12/09	14.25	— —	(0.13)	0.00	2.48
Annual Growth	15.5%	— —	—	—	(0.3%)

OMV AG (Austria)

Oil and chemicals group OMV is Austria's largest industrial company. A leading oil and gas company in Central and Eastern Europe it explores for natural gas and crude oil; refines crude oil; and imports transports and stores gas. In 2012 OMV reported proved reserves of 1.2 billion barrels of oil equivalent; it produced about 303000 barrels of oil equivalent per day and sold 13 billion cu. ft. of gas. The bulk of OMV's sales come from refining and marketing with the company operating five refineries and more than 4500 gas stations in 13 countries.

Operations

The company operates in three major segments. OMV Exploration and Production's core countries in Romania and Austria OMV is focusing on reducing the natural decline and on enhancing the recovery rates from mature fields. It is looking to find new growth areas within the Caspian Middle East and Africa regions..

OMV Gas and Power ensures the supply of natural gas to its customers via a 2000 km gas pipeline in Austria. Its natural gas network serving about 90% of Austria's natural gas demand draws gas supplies from Russia Norway and Germany as well as from domestic reserves. Austria's gas market now dominated by OMV is slated for full competition and OMV is among state-controlled companies set for full privatization.

OMV Refining and Marketing serves about 1.5 million people a day through retail gas stations in 13 countries and is the market leader in Central and South Eastern Europe.

A fourth segment OMV Solutions is the integrated shared service center for all of the OMV Group companies. Its portfolio spans IT financial services and human resources administration.

Financial Performance

OMV's revenue increased by 28% in 2012 thanks to higher oil prices increased demand and the sale of higher volumes of oil and petroleum products.

However net income decreased by more than 11% in 2012 (before the restatement of 2011 results).

Strategy

Exploration and production is the growth driver of OMV and in 2013 the company announced plans to direct more than two-thirds of future investments towards exploration and production of oil and gas. It also plans to grow its integrated natural gas assets and restructure its downstream business by selling non-core refining and marketing assets.

In 2012 the company sold its gas station subsidiary in Croatia. That year it boosted it E&P assets entering Abu Dhabi and acquiring natural gas assets in Norway.

In a further push to grow in the Middle East in 2011 the company acquired two Tunisia-based exploration and production units from Pioneer Natural Resources for $866 million. It also boosted its footprint in Pakistan acquiring Petronas Carigali (Pakistan) Ltd. in 2011.

The Refining and Marketing portfolio will be adjusted in response to falling demand for crude oil products in Europe. The restructuring of the R&M portfolio will prioritize highquality products the integration with petrochemicals and improved performance.

The aquisition of full control (in 2010) of Petrol Ofisi Turkey's leading filling station and retail business with the only nationwide filling station network in the country (approximately 2300 stations)

built a strategic bridge in the growth market of Turkey.

Ownership

OMV's largest shareholders are Austrian state holding company OIAG (32%) and the International Petroleum Investment Company (IPIC) of Abu Dhabi (20%).

HISTORY

Oil exploration began in Austria in the 1920s largely as joint ventures with foreign firms such as Shell and Socony-Vacuum. Full-scale production did not get underway until 1938 when the Anschluss (the absorption of Austria by Germany) paved the way for Germany to exploit Austria's natural resources to fuel its growing war machine. In the division of spoils following WWII Russia gained control of Austria's oil reserves.

The Russian-administered oil assets were transferred to the new Austrian government in 1955 which authorized the company Osterreichische Mineralolverwaltung (OMG) in 1956 to control state oil assets. OMG state-controlled by the Austrian Mineral Oil Administration set about building a major refinery in 1960 and acquiring marketing companies Martha and OROP in 1965.

In 1968 OMG became the first Western company to sign a natural gas supply contract with Russia. In 1974 the company commissioned the Trans-Austria Gas Pipeline which enabled the supply of natural gas to Italy. That year OMG changed its name to OMV Aktiengesellschaft (OMV became OMV in 1995 for international markets).

During the 1970s OMV expanded its crude supply arrangements tapping supplies from Iran Iraq Libya and other Middle Eastern countries. It moved into oil and gas exploration in the mid-1980s forming OMV Libya (acquiring 25% of Occidental's Libyan production) and OMV UK.

With Austria moving toward increasing privatization in 1987 about 15% of OMV's shares were sold to the public. The government sold another 10% two years later. In 1989 OMV acquired PCD Polymere. With the aim of merging state-owned oil and chemical activities OMV acquired Chemie Linz in 1990. The company also opened its first OMV-branded service station that year. In 1994 OMV reorganized itself as an integrated oil and gas group based in Central Europe with international exploration and production activities and with other operations in the chemical and petrochemical sectors.

In 1995 OMV acquired TOTAL-AUSTRIA expanding its service stations by 59. The company introduced OMV lubricants to the Greek market in 1996. It also expanded its OMV service station network in Hungary to 66 stations after acquiring 31 Q8 (Kuwait) sites. In 1997 the Stroh Company's retail network in Austria was merged into OMV.

Expanding its retail network even farther OMV acquired BP's retail network in the Czech Republic Slovakia and Hungary in 1998. It also sold its stake in Chemie Linz and acquired a 25% stake in major European polyolefin producer Borealis which in turn acquired PCD Polymere. In 1999 the company pushed its retail network into Bulgaria and Romania. That year OMV also acquired Australian company Cultus Petroleum.

OMV and Shell agreed to develop North Sea fields together in 2000. That year OMV also formed a joint venture with Italy's Edison International to explore in Vietnam and acquired more than 9% of Hungarian rival MOL. It upped that stake to 10% in 2001.

In 2002 OMV opened its first gas station in Serbia and Montenegro. It also increased its German gas station count from 79 to 151 with the purchase of 32 units from Royal Dutch Shell and 40 stations from Martin GmbH & Co.

In 2003 the company acquired Preussag Energie's exploration and production assets for $320 million. That year the company moved into Bosnia-Herzegovina opening nine gas stations.

During 2004 the company bought up 51% of Romania's Petrom making it the top oil and gas producer in Central Europe. As part of the deal OMV chose to divest itself of its quarter-chunk of Rompetrol.

In 2006 Russian energy giant Gazprom signed long-term contracts for gas deliveries with OMV.

In a major consolidation move in 2006 OMV agreed to buy Austrian power firm Verbund for $17 billion but the move was rebuffed by government regulators. The next year the company announced plans to merge with Hungary's energy powerhouse MOL but those plans were called off as well due to European Commission regulatory concerns in 2008.

After plans to merge with Hungary's MOL went south OMV the next year sold its 21% stake in it to Russian oil company Surgutneftegas for E1.4 billion ($1.85 billion). Also in 2009 in keeping with its focus on retail markets in the Danube region southeastern Europe and the Black Sea region OMV sold subsidiary OMV Italia; San Marco Petroli acquired the network of about 100 gas stations in the northern Italian region of Triveneto.

OMV has been disposing of some of its heating oil operations. In 2008 it unloaded Bayern GmbH and it plans to sell its OMV Warme VertriebsgmbH by the end of 2010. At that point the sale of heating oil to private clients will be handled by partners but OMV will continue to service corporate customers.

Eyeing new areas of exploration that year OMV also acquired a 10% stake in Pearl Petroleum giving it access to gas-condensate fields in Iraq.

In 2010 the company boosted its share of Turkey-based oil products company Petrol Ofisi (renamed OMV Petrol Ofisi) from 42% to 96% by acquiring a 54% stake from Doan Holding for about $1.4 billion. The deal gave OMV access to not only Turkey but the Caspian region and the Middle East.

EXECUTIVES

Deputy Chairman Supervisory Board, Wolfgang C. G. Berndt, age 71
Deputy Chairman Executive Board, David C. Davies, age 60, $1,096,338 total compensation
Executive Board Member, Jaap Huijskes, age 50
Chairman Supervisory Board, Markus Beyrer, age 49
CEO, Doris Bures
Chairman of the Intergovernmental Panel on Climate Change, Rajendra Pachauri
Deputy Chairwoman of the Supervisory Board, Alyazia Kuwaiti
Deputy Chairman of the Supervisory Board, Khadem Qubaisi
Head of Investor Relations, Lacramiorara Diaconu
Member of the Executive Board, Manfred Leitner
Deputy Chairman Supervisory Board, Wolfgang C. G. Berndt, age 71
Director, Helmut Draxler, age 64
Director, Herbert Stepic, age 68
Member of the Supervisory Board, Wolfram Littich
Director, Herbert Werner, age 67
Director, Norbert Zimmermann, age 67
Director, Alyazia Ali Saleh Al Kuwaiti, age 37
Deputy Chairman Supervisory Board, Khadem A. Al Qubaisi, age 42
Member of the Supervisory Board, Elif Bilgi-Zapparoli
Member of the Supervisory Board; Employee Representative, Ferdinand Nemesch
Member of the Supervisory Board; Employee Representative, Franz Kaba

Member of the Supervisory Board; Employee Representative, Leopold Abraham
Member of the Supervisory Board; Employee Representative, Martin Rossmann
Member of the Supervisory Board; Employee Representative, Wolfgang Baumann

LOCATIONS

HQ: OMV AG (Austria)
  Trabrennstrasse 6-8, Vienna 1020
Phone: (43) 1 40440 0   **Fax:** (43) 1 40440 27900
Web: www.omv.com

Sales

	% of total
Europe	
Central & Europe	
Austria	37
Germany	16
Turkey	13
Romania	11
Other	15
Other	8
Total	**100**

PRODUCTS/OPERATIONS

Sales

	% of total
Refining &	62
Gas &	25
Exploration &	12
Corporate &	1
Total	**100**

COMPETITORS

BP	MOL
Eni	PKN ORLEN
Exxon Mobil	Royal Dutch Shell
Hellenic Petroleum	Unipetrol

HISTORICAL FINANCIALS

Company Type: Public

Income Statement

FYE: December 31

	REVENUE ($ mil.)	NET INCOME ($ mil.)	NET PROFIT MARGIN	EMPLOYEES
12/13	58,393	1,600	2.7%	26,863
12/12	56,213	1,796	3.2%	28,658
12/11	44,046	1,375	3.1%	29,800
12/10	31,215	1,232	3.9%	31,398
12/09	25,811	823	3.2%	34,676
Annual Growth	22.6%	18.1%	—	(6.2%)

2013 Year-End Financials

Debt ratio: 21.2%   No. of shares (mil.): 326
Return on equity: 9.8%   Dividends
Cash ($ mil.): 970   Yield: 2.4%
Current ratio: 0.92   Payout: 42.0%
Long-term debt ($ mil.): 5,368   Market value ($ mil.): 15,591

	STOCK PRICE ($) FY Close	P/E High/Low		PER SHARE ($) Earnings	Dividends	Book Value
12/13	47.79	27	19	4.89	1.16	49.01
12/12	36.70	17	10	5.50	1.05	48.09
12/11	30.38	26	15	4.36	1.95	43.52
12/10	41.80	30	16	4.11	1.51	40.67
12/09	44.10	51	23	2.75	2.00	39.05
Annual Growth	2.0%		—	15.4%	(12.7%)	5.8%

Onex Corp.

Investment firm Onex holds equity interests in companies across several industries in North America. It mainly focuses on manufacturing and health care but also has holdings in the financial services building products and transportation sectors. While large-cap private equity is its biggest segment the company also invests in debt and credit securities and real estate including real estate investment trusts commercial real estate loans and residential developments. Its ONCAP family of private equity funds invests in mid-cap firms. Altogether Onex has some $11.8 billion in third-party capital under management and about $14.1 billion in all. Onex also owns US insurance brokerage firm USI.

Geographic Reach

Onex is stationed in Ontario Canada and has other offices in London and New York. The US accounts for 60% of its revenue. Other major markets include Europe(19%) and Asia and Oceania (13%).

Operations

The company's portfolio includes interests in Spirit AeroSystems The Warranty Group electronics manufacturer Celestica and business process outsourcer Sitel in addition to minority stakes in airplane manufacturer Hawker Beechcraft. (It sold off its remaining stake in Allison Transmission in late 2014.) Onex's health care holdings include Res-Care Skilled Healthcare Group and the Center for Diagnostic Imaging.

Financial Performance

Onex achieved a revenue milestone in 2013 generating a record-setting $27.8 billion. However the firm posted net losses of $121 million in 2012 and $354 million in 2013 primarily due to higher operating expenses and a loss from continuing operations.

The historic revenue growth for 2013 was driven by a 9% increase in its building products segment revenue as a result of higher revenue from North America and Europe. North American segment revenue climbed due to increased demand from new customers in addition to a previous acquisition.

Strategy

When considering acquisitions Onex seeks out growth investments restructurings and subsidiaries or divisions being sold by large corporations. It prefers to take a controlling position in its holdings which enables it to make strategic decisions though Onex does not usually get involved in the day-to-day activities of its companies.

In late 2014 it agreed to pay up to $4.6 billion for Swiss packaging company SIG Combibloc. Onex subsidiary USI also in 2014 agreed to acquire more than 40 insurance brokerage and consulting locations nationwide from financial services company Wells Fargo & Company.

EXECUTIVES

CFO, Donald W. (Don) Lewtas
Senior Managing Director, Seth M. Mersky, age 54
Senior Managing Director, Anthony Munk, age 54
Senior Managing Director, Ewout R. (Eve) Heersink, age 64
Chairman and CEO, Gerald W. (Gerry) Schwartz, age 71, $811,380 total compensation
Director Corporate Administration, Danica Oldford
Director Taxation, David W. Copeland
Senior Managing Director, Robert M. (Bobby) Le Blanc, age 46
Co-Founder and Chief Investment Officer Onex Credit Partners, Michael J. Gelblat

Co-Founder and Chief Investment Officer Onex Credit Partners, Stuart R. Kovensky
Vice President; General Counsel; Secretary, Andrea E. Daly
Principal Onex Partners, Kosty Gilis
Principal Onex Partners, Joshua (Josh) Hausman
Principal Onex Partners, David R. Hirsch, age 37
Principal and CFO Onex Real Estate Partners, Edward J. Santoro, age 63
VP Investor Relations, Emma Thompson
Senior Associate Onex Partners, Tate A. M. Abols
Vice President - Finance, Christine M. Donaldson
Director Onex Partners, Andrew P. Lapham
Director Onex Partners, John T. McCoy
Senior Associate Onex Partners, Amir Motamedi
Principal Onex Partners, Adam Reinmann
Director Taxation, Robert (Rob) Auld
Director Information Technology, Jason MacKenzie
Director Onex Partners Finance, Susan J. Soenderop
Associate Onex Partners, Matthew Alexander
Associate Onex Partners, Aneil Manhas
President Chief Executive Officer, Michael Dana
Managing Partner ONCAP, Michael Lay
Associate Onex Partners, David Armstrong
Associate Onex Partners, Adam Cobourn
Associate Onex Partners, Kelvin Kwong
Associate Onex Partners, Adina Radu
Chief Investment Officer, Steven E. Talles
Principal Asset Management Onex Real Estate Partners, Michael J. Koep
Principal Acquisitions Onex Real Estate Partners, Sorabh Maheshwari
Associate ONCAP, Manica Gautam
Associate ONCAP, Adam Shantz
Senior Associate ONCAP, Wole James
Associate ONCAP, Jared Waldron
Director, Serge Gouin, age 69
Managing Director and Director, Ewout R. (Eve) Heersink, age 64
Director, Peter C. Godsoe, age 73
Director, John B. McCoy, age 69
Director, Heather M. Reisman, age 63
Director, J. Robert S. Prichard, age 65
Director, Arni C. Thorsteinson, age 63
Director, Daniel C. Casey, age 64
Director, William A. (Bill) Etherington, age 70
Auditors: PricewaterhouseCoopersLLP

LOCATIONS

HQ: Onex Corp.
49th Floor, 161 Bay Street, P.O. Box 700, Toronto, Ontario M5J 2S1
Phone: 416 362-7711   **Fax:** 416 362-6803
Web: www.onex.com

Sales

	% of total
North	64
Asia &	20
Europe	13
Other	3
Total	**100**

PRODUCTS/OPERATIONS

Sales

	% of total
Electronic manufacturing	27
Health	26
Aerostructures	18
Metal	9
Customer support	6
Financial	5
Other	9
Total	**100**

Selected Holdings

Allison Transmission
Carestream Health
Celestica

Center for Diagnostic Imaging
Hawker Beechcraft
JELD-WEN
Res-Care
RSI Home Products
Sitel
Skilled Healthcare Group
Spirit AeroSystems
Sport Supply Group
Tomkins
The Warranty Group

COMPETITORS

Berkshire Hathaway	Forstmann Little
Blackstone Group	HM Capital Partners
Brookfield Asset	Heico Companies
Management	Investor AB
Caisse de depot et	KKR
placement du Quebec	Power Financial
Clayton Dubilier &	TPG
Rice	Thomas H. Lee Partners
Counsel Corporation	

HISTORICAL FINANCIALS

Company Type: Public

Income Statement

FYE: December 31

	REVENUE ($ mil.)	NET INCOME ($ mil.)	NET PROFIT MARGIN	EMPLOYEES
12/13	27,809	(354)	—	0
12/12	27,443	(121)	—	250,000
12/11	24,642	1,327	5.4%	246,000
12/10*	19,734	(167)	—	0
01/10	0	0	—	0
Annual Growth	—	—	—	—

*Fiscal year change

2013 Year-End Financials

Debt ratio: 32.4%
Return on equity: (-25.4%)
Cash ($ mil.): 3,191
Current ratio: 1.56
Long-term debt ($ mil.): 11,319

No. of shares (mil.): 111
Dividends
　Yield: 0.0%
　Payout: —
Market value ($ mil.): 6,018

	STOCK PRICE ($) FY Close	P/E High/Low		Earnings	PER SHARE ($) Dividends	Book Value
12/13	53.95	—	—	(3.12)	0.13	10.35
12/12	42.27	—	—	(1.05)	0.11	14.18
12/11	33.11	3	3	11.31	0.11	15.80
12/10*	30.33	—	—	(1.40)	0.11	4.26
01/10	22.30	—	—	(0.00)	0.09	(0.00)
Annual Growth	**24.7%**	—	—		**7.5%**	—

*Fiscal year change

Orange

For many in Europe and elsewhere the telecom landscape has an Orange glow. Formerly France Telecom Orange provides fixed-line and mobile voice and data services to consumers and commercial clients around the world. The company serves some 230 million customers in more than 30 countries. It is a leading European wireless operator and broadband service provider with more than 170 million mobile customers and some 15 million broadband subscribers. Orange's services for corporate clients are provided by its Orange Business Services unit which offers a wide range of managed business networking and data services. The company had been coalescing around its

Orange brand since 2006 culminating in the mid-2013 name change.

Geographic Reach

Orange divides up its primary business —mobile and fixed-line telephony along with Internet access services —by region with France comprising nearly half of total operations. Spain and Portugal are its other two major regions with these services. The rest of the world makes up nearly a fifth of total revenues. The remaining business about 15% of sales is largely the company's enterprise services operations.

Strategy

The company's near-term strategy includes efforts to simplify its products and services by focusing on customer-facing improvements and marketing. It also continues to look beyond France for new business including doubling revenues in Africa and the Middle East by 2015 and expanding in Europe. That expansion will not only benefit Orange's core business but also its enterprise services success.

HISTORY

Shortly before he abdicated King Louis Philippe laid the groundwork for France's state-owned telegraphic service. Established in 1851 the operation became part of the French Post Office in the 1870s about the time Alexander Graham Bell invented the telephone. The French government licensed three private companies to provide telegraph service and during the 1880s they merged into the Societe Generale de Telephones (SGT). In 1883 the country's first exchange was initiated in Rheims. Four years later an international circuit was installed connecting Paris and Brussels. The government nationalized SGT in 1889.

By the turn of the century France had more than 60000 phone lines and in 1924 a standardized telephone was introduced. Long-distance service improved with underground cabling and phone exchanges in Paris and other leading cities became automated during the 1930s.

WWII proved a major setback to the French government's telephone operations Direction Generale des Telecommunications (DGT) because a large part of its equipment was destroyed or damaged. For the next two decades France lagged behind other nations in telephony infrastructure development. An exception to this technological stagnation was Centre National d'Etudes des Telecommunications (CNET) the research laboratory formed in 1944 that eventually became France Telecom's research arm.

In 1962 DGT was a key player in the first intercontinental television broadcast between the US and France via a Telstar satellite. The company began to catch up with its peers when it developed a digital phone system in the mid-1970s. In 1974 CNET was instrumental in the launch of France's first experimental communications satellite. In another technological advance DGT began replacing its paper directories with the innovative Minitel online terminals in 1980.

The French government created France Telecom in 1988. In 1993 France Telecom and Deutsche Telekom (DT) teamed up to form the Global One international telecommunications venture and Sprint joined the next year. Global One was formally launched in 1996. Also that year France Telecom began providing Internet access though Minitel still reigned as the country's top online service.

In 1997 the government sold about 20% of France Telecom to the public. With Europe's state telephone monopolies ending in 1998 France Telecom reorganized and brought prices in line with those of its competitors.

France Telecom paid $4.3 billion to DT and Sprint in 2000 to take full ownership of Global One. Later that year it snatched up UK mobile phone operator Orange in a $37.5 billion cash and stock deal after Vodafone was forced to divest the company before merging with Mannesmann. France Telecom also invested $4.5 billion in UK cable operator NTL and sold its stake in Mexican telecom giant Telmex.

In 2001 the company sold its 49.9% stake in Noos France's #1 cable-TV operator. It sold its nearly 11% stake in Greek mobile carrier Vodafone-Panafon to Vodafone Group for Â311 million the following year.

France Telecom took full ownership of Orange and Wanadoo a European directory publisher and ISP in 2004. In 2006 the company sold its 54% stake in directories business PagesJaunes Groupe to Kohlberg Kravis Roberts (now KKR) in a deal valued at about $4.2 billion. Also that year it acquired the remaining shares that it did not already own of Dutch-based carrier Equant; it subsequently changed the name to Orange Business Services.

The company in 2007 sold the mobile phone unit of France Telecom Espana to Deutsche Telekom in return for that company's Ya.com Internet unit. It also acquired a controlling stake in security network specialist Silicomp.

In 2011 it helped that plan along when it bought Congo Chine Telecom (CCT) from ZTE and the government of Congo for $17 million. Orange sees Congo as an underpenetrated market with considerable growth potential and will make a multi-installment capital investment in CCT of $185 million.The company in 2010 paid $840 million for a 40% stake in Moroccan network operator Meditel in a move to push further into emerging markets. The deal put the company in direct competition in that country with fellow French rival Vivendi which owns a controlling stake in former Moroccan telecom monopoly Maroc Telecom.

Also that year Orange bought submarine communications cable laying and maintenance specialist Elettra from Telecom Italia to expand its capacity to install and service undersea networks. The company combined the operations of Elettra including its two cable ships with its existing cable laying subsidiary.

In 2012 it expanded in Egypt by completing the purchase of Orascom Telecom's wireless services provider Mobinil Egypt's biggest wireless carrier. Also that year to focus on higher growth areas in Europe Orange sold Orange Switzerland for Â1.6 billion ($2.1 billion) to investment firm Apax Partners.

EXECUTIVES

SEVP Communication and Brand, Xavier Couture, age 63

EVP Group Human Resources, Bruno Mettling, age 56

Deputy CEO Quality Corporate Social Responsibility, Jean-Philippe Vanot, age 62

SEVP Marketing and Innovation, Jean-Paul Cottet, age 59

EVP Group General Secretary and France Carriers Division, Pierre Louette, age 51

EVP Africa the Middle-East and Asia, Marc Rennard, age 57

SEVP Enterprise Communication Services, Vivek Badrinath, age 43

SEVP Events Cultural and Institutional Partnerships and Philanthropy, Christine Albanel, age 58

SEVP Networks and Carriers and Research and Development, Thierry Bonhomme, age 57

SEVP Strategy and Development, Elie Girard, age 34

SEVP Europe, Benoit Scheen, age 46

Executive Vice President - Group Strategy & Development; Member of the Executive Committee, Elie Girard

Executive Vice President Marketing and Innovation; Member of the Executive Committee, Jean Cottet

Executive Vice President - Operations in Europe (excluding France); Member of the Executive Committee, Benoit Scheen

Deputy Chief Executive Officer - Orange France; Member of the Executive Committee, Delphine Delphine Ernotte Cunci Cunci

Director, Charles-Henri Filippi, age 61

Director, Jose-Luis Duran, age 48

Director, Marcel Roulet, age 79

Director, Gilles Michel, age 57

Director, Henri Martre, age 85

Director, Bernard Dufau, age 72

Director, Jean Simonin, age 68

Director, Stephane Tierce, age 44

Director, Claudie Haignere, age 55

Director, Bruno Bezard, age 49

Director, Pascal Faure, age 51

Director, Caroline Angeli, age 56

Director, Ghislaine Coinaud, age 57

Director, Daniel Guillot, age 56

Director, Marc Maouche, age 49

Director, Patrick Roussel

Director, Thierry Franchi

Independent Director, Claudie Haignere

Independent Director, Jean Severino

Independent Director, Jose Duran

Independent Director, Muriel Penicaud

Auditors: Deloitte&Associes

LOCATIONS

HQ: Orange
78 rue Olivier de Serres, Paris 75015
Phone: (33) 1 44 44 21 05
Web: www.orange.com

PRODUCTS/OPERATIONS

Sales

	% of total
Personal and communicat	
France	47
Spain	9
Poland	8
Enterprise	15
International operators and shared	2
Rest of the	19
Total	**100**

2011 Mobile Customers

	# mil.	% of total
France	27	16
Poland	14	9
UK	13	8
Spain	12	8
Rest of the world	99	60
Total	**167**	**100**

2011 Broadband Customers

	mil.	% of total
France	9	67
Poland	2	16
Spain	1	9
UK	0	2
Rest of the world	0	6
Total	**14**	**100**

Selected Operations

Audience and advertising (Internet advertising business)
Content (partnerships with content providers and development of related technology platforms)
Enterprise communication services (communication services to companies)
Health (services to the health care industry)
Home communication services (residential communication services especially fixed-line broadband)

Personal communication services (communication services for individuals using mobile devices)

COMPETITORS

AT&T	KPN
BSkyB	Maroc Telecom
BT	SFR
Belgacom	TalkTalk
Bouygues	Tele2
COLT Group	Telecom Italia
Cable & Wireless	Telefonica
Deutsche Telekom	Telefonica Europe
Equinix Group	Tiscali
HP Enterprise Services	Unisys
Hutchison Whampoa	Virgin Mobile
IBM Global Services	Vivendi
Jazztel	Vodafone

HISTORICAL FINANCIALS
Company Type: Public

Income Statement
FYE: December 31

	REVENUE ($ mil.)	NET INCOME ($ mil.)	NET PROFIT MARGIN	EMPLOYEES
12/13	56,063	2,578	4.6%	165,488
12/12	57,009	1,080	1.9%	170,531
12/11	58,438	5,038	8.6%	171,949
12/10	60,881	6,531	10.7%	168,694
12/09	66,218	4,317	6.5%	167,148
Annual Growth	(4.1%)	(12.1%)	—	(0.2%)

2013 Year-End Financials

Debt ratio: —	No. of shares (mil.): —
Return on equity: 7.7%	Dividends
Cash ($ mil.): 8,144	Yield: 5.4%
Current ratio: 0.61	Payout: 127.3%
Long-term debt ($ mil.): —	Market value ($ mil.): —

	STOCK PRICE ($) FY Close	P/E High/Low	PER SHARE ($) Earnings	Dividends	Book Value
12/13	12.35	39 23	0.98	0.68	12.77
12/12	11.05	90 56	0.41	2.88	12.19
12/11	15.66	31 17	1.89	3.66	13.54
12/10	21.08	27 15	2.44	2.87	14.70
12/09	25.24	52 34	1.63	4.00	14.16
Annual Growth(16.4%) (2.6%)		—	—(12.0%)	(35.8%)	

Orix Corp. (Japan)

An international financing leviathan ORIX is one of Japan's largest public financial services firms. The company finances leases of everything from computers and measuring equipment to aircraft and ships; it rents out some 30000 different items and is adding more. ORIX also engages in consumer and corporate finance investment banking brokerage car rental and property development and management services in Japan and more than 35 other countries. Its retail offerings include banking life insurance credit cards and trust services. ORIX even has its own professional baseball team the Kobe-based ORIX Buffaloes.

Geographic Reach

The company operates around 1800 offices in Japan (where it earns more than 80% of its revenues) and 260 more overseas. ORIX USA acts as the holding company for the firm's operations in the US which ORIX is targeting for growth. Among its holdings are Los Angeles-based investment

bank Houlihan Lokey which specializes in middle-market mergers and acquisitions.

Strategy

ORIX is also looking to build its fee-based business in Japan and abroad. Asia and China in particular are additional areas of focus for the company. It also plans to continue to expand its already diverse array of offerings by moving into energy and environmental products. ORIX has been able to remain profitable during the global credit crunch but the stagnant economy as well the company's internal deleveraging have been a drag on its bottom line.

EXECUTIVES

President ORIX Baseball Club, Hiroaki Nishina, age 70
Chairman and CEO, Yoshihiko Miyauchi, age 79
Deputy President and CIO, Tamio Umaki, age 66
Corporate EVP, Shintaro Agata, age 64
Corporate EVP, Yuki Oshima, age 67
Deputy President and CFO, Haruyuki Urata, age 60
EVP; President ORIX Real Estate, Yoshiyuki Yamaya, age 58
SVP; President ORIX Auto, Katsunobu Kamei
EVP; President NS Lease, Katsutoshi Kadowaki
President and COO, Mikoto Inoue, age 62
Corporate EVP, Kazuo Kojima
SVP; President ORIX Credit, Masatoshi Kemmochi
Vice Chairman; Chairman ORIX Real Estate Corporation, Hiroaki Nishina, age 69
Director, Yoshinori Yokoyama, age 71
Director, Takeshi Niinami
Director, Hirotaka Takeuchi, age 67
Deputy President CFO and Director, Haruyuki Urata, age 59
President COO and Director, Makoto Inoue, age 61
Director, Takeshi Sasaki, age 71
Director, Eiko Tsujiyama
Director, Robert Feldman
Auditors: KPMGAZSA&Co.

LOCATIONS

HQ: Orix Corp. (Japan)
 Mita NN Building, 4-1-23 Shiba, Minato-ku, Tokyo 108-0014
Phone: (81) 3 5419 5042   **Fax:** (81) 3 5419 5901
Web: www.orix.co.jp

Sales

	% of total
Japan	85
Asia Europe &	9
Americas	6
Total	**100**

PRODUCTS/OPERATIONS

Sales

	% of total
Operating	27
Interest on loans &	19
Life insurance premiums & related	11
Real estate	7
Direct financing	6
Gain on sales of real estate under operating	2
Other	28
Total	**100**

Selected Subsidiaries and Segments

ORIX Aircraft (aircraft leasing)
ORIX Asset Management & Loan Services Corporation (commercial mortgage servicing)
ORIX Auto (car rental and leasing)
ORIX Baseball Club (professional baseball team)
ORIX Life Insurance
ORIX Real Estate (real estate development and investment)
ORIX Real Estate Investment Advisors (asset management)

ORIX Rentec (rental operations)
ORIX Trust and Banking
ORIX USA
SUN Leasing Corporation (medical equipment leasing)

COMPETITORS

CIT Group	Mizuho Financial
GE Capital	Rentokil Initial
ILFC	Sumitomo
Mitsubishi UFJ Financial Group	

HISTORICAL FINANCIALS
Company Type: Public

Income Statement
FYE: March 31

	ASSETS ($ mil.)	NET INCOME ($ mil.)	INCOME AS % OF ASSETS	EMPLOYEES
03/14	87,865	1,809	2.1%	25,977
03/13	89,696	1,189	1.3%	19,043
03/12	101,851	1,050	1.0%	17,488
03/11	103,634	812	0.8%	17,578
03/10	82,860	404	0.5%	17,725
Annual Growth	1.5%	45.5%	—	10.0%

2014 Year-End Financials

Return on assets: 2.1%	Dividends
Return on equity: 10.4%	Yield: 0.9%
Long-term debt ($ mil.): —	Payout: 61.6%
No. of shares (mil.): 1,309	Market value ($ mil.): 92,277
Sales ($ mil): 12,998	

	STOCK PRICE ($) FY Close	P/E High/Low	PER SHARE ($) Earnings	Dividends	Book Value
03/14	70.47	0 0	1.38	0.65	14.20
03/13	63.58	0 0	0.93	0.00	14.30
03/12	48.25	0 0	0.82	0.00	15.83
03/11	46.57	0 0	0.64	0.40	14.82
03/10	44.11	0 0	0.34	0.36	(0.00)
Annual Growth	12.4%	— —	42.2%	15.7%	—

Oversea-Chinese Banking Corp. Ltd. (Singapore)

Singapore bank Oversea-Chinese Banking Corporation (OCBC Bank) operates more than 470 branches and offices in 15 countries including some 350 offices in Indonesia through its Bank OCBC NISP subsidiary. The company offers traditional banking services for individuals and businesses as well as financial services such as brokerage and asset management. Private banking for high-net-worth families is offered through the Bank of Singapore while Great Eastern Holdings which provides life and property/casualty insurance is the largest insurance company in Singapore and Malaysia. OCBC Bank was founded in 1912 to serve the Chinese business community of Singapore and other parts of Asia but now serves the general public.

Geographic Reach

The bank's main operations are in its home country of Singapore which accounts for 60% of business. Malaysia where it operates as OCBC Bank Malaysia and offers Islamic banking services through OCBC Al-Amin Bank accounts for about 20% of business. Indonesia and China each account for less than 10% of business.

In addition to its core markets OCBC also has a presence in Australia Brunei Dubai Hong Kong Japan The Philippines South Korea Taiwan Thailand the UK the US (in New York and Los Angeles) and Vietnam through branches and representative offices.

Strategy

With Singapore's population only 5 million people the bank has targeted China Indonesia and Malaysia as international growth markets. It plans to increase its Islamic banking and insurance operations in Malaysia home to almost 30 million people. In Indonesia (population 247 million) the bank consolidated its banking subsidiaries in order to grow the OCBC NISP brand there. And in China with 1.3 billion people the bank plans to cater to wealthy citizens by offering private banking services through the Bank of Singapore.

EXECUTIVES

Chairman, Cheong Choong Kong, age 72
Director and CEO OCBC Bank Malaysia, Jeffrey S. T. Chew, age 49
CEO and Director, David P. Conner
SVP Group Corporate Communications, Koh Ching Ching, age 46
Chief Operating Officer, Ching Wei Hong, age 54
EVP Group Investment Banking, George L. W. Lee, age 61
EVP Group Audit, Lai Teck Poh, age 69
EVP Group Human Resources, Cynthia G. H. Tan, age 63
EVP Group Quality and Service Excellence, Teng Soon Lang, age 63
Company Secretary, Peter B. A. Yeoh, age 59
Group Chief Executive Officer, Samuel N. (Sam) Tsien, age 59
EVP Enterprise Banking and Financial Institutions, Linus T. L. Goh, age 51
SVP Group Property Management, Vincent Soh, age 58
SVP Group Transaction Banking, Neo Bock Cheng, age 49
Senior Executive Vice President Head of Global Treasury, Lam Kun Kin, age 51
EVP International, Na Wu Beng, age 57
EVP Group Risk Management, Gilbert Kohnke, age 55
Chairman OCBC Bank China, Leong Wai Leng, age 48
Head Group Operations and Technology, Lim Khiang Tong, age 54
Head of Audit, Kng Tin
General Counsel, Loretta Yuen
Executive Vice President, Cynthia Hiang
Executive Vice President, Gan Kim
Chief Financial Officer, Darren T.S. Peng, age 43
Head of Global Commercial Banking, Linus G.T. Liang, age 51
Executive Vice President Head of Global Corporate Banking, George L.L. Wah
Chief Executive Officer Bank of Singapore, Renato de Guzman
CEO OCBC Bank China, Kng Hwee Tin
CEO and Director, David P. Conner
Director, Bobby Chin, age 62
Director, Lee Seng Wee, age 82
Director, Lee Tih Shih, age 50
Director, Prof Neo Boon Siong, age 56
Director, Patrick K. H. Yeoh, age 75
Director, Pramukti Surjaudaja, age 51
Auditors: KPMGLLP

LOCATIONS

HQ: Oversea-Chinese Banking Corp. Ltd. (Singapore)
65 Chulia Street, #06-00 OCBC Centre, 049513
Phone: (65) 6318 7222   **Fax:** (65) 6533 7955
Web: www.ocbc.com

Sales

	% of total
Singapore	63
Malaysia	20
Indonesia	7
China	7
Rest of	2
Rest of	1
Total	**100**

PRODUCTS/OPERATIONS

Sales

	% of total
Interest	59
Noninterest	
Fees &	12
Life	7
General	1
Rental	1
Dividends	1
Other	19
Total	**100**

Selected Subsidiaries

Banking
  Bank of Singapore Limited
  OCBC Al-Amin Bank Berhad
  OCBC Bank (Malaysia) Berhad
  Singapore Island Bank Limited
Insurance
  Great Eastern Life Assurance (Malaysia) Berhad
  Overseas Assurance Corporation (Malaysia) Berhad
  The Great Eastern Life Assurance Company Limited
  The Overseas Assurance Corporation
Asset management
  Lion Global Investors Limited
  Great Eastern Holdings Limited
Stockbroker
  OCBC Securities Private Limited

COMPETITORS

ABN AMRO Group	Citigroup
AmBank Group	DBS Group Holdings
BNP Paribas	HSBC
Bank Central Asia	Hong Leong Finance
Bank Danamon Indonesia	Maybank
Bank Mandiri	Standard Chartered
Bank Rakyat	United Overseas Bank

HISTORICAL FINANCIALS

Company Type: Public

Income Statement
FYE: December 31

	ASSETS ($ mil.)	NET INCOME ($ mil.)	INCOME AS % OF ASSETS	EMPLOYEES
12/13	267,902	2,190	0.8%	25,350
12/12	241,962	3,264	1.3%	24,628
12/11	213,713	1,779	0.8%	22,892
12/10	178,808	1,757	1.0%	21,585
12/09	138,624	1,400	1.0%	19,561
Annual Growth	**17.9%**	**11.8%**	**—**	**6.7%**

2013 Year-End Financials

Return on assets: 0.8%
Return on equity: 10.8%
Long-term debt ($ mil.): —
No. of shares (mil.): —
Sales ($ mil): 14,535
Dividends
  Yield: —
  Payout: —
Market value ($ mil.): —

STOCK PRICE ($) / P/E / PER SHARE ($)

	STOCK PRICE ($) FY Close	P/E High/Low		Earnings	Dividends	Book Value
12/13	7.92	7	6	0.62	0.00	5.79
12/12	7.92	5	3	0.92	0.00	6.15
12/11	6.18	8	5	0.50	0.00	5.05
12/10	7.72	7	5	0.51	0.00	4.86
12/09	6.20	5	2	0.42	0.00	4.19
Annual Growth	**6.3%**	**—**		**9.9%**	**—**	**8.4%**

P.T. Aqua Golden Mississippi (Indonesia)

LOCATIONS

HQ: P.T. Aqua Golden Mississippi (Indonesia)
17, Boulevard Haussmann, Paris 75009
Phone: (33) 1 4435 2020
Web: www.danone.com

HISTORICAL FINANCIALS

Company Type: Public

Income Statement
FYE: December 31

	REVENUE ($ mil.)	NET INCOME ($ mil.)	NET PROFIT MARGIN	EMPLOYEES
12/13	29,321	1,957	6.7%	104,642
12/12	27,506	2,203	8.0%	102,401
12/00	55	3	7.0%	1,273
12/99	57	2	4.9%	1,351
12/98	46	2	5.3%	0
Annual Growth	**53.6%**	**56.0%**	**—**	**—**

2013 Year-End Financials

Debt ratio: 38.6%
Return on equity: 12.4%
Cash ($ mil.): 1,334
Current ratio: 0.74
Long-term debt ($ mil.): 9,053
No. of shares (mil.): 586
Dividends
  Yield: —
  Payout: —
Market value ($ mil.): —

Panasonic Corp

Panasonic has been one of the world's most prolific electronics manufacturers since 1919. It operates worldwide through about 600 companies under brands Panasonic Quasar Technics and others. The company spans multiple fields: Its consumer business consists of AVC (audio video and communications) equipment along with hardware and software for linking it together and home appliances (washing machines vacuum cleaners personal grooming aids and commercial HVAC). In the field of devices Panasonic covers multimedia and eco-car equipment industrial electronic components and batteries. The company's solutions equipment targets environmentally conscience businesses manufacturers and health care firms.

Geographic Reach

The company sells its products and services in Asia Europe and North and South America. Japan accounts from just over 50% of net sales. While

North and South America accounts for over 10% of net sales. Europe also represents some 10% of net sales.

Operations

Within the company's businesses are eight segments: digital AVC networks appliances eco solutions industrial devices systems and communications automotive systems energy and other. Panasonic is weighing the sale of its medical products unit to shore up its balance sheet.

Panasonic is financially diversified across its segments with the digital AVC networks segment consisting of imaging equipment AVC network equipment such as flat-panel TVs blu-ray disc recorders digital cameras notebook PCs projectors and in-flight entertainment systems. Its appliances segment manufactures products like air conditioners refrigerators washing machines and other home appliances. Its eco solutions group includes four business groups which include the lighting (lamps devices and equipment) energy systems (distribution panelboards energy management products and wiring equipment) housing systems (home and building products) and environmental systems (air quality appliances and solutions).

Financial Performance

Panasonic's overall sales for fiscal 2012 (ends March 31) came in at Å7.8 trillion (about $97 billion) a decrease of 10% from Å8.7 trillion (about $105.7 billion) in fiscal 2011. The company reported a net loss of Å77.2 billion (about $9.6 billion) in fiscal 2012 compared to a net income of Å74 billion (about $946 million) in fiscal 2011. The affects of the Great East Japan Earthquake flooding in Thailand the European financial crisis and the high yen resulted in lower sales and net income.

In fiscal 2012 the company's business tumbled in the wake of supply chains affected by the flooding in Thailand and the unwavering European financial crisis. In the US business remained sluggish but emerging markets such as China and India provided a relative boost to the company's bottom line.

Strategy

Panasonic however along with other Japanese consumer electronics makers is struggling to make money on products like TVs VCRs and DVD players. To compensate Panasonic's management has announced a three-year plan called the "Green Transformation 2012" designed to accelerate the company's push toward becoming #1 in green technology in the electronics industry. SANYO Electric fits neatly into this strategy. Purchased for 400 billion-plus yen ($4.6 billion) in 2011 SANYO Electric repositioned Panasonic as Japan's second-largest electronics company after Sony. In addition the deal gave Panasonic the keys to the growing hybrid car battery market; SANYO Electric is the world's largest maker of rechargeable batteries and Volkswagen's partner in developing lithium-ion batteries.

During 2012 Panasonic has moved to reposition SANYO's operations including the rechargeable battery business as part of its global branding strategy. The change follows the transfer of SANYO Electric's low-margin washing machine and refrigerator business to China-based Haier Group. The deal valued at about $130 million is intended to allow Panasonic to concentrate on SANYO's more profitable and greener operations. Panasonic expects to have unified all of its branding by April 2013.

As one of the conditions for the deal Chinese officials urged Panasonic to decrease its stake in its hybrid-car-battery joint venture with Toyota Motor Corporation. To this end Panasonic exited its Primearth EV joint venture (formerly Panasonic EV Energy Co.) but acquired a 2% stake in Tesla Motors to co-develop electric vehicle batteries with

the US car maker. The deal follows a previous agreement with Tesla under which Panasonic supplies lithium ion batteries for Tesla's electric cars. Also Panasonic sold its automotive nickel hydride battery business to a Chinese firm for about JPY500 million ($6 million).

HISTORY

Grade school dropout Konosuke Matsushita took $50 in 1918 and went into business making electric plugs (with his brother-in-law Toshio Iue founder of SANYO). His mission to help people by making high-quality low-priced conveniences while providing his employees with good working conditions earned him the sobriquet "god of business management." Matsushita Electric Industrial grew by developing inexpensive lamps batteries radios and motors in the 1920s and 1930s.

During WWII the Japanese government ordered the firm to build wood-laminate products for the military. Postwar occupation forces prevented Matsushita from working at his firm for four years. Thanks to unions' efforts he rejoined his namesake company shortly before it entered a joint venture with Dutch manufacturer Philips in 1952. The following year it moved into consumer goods making televisions refrigerators and washing machines and later expanding into high-performance audio products. Matsushita bought a majority stake in Victor Company of Japan (JVC originally established by RCA Victor) in 1954. Its 1959 New York subsidiary opening began Matsushita's drive overseas.

Sold under the National Panasonic and Technics names the firm's products were usually not cutting-edge but were attractively priced. Under Masaharu Matsushita the founder's son-in-law who became president in 1961 the company became Japan's largest home appliance maker introducing air conditioners microwave ovens stereo components and VCRs in the 1960s and 1970s. JVC developed the VHS format for VCRs which beat out Sony's Betamax format.

Matsushita built much of its sales growth on new industrial and commercial customers in the 1980s. The company expanded its semiconductor office and factory automation auto electronics audio-visual housing and air-conditioning product offerings that decade. Konosuke died in 1989.

The next year Matsushita joined the Japanese stampede for US acquisitions buying Universal Studios' then-owner MCA. In 1993 Yoichi Morishita was named president and the company acquired Philips' stake in their joint venture. Two years later when cultural incompatibility depressed MCA's performance Matsushita sold 80% of the company (now Universal) to liquor mogul Seagram resulting in a fiscal 1996 loss. That year Matsushita pushed the technology envelope introducing the first DVD player.

Declining sales forced the firm to rethink its strategy; it began a multiyear restructuring including a buildup in parts of Asia with cheaper labor and job cuts. In 1997 Matsushita consolidated most of its business units into basic categories: consumer products industrial products and components. The downside of Matsushita's move into emerging Asian markets became apparent that year as many Southeast Asian countries suffered currency crises.

In fiscal years 1998 and 1999 the company's income dropped partly due to a slow domestic economy. A lagging market led Matsushita to close its North American semiconductor operations in late 1998. Also that year the company bought a stake in Mobile Broadcasting (a digital satellite broadcasting venture of nine companies) and introduced digital TVs.

Matsushita in 1999 bought a 9% stake in Symbian a venture created by the makers of 85% of the world's mobile phones (including Motorola and Nokia).

In June 2000 Yoichi Morishita became chairman and Kunio Nakamura took the reins as president of Matsushita. The next December following a year with a three-fold increase in expenditures on chip-making ($1.2 billion) the company began making chips for cell phones digital cameras and digital TVs.

In early 2002 Matsushita announced plans to turn around its financial slump by cutting 13000 local jobs (through early retirement) and trimming directors' salaries. The company also reclassified its former consumer industrial and components categories into four new divisions: AVC networks home appliances industrial equipment and components and devices.

In April 2002 Matsushita teamed up with Chinese home appliance manufacturer TCL Holdings; the move was intended to help Matsushita increase its presence in China's growing consumer electronic market. That month the firm established a joint venture with Toshiba for the manufacture and sale of liquid crystal display (LCD) panels and next-generation display devices.

The company launched a global brand consolidation strategy in 2003 rebranding all home appliance products in non-Japanese markets to Panasonic from National. (The National brand continues to be used along with the Panasonic brand in Japan.) It further expanded the Panasonic brand's reach in 2004 when it increased its stake (to 60%) in Indonesian manufacturing PT Panasonic Gobel a joint venture between Matsushita and the Gobel family. The transaction allowed Matsushita to assume control of Panasonic sales in that country.

In early 2004 Matsushita acquired affiliate Matsushita Electric Works (MEW) a company in which it previously held a 32% share. MEW which makes lighting security systems and kitchen and bathroom fittings was spun off from Matsushita in 1935. The acquisition makes Matsushita the largest Japanese electronic and electrical equipment manufacturer. Many of the two companies' overlapping research and development sales marketing and manufacturing capabilities have been combined so that a unified brand V-products is presented to the public. In late 2004 the company closed down its MT Picture Display Corporation of America operations which made CRTs (cathode ray tubes) for TVs. The unit was part of the Matsushita Toshiba Picture Display family a joint venture of MEI and Toshiba.

In 2005 Matsushita continued to collaborate with other companies to create new products. That January the company agreed to work with Olympus to develop new digital cameras. It also announced a deal with Hitachi to produce plasma display panels.

In June 2006 senior managing director Fumio Ohtsubo was named president succeeding Kunio Nakamura who became chairman of the company's board of directors.

In a rather large shift to leverage the strength of its Panasonic brand name Matsushita in October 2008 changed the name of its company to Panasonic Corporation. The company also adopted the Panasonic name worldwide for its brands including the National brand it uses in Japan. Matsushita's founder's name means "lucky man under the pine tree."

In late 2009 Panasonic purchased a 51% stake in rival SANYO Electric after about a year of battling antitrust regulators across the globe. The deal put Panasonic in the driver's seat in the hybrid car battery market.

In October 2010 Panasonic completed a tender offer for SANYO Electric's shares raising its stake in the company to more than 80% and making SANYO Electric a wholly-owned subsidiary. At the same time it completed another tender offer which raised its stake in Panasonic Electric Works from 51% to 84%.

EXECUTIVES

Chairman, Kunio Nakamura, age 75
EVP, Yasuo Katsura, age 67
Vice Chairman, Masayuki Matsushita, age 69
Chairman, Fumio Ohtsubo, age 69
Senior Managing Director and President Automotive and Industrial Systems Company, Yoshihiko (Yoshi) Yamada, age 63
President, Kazuhiro Tsuga
Managing Executive Officer; President Panasonic Electronic Devices, Toshiaki Kobayashi
Managing Executive Officer and Director Corporate Management Division for Asia and Oceania; Managing Director Panasonic Asia Pacific Pte. Ltd., Ikuo Miyamoto
Managing Executive Officer and Head China and Northeast Asia, Hidetoshi Osawa
Executive Officer; Director Corporate Management Division for North America; Chairman and CEO North America, Joseph M. (Joe) Taylor
Managing Director; President AVC Networks Company, Yoshiyuki Miyabe
Senior Managing Director and President Appliances Company, Kazunori Takami, age 60
Managing Director Accounting and Finance, Hideaki Kawai
Managing Executive Officer and Chairman and CEO Panasonic Europe, Laurent Abadie
EVP and President Eco Solutions Company, Shusaku Nagae
Managing Executive Officer and Head Asia the Middle East and Africa, Yorihisa Shiokawa
Managing Director Technology Intellectual Property and Information Systems, Mamoru Yoshida
President Panasonic Healthcare Co. Ltd., Kenji Yamane
President CEO*, Patrick D. O'Brien
Chairman, Kunio Nakamura, age 74
EVP and Representative in Tokyo Director Corporate Division for Government and Public Affairs and Board Member, Yasuo Katsura, age 66
Vice Chairman, Masayuki Matsushita, age 69
Board Member, Ikuo Uno, age 78
Board Member, Masayuki Oku, age 69
Chairman, Fumio Ohtsubo, age 69
EVP Domestic Consumer Marketing General Director Consumer Products Marketing Domestic Customer Satisfaction and Design and Board Member, Toshihiro Sakamoto, age 67
Managing Director Industrial Sales and Board Member, Yoshihiko (Yoshi) Yamada, age 62
Senior Managing Director Overseas Operations and Board Member, Hitoshi Otsuki, age 66
EVP Corporate Division for Promoting System & Equipment Business and Electrical Supplies Sales Project Sales and Building Products Sales and Board Member, Takahiro Mori, age 66
Executive Officer Manufacturing Innovation Facility Management Quality Administration FF Customer Support and Management and Environmental Affairs and Board Member, Masashi Makino, age 65
Senior Managing Director and Board Member; President AVC Networks Company, Ken Morita, age 65
Senior Managing Director Intellectual Property and Board Member, Ikusaburo Kashima, age 65
Senior Managing Director Corporate Division for Promoting Energy Solutions Business and Board Member, Junji Nomura, age 66

Managing Director Accounting Finance and Information Systems and Board Member, Makoto Uenoyama, age 60
Managing Director and Board Member; President Home Appliances Company In Charge Of Lighting Company, Kazunori Takami, age 59
Board Member; President System Networks Company and Panasonic System Networks Co. Ltd., Takashi Toyama, age 58
Managing Director Personnel General Affairs Social Relations and e-Work Promotion Office and Board Member, Masatoshi Harada, age 58
Auditors: KPMGAZSA&Co.

LOCATIONS

HQ: Panasonic Corp
1006 Oaza Kadoma, Kadoma, Osaka 571-8501
Phone: (81) 6 6908 1121
Web: www.panasonic.co.jp

Sales

	% of total
Japan	53
North & South	12
Europe	10
Asia &	25
Total	**100**

PRODUCTS/OPERATIONS

Sales

	% of total
AVC	17
Appliance	15
Eco	15
Industrial	14
Systems &	8
Automotive	7
Energy	6
Other	18
Total	**100**

Selected Segments and Products

AVC Networks
  Camcorders
  Computer drives (CD-ROM DVD-ROM/RAM)
  Computers (PCs)
  Digital cameras
  DVD players and recorders
  Fax machines
  Printers
  Telephones
  TVs (color LCD plasma display)
PEW and PanaHome
  Automation controls
  Beauty and personal care products
  Electronic and plastic materials
  Home security systems
  Interior furnishings
Home appliances
  Air conditioners and purifiers
  Dishwashers
  Dryers
  Fans
  Refrigerators
  Vacuum cleaners
  Water heaters
  Washing machines
Components and devices
  Batteries (dry rechargeable)
  Displays (CRTs LCDs PDPs)
  Electric motors
  General components (capacitors resistors printed circuit boards)
  Magnetic recording heads
  Semiconductors

Selected Brands

National
Panasonic
Quasar
Technics
Victor

COMPETITORS

A123 Systems	Konica Minolta
Apple Inc.	LG Electronics
BSH Bosch und Siemens Hausgerate	Motorola Solutions
	NEC
BYD	Nokia
Canon	Olympus
Dell	Philips Electronics
Eastman Kodak	Procter & Gamble
Electrolux	Samsung Electronics
Fujitsu Technology Solutions	Sharp Corp.
	Sony
GE Appliances & Lighting	TE Connectivity
	Technicolor
Haier Group	Toshiba
Hewlett-Packard	Truly International
IBM	Whirlpool
Intel	Yuasa Battery Thailand

HISTORICAL FINANCIALS

Company Type: Public

Income Statement

	REVENUE ($ mil.)	NET INCOME ($ mil.)	NET PROFIT MARGIN	FYE: March 31 EMPLOYEES
03/14	74,952	1,166	1.6%	271,789
03/13	77,615	(8,016)	—	293,742
03/12	95,650	(9,413)	—	330,767
03/11	104,975	893	0.9%	366,937
03/10	79,415	(1,107)	—	384,586
Annual Growth	**(1.4%)**	**—**	**—**	**(8.3%)**

2014 Year-End Financials

Debt ratio: 0.1%
Return on equity: 8.5%
Cash ($ mil.): 5,739
Current ratio: 1.09
Long-term debt ($ mil.): 5,399

No. of shares (mil.): —
Dividends
  Yield: 0.4%
  Payout: 9.7%
Market value ($ mil.): —

	STOCK PRICE ($) FY Close	P/E High/Low		PER SHARE ($) Earnings	Dividends	Book Value
03/14	11.44	0	0	0.50	0.05	6.53
03/13	7.33	—	—	(3.47)	0.00	5.85
03/12	9.25	—	—	(4.07)	0.00	10.18
03/11	12.59	0	0	0.43	0.11	14.93
03/10	15.32	—	—	(0.53)	0.14	14.44
Annual Growth (18.0%)	**(7.0%)**	**—**	**—**	**—**	**(22.5%)**	

Pegatron Corp

LOCATIONS

HQ: Pegatron Corp
5/F., No. 76, Ligong Street, Beitou District, Taipei 112
Phone: (886) 2 8143 9001   **Fax:** (886) 2 8143 7984
Web: www.pegatroncorp.com

HISTORICAL FINANCIALS

Company Type: Public

Income Statement

	REVENUE ($ mil.)	NET INCOME ($ mil.)	NET PROFIT MARGIN	FYE: December 31 EMPLOYEES
12/13	31,848	320	1.0%	0
12/12	30,363	219	0.7%	177,948
12/11	19,793	109	0.6%	112,318
12/10	18,231	364	2.0%	104,608
12/09	16,819	329	2.0%	96,534
Annual Growth	**17.3%**	**(0.7%)**	**—**	**—**

Debt ratio: 0.4% No. of shares (mil.): —
Return on equity: 9.4% Dividends
Cash ($ mil.): 2,490 Yield: —
Current ratio: 1.37 Payout: —
Long-term debt ($ mil.): 962 Market value ($ mil.): —

Permanent TSB Group Holdings Plc

Taking the "Ireland first" motto to heart permanent tsb Group Holdings (formerly Irish Life & Permanent) provides financial services across the grassy hills of Ireland. The company provides banking mortgage loans and asset management services to its home country. The permanent tsb banking unit operates more than 70 retail branches while its Capital Home Loans subsidiary provides residential mortgage loans. Slow to recover from economic troubles the firm has been restructuring in recent years; its efforts culminated with the sale of its life insurance operations to Ireland's Minister for Finance office in 2012. The Irish government also holds a majority stake in permanent tsb Group Holdings.

The company's Irish Life unit provides life insurance and investment products to individuals through its own sales force independent agents and the branches of permanent tsb. In addition Irish Life owns 30% of Allianz-Irish Life; German insurance giant Allianz is the majority owner of the nonlife insurance firm. Overall IL&P serves 1.6 million customers.

In addition to its banking and insurance divisions other divisions provide asset management and group pension and insurance products.

Like many Irish banks and lenders the company has been hurt by the global credit crunch and subprime mortgage market collapse. It stopped writing home loans in the UK market late in 2008. Early the following year Irish Life & Permanent came under fire for financial transactions conducted with Anglo Irish Bank (renamed Irish Bank Resolution Corporation Limited in 2011) during 2008 and during the ensuing regulatory investigation CEO Denis Casey resigned. Kevin Murphy took over the CEO role the following year.

By mid-2009 the company had turned to its "worst-case scenario" for dealing with bad loan losses. It then announced plans to split apart its insurance banking and asset management operations into separate companies.

Irish Life is the result of a 1999 merger between Irish Life and Irish Permanent.

HISTORY

One of the two strands that make up Irish Life & Permanent began in 1884 with the founding of The Irish Temperance Permanent Benefit Building Society. In 1940 however the company was refitted with the more manageable moniker: The Irish Permanent Building Society. This was also the event that kicked off the company's efforts to advertise and build a major national brand name.

During the 1940s and 1950s the Irish Permanent Building Society continued to put its energy into developing its reputation and brand through advertising. This strategy paid off in spades and by the end of the 1960s the company had nearly 200 locations in Ireland.

With the passing of the Building Societies Act at the end of the 1980s Irish Permanent Building Society began to set up subsidiaries to handle other business ventures. Its Irish Permanent Finance provided unsecured lending and leasing and its Irish Permanent Life & Pensions sold pension policies and life insurance.

In 1994 Irish Permanent bought Prudential Life of Ireland a company whose life assurance and pensions business in Ireland helped Irish Permanent in its campaign to expand its product range. That year the company also picked up private bank Guinness & Mahon. The buying spree continued in 1996 as Irish Permanent acquired Capital Home Loans a mortgage lender operating in the UK.

On the other side of the family Irish Life Assurance was founded in 1939 from several Irish and British life assurance companies. This (and subsequent) dealings left Ireland's Minister of Finance with a 90% share of the company.

Irish Life Assurance was restructured as Irish Life and listed on the Irish and London stock exchanges in the summer of 1991. This event began the Minister of Finance's dissolution of most of his stake in the company (a purging that was complete by 1995). In 1992 the company came to Belfast and London moving beyond Ireland for the first time.

Then in 1999 Irish Life and Irish Permanent came together effectively pairing the Emerald Isle's biggest life insurer and biggest mortgage firm. Both companies boasted a market share above 20 percent in their respective industries and while life insurance is still its bread and butter the company is angling to become an ever-more central player in Ireland's burgeoning personal financial services market. In 2001 the company completed its acquisition of Irish retail banker TSB.

In line with Irish Life & Permanent's strategy to focus on its domestic market the company sold the last of several US insurance subsidiaries in 2003.

EXECUTIVES

CEO and Director, Kevin Murphy, age 62, $428,527 total compensation
Chief Actuary, Bruce Maxwell
Secretary, Ciaran Long, age 61
Chairman, Gillian Bowler, age 61
Director of Communications, Ray Gordon
Group Finance Director and Board Member, David McCarthy, age 53
CIO, Brendan Healy
Chief Executive Irish Life Investment Managers, Gerry Keenan
Head of Investor Relations, Barry Walsh
Chief Executive permanent TSB Bank, David Guinane, age 53
Chief Executive Irish Life Retail, Gerry Hassett, age 49
Head Human Resources & Organizational Development, Tony Hession
CEO and Director, Kevin Murphy, age 62
Director, Ray MacSharry, age 75
Director, Finbar M. Sheehan, age 75
Director, Danuta Gray, age 55
Director, Roy Keenan, age 68
Director, Eamonn Heffernan, age 69
Director, Breffni Byrne, age 68
Group Finance Director and Board Member, David McCarthy, age 53
Director, Liam O'Reilly, age 66
Director, Margaret Hayes, age 59
Auditors: KPMG

LOCATIONS

HQ: Permanent TSB Group Holdings Plc
56 - 59, St. Stephen's Green, Dublin 2
Phone: (353) 1 704 2000 **Fax:** (353) 1 704 1900
Web: www.permanenttsbgroup.ie

COMPETITORS

AIB	National Irish Bank
Azimut	Royal Bank of Scotland
Bank of Ireland	St. Andrew's Group
FBD Holdings	Shannon
Hibernian General Insurance	Standard Life
Jupiter Fund Management	

HISTORICAL FINANCIALS

Company Type: Public

Income Statement

FYE: December 31

	ASSETS ($ mil.)	NET INCOME ($ mil.)	INCOME AS % OF ASSETS	EMPLOYEES
12/13	51,766	(359)	—	2,041
12/12	53,933	(1,316)	—	2,305
12/11	93,176	(553)	—	4,407
12/10	101,313	(171)	—	4,338
12/09	115,275	(450)	—	4,694
Annual Growth	(18.1%)	—	—	(18.8%)

2013 Year-End Financials

Return on assets: (-0.6%) Dividends
Return on equity: (-10.0%) Yield: —
Long-term debt ($ mil.): — Payout: —
No. of shares (mil.): — Market value ($ mil.): —
Sales ($ mil): 1,438

PetroChina Co Ltd

If you want petroleum in China or elsewhere then PetroChina is your company. A subsidiary of state-owned China National Petroleum Corporation (CNPC) PetroChina produces two-thirds of China's oil and gas. The company has proved reserves of 10.8 billion barrels of oil and 69.3 trillion cu. ft. of natural gas. In China it owns more than 53400 kilometers of natural gas and refined products pipeline and operates 29 refineries and 13 chemical plants. PetroChina was created in 2000 as a separate company to initially manage the domestic operations —and in recent years some key international assets —of CNPC.

Strategy

PetroChina is taking advantage of the growing consumption of natural gas in China by expanding its transmission infrastructure. It is also expanding its oil reserves and refining operations through the purchase of international oil fields and refineries including several assets from its parent.

EXECUTIVES

Chairman, Jiang Jiemin, age 58
General Accountant; Director, Wang Guoliang, age 61
Chairman of the Board; President, Zhou Jiping, age 61
VP and Deputy General Manager and Safety Director; Director, Liao Yongyuan, age 51
VP, Li Hualin, age 51
Supervisor, Wen Qingshan, age 55

VP and General Manager Exploration and Production, Zhao Zhengzhang, age 57
Chief Geologist and General Manager Changqing Oilfield, Wang Daofu, age 58
Chief Engineer and General Manager Natural Gas and Pipelines, Huang Weihe, age 56
VP, Sun Longde, age 52
VP, Liu Hongbin, age 51
Supervisor, Li Yuan, age 68
Supervisor, Sun Xianfeng, age 62
Supervisor, Wang Daocheng, age 74
CFO, Zhou Mingchun, age 46
Chief Engineer, Lin Aiguo, age 55
VP and General Manager China National Oil and Gas Exploration and Development Corporation, Qiliang Bo, age 51
VP and General Manager Trans-Asia Gas Pipeline Company Limited, Bo Sun, age 53
Chairman, Jiang Jiemin, age 57
General Accountant; Director, Wang Guoliang, age 61
Deputy General Manager; Director, Wang Fucheng, age 62
Director, Franco Bernabe, age 65
Chairman of the Board; President, Zhou Jiping, age 61
Director, Zeng Yukang, age 62
VP and Deputy General Manager and Safety Director; Director, Liao Yongyuan, age 51
Director, Chee-Chen Tung, age 70
Director, Liu Hongru, age 82
Director, Li Yongwu, age 69
Director, Li Xinhua, age 60
Director, Cui Junhui, age 69
Director, Jiang Fan, age 50
Auditors: PricewaterhouseCoopers

LOCATIONS

HQ: PetroChina Co Ltd
No. 9 Dongzhimen North Street, Dongcheng District, Beijing 100007
Phone: (86) 10 5998 5667   **Fax:** (86) 10 6209 5667
Web: www.petrochina.com.cn

Sales

	% of total
China	78
Other	22
Total	**100**

PRODUCTS/OPERATIONS

Sales

	% of total
Marketing	72
Refining &	12
Exploration &	10
Natural gas &	6
Total	**100**

COMPETITORS

Bangchak Petroleum Public	Exxon Mobil
CNOOC	Sinopec Shanghai Petrochemical
Chevron	

HISTORICAL FINANCIALS

Company Type: Public

Income Statement

FYE: December 31

	REVENUE ($ mil.)	NET INCOME ($ mil.)	NET PROFIT MARGIN	EMPLOYEES
12/13	373,003	21,407	5.7%	544,083
12/12	352,134	18,498	5.3%	548,355
12/11	318,353	21,123	6.6%	552,810
12/10	222,315	21,237	9.6%	552,698
12/09	149,278	15,141	10.1%	539,168
Annual Growth	**25.7%**	**9.0%**	**—**	**0.2%**

2013 Year-End Financials

Debt ratio: 3.5%
Return on equity: 11.8%
Cash ($ mil.): 8,491
Current ratio: 0.67
Long-term debt ($ mil.): 50,027

No. of shares (mil.): —
Dividends
Yield: 3.8%
Payout: 3,831.3%
Market value ($ mil.): —

	STOCK PRICE ($) FY Close	P/E High/Low		PER SHARE ($) Earnings	Dividends	Book Value
12/13	109.74	5	4	0.12	4.21	1.02
12/12	143.78	6	5	0.10	4.47	0.93
12/11	124.31	5	4	0.12	0.12	0.87
12/10	131.49	4	3	0.12	3.80	0.78
12/09	118.96	5	2	0.08	3.57	0.68
Annual Growth	**(2.0%)**	**—**	**—**	**9.4%**	**4.3%**	**10.8%**

Petroleo Brasileiro S.A.

PETROLEO BRASILEIRO (PETROBRAS) isn't brash but it is Brazil's top company and has assets in 30 countries. The integrated energy company explores for oil and gas and produces refines and transports oil and gas products. With extensive assets in offshore Brazil in 2011 PETROBRAS reported proved reserves of 12.9 billion barrels of oil equivalent. In Brazil it also operates 12 refineries an extensive oil and gas pipeline network and more than 7300 gas stations. Petrobras Distribuidora is Brazil's #1 retailer of oil products and fuel alcohol. Petrobras Argentina is a top Argentine oil firm. Other units operate electricity (10 power plants) petrochemicals and natural gas assets.

Petrobras Internacional also known as Braspetro conducts exploration worldwide including in Angola Nigeria Tanzania Portugal the US and across Latin America.

The bulk of PETROBRAS' production comes from its operations in Brazilian waters; the company is recognized as a leader in offshore drilling technology and deepwater wells. In 2011 it was operating more than 130 production platforms. PETROBRAS has made a number of major offshore oil discoveries in offshore Brazil since 2000 including the Tupi field (found in 2007) and which has the potential to boost Brazil's oil reserves by 40%. In 2010 PETROBRAS announced another major discovery a 3.7 to 15 billion-barrels-of-oil-reserves find (offshore of Rio de Janeiro) that could double Brazil's known reserves.

PETROBRAS is also a major ethanol producer and plans (through Petrobras Transporte S.A. which oversees oil and derivatives ethanol biofuels and natural gas transportation and storage activities) to invest billions of dollars in biofuel development to ensure Brazil's fuel independence as its economy and population grows.

The global recession hurt the company's financial performance in 2009 as low commodity prices and weak sales pulled down revenues and income. However PETROBRAS is well positioned for economic growth. In 2010 the company raised $70 billion to develop its lucrative offshore oilfields in the world's largest ever public share offerings.

That year PETROBRAS reported robust revenues and income growth fueled by a growing economy higher commodity prices and increased production.

Streamlining its Petrobras Argentina operations in 2011 the company acquired that unit's Brazilian petrochemicals business (Innova SA) for $332 million.

In 2012 it teamed up with GE Oil & Gas in a $1.1 billion deal through which the GE unit will supply 380 subsea wellhead systems to a number of PETROBRAS' oil and gas fields in offshore Brazil.

Brazil's government owns more than 55% of PETROBRAS.

HISTORY

O petroleo e nosso!"

"The oil is ours!" proclaimed the Brazilian nationalists' slogan in 1953 and President Getulio Vargas approved a bill creating a state-run monopoly on petroleum discovery development refining and transport. The same year that PETROLEO BRASILEIRO (PETROBRAS) was created a team led by American geologist Walter Link reported that the prospects of finding petroleum in Brazil were slim. The report outraged Brazilian nationalists who saw it as a ploy for foreign exploitation. PETROBRAS proved it could find oil but Brazil continued to import crude oil and petroleum products. By 1973 the company produced about 10% of the nation's needs.

When oil prices soared during the Arab embargo the government instead of encouraging exploration for domestic oil pushed PETROBRAS into a program to promote alcohol fuels. The company was forced to raise gasoline prices to make the more costly gasohol attractive to consumers. During the 1979 oil crunch the price of gasohol was fixed at 65% of gasoline. But during the oil glut of the mid-1980s PETROBRAS' cost of making gasohol was twice what it cost to buy gasoline —in other words PETROBRAS lost money.

PETROBRAS soon began overseas exploration. In 1980 it found an oil field in Iraq an important trading partner during the 1980s. The company also drilled in Angola and through a 1987 agreement with Texaco in the Gulf of Mexico.

In the mid-1980s PETROBRAS began production in the deepwater Campos basin off the coast of Rio de Janeiro state. Discoveries there in 1988 in the Marlim and Albacora fields more than tripled its oil reserves. It plunged deep into the thick Amazon jungle in 1986 to explore for oil and by 1990 Amazon wells were making a significant contribution to total production. That year to ease dependence on imports PETROBRAS launched a five-year $16.9 billion plan to boost crude oil production. It also began selling its mining and trading assets.

Before the invasion of Kuwait Brazil relied heavily on Iraq trading weapons for oil. After the invasion spawned increases in crude prices PETROBRAS raised pump prices but yielding to the government's anti-inflation program still did not raise them enough to cover costs. It lost $13 million a day.

The company sold 26% of Petrobras Distribuidora to the public in 1993 and privatized several of its petrochemical and fertilizer subsidiaries. A 1994 presidential order bent on stabilizing Brazil's 40%-per-month inflation cut the prices of oil products. In 1995 the government loosened its grip on the oil and gas industry and allowed foreign companies to enter the Brazilian market. In the wake of this reform PETROBRAS teamed up with a Japanese consortium to build Brazil's largest oil refinery.

In 1997 PETROBRAS appealed a $4 billion judgment from a 1992 shareholder lawsuit; the suit alleged PETROBRAS had undervalued shares during the privatization of the loss-making Petroquisa affiliate. (The appeal was granted in 1999.)

As part of an effort to boost oil production PETROBRAS also began to raise money abroad in 1999. The next year PETROBRAS and Spanish oil giant Repsol YPF agreed to swap oil and gas assets in Argentina and Brazil in a deal worth more than $1 billion.

In 2000 the company announced plans to change its corporate name to PETROBRAX but fierce political and popular reaction forced the company to abort this plan in 2001. In an even greater public relations disaster that year one of PETROBRAS' giant rigs sank off of Brazil and 10 workers were killed. In 2001 PETROBRAS announced that it was going to spend as much as $3 billion to buy an oil company in order to increase its production in the Gulf of Mexico.

In 2002 the company expressed an interest in buying Argentina's major oil company (YPF) from Spanish/Argentine energy giant Repsol YPF. That year PETROBRAS bought control (59%) of Argentine energy company Perez Companc in a deal valued at $1 billion. PETROBRAS also reported its first oil find in Argentina in 2002.

In 2006 the company acquired a 50% stake in a deepwater block in Equatorial Guinea from a private group of companies for an undisclosed sum.

The company also restructured the Brazilian petrochemical industry to make it more efficient. Its actions included the purchase of the petrochemical assets of the Ipiranga Group in 2007 and Suzano Petroquimica a leader in Latin American polypropylene resin production in 2008.

In 2007 PETROBRAS announced a major offshore oil discovery in the Tupi. In 2008 it reported it had discovered a major natural gas field near the Tupi find.

EXECUTIVES

Chief Downstream Officer, Paulo R. Costa, age 60
CFO and Chief Investor Relations Officer, Almir G. Barbassa, age 67
Chairman, Guido Mantega, age 65
Chief International Officer, Jorge L. Zelada, age 57
Exploration and Production Officer; Member of the Executive Board, Guilherme Guilherme de Oliveira Estrella Estrella
Chief Executive Officer; Member of the Executive Board; Director, Maria Maria das Gracas Silva Foster Foster
Services Officer; Member of the Executive Board, Renato Renato de Souza Duque Duque
Director, Jorge Gerdau Johannpeter, age 76
Director, Josue Christiano Gomes da Silva
Director, Luciano Galv?o Coutinho, age 67
CEO and Director, Maria das Gracas Silva Foster, age 60
Director, Francisco Roberto de Albuquerque, age 76
Director, Sergio F. Quintella, age 79
Director, Marcio Pereira Zimmermann, age 58
Director, Miriam Aparecida Belchior
Auditors: Ernst&YoungAuditoresIndependentesS/C

LOCATIONS

HQ: Petroleo Brasileiro S.A.
Avenida Republica do Chile, 65, Rio de Janeiro 20031-912
Phone: (55) 21 3224 4477
Web: www.petrobras.com.br

Sales

	% of total
Brazil	74
Other	28
Total	**100**

PRODUCTS/OPERATIONS

Sales

	% of total
Refining transportation &	46
Exploration &	26
Distribution	18
International	6
Gas &	4
Total	**100**

Selected Subsidiaries

Downstream Participac?es S.A. (asset exchanges between Petrobras and Repsol-YPF)
Petrobras Argentina (59%; oil and gas Argentina)
Petrobras Comercializadora de Energia Ltda
Petrobras Distribuidora SA (BR; distribution and marketing of petroleum products fuel alcohol and natural gas)
Petrobras Gas SA (Gaspetro management of the Brazil-Bolivia pipeline and other natural gas assets)
Petrobras Internacional SA (Braspetro; overseas exploration and production marketing and services)
Petrobras International Finance Company PIFCO (oil imports)
Petrobras Negocios Eletronicos S.A.
Petrobras Quimica SA (Petroquisa petrochemicals)
Petrobras Transporte SA (Transpetro oil and gas transportation and storage)

COMPETITORS

Ashland Inc.	Marathon Oil
BHP Billiton	Norsk Hydro ASA
BP	Occidental Petroleum
Chevron	PEMEX
Devon Energy	Petroleos de Venezuela
Eni	Royal Dutch Shell
Exxon Mobil	Sunoco
Imperial Oil	TOTAL
Koch Industries Inc.	

HISTORICAL FINANCIALS

Company Type: Public

Income Statement

FYE: December 31

	REVENUE ($ mil.)	NET INCOME ($ mil.)	NET PROFIT MARGIN	EMPLOYEES
12/13	141,462	11,094	7.8%	86,111
12/12	144,103	11,034	7.7%	85,065
12/11	145,915	20,121	13.8%	81,918
12/10	120,052	19,184	16.0%	80,492
12/09	91,869	15,504	16.9%	74,240
Annual Growth	11.4%	(8.0%)	—	3.8%

2013 Year-End Financials

Debt ratio: 35.5%	No. of shares (mil.): —
Return on equity: 7.0%	Dividends
Cash ($ mil.): 15,868	Yield: 1.5%
Current ratio: 1.49	Payout: 24.2%
Long-term debt ($ mil.): 106,308	Market value ($ mil.): —

	STOCK PRICE ($) FY Close	P/E High/Low	PER SHARE ($) Earnings	Dividends	Book Value
12/13	13.78	24 14	0.85	0.21	11.39
12/12	19.47	38 21	0.85	0.86	12.87
12/11	24.85	27 14	1.54	0.93	13.48
12/10	37.84	25 16	1.94	0.99	24.39
12/09	47.68	30 13	1.77	1.05	18.54
Annual Growth (11.5%)	(26.7%)	— —	(16.8%)	(33.4%)	

Petroliam Nasional Berhad (Malaysia)

LOCATIONS

HQ: Petroliam Nasional Berhad (Malaysia)
Tower 1, Petronas Twin Towers, Kuala Lumpur City Centre, Kuala Lumpur 50088
Phone: (60) 3   **Fax:** (60) 3
Web: www.petronas.com

HISTORICAL FINANCIALS

Company Type: Public

Income Statement

FYE: December 31

	REVENUE ($ mil.)	NET INCOME ($ mil.)	NET PROFIT MARGIN	EMPLOYEES
12/13	96,864	16,518	17.1%	49,193
12/12	95,035	16,130	17.0%	46,145
12/11*	70,305	15,419	21.9%	43,266
03/11	79,744	18,131	22.7%	41,628
03/10	66,332	12,348	18.6%	40,992
Annual Growth	9.9%	7.5%	—	4.7%

*Fiscal year change

2013 Year-End Financials

Debt ratio: 2.4%	No. of shares (mil.): 0
Return on equity: 16.9%	Dividends
Cash ($ mil.): 35,751	Yield: —
Current ratio: 2.27	Payout: —
Long-term debt ($ mil.): 8,853	Market value ($ mil.): —

Peugeot S.A.

Peugeot S.A. enjoys its space under L'Arc de Triomphe besting rival Renault to claim the top spot in the battle for auto sales in France. Peugeot makes cars and light commercial vehicles under the Peugeot and Citroen brands. Peugeot is among the top manufacturers in European passenger car and commercial vehicle sales. Also part of Peugeot's automotive operations are Faurecia (auto parts) GEFCO (transportation and logistics) and Banque PSA Finance (financial services for dealers and customers). Other group products include motorcycles and scooters. Peugeot makes most of its sales in Europe. The Peugeot family controls about 38% of the voting stock.

The Peugeot brand rolled out more than 2.1 million vehicles in 2011. Sales outside Europe accounted for 48% of the total. Peugeot models include the Peugeot 508 RXH the Peugeot 3008 crossover and the RCZ coupe. Citroen sold more than 1.4 million cars in 2011. Citroen models include the DS4 DS5 C3 Picasso C4 and C-Crosser. Both brands boast electric cars the Peugeot iOn and the Citroen C-ZERO as well as electric commercial vehicles the Peugeot Partner Origin and Citroen Berlingo First. The company has sold about 4000 electric vehicles and has orders for more than 6000.

Financing vehicle sales as well as vehicle and replacement part inventories at dealers Banque PSA Finance operates in more than 20 countries. It annually provides financing for more than 840000 vehicles. Deriving about 38% of its sales from non-Peugeot clients Gefco provides upstream and downstream logistics services in about 150 countries. Peugeot plans to sell all or part of Gefco in 2012. Faurecia 57% owned by Peugeot focuses its automotive equipment operations on automotive seating emissions control technologies interior systems and automotive exteriors. Faurecia operates at about 240 locations and about 40 research and development centers in more than 30 countries.

Peugeot's consolidated sales and revenue rose about 7% in 2011 compared with 2010. By segment the automotive division's consolidated revenue increased 3% over the same period. New vehicle sales similarly went up about 3%. By region the division responded to strong demand in Latin America China and Russia. Also the percentage of premium cars sold rose from 13% in 2010 to 18% in 2011.

Faurecia soared 17% in 2011 versus 2010. Sales of the division's catalytic converter monoliths rose about 24% while sales of R&D tooling and prototypes headed up 19%. The division also enjoyed strong sales in all regions. European sales were up 11 while North America jumped about 33% Asia headed up 15% South America surged about 15% and the rest of the world increased about 31%.

Gefco jumped about 13% in 2011 versus 2010 supported by the acquisition of 70% of the Italy-based Mercurio group which transports vehicles worldwide in May 2011. The Mercurio acquisition boosted the segment's business in downstream logistics. Services for external customers rose 19%.

Banque PSA Finance inched up about 3%. The segment financed about 28% of all new Peugeot and Citroen cars in 2011. It enjoyed especially strong demand in Argentina Brazil and Russia.

While Peugeot is anticipating a contraction of auto sales in the European auto market it expects to see strong growth in China Latin America and Russia. In China where the company has a market share of more than 3% the Peugeot brand boasts more than 500 sales outlets while Citroen has about 860. To boost Latin American sales the company has launched two locally produced models the Peugeot 408 and Citroen C3 Picasso. In Russia the two brands operate more than 140 sales outlets that cover 90% of the country.

In 2012 Peugeot and General Motors announced that they would form an alliance to share vehicle platforms components and modules and to establish a global purchasing joint venture. The companies hope the partnership will create annual savings of $2 billion within five years. As part of the deal GM will pay $400 million to $470 million (depending on market conditions) for a 7% stake in Peugeot. The company's engine partnership with BMW gave birth to a 50/50 joint venture in 2011 to produce powertrain components such as battery packs power electronics and software for hybrid vehicles. The main components used in BMW's and Peugeot's hybrid vehicles will be standardized thus saving manufacturing and development costs for both car companies.

HISTORY

In 1810 brothers Frederic and Jean-Pierre Peugeot made a foundry out of the family textile mill in the Alsace region of France and invented the cold-roll process for producing spring steel. Bicycle production began in 1885 at the behest of avid cyclist Armand Peugeot Jean-Pierre's grandson.

Armand turned to automobiles and built Peugeot's first car a steam-powered three-wheeler in 1889. A gas-fueled Peugeot tied for first place in the 1894 Paris-Rouen Trials the earliest auto race on record. That year the budding carmaker built the first station wagon followed in 1905 by the first compact the 600-pound "Le Bebe."

Peugeot built factories in France including one in Sochaux (1912) that remains the company's main plant. It made the first diesel passenger car in 1922. The 1929 introduction of the reliable 201 model was followed by innovations such as synchromesh gears in 1936. The company suffered heavy damage in WWII but quickly bounced back and began expanding overseas after the war.

In 1954 CEO Roland Peugeot rebuffed a board proposal calling for global expansion that would place the company in competition with US automakers. By 1976 the French government persuaded Peugeot to merge with Citroen.

Andre Citroen founded his company in 1915 and in 1919 it became the first in Europe to mass-produce cars. Citroen hit the skids during the Depression and in 1934 handed Michelin a large block of stock in lieu of payment for tires. Citroen never fully recovered though by 1976 the company's line ranged from the 2CV minicar (discontinued in 1990) to limousines.

In 1978 Peugeot bought Chrysler's aging European plants and withering nameplates including Simca (France) and Rootes (UK). Peugeot changed the nameplates to Talbot but sales continued to slide. It lost nearly $1.2 billion from 1980 to 1984.

Jacques Calvet took over as CEO in 1984. He cut 30000 jobs and spent heavily on modernization. Aided by the strong launch of the 205 superminicar Peugeot returned to profitability in 1985 and by 1989 had halved its production break-even point. In the 1980s Peugeot inked production deals with Renault (industrial vehicles motors gearboxes) and Fiat (light trucks) and introduced a reasonably priced electric van in 1990.

Peugeot withdrew from the US in 1991 after five years of declining sales. A year later Renault and Peugeot developed electric cars and set up servicing centers throughout France. Citing an economic slump in 1993 Peugeot suffered its first loss ($239 million) since 1985. A French government incentive to replace cars more than 10 years old boosted 1994 sales.

Peugeot and rival Renault together introduced a V6 engine in 1996. Jean Martin Folz replaced Calvet as managing board chairman in 1997; Folz headed up Peugeot for 10 years and was replaced by Christian Streiff in 2007. In 1998 the company began building Peugeots and Citroens in the same plants and created its Faurecia unit when its ECIA subsidiary merged with car parts maker Bertrand Faure. In an effort to capitalize on the growing South American car market the company purchased more than 80% of Argentina's Sevel and built a plant in Brazil. In 1999 the company sold its flight systems supplier SAMM to TRW's Lucas Aerospace unit.

With demand for its cars falling steeply in South America due to the region's continuing economic crisis Peugeot restructured its Brazil operations in 2000 and formed a new subsidiary Citroen do Brasil.

In 2001 Peugeot announced that it was building an engine plant in Brazil and agreed to produce a subcompact car for the European market

with Toyota. The following year Peugeot formed an alliance with BMW to develop and build a line of small diesel engines for use in vehicles made by both companies.

In 2005 Peugeot achieved a major milestone when for the first time it sold more than 1 million units outside its traditional market of Western Europe or 30% of total sales. Large gains were made in South America and even more so in China. In 2006 the company repeated the feat. With Western Europe a mature market Peugeot was looking to three key emerging markets to drive future growth: China the Mercosur region (Argentina Brazil Paraguay and Uruguay) and Central and Eastern Europe.

EXECUTIVES

Vice Chairman, Jean-Philippe Peugeot
Chairman, Thierry Peugeot
Executive Vice-President of Human Resources at PSA Peugeot Citro, Philippe Dorge
Vice Chairman, Jean-Louis Silvant
Director, Robert Peugeot
Director, Jean-Paul Parayre, age 76
Director, Joseph F. Toot Jr.
Vice Chairman, Jean-Philippe Peugeot
Director, Marc Freidel, age 65
Director, Jean-Louis Masurel
Director, Marie-Helene Roncoroni
Director, Henri-Philippe Reichstul, age 64
Director, Ernest-Antoine Seilliere
Director, Geoffroy Roux de Bezieux
Auditors: PricewaterhouseCoopers

LOCATIONS

HQ: Peugeot S.A.
   75, avenue de la Grande-Armee, Paris 75116
Phone: (33) 1 40 66 55 11   **Fax:** (33) 1 40 66 54 14
Web: www.psa-peugeot-citroen.com

Sales

	% of total
Europe	73
Latin	9
Asia	5
Russia	3
Rest of the	10
Total	**100**

PRODUCTS/OPERATIONS

Sales

	% of sales
Automotive division	66
Faurecia	25
Gefco	6
Banque PSA Finance	3
Total	**100**

Sales

Units % of total		
Peugeot brand	2,114,000	60
Citroen brand	1,436,000	40
Total	**3,550,000**	**100**

Selected Subsidiaries

Citroen
Peugeot
Banque PSA Finance
Faurecia (57% automotive components)
GEFCO (transportation and logistics services)

COMPETITORS

BMW	Nissan
CRCAM IDF CCI	Norbert Dentressangle
Chrysler	Piaggio & Co.
Daimler	Renault
Fiat	Saab Automobile
Ford Motor	Suzuki Motor
General Motors	Toyota

Honda
Isuzu
Kia Motors
Mazda

Volkswagen
Volvo Car Corp.
Yamaha Motor

HISTORICAL FINANCIALS
Company Type: Public

Income Statement
FYE: December 31

	REVENUE ($ mil.)	NET INCOME ($ mil.)	NET PROFIT MARGIN	EMPLOYEES
12/13	74,467	(3,189)	—	196,885
12/12	73,080	(6,603)	—	204,287
12/11	77,493	760	1.0%	0
12/10	75,030	1,517	2.0%	198,220
12/09	69,748	(1,672)	—	186,220
Annual Growth	1.7%	—	—	1.4%

2013 Year-End Financials
Debt ratio: 72.2%
Return on equity: (-27.7%)
Cash ($ mil.): 10,676
Current ratio: 1.02
Long-term debt ($ mil.): 11,125

No. of shares (mil.): 342
Dividends
  Yield: —
  Payout: —
Market value ($ mil.): —

PFA Pension Forsikringsaktieselskab (Denmark)

LOCATIONS
HQ: PFA Pension Forsikringsaktieselskab (Denmark)
Sundkrogsgade 4, Copenhagen DK-2100

Phone: (45) 39 17 50 00 **Fax:** (45) 39 17 59 50
Web: www.pfa.dk

HISTORICAL FINANCIALS
Company Type: Public

Income Statement
FYE: December 31

	ASSETS ($ mil.)	NET INCOME ($ mil.)	INCOME AS % OF ASSETS	EMPLOYEES
12/13	77,051	39	0.1%	1,235
12/12	65,365	67	0.1%	0
12/02	23,678	148	0.6%	1,007
12/01	18,279	(437)	—	847
12/00	19,321	51	0.3%	798
Annual Growth	11.2%	(2.0%)	—	3.4%

PICC Property and Casualty Co Ltd

PICC Property and Casualty (PICC P&C) is the leading property and casualty (P&C) insurer in bustling China. Founded in 1949 as the state-owned People's Insurance Company of China (now known as PICC Group) PICC P&C was spun off in 2003. It operates throughout most of China with more than 10000 branch offices providing primarily auto insurance (more than 70% of sales). Additional types of coverage include commercial property liability accident and homeowners insurance. PICC Group holds 70% of the company while beleaguered US firm AIG holds 10% of its shares.

Founded just 20 days after ceremonies marking the founding of China PICC P&C survived a twenty-year suspension of insurance activities within China. It eventually came to control 70% of the P&C market in spite of increasing competition both from China-based insurers and from foreign companies entering the burgeoning marketplace.

The company has sisters: PICC Life Insurance Company and PICC Health Insurance Company which offer complementary coverage.

EXECUTIVES
Chairman, Wu Yan, age 49
Vice Chairman and President, Wang Yincheng, age 49
EVP Board Secretary and Director, Liu Zhenghuan, age 60
EVP, Guo Shengchen, age 55
EVP, Zhao Shuxian, age 57
EVP, Jia Haimao, age 56
EVP, Wang He, age 53
Chief Compliance Officer, Wang Yueshu, age 54
EVP, Wang Dedi, age 52
EVP, Jiang Caishi, age 45
Secretary, Man Kam Ching
Vice Chairman and President, Wang Yincheng, age 49
EVP Board Secretary and Director, Liu Zhenghuan, age 60
Director, Zhou Shurui, age 57
Director, Edmund S.W. Tse, age 72
Director, Christopher W. C. Cheng, age 61
Director, Lu Zhengfei, age 46
Director, Peter K. Y. Luk, age 69
Director, Ding Ningning, age 62
Auditors: Ernst&Young

LOCATIONS
HQ: PICC Property and Casualty Co Ltd
Tower 2, No. 2 Jianguomenwai Avenue, Chaoyang District, Beijing 100022
Phone: (86) 10 85176084   **Fax:** (86) 10 85176084
Web: www.piccnet.com.cn

PRODUCTS/OPERATIONS

Sales

	% of total
Motor	68
Commercial	13
Cargo	4
Liability	4
Accidental	4
Homeowners	2
Other	5
Total	**100**

COMPETITORS
AIG
Allianz Guangzhou
CNinsure
China Life Insurance
China Pacific Property Insurance
Chubb Corp
Ping An Insurance

HISTORICAL FINANCIALS
Company Type: Public

Income Statement
FYE: December 31

	ASSETS ($ mil.)	NET INCOME ($ mil.)	INCOME AS % OF ASSETS	EMPLOYEES
12/13	52,763	1,744	3.3%	160,190
12/12	46,585	1,669	3.6%	156,364
12/11	42,203	1,275	3.0%	140,942
12/10	30,612	790	2.6%	60,629
12/09	24,221	261	1.1%	60,202
Annual Growth	21.5%	60.8%	—	27.7%

2013 Year-End Financials
Return on assets: 3.4%
Return on equity: 20.5%
Long-term debt ($ mil.): —
No. of shares (mil.): —
Sales ($ mil.): 31,783

Dividends
  Yield: 0.0%
  Payout: —
Market value ($ mil.): —

	STOCK PRICE ($) FY Close	P/E High/Low		PER SHARE ($) Earnings	Dividends	Book Value
12/13	36.80	1	1	0.13	0.05	0.70
12/12	32.21	1	1	0.14	0.02	0.59
12/11	25.30	2	1	0.11	0.04	0.46
Annual Growth	20.6%	—	—	4.9%	8.6%	11.3%

Ping An Bank Co Ltd

LOCATIONS
HQ: Ping An Bank Co Ltd
Shenzhen Devolopment Bank Building, No. 5047, Shennan East Road, Shenzhen, Guangdong Province 518001
Phone: (86) 755 82080387   **Fax:** (86) 755 82080386
Web: www.bank.pingan.com

HISTORICAL FINANCIALS
Company Type: Public

Income Statement
FYE: December 31

	ASSETS ($ mil.)	NET INCOME ($ mil.)	INCOME AS % OF ASSETS	EMPLOYEES
12/13	312,483	2,515	0.8%	0
12/12	257,695	2,149	0.8%	0
12/11	199,888	1,632	0.8%	0
12/10	110,384	953	0.9%	0
12/09	86,088	736	0.9%	0
Annual Growth	38.0%	35.9%	—	—

2013 Year-End Financials
Return on assets: 0.8%
Return on equity: 15.4%
Long-term debt ($ mil.): —
No. of shares (mil.): —
Sales ($ mil): 8,639

Dividends
  Yield: —
  Payout: —
Market value ($ mil.): —

Ping An Insurance (Group) Co of China Ltd.

Ping An Insurance is China's second-largest life insurance company (after China Life Insurance Company) and offers a variety of products including fire marine cargo and accident insurance as well as a home protection plan. The company also provides stock trading equity investment funds and bonds property leasing and asset management services through Ping An Trust; and its Shenzhen Ping An Bank subsidiary offers retail banking and other consumer services such as credit card and mortgage lending. In addition Ping An Insurance founded in 1988 has launched Ping An Health Insurance Company of China.

While insurance is still the company's main staple it is hoping to secure a prime spot in China's developing asset management industry.

London-based HSBC Holdings which has had operations in China for more than 140 years doubled its stake in Ping An to about 20% in 2006 through a $1 billion deal with shareholders Goldman Sachs Group and a unit of the private equity business of Morgan Stanley.

In 2008 Ping An agreed to acquire half of the asset management business of Fortis in an attempt to diversify its operations and make them more global in scope. However the deal valued at nearly $3.4 billion was terminated when Fortis foundered in late 2008.

Meanwhile the company's insurance arm set to investigating and paying claims from the 2008 earthquake and aftershocks in the Sichuan province. By 2009 the company had already paid out its largest claim ever: $105 million to Lafarge Shui Cement the worlds' largest cement manufacturer for damages to several cement plants it operated in that area.

EXECUTIVES

Chairman and CEO, Peter M. Z. Ma, age 57
President, Alex H. C. Ren, age 44
Chief Legal Officer and Joint Secretary, Jun Yao, age 46
Chief Finance Business Officer, Richard Jackson, age 57
SVP, Liping Wang, age 56
SVP and General Manager, Kexiang Chen, age 55
SVP and CIO, Sai Lai Lo, age 50
Investor Relations, Shaoliang Jin
Investor Relations, Zhang Xuewu
EVP Vice Chief Executive Officer and Director, Jianyi Sun, age 60
SVP and Chief Investment Officer, John Pearce, age 50
SVP, Shifan Cao, age 57
Director, Louis C. Y. Cheung, age 49
EVP Vice Chief Executive Officer and Director, Jianyi Sun, age 60
Director, Lijun Lin, age 50
Director, Peter T. S. Wong, age 61
Director, Sing Yip Ng, age 62
Director, Hongyi Zhang, age 67
Director, Su Chen, age 55
Director, Liping Xia, age 75
Auditors: Ernst&Young

LOCATIONS

HQ: Ping An Insurance (Group) Co of China Ltd. Offices at 15, 16, 17, 18 Floors, Galaxy Development Center, Fu Hua No. 3 Road, Futian District, Shenzhen, Guangdong Province 518048
Phone: (86) 400 8866 338   **Fax:** (86) 755 8243 1029
Web: www.pingan.com

PRODUCTS/OPERATIONS

2007 Revenues

	% of total
Life	56
Property/casualty	11
Banking	8
Securities	8
Other	17
Total	**100**

Selected Subsidiaries & Affiliates

China Ping An Insurance Overseas (Holdings) Limited
   China Ping An Insurance (Hong Kong) Company Limited (75%)
   Ping An of China Asset Management (Hong Kong) Company Limited
China Ping An Trust & Investment Co. Ltd.
   Ping An Securities Co. Ltd.
Ping An Annuity Insurance Company of China Ltd.
Ping An Health Insurance Company of China Ltd.
Ping An Life Insurance Company of China Ltd.
Ping An Property & Casualty Insurance Company of China Ltd.
Shenzhen Ping An Bank Co. Ltd.

COMPETITORS

CNinsure	China Pacific Property
China Insurance	Insurance
China Life Insurance	Chubb Corp
China Pacific	PICC Property
Insurance	

HISTORICAL FINANCIALS

Company Type: Public

Income Statement

FYE: December 31

	ASSETS ($ mil.)	NET INCOME ($ mil.)	INCOME AS % OF ASSETS	EMPLOYEES
12/13	555,066	4,650	0.8%	203,366
12/12	456,232	3,216	0.7%	190,284
12/11	363,088	3,094	0.9%	175,136
12/10	177,745	2,626	1.5%	128,808
12/09	137,040	2,033	1.5%	100,267
Annual Growth	**41.9%**	**23.0%**	**—**	**19.3%**

2013 Year-End Financials

Return on assets: 0.9%
Return on equity: 16.4%
Long-term debt ($ mil.): —
No. of shares (mil.): —
Sales ($ mil): 69,578
Dividends
Yield: 0.7%
Payout: 0.5%
Market value ($ mil.): —

	STOCK PRICE ($) FY Close	P/E High/Low		PER SHARE ($) Earnings	Dividends	Book Value
12/13	18.03	0	0	0.59	0.13	3.81
12/12	17.19	0	0	0.41	0.10	3.23
12/11	13.11	0	0	0.40	0.00	2.63
12/10	22.45	0	0	0.35	0.11	2.22
12/09	17.59	0	0	0.28	0.08	1.69
Annual Growth	**0.6%**	**—**	**—**	**20.6%**	**11.8%**	**22.5%**

Piraeus Bank SA

Greece is the word and Piraeus has most certainly heard. Piraeus Bank provides retail banking investment banking leasing and insurance services in the Mediterranean and in Central and Eastern Europe. Its network of branches across Greece numbers more than 1000 plus it has about 400 more in Albania (Tirana Bank) Romania Bulgaria Serbia the Ukraine and the US (New York's Marathon Bank). Piraeus Bank also provides its services through its electronic Winbank business which includes about 1900 ATMs Internet and phone banking. The company maintains a diverse loan portfolio with energy and transportation loans making up 30% of its portfolio. Piraeus Bank was founded in 1916 and under state control until 1991.

Since Piraeus Bank was privatized it has grown rapidly through acquisitions of other banks in Greece. The company also has expanded internationally into Central and Eastern Europe and elsewhere in the Mediterranean. It acquired Bulgarian Eurobank (now Piraeus Bank Bulgaria) Atlas Bank (renamed Piraeus Bank Beograd) Egyptian Commercia Bank (Piraeus Bank Egypt) Share Capital of International Commerce Bank in the Ukraine and the Cyprus branch network of Arab Bank (Piraeus Bank Cyprus).

In 2009 Piraeus Bank teamed with BNP Wealth Management to begin offering wealth management services. In another partnership that year the company signed an agreement with Victoria General Insurance Group in order to offer insurance. Piraeus Bank continues to seek investments for further growth.

EXECUTIVES

Chairman Board of Director and Executive Board, Michalis G. Sallas, age 65
Board Member and Managing Director; Chairman Romania and Beograd, Stavros M. Lekkakos, age 62
Board Member and Managing Director Chairman Piraeus Securities, Alexandros S. Manos
Board Member and Deputy Managing Director Retail Branch Network and Medium-Sized Enterprises, Christodoulos G. Antoniadis, age 59
Board Member and Deputy Managing Director International Banking, Ilias D. Milis
Board Member and Deputy Manager Director Retail Lending and Business Development, Spyros A. Papaspyrou, age 54
Director-Representative of the Hellenic Financial Stability Fund, Ekaterini Mperitsi
Chief Risk Officer, Georgios Mantakas
Chief Financial Officer; General Manager of Financial Management and Strategic Planning, Georgios Poulopoulos
Non-Executive Vice Chairman of the Board, Ioannis Vardinogiannis
Assistant General Manager, Konstantinos Paschalis
Non-Executive Vice Chairman of the Board, Panagiotis Roumeliotis
Director-Representative of the Hellenic Financial Stability Fund, Solomon Beracha
Board Member, Iakovos G. Georganas, age 82
Board Member, Georgios P. Alexandridis, age 81
Board Member and Managing Director; Chairman Romania and Beograd, Stavros M. Lekkakos, age 62
Board Member, Chariklia A. Apalagaki, age 55
Board Member, Vassilios S. Fourlis, age 54
Board Member, Stilianos D. Golemis
Board Member and Managing Director Chairman Piraeus Securities, Alexandros S. Manos

Board Member and Deputy Managing Director
Retail Branch Network and Medium-Sized
Enterprises, Christodoulos G. Antoniadis, age 59
Board Member and Deputy Managing Director
International Banking, Ilias D. Milis
Board Member and Deputy Manager Director
Retail Lending and Business Development,
Spyros A. Papaspyrou, age 54
Board Member, Theodoros P. Mylonas, age 65
Director; Representing the Greek State, Athanasios
Tsoumas
Non-Executive Member of the Board, Eftychios
Vasilakis
Non-Executive Director, Jiri Smejc
Non-Executive Director, Konstantin Yanakov
Non-Executive Independent Member of the Board,
Stylianos Gkolemis

LOCATIONS

HQ: Piraeus Bank SA
  4 Amerikis str., Athens 105 64
Phone: (30) 210 333 5000   Fax: (30) 210 333 5080
Web: www.piraeusbankgroup.com

PRODUCTS/OPERATIONS

Selected Subsidiaries
ATEbank
ETBA Industrial Areas S.A.
Marathon Bank of New York (USA)
OJSC Piraeus Bank ICB (Ukraine)
Picar S.A.
Piraeus Asset Management Mutual Funds S.A.
Piraeus Bank AD Beograd (Serbia)
Piraeus Bank Bulgaria AD
Piraeus Bank (Cyprus) Ltd
Piraeus Bank Egypt SAE
Piraeus Capital Management
Piraeus Card Services
Piraeus Direct Services S.A.
Piraeus Insurance and Reinsurance Brokerage S.A.
Piraeus Insurance Agency S.A.
Piraeus Factoring S.A.
Piraeus Leaases SA
Piraeus Leasing Bulgaria
Piraeus Bank Romania S.A.
Piraeus Leasing Romania
Piraeus Private Equity
Piraeus Real Estate S.A.
Piraeus Securities S.A.
Piraeus Wealth Management
Tirana Bank S.A. (Albania)
Tirana Leasing (Albania)

COMPETITORS

Alpha Bank	Emporiki Bank
Bank of Cyprus	National Bank of
EFG Eurobank Ergasias	Greece

HISTORICAL FINANCIALS
Company Type: Public

Income Statement   FYE: December 31

	ASSETS ($ mil.)	NET INCOME ($ mil.)	INCOME AS % OF ASSETS	EMPLOYEES
12/13	126,672	3,505	2.8%	22,718
12/12	92,798	(671)	—	18,872
12/11	63,834	(8,554)	—	12,806
12/10	77,038	(27)	—	13,320
12/01	10,922	45	0.4%	0
Annual Growth	22.7%	43.7%	—	—

2013 Year-End Financials
Return on assets: 3.1%	Dividends
Return on equity: 85.1%	Yield: —
Long-term debt ($ mil.): —	Payout: —
No. of shares (mil.): —	Market value ($ mil.): —
Sales ($ mil): 10,826	

STOCK PRICE ($)

	FY Close	P/E High/Low	Earnings	PER SHARE ($) Dividends	Book Value
12/13	4.11	9 1	1.28	0.00	1.81
12/12	6.45	— —	(0.58)	0.00	(1.30)
12/11	6.45	— —	(7.91)	0.00	(1.08)
12/10	6.45	— —	(0.04)	0.00	10.20
Annual Growth	(13.9%)	— —	—	—	(13.4%)

Polski Koncern Naftowy Orlen S.A.

Crudely moving into the private market PKN ORLEN is the largest refiner and distributor of oil in Poland. The company owns a total of seven refineries (including three in the Czech Republic and one in Lithuania) and has some 2700 retail sites in the Czech Republic Germany Lithuania and Poland. PKN ORLEN owns chemical maker Anwil has holdings in several other Polish companies and controls Czech refiner and retailer UNIPETROL. Two former state monopolies Petrochemia Plock (Poland's largest refinery) and Centrala Produktow Naftowych (Poland's #1 petroleum distributor) merged in 1999 to create PKN ORLEN. The Polish government still owns 27% of the company.

The company also manufactures liquefied propane-butane gas (LPG) for use at industrial plants and for heating public buildings. Other PKN ORLEN products include polyvinyl chloride plastics used in foils containers bottles cable insulation and auto parts; nitric fertilizers; asphalts for construction of roads airports and sports facilities; and basic industrial and engine oils.

Its Eko subsidiary burns hazardous waste while its ORLEN Transport division handles the distribution of fuel to its gas stations. Its Solino holdings (70%) produce salt and brine and use salt caverns for underground storage of petroleum and fuels.

HISTORY

The merger between Petrochemia Plock Poland's largest refiner and petrochemicals maker and CPN (Centrala Produktow Naftowych) the nation's largest motor fuel distributor created Polski Koncern Naftowy (PKN) in 1999.

Poland's oil industry stretches back to the late 1800s when five refineries were built in the nation's southern region. The Polish Oil Monopoly was formed in 1944 to oversee the country's oil distribution operations; it assumed the CPN name a year later.

While the rest of the world increasingly turned to oil as an energy source after WWII Poland continued to rely on coal and its oil industry grew slowly. CPN was split into 17 regional branches in 1955. The branches controlled local operations and the head office in Warsaw handled pricing and purchasing.

In the late 1950s the Soviet Union began building the Friendship pipeline to deliver crude oil to East Germany and Poland. The Polish government responded by forming Petrochemia to develop a refinery next to the pipeline in the city of Plock.

The Petrochemia refinery began producing refined products in 1964; four years later it started processing crude oil to make fuels lubricants and bitumen. The refinery also began making products such as detergents and plastics from processed refinery gases and other hydrocarbons. It added petrochemicals in 1970.

Because of the oil industry's slow growth in Poland the country managed to avoid some of the impact of the 1970s energy crisis. (Even as late as 1995 oil accounted for only 17% of Poland's energy consumption.) But it was forced to pay higher prices for Russian crude. In 1975 the government decided to expand its refining operations and created a second major refiner Rafineria Gdanska to focus on motor oils.

Locked behind the Iron Curtain Poland was not able to build its oil operations until the early 1990s. In 1992 Petrochemia began expanding its refinery facilities to reach a production capacity of 820000 barrels per day within 10 years.

After Communism's demise the Polish government started planning the privatization of its oil operations. After several plans were adopted and discarded in the early 1990s the government finally decided in 1996 to split CPN up among the nation's refineries. Holding company Nafta Polska was formed that year to own 75% stakes in Poland's refineries and in CPN and carry out the privatization process.

In 1997 CPN was stripped of its fuel depots and rail transport operations which were placed under the Nafta Polska umbrella. Displeased with the plan to carve up CPN the distributor's management rallied against the government's plan. The Polish government gave in and went back to the drawing board.

A successful plan was formed in 1998 namely to merge Petrochemia and CPN. The companies were combined in 1999 and 30% of the new PKN was floated on the Warsaw and London stock exchanges. The next year the government spun off an additional 42% stake and the company added ORLEN to its name (combining the Polish words for eagle and energy). Also in 2000 the government began preparing to float Refineria Gdanska. PKN hoped to get a piece of its regional rival but the state left PKN out of the bidding to encourage competition.

PKN acquired some 494 gas stations in Germany from BP who sold them to meet German antitrust regulations for its merger with Veba Oel in late 2002.

In 2004 PKN purchased 63% of UNIPETROL; the European Commission's Competition Directorate granted approval of the purchase in mid-2005.

LOCATIONS

HQ: Polski Koncern Naftowy Orlen S.A.
  Chemikow 7, Plock 09-411
Phone: (48) 24 256 81 80   Fax: (48) 24 367 77 11
Web: www.orlen.pl

PRODUCTS/OPERATIONS

HISTORICAL FINANCIALS
Company Type: Public

Income Statement   FYE: December 31

	REVENUE ($ mil.)	NET INCOME ($ mil.)	NET PROFIT MARGIN	EMPLOYEES
12/13	37,762	58	0.2%	21,565
12/12	38,822	758	2.0%	21,956
12/11	31,044	685	2.2%	22,380
12/10	28,238	801	2.8%	22,040
12/09	23,806	458	1.9%	22,535
Annual Growth	12.2%	(40.3%)	—	(1.1%)

2013 Year-End Financials

Debt ratio: 4.8%   No. of shares (mil.): 427
Return on equity: 0.6%   Dividends
Cash ($ mil.): 959   Yield: —
Current ratio: 1.54   Payout: —
Long-term debt ($ mil.): 2,190   Market value ($ mil.): —

	STOCK PRICE ($) FY Close	P/E High/Low		PER SHARE ($) Earnings	Dividends	Book Value
12/13	0.00	9	8	0.14	0.00	20.12
12/12	32.00	1	0	1.77	0.00	20.01
12/11	19.50	1	0	1.60	0.00	16.65
12/10	32.05	1	0	1.87	0.00	17.09
Annual Growth	—	—	—	(48.1%)	—	4.2%

POSCO (South Korea)

POSCO has steeled itself for any set of business conditions. The company makes hot- and cold-rolled steel products (plate steel stainless steel electrical steel and wire rods) which it sells to the auto shipbuilding home appliance engineering and machinery industries. It produces more than 39 million tons of steel a year making it the world's #3 steelmaker behind ArcelorMittal and Nippon Steel. Majority-owned POSCO Engineering & Construction builds industrial facilities such as steel plants and energy plants. POSCO Energy is Korea's largest private power generator and subsidiary Daewoo International is a global steel and raw materials trading company. Most of POSCO's sales are to Korean markets.

POSCO's hot- and cold-rolled products segments account for about two-thirds of sales. Hot-rolled products are used in the construction of automobile chassis buildings and bridges industrial pipes and tanks and railway rolling stocks. The company's cold-rolled products such as cold-rolled coils and galvanized cold-rolled products are used in the automotive industry to manufacture car body panels and for other uses like household goods electrical appliances and engineering and metal parts. It produces most of its steel at its integrated steel facilities Pohang Works and Gwangyang Works. POSCO also engages in steel and raw materials trading and invests in energy and mineral development projects around the world though its Daewoo International unit.

South Korea has little native iron ore and POSCO has had to look elsewhere for its raw materials. It purchases iron ore or coal from Australia Brazil Canada South Africa and the US from companies such as Vale Rio Tinto and BHP Billiton. To expand its production operations POSCO has developed joint ventures with companies in China Southeast Asia and Latin America.

In 2011 the company reported an 11% rise in revenues (a more than 40% increase in local revenues) thanks in part to higher selling prices for its steel and wire rod products but primarily because of a 200%-plus growth in trading revenues as the result of the Daewoo acquisition in 2010. However POSCO reported a drop of 13% in net income for the year as major cost increases related to the Daewoo purchase outpaced revenue growth.

To geographically expand its operations POSCO has an alliance with long-time rival Nippon Steel whereby each has taken a small stake in the other; it has also formed a joint venture with Steel Authority of India and plans to establish agreements with other steelmakers in China and Europe.

POSCO is looking to expand into the energy industry market for steel plate (used in the construction oil platforms). In 2012 it secured a steel supply contract from rig maker Samkang M&T for North Sea rigs and has set its sights on getting a 10% global share of the oil and gas industry's steel plate market by 2020.

In 2011 POSCO entered a $6 billion joint venture with Vale's Mozambique operations to mine coal in the southern part of that country. The mine expected to produce 11 million tons of metallurgical coal a year will help POSCO maintain a steady supply of raw materials for its steel mills. At the same time POSCO agreed to set up a similar joint mining venture in neighboring Zimbabwe with Anchor Holdings to develop chrome coal iron ore and other minerals.

That same year POSCO acquired a 20% stake in US-based graphene company XG Sciences in a move to diversify its business. Graphene is a raw material used to manufacture high-tension nanocarbon. POSCO also moved to acquire all of Thailand-based stainless steel producer Thainox Stainless pcl in 2011. POSCCO already owned a 16% stake but had waited for political stability to return to Thailand before acquiring the balance.

HISTORY

After the Korean War South Korea the US and its allies wanted to rebuild South Korea's infrastructure as quickly as possible. Steel was given a high priority and before long about 15 companies were making various steel products. Quality was a problem though as the companies used dated production processes.

With the backing of South Korean president Chung Hee Park momentum for a large steel plant grew in the late 1960s. In 1967 the South Korean government and Korean International Steel Associates (KISA) —a consortium of seven Western steelmakers - signed an agreement that called for the completion of an integrated mill by 1972. Pohang Iron & Steel Co. (POSCO) the operating company was incorporated in 1968. Efforts to raise the necessary capital failed however and KISA was dissolved in 1969.

Undaunted the South Koreans turned to the Japanese who arranged loans covering most of the mill's costs and the early phases of planning and construction. The Japanese also transferred the technology needed to run such a plant. Slow and deliberate planning resulted in a plant far away from Seoul (part of a plan to locate industries throughout the country) and a design that lent itself to future expansion. The first stage including a blast furnace and two steel converters was completed in 1973. By the time the fourth stage of construction began in 1979 the Koreans had gained enough confidence to take over many of the tasks. When the last stage was completed in 1981 the plant had an annual capacity of 8.5 million tons.

To ensure steel of acceptable quality POSCO focused first on plain high-carbon steel for general construction rather than on specialized (and difficult to produce) varieties. The company gradually broadened its specialized offerings.

In 1985 POSCO began construction on a second integrated steel plant located in Kwangyang. That plant was also built in four stages; its annual production capacity when it was completed in 1992 was 11.4 million tons. By 1987 POSCO was exporting almost 3 million tons of steel a year and using its knowledge to assist in plant construction projects in other countries.

By the mid-1990s POSCO was exporting 6 million tons of steel annually. The South Korean government sold a 5% stake in POSCO to the public in 1998 and vowed to open up the primary steelmaking industry to competition. However facing a

severe downturn in steel demand that year because of sluggishness in Asian and domestic markets the company canceled two projects in China and suspended two in Indonesia. In 1999 POSCO merged its two subsidiaries Pohang Coated Steel and Pohang Steel Industries to create Pohang Steel Co. That same year POSCO Machinery & Engineering POSEC-HAWAII and P.T. Posnesia Stainless Steel Industry were joined to form POSCO Machinery & Engineering. The South Korean government continued selling off its 13% stake in 1999.

In 2000 POSCO sold its 51% stake in telecommunications company Shinsegi Telecom to SK Telecom in exchange for cash and a 6.5% stake in SK Telecom. It also formed a strategic alliance —exploration of joint ventures shared research and joint procurement —with Nippon Steel the world's #1 steelmaker. The deal also calls for each to take increased equity stakes (2% or 3%) in the other. After about 30 years of government control the South Korean government sold its remaining shares of POSCO in 2001.

In June 2002 Chairman Yoo was indicted for influencing POSCO subsidiaries and contractors to buy inflated shares of Tiger Pools International (South Korea's sole sports lottery business) for Kim Hong-Gul the third son of South Korean President Kim Dae-Jung. That same year Pohang Iron & Steel Co. officially changed its company name to POSCO to try and strengthen brand recognition.

In 2003 Yoo resigned ahead of the company's shareholder meeting amid his possible involvement in illegal stock transactions.

The company invested in its Mexican operations in 2006 announcing a joint venture coil processing facility with Daewoo International to serve local carmakers. In 2010 POSCO acquired a majority stake in Daewoo International. Daewoo shareholders voted to put the company's depressed shares up for sale after the South Korean government gave its approval for the deal early in 2010.

EXECUTIVES

CEO, Joon-Yang Chung, age 67
EVP and Head of Growth and Investment Division, Yoon Yong-Won, age 62
President Chief Financial and Planning Officer and Director, Choi Jong-Tae, age 63
CEO and Director, Joon-Yang Chung, age 65
Director, Sun Wook, age 68
Director, Charles Ahn, age 51
Director, Yoo Jang-Hee, age 72
Director, Han Joon-Ho, age 67
Director, Kim Byung-Ki, age 33
Director, Lee Chang-Hee, age 53
Director, Park Sang-Yong, age 62
Auditors: KPMGSamjongAccountingCorp.

LOCATIONS

HQ: POSCO (South Korea)
6261 Donghaean-ro Nam-gu, Pohang-si,
Gyeongsangbuk-do 790-300
Phone: (82) 54 220 0114   **Fax:** (82) 54 220 6000
Web: www.posco.co.kr

Sales

	$ mil.	% of total
Asia/Pacific		
China	9	
Other Asia	4	
Other regions	4	

PRODUCTS/OPERATIONS

Sales

	$ mil.	% of total
Steel	57	
Construction	8	
Total	**0**	**100**

COMPETITORS

ArcelorMittal
Baosteel
Bechtel
Fluor
Hitachi
Hyundai Steel
JFE Holdings
Kobe Steel
Mitsubishi Steel Mfg.
Nippon Steel & Sumitomo Metal Corporation
Samsung Group
Severstal
Tata Steel
ThyssenKrupp Steel
United States Steel

HISTORICAL FINANCIALS

Company Type: Public

Income Statement

FYE: December 31

	REVENUE ($ mil.)	NET INCOME ($ mil.)	NET PROFIT MARGIN	EMPLOYEES
12/13	58,826	1,308	2.2%	17,832
12/12	59,571	2,305	3.9%	17,623
12/11	59,496	3,148	5.3%	17,553
12/10	42,707	3,661	8.6%	16,390
12/09	31,852	2,781	8.7%	16,516
Annual Growth	16.6%	(17.2%)	—	1.9%

2013 Year-End Financials

Debt ratio: 0.0%
Return on equity: 3.3%
Cash ($ mil.): 4,001
Current ratio: 1.56
Long-term debt ($ mil.): 14,770

No. of shares (mil.): 79
Dividends
  Yield: 2.2%
  Payout: 8.4%
Market value ($ mil.): 6,223

	STOCK PRICE ($) FY Close	P/E High/Low	PER SHARE ($) Earnings	Dividends	Book Value
12/13	78.00	— —	16.55	1.77	501.12
12/12	82.15	— —	29.85	2.09	478.38
12/11	82.10	— —	40.76	0.00	428.55
12/10	107.69	— —	48.09	1.97	423.45
12/09	131.10	— —	36.28	1.57	346.78
Annual Growth	(12.2%)	— —	(17.8%)	3.1%	9.6%

Power Corp. of Canada

Founded in the 1920s to develop hydroelectric power Power Corporation of Canada now generates cash not electricity. Through its majority stake in Power Financial the company controls one of Canada's leading mutual fund firms (IGM Financial) one of its largest life insurers (Great-West Lifeco) and other insurance firms. It also owns Gesca which publishes Montreal's "La Presse" and six other daily newspapers in Quebec and Ontario and a majority of Pargesa Group which has stakes in large companies involved in energy (TOTAL) utilities (GDF SUEZ) construction (Lafarge) wines and spirits (Pernod Ricard) and other sectors in Europe through a controlling stake in Groupe Bruxelles Lambert.

In addition Power Corporation has investments in hedge funds private equity fund managers in France and the US and companies involved in biotechnology clean tech digital media and television production. Through Great-West Lifeco the company owns US-based mutual fund manager Putnam which it acquired from insurance brokerage Marsh & McLennan in 2007. The nearly $4 bil-

lion deal gave Power Corporation a significant presence in the US.

The company proved to be rather resilient during the economic downturn as its portfolio companies for the most part performed relatively well. Earnings were up in 2010 as IGM Financial and Great-West Lifeco reported higher sales. Power Corporation continues to focus on its core asset management and retirement planning operations and build the online presence of its media holdings. In 2011 the company made a move to enter China's fast-growing fund management sector by arranging to buy a 10% state in China Asset Management.

Former chairman Paul Desmarais (whose sons Paul and Andre are co-CEOs) owns more than 60% of Power Corporation of Canada.

EXECUTIVES

VP and Controller, Denis Le Vasseur
Director; Vice Chairman Power Financial, Raymond L. McFeetors, age 69
Director; President and CEO Power Financial, R. Jeffrey Orr
VP, Peter Kruyt, age 59
SVP General Counsel and Secretary, Edward Johnson
SVP, Arnaud Vial, age 62, $452,627 total compensation
Executive Vice President, John A. Rae, $426,128 total compensation
Deputy Chairman, Robert Gratton, age 70
Chairman and Co-CEO; Co-Chairman Power Financial, Paul Desmarais Jr., age 60, $952,900 total compensation
EVP and CFO Power Corporation of Canada and Power Financial, Gregory D. Tretiak
Vice Chairman Power Corporation of Canada and Power Financial, Henri-Paul Rousseau, age 65
Treasurer, Isabelle Morin
VP, Daniel Friedberg
VP and Assistant General Counsel, Stephane Lemay
VP and Head Corporate Finance, Richard Pan
VP, Luc Reny
Vice President; Controller, Denis Vasseur
Vice President, Pierre Larochelle
Vice President, Yuhong Liu
Vice President; General Counsel; Secretary, Stephane Lemay
Director; Vice Chairman Power Financial, Raymond L. McFeetors, age 69
Director; President and CEO Power Financial, R. Jeffrey Orr
EVP and Director, John A. Rae
Deputy Chairman President and Co-CEO; Co-Chairman Power Financial, Andre R. Desmarais, age 56
Director, Isabelle Marcoux, age 44
Vice Chairman, Michel Plessis-Belair, age 71
Deputy Chairman, Robert Gratton, age 70
Vice Chairman Power Corporation of Canada and Power Financial, Henri-Paul Rousseau, age 65
Director, James R. Nininger
Director, Paul Desmarais Sr., age 86
Director, Pierre Beaudoin, age 56
Director, Rt. Hon. Donald F. (Don) Mazankowski, age 79
Director, Laurent Dassault, age 61
Director, Anthony R. Graham, age 57
Director, Jerry E. A. Nickerson, age 78
Director, Emoke J. E. Szathmary
Director, Robert Parizeau
Director, Guy Fortin
Independent Director, Emoke Szathmary
Independent Director, Marcel Coutu
Auditors: Deloitte&ToucheLLP

LOCATIONS

HQ: Power Corp. of Canada
  751 Victoria Square, Montreal, Quebec H2Y 2J3
Phone: 514 286-7400   Fax: 514 286-7484
Web: www.powercorporation.com

Sales

	% of total
Canada	52
Europe	28
US	20
Total	100

PRODUCTS/OPERATIONS

Sales

	% of total
Premium	54
Net investment	29
Fees & media	17
Total	100

Sales by Segment

	% of total
Great-West	91
IGM	8
Other	1
Total	100

Selected Investments

Communications
  Gesca Ltee (newspaper publisher)
  Square Victoria Communications Group Inc.
  Square Victoria Digital Properties Inc.
Financial Services
  Great-West Lifeco Inc. (68%)
    The Canada Life Assurance Company
    Great-West Life & Annuity Insurance Company
    The Great-West Life Assurance Company
    London Life Insurance Company
    Putnam Investments LLC
  IGM Financial Inc. (57%)
    Investment Planning Counsel (91%)
    Investors Group
    Mackenzie Financial Corporation
  Power Financial Corporation (66%)
  Victoria Square Ventures Inc.
Other
  Pergesa Holding S.A. (Switzerland)

COMPETITORS

AGF Management	Counsel Corporation
Berkshire Hathaway	Dundee Corp.
Brookfield Asset Management	Loews
CI Financial	Manulife Financial
CPP Investment Board	Onex
Caisse de depot et placement du Quebec	Ontario Teachers' Pension Plan

HISTORICAL FINANCIALS

Company Type: Public

Income Statement

FYE: December 31

	ASSETS ($ mil.)	NET INCOME ($ mil.)	INCOME AS % OF ASSETS	EMPLOYEES
12/13	324,456	48	0.0%	0
12/12	273,127	50	0.0%	30,900
12/11	250,461	40	0.0%	30,700
12/10	248,053	41	0.0%	31,126
12/09	136,405	650	0.5%	30,744
Annual Growth	24.2%	(47.6%)	—	—

2013 Year-End Financials

Return on assets: 0.0%
Return on equity: 0.4%
Long-term debt ($ mil.): —
No. of shares (mil.): 411
Sales ($ mil): 27,976

Dividends
  Yield: 0.0%
  Payout: 55.7%
Market value ($ mil.): 12,379

	STOCK PRICE ($) FY Close	P/E High/Low		PER SHARE ($) Earnings	Dividends	Book Value
12/13	30.09	13	11	1.96	1.09	25.27
12/12	25.58	16	11	1.80	1.17	24.70
12/11	23.33	13	8	2.27	1.14	23.43
12/10	27.79	19	14	1.57	1.16	23.06
12/09	27.68	19	6	1.34	1.11	56.40
Annual Growth (18.2%)	2.1%	—	—	10.0%	(0.4%)	

Power Financial Corp

Power Financial gets a charge out of insurance and investments. The holding company seeks controlling stakes in financial services companies in the US the UK and Canada. Core investments include 68%-owned Great-West Lifeco (subsidiaries include Great-West Life Assurance Canada Life and London Life Insurance leading providers of insurance in Canada). Lifeco's US subsidiary Great-West Life & Annuity Insurance provides employee benefits and retirement plans. Boston-based fund manager Putnam Investments is also part of the family. Power Financial owns about half of IGM Financial which owns Investors Group and Mackenzie Financial distributors of mutual funds and other investment products and services.

Power Financial also is a 50% partner in Dutch holding company Parjointco with the Frere-Bourgeois and CNP groups the joint venture that owns a 54% stake in Pargesa which invests in building materials utilities minerals and energy companies (with Groupe Bruxelles Lambert it owns stakes in Imerys and TOTAL).

In 2007 Power Financial surprised many when it purchased the once-venerable but recently disgraced Putnam Investments. Speculation turned to I-told-you-so the following year when Putnam like most money managers was slammed by the subprime mortgage and credit market collapse. In mid-2008 Power Financial brought in long-time Fidelity Investments COO Robert Reynolds as president and CEO of Putnam. The new leader trimmed staff tied pay to performance and started two new funds to attract fresh money.

Power Corporation of Canada the country's fifth largest firm by revenue owns two-thirds of Power Financial. Canada's well-known billionaire Desmarais family controls Power Corporation.

EXECUTIVES

VP and Controller, Denis Le Vasseur
Vice Chairman, Raymond L. McFeetors, age 69, $1,821,767 total compensation
President Chief Executive Officer, R. Jeffrey Orr, $2,880,391 total compensation
Senior Vice-President, Arnaud Vial, age 62, $132,548 total compensation
SVP General Counsel and Secretary, Edward D. Johnson
Co-Chairman, Paul Desmarais Jr., age 60, $408,900 total compensation
Vice Chairman, Henri-Paul Rousseau, age 65
Human Resources Director, Luc Reny
Managing Director Power Financial Europe, Jocelyn Lefebvre, age 57
Treasurer, Isabelle Morin
Executive Vice-President Chief Financial Officer, Gregory D. Tretiak
Vice-President Controller, Denis Vasseur
Vice President, Richard Pan

Vice President; General Counsel; Secretary, Stephane Lemay
Vice Chairman, Raymond L. McFeetors, age 69
President CEO and Director, R. Jeffrey Orr
Co-Chairman, Andre R. Desmarais, age 56
Director, Raymond Royer, age 75
Director, Michel Plessis-Belair, age 71
Director, Robert Gratton, age 70
Vice Chairman, Henri-Paul Rousseau, age 65
Director, Paul Desmarais Sr., age 86
Director, Rt. Hon. Donald F. (Don) Mazankowski, age 77
Director, J. Brian Aune, age 73
Director, Louise Roy
Director, Anthony R. Graham, age 57
Director, Gerald Frere, age 62
Director, Jerry E. A. Nickerson, age 76
Director, Emoke J. E. Szathmary
Director, V. Peter Harder, age 61
Director, Marc A. Bibeau
Director, Amaury de Seze
Independent Director, Emoke Szathmary
Independent Director, Gerald Frere
Auditors: Deloitte&ToucheLLP

LOCATIONS

HQ: Power Financial Corp
751 Victoria Square, Montreal, Quebec H2Y 2J3
Phone: 514 286-7400   **Fax:** 514 286-7484
Web: www.powerfinancial.com

2010 Revenues

Canada	52
US	20

PRODUCTS/OPERATIONS

2010 Revenues

Great-West Lifeco	70
Pargesa	7

Selected Subsidiaries & Affiliates

Great-West Lifeco Inc. (68%)
  Great-West Life & Annuity Insurance Company (US)
  Great-West Life Assurance Company
    Canada Life Financial Corporation
    London Insurance Group Inc.
  Putnam LLC
IGM Financial Inc. (57%)
  Investment Planning Counsel (94%)
  Investors Group Inc.
  Mackenzie Financial Corporation

COMPETITORS

AXA Financial
Allstate
CIGNA
Industrial Alliance Insurance and Financial Servic
Manulife Financial
Prudential
RBC Financial Group
State Farm
Sun Life

HISTORICAL FINANCIALS

Company Type: Public

Income Statement

FYE: December 31

	ASSETS ($ mil.)	NET INCOME ($ mil.)	INCOME AS % OF ASSETS	EMPLOYEES
12/13	321,358	1,783	0.6%	0
12/12	270,058	1,634	0.6%	17,870
12/11	247,698	1,688	0.7%	29,100
12/10*	245,165	1,471	0.6%	0
01/10	222,678	0	—	0
Annual Growth	9.6%	—	—	—

*Fiscal year change

2013 Year-End Financials

Return on assets: 0.6%
Return on equity: 12.5%
Long-term debt ($ mil.): —
No. of shares (mil.): 711
Sales ($ mil): 27,238
Dividends
Yield: 0.0%
Payout: 53.2%
Market value ($ mil.): 24,194

	STOCK PRICE ($) FY Close	P/E High/Low		PER SHARE ($) Earnings	Dividends	Book Value
12/13	34.02	12	9	2.47	1.32	21.31
12/12	27.29	13	10	2.31	1.41	19.89
12/11	25.07	14	9	2.36	1.37	18.72
12/10*	30.84	16	12	2.06	1.37	18.13
01/10	29.49	—	—	(0.00)	1.33	17.27
Annual Growth	3.6%	—	—	—	(0.3%)	5.4%

*Fiscal year change

Prudential Plc

When it comes to life insurance a little prudence goes a long way. Working through its subsidiaries Prudential is the UK's largest life insurer and the largest European insurer operating in Asia. In addition to insurance Prudential UK's products include pensions annuities investment bonds and fund management. Other businesses include UK fund manager M&G. In Asia the company sells life insurance savings and investment products in about a dozen countries through its Prudential Corporation Asia unit. In the US Prudential owns Jackson National Life Insurance which offers annuities and life insurance. Prudential plc was formed in 1848 to offer life insurance and loans to the middle class.

Operations

Prudential serves more than 24 million policyholders through its global insurance divisions and it has a total of some Å405 million in assets under management. About 13 million customers are in Asian markets.

The company's operations are divided into four segments: Jackson National in the US Prudential Corporation Asia and Prudential UK and M&G based in the UK market. Operating subsidiaries within the UK-based divisions include Prudential Assurance Prudential Annuities Prudential Retirement and Prudential Assurance Singapore.

Insurance revenues account for more than 90% of annual earnings while asset management services provided by the M&G division make up the remainder of annual revenue.

Geographic Reach

Through its UK-based businesses Prudential has about 50 branch locations in the UK other European countries and India. Jackson National distributes products in all 50 US states from about 20 regional offices. In Asia Prudential has about 30 businesses that are spread over 14 markets.

Sales and Marketing

Prudential conducts sales through independent brokers and agents institutional product distributors regional brokers captive agents banks and investment advisors.

In addition to joint ventures with banks in China (with CITIC Group) and India (with ICICI Bank) Prudential has bank distribution agreements in other Asian markets. It life accident and health insurance policies are sold in Singapore Indonesia and Thailand through the more than 500 branches of United Overseas Bank.

Financial Performance

Rises in earned premiums and investment returns led to a 54% revenue increase to some Â55.5 billion ($89.6 billion) in 2012. The company reported premium growth in all three core markets (the US Asia and the UK).

However sales declined in both 2010 and 2011 after a large jump in 2009. Prudential has seen volatile earnings in recent years due to the fact that the company relies on investment returns for more than 40% of its insurance income (in addition to premiums and fees) which makes it vulnerable to changes in market conditions.

Profits rose 55% to Â2.2 billion ($3.6 billion) in 2012 due to higher revenues. Prudential has seen steadily climbing net income over the past five years as revenues outweigh expenses.

Strategy

A key part of Prudential's growth strategy and differentiation from its competitors is its presence in Asia particularly in markets including Southeast Asia Singapore and Hong Kong. The company entered the new Asian market of Cambodia in 2013. It is especially working to increase sales of savings and insurance products to the emerging group of middle class individuals in Asian markets.

Another strategic area of focus is retirement savings products (such as variable annuities) in the US. Its Jackson National Life Insurance takes advantage of the fact that the US has the largest market for retirement-related financial products. Prudential is also focused on strengthening existing life insurance operations in the US. In the UK the company is maximizing its asset management operations and focusing on core insurance markets.

Prudential also looks to diversify its earnings and offerings by making bolt-on acquisitions when opportunities emerge.

Mergers and Acquisitions

In 2013 the company widened its operations in Southeast Asia through the purchase of Thailand-based Thanachart Life Assurance from Thanachart Bank for some Â368 million; the transaction also included a deal in which Prudential distributes policies through Thanachart's banking branches. To expand in the US market Prudential acquired SRLC America a US division of Swiss Re for some Â370 million ($587 million) in 2012. The purchase diversified Jackson's life insurance underwriting activities in the US market.

Ownership

Capital Group International owns about 10% of the company.

HISTORY

Actually prudence almost killed Prudential before it ever got started. Founded in 1848 as Prudential Mutual Assurance Investment and Loan Association the firm initially insured middle-class customers. The Dickensian conditions of the working poor made them too risky for insurers. Unfortunately the company found few takers of the right sort and by 1852 Prudential was in peril.

Two events saved Prudential: The House of Commons pressed for insurance coverage for all classes and Prudential's own agents pushed for change. The company expanded into industrial insurance a modest coverage for the working poor. In 1864 to quell criticism of the insurance industry Prudential brought in independent auditors to confirm its soundness. This soon became a marketing tool and business took off. The Pru as it came to be known became the leading industrial insurer by the 1880s. It covered half the country's population by 1905. The firm's salesmen were known for making personal visits to customers (the "Man from the Pru" became a ubiquitous icon in the 1940s and was revived in 1997).

During the two world wars Prudential boosted its reputation by honoring the policies of war victims when it could have legally denied them. Between wars the company added fire and accident insurance in Europe.

The 1980s were volatile for insurance companies especially in the wake of Britain's financial deregulation in 1986. Therefore in 1982 under the direction of CEO Brian Corby the Pru reorganized product lines and in 1985 entered the real estate business. In 1986 it entered the US market by buying US-based Jackson National Life Insurance.

Prudential which had considered selling Mercantile and General Reinsurance in the early 1990s (purchased in 1969) sold the reinsurer back to Swiss Re in 1996. It also formed Prudential Bank and created an Asian emerging-market investment fund that year.

Insurance regulators reprimanded the company for mis-selling financial products in 1997. In 1998 Jackson National bought a California savings and loan enabling it to sell investment products in the US. Also that year the Pru sold its Australian and New Zealand businesses and Prudential Bank launched its pioneering Internet bank Egg Banking.

In 1999 Prudential bought investment manager M&G Group. The company then changed its name to Prudential plc and began talks with the Prudential Insurance Company of America to resolve confusion of their similar names as they expanded into new markets. Also in 1999 the Pru joined forces with the Bank of China to offer pension and asset management in Hong Kong.

The company announced plans in 2000 to sell a chunk of its institutional fund management business as well as its traditional balanced pension business to Deutsche Bank. That year the company spun off 20% of Egg (it sold the rest in 2007).

Entering the Japanese life insurance market Prudential bought Orico Life in 2001. Prudential's hopes of capturing the lucrative annuities market by acquiring American General were dashed that year as American General instead embraced American International Group leaving the Pru with a $600 million break-up fee. To consolidate operations the firm sold its general insurance business in 2001 to Swiss insurer Winterthur (a subsidiary of Credit Suisse).

In early 2006 Prudential rejected a takeover offer from larger rival Aviva valued at nearly $30 billion.

After helping oversee the shift in focus that brought the company growth in Asia and stability during the 2008 economic downturn CEO Mark Tucker stepped down at the end of September 2009. The company chose CFO Tidjane Thiam to replace him. Thiam a native of Ivory Coast became the first black CEO of a FTSE 100 company.

In early 2010 the company expanded its operations in Singapore by acquiring United Overseas Bank's life insurance unit for S$428 million ($307 million). Along with becoming owner of UOB Life Assurance Ltd. Prudential entered into an agreement through which UOB sells Prudential's life accident and health insurance policies for 12 years at the bank's more than 400 branches in Singapore Indonesia and Thailand giving Prudential a greater presence in those markets. In 2011 Prudential targeted the business of Singapore's class of "rising rich" individuals as an important area for growth.

Prudential made a splashy bid on AIG's Hong Kong-based American International Assurance (AIA) business in 2010. The $35.5 billion deal ($25 billion in cash $8.5 billion in securities and $2 billion in stock) would have made Prudential the largest life insurer in Hong Kong and allowed AIG to pay off a chunk of its debt to the US government. However Prudential's shareholders were not impressed and raised a ruckus over the deal. To appease them Prudential attempted to reduce its offer to $30 billion —which AIG coolly refused —and then simply withdrew its entire offer.

EXECUTIVES

COO M&G Group, Martin Lewis
Executive Director; President and CEO Jackson National Life, Michael A. (Mike) Wells, age 53
Chief Risk Officer Prudential UK and Europe, Marcia Cantor-Grable
Executive Director; Chief Executive Prudential UK and Europe, Robert A. (Rob) Devey, $109,889 total compensation
COO Prudential Property Investment Managers (PRUPRIM) M&G, Malcolm Smith
Deputy Chief Executive Prudential UK and Europe, Barry O'Dwyer
Deputy Chief Executive Prudential UK and Europe, Andrew M. (Andy) Crossley
Chief Actuary Prudential UK, David Belsham
Chief Executive Fund Management Prudential Corporation Asia, Graham Mason
Director Human Resources Prudential UK and Europe, Catherine (Cathy) Lewis
Managing Director Prudential Property Investment Managers (PRUPRIM) M&G, Martin R. Moore
Group Chief Risk Officer and Director, John Foley, age 57
Director, Michael W.O. Garrett, age 71
Director, Kathleen A. O'Donovan, age 55
Executive Director; Chief Executive The M&G Group, Michael G.A. McLintock, age 52
Director, James H. Ross, age 75
Director, Keki B. Dadiseth, age 67
Director, Bridget A. Macaskill, age 63
Director, Ann F. Godbehere, age 57
Executive Director; President and CEO Jackson National Life, Michael A. (Mike) Wells, age 53
Director, Sir Howard J. Davies, age 62
Director, Paul Manduca, age 61
Director, Lord Andrew Turnbull, age 68
Group Chief Executive and Director, Tidjane C. Thiam, age 50
CFO and Director, Nicolaos (Nic) Nicandrou
Executive Director; Chief Executive Prudential UK and Europe, Robert A. (Rob) Devey
Group Chief Risk Officer and Director, John Foley, age 56
Auditors: KPMGAuditPlc

LOCATIONS

HQ: Prudential Plc
Laurence Pountney Hill, London EC4R 0HH
Phone: (44) 20 7548 3640
Web: www.prudential.co.uk

Sales

	% of total
US	27
Asia	15
UK	14
Investment	44
Total	**100**

PRODUCTS/OPERATIONS

Sales

	% of total
Insurance	96
Asset	4
Total	**100**

COMPETITORS

AEGON	Lincoln Financial
AIA Group	Group
AIG	Lloyds Banking Group

AXA
Allianz
Aviva
BlackRock
Canada Life
Cathay Life Insurance
China Life Insurance
China Pacific
  Insurance
Citigroup
FMR
Friends Provident
Great Eastern Holdings
HSBC
ING
Invesco Perpetual
Jupiter Fund
  Management
Legal & General
  Group

Manulife Financial
MetLife
Mitsui Sumitomo
  Insurance
Nationwide Financial
New York Life
Nippon Life Insurance
Ping An Insurance
Prudential
RSA Insurance
Resolution Ltd
Samsung Life Insurance
Schroders
Sompo Japan Insurance
Standard Life
State Farm
TIAA-CREF
The Hartford
Tokio Marine
Zurich Insurance Group

HISTORICAL FINANCIALS
Company Type: Public

Income Statement
FYE: December 31

	ASSETS ($ mil.)	NET INCOME ($ mil.)	INCOME AS % OF ASSETS	EMPLOYEES
12/13	538,628	2,224	0.4%	20,052
12/12	500,086	3,541	0.7%	27,619
12/11	422,641	2,301	0.5%	25,414
12/10	404,937	2,221	0.5%	25,992
12/09	368,866	1,094	0.3%	27,389
Annual Growth	9.9%	19.4%	—	(7.5%)

2013 Year-End Financials
Return on assets: 0.4%
Return on equity: 13.4%
Long-term debt ($ mil.): —
No. of shares (mil.): —
Sales ($ mil): 86,796

Dividends
  Yield: 2.0%
  Payout: 272.3%
Market value ($ mil.): —

	STOCK PRICE ($) FY Close	P/E High/Low		PER SHARE ($) Earnings	Dividends	Book Value
12/13	45.00	230	135	0.87	0.94	6.23
12/12	28.55	89	57	1.39	0.81	6.53
12/11	19.74	113	66	0.91	2.00	5.53
12/10	20.86	94	57	0.88	0.60	4.90
12/09	20.39	218	47	0.44	0.61	4.01
Annual Growth	21.9%		—	18.8%	11.3%	11.6%

PTT Public Co Ltd.

Thailand fills its tanks thanks to integrated oil company PTT the nation's largest company. Its PTT Oil transportation and marketing unit operates more than 1200 gas stations. PTT Gas procures processes transports and distributes natural gas. PTT owns 49% of the nation's largest refiner Thai Oil. Other PTT units engage in oil and gas exploration and production (in Thailand and elsewhere) produce petrochemicals and mine coal. It is also has major oil and gas trading operations. The company is majority-owned by the Government of Thailand.

Operations

PTT's core businesses are Exploration & Production and Gas and Oil.

PTT Exploration and Production Public Company Limited (PTTEP). PTT has also invested in natural gas-related corporations both in Thailand and abroad.

The Gas Business Group engages in natural gas supply procurement pipeline transmission separation and distribution.

The Oil Business Group engages in distribution of refined fuel and lubricating products covering retail marketing run through PTT service stations wholesale marketing and commercial marketing for government agencies industry sector airlines and oil vessels.

The International Trading Business Group covers procurement and import-export trading of crude oil condensate petroleum and petrochemical products .

On the investment side PTT invests in a wide range of its related businesses with an emphasis on petrochemical and oil refining businesses.

Financial Performance

The company's revenues increased by 28% in 2011 with a jump in profits of 25% reflected the success in natural gas procurement to meet growing demand efficiency improvement of gas separation plants (GSPs) and the commercial operation of GSP unit 6 (Rayong) which boosted production capacity.

Other factors include PTTEP's production increase (especially from the oil sands KKD project in Canada); production capacity expansion in the petrochemical group; improved returns from portfolio risk management investment and development programs; and pricing risk management for PTT and PTT group.

Strategy

The company sees its role as being the lead player in Thailand's oil and gas development and revenue production. PTT is relying on the synergy between various downstream businesses to add business value and reduce operating costs.

Ownership

The Government of Thailand owns 51% of PTT.

Company Background

Thailand which created PTT to secure energy supplies during the oil crunch of the late 1970s sold a third of the company in a 2001 IPO.

In 2008 as part of PTT's energy diversification drive the company opened the world's largest NGV (natural gas vehicle) gas station in Thailand to respond to the growing number of NGV vehicles in the country.

EXECUTIVES
President CEO Secretary and Director, Pailin Chuchottaworn
Chairman, Norkun Sitthiphong
Director Chairman of the Audit Committee, Chulasingh Vasantasingh
Auditors: OfficeoftheAuditorGeneralofThailand

LOCATIONS
HQ: PTT Public Co Ltd.
  555 Vibhavadi-Rangsit Road, Chatuchak, Bangkok 10900
Phone: (66) 2 537 2000   **Fax:** (66) 2 537 3498 9
Web: www.pttplc.com

PRODUCTS/OPERATIONS

Sales

	% of total
International	53
Oil	21
Natural	16
Exploration &	6
Petrochemical	3
Coal	1
Other	-
Total	**100**

Selected Subsidiaries and Affiliates:
PetroAsia (Huizhou) Co. Ltd. (25%)

PTT Exploration and Production Public Co. Ltd. (66%)
PTT Mart Co. Ltd. (49%)
PTT Natural Gas Distribution Co. Ltd. (58%)
Star Petroleum Refining Co. Ltd. (36%)
Thai Lube Blending Co. Ltd. (49%)
Thai Oil Plc. (50%)

COMPETITORS
BP
Chevron
Salamander Energy

HISTORICAL FINANCIALS
Company Type: Public

Income Statement
FYE: December 31

	REVENUE ($ mil.)	NET INCOME ($ mil.)	NET PROFIT MARGIN	EMPLOYEES
12/13	86,831	2,891	3.3%	25,251
12/12	91,301	3,420	3.7%	20,816
12/11	77,158	3,345	4.3%	18,240
12/10	63,259	2,766	4.4%	9,015
12/09	47,611	1,787	3.8%	7,952
Annual Growth	16.2%	12.8%	—	33.5%

2013 Year-End Financials
Debt ratio: 0.8%
Return on equity: 14.6%
Cash ($ mil.): 4,816
Current ratio: 1.29
Long-term debt ($ mil.): 12,907

No. of shares (mil.): —
Dividends
  Yield: —
  Payout: —
Market value ($ mil.): —

	STOCK PRICE ($) FY Close	P/E High/Low		PER SHARE ($) Earnings	Dividends	Book Value
12/13	8.75	0	0	1.01	0.00	7.30
12/12	10.85	0	0	1.20	0.00	6.93
12/11	9.00	0	0	1.17	0.00	6.18
12/10	10.50	0	0	0.97	0.00	5.74
12/09	7.20	0	0	0.63	0.00	4.55
Annual Growth	5.0%		—	12.6%	—	12.6%

Public Bank Berhad (Malaysia)

Public Bank stakes its success on providing banking services to the public. The company has about 250 branches throughout Malaysia where it is one of the top lenders and fund operators. Offerings include deposit accounts credit cards home loans and insurance plans. In addition to retail and commercial services it provides corporate banking brokerage investment banking wealth management and Islamic banking. Public Bank has more than 100 overseas branches in countries including Cambodia China Hong Kong Laos Sri Lanka and Vietnam. The company was founded in 1966 by chairman Tan Sri Dato' Sri Dr. Teh Hong Piow.

LOCATIONS
HQ: Public Bank Berhad (Malaysia)
  27th Floor, Menara Public Bank, 146 Jalan Ampang, Kuala Lumpur 50450
Phone: (60) 3 2163 8888   **Fax:** (60) 3 2163 9917
Web: www.publicbank.com.my

PRODUCTS/OPERATIONS

HISTORICAL FINANCIALS

Company Type: Public

Income Statement

FYE: December 31

	ASSETS ($ mil.)	NET INCOME ($ mil.)	INCOME AS % OF ASSETS	EMPLOYEES
12/13	93,326	1,240	1.3%	17,924
12/12	89,694	1,263	1.4%	17,625
12/11	78,703	1,099	1.4%	17,500
12/10	73,435	989	1.3%	17,369
12/09	63,406	735	1.2%	17,169
Annual Growth	10.1%	14.0%	—	1.1%

2013 Year-End Financials

Return on assets: 1.4%
Return on equity: 21.1%
Long-term debt ($ mil.): —
No. of shares (mil.): —
Sales ($ mil): 4,454

Dividends
Yield: —
Payout: —
Market value ($ mil.): —

	STOCK PRICE ($) FY Close	P/E High/Low		PER SHARE ($) Earnings	Dividends	Book Value
12/13	0.00	—	—	0.35	0.00	1.78
12/12	0.00	0	0	0.36	0.00	1.67
12/11	4.08	0	0	0.31	0.00	1.34
Annual Growth	—			3.1%	—	7.4%

Qatar National Bank

Qatar National Bank (QNB) is a leading financial institution in the State of Qatar one of the wealthiest nations in the world. Boasting 45% of the total assets in Qatar's banking sector QNB offers customers private and commercial deposit accounts and loans investment management credit cards insurance and mutual funds. International branches are located in a dozen other countries across Africa Asia Europe and the Middle East. Through associate and affiliated companies QNB has a presence in about 25 countries. The company has a local network of more than 50 branches (some cater specifically to women) and hundreds of ATMs. QNB was established in 1964.

LOCATIONS

HQ: Qatar National Bank
P.O. Box 1000, Doha
Phone: (974) 44425 444   **Fax:** (974) 4441 3753
Web: www.qnb.com.qa

PRODUCTS/OPERATIONS

HISTORICAL FINANCIALS

Company Type: Public

Income Statement

FYE: December 31

	ASSETS ($ mil.)	NET INCOME ($ mil.)	INCOME AS % OF ASSETS	EMPLOYEES
12/14	133,632	2,872	2.1%	0
12/13	121,790	2,603	2.1%	0
12/12	100,734	2,289	2.3%	0
12/11	82,910	2,061	2.5%	0
12/10	61,340	1,566	2.6%	0
Annual Growth	21.5%	16.4%	—	—

2014 Year-End Financials

Return on assets: 2.2%
Return on equity: 19.0%
Long-term debt ($ mil.): —
No. of shares (mil.): 699
Sales ($ mil): 6,155

Dividends
Yield: —
Payout: —
Market value ($ mil.): —

Quanta Computer Inc

Quanta Computer is an original design manufacturer (ODM) serving some of the leading names in computer hardware including Dell Apple and HP. It is one of the world's largest manufacturers of notebook computers and also produces network servers television set-top boxes monitors LCD TVs and smartphones. Quanta Computer's other business units include Quanta Storage (data storage products) and RoyalTek Company (personal navigation devices and other GPS products). While well known for its notebooks and their smaller computer cousins the netbooks Quanta Computer is diversifying into other consumer electronics and IT products.

Geographic Reach The company is based in Taiwan with additional facilities in Asia Europe and North and South America.

Financial Performance Quanta Computer's 2011 revenue fell just over 1% to NT$1.1 trillion (around $37 billion). Its net income however rose by 22% for the same period to NT$23 billion (about $780 million) as a result of strict cost controls it put in place. The company is focused on inventory reductions and yield rate improvements among other measures.

Strategy The company is focusing its R&D efforts on cloud computing connectivity and client devices. All three areas are part of a broader cloud computing initiative that involves the design and manufacture of data storage products and servers (for providing cloud-computing services) next-generation data networking products (for enabling uninterrupted cloud-computing connections and service coverage) and client devices (for accessing cloud networks). Outside of notebooks other areas of focus include mobile devices automotive electronics high-definition video conferencing and satellite technology.

Auditors: KPMG

LOCATIONS

HQ: Quanta Computer Inc
No. 188, Wen Hwa 2nd Road, Kuei Shan Hsiang, Taoyuan
Phone: (886) 3 327 2345   **Fax:** (886) 3 327 1511
Web: www.quantatw.com

COMPETITORS

ASUSTeK	Hon Hai
BenQ	Inventec
Celestica	MiTAC
China Techfaith	Pegatron
Compal Electronics	Super Micro Computer
First International Computer	Tatung
Flextronics	TriGem
Foxconn International	Wistron

HISTORICAL FINANCIALS

Company Type: Public

Income Statement

FYE: December 31

	REVENUE ($ mil.)	NET INCOME ($ mil.)	NET PROFIT MARGIN	EMPLOYEES
12/13	29,522	624	2.1%	0
12/12	35,317	794	2.2%	121,917
12/11	36,612	775	2.1%	108,872
12/10	38,651	664	1.7%	68,720
12/09	26,250	729	2.8%	64,719
Annual Growth	3.0%	(3.8%)	—	—

2013 Year-End Financials

Debt ratio: 1.1%
Return on equity: 15.2%
Cash ($ mil.): 6,956
Current ratio: 1.26
Long-term debt ($ mil.): 1,052

No. of shares (mil.): —
Dividends
Yield: —
Payout: 0.3%
Market value ($ mil.): —

	STOCK PRICE ($) FY Close	P/E High/Low		PER SHARE ($) Earnings	Dividends	Book Value
12/13	8.87	—	—	0.16	0.00	1.07
12/12	8.87	—	—	0.20	0.00	1.08
12/11	8.87	—	—	0.20	0.00	1.06
12/10	7.75	—	—	0.16	0.00	1.07
12/09	7.75	—	—	0.19	0.00	0.94
Annual Growth	3.4%			(3.6%)	—	3.2%

Raiffeisen Zentralbank Oesterreich AG (Austria)

Being among the largest bankers in Austria's mature market only gets you so far so Raiffeisen Zentralbank has branched out into other countries and now operates across Central and Eastern Europe from Albania to the Ukraine. It has more than 3000 banking branches in the region offering commercial and investment services. Raiffeisen Zentralbank owns about 70% of Raiffeisen International Bank (RIB) through which it provides central services to its regional banks which in turn provide services to local Raiffeisen banks operating more than 3000 branches in Central and Eastern Europe. The company was founded in 1927 and is owned by its regional banks.

Raiffeisen Zentralbank is growing through acquisitions and other transactions outside Austria. It spun off 30% of RIB in 2005 and used the proceeds to go on a buying spree acquiring banks in the Czech Republic (eBanka) Russia (Impexbank) and the Ukraine (Bank Aval). It is also expanding its presence by opening new branches particularly in markets outside of Austria. Subsidiary Raiffeisen Investment teamed up with Lazard in 2007 to garner more M&A advisory business in Russia and other countries.

The company also has a limited presence in Western Europe Asia and the US.

LOCATIONS

HQ: Raiffeisen Zentralbank Oesterreich AG (Austria)
Am Stadtpark 9, Vienna A-1030
Phone: (43) 1 26 261 0   **Fax:** (43) 1 707 1715
Web: www.rzb.at

PRODUCTS/OPERATIONS

HISTORICAL FINANCIALS

Company Type: Public

Income Statement

FYE: December 31

	ASSETS ($ mil.)	NET INCOME ($ mil.)	INCOME AS % OF ASSETS	EMPLOYEES
12/13	202,826	581	0.3%	59,372
12/12	192,375	488	0.3%	0
12/10	182,683	955	0.5%	60,356
12/09	213,115	624	0.3%	59,800
12/08	219,389	66	0.0%	66,651
Annual Growth	(1.6%)	54.1%	—	(2.3%)

2013 Year-End Financials

Return on assets: 0.2%
Return on equity: 5.9%
Long-term debt ($ mil.): —
No. of shares (mil.): —
Sales ($ mil): 13,093

Dividends
Yield: —
Payout: —
Market value ($ mil.): —

Rallye S.A. Neuilly-Sur-Seine

LOCATIONS

HQ: Rallye S.A. Neuilly-Sur-Seine
83, rue du Faubourg Saint-Honore, Paris 75008
Phone: (33) 1 44 71 13 73   **Fax:** (33) 1 44 71 13 70
Web: www.rallye.fr

HISTORICAL FINANCIALS

Company Type: Public

Income Statement

FYE: December 31

	REVENUE ($ mil.)	NET INCOME ($ mil.)	NET PROFIT MARGIN	EMPLOYEES
12/13	67,881	238	0.4%	333,722
12/12	56,231	322	0.6%	321,385
12/11	45,344	19	0.0%	227,995
12/10	39,856	9	0.0%	175,380
12/09	39,583	145	0.4%	168,046
Annual Growth	14.4%	13.1%	—	18.7%

2013 Year-End Financials

Debt ratio: 46.3%
Return on equity: 10.6%
Cash ($ mil.): 8,023
Current ratio: 0.93
Long-term debt ($ mil.): 15,404

No. of shares (mil.): 48
Dividends
Yield: —
Payout: —
Market value ($ mil.): 2,067

	STOCK PRICE ($) FY Close	P/E High/Low		PER SHARE ($) Earnings	Dividends	Book Value
12/13	42.75	22	11	4.89	0.00	40.42
Annual Growth	—	—	—	—	—	—

Reliance Industries Ltd

India and Reliance Industries rely on each other. The company is India's largest petrochemical firm and among the country's largest companies (along with Indian Oil and Tata Group) accounting for 14% of India's total exports and 4% of its total market capitalization. Oil refining and the manufacture of polyolefins and related chemicals account for the bulk of Reliance Industries' sales. It also makes textiles and explores for oil and gas. Reliance Industries operates more than a dozen manufacturing plants in India. The company has fully integrated its oil and gas refining subsidiary Reliance Petroleum in an effort to consolidate the company's position as a major player in the global refining business.

Reliance Industries' diverse portfolio includes the exploration and production of oil and gas petroleum refining and marketing and petrochemicals (including the production of polyester fiber intermediates plastics and chemicals) as well as textiles retail telecommunications and special economic zones.

In India the company has manufacturing plants in Allahabad Barabanki Dahej Hazira Hoshiarpur Jamnagar Nagothane Nagpur Naroda Patalganga Silvassa and Vadodara. Reliance Industries has operations around the world including in Kenya the Netherlands Singapore the UAE the US (oil and gas) and the UK (retail).

In Fiscal 2012 the company reported a 35% spike in revenues driven by a jump in oil prices and increased demand from petroleum products in developing countries coupled with an increase in Indian domestic demand for textiles chemicals and petroleum products. However its net income dipped by 1% due to a spike in current taxation charges. Buoyed by a recovering global economy the expansion of its own operations and higher oil prices in 2011 Reliance Industries posted a 30% rise in revenues.

Reliance Industries operates in the retail sector through subsidiary Reliance Retail Limited. That unit has big ideas about starting an Indian retail revolution with supermarket outlets across the country under the name Reliance Fresh. It operates a joint venture with UK retail legend Marks & Spencer that hopes to open 50 retail locations by 2014. Moving into the financial services sector in 2011 the company formed a joint venture with US-based investment firm D. E. Shaw.

Reliant Industries is targeting oil and gas as a key growth segment. Seeking funds and expertise to boost its oil and gas exploration and production operations in India in 2011 the company sold BP a 30% stake in 23 oil and gas blocks for about $7.2 billion.

The company is also growing its oil and gas exploration and production assets outside of India. In 2010 it also got a strong foothold in the North American gas market by forming a $1.7 billion Marcellus Shale joint venture with Atlas Energy. Atlas Energy is the development operator for the Appalachian joint venture. In return Reliance Industries owned 40% of Atlas Energy's core Marcellus Shale acreage. In 2011 Chevron stepped in and paid $4.3 billion to acquire Atlas and take over its joint venture with Reliant.

In 2010 Reliance Industries formed a 60%-owned joint venture with Carrizo Oil & Gas which acquired 104400 additional acres in the Marcellus Shale play. That same year Reliance Industries acquired a 45% share in a Pioneer Natural Resources tract in southern Texas for $1.35 billion.

The company began to further diversify in 2010. Reentering the telecommunications sector the company acquired 95% of Infidel Broadband Services a national broadband provider for about $1.02 billion. Infotel was the only company to secure a nationwide license to offer wireless broadband service across India a market with 600 million cell phone users. The deal marked Reliance Industries' return to the telecom market after a 5-year hiatus.

Following a prolonged dispute among the founding Ambani family after the death of patriarch Dhirubai Ambani the company demerged into separate entities –including Reliance Capital (financial services) Reliance Communications (telecommunications) and Reliance Energy (utilities) –in 2006. Mukesh Ambani took control of Reliance Industries and Indian Petrochemicals while his brother Anil took over Reliance Capital Reliance Communications and Reliance Energy.

Mukesh Ambani controls almost half of Reliance Industries.

EXECUTIVES

Executive Director, Hital R. Meswani, $34,530 total compensation
Executive Director, Nikhil R. Meswani, $37,590 total compensation
Chairman and Managing Director, Mukesh D. Ambani, age 57, $11,510 total compensation
Executive Director, P.M.S. Prasad
Executive Director, Pawan K. Kapil
Vice President Corporate Secretarial, S Sudhakar
Executive Director, Hital R. Meswani
Executive Director, Nikhil R. Meswani
Director, Prof Dipak C. Jain, age 56
Executive Director, P.M.S. Prasad
Director, Ramniklal H. Ambani
Director, Mansingh L. Bhakta
Director, Yogendra P. Trivedi
Director, Prof Ashok Misra
Director, Dharam V. Kapur
Director, Mahesh P. Modi
Director, Raghunath Anant Mashelkar
Executive Director, Pawan K. Kapil
Auditors: Chaturvedi&Shah

LOCATIONS

HQ: Reliance Industries Ltd
3rd Floor, Maker Chambers IV, 222, Nariman Point, Mumbai 400 021
Phone: (91) 22 2278 5000   **Fax:** (91) 22 2278 5111
Web: www.ril.com

PRODUCTS/OPERATIONS

Sales

Petroleum	72
Oil & Gas	4
Total	**100**

Selected Products

Chemicals
  Benzene
  Linear alkyl benzene
  Solvents
  Toluene
  Xylenes
Fiber Intermediates
  Di-Ethylene Glycol
  Mono ethylene glycol (MEG)
  Purified terephalic acid (PTA)
  Tri-Ethylene Glycol
Oil and Gas
  Crude oil
  Natural gas
Polyester
  Polyester filament yarn (PFY)
  Polyester staple fiber (PSF)
Polymers
  Polyethylene (HDPE & LLDPE)
  Polypropylene
  Polyvinyl chloride
Textiles

Furnishings fabrics
Sleep products
Texturized yarns

COMPETITORS

Adani Enterprises	Hindustan Petroleum
Asahi Kasei	Indian Oil
Bharat Petroleum	LyondellBasell
Chargeurs	Milliken
DuPont	Reliance
Eastman Chemical	Communications
Essar Group	Shell Chemicals
ExxonMobil Chemical	Tata Group

HISTORICAL FINANCIALS

Company Type: Public

Income Statement

FYE: March 31

	REVENUE ($ mil.)	NET INCOME ($ mil.)	NET PROFIT MARGIN	EMPLOYEES
03/13	74,592	3,846	5.2%	0
03/12	71,684	3,876	5.4%	23,166
03/11	61,189	4,327	7.1%	22,661
03/10	49,127	5,457	11.1%	23,365
03/09	30,546	2,942	9.6%	24,679
Annual Growth	**25.0%**	**6.9%**		

2013 Year-End Financials

Debt ratio: —
Return on equity: 11.8%
Cash ($ mil.): 9,294
Current ratio: 1.59
Long-term debt ($ mil.): —

No. of shares (mil.): —
Dividends
 Yield: —
 Payout: —
Market value ($ mil.): —

Renault S.A. (France)

In Renault's road race against rival Peugeot Citroen to be France's dominant automaker second place will have to deux. Renault manufactures and markets small to midsize cars and light trucks under three brands: Renault Dacia and Renault Samsung Motors (Renault holds 80% Samsung 20%). The company owns Automobile Dacia (Romania's leading automaker) and holds just under half of the Renault-Nissan Alliance (and 43% of Nissan). It also participates in an alliance with Russian car maker AvtoVAZ and helps Germany's Daimlerbuild smart cars. Renault which has become an international brand operates nearly 40 manufacturing facilities in more than 15 countries and sells into 118 nations.

The synergies between Renault and Nissan have produced a reciprocal benefit — Renault has adopted a better production system with Nissan's support and Nissan has embraced better cost-control measures practiced by Renault. The Alliance gives both companies a competitive edge over other automotive companies through shared technologies and platforms. For example Nissan can use Renault's research when developing a diesel engine and Renault can benefit from Nissan's battery technology. By sharing production facilities – which the companies do in Mexico South Africa South Korea and Spain –they save on production purchasing and related costs. The Alliance also allows Renault and Nissan to tackle projects such as electric vehicles the cost of which would be prohibitive if each company had to bear it separately. As is both companies have invested E4 billion (almost $5 billion) into research and development and the manufacturing of vehicles and batteries. The Renault-Nissan Alliance is making a tandem

expansion into emerging countries such as Russia India and Brazil. In an attempt to get a larger piece of the growing car market in India Renault has made a point of introducing a steady stream of new models there. To get a larger chunk of the rapidly growing Russian car market Renault-Nissan forged an alliance with Russian carmaker AvtoVAZ. Renault holds about 50% of the company and has invested heavily in upgrading its production plants.

Like most other carmakers Renault-Nissan is investing heavily in Asia. In China the Alliance is principally represented by Nissan which has a partnership with local carmaker Dongfeng Motor. The joint venture plans to produce 40000 vehicles annually. The Alliance is also making concerted steps to expand in India where it has a plant in Chennai. Renault-Nissan entered yet another collaborative agreement in early 2010 when it joined up with Daimler to give Toyota and Volkswagen a run for their money. Renault will provide its small-car technology to Daimler for use in some of its models. As part of the deal Renault and Nissan each took a 1.55% share in Daimler while Daimler has a 3.1% stake in each of them. The company expects the partnership to provide a benefit of about E2 billion ($3.6 billion) to Renault-Nissan by 2015.

Going forward Renault is focusing on the mass marketing of electric vehicles with plans to produce 500000 by 2015. Not just content to make electric cars Renault and Nissan together with German power utility RWE set up 1000 charging stations in Germany to help sell its cars.

The French government and Nissan each hold about 15% of Renault though Nissan has agreed not to exercise the voting control associated with its shares.

HISTORY

In the Paris suburb of Billancourt in 1898 21-year-old Louis Renault assembled a motorized vehicle with a transmission box of his own design. Louis and his brothers Marcel and Fernand established Renault Freres and produced the world's first sedan in 1899. Marcel died in a racing accident (1903) and Fernand left the business (1908) leaving Louis in sole possession of the company. He renamed it La Societe Louis Renault in 1908.

In 1914 a fleet of 600 Paris taxis shuttled French troops to fight the Germans in the Battle of the Marne. Renault also built light tanks and airplane engines. Between world wars Renault expanded into trucks tractors and aircraft engines. Renault sustained heavy damage in WWII but Louis Renault operated the remaining Paris facilities for the Germans during their occupation of France. After the liberation of Paris he was accused of collaboration and died in prison while awaiting trial in 1944. The de Gaulle government nationalized Renault in 1945 and gave the company its present name.

Worldwide economic growth aided Renault's postwar comeback. The company achieved its greatest success in high-volume low-cost cars such as the 4 CV in the late 1940s and 1950s the Renault 4 in the 1960s and 1970s and the Renault 5 in the 1970s and 1980s.

In 1979 Renault acquired 46% of American Motors Corporation (AMC). In the early 1980s AMC fared poorly and Renault suffered from a worldwide slump in auto sales an aging product line and stiff competition from Japanese carmakers. Decreasing sales an unwieldy bureaucracy and above-average wages contributed to a $1.5 billion loss in 1984.

Georges Besse took over Renault in 1985 and trimmed employment by 20000. When Besse was assassinated by Red Army Faction terrorists in 1986 Raymond Levy assumed his role and contin-

ued his policies laying off 30000 more workers and selling AMC to Chrysler (1987).

Renault and AB Volvo agreed to extensive cross-ownership and cooperation in 1990. In 1994 Renault swapped its 25% stake in Volvo's car division for the latter's 45% stake in Renault's troubled truck unit. (Volvo sold its remaining 11% stake in 1997.)

The French government reduced its share of the firm from 80% to 52% in 1995 and to 44% the following year. In 1997 it shut down a Belgian plant that employed more than 3000 workers and fired a similar number of employees in France. Renault paid a $13 million civil penalty to the EPA in 1998 to settle allegations that its Mack Trucks unit cheated on its diesel engine emissions tests.

Renault and Fiat struck several deals in 1999. They combined their bus-making operations under the name Irisbus and their foundry operations into jointly owned Teksid. Renault sold a 51% stake in Renault Automation to Fiat's Comau robotics unit. Also that year Renault bought a 51% stake in Romanian automaker Automobile Dacia SA and paid $5.4 billion for a 37% stake in Nissan and a 15% (later increased to 23%) stake in truck affiliate Nissan Diesel Motor.

Early in 2000 the company announced that it would spend around $100 million to build an SUV factory in Brazil and announced plans to trim almost $3 billion in costs between 2001 and 2003. The same year Renault agreed to buy a 70% stake in Samsung Motors' automobile business for around $550 million. It also sold its Mack truck unit to Volvo in exchange for a 15% stake in the Swedish truck maker. Renault planned to buy another 5% of Volvo on the open market. Renault and Nissan also announced plans to save about $1 billion by combining their European sales and marketing operations.

Renault sold its Renault V.I. subsidiary and its Mack Trucks unit to Volvo in return for a 20% stake in the Swedish truck maker.

Later in 2001 Renault furthered strengthen ties with Nissan. The plan increased Renault's stake in Nissan to 44% while granting Nissan a 15% stake in Renault. The French Finance Ministry also announced that it would reduce the French government's stake in Renault from 44% to 25% through a public offering. The two deals were completed in 2002. In 2003 the French government further reduced its stake in Renault from 25% to about 15%.

Early in 2005 Renault sold its 18% stake in Nissan Diesel Motor Co. Ltd. to J.P. Morgan Securities Ltd. who in turn sold the shares on the open market.

The following year Renault called an emergency board meeting to ponder a proposal put forth in writing by billionaire General Motors investor Kirk Kerkorian (he owned about a 10% stake in GM at the time). Kerkorian suggested GM Renault and Nissan form a three-way global automotive alliance but the parties decided otherwise and announced at the Paris Auto Show in 2006 that no such alliance would be formed.

In 2005 Carlos Ghosn was appointed as CEO; he also remained as CEO with Nissan. Ghosn had been Renault's chief cost cutter since 1999. Ghosn made public his plans to revamp Renault by slashing the number of suppliers close five plants and cut its workforce by 14%. While not in the same precarious position as its North American counterparts Chrysler Ford and GM Renault's 2005 profits fell by more than 35% from the previous year and its lineup of products is growing stale.

In 2006 Renault formed a car manufacturing joint venture with India's Mahindra & Mahindra which produced the no-frills midsized Logan model sedan. In 2010 Renault sold its 49% interest in the venture to Mahindra but continued to supply key engine and transmission components.

Sales of the Logan never reached expected levels and Renault stated it would rather focus on more profitable alliances in the region including its Renault-Nissan alliance.

EXECUTIVES

President of Renault, Louis Schweitzer, age 72
Chairman Chief Executive Officer, Carlos Ghosn, age 60
EVP and Leader Asia Africa Management Committee, Katsumi Nakamura, age 61
SVP Global Supply Chain, Michel Faivre-Duboz, age 63
Chairman Renault Sport and Renault F1 Team, Bernard Rey, age 68
EVP Engineering and Quality, Jean-Michel Billig, age 51
Leader Euromed Region Management Committee, Jacques Chauvet, age 65
EVP Engineering and Quality, Odile Desforges, age 63
Executive Vice President Corporate Planning, Philippe Klein, age 57
Advanced Process Design Engineer and Director, Yves Audvard, age 61
Document Manager Quality and Director, Alain Champigneux, age 60
Chief Operating Officer for Renault, Carlos Tavares, age 55
EVP Sales and Marketing & Light Commercial Vehicles, Jerome Stoll, age 60
SVP Pre-Engineering Projects and Requirements, Michel Balthazard, age 60
Executive Vice President Chief Financial Officer Chairman CEO, Dominique Thormann, age 60
SVP Corporate Design, Laurens G. van den Acker, age 48
SVP and Alliance Managing Director Global Logistics, Christian Mardrus, age 54
Corporate Controller, Eric Nicolas, age 54
EVP Human Resources, Marie-Francoise Damesin, age 57
SVP Global Marketing, Stephen Norman, age 60
EVP and Chairman France Operations, Gerard Leclercq, age 66
SVP Powertrain Engineering, Jacques Prost, age 61
Cost Control - Technocentre Guyancourt and Director, Patrick Biau, age 57
SVP Vehicle Engineering, Nadine Leclair, age 57
SVP Market Area France, Bernard Cambier, age 61
Managing Director Russia; Chairman Eurasia Region, Bruno Ancelin, age 58
SVP Purchasing; Chairman RNPO, Christian Vandenhende, age 54
SVP Quality, Jean-Pierre Vallaude, age 62
SVP Light Commercial Vehicles, Jean-Christophe Kugler, age 53
Expert Fellow, Christian Deleplace
SVP and Chairman Americas Region, Denis Barbier, age 56
Chief Executive Renault Samsung Motors, Francois Provost
Director of Investor Relations, Thierry Huon
EVP Manufacturing and Supply Chain, Thierry Bollore
EVP and Chairman Europe Region, Stefan Mueller
Director, Alain J. P. Belda, age 70
Director, Thierry Desmarest, age 68
Director, Franck Riboud, age 58
Director, Jean-Pierre (JP) Garnier, age 66
Director, Marc Ladreit de Lacharriere, age 73
Director, Charles F. W. de Croisset, age 70
Director, Hiroto Saikawa, age 60
Director, Pascale Sourisse
Director, Philippe Lagayette, age 70
Advanced Process Design Engineer and Director, Yves Audvard, age 61
Document Manager Quality and Director, Alain Champigneux, age 60

Director, Dominique de La Garanderie, age 70
Director, Takeshi Isayama
Director, Luc Rousseau
Cost Control - Technocentre Guyancourt and Director, Patrick Biau, age 57
Head Sociotechnics UET and Director, Michel Sailly
Director, Alexis Kohler
Director, Bernard Delpit, age 48
Auditors: Deloitte&Associes

LOCATIONS

HQ: Renault S.A. (France)
13-15, quai Le Gallo, Boulogne-Billancourt, Cedex 92513
Phone: (33) 1 76 84 04 04
Web: www.renault.com

Sales

	% of total
Europe	70
Americas	10
Asia &	10
Euromed (Algeria Morocco Romania	7
Eurasia (former Soviet	3
Total	**100**

PRODUCTS/OPERATIONS

Sales

	% of total
Automobiles	95
Sales	5
Total	**100**

COMPETITORS

BMW	Mahindra
Chrysler	Mazda
Daimler	Peugeot
Fiat	Saab Automobile
Ford Motor	Suzuki Motor
General Motors	Tata Motors
Honda	Toyota
Isuzu	Volkswagen
Kia Motors	Volvo Car Corp.

HISTORICAL FINANCIALS

Company Type: Public

Income Statement

FYE: December 31

	REVENUE ($ mil.)	NET INCOME ($ mil.)	NET PROFIT MARGIN	EMPLOYEES
12/13	56,352	806	1.4%	121,807
12/12	54,395	2,335	4.3%	127,086
12/11	55,137	2,705	4.9%	128,322
12/10	52,157	4,577	8.8%	124,749
12/09	48,564	(4,501)	—	124,307
Annual Growth	**3.8%**	**—**		**(0.5%)**

2013 Year-End Financials

Debt ratio: 62.0%	No. of shares (mil.): 291
Return on equity: 2.4%	Dividends
Cash ($ mil.): 16,054	Yield: —
Current ratio: 1.05	Payout: —
Long-term debt ($ mil.): 9,774	Market value ($ mil.): 23,428

	STOCK PRICE ($) FY Close	P/E High/Low		PER SHARE ($) Earnings	Dividends	Book Value
12/13	80.25	79	47	2.95	0.00	107.70
12/12	55.45	15	9	8.57	0.00	109.78
12/11	35.27	16	7	9.93	0.00	106.82
12/10	56.82	8	4	17.00	0.00	101.63
12/09	50.55	—	—	(17.47)	0.00	82.10
Annual Growth	**12.2%**	—	—	—	—	**7.0%**

Repsol S.A.

The sun shines on Repsol (formerly Repsol YPF) Spain's largest oil company. A fully integrated oil and gas company it operates in Latin America the Middle East and North Africa. Repsol operates five refineries in Spain and one in Peru and produces chemicals plastics and polymers. It sells gas under the brands Campsa Petronor and Repsol at 4500 service stations in Europe and Latin America. It is one of Spain's largest sellers of liquefied petroleum gas and liquefied natural gas. Repsol has proved reserves of 2.2 billion barrels of oil equivalent. Affiliate YPF conducts exploration production refining logistics marketing and chemicals in Argentina. Repsol also owns 30% of Gas Natural Fenosa.

Change in Company Type

In 2012 the Argentine government shocked the company when it seized control of subsidiary YPF as part of a nationalization drive.

Repsol had owned YPF Argentina's #1 oil company since 1999. However the Fernandez government took back a 51% stake in YPF. The bid reflects a growing trend towards nationalization of key industries (airlines private pension funds) that have drawn warnings from Argentina's trading partners.

Geographic Reach

Repsol operates globally and has major assets primarily in Spain and Argentina. In 2011 Europe accounted for 63% of company's revenues.

Operations

Repsol upstream's division is engaged in oil and natural gas exploration and production activities based on key traditional regions located in Latin America (mainly Trinidad and Tobago Peru Venezuela Bolivia Colombia and Ecuador) and in North Africa (Algeria and Libya). Strategic areas for short and medium-term growth include the US Gulf of Mexico and offshore fields in Brazil.

The company's LNG activities include the liquefaction transportation marketing and regasification of liquefied natural gas in addition to electricity generation activities in Spain at the Bahia de Bizkaia Electricidad plan and natural gas marketing in North America.

Repsol's downstream business includes the supply and trading of crude and other products oil refining marketing of oil products and LPG and the production and marketing of chemicals.

Financial Performance

Higher oil prices and increased demand lifted Repsol's revenues by 6% in 2011. Net income decreased by 53% in 2011 due to the impact on revenues of the depreciation of the dollar against the euro and increase in personnel expense.

Strategy

Repsol plans to invest more than €21 billion (more than $26 billion) over the next few years in its operations particularly in exploration and production including its Spanish refineries which will receive an investment of about €4 billion (more than $4 billion).

To raise cash and to rebalance its global portfolio in 2011 Repsol sold about 4% of its stake in YPF to Lazard Asset Management for $639 million.

Repsol created the New Energies Business Unit in 2010 assigned to the Downstream Division to promote and new cleaner energy initiatives to reduce carbon dioxide emissions.

Mergers and Acquisitions

Growing its operations in 2014 Repsol agreed to acquire Canada-based Talisman Energy for $8.3 billion plus debt.

HISTORY

Repsol officially created in 1987 is actually the result of efforts that began as early as the 1920s to organize Spain's fragmented energy industry.

Following an era of dependency on foreign investment prior to and during Francisco Franco's dictatorship (1939-75) Spain began reorganizing its energy industry. In 1979 it set up the Instituto Nacional de Hidrocarburos which in 1981 incorporated all public-sector firms involved in gas and oil under one government agency.

Repsol was formed six years later to provide central management to a Spanish oil company that could compete in the unified European market. The government chose the name Repsol after a well-known brand of Spanish lubricant products. The firm was charged with pursuing a global strategy to bring together all levels of the industry.

In 1989 Repsol offered 26% of the firm on the Madrid and New York stock exchanges raising more than $1 billion. That year Repsol increased its marine fleet with the purchase of the Naviera Vizcaina shipping company and bought Carless Refining & Marketing a UK business with a chain of 500 service stations operating mainly under the Anglo brand. Although Spain was opening its doors to foreign investment the Spanish government maintained control over the country's energy industry including a tightly guarded distribution network under state-controlled Campsa. Campsa oversaw a marketing/logistics system of pipelines storage terminals and sales outlets.

The European Community demanded that Spain open its markets to other EC members forcing Campsa in 1991 to divide its 3800 gasoline stations among its four major shareholders: Cepsa (Spain's largest private refiner) Petromed Ertoil and Repsol. Repsol gained 66% of the logistical network and use of the Campsa brand name.

Repsol and Spanish bank La Caixa merged their interests in natural gas in 1992 to create Gas Natural a new gas distributor. That year the Spanish government began reducing its majority holding and by 1996 its stake had dwindled to 10%. (It sold its remaining stock in 1997.)

Expanding its South American operations Repsol acquired control of Argentinian oil company Astra CAPSA and a Peruvian oil refinery in 1996. That year Repsol purchased a 30% stake in the Tin Fouye Tabankort field in Algeria.

In 1999 Repsol paid $2 billion for a 15% stake in giant oil company YPF which was auctioned off by Argentina's government. After acquiring another 83% of YPF for $13.2 billion Repsol changed its name to Repsol YPF. To help pay down debt incurred in the acquisition Repsol YPF sold its UK North Sea oil and gas operations to US independent Kerr-McGee for $555 million in 2000. That year the company (as part of its commitment to Argentina's government after acquiring YPF) agreed to swap some of its Argentine refining and marketing assets for Brazilian oil and gas operations owned by Petrobras.

In 2002 Repsol YPF sold oil and gas assets in Indonesia to CNOOC for about $585 million. Former chairman of Spain's top gas supplier Gas Natural S.A. Antonio Brufau replaced Alfonso Cortina de Alcocer in 2004 as chairman of Repsol.

In 2006 the company acquired BP's 28% stake in the Shenzi field in the Gulf of Mexico. The next year Repsol YPF began selling minority stakes in YPF to generate cash to support the Argentine company's growth.

EXECUTIVES

Executive Managing Director YPF, Antonio Gomis Saez

Executive Managing Director Downstream, Pedro Fernandez Frial

Executive Managing Director Upstream, Nemesio Fernandez-Cuesta Luca de Tena

General Counsel Secretary and Director, Luis Suarez de Lezo Mantilla, age 64

CFO, Miguel Martinez San Martin

Executive Managing Director HR and Organization, Cristina Sanz Mendiola

Executive Director Communications and Chairman's Office, Bego?a Elices Garcia

Deputy Director National International and Financial Media, Maria Ritter

International and Financial Media Manager, Kristian Rix

Media Director, Juan Valdemoro

General Director of Exploration and Production, Luis Cabra

General Counsel; General Secretary; Secretary of the Board; Executive Director, Luis Mantilla

Director of Investor Relations, Maria Zingoni

General Director of Economics and Finance; Director, Miguel Barrio

Chief Financial and Economic Officer; General Director of Subsidiaries; Affiliates and Development, Miguel Martin

Chief Operating Officer; Business Director, Nemesio Tena

Executive Director of Commercial Area, Pascual Olmos

General Director of Strategy and Control, Pedro Frial

Executive Director of Resources, Andreu Punet

Executive President; Chief Executive Officer; Chairman of the Board; Executive Director, Antonio Niubo

General Manager of YPF SA, Antonio Saez

General Director of Communication and Chairmans Office; Director, Begona Garcia

Executive Director of GNL, Benjamin Palomo

Director of Human Resources and Organization, Cristina Mendiola

Executive Director of Trading and Transport, Ignacio Egea

Vice Chairman of the Board, Isidro Casas

General Director of Industrial Area and New Energies, Josu Miguel

Vice Chairman of the Board, Juan Gallo

Vice Chairman, Isidro Faine Casas, age 71

Director, Juan Maria Nin Genova, age 60

General Counsel Secretary and Director, Luis Suarez de Lezo Mantilla, age 64

Director, Carmelo de las Morenas Lopez, age 75

Director, Henri-Philippe Reichstul, age 65

Vice Chairman, Juan Abello Gallo, age 72

Director, Paulina Beato Blanco, age 69

Director, Artur Carulla Font, age 67

Director, Luis Carlos Croissier Batista, age 65

Director, Angel Durandez Adeva, age 72

Director, Javier Echenique Landiribar, age 62

Director, Jose Manuel Loureda Manti?an, age 76

Director, Maria Isabel Gabarro Miquel, age 59

Director, Jose M. Carrera Panizzo

Independent Director, Mario Pelaz

Independent Director, Javier Landiribar

Director; Representative of Pemex Internacional Espana SA, Jose Panizzo

Auditors: DeloitteSL

LOCATIONS

HQ: Repsol S.A.
Mendez Alvaro, 44, Madrid 28045
Phone: (34) 91 75 38 100   **Fax:** (34) 902 303 145
Web: www.repsol.com

PRODUCTS/OPERATIONS

Sales

	% of total
Downstream	63
YPF	17
Gas Natural	10
Upstream	6
LNG	4
Corporate	-
Total	**100**

COMPETITORS

Anadarko Petroleum	Murphy Oil
Apco Oil and Gas	Noble Energy
International	Norsk Hydro ASA
BHP Billiton	Occidental Petroleum
BP	PEMEX
Devon Energy	PETROBRAS
Endesa S.A.	Petrobras Argentina
Eni	Petroleos de Venezuela
Exxon Mobil	Pioneer Natural
IBERDROLA	Resources
Imperial Oil	RasGas
Koch Industries Inc.	Royal Dutch Shell
Marathon Oil	TOTAL

HISTORICAL FINANCIALS

Company Type: Public

Income Statement

FYE: December 31

	REVENUE ($ mil.)	NET INCOME ($ mil.)	NET PROFIT MARGIN	EMPLOYEES
12/13	76,433	268	0.4%	30,296
12/12	77,152	2,715	3.5%	29,985
12/11	80,848	2,836	3.5%	46,575
12/10	75,018	6,280	8.4%	43,298
12/09	68,241	2,245	3.3%	41,014
Annual Growth	2.9%	(41.2%)	—	(7.3%)

2013 Year-End Financials

Debt ratio: 37.3%	No. of shares (mil.): 1,301
Return on equity: 0.7%	Dividends
Cash ($ mil.): 10,234	Yield: 4.0%
Current ratio: 1.52	Payout: 915.8%
Long-term debt ($ mil.): 18,069	Market value ($ mil.): 32,904

	STOCK PRICE ($) FY Close	P/E High/Low		Earnings	PER SHARE ($) Dividends	Book Value
12/13	25.29	338	238	0.21	1.01	28.79
12/12	20.90	32	13	2.24	1.29	29.51
12/11	30.51	38	24	2.33	2.08	27.71
12/10	27.94	14	8	5.14	0.93	26.46
12/09	26.66	48	20	1.86	1.65	23.54
Annual Growth	(1.3%)	—	—	(42.3%)	(11.6%)	5.2%

Resona Holdings Inc
Osaka

Resona Holdings resonate in Japan's retail banking market. It's the holding company of Resona Bank and smaller regional banks Kinki Osaka Bank and Saitama Resona Bank. Resona Holdings focuses on consumer and small business banking in the greater Tokyo area and the Kansai region. Resona Bank provides corporate pension management as well as banking and trust services. Personal banking services include loans for individuals asset management and estate planning. The company also provides corporate banking services such as loans pension management and real estate services. Altogether Resona Holdings boasts about 1425 branches (593 manned and 832 unmanned) throughout Japan.

EXECUTIVES

Chairman and Representative Executive Officer; Chairman Resona Bank, Eiji Hosoya, age 69

President and Representative Executive Officer, Kazuhiro Higashi, age 57

Director President and Representative Executive, Seiji Higaki

Executive Officer; Representative Director and President Resona Bank, Naoki Iwata

Executive Officer; Representative Director President and Executive Officer The Kinki Osaka Bank, Kazuyoshi Ikeda

President Saitama Resona Bank, Masahito Kamijo

Representative Executive Officer, Toshiki Hara

Representative Executive Officer, Tetsuya Kan

President The Kinki Osaka Bank, Koji Nakamae

Deputy President Representative Executive Officer and Director; Executive Officer of Resona Bank, Kazuhiro Higashi, age 57

President Representative Executive Officer and Director, Seiji Higaki

Director, Kaoru Isono

Auditors: DeloitteToucheTohmatsu

LOCATIONS

HQ: Resona Holdings Inc Osaka
1-5-65 Kiba, Koto-ku, Tokyo 135-0042
Phone: (81) 3 6704 3111
Web: www.resona-gr.co.jp

PRODUCTS/OPERATIONS

Selected Subsidiaries

Daiwa Guarantee Co. Ltd. (credit guarantee)
Resona Bank Ltd. (bank)
Resona Guarantee Co. Ltd. (credit guarantee)
Saitama Resona Bank Ltd. (bank)
Kinki Osaka Shinyo Hosho Co. Ltd. (credit guarantee)
The Kinki Osaka Bank Ltd. (bank)
P.T. Bank Resona Perdania (bank)
Resona Kessai Service Co. Ltd. (collections agency)
Resona Card Co. Ltd. (credit cards)
Resona Capital Co. Ltd. (private equity)
Resona Research Institute Co. Ltd. (consulting)
Resona Business Service Co. Ltd. (staffing)

COMPETITORS

Aozora Bank	Joyo Bank
Bank of Yokohama	Juroku Bank
Chiba Bank	Mitsubishi UFJ
Chugoku Bank	Financial Group
Chuo Mitsui Trust	Mizuho Financial
Citigroup	NORTH PACIFIC BANKLTD.
Fukuoka Financial	Nishi-Nippon City Bank
Group	Shinsei Bank
Gunma Bank	Shizuoka Bank
Hachijuni Bank	Sumitomo Mitsui
Hokuhoku Financial	Yamaguchi Financial
Group	Group
Iyo Bank	

HISTORICAL FINANCIALS

Company Type: Public

Income Statement

FYE: March 31

	ASSETS ($ mil.)	NET INCOME ($ mil.)	INCOME AS % OF ASSETS	EMPLOYEES
03/14	433,246	2,137	0.5%	16,536
03/13	458,175	2,924	0.6%	16,826
03/12	526,633	3,092	0.6%	16,881
03/11	515,742	1,933	0.4%	16,941
03/10	436,191	1,415	0.3%	16,756
Annual Growth	(0.2%)	10.9%	—	(0.3%)

2014 Year-End Financials

Return on assets: 0.5%
Return on equity: 11.3%
Long-term debt ($ mil.): —
No. of shares (mil.): —
Sales ($ mil): 8,040

Dividends
Yield: —
Payout: —
Market value ($ mil.): —

	STOCK PRICE ($) FY Close	P/E High/Low		PER SHARE ($) Earnings	Dividends	Book Value
03/14	4.81	—	—	0.63	0.00	8.64
03/13	5.47	—	—	0.77	0.00	9.49
03/12	4.42	—	—	0.83	0.00	9.17
03/11	5.86	—	—	0.50	0.00	7.85
03/10	11.16	—	—	0.57	0.00	21.14
Annual Growth	(19.0%) (20.0%)	—	—	2.7%		—

Rewe-Zentral AG (Germany, Fed. Rep.)

REWE Group sells the fuel that Germans love best —food and drink. REWE is one of the largest food retailers in Germany (along with METRO AG ALDI and Lidl) and one of the largest in Europe overall. REWE operates some 15000 stores in about a dozen European countries (about 10000 in Germany) including Russia and Ukraine. Store formats include supermarkets (REWE) hypermarkets (toom) discount stores (Penny) drugstores (BIPA) DIY stores (toom Baumarkt) and consumer electronics stores (ProMarkt) among others. The company's other businesses include about 2100 travel agencies several tour operators and foodservice. Founded in 1927 REWE is a cooperative owned by its independent retail members.

REWE has expanded mainly through acquisitions and targeting growth in the Czech Republic Hungary Romania and the Ukraine. REWE's Penny Market chain (with 320-plus stores) jumped into first place in the Czech discount market with the 2008 purchase of Plus stores from rival Tengelmann. Previously REWE acquired about 95 Delvita supermarkets there from Belgium's Delhaize Group in 2007. REWE is also focusing on expanding Penny Market in Romania where it operates about 100 stores. It has also opened about 20 Billa supermarkets in Russia as well as SEL-GROS Cash & Carry stores. Currently about 30% of the company's annual revenue is derived from international sales; REWE plans to increase this to 60% by 2015.

To better focus on its core food retailing and travel-related businesses REWE sold its 50% stake in its business-to-business cash-and-carry and foodservice activities —which came under the umbrella of transGourmet Group —to its joint venture partner Switzerland's Coop. The deal which closed in early 2011 strengthens Coop's concentration on the wholesaling business.

REWE's core food retail operations provide about 80% of the company's sales but have faced intense competition from discounters including compatriot ALDI. As a result REWE has shuttered more than 400 outlets in Germany in recent years. On the plus side the German grocery chain acquired about 120 supermarkets in southern and eastern Germany from rival METRO and more than 325 Plus locations from Tengelmann.

While food retailing represents most of REWE's revenue other sources include its leisure travel group (tour operators including ITS Reisen Jahr Reisen Tjaereborg Dertour Meier's Weltreisen and ADAC Reisen) and travel agencies (Atlas Der and Derpart).

REWE is an acronym for Revisionsverband der Westkauf-Genossenschaften or the Auditing Association of the Western Purchasing Cooperatives.

HISTORY

In 1927 17 German food wholesale companies joined forces to create the cooperative that would become REWE-Zentral. The cooperative expanded and had 64 members by 1933. In 1935 the group centralized management giving the head office in Cologne more authority over operations.

WWII caused a slowdown in business during the early 1940s. However by 1947 REWE was again in expansion mode and entered the import business. In 1950 the cooperative expanded internal operations including the addition of an advertising department. Importing became a successful venture and in 1956 the group started a freight and cargo business. The cooperative had multiple regional wholesale businesses and more than 100 members by 1960. In 1974 it added retail outlets including miniMAL Penny and Idea.

In the 1980s REWE continued retail and wholesale acquisitions throughout Germany. The group bought the food retail chains Desuma Hill Otto Mess and Supermarket Handels in 1988.

The cooperative bought Germany's Kafu supermarket chain (2500 stores) in 1992. It entered the UK the next year by purchasing a 28% stake in the Budgens convenience store chain. Also in 1993 REWE opened its first store in Poland. A year later it expanded to Slovakia and Italy. In 1995 REWE opened stores in Spain and scaled back its UK business closing 12 Penny stores and selling four others. The company bought Austria's Billa supermarket chain the following year. In 1997 REWE moved into the Czech Republic.

In 1998 REWE bought another Austrian supermarket chain but was forced to sell 20% of its stores by Austrian regulators (REWE had more than 50% of market share). The company opened stores in Romania and Croatia in 1999.

REWE opened a store in Ukraine in January 2000. In August it sold its stake in Budgens leaving the company without any operations in the UK. Also in August REWE bought parts of the LTU travel group giving it 100% of the LTU Touristik travel agency and 40% of the LTU airline. Early in 2001 REWE bought Italian supermarket chain Standa (about 120 stores in northern and central Italy and Sardinia).

In 2002 REWE sold its Billa supermarkets in Hungary to Spar Ungarn the Hungarian subsidiary of Switzerland's Aspiag Management for an undisclosed price.

To fill a gap in its international presence and reduce its exposure to the depressed German economy REWE acquired Swiss rival Bon Appetit in November 2003.

Long-serving Chief Executive Hans Reischl stepped down in April 2004 eight months ahead of schedule. He was replaced by Dieter Berninghaus who had been in charge of REWE's international business.

In May 2007 REWE acquired about 95 Delvita supermarkets in the Czech Republic from Belgium's Delhaize Group for about $128 million. Previously in mid-2005 Delvita sold its 11 stores in Slovakia to Rewe.

In December 2008 the first SELGROS Cash & Carry store opened in Russia near Moscow.

LOCATIONS

HQ: Rewe-Zentral AG (Germany, Fed. Rep.)
Domstrasse 20, Cologne D-50668
Phone: (49) 221 149 0   **Fax:** (49) 221 149 9000
Web: www.rewe.de

2009 Stores

	No.
Germany	10,893
International	4,552
Total	**15,445**

Sales

	% of total
Germany	69
International	
Western	19
Eastern	12
Total	**100**

PRODUCTS/OPERATIONS

HISTORICAL FINANCIALS

Company Type: Public

Income Statement

FYE: December 31

	REVENUE ($ mil.)	NET INCOME ($ mil.)	NET PROFIT MARGIN	EMPLOYEES
12/13	61,379	270	0.4%	214,584
12/12	57,341	121	0.2%	0
12/01	4,822	58	1.2%	186,834
12/00	4,502	30	0.7%	179,000
12/92	3,489	13	0.4%	7,494
Annual Growth	**14.6%**	**15.6%**	**—**	**17.3%**

2013 Year-End Financials

Debt ratio: 12.1%
Return on equity: 4.2%
Cash ($ mil.): 1,119
Current ratio: 0.69
Long-term debt ($ mil.): 969

No. of shares (mil.): 1
Dividends
 Yield: —
 Payout: —
 Market value ($ mil.): —

RHB Bank Berhad (Malaysia)

RHB Bank Berhad lends a helping hand for Malaysians' financial future. The bank a subsidiary of RHB Capital Berhad offers a wide range of financial services such as personal and corporate loans savings accounts and credit cards. RHB Bank Berhad also provides a variety of Islamic products and online banking. The company operates a network of some 200 offices across Malaysia as well as branches throughout Singapore Bangkok and Brunei. It is purchasing an 80% stake in Indonesian financial institution Bank Mestika. RHB Bank Berhad was established through the merging of

DCG Bank Berhad and Kwong Yik Berhad in 1997.

LOCATIONS

HQ: RHB Bank Berhad (Malaysia)
Towers Two & Three, RHB Centre, Jalan Tun Razak, Kuala Lumpur 50400
Phone: (60) 3 9287 8888   **Fax:** (60) 3 9287 9000
Web: www.rhb.com.my

PRODUCTS/OPERATIONS

HISTORICAL FINANCIALS

Company Type: Public

Income Statement

FYE: December 31

	ASSETS ($ mil.)	NET INCOME ($ mil.)	INCOME AS % OF ASSETS	EMPLOYEES
12/13	53,163	538	1.0%	0
12/12	55,410	589	1.1%	0
12/11	45,119	491	1.1%	0
12/10	38,758	462	1.2%	0
12/09	30,981	346	1.1%	0
Annual Growth	**14.5%**	**11.6%**	**—**	**—**

2013 Year-End Financials

Return on assets: 1.0%
Return on equity: 13.8%
Long-term debt ($ mil.): —
No. of shares (mil.): —
Sales ($ mil): 2,479

Dividends
 Yield: —
 Payout: —
 Market value ($ mil.): —

RHB Capital Bhd (Malaysia)

RHB Capital is the holding company for RHB Banking Group which offers retail small business and commercial banking services (through RHB Bank) and insurance securities asset management unit trusts derivatives corporate finance and underwriting (through RHB Investment Bank and RHB Insurance). The group's RHB Islamic Bank unit offers retail and commercial banking services that are sensitive to Islamic and regional laws. RHB Capital operates through more than 200 locations mainly in Malaysia but also Brunei Cambodia Hong Kong Indonesia Singapore Thailand and Vietnam. In 2013 RHB Investment Bank bought OSK Investment Bank. RHB Capital acquired and merged Kwong Yik Bank with DCB Bank in 1997.

EXECUTIVES

Director Group Corporate Services, Norazzah Sulaiman
Director Group Finance, Kellee Kam
CEO, Dato' Tajuddin Atan
Head of Retail Banking, Renzo Viegas
Chairman, Dato? Mohamed Khadar Merican, age 58
Director Group Transaction Banking, Michael L.K. Boon

Chief Operating Officer of RHB Capital Berhad on, Puan Sulaiman

LOCATIONS

HQ: RHB Capital Bhd (Malaysia)
Level 10, Tower One, RHB Centre, Jalan Tun Razak, Kuala Lumpur 50400
Phone: (60) 3 9285 2233   **Fax:** (60) 3 9281 9314
Web: www.rhb.com.my

COMPETITORS

AmBank Group	Hang Seng Bank
Bank of China	Malaysian Industrial
Bank of East Asia	Development Finance
CIMB Group	Maybank

HISTORICAL FINANCIALS

Company Type: Public

Income Statement

FYE: December 31

	ASSETS ($ mil.)	NET INCOME ($ mil.)	INCOME AS % OF ASSETS	EMPLOYEES
12/13	58,332	558	1.0%	16,692
12/12	61,754	582	0.9%	12,154
12/11	48,088	473	1.0%	11,299
12/10	41,961	460	1.1%	11,722
12/09	33,567	350	1.0%	10,329
Annual Growth	**14.8%**	**12.4%**	**—**	**12.7%**

2013 Year-End Financials

Return on assets: 0.9%
Return on equity: 11.5%
Long-term debt ($ mil.): —
No. of shares (mil.): —
Sales ($ mil): 2,923

Dividends
 Yield: —
 Payout: —
 Market value ($ mil.): —

Rio Tinto Ltd

Rio Tinto is on the lookout for pay dirt. Rio Tinto Limited one of the world's largest mining operations (along with BHP Billiton and Vale) is the Australian half of dual-listed sister companies with Rio Tinto plc taking up residence in London. Although each company trades separately the two Rio Tintos operate as one business. Rio Tinto explores for a variety of commodities: bauxite coal copper diamonds gold iron ore minerals (borates and titanium dioxide) nickel and potash. Iron ore makes up about 44% of the group's sales. It also produces aluminum through its Rio Tinto Alcan unit. Most of its businesses are in Australia and North America but it is expanding its operations in China and Mongolia.

By focusing on a strategy of developing large-scale long-term mining operations and businesses Rio Tinto has tried to weather commodity prices that have dipped and risen over several years. The mining industry is affected by both oversupply and rising costs in raw materials. Like its rivals the company continues to seek acquisitions that will grow shareholder value as it cuts costs and improves productivity.

Despite a year of challenges including six fatalities at its mining sites and flooding that disrupted production in Australia Rio Tinto recorded revenues of $60.5 billion in 2011. Net income however fell about 59% —from $15.3 billion in 2010 to $6.8 billion in 2011. The company attributes an $8.9 billion impairment charge related to its aluminum assets as the cause of its precipitous fall in net earnings that year.

The company's iron ore business also contributed 78% of the group's net income in 2011. Rio Tinto is the world's second-largest supplier of iron ore which is used in steelmaking operations. Its key iron ore operations are in the Pilbara region of Western Australia and in Quebec in Canada.

In 2011 the company started trimming its aluminum operations. It placed 13 assets on the chopping block allowing Rio Tinto Alcan to focus on its high-quality tier one assets (mostly in Canada) and improve performance. The company also planned to transfer its stakes in six Australian and New Zealand operations to a new business unit Pacific Aluminium that would be managed and reported separately from Rio Tinto Alcan.

In 2011 to raise cash the company sold its talc business to Imerys for $340 million. That year Rio Tinto also increased its stake to 49% in Canada-based Ivanhoe Mines which manages the Oyu Tolgoi mine in Mongolia one of the world's largest undeveloped copper-gold projects. In 2012 it upped its holding in Ivanhoe Mines to 51% to become the majority owner. Commercial production at the mine may be delayed however because an agreement to supply electricity has not yet been reached between China and Mongolia.

In another strategic move in 2011 Rio Tinto made an all-cash offer for Canada-based uranium producer Hathor Exploration valued at $578 million after rival Cameco Corp. made a takeover bid for the company. In 2012 Rio Tinto was successful in acquiring Hathor which supplies about a fifth of the world's uranium.

In the first half of 2011 the company completed the acquisition of the Riversdale coal mine which has now been renamed Rio Tinto Coal Mozambique.

In 2012 the company began an overview of operations and announced that it may sell its diamond business. The company operates diamond mines in Canada Zimbabwe and Australia. At its Argyle mine in Australia the company unearthed a rare pink diamond in the rough in 2012. The Argyle mine is undergoing a $2.1 billion expansion and is the world's largest producer of pink diamonds. However in 2011 diamond operations made up only 2% of the company's total earnings before interest tax depreciation and amortization. Argyle's lower production also helped lead to an 86% drop in overall earnings for its diamonds unit that year.

Slimming down further in 2012 the company agreed to sell one of its noncore US operations Atlanta-based wire and cable business Alcan Cable to Kentucky-based General Cable for $185 million. General Cable makes and distributes copper aluminum and fiber-optic wire and cable products. Alcan Cable serves the energy and construction markets.

HISTORY

Rio Tinto Limited began life as the Zinc Corporation in 1905 to recover zinc from the tailings of the silver and lead mines around Australia's mineral-rich Broken Hill area. The company expanded steadily extending its operations into a wide range of mining and metallurgical activities primarily in Australia. By 1914 it had changed its name to Consolidated Zinc Corporation. The company discovered the world's largest deposit of bauxite (1955) and formed Hamersley Holdings with Kaiser Steel (1962) to mine iron ore.

Rio Tinto plc (UK) began with mining operations in Spain in 1873. It sold most of its Spanish holdings in 1954 and branched out to Australia Africa and Canada. In 1962 Rio Tinto and Australia's Consolidated Zinc merged to form RTZ. The companies merged their Australian interests as a partially owned subsidiary CRA (from Conzinc Riotinto of Australia).

In 1968 RTZ bought U.S. Borax which was built on one of the earth's few massive boron deposits. (The use of boron in cleansers was widespread in the late 19th century.) A 1927 discovery in the Mojave Desert led to development of a large boron mine. Until its Turkish mine was nationalized RTZ controlled the world's boron supply. It sold U.S. Borax's consumer products operations in 1988.

RTZ opened a large copper mine at Bougainville in Papua New Guinea in 1969. Subsidiary CRA discovered diamonds in Western Australia's Argyle region three years later. CRA then opened Australia's largest thermal-coal development at Blair Athol in 1984.

RTZ bought Kennecott Corporation in 1989 and expanded its copper operations. Kennecott had been formed by Stephen Birch and named for Robert Kennicott (a typo altered the spelling of the company's name); it had begun mining at Bingham Canyon Utah in 1904. Kennicott had died in Alaska while trying to establish an intercontinental telegraph line. Backed by J.P. Morgan and the Guggenheims Birch also built a railroad to haul the ore. Kennecott merged its railroad and mine operations in 1915. Kennecott consolidated its hold on Chile's Braden copper mine (1925) and on the Utah Copper Company (1936) and other US mines. When copper prices slumped British Petroleum's Standard Oil of Ohio subsidiary bought Kennecott (1981). In 1989 RTZ purchased British Petroleum's US mineral operations including Kennecott.

By the 1990s RTZ and CRA (by then 49%-owned by RTZ) were increasingly competing for mining rights to recently opened areas of Asia and Latin America. RTZ sold the last of its nonmining holdings (building products group) in 1993. In 1995 RTZ brought CRA into its operations. Through Kennecott RTZ purchased US coal mine operators Nerco Cordero Mining Company and Colowyo Coal Company. Also in 1995 the company acquired 13% of Freeport-McMoRan Copper & Gold (sold in 2004).

The RTZ and CRA company names were changed to Rio Tinto plc and Rio Tinto Limited respectively in 1997. Rio Tinto bought a Wyoming coal mine from Kerr-McGee for about $400 million in 1998. The next year Rio Tinto bought 80% of Kestrel (coal Australia) increased its ownership of Blair Athol from 57% to 71% and increased its stake in Comalco (aluminum) to 72%.

In 2000 CEO Leon Davis retired; his position passed to energy group executive Leigh Clifford. In a move that sparked an outcry from union officials Davis accepted a position as non-executive deputy chairman (he retired from the board in 2005). Later that year Rio Tinto acquired both North Limited and Ashton Mining. The company also bought Comalco's outstanding shares and the Peabody Group's Australian subsidiaries.

Rio Tinto sold its Norzink Zink Smelter to Outokumpu in 2001. It also increased its holdings in Queensland Alumina Coal & Allied Industries and Palabora Mining and it began developing the Hail Creek Coal Project in Australia which is based on one of the largest coking coal deposits in the world. In 2003 Rio Tinto sold its 25% stake in Minera Alumbrera (Argentina) and Peak Gold Mine (Australia) to Wheaton River Minerals for around $210 million.

Rio Tinto had owned 14% of Lihir Gold but divested its stake in the company. Prior to that decision the company had controlled Lihir and its management. In late 2005 though Rio Tinto relinquished its management rights and decided to sell its entire stake in Lihir.

Tom Albanese succeeded Clifford in 2007.

In 2007 Rio Tinto swooped in and made a successful $38 billion offer to buy Alcan then the world's #3 aluminum producer. That came not long after Alcoa #2 in the world had offered $33 billion. The deal combined Rio Tinto's own aluminum operations with Alcan's to form the new world leader Rio Tinto Alcan based in Canada. Rio Tinto's operations were located in Australia New Zealand and Africa as well as in Italy and the UK. Alcan's geographic strengths were in North America throughout Europe and in the Asia/Pacific region.

After that acquisition Rio Tinto announced a major divestment program saying it wanted to sell off $15 billion worth of assets. In early 2008 it began that program selling stakes in two North American properties to Hecla Mining and Barrick Gold. The properties had been a part of Kennecott Minerals and netted Rio Tinto about $2.5 billion. Later that year the company spun off most of its North American coal operations into a company called Cloud Peak Energy which it spun off through a public offering in 2009 using the almost $750 million it received to help recoup expenses from the purchase of Alcan. A major step in the divestment plan was taken in early 2009 when the company sold its undeveloped potash assets and a Brazilian iron ore mine to Vale for about $1.5 billion.

The company's most significant deals though have been the ones that didn't happen. In 2008 BHP Billiton approached Rio Tinto with an offer to buy its Anglo-Australian rival at a price that valued the company at nearly $150 billion. Rio Tinto's Board rejected the notion but BHP Billiton kept up its pursuit. The combination would have created the world's largest minerals company and one of the largest companies of any sort in terms of market cap. Months later though at the end of a year mired by the global economic meltdown BHP Billiton announced that the deal no longer provided value to its shareholders and called it off.

In an effort to obstruct BHP Billiton's takeover bid for Rio Tinto in 2008 Alcoa and Aluminum Corporation of China (Chinalco) had acquired 14% of Rio Tinto for $14 billion. Early the next year Chinalco stepped in with an offer to assist Rio Tinto out of a portion of its debt which was considerable. The complicated arrangement would have given Rio Tinto $19.5 billion through investments in aluminum copper and iron ore joint ventures as well as through convertible bonds. Chinalco's stake in Rio Tinto would have been raised to 19% and the Chinese company would have had the right to name two members to Rio Tinto's Board.

However the transaction —never popular with domestic investors —fell through by mid-2009. Rio Tinto instead went with a rights issue hoping to raise $15 billion and an agreed-upon joint venture with BHP Billiton that would have combined the two companies' iron ore projects in Western Australia. However that deal fell through also after German authorities ruled in 2010 that it was anticompetitive.

In late 2010 Rio Tinto made a $3.5 billion tender offer for Australian coal producer Riversdale Mining Ltd. but ran into problems convincing two large institutional shareholders to sell their stakes. Rio Tinto upped the offer to about $4 billion in early 2011 but India's Tata Steel and Brazil's CSN —which together held about 47% of Riversdale — were still not willing to part with their shares. A couple of deadline extensions and price bumps later Rio Tinto acquired both the CSN and Tata stakes to control close to 100% of Riversdale's shares.

EXECUTIVES

Chief Executive Aluminum, Oscar Y. L. Groeneveld, age 59, $1,261,000 total compensation
Chairman, Jan P. du Plessis, age 60
CEO and Board Member, Tom Albanese, age 56, $1,664,000 total compensation
Finance Director and Board Member, Guy R. Elliot, age 58, $1,239,000 total compensation
Chief Executive Iron Ore, Sam Walsh, age 64, $1,245,000 total compensation
Company Secretary, Stephen Consedine, age 52
Group Executive Business Support and Operations, Bret Clayton, age 52, $680,000 total compensation
Managing Director Australia, David Peever
Chief Executive Technology and Innovation, Preston Chiaro, age 60, $714,000 total compensation
Global Head Legal, Debra A. Valentine, age 60, $548,000 total compensation
Company Secretary, Ben Mathews, age 46
Global Practice Leader Media Relations, Christina Mills
Group Executive Technology and Innovation, Grant Thorne, age 64, $773,000 total compensation
Managing Director; President Simandou, David Smith
Chief Executive Copper, Andrew Harding, age 48
Country Manager Mozambique; CEO Riversdale Mining, Eric Finlayson
Chief Executive Energy, Doug Ritchie, age 58
Managing Director China, Ian Bauert
Chief Executive - Copper, Jean-Sebastien Jacques
Board Member, Richard R. Goodmanson, age 66
Board Member, Andrew Gould, age 67
Board Member, Paul M. Tellier, age 74
Board Member, John S. Varley, age 57
Board Member, Sir Roderick I. (Rod) Eddington, age 63
CEO and Board Member, Tom Albanese, age 56
Finance Director and Board Member, Guy R. Elliot, age 58
Board Member, Lord John O. Kerr of Kinlochard, age 72
Board Member, Ann F. Godbehere, age 58
Board Member, Robert E. (Bob) Brown, age 68
Board Member, Vivienne Cox, age 54
Board Member, Michael Fitzpatrick, age 61
Board Member, Yves Fortier, age 76
Auditors: PricewaterhouseCoopers

LOCATIONS

HQ: Rio Tinto Ltd
Level 33, 120 Collins Street, Melbourne, Victoria 3000
Phone: (61) 3 9283 3333   **Fax:** (61) 3 9283 3707
Web: www.riotinto.com

Sales by Destination

	% of total
Asia	
Japan	17
Other countries	16
US	14
Canada	3
UK	1
Australia	2
Total	**100**

PRODUCTS/OPERATIONS

Sales

	% of total
Iron Ore	44
Aluminum	18
Copper	11
Energy	10
Other	12

Selected Holdings

Aluminum
Bell Bay
Boyne Island (59% smelting)
Queensland Alumina Ltd. (80%)
Tiwai Point (79% New Zealand)
Weipa (Australia)
Iron Ore
Hamersley Iron Pty. Ltd.
Channar (60%)
Marandoo mine (Pilbara Australia)
Nammuldi
Iron Ore Co. of Canada (59%)
Robe River Iron Associates (53%)
Energy & Minerals
Coal
Bengalla (30% Australia)
Blair Athol Coal (71%)
Hail Creek Coal (82%)
Hunter Valley Operations (76%)
Kestrel (80%)
Mt Thorley (61%)
Warkworth (42%)
Rio Tinto Diamonds & Minerals
Rio Tinto Diamond (diamonds Australia Canada Zimbabwe)
Rio Tinto Minerals (borates titanium dioxide Argentina/Australia/US)
Copper Products
Escondida (30% Chile)
Grasberg (40% Indonesia)
Kennecott Utah Copper (US)
Northparkes (80%)
Palabora (58% South Africa)
Gold
Barneys Canyon (US)
Bingham Canyon (US)
Escondida (30% Chile)
Rawhide (51% US)

COMPETITORS

ALROSA	Glencore Xstrata
ASARCO	Goldcorp
Alcoa	Grupo Mexico
Anglo American	ITOCHU
AngloGold Ashanti	Kaiser Aluminum
BHP Billiton	Marubeni
Barrick Gold	Newmont Mining
CONSOL Energy	Norsk Hydro ASA
Cliffs Natural Resources	RUSAL
	Recylex
Codelco	Southern Copper
Fortescue Metals	Teck
Freeport-McMoRan	Vale

HISTORICAL FINANCIALS

Company Type: Public

Income Statement

FYE: December 31

	REVENUE ($ mil.)	NET INCOME ($ mil.)	NET PROFIT MARGIN	EMPLOYEES
12/13	51,171	3,665	7.2%	66,331
12/12	50,967	(2,990)	—	61,305
12/11	60,537	5,826	9.6%	56,965
12/10	56,576	14,324	25.3%	69,002
12/09	41,825	4,872	11.6%	95,608
Annual Growth	5.2%	(6.9%)	—	(8.7%)

2013 Year-End Financials

Debt ratio: 25.7%
Return on equity: 7.9%
Cash ($ mil.): 10,216
Current ratio: 1.40
Long-term debt ($ mil.): 24,625
No. of shares (mil.): 1,848
Dividends
Yield: —
Payout: —
Market value ($ mil.): 112,867

	STOCK PRICE ($) FY Close	P/E High/Low		PER SHARE ($) Earnings	Dividends	Book Value
12/13	61.06	37	24	1.97	0.00	24.82
12/12	68.06	—	—	(1.62)	0.00	25.18
12/11	61.46	30	18	3.01	0.00	27.81
12/10	86.52	12	7	7.26	0.00	29.73
12/09	65.75	24	10	2.75	0.00	22.37
Annual Growth	(1.8%)	—	—	(8.0%)	—	2.6%

Rio Tinto Plc

You aren't seeing double. Rio Tinto plc one of the world's largest mining operations (along with BHP Billiton and Vale) is the British half of dual-listed companies. Its Australian counterpart is Rio Tinto Limited with headquarters in Melbourne. Rio Tinto explores for a variety of commodities: bauxite coal copper diamonds gold iron ore minerals (borates and titanium dioxide) nickel and potash. Iron ore makes up about 44% of the group's sales. The company also produces aluminum through its Rio Tinto Alcan unit. Rio Tinto may sell its diamond business. For more information see Hoover's Rio Tinto Limited profile.

By focusing on a strategy of developing large-scale long-life mining operations Rio Tinto has tried to weather commodity prices that have dipped and risen over several years. Like its rivals the company continues to seek strategic acquisitions as it cuts costs and improves productivity. Rio Tinto's tight-fisted operating style while providing exceptional margins for its industry has drawn the ire of unions which have been critical of the company's employment and environmental records.

Following a tough 2009 in which the global recession depressed commodity prices Rio Tinto rebounded strongly in 2010 posting a 35% increase in overall revenues due primarily to increased sales volumes and prices generated by the beginnings of an economic recovery. Leading the pack for Rio Tinto was its Iron Ore segment which saw an increase of 91% over the previous year followed by the Copper segment with a hike of 24% and the Energy unit with 15%. Profitability soared in 2010 as net income jumped more than 184% due to lower operating costs and significant reductions in debt.

Despite its failed effort the previous year to hike its 9% stake in Rio Tinto to 19% Aluminum Corporation of China (Chinalco) formed a joint venture with Rio Tinto in 2010 to operate an iron ore project in Guinea West Africa. A Chinalco subsidiary will hold 47% of Rio Tinto's Simandou project which is expected to begin producing up to 70 million tons of ore per year by 2015.

In 2011 Rio Tinto and Chinalco teamed up again on a new joint venture that will focus on mineral exploration in China. Chinalco is seeking to find and develop domestic sources of copper coal and potash to offset the cost of importing those raw materials. Chinalco will hold a 51% interest in the joint venture Chinalco Rio Tinto Exploration with Rio Tinto holding the remaining 49%.

One of the world's largest producers of copper Rio Tinto operates the Oyu Tolgoi project in Mongolia along with Canada's Ivanhoe Mines and the Mongolian government. Vancouver-based Ivanhoe controlled one of the world's largest untapped copper and gold deposits in Mongolia and Rio Tinto expects the mine to be one of the world's top 10 copper producers as well as one of the top gold producers by 2018. In 2012 Rio Tinto upped its holding in Ivanhoe from 49% to 51% to become the majority owner.

Also in early 2012 Rio Tinto completed its offer for Canada-based uranium producer Hathor Exploration valued at $578 million after rival Cameco Corp. made a takeover bid for the company in 2011. Hathor supplies about a fifth of the world's uranium.

In 2011 the company also started slimming its aluminum operations. It placed 13 assets on the chopping block allowing Rio Tinto Alcan to focus on its high-quality tier one assets (mostly in Canada) and improve performance. The company also planned to transfer its stakes in six Australian and New Zealand operations to a new business unit Pacific Aluminium. The new unit managed and reported separately from Rio Tinto Alcan would include the company's Gove bauxite mine and alumina refinery Boyne Smelters and Gladstone Power Station Tomago smelter and Bell Bay smelter in Australia. In New Zealand it would include the New Zealand Aluminium Smelters.

For at least a while longer the company is holding on to seven noncore assets managed by Rio Tinto Alcan including operations in France Germany the UK and the US. The company is in no hurry to sell and may wait until the economy improves before divesting certain operations. Rio Tinto has tried a similar divestment strategy before. It embarked on a divestment plan in the mid-2000s with the long-term goal of turning out $15 billion from its divestments. By 2010 the company had gained more than $10 billion from the divestment program.

EXECUTIVES

Chief Executive, Sam Walsh, age 64
CFO and Director, Guy Elliott, age 58
Group Executive Business Support and Operations, Bret Clayton, age 52
Group Executive Technology and Innovation, Preston Chiaro, age 60
Group Executive Legal and External Affairs, Debra A. Valentine, age 60
Chief Executive Rio Tinto Alcan, Jacynthe Cote, age 56
Chief Executive Copper, Andrew Harding, age 48
Group Executive People and Organisation, Hugo Bague, age 53
Chief Executive Energy, Harry Kenyon-Slaney
Chairman, Jan du Plessis
Chief Executive Diamonds and Minerals, Alan Davies
Director, Richard R. Goodmanson, age 66
Chief Executive and Director, Tom Albanese, age 54
Chief Executive Iron Ore and Australia and Director, Sam Walsh, age 62
CFO and Director, Guy Elliott, age 58
Director, Michael Fitzpatrick, age 61
Director, Lord Kerr Kinlochard, age 71
Non-Executive Independent Director, Christopher Lynch
Non-Executive Independent Director, John Kerr
Auditors: PricewaterhouseCoopersLLP

LOCATIONS

HQ: Rio Tinto Plc
2 Eastbourne Terrace, London W2 6LG
Phone: (44) 20 7781 2000   **Fax:** (44) 20 7781 1800
Web: www.riotinto.com

Sales by Destination

	% of total
Asia	
China	31
Japan	17
Other countries	16
US	14
Canada	3
Europe	
UK	1
Other countries	11
Australia	2
Total	**100**

PRODUCTS/OPERATIONS

	% of total
Iron ore	44
Copper	11
Energy	10
Diamonds & minerals	5
Total	**100**

COMPETITORS

ALROSA	Freeport-McMoRan
ASARCO	Glencore Xstrata
Alcoa	Goldcorp
Anglo American	Grupo Mexico
AngloGold Ashanti	ITOCHU
BHP Billiton	Kaiser Aluminum
Barrick Gold	Marubeni
CONSOL Energy	Newmont Mining
Cliffs Natural	Norsk Hydro ASA
Resources	RUSAL
Codelco	Southern Copper
DeBeers	Teck
Fortescue Metals	Vale

HISTORICAL FINANCIALS

Company Type: Public

Income Statement
FYE: December 31

	REVENUE ($ mil.)	NET INCOME ($ mil.)	NET PROFIT MARGIN	EMPLOYEES
12/13	51,171	(2,586)	—	66,331
12/12	50,967	(14)	—	71,219
12/11	60,537	939	1.6%	67,930
12/10	56,576	860	1.5%	76,894
12/09	41,825	463	1.1%	101,994
Annual Growth	**5.2%**	**—**		**(10.2%)**

2013 Year-End Financials

Debt ratio: —
Return on equity: (-5.5%)
Cash ($ mil.): 10,216
Current ratio: 1.40
Long-term debt ($ mil.): —

No. of shares (mil.): 1,412
Dividends
 Yield: 3.1%
 Payout: 89.3%
Market value ($ mil.): 79,718

	STOCK PRICE ($) FY Close	P/E High/Low	PER SHARE ($) Earnings	Dividends	Book Value
12/13	56.43	30 20	1.97	1.76	32.48
12/12	58.09	— —	(1.62)	1.66	33.21
12/11	48.92	25 14	3.01	1.17	36.57
12/10	71.66	34 5	7.26	0.88	38.22
12/09	215.39	80 29	2.75	6.38	28.76
Annual Growth	**(28.5%)**	**— —**	**(8.0%)**	**(27.5%)**	**3.1%**

Riyad Bank (Saudi Arabia)

One of the largest financial institutions in the Middle East Riyad Bank's palette of services includes something for just about every customer including those who require Sharia-compliant banking. The Saudi financial services firm offers retail and corporate banking services including credit cards mutual fund products electronic trade financing treasury services financing and IPO advice for the oil gas and petrochemical sector. The Riyad Bank network includes 304 branches with 64 dedicated branches for women and 19 female-only sections in other branches as well as 20 self-service electronic branches and more than 2500 automated teller machines. It also has offices in London Houston and Singapore.

Operations

The bank operates an investment arm Riyad Capital that provides asset management services. The firm is also a major player in IPO advisory business in Saudi Arabia.

EXECUTIVES

President and CEO, Talal I. Al-Qudaibi
Deputy CEO, Suliman A. Al-Gwaiz
EVP and Chief Risk Officer, Thalib A. Al-Shamrani
Deputy CEO, Abdulaziz S. Al-Furaih
EVP Treasury and Investment, Abdulaziz S. Al-Malki
EVP Corporate Banking, Abdul Majeed A. Al-Mubarak
Chairman, Rashed Abdulaziz Al-Rashed
EVP Corporate Banking, Ossama A. Bukhari
EVP Operations, Riyadh O. Al-Zahrani
EVP Marketing, Mohamad A. Al-Rabeah
Executive Vice President Support Services, Saeed S. Al-Siairri
Executive Vice President Information Technology, Abdulrahman M. Al-Odan
EVP Retail Banking, Adel A. Al-Sheikh
EVP Human Resources, Adnan S. Al-Joyan
EVP Risk Management, Ahmed Y. Al-Tayeb
EVP Credit, Majid A. Al-Gwaiz
EVP Branches, Hani A. Abu Al Naja
EVP Information Technology, Aiedh M. Al-Zahrani
Director, Abdullah M. Al-Issa
Director, Abdulrahman Hassan Sharbatly
Director, Abdulaziz Saleh Al-Jarbou
Director, Mohammed Abdulaziz Al-Afaleq
Director, Khaled Hamza Nahas
Director, Abdullah Ibrahim Al-Ayadhi
Director, Faris Abdullah AbaalKhail

LOCATIONS

HQ: Riyad Bank (Saudi Arabia)
King Abdul Aziz Road, P.O. Box 22622, Riyadh 11416
Phone: (966) 1 401 3030   **Fax:** (966) 1 404 2707
Web: www.riyadbank.com

COMPETITORS

Arab National Bank	Gulf International
Banque Saudi Fransi	Bank
Dallah Albaraka Group	

HISTORICAL FINANCIALS

Company Type: Public

Income Statement
FYE: December 31

	ASSETS ($ mil.)	NET INCOME ($ mil.)	INCOME AS % OF ASSETS	EMPLOYEES
12/13	54,723	1,052	1.9%	5,677
12/12	50,708	924	1.8%	5,334
12/11	48,236	839	1.7%	5,256
12/10	46,280	753	1.6%	5,502
12/09	47,028	807	1.7%	0
Annual Growth	**3.9%**	**6.8%**	**—**	**—**

2013 Year-End Financials

Return on assets: 2.0%
Return on equity: 11.9%
Long-term debt ($ mil.): —
No. of shares (mil.): 1,500
Sales ($ mil): 1,634

Dividends
 Yield: —
 Payout: —
Market value ($ mil.): —

Roche Holding Ltd.

Roche is on a medicinal roll. The company operates two segments pharmaceuticals and diagnostics and sells its products in some 180 countries. Roche's prescription drugs include cancer therapies MabThera/Rituxan and Avastin anemia treatment NeoRecormon/Epogin hepatitis drug

Pegasys transplant drug CellCept macular degeneration therapy Lucentis and Tamiflu which is used to prevent and treat influenza (including pandemic strains). The company markets many of its best-sellers through subsidiary Genentech and affiliate Chugai Pharmaceutical. Roche's diagnostics arm offers clinical lab supplies genetic tests diabetes monitoring supplies and point-of-care diagnostics for health care providers.

Operations

Roche's pharmaceuticals division accounts for more than three-fourths of annual revenues with oncology drugs making the largest sales contribution (45% of revenues). The smaller yet faster-growing diagnostics segment is a leading maker of in vitro clinical diagnostic tests through its professional diagnostics segment; it is also an established provider of diabetes tests and glucose monitors.

Geographic Reach

The largest geographic markets for the pharma segment are the US and Western Europe. Product marketing efforts in the US are conducted through Roche's main US subsidiary Genentech which is one of the world's largest biotech companies. The company also has a solid stance in the Japanese drug market through its 60% stake in Chugai Pharmaceutical and it is experiencing growth in Latin America and Asia.

Financial Analysis

As one of the top 10 global pharmaceutical companies Roche has steadily grown its revenues and profits over the last decade. But while the company reported net income growth of 13% to more than $10 billion in 2011 largely attributed to its cost-control and efficiency programs (including workforce reductions and facility consolidation efforts) its revenues took a 9% dip to about $47 billion due to poor currency exchange rates for the Swiss Franc. However Roche reported a group sales increase of 1% at constant exchange rates due to increased returns from sales of key pharmaceutical and diagnostic products.

Key drivers for growth in 2011 included rising global sales of Lucentis Actemra/RoActemra Mircera (for anemia in kidney disease patients) and four of the top cancer drugs (MabThera/Rituxan Herceptin Tarceva and Xeloda). However sales of one top selling cancer drug —Avastin —fell after the FDA revoked its indication for breast cancer. Revenues from bestseller Tamiflu also declined in 2010 and 2011 following a sharp rise in demand from flu pandemics and resulting government stockpiling in previous years. Growth in the smaller diagnostics business segment is attributed to increased sales of clinical laboratory supplies and cancer diagnostic products.

Strategy

In order to expand its pharmaceutical product offerings and stave off revenue losses from patent expirations and other competitive pressures Roche invests heavily in internal research and development programs to expand its pipeline of small-molecule and biotechnology drug candidates. The company has about 100 drugs in clinical development stages the bulk of which aim to treat oncology cardiovascular metabolic viral inflammatory autoimmune and central nervous system disorders. New drugs that have emerged from Roche's pipeline include Zelboraf a melanoma medicine marketed in partnership with Daiichi Sankyo and launched in 2011 Perjeta (pertuzumab) a new Genentech-developed breast cancer drug approved by the FDA in 2012.

The firm has also widened its R&D programs by forming partnerships with other drugmakers such as Biogen Idec and Pharmasset as well as through acquisitions. In addition to new drug formulas Roche conducts R&D programs on existing drugs to gain regulatory approval for new indications

which typically helps to extend a drug's patent protection and increase sales volumes.

Not one to neglect its smaller division Roche has been aggressively adding to its diagnostic testing stable through R&D partnership and acquisition efforts. In addition to clinical and diabetes tests focus areas for the diagnostics division include tissue-based cancer diagnostics (through its Ventana Medical Systems subsidiary) life science (gene sequencing) technologies and molecular diagnostics which include personalized (or companion) tests that are used to determine the best treatment regimen for a specific patient.

Mergers and Acquisitions

Acquisitions are also key elements in Roche's R&D growth strategy and have expanded its pharmaceutical segment in focused therapeutic areas. For instance the 2011 purchase of drug developer Anadys Pharmaceuticals expanded its hepatitis C virus (HCV) development portfolio.

In the diagnostics segment the company would have become a market leader in the gene sequencing market in 2012 had it been successful in its hostile attempts to acquire research equipment maker Illumina. Past purchases have expanded its professional and cancer testing operations.

In 2013 it did enhance its diagnostics business and strengthened its hematology offerings with the $220 million purchase (plus contingent payments) of Constitution Medical Investors which makes tests for blood diseases. Two years later it agreed to buy a controlling stake in Foundation Medicine which makes the FoundationOne cancer test for just over $1 billion.

The company also announced plans to buy private French company Trophos which makes olesoxime (an experimental treatment for spinal muscular atrophy a debilitating genetic neuromuscular disease) for an upfront payment of Â120 million ($140 million) plus further payments up to Â350 million.

Ownership

Descendants of the founding Hoffmann and Oeri families own about half of Roche. In addition fellow Swiss drugmaker Novartis owns 33% of the company.

HISTORY

Fritz Hoffmann-La Roche backed by family wealth began making pharmaceuticals in a lab in Basel Switzerland in 1894. At the time drug compounds were mixed at pharmacies and lacked uniformity. Hoffmann was not a chemist but saw the potential for mass-produced standardized branded drugs.

By WWI Hoffman had become successful selling Thiocal (cough medicine) Digalen (digitalis extract) and other products on four continents. During the war the Bolsheviks seized the firm's St. Petersburg Russia facility and its Warsaw plant was almost destroyed. Devastated Hoffmann sold company shares outside the family in 1919 and died in 1920.

As WWII loomed Roche divided its holdings between F. Hoffman-La Roche and Sapac which held many of Roche's foreign operations. US operations became more important during the war. Roche synthesized vitamins C A and E (eventually becoming the world's top vitamin maker) and built plants and research centers worldwide.

Roche continued to develop such successful products as tranquilizers Librium (1960) and Valium (1963) —the world's best-selling prescription drug prior to anti-ulcer successors Tagamet (SmithKline Beecham now part of GlaxoSmithKline) and Prilosec (AstraZeneca). Roche made its first fragrance and flavor buy Givaudan in 1963.

In the 1970s after several governments accused it of price-gouging on Librium and Valium Roche

agreed to price restraints. The company was fined for vitamin price-fixing in 1976. It was also rapped that year for its slow response to an Italian factory dioxin leak that killed thousands of animals and forced hundreds of families to evacuate.

Roche became one of the first drugmakers to sell another's products when it agreed to sell Glaxo's Zantac ulcer treatment in the US in 1982. The move let Roche maintain its large US sales force at the time when Valium went off patent decimating the company's drug sales.

Roche acquired a product pipeline when it bought a majority stake in genetic engineering firm Genentech in 1990. In 1994 it bought the struggling Syntex solidifying its position in North America. The company gained Aleve and other products in 1996 when it bought out its joint venture with Procter & Gamble and also acquired Cincinnati-based flavors and fragrances firm Tastemaker.

In its biggest acquisition ever Roche bought Corange in 1998 for $10.2 billion; its subsidiary Boehringer Mannheim was renamed Roche Molecular Biochemicals. In 1999 Roche announced it had located the gene that causes osteoarthritis. The company began to market anti-obesity pharmaceutical Xenical in the US that year despite reports of some unpleasant side effects.

Also in 1999 Roche agreed to a record-setting fine to end a US Justice Department investigation into Roche's role in an alleged vitamin price-fixing cartel; in 2000 it agreed to pay out again (to 22 states) to settle a lawsuit regarding the cartel. A related European Union probe the following year also found Roche guilty and levied heavy fines against the firm. In 1999 and 2000 Roche squeezed cash out of its high-flying biotech progeny; it bought the 33% of Genentech it didn't own in 1999 then raised a total of almost $8 billion by reselling 42% of Genentech in three public offerings in 1999 and 2000.

Influenza drug Tamiflu failed to win European Union approval in 2000 but breast cancer drug Herceptin was OK'd there. Also that year the company spun off its fragrances and flavors unit Givaudan SA and divested its BASILEA Pharmaceutica biotech division which focused on infectious disease and skin disorder drugs. Two long-time Roche leaders chairman Fritz Gerber and CFO Henri Meier retired that year; both remained on Roche's board for a brief time thereafter.

In 2001 rival Swiss pharmaceuticals firm Novartis bought a 20% stake in Roche from financier Martin Ebner's BZ Gruppe Holding. The company sold its fine chemicals business to DSM in 2003 to further narrow its focus and in 2005 Roche sold its consumer health business which included vitamins the analgesic Aleve and antacid Rennie to Bayer HealthCare.

In 2006 Roche received approval for the application of its cancer drug MabThera (known as Rituxan in the US) in treating rheumatoid arthritis throughout the EU. It also put its post-menopausal osteoporosis treatment Boniva out on the EU and US markets at that time.

One major acquisition came with the $3.4 billion purchase of Ventana Medical Systems a diagnostic firm focusing on cancers in 2008. The purchase expanded the company's operations into tissue-based diagnostics.

The company added to its oncology R&D efforts in 2008 through the $160 million acquisition and integration of UK biotech research firm Piramed and the purchase of Canadian antibody developer ARIUS Research (later integrated into Roche Canada). Roche also expanded its neurology pipeline through the purchase of Memory Pharmaceuticals in 2008 for $50 million to gain access to the company's memory loss and cognition therapies.

In a move to secure its global presence in 2008 Roche upped its stake in Japan's Chugai Pharmaceutical from 50.1% to about 60% through a shareholder tender offer worth some $900 million.

Roche also began making attempts to take full control of Genentech in late 2008 when the company made a $44 billion offer to purchase the 44% of Genentech that it didn't already own; however Genentech rejected the takeover offer as undervalued. In early 2009 Roche issued a hostile $42 billion tender offer but after a tepid response from Genentech shareholders Roche upped the offer to its final value of about $47 billion. The deal was completed later that year. While Roche and Genentech already shared rights to numerous commercial and development-stage drugs (including some bestselling cancer therapies) Roche wanted Genentech as a wholly owned subsidiary to gain full access to its drugs and keep its pipeline full of new biotech development projects for years to come. Roche also cut costs and increased efficiencies through the acquisition by combining certain functions of Genentech with its existing US operations (while at the same time aiming to keep Genentech's innovative identity and culture intact). As a result in 2010 Genentech became Roche's US sales marketing manufacturing and administrative headquarters

Roche gained marketing approval for Actemra (or RoActemra in some markets) a rheumatoid arthritis medicine in the EU in 2009 and in the US in 2010.

As a result in 2010 Genentech became Roche's US sales marketing manufacturing and administrative headquarters taking over those roles from the previous main location in Nutley New Jersey (operating as Hoffman-La Roche Inc.).

On top of the Genentech integration efforts in late 2010 the company announced plans to cut some 6% of its global workforce (about 4800 jobs) primarily in its manufacturing and sales and marketing organizations to improve operational efficiency and production levels.

EXECUTIVES

Chairman, Franz B. Humer, age 68, $5,709,204 total compensation

Chairman President and CEO Chugai, Osamu Nagayama, age 67

Head Genentech Research and Early Development, Richard H. Scheller, age 61

Vice Chairman, Prof Bruno Gehrig, age 68

CEO Genentech, Ian T. Clark, age 54

Chief Financial and IT Officer, Alan Hippe, age 46

General Counsel, Gottlieb A. Keller, age 60, $1,420,200 total compensation

Head Human Resources, Silvia Ayyoubi, age 61, $686,434 total compensation

Vice Chairman, Andre Hoffman, age 56

CEO, Severin Schwan, age 46, $2,722,052 total compensation

Head CEO Office and Secretary to the Corporate Executive Committee, Per-Olof Attinger, age 54

COO Pharmaceuticals, Daniel O'Day, age 50

Head Group Communications, Stephan Feldhaus

COO Diagnostics, Roland Diggelmann

Head of Roche Pharma Research & Early Development, Mike Burgess

Head of Roche Partnering, Sophie Kornowski-Bonnet

Director, Lodewijk J.R. de Vink, age 68

Director, Pius Baschera, age 63

Director, DeAnne S. Julius, age 64

Vice Chairman, Prof Bruno Gehrig, age 68

Director, Sir John Irving Bell, age 61

Vice Chairman, Andre Hoffman, age 56

Director, Andreas Oeri, age 64

Director, Prof Beatrice Weder di Mauro, age 48

Auditors: KPMGKlynveldPeatMarwickGoerdelerSA

LOCATIONS

HQ: Roche Holding Ltd.
Grenzacherstrasse 124, Basel CH-4070
Phone: (41) 61 688 1111   **Fax:** (41) 61 691 93 91
Web: www.roche.com

Sales

	% of total
North	36
Europe	35
Asia	19
Latin	7
Africa Australia &	3
Total	**100**

PRODUCTS/OPERATIONS

Sales

	% of total
Pharmaceuticals	
Oncology	45
Inflammatory autoimmune &	7
Virology	6
Metabolic &	5
Ophthalmology	4
Respiratory	2
Renal	2
Cardiovascular	2
Central nervous	2
Infectious	1
Other	1
Diagnostics	23
Total	**100**

Selected Products

Top 20 Products (listed alphabetically)
Actemra/RoActemra (rheumatoid arthritis)
Activase/TNKase (cardiovascular)
Avastin (colorectal cancer non-small cell lung cancer breast cancer kidney cancer)
Bonviva/Boniva (osteoporosis)
CellCept (transplantation)
Herceptin (HER2-positive breast cancer)
Lucentis (wet age-related macular degeneration diabetic macular edema)
MabThera/Rituxan (non-Hodgkin's lymphoma rheumatoid arthritis chronic lymphocytic leukemia)
Madopar (Parkinson's disease restless leg syndrome)
Mircera (predialysis)
NeoRecormon/Epogen (anemia oncology)
Neutrogin/Neupogen (neutropenia associated with chemotherapy)
Nutropin (growth hormone deficiency)
Pegasys (hepatitis B and C)
Pulmozyme (cystic fibrosis)
Tamiflu (treatment and prevention of influenza)
Tarceva (advanced non-small cell lung cancer advanced pancreatic cancer)
Valcyte/Cymevene (cytomegalovirus infection)
Xeloda (colorectal cancer breast cancer colon cancer)
Xolair (asthma)
Other Products
Anaprox (pain fever and inflammation)
Bactrim (anti-infective)
Bondronat (bone disease in breast cancer patients)
Dilatrend (hypertension)
Dormicum (sedation)
Erivedge (basal cell carcinoma)
Fuzeon (HIV)
Invirase (HIV)
Kytril (nausea and vomiting induced by chemotherapy or radiation therapy)
Lariam (malaria)
Perjeta (breast cancer)
Roaccutane/Accutane (acne)
Rocaltrol/Calcitriol (osteoporosis)
Rocephin (bacterial infections)
Roferon-A (hepatitis C hairy cell leukemia AIDS-related Kaposi's sarcoma)
Toradol (acute pain)
Valium (anxiety disorders)
Vesanoid (leukemia)
Viracept (HIV)
Xenical (weight loss weight control)
Zelboraf (metastatic melanoma)
Zenapax (transplant rejection)

Selected Acquisitions

2011
Anadys Pharmaceuticals ($230 million; San Diego California; virology drugs)
mtm laboratories AG (E190 million or $265 million; Germany; cervical cancer testing)
PVT (E85 million or $120 million; Germany and US; in vitro diagnostic tests and lab equipment)
2010
BioImagene ($100 million; tissue-based cancer diagnostics for personalized tests)
Medingo (up to $200 million; Israel; insulin pump manufacturing)

COMPETITORS

Abbott Labs	GlaxoSmithKline
Actavis Inc.	Johnson & Johnson
Amgen	Merck
Astellas	Merck KGaA
AstraZeneca	Novartis
Bayer AG	Pfizer
Becton Dickinson	Ranbaxy Laboratories
Biogen Idec	Sanofi
Bristol-Myers Squibb	Siemens Healthcare
Eisai	Diagnostics
Eli Lilly	Takeda Pharmaceutical
Gilead Sciences	Teva

HISTORICAL FINANCIALS

Company Type: Public

Income Statement

FYE: December 31

	REVENUE ($ mil.)	NET INCOME ($ mil.)	NET PROFIT MARGIN	EMPLOYEES
12/14	50,411	9,434	18.7%	88,509
12/13	54,555	12,528	23.0%	85,080
12/12	51,755	10,405	20.1%	82,089
12/11	46,889	9,930	21.2%	80,129
12/10	52,540	9,260	17.6%	80,653
Annual Growth	(1.0%)	0.5%	—	2.4%

2014 Year-End Financials

Debt ratio: 34.3%	No. of shares (mil.): 160
Return on equity: 48.0%	Dividends
Cash ($ mil.): 3,782	Yield: 3.2%
Current ratio: 1.35	Payout: 11.5%
Long-term debt ($ mil.): 19,558	Market value ($ mil.): 5,438

	STOCK PRICE ($) FY Close	P/E High/Low		PER SHARE ($) Earnings	Dividends	Book Value
12/14	33.99	8	3	10.93	1.11	123.75
12/13	70.20	7	5	14.51	0.97	135.33
12/12	50.50	5	4	12.17	0.92	98.82
12/11	42.55	6	3	11.67	1.02	80.49
12/10	36.65	5	3	10.80	0.70	63.24
Annual Growth	(1.9%)	—	—	0.3%	12.4%	18.3%

Rosneft Oil Co OJSC (Moscow)

LOCATIONS

HQ: Rosneft Oil Co OJSC (Moscow)
26/1, Sofiyskaya Embankment, Moscow 115035
Phone: (7) 499 517 88 99   **Fax:** (7) 499 517 72 35
Web: www.rosneft.com

Company Type: Public

Income Statement

FYE: December 31

	REVENUE ($ mil.)	NET INCOME ($ mil.)	NET PROFIT MARGIN	EMPLOYEES
12/13	142,824	16,582	11.6%	0
12/12	101,114	11,202	11.1%	166,110
12/11	84,202	9,789	11.6%	160,837
12/10	62,888	9,602	15.3%	159,771
12/09	46,826	6,514	13.9%	0
Annual Growth	32.2%	26.3%	—	—

2013 Year-End Financials

Debt ratio: 0.9%	No. of shares (mil.): —
Return on equity: 20.3%	Dividends
Cash ($ mil.): 8,367	Yield: 0.0%
Current ratio: 1.05	Payout: 0.0%
Long-term debt ($ mil.): 51,239	Market value ($ mil.): —

	STOCK PRICE ($) FY Close	P/E High/Low		PER SHARE ($) Earnings	Dividends	Book Value
12/13	7.85	0	0	1.61	0.00	8.97
12/12	8.85	0	0	1.19	0.00	7.93
Annual Growth	(11.3%)	—	—	7.8%	34.0%	3.1%

Royal Bank of Canada

Royal Bank of Canada is Canada's #1 bank by assets and market capitalization and is a leading North American financial services company. Royal Bank of Canada and its subsidiaries operate under the brand name RBC providing a diversified set of personal and commercial banking wealth management insurance investor and wholesale banking services globally. RBC serves large and small personal business public sector and institutional clients through offices in Canada the US and about 49 other countries including the UK and other select parts of Europe and Asia/Pacific.

Geographic Reach

Canada is RBC's largest market accounting for more than two-thirds of total revenue. The remainder of revenue is balanced between the US and other international markets (which include Europe and Asia).

Operations

The company has realigned its business segments into five units. It eliminated its International Banking segment and created a new Investor & Treasury Services segment which offers advisory custodial and financing services to safeguard assets and manage risk to institutional investors. That segment includes RBC Investor Services the largest custodian in Canada and formerly a joint venture called RBC Dexia. The company also operates a Personal & Commercial Banking segment which includes personal and business banking operations and certain investment businesses in Canada the US and the Caribbean.

Wholesale banking business Capital Markets continues to provide a full suite of products and services —including corporate and investment banking equity and debt origination and structuring and trading —to public and private companies institutional investors governments and central banks. Rounding out RBC's business segments are Wealth Management and Insurance.

Financial Performance

The company has seen stable growth in its revenues over the past few years. RNC's revenues increased by 9% in 2013 due to higher interest and non interest income. Net interest income rose due to solid volume growth of 5% across most of its businesses in the Canadian Banking segment and higher trading-related net interest income (and higher lending activity) in Capital Markets. RBC's net income increased by 8% in 2013 due to a decline in the provision for loan losses.

Strategy

With Canada generating more than two-thirds of RBC's revenue it's no surprise that the company's primary strategy in that market is to remain the undisputed leader in financial services. Other initiatives the company is undertaking to achieve its growth strategy are tightly managing costs deepening client relationships increasing price competitiveness and investing in technology.

Outside of Canada in an effort to be a leading provider of capital markets and wealth management services the company is focusing on high-net-worth corporate and institutional clients in the US the UK and key emerging markets like Hong Kong and Singapore. RBC is the sixth-largest global wealth manager by assets under management. Streamlining its operations in 2014 RBC sold RBC Royal Bank (Jamaica) Limited and RBTT Securities Jamaica Limited to Sagicor Group Jamaica Limited.

Mergers and AcquisitionsGrowing its position in Canada in 2013 RBC acquired the Canadian auto finance and deposit business of Ally Financial in a deal valued at $1.4 billion. The deal positions RBC as a leader in the Canadian auto finance business.

Diversifying its portfolio that year the bank acquired the Athena Energy Group a market leading natural gas supplier in Quebec.

Company Background

In 2012 RBC acquired the Latin American Caribbean and African private banking business of Coutts the wealth management division of Royal Bank of Scotland to increase market share with high-net-worth clients.

RBC in 2012 also shed its money-losing US retail bank operations RBC Bank (USA) and a US credit card business selling them to PNC Financial for $3.6 billion. RBC said those operations lacked the scale to accomplish what the company wanted to do in the US. RBC had also been struggling with credit losses in the US following the economic downturn.

RBC was created as Merchants Bank in 1864 and was incorporated in 1869. It changed its name to The Royal Bank of Canada in 1901 and to Royal Bank of Canada in 1990.

HISTORY

Royal Bank of Canada (RBC) has looked south of the border ever since its 1864 creation as Merchants Bank in Halifax Nova Scotia a port city bustling with trade spawned by the US Civil War. After incorporating in 1869 as Merchants Bank of Halifax the bank added branches in eastern Canada. Merchants opened a branch in Bermuda in 1882. Gold strikes in Canada and Alaska in the late 1890s pushed it into western Canada.

Merchants opened offices in New York and Cuba in 1899 and changed its name to Royal Bank of Canada in 1901. RBC moved into new Montreal headquarters in 1907 and grew by purchasing such banks as Union Bank of Canada (1925). In 1928 it moved into the 42-story Royal Bank Building then the tallest in the British Empire.

The bank faltered during the Depression but recovered during WWII. After the war RBC financed the expanding minerals and oil and gas industries. When Castro took power in Cuba RBC tried to operate its branches under communist rule but sold out to Banco Nacional de Cuba in 1960.

RBC opened offices in the UK in 1979 and in West Germany Puerto Rico and the Bahamas in 1980. As Canada's banking rules relaxed RBC bought Dominion Securities in 1987. The US Federal Reserve approved RBC's brokerage arm for participation in stock underwriting in 1991.

The bank faced a $650 million loss in 1992 after backing the Reichmann family's Olympia & York property development company which failed under the weight of its UK projects. The next year an ever-diversifying RBC bought Royal Trustco Canada's #2 trust company and Voyageur Travel Insurance its largest retail travel insurer. A management shakeup in late 1994 ended with bank president John Cleghorn taking control of the company.

In 1995 RBC listed on the New York Stock Exchange and the next year joined with Heller Financial (an affiliate of Japan's Fuji Bank) to finance trade between Canada and Mexico. It began offering PC home banking in 1996 and Internet banking in 1997. That year RBC became one of the world's largest securities-custody service providers with its acquisition of The Bank of Nova Scotia's institutional and pension custody operations.

The company and Bank of Montreal agreed to merge in 1998 but Canadian regulators fearing the concentration of banking power seen in the US rejected the merger. In response the bank trimmed its workforce and orchestrated a sale-leaseback of its property portfolio (1999).

In the late 1990s RBC grew its online presence by purchasing the Internet banking operations of Security First Network Bank (now Security First Technologies 1998) the online trading division of Bull & Bear Group (1999) and 20% of AOL Canada (1999). It also bought several trust and fiduciary services businesses from Ernst & Young.

It acquired US mortgage bank Prism Financial and the Canadian retail credit card business of BANK ONE in 2000. RBC also sold its commercial credit portfolio to U.S. Bancorp. The company agreed to pay a substantial fine after institutional asset management subsidiary RT Capital Management came under scrutiny from the Ontario Securities Commission for alleged involvement in illegal pension-fund stock manipulation. RBC ended up selling RT Capital to UBS AG the following year.

Also in 2001 RBC made another US purchase: North Carolina's Centura Banks (now RBC Centura Banks). It sold Houston-based home lender RBC Mortgage to New Century Financial in 2005. Also that year it acquired private bank Abacus Financial which adding locations in the UK and Amsterdam.

RBC spent the decade prior to the global recession building up its US operations. The company moved into the US trust business in 2006 when it purchased American Guaranty & Trust a unit of National Life Insurance Company. In 2007 it bought the electronic brokerage business of New York boutique Carlin Financial Group. Other acquisitions made during that period include debt securities investor Access Capital Strategies energy advisory firm Richardson Barr and DC-area investment bank Ferris Baker Watts.

In 2008 RBC acquired community banks in Alabama Georgia and Florida including Alabama National BanCorporation. That same year RBC agreed to buy back some $850 million in auction-rate securities and pay the New York State attorney general's office a nearly $10 million fine. Auction-rate securities were sold to investors as a low-risk investment but as the economy worsened in 2007 and 2008 banks canceled the regular auctions rendering the securities worthless. Customers and regulators claimed that banks continued to sell them the securities even though they knew the investments had become very high risk.

Also in 2008 RBC Bank expanded its finance operations when it bought the Canadian commercial leasing business of ABN AMRO. It renamed the unit RBC Equipment Finance Group.

To cement its place among the world's 10 largest wealth managers RBC bought UK-based fixed income specialist BlueBay Asset Management for some $1.5 billion in 2010. Also that year it bought BNP Paribas Fortis' Hong Kong wealth management business.

In 2010 it also sold Liberty Life its US life insurance subsidiary that had posted losses for two years to Apollo affiliate Athene Holding. To boost brand recognition of another US unit the company changed the name of Voyageur Asset Management to RBC Global Asset Management (US).

EXECUTIVES

Group Head International Banking and Insurance; Chairman and CEO RBC Bank (USA), W. James (Jim) Westlake, $559,500 total compensation
Chairman, David P. O'Brien, age 72
President Chief Executive Officer, Gordon M. Nixon, age 57, $1,466,500 total compensation
Chief Administrative Officer Chief Financial Officer, Janice R. Fukakusa, $547,844 total compensation
Co-Group Head Capital Markets; Chairman and Co-CEO RBC Capital Markets, A. Douglas (Doug) McGregor, age 58, $165,400 total compensation
Group Head Wealth Management; President and CEO RBC Asset Management, M. George Lewis
SVP & Chief Economist, Craig Wright
Chief Operating Officer, Barbara G. Stymiest, $652,750 total compensation
Co-Group Head Capital Markets; President and Co-CEO RBC Capital Markets, Mark A. Standish, age 53, $178,946 total compensation
Chief Risk Officer, Morten N Friis
Regional President Atlantic Provinces, Greg Grice
Group Head Canadian Banking, David I. (Dave) McKay, age 51, $413,500 total compensation
Chief Human Resources Officer, Zabeen Hirji
President RBC Asset Management, Douglas (Doug) Coulter
Head RBC Global Asset Management Institutional Client Group; President Phillips Hager & North, Damon Williams
CEO RBC Global Asset Management, John S. Montalbano
Regional VP Newfoundland and Labrador, Sean Munro
CEO Caribbean Banking, Suresh Sookoo
Executive Vice President, Charlie Coffey
Independent Chairman of the Board, David OBrien
Director, Douglas T. (Doug) Elix, age 64
Director, Alice D. Laberge, age 58
Director, J. Pedro Reinhard, age 69
Director, Richard L. (Rick) George, age 63
Director, Michael H. McCain, age 55
Director, John T. Ferguson, age 71
Director, Jacques Lamarre, age 71
President CEO and Director, Gordon M. Nixon, age 56
Director, Timothy J. (Tim) Hearn, age 69
Director, Brandt C. Louie, age 71
Director, Paule Gauthier, age 70
Director, Heather E. L. Munroe-Blum, age 64
Director, W. Geoffrey (Geoff) Beattie, age 54
Director, Kathleen P. (Katie) Taylor, age 57
Director, Victor L. Young, age 69
Director, Edward Sonshine, age 68
Director, Bridget van Kralingen
Director, David Denison
Independent Director, Bridget Kralingen
Auditors: Deloitte&ToucheLLP

LOCATIONS

HQ: Royal Bank of Canada
  200 Bay Street, Toronto, Ontario M5J 2J5
Phone: 416 974-5151   **Fax:** 416 955-7800
Web: www.rbc.com

Sales

	% of total
Canada	67
US	16
Other	17
Total	**100**

PRODUCTS/OPERATIONS

Sales

	% of total
Personal & commercial	56
Capital	22
Wealth	11
Insurance	10
Investor & treasury	1
Total	**100**

COMPETITORS

AGF Management	Dundee Corp.
BMO Financial Group	Goldman Sachs
Bank of America	Great-West Lifeco
Barclays	Guardian Capital Group
CI Financial	HSBC Bank Canada
CIBC	JPMorgan Chase
Caisse de depot et	Laurentian Bank
placement du Quebec	National Bank of
Caisses centrale	Canada
Desjardins	Nomura Securities
Canadian Western Bank	Power Financial
Central 1 Credit Union	Scotiabank
Citigroup	TD Bank
Deutsche Bank	UBS

HISTORICAL FINANCIALS

Company Type: Public

Income Statement

FYE: October 31

	ASSETS ($ mil.)	NET INCOME ($ mil.)	INCOME AS % OF ASSETS	EMPLOYEES
10/14	840,559	7,962	0.9%	0
10/13	823,013	7,965	1.0%	0
10/12	827,347	7,462	0.9%	80,000
10/11	796,996	6,368	0.8%	74,000
10/10	712,875	5,127	0.7%	79,000
Annual Growth	**4.2%**	**11.6%**	**—**	**—**

2014 Year-End Financials

Return on assets: 0.9%
Return on equity: 17.6%
Long-term debt ($ mil.): —
No. of shares (mil.): 1,441
Sales ($ mil): 37,544

Dividends
Yield: 3.9%
Payout: 53.1%
Market value ($ mil.): 102,580

	STOCK PRICE ($) FY Close	P/E High/Low		PER SHARE ($) Earnings	Dividends	Book Value
10/14	71.17	10	8	5.36	2.57	32.67
10/13	67.18	11	9	5.30	2.48	32.22
10/12	57.03	12	8	4.94	2.27	30.72
10/11	48.92	16	10	4.21	2.13	27.71
10/10	53.38	18	12	3.40	1.96	26.87
Annual Growth	**7.5%**	**—**	**—**	**12.1%**	**7.0%**	**5.0%**

Royal Bank of Scotland Group Plc

If you have overdraft protection for your checking account you can thank The Royal Bank of Scotland (RBS) which introduced the service in 1728. Today RBS is one of Europe's largest banking groups. Through subsidiaries Royal Bank of Scotland and National Westminster Bank it has the UK's largest bank network of more than 2000 branches. RBS offers private banking and insurance products through Coutts Group and Adam & Company. Other divisions include Ulster Bank which operates in Ireland and Northern Ireland; Citizens Financial which operates as Citizens Bank and Charter One in the US; and US transaction processor RBS Lynk. After a series of bailouts in 2008 and 2009 the UK government owns 81% of RBS.

The group was crippled by both the global financial crisis and its ambitious international expansion primarily its disastrous 2007 investment in Dutch bank ABN AMRO. In late 2008 the UK took a 60% stake in RBS but the bank still ended up reporting an annual loss of some Â28 billion ($41 billion) —the largest loss in British corporate history. The government has since stepped in twice more to help RBS manage its debt and interest payments.

The government intervened with the contingency that RBS make significant efforts to get back on solid ground. Toward that end the group is cutting costs and selling operations to refocus on its core banking business. In 2010 it sold more than 300 branches and offices to Banco Santander for some Â1.65 billion ($2.6 billion). RBS is also selling noncore asset management units to Aberdeen Asset Management for a gain of Â84.7 million ($135 million). RBS sold its factoring and invoice financing unit to GE Capital and its payment services unit Global Merchant Services to Advent International and Bain Capital. It also sold its interest in RBS Sempra Commodities. In 2012 the company sold the international private banking business of Coutts to Royal Bank of Canada. Other divisions are simply being wound down and closed.

RBS also is scaling back on the international growth that weakened the group during the economic fallout with the ultimate goal of reducing non-UK operations to less than a quarter of its assets. In 2009 the group sold its 4% stake in Bank of China for some Â1.6 billion ($2.4 billion); it also sold most of its operations in Southeast Asia to Australia and New Zealand Banking Group for about $550 million. RBS divested units in Argentina Colombia Chile the United Arab Emirates Kazakhstan and Pakistan —all assets gained as part of its ABN AMRO transaction. In 2012 RBS sold all of the related investment banking operations in the Netherlands back to the reformed ABN AMRO. Additionally HSBC has agreed to buy the group's retail and commercial banking operations in India; DBS Group is buying those operations in China. Scotiabank bought the bank's business in Chile. In late 2014 it announced plans to wind down its fixed-income trading business in Japan and it is exploring scaling back or even completely exiting operations there. Altogether it is expected to exit more than half of the countries in which it operates.

The five-year plan to restore RBS has made some progress. The bank has somewhat narrowed its losses for the past three years although it still reported a nearly Â2 billion (some $3.2 billion) loss in 2011. RBS has been diligently reducing its exposure to riskier assets and strengthening its core business. However the company has been hurt by a number of factors including a Â1.1 billion impairment on Greek sovereign debt in 2011 and its exposure to bad loans from its Irish operations. Total revenues fell some 9% that year largely due to lower interest and trading earnings and the group's reduced size and scope.

More changes were announced in 2012 as the company continues to exit or downsize certain activities. It restructured its wholesale banking operations into two divisions —markets and international banking —and plans to stop doing business in cash equities corporate brokering equity capital markets and mergers and acquisitions. Its markets business is focused on fixed income while the international banking unit provides debt financing risk management and payments services. It has been selling parts of its structured retail investor products and equity derivatives businesses to BNP Paribas S.A. to de-emphasize some of its more complex structured products that are capital-intensive or costly to run.

RBS was ordered by the Federal Reserve in 2011 to improve its US operations or risk losing permission to do business in America. RBS must strengthen oversight management and risk management.

HISTORY

Royal Bank of Scotland was founded in 1727 but its roots go back to the Darien Company a merchant expedition that was established to set up a Scottish trading colony in Panama. The Darien expedition ended disastrously in 1699. In 1707 England voted to compensate Scottish creditors for the colony's failure (in part because England had promised support then reneged contributing to the collapse) and a small industry sprang up around paying creditors and loaning them money. In 1727 the Equivalent Company the combined entity of these organizations was granted a banking charter and became Royal Bank of Scotland.

In 1826 the Parliament voted to take away Scottish banks' right to issue banknotes for less than five pounds which would have required banks to use gold or silver. Few banks had such reserves and the move sparked an outcry. Novelist Sir Walter Scott's "The Letters of Malachi Malagrowther" which defended the Scottish one-pound note helped shoot down the proposal.

RBS expanded throughout Scotland over the next 50 years. It opened a London branch in 1874; it didn't establish a branch outside London until it bought Williams Deacon's Bank which had a branch network in North England. RBS continued to use the Williams Deacon's name as it did with Glyn Mills & Co. which it purchased in 1939.

In 1968 RBS took on its modern persona as a public company when it merged with National Commercial Bank. The company moved overseas during the 1970s establishing offices in Hong Kong and major US cities.

RBS spent the next 20 years trying to achieve another merger of the same scale as National Commercial. In 1981 the bank was wooed by Standard Chartered Bank and Hongkong and Shanghai Bank (now part of HSBC Holdings) but British regulators denied both suitors.

The bank moved into telephone operations in 1985 when it set up Direct Line for selling car insurance. In 1988 RBS bought New England bank Citizens Financial (but it plans to divest that business). In 1989 the company entered into an alliance with Banco Santander (now Santander Central Hispano) Spain's largest banking group. The alliance created a cross-pollination of ideas and strategies that boosted both banks' operations. The first fruit of the alliance came in 1991 with the launch of Interbank On-line Systems (IBOS) which

connected several European banks and allowed for instantaneous money transfers.

In the 1990s RBS was linked with a variety of partners. It even made a bid for the much larger bank Barclays in a move regarded as cheeky but was rebuffed. In 1997 it announced a joint venture with Richard Branson's Virgin Group called Virgin Direct to offer personal banking. The company also bought Angel Trains Contract a rolling stock leasing company and established a transatlantic banking transfer system (similar to IBOS) with US bank CoreStates (now owned by First Union).

In 2000 RBS acquired NatWest after a prolonged takeover battle with rival Bank of Scotland (now part of HBOS plc). The bank sold Gartmore Investment Management its fund management unit to Nationwide Mutual Insurance Company. Royal Bank also sold the assets of NatWest's Equity Partners unit and launched NatWest Private Banking to target wealthy investors.

In 2004 RBS made several acquisitions to boost its US presence: It paid about $360 million for the credit card business of Connecticut-based People's Bank and bought payments processor Lynk Systems (now RBS Lynk) while Citizens Financial bought Cleveland-based bank Charter One Financial. Also that year Ulster Bank bought Ireland-based retail financial services provider First Active.

In 2007 RBS led the consortium that acquired the Dutch bank for Â71 billion in a deal that was called the largest ever in the banking industry. The buyers carved ABN AMRO into pieces; RBS took the global wholesale and international retail operations in Asia Eastern Europe and the Middle East. The ambitious takeover preceded the global economic crisis though and RBS was among the hardest hit financial groups.

The troubled company made several moves to try and raise capital. Early in 2008 the company announced a Â12 billion rights issue. RBS also tried but failed to find a buyer for its insurance arm. However other assets were divested that year. The company sold rolling stock leasing firm Angel Trains to Babcock & Brown and others and it sold its joint venture Tesco Personal Finance back to supermarket giant Tesco. The efforts proved inadequate though. The government took a controlling stake in the group in 2008 the same year that RBS reported the largest corporate loss in British history.

Also as part of the government rescue RBS went through a management shakeup. Fred Goodwin the architect of the bank's international expansion was removed as CEO. He was replaced by Stephen Hester formerly the CEO of British Land Company. Johnny Cameron chairman of the group's global banking and markets segment (which lost the group's most money in 2008) was also ousted and chairman Tom McKillop retired early.

RBS also shuffled its corporate structure in 2009. It split its UK retail and commercial banking division into three segments (retail commercial and wealth) and made Ulster Bank its own segment. The group folded its operations support division into other arms and established a segment to manage the selling and runoff of noncore operations. RBS retained the Global Banking & Markets Global Transaction Services US Retail & Commercial and RBS Insurance (including Churchill Insurance) segments although several of their components were transferred to the noncore segment.

In October 2012 RBS sold a 30% stake in Direct Line Group part of its insurance group in an IPO valued at Â2.6 billion ($4.2 billion).

EXECUTIVES

CFO and Director, Bruce W. Van Saun, age 56, $530,336 total compensation

Group Chief Executive and Director, Stephen A. M. Hester, age 53, $1,765,706 total compensation

Head Human Resources, Neil Roden

Global Head Global Restructuring Group, Derek S. Sach, age 59

Chief Executive - Citizens and Head of Americas, Ellen Alemany, age 58

President Global Banking and Markets, Suneel Kamlani

Chairman, Sir Philip Hampton, age 61, $1,114,820 total compensation

Chief Administration Officer, Ron Teerlink, age 53

Head Group Corporate Affairs, Andrew Wilson, age 43

Head Restructuring and Risk, Nathan Bostock, age 53

Group Treasurer, John Cummins

CEO UK Corporate Banking Division, Chris Sullivan, age 56

Co-Head Global Banks and Markets Americas; Head Fixed Income Trading for Americas, Michael Lyublinsky

Head Investor Relations, Richard O'Connor

Chairman Asia, John McCormick

Group Chief Economist and Head Communications, Andrew McLaughlin

Head Finance Europe Middle East and Africa, John McIntyre

Co-Head Global Banking and Markets Americas; Head North America Corporate Coverage and Advisory, Bob McKillip

Director, Baroness Sheila V. Noakes, age 64

CEO Global Banking and Markets, John Hourican, age 43

Global Head Markets, Peter Nielsen

Chief Administrative Officer Markets, Jeremy Wright

CEO RBS Insurance, Paul Geddes, age 44

Chief Executive UK Retail, Ross McEwan

Chief China Economist, Ben Simpfendorfer

COO Group Manufacturing, Richard Hemsley

Deputy CEO Global Banking and Markets, Marco Mazzuchelli

Head Group Media Centre, Jason Knauf

Senior Assistant Secretary, Jan Cargill

Group Secretary, Aileen Taylor

Group General Counsel, Chris Campbell

CEO UK Corporate and Institutional Banking, Mark Catton

Head Noncore Division and Asset Protection Scheme, Rory Cullinan

Global Head Securitized Products and Head of US Credit Global Banking & Markets Division, Scott Eichel

Chairman and CEO China, Sherry Liu

Regional Head Global Banking, Matthew Kirkby

Head West Register, Helen Gordon

Owner of a start-up business, Josh Parker

Group Finance Director; Executive Director, Bruce Saun

Vice President and he, Gao Qi

CFO and Director, Bruce W. Van Saun, age 56

Director, Joseph P. (Joe) MacHale, age 62

Director, Arthur F. (Art) Ryan, age 71

Group Chief Executive and Director, Stephen A. M. Hester, age 53

Director, John McFarlane, age 66

Director, Sir Sandy Crombie, age 65

Director, Philip G. Scott, age 60

Director, Penelope L. (Penny) Hughes, age 55

Director, Alison Davis, age 52

Director, Anthony (Tony) Di Iorio, age 70

Director, Baroness Sheila V. Noakes, age 64

Director, Brendan Nelson, age 64

Independent Non-Executive Director, Tony Iorio

Auditors: Deloitte&ToucheLLP

LOCATIONS

HQ: Royal Bank of Scotland Group Plc
RBS Gogarburn, P.O. Box 1000, Edinburgh EH12 1HQ
Phone: (44) 131 626 0000   **Fax:** (44) 131 626 3081
Web: www.rbs.com

Sales

	% of total
UK	67
Rest of US	11
US	18
Other	4
Total	**100**

PRODUCTS/OPERATIONS

Sales by Segment

	% of total
Global banking &	21
UK	20
RBS	15
UK	14
US retail &	11
Global transaction	8
Wealth	4
Ulster	3
Other	4
Total	**100**

Sales

	% of total
Net	42
Fees &	21
Insurance net premium	14
Other	23
Total	**100**

Selected Subsidiaries

Citizens Financial Group Inc. (banking US)
Coutts & Co (private banking)
Direct Line Insurance Group plc
National Westminster Bank Plc
The Royal Bank of Scotland plc
Ulster Bank Limited (Northern Ireland)

COMPETITORS

AIB	JPMorgan Chase
Bank of America	Lloyds Banking Group
Bank of Ireland	PNC Financial
Barclays	Santander UK
Citigroup	Standard Chartered
HSBC	Standard Life
ING Direct UK	permanent tsb

HISTORICAL FINANCIALS

Company Type: Public

Income Statement

FYE: December 31

	ASSETS ($ mil.)	NET INCOME ($ mil.)	INCOME AS % OF ASSETS	EMPLOYEES
12/13	1,698,649	(14,783)	—	114,900
12/12	2,115,244	(9,600)	—	137,200
12/11	2,327,889	(3,085)	—	142,600
12/10	2,256,880	(1,717)	—	145,500
12/09	2,747,596	(5,749)	—	159,700
Annual Growth	(11.3%)	—	—	(7.9%)

2013 Year-End Financials

Return on assets: (-0.7%)
Return on equity: (-14.1%)
Long-term debt ($ mil.): —
No. of shares (mil.): —
Sales ($ mil): 43,723
Dividends
  Yield: 7.7%
  Payout: —
Market value ($ mil.): —

	STOCK PRICE ($) FY Close	P/E High/Low	PER SHARE ($) Earnings	Dividends	Book Value
12/13	20.46	— —	(1.33)	1.59	1.70
12/12	22.52	— —	(0.88)	1.19	1.92
12/11	11.20	— —	(0.28)	0.00	10.49
12/10	14.55	— —	(0.08)	1.19	10.66
12/09	10.35	— —	(1.02)	1.59	22.34
Annual Growth	18.6% (47.5%)	— —	—	(0.0%)	

Royal Bank of Scotland plc

LOCATIONS

HQ: Royal Bank of Scotland plc
36 St Andrew Square, Edinburgh EH2 2YB
Phone: (44) 131 556 8555
Web: www.rbs.co.uk

HISTORICAL FINANCIALS

Company Type: Public

Income Statement

FYE: December 31

	REVENUE ($ mil.)	NET INCOME ($ mil.)	NET PROFIT MARGIN	EMPLOYEES
12/13	41,180	(12,078)	—	106,100
12/12	40,424	(6,210)	—	108,100
12/11	42,138	(2,541)	—	110,900
12/10	47,931	(1,510)	—	113,600
12/09	56,029	(385)	—	0
Annual Growth	(7.4%)	—	—	—

2013 Year-End Financials

Debt ratio: —
Return on equity: (-13.5%)
Cash ($ mil.): 132,194
Current ratio: —
Long-term debt ($ mil.): —
No. of shares (mil.): —
Dividends
  Yield: —
  Payout: —
Market value ($ mil.): —

	STOCK PRICE ($) FY Close	P/E High/Low	PER SHARE ($) Earnings	Dividends	Book Value
12/13	36.24	— —	(0.00)	0.00	12.20
12/12	27.70	— —	(0.00)	0.00	14.46
12/11	24.06	— —	(0.00)	0.00	14.43
12/10	25.82	— —	(0.00)	0.00	13.39
Annual Growth	12.0%	— —	—	—	(2.3%)

Royal Dutch Shell Plc

Royal Dutch Shell which sits on an oil and gas throne that is only slightly below that of #1 oil company Exxon Mobil has worldwide proved reserves of 13.9 billion barrels of oil equivalent. Most of the oil giant's crude is produced in Nigeria Oman the UK and the US. It is also investing in the Athabasca Oil Sands Project which converts oil sands in Alberta to synthetic oil. The company operates 44000 gas stations (the world's largest re-

tail fuel network). Royal Dutch Shell also produces refined products and chemicals at more than 30 refineries (with the capacity to process 3.3 million barrels of crude oil per day) transports natural gas trades gas and electricity and develops renewable energy.

Geographic Reach

The company operates around the world in more than 70 countries including in Australia Brazil Brunei Canada China Denmark Germany Malaysia the Netherlands Nigeria Norway Oman Qatar Russia the UK and the US.

Operations

Royal Dutch Shell operates in three segments: Upstream Downstream and the Corporate segment.

Through Upstream International and Upstream Americas the company explores for and produces crude oil natural gas and natural gas liquids; transports oil and gas; and operates the upstream and midstream infrastructure required to deliver oil and gas to market. Upstream International also manages liquefied natural gas (LNG) and gas-to-liquids (GTL) businesses. Upstream Americas also extracts bitumen from oil sands in Canada which is converted into synthetic crude oil.

In 2013 Royal Dutch Shell added 1.6 billion barrels of oil equivalent of gross proved reserves. The Downstream segment is engaged in the manufacturing supply distribution and marketing of oil products and chemicals; alternative energy (excluding wind); and CO2 management. Downstream accounted for about 88% and Upstream accounted for 10% of Royal Dutch Shell's total revenues in 2013.

In 2013 the company produced 3.2 million barrels of oil equivalent a day and sold about 19.6 million tons of LNG.

The segment's Supply and Distribution infrastructure has more than 1500 storage tanks and 150 distribution facilities in 25 countries. It supplies more than 100 grades of lubricants and 20 different types of fuel serving more than 15000 vessels worldwide. Royal Dutch Shell's Corporate segment manages the company's non-operating activities including Shell's holdings and treasury organization its headquarters and central functions as well as its self-insurance activities.

Financial Performance

The company's revenues declined by 5% in fiscal 2013 primarily due to lower Downstream segment sales decreased interest and lower other income received; partially offset by higher Upstream revenues. Upstream revenues rose thanks to an 1.4% increase in global oil demand driven by emerging economies. Synthetic crude oil prices posted a 7% increase while gas prices were 6% higher than in 2012. These gains were partially offset by lower liquids prices. In the Downstream segment oil products sales volumes dipped by 1% in 2012 reflecting lower marketing and trading volumes partly offset by the increased Refinery intake volumes. The drop was also caused by field declines and the impact of the challenging operating environment in Nigeria. Royal Dutch Shell's net income decreased by 38% in 2013 due to lower revenues and high depreciation charges as a result of impairments and a change in financial reporting requirements.

Strategy

The company's key strengths include the development and application of technology the financial and project-management skills to deliver large field development projects and the management of integrated value chains.

Royal Dutch Shell committed about 85% of its capital investment in 2014 to Upstream activities. It's long term strategy includes developing shale oil and gas plays and future opportunities such as heavy oil plays and new fields in the Arctic Iraq Kazakhstan and Nigeria.

Looking to focus its onshore US drilling program on a few of the more prolific formations in an effort to boost profitability in 2014 Royal Dutch Shell agreed to sell drilling rights in shale formations in Louisiana and Wyoming for $2.1 billion in two transactions. In one of the deals the company will also receive drilling rights to land in Ohio and Pennsylvania.

To free up cash in 2014 Royal Dutch Shell also agreed to sell its Australian downstream businesses to Vitol for A$2.9 billion (US$2.6 billion).

While committed to developing clean energy as a way to reduce carbon emissions Royal Dutch Shell is focusing on clean oil production technology (such as carbon sequestration) and biofuels which are more in line with its core oil and gas competencies rather than on wind power and solar energy.

Boosting its research and development capability in 2013 the company relaunched its Shell Technology Center Houston as the global base for a number of specific technology focus areas across the upstream and downstream segment. Royal Dutch Shell spends more than a billion dollars a year on research and development activities.

Expanding its Canadian oil and gas production activities in 2012 Royal Dutch Shell announced plans to ramp up production at its Athabasca Oil Sands project in Alberta and to develop shale gas and an LNG export terminal in British Columbia.

Mergers and Acquisitions

In 2014 the company acquired Repsol's LNG portfolio outside of North America including supply positions in Peru and Trinidad and Tobago for about $4 billion.

Growing its North America shale portfolio in 2012 Royal Dutch Shell acquired 618000 net acres in the Permian Basin in West Texas (with production of 26000 barrels of oil equivalent per day) from Chesapeake Energy for $2 billion.It also agreed to buy Hess' stake in the North Sea Beryl area fields and the Scottish Area Gas Evacuation System for $525 million.

In a move to expand its position as a provider of shallow water drilling services in Asia Africa and the Middle East in 2012 it formed Shell Drilling Holdings which bought 37 jackup drilling rigs one swamp barge and associated operations from Transocean for $1.05 billion.

HISTORY

In 1870 Marcus Samuel inherited an interest in his father's London trading company which imported seashells from the Far East. He expanded the business and after securing a contract for Russian oil began selling kerosene in the Far East.

Standard Oil underpriced competitors to defend its Asian markets. Samuel secretly prepared his response and in 1892 unveiled the first of a fleet of tankers. Rejecting Standard's acquisition overtures Samuel created "Shell" Transport and Trading in 1897.

Meanwhile a Dutchman Aeilko Zijlker struck oil in Sumatra and formed Royal Dutch Petroleum in 1890 to exploit the oil field. Young Henri Deterding joined the firm in 1896 and established a sales force in the Far East.

Deterding became Royal Dutch's head in 1900 amid the battle for the Asian market. In 1903 Deterding Samuel and the Rothschilds (a French banking family) created Asiatic Petroleum a marketing alliance. With Shell's non-Asian business eroding Deterding engineered a merger between Royal Dutch and Shell in 1907. Royal Dutch shareholders got 60% control; "Shell" Transport and Trading 40%.

After the 1911 Standard Oil breakup Deterding entered the US building refineries and buying producers. Shell products were available in every state by 1929. Royal Dutch/Shell joined the 1928 "As Is" cartel that fixed prices for most of two decades.

The post-WWII Royal Dutch/Shell profited from worldwide growth in oil consumption. It acquired 100% of Shell Oil its US arm in 1985 but shareholders sued maintaining Shell Oil's assets had been undervalued in the deal. They were awarded $110 million in 1990.

Management's slow response to two 1995 controversies —environmentalists' outrage over the planned sinking of an oil platform and human rights activists' criticism of Royal Dutch/Shell's role in Nigeria —spurred a major shakeup. It began moving away from its decentralized structure and adopted a new policy of corporate openness.

In 1996 Royal Dutch/Shell and Exxon (now Exxon Mobil) formed a worldwide petroleum additives venture. Shell Oil joined Texaco (now part of Chevron) in 1998 to form Equilon Enterprises combining US refining and marketing operations in the West and Midwest. Similarly Shell Oil Texaco and Saudi Arabia's Aramco combined downstream operations on the US's East and Gulf coasts as Motiva Enterprises.

In 1999 Royal Dutch/Shell and the UK's BG plc acquired a controlling stake in Comgas a unit of Companhia Energetica de S o Paulo and the largest natural gas distributor in Brazil for about $1 billion.

In 2000 the company sold its coal business to UK-based mining giant Anglo American for more than $850 million. To gain a foothold in the US power marketing scene Royal Dutch/Shell formed a joint venture with construction giant Bechtel (called InterGen). The next year the company agreed to combine its German refining and marketing operations with those of RWE-DEA. Royal Dutch/Shell tried to expand its US natural gas reserves in 2001 by making a $2 billion hostile bid for Barrett Resources but the effort was withdrawn after Barrett agreed to be acquired by Williams for $2.5 billion.

In 2002 in connection with Chevron's acquisition of Texaco Royal Dutch/Shell acquired ChevronTexaco's (now Chevron) stakes in the underperforming US marketing joint ventures Equilon and Motiva. That year the company through its US Shell Oil unit acquired Pennzoil-Quaker State for $1.8 billion. Also that year Royal Dutch/Shell acquired Enterprise Oil for $5 billion plus debt. In addition it purchased RWE's 50% stake in German refining and marketing joint venture Shell & DEA Oil (for $1.35 billion).

In 2004 the group signed a $200 million exploration deal with Libya signaling its return to that country after a more than decade-long absence. Also that year the company reported that it had overestimated its reserves by 24%. The bad news resulted in the ouster of the chairman and CFO.

The Anglo-Dutch entity restructured to stay competitive. Revelations of overestimated oil reserves in 2004 prompted a push for greater transparency in the company's organizational structure. This led to the 2005 merger of former publicly traded owners Royal Dutch Petroleum and The "Shell" Transport and Trading Company into Royal Dutch Shell.

Searching for new oil assets in 2006 the company acquired a large swath of oil sands acreage in Alberta Canada. Further boosting its oil sands business in 2007 the company acquired the 22% of Shell Canada that it did not already own. The company also began investing some $12 billion (in addition to the $2.6 billion already spent) in offshore projects near Dubai. In 2008 Royal Dutch Shell expanded its exploration assets in Alaska by

acquiring 275 lease blocks in the Chukchi Sea for $2.1 billion.

In 2009 the company made significant oil discoveries in the deepwater eastern Gulf of Mexico at West Boreas Vito and the Cardamom Deep and in 2010 at the Appomattox prospect in the Mississippi Canyon block. The finds expanded Shell Oil's long-term development plans in the area.

Further expanding its unconventional natural gas resources in 2010 the company spent $4.7 billion to acquire East Resources which holds 1 million acres of Marcellus Shale one of the fastest-growing shale plays in the US.

On the conventional side of the oil business the Gulf of Mexico produces 370000 barrels of oil per day or about 15% of Royal Dutch Shell's worldwide production. In 2010 the company claimed an industry record starting production at the deepest floating drilling and production platform in the world. The Perdido Development operates in 8000 ft. of water in the Gulf of Mexico. In response to the BP oil rig disaster in the Gulf of Mexico the company joined forces with Exxon Mobil Chevron and ConocoPhillips to form a $1 billion rapid-response joint venture that will be able to better manage and contain future deepwater spills.

With an eye toward raising cash and focusing on its majority holdings and joint ventures rather than on minority held businesses in 2010 Royal Dutch Shell sold 10% of its 34% in Australian oil and gas enterprise Woodside Petroleum for $3.3 billion. Royal Dutch Shell also announced that it would seek to sell the rest of its stake in Woodside Petroleum over time. (Earlier in the year the company formed a $3.5 billion joint venture with PetroChina which acquired Arrow Energy a company with major natural gas assets in Northern Australia).

As part of its strategy of selling noncore downstream assets to raise cash in 2010 Royal Dutch Shell sold its Finnish and Swedish operations (including a refinery in Gothenburg and 565 gas stations) to Finland-based St1 for $640 million. In 2011 it sold its UK-based Stanlow refinery to India's Essar Group for $350 million.

In 2010 the company formed a $12 billion joint venture with Brazil's Cosan to ramp up ethanol production.

EXECUTIVES

Chairman, Jorma Ollila, age 64
Downstream Director, Mark Williams, age 63
Chief Financial Officer, Simon Henry, age 53, $643,507 total compensation
Chairman Shell Companies in Australia, Russell R. Caplan, age 67
Chief Executive Officer, Peter R. Voser, age 56, $1,815,864 total compensation
Chairman Shell U.K. Limited, James Smith
Vice President Global Business Environment, Jeremy B. Bentham
Deputy Chairman, Lord John O. Kerr of Kinlochard, age 72
President Director Upstream Americas Shell Oil Company; Chairman Shell Canada, Marvin E. Odum, age 54
Company Secretary, Michiel Brandjes, age 59
President Shell Energy North America (US), Mark Quartermain
EVP Russia and Caspian Region, Charles Watson
EVP Upstream Australia, Ann Pickard
EVP Americas Shell Gas & Power, Curtis R. Frasier
VP Shell Canada, Thomas G. Zengerly
EVP Shell Canada, John Abbott
President and Country Chair Shell Canada, Lorraine Mitchelmore
VP Shell Canada, Stephanie Sterling

Chair and Managing Director Shell Petroleum Development Company Nigeria; VP Production Africa, Mutiu Sunmonu
Head Group Media Relations, Stuart Bruseth
VP Downstream Australia, Andrew Smith, age 50
Finance Manager Shell Development Australia, Michael Carey
Technical VP Europe, John Gallagher, age 54
General Manager UK Retail, Melanie Lane
VP Human Resources UK Ireland and Nordics, Paul Milliken
Head UK Government Relations, Kate Smith
VP Corporate and UK Country Controller, Graham Talbot
Vice President Global Media Relations, Andy Norman
Vice President Investor Relations, Ken Lawrence
Board Member, Charles O. (Chad) Holliday Jr., age 67
Board Member, Josef Ackermann, age 66
CFO and Board Member, Simon Henry, age 53
Board Member, Jeroen van der Veer, age 66
Chief Executive Officer, Peter R. Voser, age 56
Board Member, Guy Elliott, age 57
Board Member, G. J. (Hans) Wijers, age 63
Executive Director Upstream International and Board Member, Malcolm Brinded, age 60
Deputy Chairman, Lord John O. Kerr of Kinlochard, age 72
Board Member, Wim Kok, age 75
Board Member, Christine Morin-Postel, age 67
Board Member, Gerard J. Kleisterlee, age 68
Independent Director, Martha Piper
Auditors: PricewaterhouseCoopersLLP

LOCATIONS

HQ: Royal Dutch Shell Plc
Carel van Bylandtlaan 30, The Hague 2596 HR
Phone: (31) 70 377 9111   Fax: (44) 20 7934 5153
Web: www.shell.com

Sales

	$ mil.	% of total
Europe	187,498	40
Africa Asia Australia/Oceania	148,260	31
US	91,946	20
Other Americas	42,467	9
Adjustments	14,318	-
Total	**484,489**	**100**

PRODUCTS/OPERATIONS

Sales

	$ mil.	% of total
Downstream	427,864	91
Upstream	42,260	9
Corporate & other	47	-
Adjustments	14,318	-
Total	**484,489**	**100**

COMPETITORS

7-Eleven	Imperial Oil
Ashland Inc.	Koch Industries Inc.
BHP Billiton	Marathon Oil
BP	Norsk Hydro ASA
Chevron	Occidental Petroleum
ConocoPhillips	PEMEX
Dow Chemical	PETROBRAS
DuPont	PetroKazakhstan
Eastman Chemical	Petroleos de Venezuela
Eni	Repsol
Exxon Mobil	Sinopec Shanghai
FEC Resources	Petrochemical
Hess Corporation	Sunoco
Huntsman International	TOTAL

HISTORICAL FINANCIALS

Company Type: Public

Income Statement

FYE: December 31

	REVENUE ($ mil.)	NET INCOME ($ mil.)	NET PROFIT MARGIN	EMPLOYEES
12/13	459,599	16,371	3.6%	92,000
12/12	481,700	26,592	5.5%	87,000
12/11	484,489	30,918	6.4%	90,000
12/10	378,152	20,127	5.3%	97,000
12/09	285,129	12,518	4.4%	101,000
Annual Growth	**12.7%**	**6.9%**	**—**	**(2.3%)**

2013 Year-End Financials

Debt ratio: 12.4%	No. of shares (mil.): —
Return on equity: 8.8%	Dividends
Cash ($ mil.): 9,696	Yield: 5.0%
Current ratio: 1.11	Payout: 136.9%
Long-term debt ($ mil.): 36,218	Market value ($ mil.): —

	STOCK PRICE ($) FY Close	P/E High/Low	PER SHARE ($) Earnings	Dividends	Book Value
12/13	71.27	28 24	2.60	3.56	28.50
12/12	68.95	17 14	4.24	3.42	29.77
12/11	73.09	16 12	4.98	3.36	27.10
12/10	66.78	21 15	3.28	3.36	23.93
12/09	60.11	31 19	2.04	3.32	21.86
Annual Growth	**4.3%**	**— —**	**6.3%**	**1.8%**	**6.9%**

Royal London Mutual Insurance Society Ltd (United Kingdom)

The Royal London Mutual Insurance Society wants to give its customers the royal treatment. The company and its subsidiaries collectively known as the Royal London Group offer products and services including life insurance pensions savings products investment products property/casualty insurance credit insurance and investment management under such brands as Royal London Asset Management Scottish Life and Bright Grey among others. The company is one of the UK's largest mutual life and pensions insurers with about 4 million customers and more than Â46 billion (almost $75 billion) under management. The Royal London Group sells both directly and through financial advisors in the UK and the Isle of Man.

Although the economic environment in the UK and the world is uncertain and likely to remain so for some time the group remains calm and carries on. Its capital strength and stability in fact continue to improve. In 2011 Royal London Group had record life and pension new business levels. Increased capital reflected this along with positive investment returns added to its assets.

During 2011 the group acquired Royal Liver Assurance and successfully integrated the business; its Royal London Asset Management (RLAM) business carries out its asset management. Royal London Group is looking to add new business in 2012 as well by acquiring The Co-operative Banking Group's life pensions and asset management businesses representing some 2 mil-

lion policyholders and Â20 billion (more than $32 billion) funds under management.

The acquisitive moves are part of the company's strategy to grow its business provide security for its policyholders and members and allow for the delivery of good financial returns.

Royal London combined its Scottish Life International Insurance and Scottish Provident International Life Assurance into Royal London 360Â in 2008. The new entity emerged as an investment savings and tax planning company with $3 billion under management.

The moves were part of other plans and consolidations. The company also bought Scottish Provident offering individual life insurance and Phoenix Life Assurance now Royal London Retail from Pearl Group in 2008.

EXECUTIVES

Director, Trevor Bish-Jones, age 52
Director, Robert Jeens, age 59
Group Chief Executive and Board Member, Mike Yardley, age 56
Group Finance Director and Board Member, Stephen Shone, age 56
Chief Executive Royal London Asset Management, Andrew (Andy) Carter
Director, Tom Ross, age 66
Director, David Williams
Executive Director, John Deane
Client Relationship Director and Director, Victoria Muir
Head Property and Director, Gareth Dickinson
Auditors: PricewaterhouseCoopersLLP

LOCATIONS

HQ: Royal London Mutual Insurance Society Ltd (United Kingdom)
55 Gracechurch Street, London EC3V 0RL
Phone: (44) 845 050 2020
Web: www.royallondongroup.co.uk

PRODUCTS/OPERATIONS

Selected Brands

Ascentric/IFDL (wrap platform investment administration and consolidation services)
Bright Grey (protection insurance)
Caledonian Life (return on investment protection products brokered in Ireland)
MoneyVista (online financial planning for consumers)
Royal London 360 (international division; offshore investment)
Royal London Asset Management (fund management; fixed income cash property and equity asset management)
Royal London Plus (life and pensions administration)
Scottish Life (pensions specialist)
Scottish Provident (personal mortgage and business protection)

COMPETITORS

AXA UK	Lloyds Banking Group
Aviva	Prudential plc
Clerical Medical	Standard Life
Friends Provident	
Legal & General Group	

HISTORICAL FINANCIALS

Company Type: Public

Income Statement

FYE: December 31

	ASSETS ($ mil.)	NET INCOME ($ mil.)	INCOME AS % OF ASSETS	EMPLOYEES
12/13	105,970	614	0.6%	3,050
12/12	64,070	419	0.7%	2,787
12/11	59,875	135	0.2%	2,692
12/10	53,168	293	0.6%	2,710
12/09	50,817	664	1.3%	2,718
Annual Growth	20.2%	(1.9%)	—	2.9%

2013 Year-End Financials

Return on assets: 0.7%
Return on equity: —
Long-term debt ($ mil.): —
No. of shares (mil.): —
Sales ($ mil): 8,104

Dividends
Yield: —
Payout: —
Market value ($ mil.): —

RWE AG

RWE doesn't stand for Runs With Electricity but it could. RWE is one of Germany's top two electricity suppliers (along with E.ON). Through its subsidiaries the energy conglomerate provides electricity and gas to residential and business customers primarily in Central and Western Europe. It also owns major UK-based utilities and German-based electricity and gas supplier RWE npower. RWE owns oil and gas exploration and production unit RWE-DEA; other businesses include companies engaged in gas transportation and storage power generation (including wind) energy trading information technology and coal mining. In 2011 RWE served 17 million electricity customers and 8 million gas customers.

Geographic Reach

RWE operates in Germany the Netherlands/Belgium the UK and in Central Eastern and South Eastern Europe. Germany accounted for more than 50% of the company's revenues in 2011.

Operations

In addition to generating power and distributing electricity and gas in its core geographic markets the company also develops renewable power through RWE Innogy; explores for and produces oil and gas through RWE-DEA; and engages in energy trading and gas midstream activities through RWE Supply & Trading.

Financial Performance

The company's revenues decreased by 3% in 2011 due to a drop in revenues from the Germany power generation Netherlands/Belgium and Trading/Gas Midstream segments. Power generation revenues declined due to the German government's shift in energy policy (exiting nuclear power) following the reactor disaster at Fukushima. Netherlands/Belgium revenues declined due to a drop in Essent's gas midstream business caused by a drop in electricity generation margins. Trading/Gas Midstream revenues declined due to a drop in the realization of successful forward transactions and in some of its gas purchase contracts.

The company's net income decreased by 45% in 2011 due to a decrease in revenues and operating income caused by an increase in the costs of material depreciation amortization and impairment losses and other operating expenses.

Strategy

RWE plans its investments in power stations networks and raw material production facilities in terms of decades not in terms of years. It is looking to compete more effectively in the deregulated German power and gas markets order by restructuring its regional energy businesses. The company's former German utility unit RWE Energie lost its regional monopoly status because of deregulation and RWE has responded by splitting its domestic power generation distribution and supply operations into new units. RWE has also responded by acquiring utilities and energy services companies in the Czech Republic Hungary Poland and Slovakia and by targeting expansion in Europe.

RWE is also focusing on the expansion of renewable energy in Germany the UK the Netherlands Poland Spain and Italy.

In 2011 the company acquired Energy Resources Holding B.V. which has owns 30 % of EPZ a Dutch electricity generator.

To meet antitrust requirements in 2011 RWE sold its 75% stake in the German natural gas transmission grid business (Thyssengas) to Macquarie Group. To pay down debt in 2011 it also sold its German long-distance power grid to a consortium of five pension funds of German and Swiss insurers for $1.4 billion. RWE retained operational control of the grid.

A possible merger between RWE and Spanish power giant IBERDROLA fell through in 2011 due to market and political concerns.

HISTORY

Founded at the end of the 19th century RWE mirrored the industrialization of Germany in its growth. It was formed as Rheinisch-Westfalisches Elektrizitatswerk in 1898 by Erich Zweigert the mayor of Essen and Hugo Stinnes an industrialist from Mulheim to provide electricity to Essen and surrounding areas. The company began supplying power in 1900.

Stinnes persuaded other cities —Gelsenkirchen and Mulheim —to buy shares in RWE in 1905. In 1908 RWE and rival Vereinigte Elektrizitatswerk Westfalen (VEW) agreed to divide up the territories that each would supply.

Germany's coal shortages caused by WWI prompted RWE to expand its coal operations and it bought Rheinische Aktiengesellschaft for Braunkohlenbergbau a coal producer in 1932. RWE also built a power line network completed in 1930 to connect populous northern Germany with the south. By 1939 as WWII began the company had plants throughout most of western Germany. However the war destroyed much of its infrastructure and RWE had to rebuild.

The company continued to rely on coal for most of its fuel needs in the 1950s but in 1961 RWE and Bayern Atomkraft sponsored the construction of a demonstration nuclear reactor the first of several such projects at Gundremmingen. The Gundremmingen plant was shut down in 1977 and to replace it RWE built two 1300-MW reactors that began operation in 1984.

RWE began to diversify and in 1988 it acquired Texaco's German petroleum and petrochemical unit which became RWE-DEA. By 1990 RWE's operations also included waste management and construction. RWE reorganized creating RWE Aktiengesellschaft as a holding company for group operations.

RWE-DEA acquired the US's Vista Chemical in 1991 and RWE's Rheinbraun mining unit bought a 50% stake in Consolidation Coal from DuPont. (The mining venture went public in 1999 as CONSOL Energy.) RWE led a consortium that acquired major stakes in three Hungarian power companies in 1995.

Hoping to play a role in Germany's telecommunications market RWE teamed with VEBA in 1997 to form the o.tel.o joint venture and RWE and VEBA gained control of large German mobile phone operator E-Plus. The nation's telecom market was deregulated in 1998 but Mannesmann and former monopoly Deutsche Telekom proved to be formidable competitors. In 1999 RWE and VEBA sold o.tel.o's fixed-line business (along with the o.tel.o brand name) and cable-TV unit Tele Columbus. The next year the companies sold their joint stake in E-Plus.

Faced with deregulating German electricity markets RWE Energie had begun restructuring as soon as the market opened up in 1998. It agreed to buy fellow German power company VEW in a $20 billion deal that closed in 2000. RWE also joined with insurance giant Allianz and France's Vivendi in a successful bid for a 49.9% stake in state-owned water distributor Berliner Wasserbetriebe (Vivendi later spurned an RWE offer to buy its energy businesses).

After taking advantage of deregulating markets in Germany RWE moved to pick up other European utilities: It acquired UK-based Thames Water (later renamed RWE Thames Water) in 2000 and bought a majority stake in Dutch gas supplier Intergas the next year. In 2002 the company issued an exchange offer to acquire UK electricity supplier Innogy (later renamed RWE npower) for a total of about $4.4 billion in cash and $3 billion in assumed debt. It also completed a $3.7 billion purchase of Czech Republic gas supplier Transgas.

In a move to further streamline operations RWE sold its 50% stake in refinery and service station subsidiary Shell & DEA Oil to Deutsche Shell and Shell Petroleum. To do battle in an increasingly competitive utility industry RWE is acquiring stakes in other European utilities. In 2003 RWE also acquired North American utility American Water Works which was combined with the US operations of RWE Thames Water for $4.6 billion in cash and $4 billion in assumed debt.

Recognizing that its international acquisitions of water utilities in the early 2000s had left it overextended RWE has been to selling its water assets in order to save cash and streamline its operations around its core power businesses. Overextended in 2006 the company sold its Thames Water unit to Kemble Water Limited a consortium led by Macquarie Bank's European Infrastructure Funds. It spun off its American Water unit in 2008.

The company saw its revenues drop in 2009 as the global recession hammered gas prices. However the same lower gas prices helped RWE to save costs enabling it to post an improved net income that year.

After being outmaneuvered by EDF in its plan to grow its Pan-European power footprint by acquiring British Energy RWE in 2009 acquired top Dutch power utility Essent for $10.7 billion. The deal boost its position as one of the top electricity and gas utilities in Europe.

Growing its energy sources in 2009 it also formed a joint venture with E.ON to develop 6000 MW of nuclear power capacity in the UK. In a move to reduce its dependency on the wholesale gas markets in 2009 RWE acquired 70% of the Breagh North Sea gas field for about $350 million.

The company announced CEO Jorgen Gro -mann who fought Germany's decision to phase out nuclear power stepped down in July 2012. Gro -mann was replaced by Peter Terium the CEO of Essent. COO Rolf Martin Schmitz was named Deputy CEO.

EXECUTIVES

Chairman Supervisory Board, Manfred Schneider, age 75

CFO and Member Executive Board, Rolf Pohlig, age 61

Deputy Chairman, Frank Bsirske

Chief Human Resources Officer, Alwin Fitting, age 61

Chairman Executive Board, Peter Terium, age 50

Manager Investor Relations Retail Shareholders, Cornelia Rath

Chief Commercial Officer, Leonhard Birnbaum, age 46

COO, Rolf Martin Schmitz, age 57

Manager Investor Relations Germany Switzerland and Asia, Martin Vahlbrock

Manager Investor Relations Scandinavia and Fixed Income, Oliver van der Mond

VP Investor Relations, Stephan Lowis

Executive Vice President of RWE Power AG, Matthias Hartung

Member of the Supervisory Board, Carl-Ludwig Boehm-Bezing

Director, Christine Merkamp

Director, Dagmar Muehlenfeld

Director, Frithjof Kuehn

Director, Manfred Holz

Director, Roger Graef

Director, Ullrich Sierau

Member of the Supervisory Board, Wolfgang Schuessel

Director, Dieter Zetsche, age 60

Director, Paul Achleitner, age 57

Director, Ekkehard D. Schulz, age 73

Chairman Supervisory Board, Manfred Schneider, age 75

Director, Carl Ludwig von Boehm-Bezing

Director, Werner Bischoff, age 66

Deputy Chairman, Frank Bsirske

Director, Dieter Faust

Director, Wolfgang Reiniger

Director, Gunter Reppien

Director, Uwe Tigges

Director, Heinz Buchel

Director, Dagmar Schmeer

Director, Dagmar Muhlenfeld

Director, Gerhard Langemeyer

Director, Andreas Henrich

Director, Manfred Weber

Director, Frithjof Kuhn

Director, Hans-Peter Lafos

Director, Wolfgang Schussel

Member of the Supervisory Board, Carl-Ludwig Boehm-Bezing

Director, Christine Merkamp

Director, Dagmar Muehlenfeld

Director, Frithjof Kuehn

Director, Manfred Holz

Director, Roger Graef

Director, Ullrich Sierau

Member of the Supervisory Board, Wolfgang Schuessel

Auditors: PricewaterhouseCoopersAG

LOCATIONS

HQ: RWE AG
Opernplatz 1, Essen 45128
Phone: (49) 201 12 00   **Fax:** (49) 201 12 15199
Web: www.rwe.com

Sales

	% of total
Germany	53
UK	17
Netherlands	11
Czech	5
Hungary	4
Other	10
Total	**100**

PRODUCTS/OPERATIONS

Sales

	% of total
Geographic Divisions	
Germany (64% see divisions)	
Central Eastern & South Eastern	17
UK	5
Netherlands &	4
Operating Divisions	
Power generation	40
Supply & distribution	22
Gas & oil	10
Renewables	2
Trading & gas	-
Other	-
Total	**100**

Selected Divisions and Subsidiaries

RWE Energy (German and continental European downstream energy operations)

RWE npower (affiliated with RWE Innogy electricity and gas supply UK)

RWE Supply & Trading (power gas coal and oil trading)

RWE-DEA AG (oil and gas exploration production and storage)

RWE Power (upstream energy operations)

COMPETITORS

BP	Enel
Centrica	Exxon Mobil
E.ON	Royal Dutch Shell
Electricite de France	Vattenfall
Endesa S.A.	

HISTORICAL FINANCIALS

Company Type: Public

Income Statement

FYE: December 31

	REVENUE ($ mil.)	NET INCOME ($ mil.)	NET PROFIT MARGIN	EMPLOYEES
12/13	70,754	(3,795)	—	67,904
12/12	66,918	1,721	2.6%	71,419
12/11	63,577	2,335	3.7%	72,068
12/10	68,151	4,427	6.5%	70,856
12/09	66,907	5,144	7.7%	70,726
Annual Growth	**1.4%**	**—**	**—**	**(1.0%)**

2013 Year-End Financials

Debt ratio: 31.7%
Return on equity: (-21.8%)
Cash ($ mil.): 5,376
Current ratio: 1.11
Long-term debt ($ mil.): 22,769

No. of shares (mil.): 575
Dividends
Yield: 5.1%
Payout: —
Market value ($ mil.): 21,187

	STOCK PRICE ($) FY Close	P/E High/Low		PER SHARE ($) Earnings	Dividends	Book Value
12/13	36.80	—	—	(6.18)	1.90	24.96
12/12	41.64	40	27	2.81	1.93	33.94
12/11	34.93	39	16	4.33	6.90	35.37
12/10	66.39	31	17	8.30	3.42	44.20
12/09	96.90	31	16	9.65	4.29	37.26
Annual Growth	**(21.5%)**	**—**	**—**	**—**	**(18.4%)**	**(9.5%)**

S-Oil Corp

S-Oil aims to become the most S-successful refiner in South Korea and beyond. The company is one of its country's leading refiners and a major provider of lubricants and gasoline. S-Oil is capable of producing 669000 barrels per day at its Onsan refinery and its product menu includes gasoline kerosene diesel lube base oil automotive and industrial oils and petrochemical products such as benzene and toluene. S-Oil operates a naphtha reforming plant with a daily capacity of 45000 barrels and a BTX production plant with an annual capacity of 900000 tons. Its joint venture with Saudi Arabia's Aramco –signed in 1991 –ensures a steady supply of crude oil.

Operations

The company operates the Onsan Refinery and other facilities at that location that can produce petrochemicals and lube base oil. S-Oil produces and supplies high quality oil products based on the world-class Bunker-C Cracking Center and the xylene Center a paraxylene plant with the world's highest production capacity for a single facility.

Geographic Reach

S-Oil exports more than 60% of its annual production to about 30 countries around the world.

Financial Performance

Thanks to high oil prices and the expansion of its refining capacity S-Oil's 2011 revenues increased by 56% and its net income by 69%.

Business Strategy

The company's long-term strategy includes further investment in the refining business integration with the petrochemical business and growing its renewable energy business.

Buoyed by increasing demand for petroleum products from China and other Asian countries in 2011 S-Oil completed its Onsan refinery expansion project. The expansion doubles the plant's production of paraxylene and benzene to 2.4 million tons a year. It also increased its refining capacity from 580000 barrels per day to 669000 barrels per day.

Company Background

S-Oil began commercial operations in 1980. The company broke off from SsangYong Group in 1999 and changed its name to S-Oil a year later.

EXECUTIVES

CFO, Yul Ryu, age 54
Account Manager, T.H. Kang
Director CEO, Nasser Al-Mahasher

LOCATIONS

HQ: S-Oil Corp
192 Baekbeom-ro Mapo-gu, Seoul 121-805
Phone: (82) 2 3772 5151   **Fax:** (82) 2 782 4879
Web: www.s-oil.com

COMPETITORS

GS Caltex	SK Group
LG International	

HISTORICAL FINANCIALS

Company Type: Public

Income Statement

FYE: December 31

	REVENUE ($ mil.)	NET INCOME ($ mil.)	NET PROFIT MARGIN	EMPLOYEES
12/13	29,628	275	0.9%	2,749
12/12	32,521	548	1.7%	2,671
12/11	27,542	1,027	3.7%	2,622
12/10*	18,292	633	3.5%	2,551
01/10	0	0	—	0
Annual Growth	**—**	**—**	**—**	**—**

*Fiscal year change

2013 Year-End Financials

Debt ratio: 0.0%
Return on equity: 5.4%
Cash ($ mil.): 555
Current ratio: 1.34
Long-term debt ($ mil.): 494

No. of shares (mil.): 112
Dividends
Yield: 0.0%
Payout: 0.0%
Market value ($ mil.): 4,188

	STOCK PRICE ($) FY Close	P/E High/Low	PER SHARE ($) Earnings	Dividends	Book Value
12/13	37.20	— —	2.36	0.00	45.22
12/12	51.00	— —	4.73	0.00	44.72
12/11	40.75	— —	8.85	0.00	40.06
12/10*	29.23	— —	5.46	0.00	(0.00)
01/10	22.81	— —	(0.00)	0.00	(0.00)
Annual Growth	13.0%	— —	—	—	—

*Fiscal year change

SAIC Motor Corp Ltd

LOCATIONS

HQ: SAIC Motor Corp Ltd
No. 489, Weihai Road, Jingan District, Shanghai 200041
Phone: (86) 21 22011138   **Fax:** (86) 21 22011199
Web: www.saicmotor.com

HISTORICAL FINANCIALS

Company Type: Public

Income Statement   FYE: December 31

	REVENUE ($ mil.)	NET INCOME ($ mil.)	NET PROFIT MARGIN	EMPLOYEES
12/13	93,461	4,097	4.4%	0
12/12	77,151	3,328	4.3%	0
12/11	69,077	3,212	4.7%	5,379
12/10	47,541	2,082	4.4%	5,536
12/09	20,450	965	4.7%	4,373
Annual Growth	46.2%	43.5%	—	—

2013 Year-End Financials

Debt ratio: 0.5%   No. of shares (mil.): —
Return on equity: 19.0%   Dividends
Cash ($ mil.): 14,717   Yield: —
Current ratio: 1.25   Payout: —
Long-term debt ($ mil.): 1,034   Market value ($ mil.): —

Samsung C&T Corp

Samsung C&T is the trading investment construction and engineering arm of the Samsung Group the largest "chaebol" (business conglomerate) in South Korea. The unit's trading and investment group is active in a number of sectors including oil and gas electronics heavy machinery and chemicals. Meanwhile the construction and engineering division handles projects including bridges and ports power plants petrochemical facilities and multifamily residential developments. It has helped build such notable projects as the Petronas Twin Towers in Malaysia and the Burj Khalifa in Dubai — both among the world's tallest buildings. Founded in 1938 Samsung C&T has more than 100 offices worldwide.

The group has experienced a decrease in sales in the construction sector as there has been a lag in the housing and architecture markets. Trading and investment has seen an increase in sales due to the success in the natural resources and chemicals market.

Samsung C&T has recently secured or completed such diverse projects as a UK airport renovation and the construction of the Incheon Bridge (one of the world's longest). The company has increasing looked to the Middle East for new construction projects. In 2011 the group won a more than $2 billion deal to build a thermal power plant in Saudi Arabia. That same year the group agreed to build a more than $2.5 billion liquefied natural gas plant also in Saudi Arabia. Early in 2012 Samsung C&T bought 90% of US oil and gas firm Parallel Petroleum from Apollo Global Management for $772 million. The deal was the largest to date of any Samsung company. It was also Samsung's first acquisition of US onshore operations.

The group is focusing more on natural resources and renewable energy sectors. The group's Samsung Renewable Energy subsidiary is developing wind and solar projects around the world. It is leading a consortium that is investing $7 billion wind and solar projects in Ontario Canada. Among the projects is a new manufacturing facility that will produce solar modules and a cluster of wind and solar power farms.

Samsung C&T entered the international housing market for the first time in 2010. The group announced that it will build an apartment complex in China. The company which typically focuses on residential building in its home country plans to expand into the international housing market if the experiment is successful.

EXECUTIVES

President CEO and Director, Sang-Dae Lee
President and CEO Trading Group; Director, Sung-Ha Chi
President CEO and Director, Sang-Dae Lee
President and CEO Trading Group; Director, Sung-Ha Chi
CFO Head of Strategic Planning and Director, Ki-cheol Jeong
Director, Nei-hei Park
Director, Yun-sik Park
Director, Sang-ju Seo
Director, Yoon-ki Paik
Auditors: SamilPricewaterhousecoopers

LOCATIONS

HQ: Samsung C&T Corp
14, Seocho-daero 74-gil Seocho-gu, Seoul 137-956
Phone: (82) 2 2145 2114   **Fax:** (82) 2 2023 2155
Web: www.samsungcnt.co.kr

Sales

	% of total
Korea	75
Asia	15
America	5
Europe	5
Total	**100**

PRODUCTS/OPERATIONS

Sales

	% of total
Trading	46
Construction	29
Manufacturing	25
Total	**100**

Selected Operations

Engineering & Construction
  Commercial construction
  Civil engineering
  Multifamily housing construction
  Power petrochemical storage and treatment facilities and industrial facilities
Trading & Investment
  Brand merchandising for textile and basic materials
  Manufacture and sale of electronic materials

Natural resources development
Plant supply and operation
Trading of chemicals iron and steel

COMPETITORS

Bechtel	LG International
Daelim Industrial	Sumitomo Mitsui
Daewoo International	Construction
GS Engineering	Taisei
Hyundai Corporation	Toyota Tsusho
Kajima	

HISTORICAL FINANCIALS

Company Type: Public

Income Statement   FYE: December 31

	REVENUE ($ mil.)	NET INCOME ($ mil.)	NET PROFIT MARGIN	EMPLOYEES
12/13	27,037	230	0.9%	8,714
12/12	23,720	422	1.8%	7,860
12/11	18,594	346	1.9%	7,233
12/10	15,835	433	2.7%	5,049
12/09	15,988	265	1.7%	4,665
Annual Growth	14.0%	(3.5%)	—	16.9%

2013 Year-End Financials

Debt ratio: 0.0%   No. of shares (mil.): 147
Return on equity: 2.1%   Dividends
Cash ($ mil.): 1,396   Yield: —
Current ratio: 1.13   Payout: 0.0%
Long-term debt ($ mil.): 2,347   Market value ($ mil.): —

Samsung Electronics Co., Ltd.

Samsung Electronics is an electronics Samson. One of the world's largest semiconductor manufacturers Samsung Electronics is also South Korea's top electronics company. It makes many kinds of consumer devices including DVD players digital TVs and digital still cameras; computers color monitors LCD panels and printers; semiconductors such as DRAMs static RAMs flash memory and display drivers; and communications devices ranging from wireless handsets and smartphones to networking gear. The company which is the flagship member of Samsung Group also makes microwave ovens refrigerators air conditioners and washing machines. Nearly half of sales come from the Asia/Pacific region.

Operations

The company operates through independent business units: Consumer Electronics (about 55% of sales) IT and Mobile Communications (20% of sales) Semiconductors (15% of sales) and Display Products (10% of sales).

A true vertically integrated company Samsung Electronics is a leader in producing many of the chips and software at the heart of its products. The company has been the leader in the worldwide memory market for more than a decade and has a significant share of the global market for CMOS image sensors for mobile phones.

Geographic Reach

Altogether Samsung has offices in 80 countries. Outside South Korea it has regional headquarters in the US (California and New Jersey through Samsung Electronics America); Europe (Germany and the UK through Samsung Electronics UK); Asia

(China Japan India and Singapore); as well as in Brazil Russia South Africa and the UAE.

It has some 40 manufacturing plants located in Brazil China Egypt Hungary India Indonesia Malaysia Mexico Poland Russia South Korea Thailand Vietnam and the US (at Samsung Austin).

America is its largest single market accounting for 30% of sales; Europe contributes about 25%; while China makes up another 20% and South Korea 10%. Other countries across Asia and Africa make up the remaining 15%.

Sales and Marketing

Samsung uses a direct sales force that operates from offices located in more than 50 countries. Its products for the consumer market (electronics appliances) are sold through major retailers worldwide. Other products such as the LCD and OLED panels made by Samsung Display are sold to OEMs. The chips made by Samsung Semiconductor are sold directly as well as through distributors.

Financial Performance

As a market leader the company has enjoyed steady growth in both its native currency (the South Korean won) and US dollars. In 2013 Samsung enjoyed strong sales for its core products — smartphones TVs and memory chips. That year it launched the Galaxy S4 smartphone a curved TV and it began mass producing the world's first 20 nanometer 4Gb ultra high-speed mobile DRAM.

Strategy

Its primary growth strategies are to solidify its market leadership by focusing on product differentiation in each business unit; identify businesses that will sustain growth over the next five to 10 years; and prepare management to anticipate and respond to business risks during times of global market uncertainty.

Over the long term Samsung Electronics is looking to grow in key product areas including mobile devices (phones and tablets) LCD panels flat-panel TVs system LSI chips IT products and home appliances. It is also promoting future growth centered around software and service opportunities while continuing to lay the foundation for future businesses particularly the health and medical equipment markets.

R&D is critical to its product development efforts and its research and development network spans six facilities in South Korea and 18 more in nine other countries including China Japan Israel India Russia the UK and the US.

In a case with potentially wide-ranging implications in August 2012 Samsung Electronics lost a patent infringement lawsuit with Apple in an ongoing copyright battle between the two. Samsung was found to have violated several Apple patents including the "bounce back" effect and the physical design of the iPhone but argued that the design similarities were not copying but benchmarking (a practice used by companies to keep up with rivals on details such as battery life screen size and other core features). Apple was awarded $1 billion in damages (the company originally sought $2.75 billion) but Samsung plans to appeal. The verdict is complicated by a decision the same week in a South Korean court that each company had infringed on the others' patents that resulted in bans and fines for both parties. Samsung continues to be nonetheless a major supplier of components for Apple products including the iPhone.

Mergers and Acquisitions

Samsung attempted to take on Apple's iTunes with the 2012 purchase of mSpot a cloud-based music service. Two-and-a-half years later it shuttered the service since renamed Samsung Music Hub in mid-2014 citing a desire to offer services as individual apps over a single bundled storefront.

The company rid itself of other operations considered non-core or poor performing. In 2013 it sold Liquavista to Amazon.com. Samsung originally bought Liquavista in 2011 hoping to increase its share of the e-reader market. In 2011 it sold its hard disk drive (HDD) business to Seagate for about $1.4 billion. As part of the transaction Seagate will supply Samsung with disk drives for its consumer electronics products while Samsung will provide Seagate with flash memory chips for storage devices. Freeing up resources to focus on newer storage technology in late 2012 it bought NVELO a California-based maker of the Dataplex storage software to add to its solid-state drives (SSDs) offerings.

Samsung Electronics is also investing in industries it isn't traditionally known for. In 2013 it bought Massachusetts-based NeuroLogica the maker of the BodyTom and CereTom portable CT scanners as part of its goal to grow as a healthcare technology player.

EXECUTIVES

Chairman, Yoon-Woo Lee, age 68
Vice Chairman and CEO, Oh-Hyun Kwon
Vice Chairman and CEO, Gee-Sung Choi, age 62
President of Samsung Telecommunications America STA, Dale Sohn
CFO and Director, Ju-Hwa Yoon, age 61
CFO, Sang-Hoon Lee, age 59
President Samsung Austin Semiconductor, Woosung Han
President and CEO Samsung Electronics North America, Yangkyu Y.K. Kim
President and CEO Samsung Semiconductor Inc., Charlie Bae
President and CEO Samsung Telecommunications America, Gregory Lee
Director, In-Ho Lee, age 70
Vice Chairman and CEO, Gee-Sung Choi, age 62
Director, Dong-Min Yoon, age 69
CFO and Director, Ju-Hwa Yoon, age 61
Director, Chae-Woong Lee, age 72
Director, Oh-Soo Park, age 61
Auditors: SamilPricewaterhousecoopers

LOCATIONS

HQ: Samsung Electronics Co., Ltd.
129, Samseong-ro, Yeongtong-gu, Suwon-si, Gyeonggi-do 443-742
Phone: (82) 31 200 1114 **Fax:** (82) 31 200 7538
Web: www.samsung.com

Sales

	% of total
Asia/Pacific	
South	17
China	16
Other	16
America	28
Europe	23
Total	**100**

PRODUCTS/OPERATIONS

Sales

	% of total
Digital	37
Telecom	27
Semiconductor	24
LCD	19
Others (7)	—
Total	**100**

Selected Products

Computers and Peripherals
  All-in-One PCs
  Hard disk drives
  Monitors
  Notebook PCs
  Personal digital assistants
  Printers
  Servers
  Storage

Tablet PCs
Consumer Electronics
  Blu-ray Disc players
  Digital cameras and camcorders
  DVD players/recorders
  Portable audio devices
  TVs (analog and digital)
Home Appliances
  Air conditioners
  Gas ovens and ranges
  Microwave ovens
  LED lighting
  Refrigerators
  Washing machines
Networking Equipment
  Ethernet hardware
  Fiber-optic cable and hardware
  Modems (cable and DSL)
  Multiplexers
  Switches
  Transceivers
Semiconductors
  Application-specific integrated circuits (ASICs)
  Communications chips (baseband and radio-frequency)
  Memory
    DRAMs
    Electrically erasable programmable read-only memories (EEPROMs)
    Flash memories
    Mask ROMs
    SRAMs
  Microcontrollers
  Smart card ICs
Telecommunications
  Enterprise communications systems
  Internet-based phones and systems
  Mobile phones
  Smartphones
  Wireless communications infrastructure

COMPETITORS

AMD	LG Electronics
AU Optronics	Lenovo
Apple Inc.	Micron Technology
Canon	Mitsubishi Electric
Chimei Innolux	Motorola Solutions
Cisco Systems	NEC
Corning	Nokia
Dalian Daxian	Nortel Networks
Elpida Memory	Panasonic Corp
Ericsson	Philips Electronics
Fujitsu	QUALCOMM
HTC Corporation	SANYO
Hewlett-Packard	SK Hynix
Hitachi	Sharp Corp.
IBM	Silicon Valley Analog
Infineon Technologies	Sony
Intel	Sony Mobile
JDS Uniphase	Spansion
Kyocera	Toshiba
LG Display	Truly International

HISTORICAL FINANCIALS

Company Type: Public

Income Statement

FYE: December 31

	REVENUE ($ mil.)	NET INCOME ($ mil.)	NET PROFIT MARGIN	EMPLOYEES
12/13	217,461	28,356	13.0%	95,794
12/12	188,351	21,715	11.5%	90,700
12/11	142,403	11,529	8.1%	101,970
12/10	137,905	14,090	10.2%	95,659
12/09	117,820	8,272	7.0%	85,085
Annual Growth	**16.6%**	**36.1%**	**—**	**3.0%**

2013 Year-End Financials

Debt ratio: 0.0%	No. of shares (mil.): 130
Return on equity: 22.8%	Dividends
Cash ($ mil.): 15,485	Yield: —
Current ratio: 2.16	Payout: —
Long-term debt ($ mil.): 2,183	Market value ($ mil.): 180,008

STOCK PRICE ($) FY Close	P/E High/Low		PER SHARE ($) Earnings	Dividends	Book Value
12/13 1,375.00	—	—	188.09	0.00	
1,049.15					
12/12 1,350.00	—	—	144.19	0.00	838.14
12/11 835.00	—	—	76.80	0.00	646.02
12/10 660.00	—	—	94.24	0.00	587.88
12/09 655.80	—	—	55.82	0.00	(0.00)
Annual Growth 20.3%			35.5%		

Samsung Life Insurance Co Ltd

LOCATIONS

HQ: Samsung Life Insurance Co Ltd
150, Taepyeongno 2-ga, Jung-gu, Seoul 100-716
Phone: (82) 2 1588 3114　　**Fax:** (82) 2 751 8100

HISTORICAL FINANCIALS

Company Type: Public

Income Statement

FYE: March 31

	REVENUE ($ mil.)	NET INCOME ($ mil.)	NET PROFIT MARGIN	EMPLOYEES
03/13	27,294	884	3.2%	6,815
03/12	20,050	837	4.2%	6,269
03/11	22,147	1,434	6.5%	6,062
03/10	22,766	800	3.5%	0
Annual Growth	6.2%	3.4%	—	—

2013 Year-End Financials

Debt ratio: —	No. of shares (mil.): 194
Return on equity: 4.9%	Dividends
Cash ($ mil.): 2,053	Yield: —
Current ratio: —	Payout: —
Long-term debt ($ mil.): —	Market value ($ mil.): —

STOCK PRICE ($) FY Close	P/E High/Low		PER SHARE ($) Earnings	Dividends	Book Value
03/13 0.00	—	—	4.54	0.00	100.32
Annual Growth	—	—	—	—	—

Sanofi

Sanofi is out to make all the world's creatures a little healthier. The company formerly known as Sanofi-Aventis develops and manufactures prescription and over-the-counter drugs and vaccines for mankind and man's best friend. Sanofi's pharmaceutical division is its biggest revenue generator with top sellers that include blood thinners Plavix and Lovenox cancer drug Taxotere and insulin brand Lantus. US consumers will recognize at least one of the brands produced by subsidiary Chattem (Gold Bond Icy Hot and Selsun Blue to name a few). Sanofi also operates Merial one of the world's largest animal health firms. Subsidiary Sanofi Pasteur makes vaccines while its Genzyme unit makes biopharmaceuticals.

The company operates worldwide marketing its products through direct sales representatives and through partnering firms. For example Sanofi co-markets cardiovascular drugs Plavix and Aprovel with Bristol-Myers Squibb (BMS). It also has agreements with Warner Chilcott to market osteoporosis drug Actonel and with Teva Pharmaceuticals for Copaxone. Products are distributed via large wholesalers and to retail chains and health care organizations. Europe and North America are the firm's largest markets.

Sanofi has worked hard to diversify its operations in the wake of and ahead of patent expirations for some of its biggest sellers. Its allergy blockbuster Allegra and sleep aid Ambien have both lost their patent protection in recent years (as has Lovenox) clearing the way for generic competition. Another top seller Plavix lost patent protection in the US in 2012 (resulting in reduced royalties from marketing partner BMS) as did blood pressure drug Avapro. Sanofi's diversification strategy hinges mainly upon making strategic acquisitions in its core therapeutic areas as well as in new markets and emerging regions poised for growth.

To boost offering of delicate biopharmaceuticals Sanofi acquired prescription drug firm Genzyme in 2011 for some $20.1 billion after months of negotiation including a lower hostile bid failed. The deal included an additional $3.8 billion that is contingent on the future performance of Genzyme's lead drug candidates (including multiple sclerosis candidate Lemtrada) and its manufacturing facilities. The purchase of Genzyme gives Sanofi a portfolio of products focused on rare inherited disorders kidney disease orthopedics transplant and immune disease cancer and diagnostic testing. Its top product is rare disease treatment Cerezyme for Gaucher's disease. Following the acquisition Genzyme became the headquarters of the parent's rare disease program. Once Genzyme was formally part of its structure the company chose to simplify the collective organization's identity by shortening its name from Sanofi-Aventis to simply Sanofi.

Another area in which the company has been particularly focused on growing is the worldwide OTC market largely through its US Chattem division which converted Allegra to an OTC product in 2011 following its patent expiration. Also in 2011 Sanofi acquired BMP Sunstone a US-based firm that markets vitamins and mineral supplements and cough and cold medicines in China for about $520 million. Through its majority owned India unit Aventis Pharma Sanofi also expanded its portfolio by buying the marketing and distribution business of Universal Medicare which makes more than 40 branded nutraceutical formulations in India.

Not one to miss an opportunity Sanofi decided it too would take advantage of patent expirations by growing its generics business especially in the European generics market where it maintains the Winthrop brand. It has also established a generic presence in emerging markets (another growth area for the company) in the Middle East Latin America and Asia.

In 2010 Sanofi took its plan to reduce its reliance on prescription drugs one step further by entering the market for medical devices. The company joined forces with medical equipment maker Agamatrix to develop blood sugar monitoring devices for diabetes patients. Sanofi already has a solid presence in the diabetes market with its insulin products Apidra and Lantus. The blood glucose monitoring systems designed to work in conjunction with the company's existing diabetes treatments were launched in European markets under the BGStar and iBGStar brands in 2011.

The next year Sanofi agreed to acquire Pluromed a medical device company that developed proprietary polymer technology used in injectable plugs for improving the safety efficacy and costs of medical interventions. The company also makes LeGoo gel a product used in surgery for temporary endovascular occlusion of blood vessels in the US and Europe.

While it has been growing some operations the company has taken a different approach to its research and development business. Beginning in 2009 Sanofi began cutting back on its pipeline of drug candidates in an effort to save on R&D costs narrowing its focus on the most promising candidates in targeted areas including cancer diabetes cardiology neurology vaccines and biologics. As of early 2011 it had about 55 candidates in its drug pipeline with about a dozen of them in late stages of clinical development. In 2009 it successfully launched a new atrial fibrillation (irregular heart beat) medicine Multaq and in 2010 it introduced prostate cancer drug Jevtana.

The company is also increasingly relying on partnerships and licensing agreements with other firms and academic institutions to support its research efforts. For instance in 2010 Sanofi formed a major outsourcing agreement with contract research organization (CRO) Covance. The deal worth up to $2.2 billion included Covance's purchase of two Sanofi R&D facilities in Europe. Covance will provide drug development services to the company through a ten-year contract.

Though it is streamlining its internal development operations the company still pursues acquisitions to bolster its late-stage pipeline in core research areas. In 2010 the company boosted its pipeline with treatments for leukemia and certain blood disorders by buying privately held TargeGen for $75 million (plus up to $485 million in potential future milestone payments).

In the vaccines market Sanofi's biggest sellers include pediatric combination vaccines and the cervical cancer vaccine Gardasil (marketed through an agreement with Merck). Subsidiary Sanofi Pasteur is also a top maker of flu vaccines and has received a boost from growing concerns over the possibility of an influenza pandemic. While its vaccine business only makes up about 10% of the company's sales Sanofi has made small acquisitions to keep its pipeline pumping.

Sanofi's animal health operations are conducted through its Merial subsidiary which was formerly a 50-50 joint venture with Merck. Sanofi acquired Merck's share of Merial (as Merck prepared for its acquisition of drugmaker Schering-Plough) in 2009 for about $4 billion. The two exercised an option to strike a fresh venture early the next year and announced plans to combine Merial with Merck's animal health business Intervet; however after spending a year planning the merger the two companies ended the agreement in 2011 citing complexities arising from anticipated divestitures to satisfy antitrust regulators. Sanofi has stated that it will instead grow its animal health operations through smaller bolt-on acquisitions.

While the company has been aggressively expanding its product offerings and R&D pipeline of potential blockbusters to help ward off the threat of generic competition it has also been pursuing cost-cutting measures as a means of offsetting future patent losses. In 2011 for instance Sanofi announced that it was reviewing options to divest its US dermatology business Dermik and later that year it sold the unit to Valeant Pharmaceuticals for some $425 million. In addition in 2010 the company downsized certain manufacturing and sales operations to reduce inefficiencies and prepare for lower production and sales volumes of selected products going off-patent. It has also conducted some layoffs.

HISTORY

The Sanofi group got its start in 1973 when French oil conglomerate Elf Aquitaine (later part of TOTAL) merged several health care cosmetics and animal nutrition companies into one subsidiary. In 1977 Sanofi set up a Japanese subsidiary through which it developed joint ventures with Japan's Meiji Seika Kaisha and Taisha Pharmaceutical firms. In 1979 Elf spun off Sanofi although it retained ownership of more than half of the company. Almost from its founding Sanofi grew through acquisitions and alliances. During the 1980s it used a massive war chest to buy stakes and set up joint ventures such as one with American Home Products in 1982.

The company bought "couturier et parfumier" Nina Ricci in 1988; such well-known fragrances as L'Air du Temps put it among the industry's top perfume houses. But Sanofi overreached the next two years and was outbid by American Home Products for AH Robins (the drug firm bankrupted by lawsuits over deaths from its Dalkon Shield IUD) and by Rhone-Poulenc (now part of Aventis) for Rorer. A chastened Sanofi and Kodak subsidiary Sterling Drug in 1991 entered into an alliance that didn't involve an exchange of cash.

In 1993 Sanofi made a splash when it bought the perfume business of fashion designer Yves Saint-Laurent. The next year it bought out much of the pharmaceutical joint venture with Kodak. Sanofi began divesting such noncore businesses as veterinarian and biotech operations in 1995. After suffering a loss in its perfume and beauty division in 1996 it sold Nina Ricci. The rest of its beauty division was sold in 1999 in preparation for the Synthelabo merger.

Synthelabo was founded in 1970 when drug firms Laboratoires Dausse and Laboratoires Robert et Carriere merged. In 1973 it became a 53%-owned subsidiary of beauty products maker L'Oreal. In 1980 drug firm Metabio-Jouillie became a part of Synthelabo making it the #3 drug company in France. In 1983 Synthelabo and US drugmaker Searle created Lorex to market the French firm's products in the UK. (Synthelabo bought Searle's interest 10 years later.)

Throughout the 1980s Synthelabo acquired merged and formed joint ventures including some in Japan with Mitsubishi Chemical Fujisawa Pharmaceutical (1985) and Tanabe Seiyaku (1987). The company continued its acquisitive ways in the 1990s buying several French rivals.

Synthelabo openly admitted its quest for a large international presence in 1996 announcing it wanted 80% of its sales to come from such foreign markets as Asia and the US. That year the company entered an alliance with Genset to research cancer-causing genes; it also signed on with SmithKline Beecham (now GlaxoSmithKline) and Human Genome Sciences to fund genetic research. Synthelabo's Hungarian subsidiary began planning to make drugs for the first time rather than just selling its parent's products as in the past. The next year Synthelabo bought Pharmacia & Upjohn's German generic drug subsidiary Sanorania Pharma.

As Synthelabo and Sanofi merged in 1999 the new company's concentration on pharmaceuticals dictated several changes including the sale of the company's interests in joint venture Pasteur Sanofi Diagnostics as well as its beauty division home to such well-known perfume lines as Yves Saint Laurent. It also sold its veterinary and animal feed division to what is now BNP Paribas.

Sanofi-Synthelabo made good on its plans to target the US in 2000 expanding its sales force

there. But the merger wasn't without its problems: Former Synthelabo CEO Herve Guerin was ousted as vice chairman and COO of Sanofi-Synthelabo after he and chairman Jean-Francois Dehecq butted heads. In 2002 the company boosted its pipeline by entering into an alliance with Immuno-Designed Molecules a biotechnology firm focusing on cancer drugs. Also that year the FDA approved the firm's colorectal cancer drug Eloxatine in record time.

Sanofi-Synthelabo acquired Aventis —and with it the Allegra franchise and Merial joint venture — in 2004. Following the merger the company changed its name to Sanofi-Aventis.

Even though key patents for Plavix weren't scheduled to expire until 2011 generics maker Apotex introduced a generic version in 2006 that flooded the US market. An injunction issued by US courts halted Apotex's manufacturing of the drug (though not sales of already distributed products) but the episode still reduced Sanofi-Aventis' Plavix sales in the US by about 16% compared to the previous year. Both companies pursued litigation.

The company received EU approval in 2006 for the use of its weight-loss drug rimonabant which entered the market under the brand name Acomplia. However in 2008 Sanofi-Aventis suspended marketing efforts for Acomplia due to reports of psychiatric side effects; the company canceled all clinical trials for the drug later that year.

In 2008 the company acquired the Australian vitamin and mineral supplements business of Symbion (now part of Primary Health Care) for $480 million. It also purchased vaccine-maker Acambis which had a history of working with Sanofi Pasteur and brought with it an approved smallpox vaccine and a solid pipeline of vaccines in development.

In late 2009 it shelled out nearly $2 billion to acquire Chattem which not only gave it a hefty line of well-known consumer products but also increased Sanofi's presence in the US (which accounted for about 30% of the company's annual sales in 2009). As part of that deal Sanofi decided to convert Allegra from a prescription to an OTC drug (following its patent expiration) and transfer it to Chattem to market. The company also expanded its presence in Asia by forming a joint venture with Chinese nutritionals firm Minsheng Pharmaceutical in 2009.

In 2009 the company paid some $1.5 billion to acquire the remaining shares of Czech generics maker Zentiva in which it already held a 25% stake. Zentiva brought with it generic operations in emerging markets including Turkey and Russia. Sanofi also expanded its Asian generics operations by forming a joint venture with Japan's Nichi-Iko Pharmaceuticals and it became sizeable in South America when it bought top Brazilian generic drug manufacturer Medley for $663 million in 2009.

In 2009 it acquired US development firm BiPar Sciences in a deal worth up to $500 million adding potential therapies for breast ovarian and other cancers; it also purchased ophthalmology development firm Fovea Pharmaceuticals for $540 million.

EXECUTIVES

Senior Vice President President Sanofi France, Christian Lajoux, age 67
President Global Operations, Hanspeter Spek, age 65
Chairman, Serge Weinberg, age 63
Chief Executive Officer, Christopher A. (Chris) Viehbacher, age 54
SVP Vaccines, Wayne F. Pisano, age 60
President Global Research and Development, Elias A. Zerhouni, age 62
Senior Vice President Secretary, Philippe Peyre, age 64

SVP Corporate Social Responsibility, Gilles Lhernould, age 59
SVP Pharmaceutical Operations Intercontinental, Antoine Ortoli, age 61
Chairman Strategic Development and Scientific Advisory Council, Richard D. Klausner
SVP Global Diabetes, Pierre Chancel, age 58
VP Media Relations and Corporate Communications, Jean-Marc Podvin
Senior Vice President Global Services, Gregory (Greg) Irace, age 55
SVP Human Resources, Roberto Pucci, age 50
SVP Industrial Development and Innovation, Jean-Philippe Santoni, age 60
SVP Legal Affairs and General Counsel, Karen Linehan, age 56
SVP Industrial Affairs, Philippe Luscan, age 51
Senior Vice President Corporate Communications, Laure Thibaud, age 55
SVP Pharmaceutical Customer Solutions, Jean-Francois Brin, age 49
SVP and Chief Medical Officer, Jean-Pierre Lehner, age 66
SVP Global Oncology, Debasish Roychowdhury, age 52
VP External and Scientific Communications, Pascal Barollier
President North America, Anne C. Whitaker
Chief Strategy Officer, David-Alexandre Gros
Senior Vice President Chief Medical Officer, Paul Chew
Director, Robert Castaigne, age 66
Director, Thierry Desmarest, age 69
Director, Gerard Van Kemmel, age 74
Director, Lindsay Owen-Jones, age 68
Director, Igor Landau, age 70
Director, Jean-Rene Fourtou, age 74
Director, Lord Douro, age 68
Director, Christian Mulliez, age 54
Director, Klaus Pohle, age 77
CEO and Director, Christopher A. (Chris) Viehbacher, age 54
Director, Uwe Bicker, age 68
Director, Claudie Haignere, age 55
Director, Partick de la Chaevardiere, age 56
Auditors: PricewaterhouseCoopersAudit

LOCATIONS

HQ: Sanofi
54, Rue La Boetie, Paris 75008
Phone: (33) 1 53 77 40 00   **Fax:** (33) 1 53 77 43 03
Web: www.sanofi.com

Sales

	$ mil.	% of total
Emerging Markets	30	
Western Europe (including France)	30	
Other regions & countries (including Japan)	11	

PRODUCTS/OPERATIONS

Sales

	% of total sales
Prescription pharmaceut	
Lantus	12
Lovenox	9
Taxotere	7
Plavix	7
Aprovel	4
Ambien/Stilnox/Myslee	3
Allegra	2
Copaxone	2
Amaryl	2
Eloxatin	1
Tritace	1
Other prescription	25
Vaccines	13
Consumer health	7
Generics	5
Total	**100**

Selected Products

Prescription pharmaceuticals
  Actonel (osteoporosis)
  Acomplia/Zimulti (obesity)
  Allegra/Telfast (allergies)
  Amaryl (diabetes)
  Ambien/Stillnox/Myslee (insomnia)
  Apidra (diabetes)
  Aprovel/Avapro (hypertension)
  Copaxone (multiple sclerosis)
  Depakine (epilepsy)
  Eloxatine (colorectal cancer)
  Jevtana (prostate cancer)
  Lantus (long-acting insulin for diabetes)
  Lovenox/Clexane (deep vein thrombosis other
    cardiovascular conditions)
  Multaq (atrial fibrillation and atrial flutter)
  Nasacort (allergic rhinitis)
  Plavix (arterial blood clots)
  Taxotere (breast and ovarian cancer)
  Tritace (hypertension)
  Vaxigrip (influenza vaccine)
  Xatral (benign prostatic hypertrophy)
Vaccines
  Adacel (diphtheria tetanus and pertussis adult booster
    vaccine)
  Fluzone (influenza vaccine)
  Insuman (diabetes)
  Menactra (meningitis and pneumonia vaccine)
  Pentaxim/Pentacel (Polio pertussis and HIB pediatric
    combination vaccine)
Consumer health
  Doliprane (pain)
  Enterogermina (intestinal health)
  Essentiale (liver therapy)
  Gold Bond (athlete's foot)
  Icy Hot (pain)
  Selsun Blue (dandruff)
  Unisom (sleep aid)
Animal health
  Frontline (antiparasitic)
  Heartgard (parasiticide)
  Ivomec (parasiticide)
Acquired Genzyme products
  Aldurazyme (genetic disease)
  Campath (oncology)
  Cerezyme (genetic disease)
  Clolar (oncology)
  Elaprase (genetic disease)
  Fabrazyme (genetic disease)
  Hectorol (kidney disease)
  Leukine (oncology)
  Mozobil (oncology)
  Myozyme/Lumizyme (genetic disease)
  Renagel/Renvela (kidney disease)
  Thymoglobulin (organ rejection)
  Thyrogen (endocrinology)

COMPETITORS

Abbott Labs	Johnson & Johnson
Actavis Inc.	LifeScan
Amgen	Medtronic Limited
Amicus Therapeutics	Merck
Apotex	Merck KGaA
Astellas	Novartis
AstraZeneca	Novo Nordisk
Bayer AG	Pfizer
Biogen Idec	Procter & Gamble
Boehringer Ingelheim	Roche Holding
Bristol-Myers Squibb	Shire
Eli Lilly	Sunovion
Fresenius	Takeda Pharmaceutical
GlaxoSmithKline	Teva
Insulet Corporation	

HISTORICAL FINANCIALS

Company Type: Public

Income Statement
FYE: December 31

	REVENUE ($ mil.)	NET INCOME ($ mil.)	NET PROFIT MARGIN	EMPLOYEES
12/13	45,853	5,117	11.2%	112,128
12/12	47,393	6,546	13.8%	111,974
12/11	45,345	7,363	16.2%	113,719
12/10	42,874	7,316	17.1%	101,575
12/09	44,296	7,584	17.1%	104,867
Annual Growth	0.9%	(9.4%)	—	1.7%

2013 Year-End Financials

Debt ratio: 20.9%
Return on equity: 6.5%
Cash ($ mil.): 11,367
Current ratio: 1.71
Long-term debt ($ mil.): 14,337

No. of shares (mil.): 1,324
Dividends
  Yield: 3.3%
  Payout: 99.6%
Market value ($ mil.): 71,023

	STOCK PRICE ($) FY Close	P/E High/Low	PER SHARE ($) Earnings	Dividends	Book Value
12/13	53.63	36 30	3.83	1.79	59.14
12/12	47.38	22 14	4.93	1.69	57.12
12/11	36.54	18 12	5.55	3.23	54.93
12/10	32.23	19 11	5.59	1.47	54.46
12/09	39.27	21 11	5.81	3.06	53.03
Annual Growth	8.1%	— —	(9.9%)	(12.5%)	2.8%

Saudi Basic Industries Corp - SABIC (Saudi Arabia)

SABIC stands for Saudi Basic Industries Corporation but it could also stand for "seriously a big industrial company." Saudi Arabia's largest non-oil company SABIC operates from six units: chemicals performance chemicals polymers (polyolefins PVC and polyester) plastics (including SABIC Innovative Plastics) fertilizers and metals (steel and aluminum). SABIC is one of the world's top makers of polyethylene and polypropylene. The company which introduces some 150 new products per year operates 60 manufacturing and compounding plants in 40 countries as well as numerous distribution centers offices and storage facilities. Founded in 1976 SABIC it is majority owned (70%) by the Saudi government.

A leading industrial player in Saudi Arabia the company primary leverages by-products of oil production to create value-added export commodities (chemicals polymers and fertilizers) and provides the commodity and financial basis for industrial diversification (such as steel production) within and outside the Kingdom.

EXECUTIVES

Vice Chairman and CEO, Mohamed H. Al-Mady
Chairman, Prince Saud bin Abdullah bin Thenayan Al-Saud
EVP Strategic Planning, Abdullah Bazid, age 58
EVP Corporate Strategy and Planning, Yousef Al-Zamel
EVP Fertilizers, Khaled Al-Mana
EVP Corporate Human Resources, Fahad Al-Sheaibi
EVP Polymers, Mosaed Al-Ohali
EVP Corporate Finance, Mutlaq Al-Morished
EVP Corporate Control, Homood A. Al-Tuwaijri
EVP Innovative Plastics, Keith J. Smith
EVP Chemicals, Yousef A. Al-Benyan
EVP Metals, Abdulaziz S. Al-Humaid
EVP Performance Chemicals, Jacobus van Haasteren
EVP Performance Chemicals, Abdullah S. Al-Rabeeah
VP Corporate Communications, Samir A. Al-Abdrabbuh
EVP Technology and Innovation, Ernesto Occhiello
EVP Shared Services, Omar A. Al-Amoudi
EVP Manufacturing, Awadh Al-Maker
Vice Chairman and CEO, Mohamed H. Al-Mady
Director, Mohammed S. Abanumay
Director, Abdullah M. Al-Issa
Auditors: Ernst&Young

LOCATIONS

HQ: Saudi Basic Industries Corp - SABIC (Saudi Arabia)
  P.O. Box 5101, Riyadh 11422
Phone: (966) 1 225 8000   **Fax:** (966) 1 225 9000
Web: www.sabic.com

PRODUCTS/OPERATIONS

Selected Subsidiaries & Affiliates

Al-Jubail Petrochemical Co
Aluminum Bahrain
Arabian Industrial Fibers Co
Arabian Petrochemical Co
Eastern Petrochemical Co
Gulf Aluminum Rolling Mill Co
Gulf Petrochemical Industries Co
Jubail Fertilizer
Jubail United Petrochemical Co
Maaden Phosphate Co.
National Chemical Carrier Company
National Chemical Fertilizer Co
National Industrial Gases Co
National Methanol Co
SABIC Innovative Plastics
Saudi Arabian Fertilizer Co
Saudi Iron & Steel Co
Saudi Kayan Petrochemical Co
Saudi Methanol Co
Saudi Organometallic Chemicals Co
Saudi Petrochemical Co
Saudi Specialty Chemicals Co
Saudi-Yanbu Petrochemical Co
Saudi-European Petrochemical Co
Sinopec SABIC Tianjin Petrochemical Co
Yanbu National Petrochemical

COMPETITORS

A. Schulman
ArcelorMittal
BASF SE
Bayer MaterialScience
Dow Chemical
DuPont
ExxonMobil Chemical
INEOS
INEOS AG
Lucite
LyondellBasell
Nippon Steel & Sumitomo Metal Corporation
POSCO
Shell Chemicals
Sumitomo Chemical

HISTORICAL FINANCIALS
Company Type: Public

Income Statement
FYE: December 31

	REVENUE ($ mil.)	NET INCOME ($ mil.)	NET PROFIT MARGIN	EMPLOYEES
12/13	50,400	6,739	13.4%	40,000
12/12	50,400	6,607	13.1%	40,000
12/11	50,639	7,797	15.4%	33,000
12/10	40,524	5,740	14.2%	33,000
12/09	27,476	2,419	8.8%	33,000
Annual Growth	16.4%	29.2%	—	4.9%

2013 Year-End Financials
Debt ratio: 6.4%
Return on equity: 16.6%
Cash ($ mil.): 10,010
Current ratio: 3.03
Long-term debt ($ mil.): 19,716

No. of shares (mil.): —
Dividends
  Yield: —
  Payout: —
Market value ($ mil.): —

Sberbank Russia

LOCATIONS
HQ: Sberbank Russia
  19 Vavilova St., Moscow 117997
Phone: (7) 495 500 55 50   Fax: (7) 495 957 5731
Web: www.sberbank.ru

HISTORICAL FINANCIALS
Company Type: Public

Income Statement
FYE: December 31

	REVENUE ($ mil.)	NET INCOME ($ mil.)	NET PROFIT MARGIN	EMPLOYEES
12/13	53,177	11,069	20.8%	0
12/12	45,370	11,458	25.3%	286,019
12/11	31,876	9,795	30.7%	266,187
12/10	31,689	5,968	18.8%	262,779
12/09	32,164	804	2.5%	260,805
Annual Growth	13.4%	92.6%	—	—

2013 Year-End Financials
Debt ratio: —
Return on equity: 20.8%
Cash ($ mil.): 40,376
Current ratio: —
Long-term debt ($ mil.): —

No. of shares (mil.): —
Dividends
  Yield: 1.9%
  Payout: 0.0%
Market value ($ mil.): —

	STOCK PRICE ($) FY Close	P/E High/Low		PER SHARE ($) Earnings	Dividends	Book Value
12/13	12.57	0	0	0.51	0.24	2.64
12/12	12.56	0	0	0.53	0.19	2.35
12/11	9.94	0	0	0.45	0.00	1.82
Annual Growth	12.5%	—	—	3.1%	—	9.7%

Schlumberger Ltd.

LOCATIONS
HQ: Schlumberger Ltd.
  42 Rue Saint-Dominique, Paris 75007
Phone: 713 375-3400
Web: www.slb.com

HISTORICAL FINANCIALS
Company Type: Public

Income Statement
FYE: December 31

	REVENUE ($ mil.)	NET INCOME ($ mil.)	NET PROFIT MARGIN	EMPLOYEES
12/14	48,871	5,438	11.1%	120,000
12/13	46,459	6,732	14.5%	123,000
12/12	42,321	5,490	13.0%	118,000
12/11	39,669	4,997	12.6%	113,000
12/10	28,931	4,267	14.7%	108,000
Annual Growth	14.0%	6.3%	—	2.7%

2014 Year-End Financials
Debt ratio: 19.9%
Return on equity: 14.0%
Cash ($ mil.): 7,501
Current ratio: 1.74
Long-term debt ($ mil.): 10,565

No. of shares (mil.): 1,275
Dividends
  Yield: 1.8%
  Payout: 30.9%
Market value ($ mil.): 108,924

	STOCK PRICE ($) FY Close	P/E High/Low		PER SHARE ($) Earnings	Dividends	Book Value
12/14	85.41	28	19	4.16	1.60	29.68
12/13	90.11	19	14	5.05	1.25	30.19
12/12	69.30	19	14	4.10	1.10	26.16
12/11	68.31	26	16	3.67	1.00	23.44
12/10	83.50	25	15	3.38	0.84	22.94
Annual Growth	0.6%			5.3%	17.5%	6.7%

Schneider Electric SE

If you're hungry for power this company can help. Schneider Electric is a leading global manufacturer of equipment for electrical power distribution and for industrial control and automation. The company helps power generators distribute electricity; designs automation systems for the automobile and water treatment industries; builds electric networks and utility management systems for energy water treatment oil and gas and marine applications; and manages electric power in residential industrial and commercial buildings. It sells its products to the construction electric power industrial and infrastructure markets.

Schneider Electric operates through five operating segments. The Power segment accounting for 37% of sales serves industrial and office buildings as well as residences through operations that include low voltage equipment installation and control systems renewable energy and electric vehicle charging. Infrastructure 22% of sales and formerly operating as Energy focuses on medium voltage operations including disconnectors circuit breakers and transformers.

The Industry segment representing 20% of sales supplies industrial firms and OEMS with products that include programmable logic controllers automation platforms contactors overload relays and motor circuit breakers. The company's smallest segments are Information Technology accounting for 14% of sales and Buildings 7% of sales. Information Technology provides critical power and cooling services especially for finance and other information technology companies. Focused on technical building management Buildings aids in the lowering of energy use and maintenance expenses among other services.

Deriving about two-thirds of its sales from outside Western Europe Schneider Electric distributes its products in some 190 countries.

Leveraging organic growth and acquisitions and focusing on areas with strong economies and on its energy management business Schneider Electric increased its revenue 14.3% at current scope and exchange rates in 2011 compared with 2010. Revenue for the power segment rose 7% on an actual basis and 7.6% at constant scope and exchange rates. The segment's uptick was supported in part by strong performance in the manufacturing and infrastructure sectors and more business development in emerging markets. Infrastructure headed up about 13% on an actual basis but 7.5% at constant scope and exchange rates. The segment did well with oil and gas and mining and metals as well as infrastructure in emerging markets.

Industry revenue enjoyed an uplift of 10.5% on an actual basis and 10.4% at constant scope and exchange rates. Machine manufacturing in emerging markets drive systems for the mining oil and gas and cement markets energy efficiency and industrial services helped boost the segment's results. Benefiting in part from demand for data centers the Information Technology sector's revenue surged about 18% on an actual basis and 10.3% at constant scope and exchange rates. Meeting demand for advanced and installed base services security systems and energy efficiency Buildings' revenue was raised 10.7% on an actual basis and 4.8% at constant scope and exchange rates. Net income rose 6% in 2011 compared with 2010 reaching a record level.

The company's Connect strategy which is being implemented from 2012 to 2014 includes four main elements: Connect to Customers Connect Everywhere Connect People and Connect for Efficiency. Connect to Customers targets opportunities for partners and distributors and improvements in the supply chain to meet the unique manufacturing and delivery needs of customers. Connect Everywhere is tasked with developing business for electric vehicle charging home automation and carbon management in mature markets and with seeking opportunities in second-tier cities in emerging markets.

Connect People is focused on workforce development including cross-business opportunities. Connect for Efficiency intends to use information technology and other functions to increase production and and to leverage research and development which now represents 5% of sales for product growth. Connect takes off from the One strategy implemented between 2008 and 2011 to organize the company around one brand served by customer segments. One was intended to position the company for opportunities in emerging markets and for more demand for energy efficiency.

In 2011 Schneider acquired Telvent GIT for about E1.4 billion ($2 billion) to expand its holdings in Spain and diversify its product line. The same year Schneider acquired US-based Summit Energy a provider of energy procurement services that complement Schneider's energy auditing and monitoring offerings. The company offers services that include energy efficiency projects risk advisory planning supply analysis contract negotiation and utility bill auditing.

Additionally in 2011 Schneider acquired India-based Luminous Power Technologies to tap growth in demand in the country for inverters and secured power products. Also in 2011 Schneider acquired Uniflair a manufacturer of precision cooling systems and other products used to cool building data centers and telecommunications facilities. The deal strengthens Schneider's presence in Europe and expands its reach in China and India. Uniflair is joining Schneider's Building segment.

HISTORY

Schneider Electric's predecessor was founded in 1782 to make industrial equipment. After the upheavals of the French Revolution and the Napoleonic Wars the company came under the control of brothers Adolphe and Eugene Schneider in 1836. Within two years they had built the first French locomotive (the country's first rail line opened in 1832).

Schneider became one of France's most important heavy industry companies branching into a variety of machinery and steel operations. However the country's industrial development continued to trail that of Britain and Germany due to recurrent political strife including the revolution of 1848 and the Franco-Prussian War. France also possessed fewer coal and iron deposits.

During WWI Schneider was a key part of France's war effort. It entered the electrical contracting business in 1929 and fought off nationalization attempts in the mid-1930s.

The blitzkrieg of 1939 brought much of France under Nazi occupation and the Schneider factories that were not destroyed were commandeered by the Germans. The company rebuilt after the war aided by the French government. It was restructured as a holding company and its operating units were split into three subsidiaries: civil and electrical engineering industrial manufacturing and construction. Charles Schneider the last family member to lead the company died in 1950.

In 1963 Schneider concluded an alliance with the Empain Group of Belgium and by 1969 three years after Schneider went public the two companies merged to become Empain-Schneider. It was a period when the company made numerous non-core acquisitions entering such fields as ski equipment fashion publishing and travel.

Schneider began reorganizing in 1980. The effort entered its final phase in 1993 with a major recapitalization that saw the merger of its former parent company Societe Parisienne d'Entreprises et de Participations with Schneider SA and the issue of new stock to existing stockholders. The company also streamlined operations. Merlin Gerin (acquired 1975) and Telemecanique (1988) became Schneider Electric in Europe and their North American operations were merged into Square D after its acquisition in 1991.

Schneider's 1994 takeover of two Belgian subsidiaries led Belgium's government to charge then-CEO Didier Pineau-Valencienne with fraud in the valuation of the stock. (A Belgian newsmagazine reported in 1997 that the government turned down an offer to settle out of court.)

In 1996 Schneider established the Schneider Electric (China) Investment Co. in Beijing China's first totally French-owned firm. The next year the company sold Spie Batignolles its electrical contracting subsidiary. Cost-cutting measures and strong sales in France and North America combined to boost the company's 1998 income.

In 1999 Schneider agreed to pay $1.1 billion for Lexel a joint venture owned by Finland's Ahlstrom and Denmark's NKT Holding to broaden its electrical equipment offerings for the household. That year the company changed its name to Schneider Electric and its main subsidiary's name to Schneider Electric Industries. Looking to add more machinery makers to its list of customers the company acquired France-based Crouzet Automatismes and Switzerland-based Positec in 2000.

Although Schneider announced in early 2001 that it would buy Legrand (a deal valued at about $6.4 billion) EU regulators blocked the acquisition in October. (In 2007 the European Court of Justice's Court of the First Instance ruled that the European Commission wrongly denied Schneider's bid to buy Legrand and ordered the EC to pay damages to Schneider for losses incurred as a result of the stymied acquisition.)

As part of the UN's "Oil for Food" program Schneider received an order from Iraq in 2002 for nearly 16000 circuit breakers to be used in that country's power grid. In September 2003 the company acquired TAC Limited (building automation and security controls). Earlier that year Schneider Electric's North American division and US-based Leviton Manufacturing inked a joint technology agreement to develop prototype voice-data-image products.

In 2004 Schneider acquired the Kavlico sensor business of Solectron for nearly $200 million and the US-based Andover Controls (building automation and security controls) from Balfour Beatty for about $400 million. Schneider continued with the purchase of France-based optoelectronics maker Dinel later that year.

The following year Schneider acquired electronic sensor specialist BEI Technologies for about $562 million. After buying the European and Middle Eastern operations of Invensys Building Systems for $150 million in 2005 Schneider in 2006 acquired the Asian and US operations of Invensys Building Systems for nearly $300 million in cash.

Also in 2006 Schneider bought the Napac subsidiary of L'Air Liquide. The French firm made intelligent remote management products for the infrastructure market allowing engineers and operators to run refineries water systems refrigerated warehouses power plants and other facilities from a distance. Napac was integrated into Schneider's Sorhodel Bardin subsidiary. That same year the company acquired GET Group a UK manufacturer of wiring devices and other electrical products. GET made lighting fixtures HVAC equipment and security systems among other offerings.

In 2007 Schneider bought video security systems specialist Pelco for $1.22 billion in cash adding to its Building Automation business. The company paid another $320 million in cash for a tax benefit held by Pelco increasing the value of the transaction to $1.54 billion. Earlier that year Schneider acquired American Power Conversion (APC) for about $6.1 billion in cash widening the company's portfolio in uninterruptible power supply systems. Schneider merged APC with the US subsidiary of its MGE UPS SYSTEMS power supplies business.

In 2008 Schneider acquired Xantrex Technology for about $500 million in cash to strengthen its product portfolio in power inverters for solar and wind energy products. Also that year the company purchased Wessen a Russia-based maker of switches sockets and other wiring devices that complements Schneider's existing wiring portfolio. Other acquisitions in 2008 included two US-based companies: RAM Industries (control systems for energy-efficiency) and Intelligent Motion System (integrated motor control and drive products). On the flip side Schneider sold its Selectron Systems AG subsidiary (automation systems for the rail industry) in 2008 as part of a change in market focus.

Reaching into Latin America in 2009 the multinational company acquired Brazil's #3 maker of UPS (uninterruptible power supplies) power protection voltage regulators and accessories Microsol Tecnologia. The purchase opened up new retail channels and local government support.

Also that year the company acquired two Indian companies: Conzerv Systems active in the Indian industrial and commercial energy market with strength in energy audits and energy management systems and Bangalore-based Meher Capacitors which became Schneider's R&D and manufacturing hub for capacitors in the region.

Schneider rang in 2010 by acquiring Cimac a Dubai-based control and system integrator. The acquisition increased the company's geographic footprint in the Gulf countries. The same year Schneider purchased Australia's SCADAgroup for A$200 million (about E140 million or around $191 million). With operations in North America and the UK in addition to Australia SCADAgroup makes telemetry products for customers in electric power generation oil and gas production and water and wastewater treatment. Its products allow end users to remotely control measure and monitor widely scattered systems.

Also in 2010 Schneider Electric and ALSTOM acquired AREVA's power transmission and distribution business (moving electricity long distances to homes and businesses). General Electric and Toshiba were ousted as potential buyers in favor of the two French companies which promised not to lay off workers and to offer positions to AREVA employees in their respective geographic areas.

EXECUTIVES

Chief Marketing Officer, Aaron L. Davis, age 48
Vice Chairman, Leo Apotheker, age 61
EVP Global Supply Chain, Annette K. Clayton, age 51
Executive Vice-President Finance, Emmanuel Babeau, age 43
Executive Vice-President Custom Sensors & Technologies Business * 1, Eric Pilaud, age 57
Secretary, Philippe Bougon
EVP Power North America and Buildings Businesses, Christopher B. (Chris) Curtis, age 57
President and CEO, Jean-Pascal Tricoire, age 51
EVP Power Global and EMEAS Business, Julio Rodriguez, age 51
Executive Vice-President IT Business, Daniel Doimo
EVP Infrastructure Business, Michel Crochon, age 63
EVP Power Asia/Pacific Business, Eric Rondolat, age 48
Executive Vice-President Customers & Alliances, Christian Wiest, age 65
EVP IT Business, Laurent Vernerey, age 54
EVP Global Human Resources, Karen Ferguson, age 50
Chairman, Henri Lachman, age 75
EVP Strategy and Innovation, Philippe Delorme, age 43
President Power Buildings and Energy US, Jeff Drees
EVP Finances, Emmauel Babeau, age 48
Chief Information Officer, Herve Coureil, age 44
EVP Industry Business, Clemens Blum, age 59
Executive Vice President China Operations 1, Zhu Hai
Executive Vice-President Global Operations 1, Julio Rodriguez
Executive Vice-President IT Business, Laurent Verneray
Director, Noel Forgeard, age 67
Director, Serge Weinberg, age 63
Director, Willy R. Kissling, age 69
Vice Chairman, Leo Apotheker, age 61
Director, Gordon R. Thoman, age 69
Director, Jerome Gallot, age 54
Director, Anand G. Mahindra, age 58
Director, Cathy Kopp, age 64
Director, Gerard de La Martiniere, age 69
Director, Claude Briquet, age 53

Director, Claude Bebear, age 77
Director, Dominique Senequier, age 61
Auditors: Ernst&YoungetAutres

LOCATIONS

HQ: Schneider Electric SE
35 rue Joseph Monier, Rueil-Malmaison, Cedex 92506
Phone: (33) 1 41 29 70 00   **Fax:** (33) 1 41 29 71 00
Web: www.schneider-electric.com

Sales

	% of total
Western	32
Asia/Pacific	27
North	23
Rest of the	18
Total	**100**

PRODUCTS/OPERATIONS

Sales

	% of total
Power	37
Infrastructure	22
Industry	20
Information	14
Buildings	7
Total	**100**

Selected Products

Advanced human-machine interface terminals
Camera sensors
Centralized building management systems
Circuit breakers
Customized sensors
Disconnectors
Electric vehicle charging infrastructure
Electrical panels
Indicator lights
InRow Cooling Systems
Installation & control systems
Medium voltage cells
Network power control
Optimum temperature control
Power supply
Programmable regulators
Renewable energies integration
Security monitoring equipment
Server cabinets
Software for the integrated management of mission
  critical infrastructure
Supervision Control & Data Acquisition (SCADA)
  management systems
Transformers
Uninterruptable power supply
  Monophase
  Three-phase

COMPETITORS

ABB	Itron
ALSTOM	Johnson Controls
Alcatel-Lucent	Legrand
Bechtel	Measurement
Beghelli	Specialties
Bharat Heavy	Mitsubishi Electric
Electricals	Nissin Electric
Checkpoint Systems	Rockwell Automation
Danaher	Roper Industries
EMCOR	Sentry Technology
Eaton	Siemens AG
Electricite de France	Technology Research
Emerson Electric	Corp.
Endress + Hauser	Transtector
Finmeccanica	Vicon Industries
Fluor	Woodhead Industries
GE	Yokogawa Electric

HISTORICAL FINANCIALS

Company Type: Public

Income Statement
FYE: December 31

	REVENUE ($ mil.)	NET INCOME ($ mil.)	NET PROFIT MARGIN	EMPLOYEES
12/13	32,423	2,599	8.0%	152,784
12/12	31,562	2,425	7.7%	152,384
12/11	28,956	2,354	8.1%	140,491
12/10	26,205	2,302	8.8%	123,482
12/09	22,750	1,227	5.4%	116,065
Annual Growth	**9.3%**	**20.6%**	**—**	**7.1%**

2013 Year-End Financials

Debt ratio: 32.9%	No. of shares (mil.): 554
Return on equity: 11.1%	Dividends
Cash ($ mil.): 7,610	Yield: 2.7%
Current ratio: 1.47	Payout: 18.8%
Long-term debt ($ mil.): 8,153	Market value ($ mil.): 9,723

	STOCK PRICE ($) FY Close	P/E High/Low		PER SHARE ($) Earnings	Dividends	Book Value
12/13	17.55	10	7	4.68	0.49	42.77
12/12	14.79	8	5	4.43	0.43	40.11
12/11	10.51	10	5	4.33	0.88	38.10
12/10	15.34	9	5	4.38	0.25	37.00
12/09	11.85	15	6	2.47	0.49	32.81
Annual Growth	**10.3%**	**—**	**—**	**17.3%**	**0.1%**	**6.9%**

Seven & i Holdings Co. Ltd.

Japan's biggest retail conglomerate Seven & i Holdings caters to six of the so-called seven deadly sins (saving wrath for its competition). The "seven" of the company's title reflects the seven areas of business that it is involved with: convenience stores general merchandise and department stores restaurants supermarkets banks and IT services. The "holding" part of the firm's name consists of its subsidiaries: Seven-Eleven Japan (parent of 7-Eleven in the US) Ito-Yokado Sogo & Seibu Co. Seven & i Food Systems Seven Bank and York-Benimaru. Created in 2005 after stock-transfer agreements absorbing its subsidiaries into the company took effect Seven & i operates some 41900 stores worldwide.

After two years of decline the holding company's fiscal 2011 (ends February) total sales inched up a bit while net income more than doubled vs. the previous year. Seven & i's convenience stores posted a sales gain while sales at its superstores and department stores were flat. Already the world's #1 convenience store operator Seven & i's worldwide network of c-stores topped 40000 in fiscal 2011. (Convenience stores account for about 40% of the group's total worldwide sales.) By March 2014 the company is planning to open a record 1500 c-stores (for a net gain of more than 900) as it works to cater to "housewives and the elderly."

While Seven & i rings up more than two-thirds of its total sales at home the holding company oversees about 100 operating companies in 15 other countries in Asia North America and Europe. With the Japanese economy in a prolonged slump and reeling from the effects of the massive earthquake in March 2011 it's looking beyond its bor-

ders for growth opportunities. China is an important emerging market for Seven & i Holdings: It currently operates more than 4800 stores and restaurants in Taiwan and supermarkets stores and restaurants in Beijing Chengdu and Shanghai. Indeed in early 2009 Seven & i Food Systems formed a joint venture company with a large Chinese corporation to establish the family restaurant chain "AllDay's" there.

Seeking to further expand its retail empire the company and Ain Pharmaciez formed Seven Health Care which plans to open drugstores inside superstores and shopping malls operated by Seven & i Holdings and to develop generic drugs. Seven Health Care is jointly owned by Seven & i Holdings (10%) and its subsidiaries Ito-Yokado (50%) and Seven-Eleven Japan (10%) as well as Ain Pharmaciez (30%). More recently the company also boosted its entertainment holdings by doubling its stake in Tower Records Japan in 2011 to about 45%. The move made Seven & i the largest shareholder in the music retail chain (ahead of NTT DoCoMo with 42%).

While the global appetite for convenience store fare is growing the hunger for department store merchandise is not. As the Japanese department store industry struggles with weak personal consumption the company rearranged its department store holdings when it merged holding company Millennium Retailing with Sogo and Seibu department stores to form Sogo & Seibu Co. in August 2009. The merger was effected to capitalize on the well-known Sogo and Seibu names reduce costs and to foster collaboration with Seven & i.

The "i" of Seven & i Holdings stands for "innovation" as well as for the similar-sounding Japanese word for "love."

EXECUTIVES

President and COO, Noritoshi Murata, age 70
Chairman and CEO, Toshifumi Suzuki, age 82
President and COO Seven-Eleven Japan, Ryuichi Isaka
Chairman Seven Bank, Takashi Anzai
President and COO York-Benimaru, Zenko Ohtaka
Managing Executive Officer and Chief Administrative Officer, Katsuhiro Goto
President and COO Ito-Yokado, Atsushi Kamei
Executive Officer, Masao Eguchi
Executive Officer, Yoshihiro Tanaka
Executive Officer, Yasuo Takaha
Executive Officer, Kazuo Otsuka
Executive Officer and CFO, Kunio Takahashi
Executive Officer, Masayuki Sato
Executive Officer, Akira Miyakawa
President Sogo & Seibu, Ryu Matsumoto
President Seven & i Food Systems, Tsuneo Okubo
Director, Takashi Anzai
Director, Zenko Ohtaka
Chief Administrative Officer and Director, Katsuhiro Goto
Director, Noritaka Shimizu
Director, Scott T. Davis
Director, Atsushi Kamei
CFO and Director, Kunio Takahashi
Director, Tsuyoshi Kobayashi
Director, Ryuchi Isaka
Director, Ikujiro Nonaka
Auditors: KPMGAZSA&Co.

LOCATIONS

HQ: Seven & i Holdings Co. Ltd.
8-8 Niban-cho, Chiyoda-ku, Tokyo 102-8452
Phone: (81) 3 6238 3000
Web: www.7andi.com

2011 Stores

	No.
Asia Oceania	

Japan	14,088
China	1,734
Other	16,454
North	8,356
Europe	506
Hawaii	55
Total	**41,193**

Sales

	% of total
Japan	69
North	29
Other	2
Total	**100**

PRODUCTS/OPERATIONS

Sales

	% of total
Convenience	39
Superstores	38
Department	18
Financial	2
Food	2
Other	1
Total	**100**

Selected Subsidiaries

Convenience stores
7-Eleven Inc.
Seven-Eleven (Beijing) Co. (65%)
Seven-Eleven China Co.
Seven-Eleven (Hawaii) Inc.
Seven-Eleven Japan Co.
Superstores
Chengdu Ito-Yokado (74%)
Hua Tang Yokado (76%)
Ito-Yokado
York Mart
York-Benimaru
Department stores
Gottsuo Bin Co.
The Loft Co. (71%)
Shell Garden Co.
Sogo & Seibu Co.
Financial services
K.K. York Insurance
Seven & i Financial Center
Seven Bank (49%)
Seven Card Service (96%)
Food services
Seven & i Food Systems
Seven & i Restaurant (Beijing) Co. (75%)

COMPETITORS

A.S. Watson	J. Front
AEON	Kirin Holdings Company
Asahi Kasei	Kokubu
Carrefour	LAWSON
Couche-Tard	McDonald's
Daiei	Nisshin Seifun Group
Dairy Farm	Seiyu
International	Takashimaya
FamilyMart	Uny
Fast Retailing	Yamazaki Baking
Isetan Mitsukoshi	

HISTORICAL FINANCIALS

Company Type: Public

Income Statement

FYE: February 28

	REVENUE ($ mil.)	NET INCOME ($ mil.)	NET PROFIT MARGIN	EMPLOYEES
02/14	55,282	1,724	3.1%	55,364
02/13	54,169	1,498	2.8%	55,011
02/12	59,516	1,614	2.7%	51,888
02/11	62,535	1,367	2.2%	50,765
02/10	57,514	504	0.9%	52,814
Annual Growth	**(1.0%)**	**35.9%**	—	**1.2%**

2014 Year-End Financials

Debt ratio: 0.1%
Return on equity: 8.8%
Cash ($ mil.): 7,784
Current ratio: 1.17
Long-term debt ($ mil.): 6,846

No. of shares (mil.): 883
Dividends
Yield: 7.0%
Payout: —
Market value ($ mil.): 66,062

	STOCK PRICE ($) FY Close	P/E High/Low	PER SHARE ($) Earnings	Dividends	Book Value
02/14	74.77	— —	1.95	1.31	24.68
02/13	58.40	— —	1.69	1.59	24.50
02/12	55.21	— —	1.83	1.47	26.19
02/11	55.83	— —	1.54	1.29	24.56
02/10	44.86	— —	0.56	0.00	22.34
Annual Growth	**13.6%**	— —	**36.7%**	—	**2.5%**

Sharp Corp. (Japan)

Sharp can give a its peers pointers on innovation. Best known for its consumer electronics the company is a top maker of electronic components and computer hardware and peripherals. Its flagship components business makes LCDs (used in everything from airplane cockpits to PCs to pinball machines) flash memory laser diodes and optical sensors. Sharp also makes printers and cell phones; consumer audio and video products such as Blu-ray disc players and LCD TVs; and a variety of appliances such as air purifiers and steam ovens. The 100-year-old company is also one of the world's largest manufacturers of photovoltaic solar cells.

Geographic Reach

Sharp gets more than half of sales from customers located outside of Japan. The company has established regional headquarters in the Americas China and in Europe as it looks to expand internationally.

Financial Performance

The company's total annual revenue increased from $26.2 billion in fiscal 2013 up to $28.4 billion in fiscal 2014. Sharp turned a net profit of roughly $126 million in fiscal 2014 after suffering a net loss of nearly $6 billion in fiscal 2013 and losing about $4.5 billion back in fiscal 2012. The company's cash flow recovered nicely in fiscal 2014 after being at dangerously low levels during 2012 and 2013.

Strategy

Sharp is focused on boosting capacity at its facilities. The company is always looking to make more of the advanced LCD panels that could give it an advantage in keeping the contract for the Apple iPhone and iPad it currently manufactures. (Sharp is one of three LCD panel suppliers for Apple. The other two are Samsung Electronics and LG Electronics.)

HISTORY

Tokuji Hayakawa got started in manufacturing in 1912 when he established Hayakawa Electric Industry to make a type of belt buckle he had designed. Three years later he invented the first mechanical pencil named the Ever-Sharp which was a commercial success. After an earthquake leveled much of Tokyo in 1923 including Hayakawa's business he moved to Osaka and sold the rights to his pencil to finance a new factory. He introduced Japan's first crystal radio sets in 1925 and four years later debuted a vacuum tube radio.

Following WWII Hayakawa Electric developed an experimental TV which it began mass-producing in 1953. The company was ready with color TVs when Japan initiated color broadcasts in 1960. Hayakawa Electric grew tremendously during the 1960s introducing microwave ovens (1962) solar cells (1963) the first electronic all-transistor-diode calculator (1964) and the first gallium arsenide LED (1969). The firm opened a US office in 1962.

In 1970 the company began to make its own semiconductor devices and changed its name to Sharp Corporation a nod to the name of its first product. It began mass production of LCDs in 1973. Sharp later introduced the first electronic calculator with an LCD (1973) solar-powered calculators (1976) and a credit card-sized calculator (1979).

The company began producing VCRs in the early 1980s and in 1984 Sharp introduced its first color copier. That year the firm introduced a fax machine and began concentrating its marketing efforts on small businesses (while its competitors were scrambling for large corporate accounts). Haruo Tsuji became president in 1986. He restructured the company and concentrated research on LCDs. Sharp blitzed the market with a new line of creative products in the late 1980s including a high-definition LCD color TV (1987) and a notebook-sized PC (1988).

Sharp introduced a cordless pocket telephone in 1992 that operated continuously for over five hours as well as a low-cost high-definition television (HDTV). That year the company announced strategic alliances with Apple to build the Newton personal digital assistant (which flopped) and with the Shanghai Radio and Television to make air conditioners fax machines copiers and printers (Shanghai Sharp Electronics began production in 1994). During the mid-1990s Sharp's ViewCam camcorder and Zaurus personal digital assistant were both big sellers.

In 1996 Sharp formed partnerships with Alcatel (now Alcatel-Lucent) Advanced Micro Devices (AMD) Fujitsu Intel and Nanjing Panda Electronics (China's second-largest TV maker). More joint ventures followed in 1997 including a partnership with Sony to develop flat-panel displays.

Katsuhiko Machida became president in 1998 as the company attempted to pump younger blood into its veins; Tsuji became company adviser. That year the company restructured around three business areas: home appliances and consumer electronics information and communications and components. Restructuring in its LCD operations reduced profits by 80% in 1999. The company rebounded the next year but a downturn in the global economy and competitive pricing in the LCD business again put Sharp's profits under pressure in 2001. The company reduced its workforce and simplified its organizational structure reorganizing its operations from 42 divisions into 24.

Also in 2001 Sharp introduced its AQUOS flat-panel TV which became a popular model among consumers; it had made 10 million AQUOS TVs by mid-2006. It set plans to build its Mihara Plant for manufacturing electronic components and agreed to collaborate on home appliances with SANYO Electric.

In 2002 Sharp built a plant for large-screen LCD TVs in Kameyama City in Japan's Mie prefecture. It began production of system LCDs at the Tenri Plant. Later that year Sharp broke ground on a new plant in Kameyama.

The following year the company began production of system LCDs at the Mie Plant No. 3. Sharp joined with eight other manufacturers of consumer electronics in forming the Blu-ray Disc Founders (later the Blu-ray Disc Association) an industry organization promoting a next-generation technology format for DVDs. SAP and Sharp agreed on partnering for mobile business applications. The company initiated production of photovoltaic modules in Europe.

Sharp launched an online music distribution service Any Music in 2004. The company built a printed circuit board manufacturing facility at the Mihara Plant and set plans to construct a second plant and technical center in Wuxi China. IBM Japan and Sharp collaborated on developing an IC card with a new operating system. Sharp and Sony Ericsson started working together on a 3G FOMA mobile phone for the Japanese market.

In 2005 the company acquired Fujitsu's LCD subsidiary Fujitsu Display Technology.

Construction finally began on Plant No. 2 in Kameyama in mid-2005; about a year later the plant started turning out LCD panels for flat-screen TVs. Later that year Sharp and the University of Tokyo established Todai-Sharp Laboratories for advanced R&D on flexible electronics.

In 2006 Sharp recalled 28000 battery packs made by Sony for laptop computers in the Japanese market because the lithium-ion batteries were at risk of overheating and catching fire. Fujitsu and other PC makers also recalled the Sony-made batteries.

Sharp spent about Â6 billion (more than $50 million) on building an LCD module assembly plant in Poland. The facility began production in 2007 providing LCD modules for TVs being sold into European markets.

Katsuhiko Machida was promoted to chairman in 2007. Succeeding him as president of the company was Mikio Katayama a corporate director since 2003 who had joined Sharp in 1981.

Also in 2007 the company teamed up with rival Pioneer to work together on developing consumer electronics products such as car navigation systems displays DVD players and home networking equipment. As part of the cooperative agreement Sharp made an equity investment in Pioneer taking a stake of 14% and becoming Pioneer's biggest shareholder (Sharp now holds more than 9%). The business and capital alliance was intended to help both companies compete better with bigger vendors such as Panasonic Samsung Electronics and Sony.

In late 2008 Sharp pleaded guilty to fixing prices on LCD panels under charges brought by the US Department of Justice and agreed to pay a fine of $120 million. Federal prosecutors and antitrust regulators previously investigated alleged price fixing in the semiconductor industry with mixed results. They found multiple violations in the DRAM business but none in the markets for graphics processing chips and cards and for static RAMs.

In 2010 Sharp and Sony formed a joint venture –Sharp Display Products Corporation –to operate an LCD panel plant in Sakai City. Sony owns about 7% of the JV with Sharp holding the remaining stake. Sony was going to invest Â100 billion ($926 million) in the LCD JV and increase its holding in the venture to 34% but weak sales of flat-panel TVs led the company to abandon the plans.

Also in 2010 the company announced two joint ventures aimed at the solar market. The first is a thin-film solar cell production venture between Sharp STMicroelectronics and Enel Green Power (EGP) a unit of Italian utility giant (and Sharp partner) Enel S.p.A. The three companies made equal initial investments of up to Â70 million to construct a plant in the Catania province of the Sicily region in Italy which began operations in 2011. Solar cells produced at the plant are marketed by Sharp and EGP in Europe the Middle East and Africa. In the second agreement Sharp and EGP set up Enel Green Power & Sharp Solar Energy S.r.l. (ESSE) with plans to build multiple independent power plants with a total generating capacity of more than 500 MW by the end of 2016.

EXECUTIVES

President, Kozo Takahashi
President and COO, Mikio Katayama, age 56
Group General Manager Global Market Development Group?Emerging Markets Asia Oceania, Takashi Okuda, age 60
Group General Manager Health and Environment Systems Group, Noboru Fujimoto
General Manager Corporate Strategy and Management Planning Board, Toshihiko Fujimoto, age 59
EVP and CTO, Shigeaki Mizushima, age 59
General Manager Liquid Crystal Display Business; Group General Manager Liquid Crystal Display Group, Yoshisuke Hasegawa, age 59
Group General Manager Audio-Visual Systems Development Group, Masatsugu Teragawa, age 62
Group General Manager Production Technology Development Group, Toshihiko Hirobe, age 58
Group General Manager Human Resources Group and Director, Nobuyuki Taniguchi, age 56
Director; Group General Manager China Group; Chairman Sharp Electronics Sales (China) Co. Ltd., Nobuyuki Sugano, age 66
General Manager Domestic Sales and Marketing; Group General Manager Domestic Sales and Marketing Group, Moriyuki Okada
Group General Manager Corporate Sales Group, Kazutaka Ihori
Senior Executive Managing Officer, Fujikazu Nakayama
General Manager Information and Communication Systems Business; Group General Manager Communication Systems Group, Masami Ohbatake
Group General Manager CS Promotion Group, Motohiko Hayashi
Group General Manager Environmental Protection Group, Hiroshi Morimoto
Director, Kunio Ito
Group General Manager CSR Promotion Group; General Manager Legal Affairs Division, Kazutoshi Goto
Operations Director, Christine Wenner
President Sharp Electronics Marketing, Akira Atarashi
IR Contact Officer, Hiroshi Hiroshi Sato Sato
Executive Officer; Chief Director of Solar System Business, Kazushi Kazushi Mukai Mukai
Executive Officer; Chief Director of Brand Strategy Promotion, Keiko Keiko Okada Okada
Executive Officer; Chief Director of AV System Business, Masayuki Masayuki Mori Mori
Executive Officer; Chief Director of Research Development, Mototaka Mototaka Taneya Taneya
Executive Officer; Chief Director of Electronic Device Sales, Noboru Noboru Yamazawa Yamazawa
Senior Executive Managing Officer, Norikazu Hoshi
Executive Officer; Chief Director of Europe & Central and Eastern Europe; President of Subsidiary, Paul Paul Molyneux Molyneux
Executive Officer; Chief Director of Electronic Device Business, Ryutaro Ryutaro Egawa Egawa
Senior Executive Managing Officer, Tetsuo Onishi
Executive Officer; Chief Director of Environment Security, Tetsuro Tetsuro Muramatsu Muramatsu
Executive Officer; Chief Director of America; President & Chairman of Subsidiary, Toshiyuki Toshiyuki Osawa Osawa
EVP and Director; Chief Officer General Administration and Solar Business and Group General Manager Global Brand Strategy Group, Toshishige Hamano, age 67
Senior Executive Managing Officer and CTO; Group General Manager Intellectual Property Group, Kenji Ohta, age 65
EVP Electronic Components and Devices Business and Director; Group General Manager Sales and Marketing Group?Electronic Components and Devices, Yoshiaki Ibuchi, age 66
EVP Audio-Visual Systems Business and Director, Masafumi Matsumoto, age 65
President and COO, Mikio Katayama, age 56
EVP Chief Legal Affairs Officer and Director; Group General Manager Tokyo Branch, Toshio Adachi, age 65
Group General Manager Human Resources Group and Director, Nobuyuki Taniguchi, age 56
Director; Group General Manager China Group; Chairman Sharp Electronics Sales (China) Co. Ltd., Nobuyuki Sugano, age 66
Director, Kunio Ito
Director, Katsuaki Nomura
Independent Director, Makoto Makoto Kato Kato
Auditors: KPMGAZSA&Co.

LOCATIONS

HQ: Sharp Corp. (Japan)
22-22 Nagaike-cho, Abeno-ku, Osaka 545-8522
Phone: (81) 6 6621 1221
Web: www.sharp.co.jp

Sales

	% of total
Japan	48
China	20
The	12
Europe	11
Other	9
Total	**100**

PRODUCTS/OPERATIONS

Sales

	% of total
Audiovisual & communication	43
LCDs	17
Health & environmental	12
Information	11
Solar	9
Other electronic	8
Total	**100**

Selected Products

Consumer/information products
  Audiovisual and communication equipment
    Audio amplifiers
    Blu-ray disc players
    Digital cameras
    High-definition televisions
    Liquid crystal display DVD televisions
    Liquid crystal display televisions
    Liquid crystal display video projectors
    Mobile phones
    Video cameras
  Information equipment
    Calculators
    Digital copiers
    Fax machines
    Mobile business tools
    Personal computers
    Printers
  Home appliances
    Air cleaning systems
    Superheated steam ovens
Electronic components
  Flash memory
  Integrated circuits
  Laser diodes and other optoelectronic devices
  Radio-frequency components
  Satellite broadcasting components
  Solar cells and other photovoltaic devices

COMPETITORS

AU Optronics	Mitsubishi Electric
Avago Technologies	Motorola Solutions
BP Solar	NEC
CASIO COMPUTER	Oki Electric
Canon	Panasonic Corp
Dell	Philips Electronics
Eastman Kodak	Pioneer Corporation

Electrolux	Q-Cells
Epson	Ricoh Company
Ericsson	SANYO
FUJIFILM	Samsung Electronics
First Solar	Siemens AG
Fuji Xerox	SolarWorld
Fujitsu	Sony
GE	SunPower
Hewlett-Packard	Suntech Power
Hitachi	TCL
IBM	TPV Technology
JDI	Tatung
Konica Minolta	Toshiba
Kyocera	Xerox
LG Electronics	Yingli
Lexmark	

HISTORICAL FINANCIALS

Company Type: Public

Income Statement

FYE: March 31

	REVENUE ($ mil.)	NET INCOME ($ mil.)	NET PROFIT MARGIN	EMPLOYEES
03/14	28,358	111	0.4%	50,253
03/13	26,342	(5,795)	—	50,647
03/12	29,938	(4,584)	—	56,756
03/11	36,494	234	0.6%	55,580
03/10	29,504	47	0.2%	53,999
Annual Growth	(1.0%)	24.2%	—	(1.8%)

2014 Year-End Financials

Debt ratio: 0.4%
Return on equity: 7.2%
Cash ($ mil.): 3,677
Current ratio: 0.89
Long-term debt ($ mil.): 2,804

No. of shares (mil.): 1,690
Dividends
 Yield: —
 Payout: —
Market value ($ mil.): 5,089

	STOCK PRICE ($) FY Close	P/E High/Low		PER SHARE ($) Earnings	Dividends	Book Value
03/14	3.01	—	—	0.08	0.00	1.19
03/13	2.78	—	—	(5.21)	0.00	1.23
03/12	7.38	—	—	(4.17)	0.00	7.15
03/11	9.83	—	—	0.20	0.23	11.51
03/10	12.40	—	—	0.04	0.15	10.37
Annual Growth (29.8%)	(41.8%)	—	—	17.2%	—	—

Shin Kong Financial Holding Co., Ltd.

Commercial banking securities dealing asset management and insurance all find a home beneath Shin Kong's umbrella. Also known as SKFH the holding company offers an array of banking and financial services through subsidiaries Shin Kong Life Insurance (SKL) Shin Kong Investment Trust (SKIT) Taiwan Shin Kong Insurance Brokers (SKIB) and Taiwan Shin Kong Commercial Bank (SKB). The company has expanded its product offerings and market presence with a focus on mainland China for growth opportunities. SKFH was established in 2002.

SKFH pursued a life-insurance joint venture in China in 2006 aiming to expand beyond Taiwan's already saturated market. The company pledged an initial capital investment of $99.6 million to fund the expansion and now has insurance offices in Shanghai and Beijing. The company is pursu-

ing a joint venture in China with Hainan Airlines to form an insurance subsidiary.

SKFH also has set up insurance and banking offices in Vietnam in an effort to expand growth in an untapped market.

LOCATIONS

HQ: Shin Kong Financial Holding Co., Ltd.
 Level 38, No. 66, Section 1, Chung-Hsiao West Road,
 Taipei 100
Phone: (886) 2 23895858
Web: www.skfh.com.tw

PRODUCTS/OPERATIONS

HISTORICAL FINANCIALS

Company Type: Public

Income Statement

FYE: December 31

	ASSETS ($ mil.)	NET INCOME ($ mil.)	INCOME AS % OF ASSETS	EMPLOYEES
12/13	85,014	334	0.4%	0
12/12	79,583	338	0.4%	20,677
12/11	70,479	181	0.3%	20,653
12/10	70,935	87	0.1%	20,693
12/09	59,455	35	0.1%	20,888
Annual Growth	9.4%	75.5%	—	—

2013 Year-End Financials

Return on assets: 0.4%
Return on equity: 11.0%
Long-term debt ($ mil.): —
No. of shares (mil.): —
Sales ($ mil.): 5,150

Dividends
 Yield: —
 Payout: —
Market value ($ mil.): —

Shinhan Financial Group Co. Ltd.

Shinhan Financial Group one of South Korea's largest financial companies in terms of assets provides retail and corporate banking credit cards insurance investment management securities brokerage and credit reporting services to almost 19 million customers. Its primary subsidiary is Shinhan Bank which with about 950 locations has one of the largest branch networks in the country. It also owns a stake in the 40-branch Jeju Bank. Shinhan Financial Group has international operations in about a half-dozen other countries including Shinhan Bank America in New York. Other units include Shinhan Investment Corp. (about 100 offices) and Shinhan Life Insurance (about 225 offices).

Geographic Reach
International branches of Shinhan Bank are located in Cambodia Canada China Germany India Japan Kazakhstan the UK and Vietnam. It has representatives in Mexico and Uzbekistan.

Strategy
In South Korea most retail transactions use cash or credit cards and conventional checking accounts are generally not offered or used as widely as in the US. As a result Shinhan Bank maintains an extensive retail branch network since customers handle most transactions at bank branches. It also operates about 25 private banks that serve high net-worth individuals.

EXECUTIVES

Director; CEO Shinhan Bank, Jin Won Suh, age 63
Deputy President, Jae Gwang Soh, age 53
Deputy President and CFO, Jung Kee Min, age 55
Deputy President, Dong Hwan Lee, age 55
Deputy President, Buhmsoo Choi, age 58
Chairman and CEO, Dong Woo Han, age 66
Vice President, Se Se Yil Oh Oh
Deputy President, Sung Ho Wi, age 56
IR Contact Officer, Seung Seung Heon Ryu Ryu
Deputy President, Sin Gee Lee, age 58
Director; CEO Shinhan Bank, Jin Won Suh
Chairman CEO and Director, Dong Woo Han
Director, Ke Sup Yun, age 68
Director, Yoji Hirakawa, age 60
Director, Philippe Aguignier, age 55
Non-Executive Independent Director, Gi Gi Yeong Kim Kim
Non-Executive Independent Director, Gye Gye Seop Yoon Yoon
Non-Executive Independent Director, Haruki Haruki Hirakawa Hirakawa
Non-Executive Independent Director, Hun Hun Namgoong Namgoong
Non-Executive Independent Director, Jae Jae Geun Yoo Yoo
Non-Executive Independent Director, Sang Sang Gyeong Lee Lee
Non-Executive Independent Director, Seok Seok Won Kim Kim
Non-Executive Independent Director, Tae Tae Eun Gwon Gwon
Auditors: KPMGSamjongAccountingCorp.

LOCATIONS

HQ: Shinhan Financial Group Co. Ltd.
 20 Sejong-daero 9-gil Jung-gu, Seoul 100-865
Phone: (82) 2 6360 3000   **Fax:** (82) 2 6263 8070
Web: www.shinhangroup.com

PRODUCTS/OPERATIONS

Selected Subsidiaries
Good Morning Shinhan Securities Co. Ltd.
Jeju Bank (62%)
Shinhan Bank
Shinhan Capital Co. Ltd.
Shinhan Card Co. Ltd.
Shinhan Credit Information Co. Ltd.
Shinhan Life Insurance Co. Ltd.
Shinhan Macquarie Financial Advisory (51%)

COMPETITORS

KB Financial Group	Samsung Life Insurance
Korea Exchange Bank	Woori

HISTORICAL FINANCIALS

Company Type: Public

Income Statement

FYE: December 31

	ASSETS ($ mil.)	NET INCOME ($ mil.)	INCOME AS % OF ASSETS	EMPLOYEES
12/13	296,009	1,809	0.6%	148
12/12	281,771	2,175	0.8%	155
12/11	248,656	2,675	1.1%	158
12/10	239,510	2,394	1.0%	145
12/09	220,404	1,128	0.5%	135
Annual Growth	7.7%	12.5%	—	2.3%

2013 Year-End Financials

Return on assets: 0.6%
Return on equity: 7.0%
Long-term debt ($ mil.): —
No. of shares (mil.): 474
Sales ($ mil): 15,719

Dividends
 Yield: 1.3%
 Payout: 18.5%
Market value ($ mil.): 21,671

	STOCK PRICE ($)	P/E	PER SHARE ($)		
	FY Close	High/Low	Earnings	Dividends	Book Value
12/13	45.70	— —	3.63	0.62	55.23
12/12	36.64	— —	4.39	0.66	51.97
12/11	68.21	— —	5.03	0.00	44.40
12/10	93.82	— —	4.53	0.71	46.52
12/09	74.28	— —	1.98	0.82	37.77
Annual Growth (11.4%)		— —	16.4%	(6.8%)	10.0%

Shinsei Bank Ltd. (Japan)

Shinsei Bank provides financial services from about 40 branches throughout Japan. The company organizes its business into three segments: Institutional Banking Consumer and Commercial Finance and Retail Banking. Shinsei used to focus on financing Japan's large industrial firms but has been cultivating its retail and small business banking operations. It offers services such as deposits mortgages and investments. Institutional activities include asset management bond sales and underwriting and trust services as well as real estate finance and public sector finance. Founded as the Long-Term Credit Bank of Japan in 1952 the company was reborn as Shinsei (Japanese for "new birth") Bank in 2000.

The Japanese government nationalized Shinsei Bank's debt-ridden Long-Term Credit Bank in 1998. It sold the bank to an international group led by US-based Ripplewood Holdings in 2000 making it one of the few major Japanese banks to come under foreign control. Ripplewood spun off the bank in 2004 placing it on the Tokyo Stock Exchange.

Today investment firm J.C. Flowers is Shinsei's largest shareholder with a 33% stake; the Japanese government owns some 25%. The company is still working to repay public funds received when it was nationalized.

In 2010 Shinsei Bank sold Shinsei Asset Management its Mumbai-based asset management operation to Daiwa Bank. The company will use the proceeds to pay down its debt.

Shinsei has been battered by its exposure to toxic assets including loans to failed Lehman Brothers and structured asset-backed securities. It has also taken a hit in the domestic real estate market in which the company has been a significant lender. Record losses reported for 2008 sparked rumors that Shinsei would merge with Aozora Bank another struggling midsized bank that was nationalized in 2001. The two banks reached a merger agreement in 2009 but called those plans off due to strategic differences.

Also as part of its restructuring efforts the company is realigning its retail and consumer finance operations. It it building up its stakes in majority-owned consumer lender APLUS which it may eventually spin off to another subsidiary Shinsei Financial.

In 2007 Shinsei acquired a minority stake in global advisory firm Duff & Phelps. The following year it acquired GE's consumer finance business in Japan consisting of credit card personal lending and mortgage operations.

EXECUTIVES

President and CEO, Shigeki Toma, age 66
Senior Managing Executive Officer, Hitomi Sato, age 66
Senior Managing Executive Officer and Group CIO, Michiyuki Okano, age 54
Senior Managing Executive Officer, Sanjeev Gupta, age 54
Deputy President, Yukio Nakamura, age 60
Senior Managing Executive Officer and CFO, Shigeru Tsukamoto, age 63
Managing Executive Officer, Norio Funayama, age 57
Managing Executive Officer, Toru Myochin, age 49
Head of Structured Finance Sub-Group, Yoshiaki Kozano
Managing Executive Officer, Yoshiaki Kozano, age 52
Managing Executive Officer, Hideyuki Kudo, age 51
Managing Executive Officer, Hironobu Satou, age 54
Managing Executive Officer, Shinichirou Seto, age 53
Managing Executive Officer, Masashi Yamashita, age 56
Director, J. Christopher Flowers, age 56
President CEO and Director, Shigeki Toma, age 65
Director, Shigeru Kani, age 70
Director, Oki Matsumoto, age 49
Director, Hiroyuki Takahashi, age 77
Senior Managing Executive Officer Head Risk Management Chief Risk Officer and Director, Yukio Nakamura, age 59
Auditors: DeloitteToucheTohmatsu

LOCATIONS

HQ: Shinsei Bank Ltd. (Japan)
2-4-3 Nihonbashi-Muromachi, Chuo-ku, Tokyo 103-8303
Phone: (81) 3 6880 7000
Web: www.shinseibank.com

PRODUCTS/OPERATIONS

Sales

	% of total
Interest	
Loans &	61
Dividends on	9
Other	2
Noninterest	
Fees &	12
Other	16
Total	**100**

COMPETITORS

Aozora Bank	Mizuho Trust &
Bank of Yokohama	Banking Ltd
Chuo Mitsui Trust	Resona
Mitsubishi UFJ	Sumitomo Mitsui
Financial Group	Sumitomo Trust and
Mizuho Financial	Banking

HISTORICAL FINANCIALS

Company Type: Public

Income Statement

	ASSETS ($ mil.)	NET INCOME ($ mil.)	INCOME AS % OF ASSETS	EMPLOYEES
03/14	90,303	400	0.4%	5,064
03/13	95,962	542	0.6%	4,863
03/12	104,957	78	0.1%	4,830
03/11	123,559	515	0.4%	5,718
03/10	121,797	(1,500)	—	6,116
Annual Growth (7.2%)		—		(4.6%)

FYE: March 31

2014 Year-End Financials

Return on assets: 0.4%
Return on equity: 6.4%
Long-term debt ($ mil.): —
No. of shares (mil.): —
Sales ($ mil): 3,672
Dividends
Yield: —
Payout: —
Market value ($ mil.): —

	STOCK PRICE ($)	P/E	PER SHARE ($)		
	FY Close	High/Low	Earnings	Dividends	Book Value
03/14	3.91	— —	0.15	0.00	2.64
03/13	4.57	— —	0.20	0.00	2.74
03/12	2.58	— —	0.03	0.00	2.88
03/11	2.39	— —	0.26	0.00	2.78
03/10	2.37	— —	(0.76)	0.00	3.46
Annual Growth 13.3%		— —	—	—	(6.6%)

Shizuoka Bank, Ltd. (Japan)

One of Japan's largest regional banks The Shizuoka Bank has more than 190 branches in and around Shizuoka prefecture a major manufacturing region southwest of Tokyo. The bank specializes in making commercial and industrial loans to businesses such as manufacturers wholesalers and retailers within Shizuoka. Other offerings include deposit accounts consumer loans asset management and investment banking services. The Shizuoka Bank also boasts about a dozen major subsidiaries that are devoted to leasing credit cards mortgages securities brokerage and management consulting. It has representative offices and branches in Belgium Hong Kong Shanghai China Singapore and the US.

EXECUTIVES

Chairman, Yasuo Matsuura, age 72
President and CEO, Katsunori Nakanishi, age 61
COO and Director, Tohru Sakurai
Chairman, Seiya Ito
Deputy Chairman, Kazuhiro Satomi
Deputy President and COO, Masahiro Goto
Senior Managing Executive Officer, Toshihiko Yamamoto
Senior Managing Executive Officer, Akihiro Nakamura
Senior Executive Officer, Itsuro Hitosugi
Senior Executive Officer, Hiroki Saito
Director, Masakazu Oishi, age 69
COO and Director, Tohru Sakurai
CFO and Director, Seiya Ito
Deputy Chairman, Kazuhiro Satomi
Deputy Chairman, Moritaka Nakamura
Senior Executive Officer and Director, Masahiro Goto
Senior Executive Officer and Director, Toshihiko Yamamoto
Senior Executive Officer and Director, Akihiro Nakamura
Director, Toshiaki Sugiyama
Auditors: DeloitteToucheTohmatsu

LOCATIONS

HQ: Shizuoka Bank, Ltd. (Japan)
1-10 Gofuku-cho, Aoi-ku, Shizuoka 420-8761
Phone: (81) 54 261 3131
Web: www.shizuokabank.co.jp

COMPETITORS

Bank of China	Norinchukin Bank
Chuo Mitsui Trust	Shimizu Bank
HSBC	Sumitomo Mitsui
Mitsubishi UFJ	Sumitomo Trust and
Financial Group	Banking
Mizuho Financial	Suruga Bank

HISTORICAL FINANCIALS

Company Type: Public

Income Statement

FYE: March 31

	ASSETS ($ mil.)	NET INCOME ($ mil.)	INCOME AS % OF ASSETS	EMPLOYEES
03/14	103,642	452	0.4%	4,246
03/13	109,624	605	0.6%	4,269
03/12	118,194	453	0.4%	4,257
03/11	114,025	436	0.4%	4,252
03/10	96,783	350	0.4%	4,210
Annual Growth	1.7%	6.6%	—	0.2%

2014 Year-End Financials

Return on assets: 0.4%
Return on equity: 5.7%
Long-term debt ($ mil.): —
No. of shares (mil.): 628
Sales ($ mil): 2,142

Dividends
  Yield: —
  Payout: —
Market value ($ mil.): 7,159

	STOCK PRICE ($) FY Close	P/E High/Low	PER SHARE ($) Earnings	Dividends	Book Value
03/14	11.39	— —	0.68	0.00	12.59
03/13	9.97	— —	0.93	0.00	13.29
03/12	9.34	— —	0.69	0.00	13.96
03/11	8.65	— —	0.64	0.00	12.76
03/10	8.65	— —	0.50	0.00	11.06
Annual Growth	7.1%	— —	7.9%	—	3.3%

Showa Shell Sekiyu K.K.

Show and tell? When is comes to oil and petroleum products Showa Shell Sekiyu has plenty to show and talk about. Showa Shell 35%-owned by Royal Dutch Shell and 15% by Saudi Aramco is one of Japan's leading oil refiners. The company imports refines and distributes petroleum products. The firm's three local refining affiliates Showa Yokkaichi Toa Oil and Seibu Oil have a collective refining capacity of 395000 barrels a day. Showa Shell markets its products through 3800 gas stations; it also has solar power electricity city gas (liquefied petroleum gas) and property businesses.

Operations

The company operates the Yokkaichi Refinery of Showa Yokkaichi Sekiyu Co. Ltd. (210000 barrels per day) the Keihin Refinery of Toa Oil Co. Ltd. (65000 barrels per day) and the Yamaguchi Refinery of Seibu Oil Co. Ltd. (120000 barrels per day). These refineries produce fuel oils such as gasoline; diesel oil; kerosene; basic materials for petrochemical products such as mixed xylene benzene and propylene; lubricants; asphalt; and other products.

Showa Shell markets its products through 3800 gas stations;

The company has developed the technology for manufacturing next-generation CIS thin-film solar panels.

It also operates Ohgishima Power which has two natural gas-fired power plants as a joint venture with Tokyo Gas. Electricity produced at the plants is sold primarily to customers in or near Tokyo.

Sales and Marketing

Showa Shell sells petroleum products in Japan primarily through its gas station network. Products sold include gasolines kerosene and a range of automotive lubricants. The company also directly sells fuel oil gas oil naphtha lubricants bitumen and LP gas to construction firms electric power and gas utilities fishing fleets manufacturers and shipping companies. Showa Shell's international sales include aviation fuel to airlines and marine bunker fuels and lubricants to shipping firms.

Financial Performance

Showa Shell's revenues increased by 18% in 2011 due to a 17% hike in prices on petroleum products which rose in tandem with higher crude oil prices pushing up sales for the oil business. The increase in crude oil prices also had a positive effect on inventory valuation. In addition the sales volume increased for kerosene and other middle distillates; and 128% increase in Energy Solution Businesses due to the greater scale of sales in the solar business stemming from the start of operations at the third Miyazaki Plant.

Net income increased by 45% in 2011 thanks to higher prices on petroleum products and higher net sales. It also benefited from increased demand for heating fuels due to particularly cold weather at the beginning of the year as well as a recovery in petroleum product margins.

Strategy

In addition to growing its core refining and petroleum products businesses the company is expanding its solar energy assets. In 2011 it launched the Kunitomi Plant its Solar Frontier unit's third Miyazaki plant and one of the largest solar plants in the world.

Ownership

Showa Shell is 35%-owned by Royal Dutch Shell and 15% by Saudi Aramco.

Company Background

The company was founded in 1985 through a merger between Japan's Showa Oil and Royal Dutch Shell's Shell Sekiyu.

EXECUTIVES

Senior Managing Director Solar Business Center; President Solar Frontier K.K., Shigeaki Kameda
Senior Executive Officer, Tomonori Okada
COO, Jun Arai, age 55
Senior Executive Officer, Atsuhiko Hirano
Chairman and CEO, Shigeya Kato
EVP; President Solar Frontier, Hiroto Tamai
Corporate Executive Officer Group Functions (Public Affairs Secretariat and HSSE), Kiyotaka Yamada
EVP, Tsuyoshi Kameoka
Executive Officer Group Functions (Legal and Personal Data Protection), Yuri Inoue
Corporate Executive Officer Oil Business Center (New Business Promotion); Group Functions (Corporate Planning (Including Corporate Governance), Misao Hamamoto
Corporate Executive Officer Solar Business Center (Executive Officer Solar Frontier K.K.; Miyazaki Plant and Procurement), Tomoaki Itou
Executive Officer Solar Frontier K.K. (Communications and Operations), Brooks Herring
Executive Officer Oil Business Center (Supply Oil Products Crude Oil & Marine and Marine), Masayuki Kobayashi
Executive Officer Group Functions (Finance & Control and Credit & Financial Risk Management), Tsutomu Yoshioka
CFO, Douglas Wood
President and Director, Jun Arai, age 55
VP CFO and Director, Richard A. Carruth
Auditors: ChuoAoyamaAuditCorporation

LOCATIONS

HQ: Showa Shell Sekiyu K.K.
  2-3-2 Daiba, Minato-ku, Tokyo 135-8074
Phone: (81) 3 5531 5591   Fax: (81) 3 5531 5598
Web: www.showa-shell.co.jp

PRODUCTS/OPERATIONS

Sales

	% of total
Oil	97
Energy Solution	3
Total	**100**

COMPETITORS

Cosmo Oil	JX Nippon Oil &
Exxon Mobil	Energy
Idemitsu Kosan	SK Innovation
JX Holdings	
JX Nippon Mining &	
Metals	

HISTORICAL FINANCIALS

Company Type: Public

Income Statement

FYE: December 31

	REVENUE ($ mil.)	NET INCOME ($ mil.)	NET PROFIT MARGIN	EMPLOYEES
12/13	28,139	574	2.0%	5,829
12/12	30,526	11	0.0%	5,848
12/11	35,812	298	0.8%	5,947
12/10	28,843	196	0.7%	5,761
12/09	21,890	(623)	—	5,439
Annual Growth	6.5%	—	—	1.7%

2013 Year-End Financials

Debt ratio: 0.1%
Return on equity: 21.9%
Cash ($ mil.): 272
Current ratio: 1.07
Long-term debt ($ mil.): 1,159

No. of shares (mil.): 376
Dividends
  Yield: —
  Payout: —
Market value ($ mil.): 3,916

	STOCK PRICE ($) FY Close	P/E High/Low	PER SHARE ($) Earnings	Dividends	Book Value
12/13	10.40	— —	1.53	0.00	8.23
12/12	5.75	— —	0.03	0.00	8.44
12/11	10.75	— —	0.79	0.00	9.58
12/10	9.56	— —	0.52	0.00	8.59
12/09	9.56	— —	(1.66)	0.00	7.41
Annual Growth	2.1%	— —	—	—	2.7%

Siemens AG (Germany)

For Siemens one of the largest electronics and industrial engineering companies in the galaxy everything comes down to four main objectives: Industry Energy Healthcare and City Infrastructure. Siemens' operations which encompass some 750 subsidiaries and associated companies around the globe make everything from automation equipment and building technologies for manufacturers and construction companies to diagnostic and imaging systems for hospitals and clinics. Other key products include power generation and distribution equipment for the oil and gas and renewable energy sectors. Siemens Energy Siemens Healthcare Siemens Industry and Siemens Infrastructure & Cities are its primary targeted segments.

HISTORY

In 1847 electrical engineer Werner von Siemens and craftsman Johann Halske formed Siemens & Halske. The firm's first major project linked Berlin and Frankfurt with the first long-distance telegraph system in Europe (1848). In 1870 it completed a 6600-mile telegraph line from London to Calcutta India and in 1874 it made the first transatlantic cable linking Ireland to the US.

The company's history of firsts includes Europe's first electric power transmission system (1876) the world's first electrified railway (1879) and one of the first elevators (1880). In 1896 it patented the world's first X-ray tube and completed the first European subway in Budapest Hungary.

By the next century it had formed light-bulb cartel OSRAM with German rivals AEG and Auer (1919) and created a venture with Furukawa Electric called Fuji Electric (1923). It developed radios and traffic lights in the 1920s and began producing electron microscopes in 1939.

Siemens & Halske played a critical role in Germany's war effort in WWII and suffered heavy losses. During the 1950s it recovered by developing data processing equipment silicates for semiconductors and the first implantable pacemaker. It moved into the nuclear industry in 1959 when its first reactor went into service at Munich-Garching. In 1966 the company reincorporated as Siemens AG. It formed joint ventures with Bosch (BSH Bosch und Siemens Hausergate appliances 1967) and AEG (Kraftwerk Union nuclear power 1969) among others. AEG dropped out of Kraftwerk Union (later Siemens Power Generation) in 1977.

In 1981 Karlheinz Kaske became the first CEO from outside the von Siemens family. Under his lead the firm entered joint ventures with Philips Intel and Advanced Micro Devices. In 1988 and 1989 it made several buys including Bendix Electronics (US) and was a willing buyer when IBM wanted to unload ROLM (then the #1 maker of PBXs). It had acquired all of ROLM's businesses by 1992. That year Heinrich von Pierer replaced Kaske as CEO.

The 1990s saw more consolidation: Siemens and German computer maker Nixdorf combined computer businesses to form Siemens Nixdorf Informationssysteme (SNI 1990); the firm acquired Sylvania's North American lamp business from GTE and merged it with the OSRAM companies in North America to form OSRAM SYLVANIA (1993).

The Asian economic crisis combined with other factors to make 1998 the worst year in the company's 150-year history. That year Siemens sold its defense electronics operations to British Aerospace (now BAE SYSTEMS) and Daimler-Benz (now Daimler) and bought CBS's power generation business (formerly Westinghouse Electric).

SNI's operations were juggled in a 1999 revamping of the company's information and communications units. That year Siemens held an IPO for its passive components and electron tubes unit. It spun off its semiconductor operations into Infineon Technologies but kept a 71% stake after Infineon's IPO in 2000. Siemens also sold its electromechanical components unit to Tyco International and its fiber-optic cable and hardware businesses to Corning.

In 2000 BSH paid $9.2 billion for the engineering and automotive parts unit Atecs Mannesmann. Also that year Siemens boosted its IT Service unit in the US by purchasing information services company ENTEX and it merged its nuclear business

with that of Framatome (the combined business is known as AREVA NP).

Siemens shares began trading on the New York Stock Exchange in 2001. The company bought Dallas-based Efficient Networks for $1.5 billion that year. The slump in the telecommunications industry hurt Siemens that year and the company cut 9700 jobs.

Late in 2001 Siemens cut its stake in Infineon Technologies to less than 50% and in 2002 it announced an additional 6500 jobs to be cut from its telecom unit. The company continued to trim its information and communications holdings with the July 2002 sale of Unisphere Networks to Juniper Networks. Later that year the company sold seven non-core subsidiaries (including Mannesmann Plastics Machinery Stabilus Demag Cranes & Components and Gottwald Port Technology) to buyout firm Kohlberg Kravis Roberts (now KKR) for $1.7 billion.

Siemens in 2004 bought the equipment treatment and technology components of US Filter for more than $990 million in cash as part of its expansion into the US. The purchase the company's largest since the 2001 acquisition of Efficient Networks was intended to strengthen its presence in the industrial water treatment and supply equipment market and to help it better compete against General Electric.

At the beginning of 2005 Klaus Kleinfeld who headed Siemens' US operations was named CEO; von Pierer became chairman of the company's supervisory board.

Also in 2005 Siemens bought medical-imaging equipment maker CTI Molecular Imaging in a deal valued at about $1 billion; it bolstered its financial services division especially in the medical equipment financing sector with the acquisition of UK-based financial services firm Broadcastle; and it purchased Flender Holding a German supplier of gear systems from a unit of Citigroup in a deal valued at $1.5 billion.

In 2005 Siemens sold its mobile phone business to Taiwanese electronics manufacturer BenQ (BenQ Mobile filed for insolvency the following year). Siemens restructured its entire communications group in 2006; its enterprise communications unit became a standalone company and its wireless modules business became part of the Siemens Group Automation and Drives division. It streamlined its telecommunications product line by discontinuing its enterprise networks business and selling its mobile phone operations. Later in 2006 the company announced that it was combining its carrier-related network operations with those of Nokia creating a joint venture called Nokia Siemens Networks. Each company took a 50% stake in the joint venture which commenced operations in 2007. The company also exited the auto parts market; Siemens sold its VDO Automotive unit to Continental for $16.7 billion in 2007.

The company augmented the automation and drives part of its Industry division when it bought UGS a developer of product lifecycle management software for about $3.5 billion in 2007. The company also grew its Healthcare division with major acquisitions. It purchased Diagnostic Products Corporation (DPC) a maker of immunodiagnostic systems for about $1.9 billion in 2006. On the heels of the DPC buy the company acquired the diagnostics division of Bayer for more than $5 billion. In 2007 the company purchased Dade Behring Holdings a provider of diagnostic testing kits for $7 billion.

Siemens attracted unwanted attention in 2006 when it was accused of making improper payments to secure contracts in Eastern Europe and the Middle East; embezzlement and tax evasion were also among the charges levied against the company. Siemens which was involved in a num-

ber of bribery cases prior to 2006 uncovered more than $500 million worth of suspicious transactions made over a seven-year period with its own probe. The investigation led to the arrest of several Siemens managers and in 2007 Heinrich von Pierer the chairman of Siemens' supervisory board who served as the company's CEO from 1992 to 2005 announced his resignation. German authorities later filed civil proceedings against von Pierer seeking damages. Siemens' CEO Klaus Kleinfeld then stepped down. Peter Loscher a veteran of General Electric and Merck succeeded Kleinfeld. After cooperating with various investigations by the SEC the US Department of Justice and other prosecutors and regulators around the world as a result of the corruption cases Siemens settled the claims in late 2008. The company agreed to pay record-setting fines of $1.6 billion to American and European authorities (including $450 million to the Justice Department $350 million to the SEC and $540 million to German prosecutors). Siemens pleaded guilty to US federal charges that it violated a law banning the use of corrupt practices in foreign business dealings but it avoided pleading guilty to bribery charges allowing it to remain a potential government contractor in the US and elsewhere.

Soon after Loscher took over Siemens announced its reorganization. Though its holdings remain vast the Siemens group initiated a significant shift in its operations. In 2009 the company designated Industry Energy and Healthcare as its primary business divisions while its IT Solutions and Financial Services segments filled supportive functions across its three main divisions in addition to growing their own customer bases. In 2011 the company announced its plans to divest its IT Solutions and Services unit to French IT company Atos Origin for approximately Å850 million (more than $1 billion).

Starting in 2008 it began divesting non-core operations including its majority stake (51%) in Siemens Enterprise Communications to the US management firm The Gores Group; an over 80% stake in Siemens Home and Office Communication Devices to ARQUES Industries; OSRAM's Global Tungsten & Powders unit; and its Wireless Modules Business.

In 2009 it continued its restructuring plan set in motion in 2008 by divesting a number of non-core operations. Fujitsu bought Siemens' 50% share in Fujitsu Siemens Computers (now Fujitsu Technology Solutions) for about Å450 million. In the latter part of the year the company sold its airfield lighting company ADB Airfield Solutions to UK-based Montagu Private Equity. Siemens also spun off its Munich-based Electronic Device Manufacturing (EDM) unit and subsequently withdrew from its joint venture Areva NP by selling its interest to Areva S.A. In 2010 the company shed its 35% stake in Hydro Power a joint venture with Voith. Hong Kong's ASM Pacific Technology acquired Siemens Electronics Assembly Systems a manufacturer of surface-mount technology equipment in early 2011. In an agreement to support the loss-making business which is burdened by Å160 million ($208 million) in loans Siemens shelled out Å29 million (about $38 million) to ASM Pacific.

The company sold its IT Solutions and Services unit (part of Siemens Industry business) to France-based Atos (formerly Atos Origin) for approximately Å850 million (more than $1 billion). Siemens accepted a 15% stake in Atos.

EXECUTIVES

EVP Head Corporate Legal and Compliance; Member Managing Board and General Counsel Siemens AG, Peter Y. Solmssen, age 60, $1,061,580 total compensation

CEO Energy Service Division; President and CEO Siemens Energy, Randy H. Zwirn

Second Deputy Chairman, Josef Ackermann, age 67, $96,616 total compensation

Chairman, Gerhard Cromme, age 71, $285,240 total compensation

CEO BSH Bosch und Siemens Hausgerate GmbH, Kurt-Ludwig Gutberlet, age 58

First Deputy Chairman, Berthold Huber, age 65, $113,984 total compensation

CEO OSRAM Division, Wolfgang Dehen, age 61, $1,126,710 total compensation

CEO Clinical Products Division USA, Norbert Gaus

CFO Siemens Building Technologies, Heribert Stumpf

President and CEO, Peter Loscher, age 56, $2,860,110 total compensation

CEO Industry Solutions Division, Jens M. Wegmann

EVP Head Supply Chain Management Chief Sustainability Officer and Member Managing Board, Barbara Kux, age 60, $982,741 total compensation

Head Corporate Supply Chain Management, Bernd Regendantz

President and CEO, Joe Kaeser, age 57, $1,126,710 total compensation

CEO Building Technologies Division, Johannes Milde

CFO Siemens Austria, Reinhard Pinzer, age 62

CFO Energy Sector, Ralf Guntermann

CEO Power Transmission Division, Udo Niehage

COO Osram, Martin Goetzeler, age 51

Chief Compliance Officer, Hans-Jorg Grundmann

CFO Siemens IT Solutions and Services, Martin Bentler, age 53

CFO Mobility Division, Michael Schulz-Drost

CEO Siemens IT Solutions and Services, Christian Oecking

CEO Financial Services, Roland W. Chalons-Browne, age 58

Head Mergers Acquistions Post Closing Management, Karl-Heinz Seibert, age 55

CEO Rail Automation, Jochen Eickholt, age 52

Member of the Managing Board; Chief Executive Officer of Healthcare Sector, Hermann Requardt, age 60, $1,126,710 total compensation

Member of the Managing Board; Chief Executive Officer of Industry Sector, Siegfried Russwurm, age 51, $1,061,580 total compensation

CEO Infrastructure and Cities Sector, Roland Busch, age 50

CEO Customer Solutions Division, Thomas (Tom) Miller

CFO Imaging and Therapy Divisions, Jochen Schmitz

CEO Siemens IT Solutions and Services US and Canada, John E. Evers Jr., age 53

CEO Siemens UK, Andreas J. Goss, age 50

Head Corporate Communications and Government Affairs, Stephan Heimbach, age 53

CEO Imaging & Therapy Systems, Bernd Montag

CFO Industry Sector, Ralf P. Thomas, age 52

Head Corporate Press Office Media Relations, Constantin Birnstiel, age 42

CFO Fossil Power Generation Division, Michael Becker

CFO Renewable Energy Division, Michael Axmann

CFO Oil and Gas Division, Volker Walprecht

CFO Energy Services Division USA, Steve Conner

CEO Power Distribution Division, Ralf Christian

CFO Power Distribution Division, Matthias Platsch

Head Corporate Information Technology, Norbert Kleinjohann

CFO Siemens Financial Services, Peter Moritz

CFO Industry Solutions Division, Wolfgang Hermann

CFO Healthcare Sector, Michael Sen, age 46

CEO VAI Metals Technologies, Werner Auer

CEO Oil and Gas Division, Tom Blades, age 58

CEO Fossil Power Generation, Roland Fischer, age 52

Chief Diversity Officer, Denice Kronau, age 55

CFO OSRAM, Thomas Schaffer

CFO Drive Technologies Division, Thomas Rathmann

CTO and Member Managing Board Siemens AG, Klaus Helmrich, age 56

CEO Industry Automation Division, Anton S. Huber

CFO Industry Automation Division, Miguel-Angel Lopez

Member of the Managing Board; Chief Executive Officer Energy Sector, Michael Suess, age 51

CFO Customer Solutions Division, Wolfgang Beitz

CEO Corporate Unit Finance and Controlling Head of the Project Stand-alone READINESS, Hannes Apitzsch

CEO Siemens Real Estate, Zsolt Sluitner

CEO Audiologische Technik, Roger Radke

President and CEO Siemens Corporation, Eric A. Spiegel

CEO Siemens Austria, Wolfgang Hesoun, age 54

Head Corporate Human Resources Director Labor and Member Managing Board of Siemens AG, Brigitte Ederer, age 58

CEO Siemens Regional Company Indonesia, Josef Winter

Chief Counsel Compliance, Klaus Moosmayer

Head EU Affairs Berlin and Brussels, Peter Witt

CEO Diagnostics Division USA, Michael Reiterman

Head Smart Grid Applications Sector Energy, Richard Hausmann

CFO Clinical Products Division, Klaus-Armin Kiesel

Head Corporate Unit Corporate Sustainability Office, Siegmar Proebstl

Head Siemens Corporate Research and Technologies, Reinhold Achatz

Head Corporate Development Siemens One, Pedro Miranda

Head Corporate Development Executives, Nicolas von Rosty

Head HR Governance Germany, Walter Huber

Head Taxes, Christian Kaeser

CEO Industry Solutions Division and CEO Customer Services Division., Dirk Hoke, age 44

CEO Drive Technologies, Ralf-Michael Franke, age 56

Chief Financial Officer, Klaus P. Stegemann

Vice President Sustainability, Alison Taylor

Vice President Corporate Affairs, Camille Johnston

Vice President and Chief Intellectual Property Counsel, Daniel J. Staudt

Senior Vice President Siemens Government Affairs, Kathleen A. Ambrose

Senior Vice President General Counsel Secretary, Rose Glazer

Sr. Vice President Communications & Marketing, Jim Whaley

President of the Managing Board; Chief Executive Officer, Peter Peter Loescher Loescher

Senior Vice President Manufacturing Engineering Software, Zvi Feuer

Senior Vice President General Manager Mainstream Engineering Software, Karsten Newbury

Senior Vice President Chief Information Officer, Craig J. Berry

Senior Vice President of Human Resources, Dan Malliet

senior Vice President of Industry Strategy for Siemens PLM Software, Stephen M. Bashada

Senior Vice President Lifecycle Collaboration Software, Eric Sterling

Senior Vice President Product Driven Services, Kevin Eustace

Senior Vice President Product Engineering Software, Jim Rusk

Senior Vice President Strategy Initiatives, Raj Khoshoo

Senior Vice President, Steve Luby

Board Member, Michael Diekmann, age 60

Board Member, Jean-Louis Beffa, age 73

Second Deputy Chairman, Josef Ackermann, age 67

Board Member, Lord Iain D. T. Vallance of Tummel, age 71

First Deputy Chairman, Berthold Huber, age 65

Board Member, Lothar Adler, age 65

Board Member, H?kan Samuelsson, age 63

Board Member, Hans-Jurgen Hartung, age 62

Board Member, Nicola Leibinger-Kammuller, age 54

Board Member, Dieter Scheitor, age 64

Board Member, Gerd von Brandenstein, age 72

Board Member, Hans Michael Gaul, age 72

Board Member, Peter Gruss, age 65

Board Member, Bettina Haller, age 55

Board Member, Harald Kern, age 54

Board Member, Werner Monius, age 59

Board Member, Rainer Sieg, age 66

Board Member, Birgit Steinborn, age 54

Board Member, Sibylle Wankel, age 50

Member of the Supervisory Board, Gerd Brandenstein

Member of the Supervisory Board, Iain Tummel

Member of the Supervisory Board, Nicola Leibinger-Kammueller

Member of the Supervisory Board; Employee Representative, Werner Moenius

Auditors: Ernst&YoungWirtschaftsprufungsgesellschaft

LOCATIONS

HQ: Siemens AG (Germany)
Wittelsbacherplatz 2, Munich 80333
Phone: (49) 89 636 32474   Fax: (49) 89 636 30085
Web: www.siemens.com

Sales

	% of total
Europe CIS Africa Middle	55
Germany	15
Other	40
Americas	27
US	19
Other	8
Asia	18
China	8
India	3
Other	7
Total	**100**

PRODUCTS/OPERATIONS

Sales

	% of total
Industry	44
Energy	33
Health	16
Other	7
Total	**100**

Selected Operations

Industry
  Building technology (heating and ventilation security fire safety systems)
  Industry automation (manufacturing and process automation)
  Industry solutions (systems integration for industrial plants)
  Mobility (transportation systems)
  Motion control (converters drives motors numerical control systems)
  OSRAM (light-emitting diodes light bulbs)
Energy
  Fossil power generation (gas and steam turbines and generators power plants)
  Oil and gas (extraction conversion and transportation systems)
  Power distribution (powergrid automation switch gear components)
  Power transmission (high-voltage equipment)
  Renewable energy (wind energy)
  Service rotating equipment (power plant services and operation)

Health care
  Diagnostics (immune diagnostics molecular analysis)
  Imaging and IT (imaging systems and networking)
  Workflow and solutions (health care systems and services)
Other
  BSH Bosch und Siemens Hausgerate (equity investment)
  ELIN GmbH & Co. (equity investment)
  Enterprise Network Holdings (equity investment)
  Financial services (cross-sector)
  Krauss-Maffei Wegmann GmbH & Co. (equity investment)
  Nokia Siemens networks (equity investment)
  Real estate (cross-sector)
  Information Technology

Selected Key Subsidiaries

Siemens Corp. (US)
Siemens Energy (Germany and US)
Siemens Enterprise Communications GmbH (Germany)
Siemens Financial Services GmbH (Germany)
Siemens Healthcare (Germany and US)
Siemens Holdings plc (UK)
Siemens Industry Automation (US; subsidiary of Siemens Industry)
Siemens Industry Inc. (US)
Siemens Industry Inc. (US)
Siemens Ltda. (Brazil)
Siemens Osakeyhtio Group (Finland)
Siemens Product Lifecycle Management Software Inc. (US; subsidiary of Siemens Industry)
Siemens Water Technologies Corp.(US; subsidiary of Siemens Industry)

COMPETITORS

ABB	Hitachi
ALSTOM	Hologic
AREVA	Honeywell
Abbott Labs	International
Affiliated Computer	Huawei Technologies
Services	Johnson Controls
Alcatel-Lucent	MAN
Avaya	McKesson
BP Solar	Mitsubishi Electric
Beckman Coulter	Mitsubishi Heavy
Bharat Heavy	Industries
Electricals	Nichia
Bombardier	Nortel Networks
Capgemini	OSRAM
Cerner	Philips Electronics
Computer Sciences	Philips Healthcare
Corp.	REpower Systems
Danfoss Turbocor	Roche Diagnostics
Danieli	Rockwell Automation
Dassault	Schneider Electric
Dresser-Rand	Sonova
Eaton	Toshiba
Emerson Electric	Tyco
FANUC	United Technologies
GE	Varian Medical Systems
GN ReSound	Veolia Environnement
Gamesa	Vestas Wind Systems

HISTORICAL FINANCIALS
Company Type: Public

Income Statement
FYE: September 30

	REVENUE ($ mil.)	NET INCOME ($ mil.)	NET PROFIT MARGIN	EMPLOYEES
09/14	90,537	6,763	7.5%	343,000
09/13	102,419	5,782	5.6%	362,400
09/12	101,236	5,764	5.7%	370,000
09/11	99,176	8,290	8.4%	350,500
09/10	103,544	5,313	5.1%	405,000
Annual Growth	(3.3%)	6.2%	—	(4.1%)

2014 Year-End Financials
Debt ratio: 25.1%
Return on equity: 18.1%
Cash ($ mil.): 10,087
Current ratio: 1.31
Long-term debt ($ mil.): 24,328
No. of shares (mil.): 835
Dividends
  Yield: 5.0%
  Payout: 65.2%
Market value ($ mil.): 99,454

	STOCK PRICE ($) FY Close	P/E High/Low		PER SHARE ($) Earnings	Dividends	Book Value
09/14	119.07	38	30	7.94	6.02	46.65
09/13	120.51	44	33	6.79	5.95	45.01
09/12	100.15	40	25	6.52	4.75	46.41
09/11	89.79	42	23	9.39	2.70	48.65
09/10	105.40	47	31	6.05	1.63	44.41
Annual Growth	3.1%	—	—	7.0%	38.6%	1.2%

Sinopharm Group Co., Ltd.

LOCATIONS

HQ: Sinopharm Group Co., Ltd.
  Sinopharm Plaza, No. 1001 Zhongshan West Road, Changning District, Shanghai 200051
Phone: (86) 21 2305 2666
Web: www.sinopharmgroup.com.cn

HISTORICAL FINANCIALS
Company Type: Public

Income Statement
FYE: December 31

	REVENUE ($ mil.)	NET INCOME ($ mil.)	NET PROFIT MARGIN	EMPLOYEES
12/13	27,563	371	1.3%	45,415
12/12	21,780	316	1.5%	40,737
12/11	16,240	247	1.5%	35,394
12/10	10,503	183	1.7%	24,117
12/09	7,713	141	1.8%	0
Annual Growth	37.5%	27.3%	—	—

2013 Year-End Financials
Debt ratio: 3.9%
Return on equity: 11.5%
Cash ($ mil.): 2,312
Current ratio: 1.27
Long-term debt ($ mil.): 682
No. of shares (mil.): —
Dividends
  Yield: —
  Payout: —
Market value ($ mil.): —

	STOCK PRICE ($) FY Close	P/E High/Low		PER SHARE ($) Earnings	Dividends	Book Value
12/13	2.87	0	0	0.15	0.00	1.40
12/12	3.15	0	0	0.13	0.00	1.14
12/11	2.57	0	0	0.10	0.00	1.04
12/10	3.52	0	0	0.08	0.00	0.78
12/09	3.65	0	0	0.08	0.00	0.77
Annual Growth	(5.8%)	—	—	17.3%	—	16.3%

Sistema JSFC

LOCATIONS

HQ: Sistema JSFC
  13 Mokhovaya Street, Moscow 125099
Phone: (7) 495 730 66 00
Web: www.sistema.com

HISTORICAL FINANCIALS
Company Type: Public

Income Statement
FYE: December 31

	REVENUE ($ mil.)	NET INCOME ($ mil.)	NET PROFIT MARGIN	EMPLOYEES
12/13	35,942	2,257	6.3%	0
12/12	34,240	946	2.8%	0
12/11	32,981	218	0.7%	0
12/10	28,098	918	3.3%	0
12/09	18,749	1,643	8.8%	0
Annual Growth	17.7%	8.3%	—	—

2013 Year-End Financials
Debt ratio: 30.6%
Return on equity: 23.1%
Cash ($ mil.): 2,059
Current ratio: 1.09
Long-term debt ($ mil.): 10,764
No. of shares (mil.): —
Dividends
  Yield: —
  Payout: —
Market value ($ mil.): —

SK Holdings Co Ltd

LOCATIONS

HQ: SK Holdings Co Ltd
  26 Jong-ro Jongno-gu, Seoul 110-110
Phone: (82) 2 2121 0114   **Fax:** (82) 2 2121 1891
Web: www.sk.co.kr

HISTORICAL FINANCIALS
Company Type: Public

Income Statement
FYE: December 31

	REVENUE ($ mil.)	NET INCOME ($ mil.)	NET PROFIT MARGIN	EMPLOYEES
12/13	106,287	268	0.3%	127
12/12	112,088	982	0.9%	196
12/11	95,985	1,443	1.5%	145
12/10	80,741	824	1.0%	300
12/09	71,018	232	0.3%	298
Annual Growth	10.6%	3.7%	—	(19.2%)

2013 Year-End Financials
Debt ratio: 0.0%
Return on equity: 2.4%
Cash ($ mil.): 7,653
Current ratio: 1.16
Long-term debt ($ mil.): 19,206
No. of shares (mil.): 40
Dividends
  Yield: —
  Payout: —
Market value ($ mil.): —

SK Innovation Co Ltd

SK Innovation (formerly known as SK Energy) is the energy lubricants and chemicals affiliate of South Korea's SK Group. Korea's largest oil refiner SK Innovation controls about 34% of Korea's fuel retailing market. The firm holds stakes in 30 oil exploration and production projects in 16 countries and has proved reserves of more than 500 million barrels of oil equivalent. It imports liquid petroleum gas (LPG) and claims a 44% share of the Korean LPG market. SK Innovation supplies natural gas to Seoul and other cities in Korea. The company also makes lubricants low-pollutant gasoline petrochemicals and batteries for electric vehicles.

In 2011 in order to be a more flexible organization in dealing with a rapidly changing marketplace SK Innovation spun off its refining unit as SK Energy its chemical operations as SK Global Chemicals and its lubricant oil business as SK Lubricants. All the units are wholly-owned subsidiaries. A part of the innovative push the company's new corporate name claims the company is looking to expand in the field of alternative energy including pursuing new battery and carbon capture technologies.

SK Innovation is focusing on strengthening its overseas oil exploration and production operations. It has formed strategic alliances with other global oil concerns such as Nippon Oil and PERTAMINA to in order to expand activities in China Vietnam and Indonesia.

In 2010 it formed a joint venture with KBR to market and license SK Innovation's petrochemical and related process technologies. That same year it agreed to sell its Brazilian oil interests to Denmark's Maersk Oil for $2.4 billion. SK Innovation plans to use the proceeds either to invest in developing oil and gas fields or to buy other international oil companies. That year the company signed a contract to operate and maintain Vietnam's first petrochemical plant.

On the innovative technology side of the ledger in 2010 Korea launched its first electric car a vehicle powered by an SK Innovation lithium-ion battery.

In 2008 the company merged with subsidiary SK Incheon Oil a major Korean refiner allowing the company to further its plans to be a major oil and fuels exporter to the growing China market.

EXECUTIVES

EVP Ethics Management Office and Director, Joon Ho Kim
Chairman and CEO, Tae-Won Chey
CEO President Corporate Planning and Global Technology and Director, Ja-Young Koo
EVP Ethics Management Office and Director, Joon Ho Kim
Director, Soon Cho
Director, Young-Suk Han
Director, Dae-Woo Nam
Director, Sei-Jong Oh
Director, Tai-Yoo Kim
Director, Myung-Hae Choi
Director, Hoon-Kyu Lee
Director, In-Goo Han
CEO President Corporate Planning and Global Technology and Director, Ja-Young Koo
Auditors: Ernst&YoungHanYoung

LOCATIONS

HQ: SK Innovation Co Ltd
26, Jong-ro Jongno-gu, Seoul 110-110
Phone: (82) 2 2121 5114   **Fax:** (82) 2 2121 2118
Web: www.skenergy.com

Sales

	% of total
Korea	41
Other	59
Total	**100**

PRODUCTS/OPERATIONS

Sales

	% of total
Petroleum	68
Petrochemicals	27
Lubricants	3
Exploration & production &	2
Total	**100**

COMPETITORS

BHP Billiton	Hyundai Corporation
Daewoo International	Idemitsu Kosan
Exxon Mobil	Nippon Oil
GS Caltex	Royal Dutch Shell

HISTORICAL FINANCIALS

Company Type: Public

Income Statement

FYE: December 31

	REVENUE ($ mil.)	NET INCOME ($ mil.)	NET PROFIT MARGIN	EMPLOYEES
12/13	63,395	694	1.1%	1,892
12/12	68,680	1,110	1.6%	1,881
12/11	59,007	2,734	4.6%	1,642
12/10	47,911	1,015	2.1%	5,457
12/09	37,913	578	1.5%	5,582
Annual Growth	**13.7%**	**4.7%**	**—**	**(23.7%)**

2013 Year-End Financials

Debt ratio: 0.0%
Return on equity: 4.6%
Cash ($ mil.): 2,708
Current ratio: 1.46
Long-term debt ($ mil.): 5,550

No. of shares (mil.): 91
Dividends
  Yield: —
  Payout: —
Market value ($ mil.): —

Skandinaviska Enskilda Banken

Snow banks are a common winter sight in Sweden; SEB banks are easy to spot year-round. Skandinaviska Enskilda Banken (SEB) provides merchant banking retail banking wealth management and life insurance in some 20 nations primarily in Northern Europe. Its merchant banking division targets large corporate clients and other financial institutions for whom it provides lending debt capital markets trading finance and custody services. Its retail division provides business services including loans and card services. SEB Wealth Management offers asset management and private banking services to institutional and wealthy clients. The group traces its roots back to 1856.

Sweden accounts for more than half of SEB's sales. The company has focused on growth in the Nordic and Baltic nations where it hopes to become the top financial services provider. Norwegian bank DnB NOR which decided to exit Sweden's mortgage market sold its portfolio of mortgage loans to SEB in 2011. Germany has been another target growth market for the group. It developed a retail branch network there but sold those operations to Banco Santander in early 2011. SEB is still dedicated to its wholesale business in Germany.

The divestiture of SEB's German branches will cut into the group's interest income. Additionally the group's fees into a nationwide banking fund have doubled to SEK 600 million ($95 million). The fund was established to maintain stability in — and prevent the collapse of —Sweden's economy. However the Nordic region is one of Europe's strongest so the company enjoys an added level of financial security.

In 2011 SEB announced plans to sell its Ukrainian retail banking operations to Eurobank Group for 250 million kronor ($37 million). The deal will include 60 branches.

The wealthy Wallenberg family controls about 21% of SEB (through holding company Investor and a family foundation).

HISTORY

Skandinaviska Enskilda Banken (SEB) was incorporated in 1972 as a result of the merger between Stockholm's Enskilda Bank (founded in 1856 by the Wallenberg family) and Skandinaviska Banken (founded in 1864 and a pioneer in commercial lending in Scandinavia). By 1974 SEB had begun expanding its operations forming an investment management subsidiary. It then became one of the first Swedish banks to go international when it took a stake in the German Deutsch-Skandinavische Bank in 1976. By the end of the 1970s SEB had reached halfway around the world establishing a subsidiary in Singapore to handle Southeast Asian operations.

By the early 1980s SEB was leading the nation in industrial as well as private accounts largely due to deregulation and the introduction of new financial instruments including Swedish treasury bills a commercial paper market and market-rate state bonds. The bank continued to expand opening branches in the Cayman Islands Hamburg London and New York; it also began cross-border banking in Scandinavia through a regional alliance with Bergen Bank of Norway Privatbanken of Denmark and Union Bank of Finland.

In another step toward deregulation the Swedish government lifted the ban on foreign banking in 1985. Within a year a dozen international banks had established themselves in Sweden but SEB continued to expand; its investment banking subsidiary Enskilda Securities opened branches in Hong Kong London New York Paris and Singapore in the latter half of the 1980s.

In 1990 the bank acquired an option to buy about a third of Skandia Sweden's largest private insurance company. But facing strong resistance from Skandia's management SEB accepted defeat and sold most of its option to two Scandinavian insurance companies. Winds of change blew through Sweden in the early 1990s as the country suffered a severe economic recession. Deregulation in the mid-1980s followed by excessive lending to the property market led to inflated real estate prices and then a collapse of the market. Banks investing in property experienced huge losses; many banks (including SEB) had to turn to the government for help to strengthen their capital bases. The mid-1990s saw the bank still trying to recover selling several of its subsidiaries including a vehicle finance unit to GE Capital.

1997 saw SEB acquire Trygg-Hansa (now SEB Trygg Liv) one of Sweden's major insurers. The bank remained acquisitive in 1998 expanding aggressively into the Baltic by buying major stakes in banks in Estonia (Eesti hlspank) Latvia (Latvija Unibanken) and Lithuania (Vilniaus Bankas).

In 1999 the bank further emphasized its Internet business making it a separate unit. Also that year SEB sold Trygg-Hansa's non-life business to Denmark's Codan Insurance in exchange for Codan's banking subsidiary and other assets. In 2000 the bank acquired Germany's almost 200-branch BfG Bank from Credit Lyonnais; it then used BfG to create a cross-selling and Internet alliance with German insurer Gerling. Also in 2000 SEB upped its stake in Eesti hispank Vilniaus Bankas and Latvijas Unibanka.

The following year SEB announced plans to acquire fellow Swedish bank ForeningsSparbanken to create SEB SwedBank. EU regulators investigated the proposal and demanded significant concession. As a result the two banks dropped plans for the merger later in 2001.

SEB continued to boost its offerings and services —largely through acquisitions —during the early years of the 21st century. Purchases included Europay in Norway (2002) Danish life insurer Codan Pension (2004) Ukraine's Bank Agio (2005) and Russia's PetroEnergoBank (2006). In 2007 it acquired nearly all of Factorial Bank adding 65 branches in Eastern Ukraine. The following year it bought London-based hedge fund Key Asset Management.

EXECUTIVES

Deputy Chairman, Urban Jansson, age 69
Deputy Chairman, Jacob Wallenberg, age 59
Executive Vice President Chief Financial Officer, Jan Erik Back, age 53
President CEO and Director, Annika Falkengren, age 52
Chairman, Marcus Wallenberg, age 59
Executive Vice President Head of Merchant Banking, Magnus Carlsson, age 58
Head Group Communications, Viveka Hirdman-Ryrberg, age 52
Deputy President Deputy CEO and Head Group Staff and Business Support, Bo Magnusson, age 51
Head Group Strategy and Business Development, Hans Larsson, age 53
Head Group Human Resources, Ulf Peterson, age 54
Executive Vice President Head of Retail Banking, Mats Torstendahl
Head of Life & Wealth Management, Anders Johnsson, age 55
Chief Risk Officer, Johan Johan Andersson Andersson
Executive Vice President Head of Business Support, Martin Johansson, age 52
Country Manager SEB Denmark and Head of Merchant Banking Denmark, Peter H?ltermand, age 51
Head of Baltic, David Teare, age 51
Country Manager SEB Norway, William Paus, age 46
Director, Carl Wilhelm Ros, age 72
Deputy Chairman, Urban Jansson, age 69
Director, Jesper Ovesen, age 56
Deputy Chairman, Jacob Wallenberg, age 59
Deputy Chairman, Tuve Johannesson, age 71
President CEO and Director, Annika Falkengren, age 52
Director, Christine Novakovic, age 50
Independent Director, Birgitta Birgitta Kantola Kantola
Director; Employee Representative, Cecilia Cecilia Martensson Martensson
Director; Employee Representative, Goran Goran Lilja Lilja
Independent Director, Johan Johan Andresen Andresen
Independent Director, Signhild Signhild Arnegard Hansen Hansen
Independent Director, Tomas Tomas Nicolin Nicolin
Auditors: PricewaterhouseCoopersAB

LOCATIONS

HQ: Skandinaviska Enskilda Banken
Kungstradgardsgatan 8, Stockholm SE-106 40
Phone: (46) 771 62 10 00
Web: www.sebgroup.com

Sales

	% of total
Scandinavia	
Sweden	55
Norway	13
Denmark	12
Finland	6
Baltics	
Lithuania	5

Estonia	4
Latvia	3
Germany	2
Total	**100**

PRODUCTS/OPERATIONS

Sales by Segment

	% of total
Merchant	53
Retail	19
Life	13
Wealth	10
Baltic	5
Total	**100**

COMPETITORS

Citigroup Global Markets	Morgan Stanley
Danske Bank	Nordea Bank
Deutsche Bank	Skandia
DnB NOR	Storebrand ASA
Goldman Sachs	Svenska Handelsbanken
KBC	Swedbank AB
	UBS Investment Bank

HISTORICAL FINANCIALS

Company Type: Public

Income Statement

FYE: December 31

	ASSETS ($ mil.)	NET INCOME ($ mil.)	INCOME AS % OF ASSETS	EMPLOYEES
12/13	387,577	2,303	0.6%	17,096
12/12	376,613	1,785	0.5%	18,168
12/11	342,561	1,610	0.5%	18,912
12/10	325,075	1,005	0.3%	20,717
12/09	324,096	156	0.0%	21,640
Annual Growth	**4.6%**	**95.9%**	**—**	**(5.7%)**

2013 Year-End Financials

Return on assets: 0.6%
Return on equity: 12.7%
Long-term debt ($ mil.): —
No. of shares (mil.): —
Sales ($ mil): 13,237

Dividends
Yield: —
Payout: —
Market value ($ mil.): —

Societe Generale

Societe Generale wants to be top brass in the French banking industry. The bank (more familiarly known as SocGen) commands a three-pronged campaign with operations entailing domestic retail banking (including regional bank Credit du Nord and majority-owned online bank and brokerage Boursorama) international retail banking and corporate and investment banking. Other key activities include specialized finance consumer finance and insurance and investment management private banking and securities services. Altogether SocGen has more than 3200 branches in France and nearly 4000 additional locations in more than 75 countries worldwide.

SocGen has international banking operations in nearly 40 countries. Key markets for the segment are Russia Central and Eastern Europe the Mediterranean basin sub-Saharan Africa and Asia particularly China India and Vietnam. The company's asset management operations include two joint ventures with fellow French banking giant Credit Agricole: Amundi (25% owned) and brokerage Newedge (50%).

SocGen reported a 3% decline in net banking income for 2011 but a nearly 40% decrease in profits from E3.9 billion to E2.4 billion (approximately $5 billion to $3.1 billion). The company attributed its results in part to a decline in corporate and investment banking earnings amid turbulent markets as well as restructuring changes and the write down of goodwill and Greek sovereign debt.

SocGen's primary strategic initiatives include controlling risk and improving customer service. Some of the ways the bank is achieving its goals include streamlining its loan application process increasing capital reserves and reducing its exposure to sovereign debt of troubled countries such as Ireland Italy Portugal and Spain. To help improve its capital position SocGen announced plans to sell US asset manager TCW Group to The Carlyle Group in 2012. It's also partnering with Tikehau Group to take over French investment company Salvepar.

HISTORY

In 1864 French steel magnate Joseph Schneider along with a group of Parisian bankers incorporated Societe Generale pour Favoriser le Developpement du Commerce et de l'Industrie en France. The bank which for obvious reasons came to be known as Societe Generale had the duty "to encourage the development of trade and industry in France." It took deposits from the public and offered lines of credit to companies. The bank also helped organize businesses and invested in them.

By the 1890s Societe Generale's branches placed shares with the public and issued private unsecured loans in France and Russia.

The bank counted 14000 shareholders in 1895 and 18 years later the number had boomed to 122000. The bank continued its brisk growth through the first decades of the 20th century opening more than 1400 branches by 1933.

Although Societe Generale managed to move into Africa and America in the 1930s the Depression and WWII forced the bank to reduce its size and close branches at home.

After WWII the bank was nationalized by the French government to help rebuild the war-ravaged country. Societe Generale (already active in New York) was well-positioned to distribute the US-sponsored postwar reconstruction initiative aka the Marshall Plan. For 30 years the bank grew steadily under state control.

The 1960s were a boom time for French exports. The decade brought the bank greater expansion both geographically (Europe Latin America) and economically thanks to the specialization of credit investment banking finance leasing for companies and home mortgages for retail customers. Societe Generale also began dealing in Eurocurrencies (money deposited outside the investing company or government's home country).

In 1973 a new law in France allowed the bank to sell up to 25% of its shares to its staff and a limited circle of institutional investors.

A year later amid the oil crisis low-quality Eurocurrency market loans came back to haunt Societe Generale. In one case the bank had unwisely lent Eurodollars to the United States National Bank of San Diego which failed and cost Societe Generale $7.5 million.

In 1975 the bank launched Agrifan an export-based food products trading company to great success. Agrifan was followed by two more companies specializing in food-industry equipment and medical supplies.

Conservatives regained power in the French government in 1986. The next year Societe Generale was officially privatized.

In 1998 the bank extended the reach of its financial services by acquiring Barr Devlin a US-based investment banker and adviser and Ya-maichi Capital Management in Japan.

The next year Societe Generale undertook a friendly merger with fellow French banking gargantuan Paribas only to have Banque Nationale de Paris swoop in and steal the prize to form BNP Paribas.

Societe Generale had to satisfy itself with a piece-meal expansion. By 2000 it had hammered out an ambitious strategic alliance with Spain-based Santander Central Hispano. The French bank also snapped up 30% of Italian insurer Societa Assicuratrice Industriale's Banca SAI subsidiary giving it access to SAI's 3 million customers. The buying spree continued into 2001 with Societe Generale acquiring Deutsche Bank's leasing and vehicle-fleet businesses Gefa and ALD. The bank then bought a controlling stake in LA-based fund manager TCW Group.

SocGen sold its South American retail banking unit Banco Societe Generale Argentina to Argentine banking group Banco Banex in 2005. The following year SocGen spun off US-based investment bank Cowen Group.

In 2008 SocGen uncovered fraud by one of its traders in one of the world's largest-ever instances of trading fraud. Soon after the company began raising funds to help cover the estimated $7.1 billion cost of the fraud and also initiated legal proceedings against the (by then former) employee. The Banking Commission of France fined the company $6.3 billion for breaches in internal controls.

Additionally chairman and then-CEO Daniel Bouton and co-CEO Philippe Citerne each gave up a half-year's salary to compensate for the company's losses. Although Bouton's offers to resign amidst the firestorm were twice rejected by SocGen's board of directors he eventually did step down. CFO Frederic Oudea succeeded him in both positions. Didier Alix and Severin Cabannes replaced Citerne as deputy CEOs.

The company spent years building up its portfolio in banks in Central and Eastern Europe including majority stakes in Russia's Rosbank in 2008 and in Macedonia's Ohridska Banka and Bauritanian Bank Banque in 2007. SocGen also expanded its private banking operations. In 2008 its SG Private Banking unit acquired a 37% stake in US-based wealth manager Rockefeller Financial Services and in 2007 it bought ABN AMRO's London private banking unit.

In 2008 SocGen merged the brokerage activities of subsidiary Fimat with Credit Agricole Corporate and Investment Bank (formerly Calyon) creating a joint venture named Newedge. The following year SocGen merged its asset management business with that of Credit Agricole creating a combined firm called Amundi with more than E690 billion ($1 trillion) of assets under management. SocGen owns 25% of the joint venture while Credit Agricole holds the other 75%.

EXECUTIVES

Director, Robert Castaigne, age 65
Director, Jean-Martin Folz, age 66
Vice Chairman, Anthony B. Wyand, age 70
Director, Luc Vandevelde, age 62
Director, Michel Cicurel, age 66
Director, Kenji Matsuo, age 64
Director, Jean Azema, age 60
Director, Elisabeth Lulin, age 46
Director, Gianemilio Osculati, age 65
Director, Nathalie Rachou
Director, Patrick Delicourt
Director, France Houssaye
Director, Jean-Bernard Levy
Auditors: Ernst&YoungAudit

LOCATIONS

HQ: Societe Generale
29, Boulevard Haussmann, Paris 75009
Phone: (33) 1 42 14 20 00
Web: www.societegenerale.com

PRODUCTS/OPERATIONS

2011 Income by Segment

	% of total
French	32
Corporate & Investment	23
International Retail	20
Specialized Financial Services &	14
Global Investment Management &	9
Corporate &	2
Total	**100**

Selected Subsidiaries and Affiliates

ALD (vehicle leasing and fleet management)
Banco Cacique (consumer finance Brazil)
Banco Pecunia (consumer finance Brazil)
Bank Republic (Georgia)
Banque de Polynesie (72% French Polynesia)
BDK Bank (consumer finance Germany)
BelRosbank (Belarus)
BFV-Societe Generale (banking Madagascar)
Boursorama SA (56% online banking and brokerage)
BRD-Groupe Societe Generale (banking Romania)
CGI (consumer finance)
CredAgoria (consumer finance Portugal)
Credit du Nord (banking France)
DeltaCredit (banking Russia)
ESSOX (consumer finance Czech Republic)
Eurobank (consumer finance Poland)
Fiditalia (consumer finance Italy)
Geniki Bank (54% Greece)
Komercni Banka (60% Czech Republic)
Lyxor (investment management)
Mobiasbanka (Moldova)
National Societe Generale Bank (Egypt)
Ohridska Banka (Macedonia)
Rosbank (Russia)
SG Mumbai (India)
SeABank (Vietnam)
SG VietFinance (Vietnam)
SKB Banka (Slovenia)
Societe Generale Albania
Societe Generale Algerie (banking Algeria)
Societe Generale Bank Cyprus
Societe Generale Benin
Societe Generale de Banque - Jordanie (Jordan)
Societe Generale de Banque au Liban (Lebanon)
Societe Generale de Banques au Cote d'Ivoire
Societe Generale de Banques au Senegal
Societe Generale Burkina Faso
Societe Generale (China) Limited
Societe Generale Expressbank (Bulgaria)
Societe Generale Maroc (Morocco)
Societe Generale - Splitska Banka (Croatia)
Societe Generale Tchad (Chad)
SOGECAP (life insurance)
Union Internationale de Banques (Tunisia)

COMPETITORS

BBVA	Credit Suisse
BNP Paribas	Deutsche Bank
CIC	HSBC France
CRCAM IDF CCI	Natixis
Caisse des Depots et Consignations	Union Financiere de France
Credit Agricole	
Credit Foncier de France	

HISTORICAL FINANCIALS

Company Type: Public

Income Statement

FYE: December 31

	ASSETS ($ mil.)	NET INCOME ($ mil.)	INCOME AS % OF ASSETS	EMPLOYEES
12/13	1,700,629	2,994	0.2%	148,324
12/12	1,648,479	1,020	0.1%	154,009
12/11	1,528,048	3,084	0.2%	159,616
12/10	1,515,133	5,242	0.3%	155,617
12/09	1,474,712	976	0.1%	156,681
Annual Growth	3.6%	32.3%	—	(1.4%)

2013 Year-End Financials

Return on assets: 0.1%
Return on equity: 4.3%
Long-term debt ($ mil.): —
No. of shares (mil.): 776
Sales ($ mil): 138,629
Dividends
Yield: 1.0%
Payout: 6.3%
Market value ($ mil.): 9,042

	STOCK PRICE ($) FY Close	P/E High/Low		PER SHARE ($) Earnings	Dividends	Book Value
12/13	11.65	9	5	3.30	0.12	90.47
12/12	7.82	22	9	0.84	0.00	87.07
12/11	4.36	8	2	4.11	0.92	81.50
12/10	10.87	6	2	6.61	0.86	85.68
12/09	14.05	76	19	0.65	1.13	84.58
Annual Growth	(4.6%)	—	—	50.3%	(43.2%)	1.7%

Societe Nationale des Chemins de Fer Francais (SNCF) (France)

France's state-owned railway company Societe Nationale des Chemins de fer Fransais (SNCF) is still blazing a trail as one of the world's largest providers of public transport. Overall the SNCF rail network covers some 120 countries more than 30000 km (almost 20000 mile) of track and about 3000 passenger stations. Through numerous subsidiaries it offers local and regional rail transport as well as long-distance high-speed rail transport. It's also a top operator of parking facilities and bicycle rentals in France. Additionally SNCF is a rail station manager and developer and a global multi-modal operator in freight transport and logistics supporting businesses that ship goods and commodities.

With the addition of the Gares & Connexions (SNCF's train station management and development unit) in 2009 SNCF now operates five divisions. SNCF Geodis (freight transport and logistics services) and SNCF Voyages (long-distance high-speed passenger transport) each represent about a quarter of revenues trailed by SNCF Infra (rail infrastructure engineering and maintenance). However with increased commuter demand followed by subsequent development activities in 2009 and 2010 SNCF's Proximites division which handles public urban and outer urban commuter travel is now the company's largest division generating roughly one-third of all revenues.

The growth of SNCF's Proximites division requires more in-service train cars to handle the increase in commuters. In early 2010 SNCF ordered 80 train cars from Canada-based Bombardier with an option for an additional 50. The contract is valued at as much as Å8 billion (almost $12 billion). Bombardier will build the trains in France for a scheduled shipment in mid-2013.

To be a major player in Europe's increasingly deregulated road and rail transport network SNCF is forging cross-border alliances: transnational ventures have included working with Deutsche Bahn to design a European high-speed rail system operating a bus and rail joint venture with UK-based Go-Ahead Group and entering into a joint venture with UK's FirstGroup to operate TransPennine Expressway in northern England.

Along with its primary rail operations SNCF has been upping its stakes in and taking over a number of other passenger and freight transportation companies to cement its market position. It took a majority stake in Keolia a French bus operator that also has operations in Algeria Australia Canada and Germany after Keolia merged with SNCF subsidiary Effia a provider of car sharing electrical car and other non-motorized transport. SNCF Geodis completed its takeover of wagon and container leasing firm Ermewa.

In late 2010 SNCF Voyages acquired a majority stake in Findworks Technologies which operates Liligo.com a travel price comparison site. The addition of Liligo strengthens SNCF's desire to develop its consumer-oriented online services both in France and across Europe. Liligo will operate as a separate entity within the SNCF family of companies.

HISTORY

France's first railway line opened in 1827 was used to haul coal from Saint-Etienne to the port of Andrezieux. Four years later the first steam locomotives and passenger service were introduced between Saint-Etienne and Lyon. Paris opened its first rail line in 1837. Although the early railway companies were under private ownership the state controlled the network of rail lines through licensing. Under Napoleon III's Second Empire (1852-1870) the government encouraged an expansion of railway lines that linked Paris to every major town and city in France. By 1870 the main routes of France's modern railway system had been laid; by 1914 the network system had grown to nearly 40000 km.

After the devastation of WWI railway companies invested heavily in rebuilding. Burdened by debt the rail network was forced to seek government intervention for its survival. In 1938 the government set up Societe Nationale des Chemins de Fer Fran - sis to unify the five largest railway systems: Compagnie de l'Est Compagnie du Midi Compagnie du Nord Compagnie du Paris-Lyon-Mediterranee and Compagnie du Paris-Orleans.

Although WWII destroyed the French railway system for a second time the massive rebuilding enabled postwar French governments to adopt modern innovations. In 1950 SNCF began a systemwide electrification of its tracks; a decade later 7600 km of its major lines were powered by electricity.

SNCF also pioneered the development of fast trains. Following an overhaul of SNCF in the early 1970s the company continued to develop high-speed trains to stay competitive with airlines. In 1981 the company's TGV ("train a grande vitesse") hit a record speed of 380 kph (236 mph). TGVs entered commercial service that year. By 1987 some 43 cities were connected to Paris by TGVs.

To add to its European logistics and freight services SNCF acquired 20% of Spanish trucking firm

TRANSFESA in 1993. In 1995 it launched Eurostar a London-Paris service using the newly opened Channel Tunnel. Partners in the joint venture were Belgian National Railroads (Societe Nationale des Chemins de Fer Belges) and European Passenger Services the British Rail unit later spun off as Eurostar (UK). That year SNCF saw its operations disrupted by a nationwide rail strike that lasted three weeks. In 1995 SNCF also created road transport and logistics group Geodis which it privatized a year later.

Diversifying further SNCF also entered telecommunications in 1996 and set up a communications network to lease spare capacity. That year the company's chairman resigned following charges of corruption related to his tenure at an oil company. SNCF also plagued by debts and strikes decided to get back on track. It began restructuring and appointed former Aerospatiale chief Louis Gallois to head the company. In 1997 it shifted most of its debt load to Reseau Ferre de France which was created to manage France's rail infrastructure.

In 1999 SNCF acquired Via-GTI France's largest privately owned public transport company which was in a joint venture with UK transport group Go-Ahead to operate the Thameslink train franchise. That year SNCF acquired Swiss rolling stock group Ermewa; it also sold its hotel interests to Accor but formed an alliance with the hotelier to offer discount lodging.

SNCF and German railway Deutsche Bahn agreed in 2000 to collaborate on developing a new generation of high-speed trains.

SNCF's rail operations were hampered by labor unrest in 2003 capped by a strike in May and June of that year. The company responded by cutting costs.

After a decade at SNCF Gallois left the company in 2006 to serve as co-CEO of defense group Airbus.

Adding steam to its European expansion in September 2009 SNCF and Channel Tunnel operator Groupe Eurotunnel bought rail freight company Veolia Cargo from Veolia Transportation (itself owned by Veolia Environnement). SNCF will take over Veolia Cargo's operations in Germany Italy and the Netherlands and Eurotunnel will take over Veolia's France operations.

LOCATIONS

HQ: Societe Nationale des Chemins de Fer Francais
(SNCF) (France)
34 rue du Commandant Mouchotte, Paris, Cedex 14
75699
Phone: (33) 1 42 85 63 13   **Fax:** (33) 1 42 85 63 16
Web: www.sncf.com

Sales

	% of total
France	80
International	20
Total	**100**

PRODUCTS/OPERATIONS

Sales

	% of total
SNCF	32
SNCF	27
SNCF	22
SNCF	16
Gares &	3
Total	**100**

HISTORICAL FINANCIALS

Company Type: Public

Income Statement

FYE: December 31

	REVENUE ($ mil.)	NET INCOME ($ mil.)	NET PROFIT MARGIN	EMPLOYEES
12/13	44,374	(247)	—	244,570
12/12	44,576	504	1.1%	249,343
12/11	42,224	161	0.4%	245,090
12/10	40,774	932	2.3%	240,978
12/09	35,844	(1,411)	—	200,097
Annual Growth	**5.5%**	—	—	**5.1%**

2013 Year-End Financials

Debt ratio: 61.6%
Return on equity: (-2.5%)
Cash ($ mil.): 6,966
Current ratio: 0.94
Long-term debt ($ mil.): 19,597

No. of shares (mil.): —
Dividends
  Yield: —
  Payout: —
Market value ($ mil.): —

Softbank Corp. (Japan)

SOFTBANK's investment strategy is anything but soft. Under the leadership of founder chairman and CEO Masayoshi Son (sometimes referred to as the Bill Gates of Japan) the company makes investments in a variety of ventures. Its portfolio holdings extend from mobile and fixed-line telecommunications to Internet commerce and content technology services marketing broadband infrastructure and more. The company also provides venture capital to technology-related concerns in Asia Europe and the US. Holdings include interests in SOFTBANK Mobile SOFTBANK Telecom SOFTBANK Commerce & Service Corp. and Yahoo Japan along with a minority stake in Yahoo!. Altogether the firm has stakes in 60-plus companies.

Mergers & Acquisitions

In order to boost its position as a global player SOFTBANK is betting big on the US wireless service market. It has entered into an agreement to acquire 78% of Sprint Nextel. If completed the deal would be the largest acquisition of a US technology company by a Japanese business in history. Under the agreement SOFTBANK will invest a whopping $21.6 billion (raised from $20.1 billion after DISH Network made an unsolicited bid) in Sprint of which $16.6 billion will be distributed to Sprint stockholders and $5 billion will be used to strengthen Sprint's balance sheet. SOFTBANK brings both cash and expansion experience to Sprint. It also allows SOFTBANK to grow its expertise in smartphones and next-generation high speed networks. The closing of the transaction is expected to occur in mid-2013.

Strategy

SOFTBANK often uses joint ventures to accomplish its goal of increasing its foothold as a global player. In the Asia/Pacific market for example it announced a joint venture with PayPal in 2012 to establish a digital payments business in Japan. The company also works with website operator Alibaba.com (of which it controls about a third) to develop mobile Internet services and an online shopping market in China and Japan. Additionally SOFTBANK participates in a joint venture with wireless network giants China Mobile Verizon Wireless and Vodafone to develop similar services.

Other strategic areas of focus for SOFTBANK include enhancing its networks sales structure and branding. Despite a soft spot for all things technological SOFTBANK also has holdings outside of the wired world: It owns the Fukuoka SOFTBANK HAWKS (formerly the Fukuoka Daiei Hawks) a professional baseball team it acquired in 2005.

Ownership

Masayoshi Son owns approximately 30% of SOFTBANK which he started in 1981 as a distributor of packaged software. In 2010 the company launched SOFTBANK Academia a program designed to identify and train potential successors to Son as CEO.

HISTORY

Ethnic Korean Masayoshi Son grew up in Japan using the name Yasumoto to conform with the Japanese policy of assimilation. In the early 1970s the 16-year-old came to the US and began using his Korean name. Son entered the University of California at Berkeley and while there invented the prototype for the Sharp Wizard handheld organizer.

Bankrolled by the nearly $1 million that Sharp paid him for his patent Son returned to Japan and founded software distributor SOFTBANK in 1981. The company got its first big break when it inked a distribution agreement with Joshin Denki one of Japan's largest consumer electronics retailers that year. Son used this agreement to gain exclusive distribution rights for much of the software he distributed.

SOFTBANK went public in 1994. That year as part of an evolving plan to control digital data delivery Son bought the trade show division of Ziff-Davis Publishing augmenting it in 1995 with the purchase of COMDEX the trade show operations of the Interface Group. The next year SOFTBANK bought the rest of Ziff-Davis. It also bought 80% of Kingston Technology (sold 1999) and a stake in Yahoo! —which laid the cornerstone for its Internet empire.

SOFTBANK accelerated its Internet investment pace in 1997 taking stakes in dozens of Web companies. That year it filed suit against Yell Publishing a Japanese firm that published a book accusing SOFTBANK of issuing phony financial statements among other improprieties.

In 1998 the firm moved into financial services entering a joint venture with E*TRADE to offer online stock trading in Japan. SOFTBANK also took Ziff-Davis public (it retained a majority stake).

Internal changes marked 1999 when SOFTBANK merged with MAC Son's private asset management company and transformed itself into a holding company focused on Internet-related companies. It teamed with the National Association of Securities Dealers to create a Japanese version of the Nasdaq stock market (launched in 2000; closed in 2002). SOFTBANK also partnered with Microsoft and Tokyo Electric Power to launch Speed-Net a Japanese Internet service provider.

In 2000 the nearly decimated Ziff-Davis announced it would transform its online arm ZDNet from a tracking stock into a stand-alone company and adopt the ZDNet name; later CNET Networks (now a part of CBS Interactive) bought both companies instead. That year SOFTBANK formed venture capital funds focusing on areas such as Latin America Japan Europe the UK and emerging markets.

The company reorganized in 2000 and placed most of its non-Japan-based holdings under a new unit called SOFTBANK Global Ventures. Sharpening its focus on Internet investments SOFTBANK sold its stake in antivirus software maker Trend Micro. Branching into banking SOFTBANK headed a consortium that paid $932 million for Japan's failed Nippon Credit Bank. SOFTBANK's share of the bank (renamed Aozora) stood at nearly 49%. The firm's stock price tumbled in

2000 and it considered taking several holding companies public.

In 2001 Cisco bought a nearly 2% stake in SOFTBANK in exchange for the firm's 12% stake in the hardware company's Japanese unit. The company also sold its SOFTBANK Forums Japan an Internet trade show company to MediaLive International. In 2002 Nasdaq Japan announced its plans to close after two loss-making years. SOFTBANK owned 43%.

In an attempt to create a larger domestic market for its e-commerce and Internet companies SOFTBANK moved aggressively into the broadband market providing asymmetric digital subscriber line (ADSL) services.

EXECUTIVES

SEVP, Ken Miyauchi, age 65
Chairman and CEO, Masayoshi Son, age 57
President SOFTBANK Holdings, Ronald D. (Ron) Fisher, age 66
President Fukuoka SoftBank Hawks Marketing, Kazuhiko Kasai
Managing Partner, Kabir Misra
VP Finance and Operations, Josh Lubov
VP Technology, Phil Shevrin
VP Fund Operations, Melanie Dyer
COO and Director, Ken Miyauchi
Director; President and Director SOFTBANK Holdings, Ronald D. (Ron) Fisher, age 65
Director, Tadashi Yanai, age 64
Director and Director Softbank Mobile, Kazuhiko Kasai
Director, Jun Murai
Director, Mark Schwartz
Director, Yun Ma
Auditors: ChuoAoyamaPricewaterhouseCoopers

LOCATIONS

HQ: Softbank Corp. (Japan)
1-9-1 Higashi-Shinbashi, Minato-ku, Tokyo 105-7303
Phone: (81) 3 6889 2290
Web: www.softbank.co.jp

COMPETITORS

3i Group	Kleiner Perkins
Accel Partners	Mayfield Fund
Alloy Ventures	Menlo Ventures
Benchmark Capital	NEA
Hummer Winblad	Sequoia Capital
ICG Group	Sevin Rosen
IVP	Trinity Ventures
JAFCO	

HISTORICAL FINANCIALS
Company Type: Public

Income Statement

	REVENUE ($ mil.)	NET INCOME ($ mil.)	NET PROFIT MARGIN	EMPLOYEES
03/14	64,587	5,105	7.9%	70,336
03/13	34,036	3,958	11.6%	24,598
03/12	39,039	3,824	9.8%	22,710
03/11	36,285	2,291	6.3%	21,799
03/10	29,584	1,035	3.5%	21,885
Annual Growth	**21.6%**	**49.0%**	**—**	**33.9%**

2014 Year-End Financials

Debt ratio: 0.5%
Return on equity: 29.5%
Cash ($ mil.): 19,022
Current ratio: 1.16
Long-term debt ($ mil.): 77,719

No. of shares (mil.): 1,188
Dividends
  Yield: 0.5%
  Payout: 0.0%
Market value ($ mil.): 45,054

	STOCK PRICE ($) FY Close	P/E High/Low		PER SHARE ($)		
				Earnings	Dividends	Book Value
03/14	37.91	0	—	4.27	0.20	15.94
03/13	22.80	0	—	3.49	0.00	14.28
03/12	14.87	—	—	3.40	0.00	15.93
03/11	19.78	—	—	2.04	0.00	9.81
Annual Growth	**24.2%**	**—**	**—**	**20.3%**	**—**	**12.9%**

Sompo Japan Nipponkoa Hldgs Inc

LOCATIONS

HQ: Sompo Japan Nipponkoa Hldgs Inc
1-26-1 Nishi-Shinjuku, Shinjuku-ku, Tokyo 160-8338
Phone: (81) 3 3349 3000
Web: www.nksj-hd.com

HISTORICAL FINANCIALS
Company Type: Public

Income Statement
FYE: March 31

	REVENUE ($ mil.)	NET INCOME ($ mil.)	NET PROFIT MARGIN	EMPLOYEES
03/14	29,001	427	1.5%	35,904
03/13	30,071	463	1.5%	35,481
03/12	33,881	(1,124)	—	35,542
03/11	31,517	(156)	—	34,203
Annual Growth	**(2.7%)**	**—**		**1.6%**

2014 Year-End Financials

Debt ratio: 0.0%
Return on equity: 3.3%
Cash ($ mil.): 5,515
Current ratio: 0.19
Long-term debt ($ mil.): 2,534

No. of shares (mil.): 411
Dividends
  Yield: —
  Payout: —
Market value ($ mil.): 10,241

	STOCK PRICE ($) FY Close	P/E High/Low		PER SHARE ($)		
				Earnings	Dividends	Book Value
03/14	24.90	—	—	1.03	0.00	32.75
03/13	21.95	—	—	1.11	0.00	32.89
03/12	22.66	—	—	(2.71)	0.00	29.40
03/11	0.00	—	—	(0.38)	0.00	31.40
Annual Growth	**—**	**—**		**—**	**1.4%**

Sony Corp

Sony is synonymous with consumer electronics. It's especially big in TVs and game consoles like the new PlayStation4. Officially named Sony Kabushiki Kaisha the company designs makes and sells a host of electronic equipment instruments and devices for consumer professional and industrial markets. Professional products include semiconductors and components. A top global media conglomerate Sony boasts additional assets in the areas of music (Sony Music Entertainment) film (Sony Pictures Entertainment and Sony Digital Production) smartphones (Sony Mobile) DVDs

(Sony Pictures Home Entertainment) and TV (Sony Pictures Television). Sony also has several financial services businesses and an advertising agency in Japan.

Geographic Reach

Sony's primary manufacturing facilities are located in Asia including Japan where it is headquartered. Japan is also its single largest market by sales (32% in fiscal 2012 ends March). The US China and Europe are also key markets.

Operations

Sony realigned its reportable segments in 2012 as part of a reorganization. The operations of the former Consumer Professional & Devices (CPD) and Networked Products & Services (NPS) segments are now part of the Consumer Products & Services (CPS) –the company's largest segment by sales –and Professional Device & Solutions (PDS) segments. CPS includes LCD televisions Blu Ray disc and DVD players digital and video cameras PCs and gaming consoles. Certain PlayStation products are marketed and distributed by Sony Computer Entertainment LLC and Sony Computer Entertainment Europe Ltd. PDS the company's second largest segment includes broadcast and other B2B products as well as semiconductors and components.

A smaller business segment Sony Ericsson was renamed Sony Mobile Communications in 2012. As a result of a reorganization that Sony is undertaking plans to even further realign its business segments are under way.

Sales and Marketing

Sony's products are marketed worldwide by sales subsidiaries and unaffiliated distributors as well as direct online sales.

Financial Performance

Sony's fiscal 2012 (ends March) sales fell 9% vs. the prior year while net income continued its steep decline. Indeed the company marked its fourth consecutive year of unprofitability in 2012 as its losses widened.

Sony's consumer products and services segment CPS remains the company's bread and butter accounting for 45% is its fiscal 2012 sales. But competition is fierce in this industry with Apple paving the way in music players with the iPod and Microsoft (Xbox 360) and Nintendo (Wii) jockeying for dominance in game console sales globally.

The rising Yen decreasing demand for its products pricing pressures and the lingering global economic crisis has sidelined Sony in recent years. After logging a record profit in 2007 the company has seen its business stall as consumers tightened their belts.

Strategy

The most pressing part of Sony's current strategy is turning around its electronics businesses. With a new management team established in April 2012 the company moves forward with a plan to strengthen certain core areas: digital imaging game and mobile. Sony is trying to develop new products expand its hardware and software offerings and integrate the operations of its smartphone business (operated by Sony Mobile) with its tablet and PC businesses. Another aspect of this strategy is to turn around its TV business to improve profitability there; TVs generate a large chunk of sales within the CPS segment.

The company may have a hit on its hands with the new PlayStation4 (PS4) which went on sale in North America in November 2013. Indeed Sony sold more than 1 million PS4s in the first 24 hours of sales. The new games console is the centerpiece of the new management team's turnaround strategy for Sony's consumer electronics and film businesses.

Sony also has been consolidating manufacturing facilities selling off businesses and facilities and reducing headcounts. Divestments include its TV production assets and personal computer division. It's closing 20 retail stores in the US and cutting 1000 jobs as part of a much larger reorganization.

In a very competitive electronics environment Sony is simultaneously trying to innovate and launch products in new markets such as it is doing with medical peripherals like printers monitors cameras and recorders. The company is drawing on its audio and visual expertise to build a 4K technology product lineup. 4K is said to deliver more than four times the resolution of full HD.

On the music side Sony's wholly owned subsidiary Sony Corporation of America (SCA) in 2012 led a group of investors in a high-profile high-dollar deal. Alongside the Estate of Michael Jackson David Geffen and Blackstone Group SCA acquired EMI Music Publishing for $2.2 billion from Citigroup. The company's Sony/ATV Music Publishing which owns more than 750000 copyrights now oversees EMI Music Publishing and its 1.3 million copyrights on behalf of the investor group. (Sony/ATV Music Publishing is co-owned by subsidiaries of SCA and trusts formed by the Estate of Michael Jackson.)

HISTORY

Akio Morita Masaru Ibuka and Tamon Maeda (Ibuka's father-in-law) started Tokyo Telecommunications Engineering in 1946 with funding from Morita's father's sake business. The company produced the first Japanese tape recorder in 1950. Three years later Morita paid Western Electric (US) $25000 for transistor technology licenses which sparked a consumer electronics revolution in Japan. His firm launched one of the first transistor radios in 1955 followed by the first Sony-trademarked product a pocket-sized radio in 1957. The next year the company changed its name to Sony (from "sonus" Latin for "sound" and "sonny" meaning "little man"). It beat the competition to newly emerging markets for transistor TVs (1959) and solid-state videotape recorders (1961).

Sony launched the first home video recorder (1964) and the first solid-state condenser microphone (1965). Its 1968 introduction of the Trinitron color TV tube began another decade of explosive growth. Sony bet wrong on its Betamax VCR (1976) which lost to rival Matsushita's (now Panasonic Corp.) VHS as the industry standard. However 1979 brought another success the Walkman personal stereo.

Pressured by adverse currency rates and competition worldwide Sony used its technology to diversify beyond consumer electronics and began to move production to other countries. In the 1980s it introduced Japan's first 32-bit workstation and became a major producer of computer chips and floppy disk drives. The purchases of CBS Records in 1988 ($2 billion) and Columbia Pictures in 1989 (a $4.9 billion deal which included TriStar Pictures) made Sony a major force in the rapidly growing entertainment industry.

The firm manufactured Apple's PowerBook but its portable CD player Data Discman was successful only in Japan (1991). In the early 1990s Sony joined Nintendo to create a new kind of game console combining Sony's CD-ROM drive with the graphic capabilities of a workstation. Although Nintendo pulled out in 1992 Sony released PlayStation in Japan (1994) and in the US (1995) to great success. Two years later in a joint venture with Intel it developed a line of PC desktop systems.

Rather than support an industry-wide standard in 1997 Sony teamed up with Philips Electronics to make another recording media called Super Audio CD which could replace videotapes and CDs. (Sony and Philips created the CD and continue to receive royalties from it.)

In 1998 Sony shipped its first digital high-definition TV to the US folded TriStar into Columbia Pictures merged its Loews Theatres unit with Cineplex Odeon and launched its Wega flat-screen TV.

Philips Sun Microsystems and Sony formed a joint venture in early 1999 to develop networked entertainment products. Also in 1999 Nobuyuki Idei became CEO and the company introduced a Walkman with the capability to download music from the Internet.

In 2000 Sony formed PlayStation.com Japan to sell game consoles and software online; it also introduced its 128-bit PlayStation 2 which plays DVD movies and connects to the Internet. The company later restructured placing all of its US entertainment holdings under a newly-formed umbrella company called Sony Broadband Entertainment.

In early 2001 Sony started an online bank with Japan's Sakura Bank and JP Morgan Chase. Struggling to coordinate its content units (music movies games etc.) with its manufacturing operations (TVs VCRs radios etc.) Sony announced yet another corporate restructuring plan; that move placed all electronics units under one upper-management group.

Adverse market conditions in 2001 aggravated by the September 11 attacks led Sony Pictures Entertainment to consolidate its two domestic television operations folding Columbia TriStar Network Television into Columbia TriStar Domestic Television (CTDT).

In February 2002 an investment group led by Onex Corporation acquired its Loews Theatres unit (which filed for bankruptcy in February 2001). In the course of the fiscal year ending March 2002 Sony laid off about 13700 employees primarily in its electronics and music businesses.

In an attempt to capitalize on the strength of its own brand Sony Pictures Entertainment renamed its Columbia TriStar Domestic Television (CTDT) and Columbia TriStar International Television (CTIT) divisions in September 2002 designating them as Sony Pictures Television (SPT) and Sony Pictures Television International (SPTI) respectively. In October 2002 Sony transformed its Aiwa unit into a wholly-owned subsidiary and absorbed the struggling firm in December 2002.

In 2003 Sony adopted a US-style corporate governance model (made possible by a revision in Japan's Commercial Code) and acquired CIS Corp. a Japanese information system consulting firm. In an effort to cut costs through manufacturing consolidation Sony closed its audio equipment plant in Indonesia that year.

Sony unveiled the Vaio Pocket in 2004 a portable music player designed to compete with Apple's iPod; Vaio Pocket debuted in the US later that year. Sony also introduced a similar product Network Walkman –its first Walkman with a hard drive –in 2004. In October 2004 the company launched a music download system in Japan dubbed MusicDrop. The system utilizes Microsoft's Windows Media Player.

To manage its financial units (Sony Life Insurance Company Sony Assurance and Sony Bank) it created Sony Financial Holdings in 2004. The company announced in 2005 that Idei would be succeeded by foreigner Howard Stringer who had been in charge of Sony's entertainment unit. In 2005 Sony sold its minority stake in music club Columbia House to BMG Direct a subsidiary of Germany's Bertelsmann. In December 2005 the company spun off Sony Communication Network the subsidiary that operates So-Net Internet service (which has nearly 3 million subscribers) through an IPO.

In June 2006 Sony created a holding company for its Japanese-based retail operations (Sony Plaza Sony Family Club B&C Laboratories CP Cosmetics Maxim's de Paris and Lifeneo) and sold 51% of the holding company to investment firm Nikko Principal Investments Japan.

In late 2008 Sony bought out NEC's 45% stake in joint venture Sony Optiarc.

The company in 2010 sold the measuring equipment business of Sony Manufacturing Systems to Mori Seiki a Japan-based precision tool maker in a deal valued at about Â6 billion (nearly $70 million). It also sold off its 90% stake in Sony Baja California its main TV factory in North America located in Tijuana Mexico to Taiwanese company Hon Hai Precision Industry. It generated $217 million for its share in HBO Latin America which it sold to Time Warner.

In February 2012 Sony acquired Telefonaktiebolaget LM Ericsson's 50% stake in Sony Ericsson Mobile Communications AB marking the completion of the previously announced transaction. As a result Sony Ericsson became a wholly-owned subsidiary of Sony and was renamed "Sony Mobile Communications."

EXECUTIVES

CEO Sony Corporation of America and Chairman and CEO Sony Pictures Entertainment, Michael M. Lynton, age 55

Chairman, Sir Howard Stringer, age 72

Co-Chairman Sony Pictures Entertainment, Amy Pascal, age 56

Vice President Chief Financial Officer, Masaru Kato

President Sony Ericsson Mobile Communications AB, Bert Nordberg

EVP and General Counsel; President Sony Corporation of America (SCA), Nicole Seligman, age 58

Executive Deputy President, Hiroshi Yoshioka, age 62

EVP and Chief Strategy Officer, Tadashi (Tan) Saito

Vice Chairman; CEO Product Quality and Safety and Environmental Affairs, Ryoji Chubachi, age 67

EVP Intellectual Property and Disc Manufacturing, Keiji Kimura, age 62

SVP New Business Professional Solutions Group, Hiromasa Otsuka, age 64

SVP External Relations and Kansai Region and Device Sales Consumer Professional and Devices Group, Tsugie Miyashita

President and CEO; Chairman Sony Corporation of America, Kazuo (Kaz) Hirai, age 54

Executive Deputy President Manufacturing Logistics and Procurement, Yutaka Nakagawa, age 69

SVP Environment and Technology Policy and Relations, Kiyoshi Nishitani

SVP Technology (System) Semiconductor Business Group, Norihisa Shirota

EVP, Shoji Nemoto

VP Product Marketing Sony Computer Entertainment America, Scott A. Steinberg

EVP China, Akira Kubota

SVP; President Advanced Materials Laboratories Core Device Development Group Research and Development and Common Software Platform, Osamu Kumagai

SVP Products Quality and Safety, Makoto Kogure

EVP, Tomoyuki Suzuki

SVP Technologies Networked Products and Services Group, Masaaki Tsuruta

SVP Japan Sales Professional Solutions Group Consumer Professional and Devices Group, Shinji Hanatani

EVP Human Resources and Corporate Workplace Solutions, Kunitaka Fujita

Chairman Sony Music Entertainment, Masao Morita, age 59

President and Group Chief Executive, Andrew House

President and CEO Sony Computer Entertainment America, Jack Tretton

President and General Manager Sony Discovery Communications and IMAX Joint Venture 3D Television Network, Tom Cosgrove

SVP Publisher Relations Sony Computer Entertainment America, Robert Dyer

VP Human Resources Sony Computer Entertainment America, Sally Buchanan

SVP and CFO Sony Computer Entertainment America, Jim Bass

VP Operations Sony Computer Entertainment America, Glenn Nash

SVP Business Development Sony Computer Entertainment America, Philip Rosenberg

EVP, Kunimasa Suzuki, age 54

SVP and Chief Transformation Officer, George Bailey

SVP; President Home Entertainment and Sound Business Group, Masashi Imamura

CFO Sony Electronics, William A. (Bill) Glaser Jr.

President and COO Sony Electronics, Phil Molyneux

CEO Sony Music Entertainment, Doug Morris

President and CEO Sony Computer Entertainment Europe, Jim Ryan

SVP and Chief Information Security Officer, Philip R. Reitinger

Director, Yorihiko Kojima

Director, Fujio Cho, age 76

Director, Roland A. Hernandez, age 56

Director, Sir Peter L. Bonfield, age 69

Vice Chairman; CEO Product Quality and Safety and Environmental Affairs, Ryoji Chubachi, age 67

Director, Yukako Uchinaga, age 68

Director, Yoshiaki Yamauchi, age 77

Director, Ryuji Yasuda, age 68

Director, Mitsuaki Yahagi, age 66

Director, Tsun-Yan Hseih, age 60

Director, Yuichiro Anzai

Auditors: PricewaterhouseCoopersAarata

LOCATIONS

HQ: Sony Corp
7-1, KONAN 1-CHOME, MINATO-KU, Tokyo 108-0075
Phone: (81) 3 6748 2111   **Fax:** (81) 3 6748 2244
Web: www.sony.co.jp

Sales

	% of total
Japan	32
Europe	19
US	19
Asia/Pacific (except Japan and	10
China	8
Other	12
Total	**100**

PRODUCTS/OPERATIONS

Sales

	% of total
Consumer Products & Services	45
Professional Device & Solutions	19
Financial	13
Pictures	10
Music	6
Sony	1
Other	6
Total	**100**

Selected Products

Consumer Products & Services (CPS)
  Digital imaging
  Game hardware and software
  Home audio and video
  Personal and mobile products
  Televisions
Professional Device & Solutions (PDS)
  Broadcast and professional-use products
  Semiconductors
  Components

COMPETITORS

Apple Inc.	Motorola Solutions
Bertelsmann	Nintendo
Dell	Nokia
Disney	Panasonic Corp
Eastman Kodak	Philips Electronics
Fujitsu	Pioneer Corporation
Hewlett-Packard	SANYO
IBM	Samsung Group
Intel	Sharp Corp.
Kyocera	Technicolor
LG Electronics	Universal Studios
Microsoft	

HISTORICAL FINANCIALS

Company Type: Public

Income Statement

FYE: March 31

	REVENUE ($ mil.)	NET INCOME ($ mil.)	NET PROFIT MARGIN	EMPLOYEES
03/14	75,250	(1,243)	—	140,900
03/13	72,278	457	0.6%	146,300
03/12	79,156	(5,566)	—	162,700
03/11	86,723	(3,134)	—	168,200
03/10	77,231	(436)	—	167,900
Annual Growth	**(0.6%)**	—		**(4.3%)**

2014 Year-End Financials

Debt ratio: 0.0%	No. of shares (mil.): 1,043
Return on equity: (-5.7%)	Dividends
Cash ($ mil.): 10,138	Yield: 1.2%
Current ratio: 0.88	Payout: 37.2%
Long-term debt ($ mil.): 8,880	Market value ($ mil.): 19,955

	STOCK PRICE ($) FY Close	P/E High/Low	PER SHARE ($) Earnings	Dividends	Book Value
03/14	19.12	— —	(1.21)	0.25	20.96
03/13	17.40	0 0	0.43	0.00	23.11
03/12	20.77	— —	(5.55)	0.00	24.65
03/11	31.83	— —	(3.12)	0.28	30.66
03/10	38.32	— —	(0.44)	0.27	31.64
Annual Growth	**(16.0%)**	— —		**(2.7%)**	**(9.8%)**

South African Reserve Bank

LOCATIONS

HQ: South African Reserve Bank
  370 Helen Joseph Street, Pretoria 0002
Phone: (27) 12 313 3911

HISTORICAL FINANCIALS

Company Type: Public

Income Statement

FYE: March 31

	ASSETS ($ mil.)	NET INCOME ($ mil.)	INCOME AS % OF ASSETS	EMPLOYEES
03/14	56,611	(132)	—	2,218
03/13	55,567	(152)	—	2,186
03/12	57,003	(77)	—	2,218
03/11	54,806	(160)	—	2,215
03/10	45,977	(120)	—	2,117
Annual Growth	**5.3%**	—	—	**1.2%**

Return on assets: (-0.2%)	Dividends
Return on equity: (-19.4%)	Yield: —
Long-term debt ($ mil.): —	Payout: —
No. of shares (mil.): 2	Market value ($ mil.): —
Sales ($ mil): 654	

SSE PLC

SSE (formerly Scottish and Southern) sees a powerful future. One of the UK's top energy firms the integrated company distributes power and gas and other services to more than 10 million customers via subsidiaries Southern Electric Scottish Hydro Electric SWALEC and Atlantic Electric and Gas and others. Regulated assets include 79300 miles of power transmission and distribution lines that serve 3.5 million end-users. SSE has more than 11300 MW of generating capacity. It also owns 50% of Scotia Gas Networks which delivers gas to 5.7 million customers. Other operations include gas exploration energy trading wind farms electrical and environmental contracting gas storage and retail appliance sales.

In response to energy deregulation in the UK SSE is looking to increase its generating capacity expand its customer base and diversify its operations. This has included moving into gas storage and fiber-optic cable operations and developing wind farms in Scotland.

In 2010 the company (as Scottish and Southern) changed its corporate name to a less geographically limiting name (SSE). That year the company acquired the ATLAS Connect fiber telecommunications network (7000 miles) which spans six business parks across Scotland. It also bought the 32 MW Calliachar wind farm project (on which construction is due to start in 2012) from I & H Brown.

SSE is also moving to boost its natural gas sources signing a deal with explorer Faroe Petroleum in 2010 to develop oil and gas fields in the North Sea. In 2011 it acquired natural gas assets and infrastructure in three regions of the North Sea from Hess Limited for $324 million.

That same year SSE acquired the Keadby Wind Farm in North Lincolnshire UK from Renewable Energy Systems Group. The 34-turbine project still in the development stage will produce between 68 and 84 MW of non-polluting energy when it is completed in 2014.

To grow its UK nuclear power assets in 2010 the company (with partners GDF SUEZ and IBERDROLA) formed NuGeneration a nuclear joint venture which aims to build up to 3600 MW of new nuclear power plants. However the Japanese nuclear plant accident in 2011 forced the global nuclear power plant industry to hit the pause button while it reviewed the safety and viability of current and future plants. In late 2011 the company announced plans to sell its 25% stake in NuGeneration to GDF SUEZ and IBERDROLA in a move to focus more on renewable energy.

The company reported a strong growth in revenues (40%) in Fiscal 2011 as a result of expanded capacity and services the acquisition of 310000 new retail customers and a generally favorable price environment. Net income also rose by about 30% due to increased demand and higher rates.

In 2012 through its Airtricity Energy Supply (Northern Ireland) unit the company acquired Phoenix Supply a regulated supplier of natural gas to 130000 customers in Northern Ireland from Phoenix Energy Holdings.

HISTORY

SSE (as Scottish and Southern Energy) was formed by the 1998 merger of Scottish Hydro-Electric and Southern Electric both of which had been created by the privatization of the UK electricity industry.

In the 1980s the Thatcherite government opened up state-owned industries to private capital and management. The electricity industry (except for nuclear power) was privatized by the Electricity Act of 1989. The next year the Central Electricity Generating Board (CEGB) the state monopoly was dismantled and CEGB's 12 regional boards transferred their assets to 12 regional electricity companies (RECs). One of these Southern Electric (first incorporated in 1989) went public in 1990.

Because the government planned to fully deregulate the industry Southern Electric expanded beyond its core electricity supply business. In 1992 it formed Southern Electric Power Generation to invest in independent power projects and the firm moved into natural gas marketing through a joint venture with Phillips Petroleum. It also developed Southern Electric Contracting an electrical contractor and formed a retail appliance company E & S Retail in alliance with fellow REC Eastern Electricity (now a unit of TXU Europe); another REC East Midlands Electricity later came onboard. The retail business renamed Powerhouse Retail lost money and was sold to the Hanson conglomerate in 1995.

That year a wave of takeovers began to swamp the privatized RECs especially by US utilities itching to try out a competitive market. Only Southern Electric was left standing after the government blocked a bid by UK power generator National Power in 1996. To avoid being run over by larger rivals in 1997 Southern Electric allied with British Energy in Sabre Power a venture to build small gas-fired plants to supply industrial customers.

Meanwhile to the north of Southern Electric Scottish Hydro-Electric had been founded in 1943 when less than 20% of northern Scotland's homes were electrified. Originally called the North of Scotland Hydro-Electric Board it built eight hydropower plants in the 1950s and by the mid-1960s most of the region had received electricity.

Like Southern Electric Hydro-Electric was incorporated in 1989 and it was taken public in 1991. However unlike its English counterpart Hydro-Electric remained integrated and encompassed power generation distribution and supply. In the 1990s it diversified into combined-cycle gas turbine plants (more efficient than coal-fired units) and cogeneration plants (producing both heat and power) in England through several joint ventures.

To prepare for deregulation of the retail power market (completed in 1999) Southern Electric acquired Hydro-Electric in 1998 in a $4.8 billion deal and formed Scottish and Southern Energy. Hydro-Electric's Lord Wilson took the chairman position and Southern's Jim Forbes became chief executive. The new company began investing in small-scale generating projects. The next year it introduced affordable renewable energy products and Internet-based billing.

In 2000 Scottish and Southern began building fiber-optic networks in southern England and Scotland. Later in 2000 the company bought British Energy's SWALEC a Wales-based electricity and gas supplier for about $315 million.

In 2002 Jim Forbes retired and Ian Marchant took his place as chief executive. The following year Scottish and Southern agreed to purchase fellow UK utility Midlands Electricity from Aquila (which held 80% of Midlands) and FirstEnergy (which held the remaining 20%); however the deal was canceled later that year.

In 2004 Scottish and Southern completed the acquisition of two power plants in the UK (2000 MW of capacity) from American Electric Power for $456 million.

Scottish and Southern considered a merger with Glasgow rival Scottish Power (acquired by IBERDROLA in 2007) to prevent that company's takeover by Germany's utility group E.ON.

Acquisitions in 2008 included Slough Heating and Power (integrated energy business) Aitricity Holdings (renewable energy) and Seeboard Trading (street lighting projects). That year the company also moved into the Irish power supply market with the purchase of CHP Supply.

EXECUTIVES

Chairman, Lord Robert Smith, age 69, $627,314 total compensation
COO Lead Director Health and Safety and Board Member, Colin Hood, age 60, $1,097,019 total compensation
Energy Supply Director and Board Member, Alistair Phillips-Davies, age 46, $688,565 total compensation
Company Secretary, Vincent Donnelly
Finance Director and Board Member, Gregor Alexander, age 52, $688,565 total compensation
Manager Investor Relations, Sally Fairbairn
Director Offshore, Jim Smith
General Manager of Solutions, Andrew Blincow
General Manager, Paul Cooley
Head of Strategy, Pamela Walsh
Chief Executive Officer, Kevin Greenhorn
Board Member, Nick Baldwin, age 62
Chief Executive and Board Member, Ian Marchant, age 52
Board Member, Rene Medori, age 56
COO Lead Director Health and Safety and Board Member, Colin Hood, age 60
Energy Supply Director and Board Member, Alistair Phillips-Davies, age 46
Finance Director and Board Member, Gregor Alexander, age 52
Board Member, Richard D. Gillingwater, age 58
Board Member, Thomas Thune Andersen, age 59
Board Member, Susan Rice, age 69
Non-executive Director, Jeremy Beeton
Auditors: KPMGAuditPlc

LOCATIONS

HQ: SSE PLC
Inveralmond House, 200 Dunkeld Road, Perth PH1 3AQ
Phone: (44) 17 38456000   **Fax:** (44) 17 38457005
Web: www.sse.com

Sales

	% of total
UK	98
Ireland & Continental	2
Total	**100**

PRODUCTS/OPERATIONS

Sales

	% of total
Generation & Power	93
Power	3
Other	4
Total	**100**

Selected Subsidiaries and Divisions

SSE Contracting Limited
  Southern Electric Contracting Limited (electrical contracting)
  SSE Utility Services plc (utility contracting)
  Thermal Transfer Limited (environmental control systems)
SSE Energy Supply Limited
  Atlantic Electric and Gas (electricity and gas supply)

Scottish Hydro-Electric (electricity and gas supply Scotland)
Southern Electric (electricity and gas supply England)
SWALEC (electricity and gas supply Wales)
SSE Gas Storage
SSE Hornsea Limited (gas storage)
SSE Generation (power generation)
SSE Network Solutions (asset management)
SSE Power Distribution (regulated electricity transmission and distribution assets)
S+S Limited (electricity connections)
SSE Retail Limited (Hienergyshop appliance sales and services)
SSE Telecommunications Limited (business-to-business telecommunications services)
SSE Neosnetworks Limited (Neos telecommunications networking services)

COMPETITORS

BG Group	Northern Powergrid
Centrica	RWE npower
E.ON UK	United Utilities
EDF Energy	Viridian Group
Edison International	Western Power
International Power	Distribution
National Grid	

HISTORICAL FINANCIALS
Company Type: Public

Income Statement
FYE: March 31

	REVENUE ($ mil.)	NET INCOME ($ mil.)	NET PROFIT MARGIN	EMPLOYEES
03/14	50,918	537	1.1%	19,894
03/13	43,012	647	1.5%	19,795
03/12	50,835	316	0.6%	19,489
03/11	45,588	2,420	5.3%	20,249
03/10	32,682	1,873	5.7%	20,177
Annual Growth	11.7%	(26.8%)	—	(0.4%)

2014 Year-End Financials

Debt ratio: 49.8%
Return on equity: 6.0%
Cash ($ mil.): 736
Current ratio: 0.95
Long-term debt ($ mil.): 9,449

No. of shares (mil.): 974
Dividends
 Yield: 5.4%
 Payout: 627.6%
Market value ($ mil.): 24,090

	STOCK PRICE ($) FY Close	P/E High/Low	PER SHARE ($) Earnings	Dividends	Book Value
03/14	24.71	209 171	0.55	1.34	8.74
03/13	22.71	132 107	0.68	2.98	8.74
03/12	21.51	292 224	0.34	2.97	7.78
03/11	20.47	33 21	2.61	1.38	8.93
03/10	16.68	37 26	2.03	1.01	5.13
Annual Growth	10.3%	— —	(27.7%)	7.3%	14.2%

Standard Bank Group Ltd

Standard Bank Group sets the standard for sub-Saharan banking. Standard Bank South Africa's largest bank offers a variety of retail and commercial banking corporate and investment banking investment management and life insurance services through about 700 locations in its home country. The group also includes 500-plus additional branches more than 15 other African nations where it operates as Stanbic Bank. Beyond Africa the bank has offices in Asia Europe and the Americas including many emerging markets. It serves in-

dividuals and business and corporate customers. Standard Bank holds a controlling stake in South African insurance firm Liberty Holdings.

Geographic Reach
Contributing almost 85% of Standard Bank Group's revenue South Africa is its largest market by far. SBG also operates in 17 other African nations (from Angola to Zambia) as well as the UK and the US. Emerging markets include Argentina Brazil China Turkey and Russia.

Operations
In addition to personal commercial and corporate banking services SBG's insurance arm 53%-owned Liberty offers life insurance and investment and wealth management services to individuals and corporations in select African markets.

Financial Performance
Standard Bank Group struggled during the prolonged global recession. Low interest rates weak demand for credit and other financial factors impacted the company's revenues in 2009 and 2010. In 2011 the bank's revenue was essentially flat (up less than 1%) vs. the prior year while net income rose 23% over the same period. The modest uptick in revenue was credited to increase in banking activities partially offset by decreasing revenues at Liberty.

The personal and business banking division (up 8% in 2011 vs. 2010) outperformed the bank's other units. Revenue in South Africa the bank's largest market declined 1% while revenue from the rest of Africa was up 15% year over year. Revenue from outside of Africa fell 6%.

Strategy
Standard Bank Group is one of four full-service South African banks and claims to be the largest by assets and earnings. SBG aspires to be Africa's leading corporate and investment bank with a deep specialization in natural resources. To that end the bank is strengthening its focus on its core market and is looking to expand in Nigeria and Namibia. The company intends to grow its commercial banking operations there by building new branches. It opened more than 70 branches in Nigeria in 2010 alone.

Despite its Afro-centric focus SBG is also active in emerging markets worldwide including Russia. Indeed Standard Bank acquired about a third of Russian investment bank Troika Dialog in 2009. The partnership helped the group establish a presence in Russia where there is an opportunity to create a substantial domestic and cross-border franchise. However in early 2012 the company sold its stake in Troika Dialog to Russia's Sberbank for $372 million plus additional funds if Troika performs well. Standard Bank hopes to utilize its relationship with Troika to establish partnerships with Sberbank in the future. Other key emerging markets for the bank are Argentina Brazil and Turkey.

LOCATIONS

HQ: Standard Bank Group Ltd
9th Floor, Standard Bank Centre, 5 Simmonds Street, Johannesburg 2001
Phone: (27) 11 636 9111   **Fax:** (27) 11 636 4207
Web: www.standardbank.com

2011 Total Income

	% of total
South	84
Rest of	10
Outside of	5
Central and	1
Total	**100**

Selected Markets

Africa
 Angola
 Botswana

DRC
Ghana
Kenya
Lesotho
Malawi
Mauritius
Mozambique
Namibia
Nigeria
South Africa
Swaziland
Tanzania
Uganda
Zambia
Americas
 Argentina
 Brazil
 US
Europe/Asia Pacific
 China
 Hong Kong
 Isle of Man
 Japan
 Jersey
 Russia
 Singapore
 Taiwan
 Turkey
 United Arab Emirates
 United Kingdom

PRODUCTS/OPERATIONS

2011 Revenue

	% of total
Liberty	45
Personal & business	34
Corporate & investment	21
Central &	—
Total	**100**

HISTORICAL FINANCIALS
Company Type: Public

Income Statement
FYE: December 31

	ASSETS ($ mil.)	NET INCOME ($ mil.)	INCOME AS % OF ASSETS	EMPLOYEES
12/13	160,533	1,571	1.0%	48,808
12/12	181,381	1,937	1.1%	49,017
12/11	184,338	1,675	0.9%	52,127
12/10	201,137	1,679	0.8%	53,351
12/09	181,034	1,565	0.9%	51,411
Annual Growth	(3.0%)	0.1%	—	(1.3%)

2013 Year-End Financials

Return on assets: 1.0%
Return on equity: 13.2%
Long-term debt ($ mil.): —
No. of shares (mil.): 1,617
Sales ($ mil): 18,573

Dividends
 Yield: 3.0%
 Payout: 0.4%
Market value ($ mil.): 20,191

	STOCK PRICE ($) FY Close	P/E High/Low	PER SHARE ($) Earnings	Dividends	Book Value
12/13	12.48	0 0	0.96	0.38	7.89
12/12	14.23	0 0	1.21	0.00	8.47
Annual Growth	(12.3%)	— —	(5.6%)	—	(1.8%)

Standard Chartered Plc

While the British Empire isn't as global as it used to be that hasn't stopped Standard Chartered. The UK-based banking group known as Stanchart primarily operates in its target markets of Asia the Middle East and Africa which offer some of the world's fastest-growing economies. It also operates in Europe and the Americas. In all Stanchart has more than 1700 offices in more than 70 countries. The company operates through two business segments: consumer banking (deposit accounts loans cards and investment products) and wholesale banking (capital markets cash management international trade custody and clearing services). Stanchart traces its roots back more than 150 years.

Geographic Reach

Based in London Stanchart operates globally in the Asia/Pacific region as well as in Africa the Middle East Europe and the Americas.

Sales and Marketing

Looking to reinforce its commitment to making a positive impact in the communities where it operates Stanchart in 2012 rolled out an international advertising campaign that spanned multiple media such as TV print outdoor and digital.

Financial Performance

Stanchart logged revenue increases of 4% in 2012 as compared to 2011 fueled by interest income and income from other operating income. Contributing to the interest income gains were revenue from treasury bills loans and advances to customers and unlisted debt securities. Its other operating income gains came from fewer losses on the disposal of financial assets and gains on the repurchase of subordinated liabilities.

Positive income growth across all its markets helped Stanchart post revenue growth during the reporting period. India was an exception however as it was impacted by depreciation of the Indian rupee against the US dollar.

Net income meanwhile dropped by $697 million in 2012 vs. 2011 thanks to declines in cash provided by financing activities attributable to more cash used to repay subordinated liabilities and less cash generated from the gross proceeds from the issue of senior debts.

Consumer banking income rose 6% in 2012 to $7.2 billion representing double-digit growth in Other Asia Africa and Americas UK and Europe. It saw strong growth in cards personal loans and unsecured lending (CCPL).

Wholesale banking revenue came in 9% higher at $11.77 billion. Stanchart points to its well diversified revenue streams for the boost.

Strategy

Africa and the Middle East are among Stanchart's targeted areas for growth. It owns First Africa Group which provides mergers and acquisitions advisory services to companies wanting to invest in Africa. Stanchart bought Barclays Bank's custody business in 2010 adding operations in eight African nations.

The Asia/Pacific region also remains a key focus for Stanchart and the company has raised capital to fund acquisitions there. Other growth markets for Stanchart include India Indonesia Korea Thailand and Taiwan. In late 2011 for example the company bought the performing segment of Barclays' credit card business in India at a discount. The company's growth in India has been rapid as that nation's economy has expanded. Stanchart was the first foreign bank to receive a license to open a branch in Iran after that country's Islamic Revolution in 1979.

Stanchart has been pursuing a new strategy in its consumer banking business shifting to a customer-focused business model and standardizing its processes. It has entered new segments such as private banking. It has used its 2008 acquisition of American Express's international banking business to not only boost its private banking operations but strengthen its presence in key markets in Asia and the Middle East. Stanchart has also aggressively added more branches and ATMs to its retail network and invested in making improvements to its online and mobile capabilities.

However the company in late 2014 agreed to sell its Hong Kong-based consumer finance business PrimeCredit to an investment consortium for between $600 million and $700 million. The deal was announced after the company announced share price underperformance in certain markets.

Mergers and Acquisitions

Helping to position Stanchart as a top South African custodian the company in 2013 acquired the South African custody and trustee business of Absa Bank. Since 2011 the group has developed a profitable custody model across more than 20 sub-Saharan African countries.

Stanchart also purchased Credit Agricole Yatirim Bankasi Turk A.S. (CAYBT) a fully-owned subsidiary of Credit Agricole Corporate and Investment Bank. The 2012 deal has allowed Stanchart to expand its wholesale banking business in Turkey.

HISTORY

Standard Chartered began in 1853 as the Chartered Bank of India Australia and China to finance trade between the UK and its Asian colonies. It began establishing offices in 1858. Over the next 40 years The Chartered Bank expanded throughout Asia. In the 20th century the bank opened branches in Germany and the US. In 1957 Chartered entered the Middle East by acquiring Eastern Bank. In 1969 it agreed to merge with Standard Bank.

In 1862 schoolmaster John Paterson established the Standard Bank of British South Africa Ltd. to fund trade with mining businesses. Within two years the bank had 15 branches. Like Chartered Standard had moved into Germany and the US by 1905 and operated in central and southern Africa by 1912.

In 1962 the bank was renamed The Standard Bank Ltd. Three years later it expanded into Gambia Ghana Nigeria and Sierra Leone but the end of colonialism meant instability; business was threatened and ruling parties often nationalized Standard's banks. In 1969 the bank agreed to merge with Chartered Bank.

Asian and Middle Eastern business flourished in the early 1970s while South African branches struggled under growing international pressure on the country's apartheid regime. In response the company diversified into metals trading and consumer finance. It also expanded in the US market with the purchase of Union Bancorp of California.

Standard Chartered failed in a 1981 attempt to gain entry to the UK market through purchasing Royal Bank of Scotland. Four years later that bank went public.

In 1986 Lloyds Bank tried to take over Standard Chartered but investors Robert Holmes a Court Yue-Kong Pao and Khoo Teck Puat acquired enough of the company to block the play. Meanwhile overseas financial deregulation brought more competition and Hong Kong Singapore and Malaysia sank into recession.

Hit by trade sanctions against South Africa the bank in 1987 sold its operations there. As the world tumbled deeper into recession Standard Chartered's loan losses climbed. But the bank began to recover the next year as it trimmed its US bank holdings.

Scandal hit the bank in the 1990s. In 1992 Standard Chartered paid $515 million in restitution after a broker in its Mumbai India office embezzled some $1.2 billion from Indian banks. In 1994 executives with Mocatta were convicted of bribery and the Hong Kong government banned Standard Chartered Securities (sold in 1996) from underwriting stock offerings for nine months after it falsified six IPOs.

In 1997 Standard Chartered refocused on retail banking with its 1998 purchase of what is now Banco Standard Chartered in Latin America and its bank/insurance tie-ups with CGU (now CGNU) and Prudential plc. The promotion of Rana Talwar to CEO brought a strategic focus on emerging markets from which other banks were withdrawing.

Standard Chartered in 1999 bought Thailand's Nakornthon Bank and the non-Swiss trade financing operations of UBS AG and expanded into China through a pact with the Bank of China. In 2000 the company bought Australia and New Zealand Banking Group's Grindlays operations in South Asia and the Middle East. The following year Stanchart began cutting 20% of its workforce. It also folded Grindlay's operations into its own while retaining the brand's name.

In 2004 Stanchart bought the majority of Australia and New Zealand Banking Group's project finance business which is headquartered in London. The business which cost Stanchart about $1.5 billion operates in four regions: the UK the US the Middle East and South Asia (especially India).

In 2005 the bank acquired Korea First Bank (now SC First Bank); the deal was the biggest foreign investment ever for South Korea's financial sector. The following year Stanchart paid about $1.2 billion for Taiwan's Hsinchu Bank making it the first foreign bank owner in that country. Also in 2006 the bank acquired 20% of China Bohai Bank.

In 2008 the UK government responded to the global financial crisis by investing Â50 billion ($87.9 billion) in the nation's top banks including Stanchart. It agreed to guarantee another Â250 billion ($438 billion) in bonds and provide additional liquidity of at least Â200 billion ($350 billion) to the banks. The bailout plan was initiated to provide capital directly to the banks in order to revitalize lending activities.

Also in 2008 the company made some acquisitions for further international expansion. It bought Asia Trust and Investment Corporation which added some 10 branches in the lucrative Taipei market. Stanchart also bought some of the Brazil operations of Lehman Brothers after that company filed for bankruptcy protection.

EXECUTIVES

Chairman, Sir John W. Peace, age 65
Global Head Credit Risk Review Wholesale Banking, Andrew Willans
Group Chief Executive, Peter A. Sands, age 53, $1,002,000 total compensation
Group Finance Director and Board Member, Richard H. Meddings, age 56, $841,000 total compensation
Regional CEO South East Asia, Neeraj Swaroop, age 54
Director People Property and Assurance, Timothy J. (Tim) Miller, age 56
Group Executive Director and CEO Asia, Jaspal Singh Bindra, age 54
Group Head of People Compliance Communications and Culture; Director, Tracy J. Clarke, age 46
Group Executive Director and CEO Wholesale Banking, Alun M. G. (Mike) Rees, age 58
Group Chief Risk Officer, Richard F. Goulding, age 54
Global Head Private Banking, Shayne K. Nelson
Chairperson Greater China Standard Greater China, Katherine Tsang, age 57
CEO Standard Chartered Afghanistan, Joseph Silvanus

CEO Standard Chartered Bangladesh, Osman Morad
CEO Standard Chartered South Africa, Ebenezer Essoka
CEO Standard Chartered Nigeria, Christopher Knight
CEO Standard Chartered Nepal, Sujit Mundul
CEO Standard Chartered Nigeria, Simon J. Millett
CEO Standard Chartered Indonesia, Simon Morris
Group Head Strategy Corporate Development and Corporate Secretariat, Annemarie Durbin
CEO Standard Chartered Botswana, David D. Cutting
CEO Standard Chartered Qatar and Egypt, Tom Aaker
CEO Standard Chartered Zimbabwe, Washington Matsaira
Group Executive Director and CEO Consumer Banking, Stefano Paolo (Steve) Bertamini, age 49
Group Head Origination and Client Coverage, Sean Wallace
Head Investor Relations, Stephen Atkinson
CEO Standard Chartered Bank Oman, Ravneet Chowdhury
CEO Standard Chartered Vietnam, Ashok Sud
CEO and Executive Vice Chairman Standard Chartered China, Lim Cheng Teck
CEO Standard Chartered Kenya, Richard Etemesi
Head of Corporate Affairs Americas, Elaine Chin
Group Executive Director and CEO Europe Middle East Africa and Americas, Viswanathan (Shankar) Shankar, age 56
CEO Standard Chartered Saadiq, Afaq Khan
Chief Economist and Group Head Global Research, Gerard Lyons, age 53
Managing Director and Regional Head Global Markets Americas, Mohammed Grimeh
Chief Information Officer and Group Head of Group Technology and Operations, Jan Verplancke, age 50
Head Corporate Communications, Tim Baxter
External Communications Manager, Yuki Finch
Global Head Sales and Financial Markets, David Carr
Global Head Financial Institutions Sales Financial Markets, Adrian Walkling
Group Head Financial Markets, Lenny Feder
CEO Standard Chartered Bahrain, Jonathan Morris
CEO Standard Chartered UK and Europe, Richard W. Holmes
CEO Standard Chartered Cameroon, Mathieu Mandeng
Chief Executive Officer, Jeremy Awori
CEO Standard Chartered Mauritius, Sridhar Nagarajan
Head of Media Relations, Jonathan Tracey
President and CEO Korea and First Bank Korea; President and CEO Standard Chartered First Bank, Richard Hill
Regional Credit Officer Wholesale Banking; Country Chief Risk Officer Americas, Peter Shaw
Head Consumer Banking Southeast Asia, Ajay Kanwal
CEO Americas, Julio Rojas
Regional CEO India and South Asia, Sunil Kaushal
Board Member, Rudy H. P. Markham, age 68
Board Member, Jamie F. T. Dundas, age 63
Board Member, Valerie F. (Val) Gooding, age 63
Board Member, Paul D. Skinner, age 70
Board Member, Oliver Stocken, age 72
Board Member, John Paynter, age 59
Board Member, Simon Lowth, age 52
Board Member, Ruth Markland, age 61
Group Chief Executive, Peter A. Sands, age 53
Group Finance Director and Board Member, Richard H. Meddings, age 56
Board Member, Gareth R. Bullock, age 60
Group Executive Director and CEO Asia, Jaspal Singh Bindra, age 54

Group Executive Director and CEO Wholesale Banking, Alun M. G. (Mike) Rees, age 58
Group Executive Director and CEO Consumer Banking, Stefano Paolo (Steve) Bertamini, age 49
Group Executive Director and CEO Europe Middle East Africa and Americas, Viswanathan (Shankar) Shankar, age 56
Board Member, Seung-Soo Han
Board Member, Richard Delbridge
Auditors: KPMGAuditPlc

LOCATIONS

HQ: Standard Chartered Plc
32nd Floor, 4-4A Des Voeux Road, Central,
Phone: (44) 20 7885 8888
Web: www.sc.com

Sales

	% of total
Asia/Pacific	
Hong	18
Singapore	11
Korea	10
Other	21
India	8
Middle East & other South	12
Americas UK &	12
Africa	8
Total	**100**

PRODUCTS/OPERATIONS

Sales

	% of total
Interest	68
Noninterest	
Fees &	17
Net trading	11
Other	4
Total	**100**

COMPETITORS

Bank of America	Hang Seng Bank
Bank of China	Lloyds Banking Group
Bank of East Asia	Maybank
Barclays	OCBC Bank
Citigroup	Royal Bank of Scotland
DBS Group Holdings	Standard Bank Group
Deutsche Bank	State Bank of India
Grupo Santander	United Overseas Bank
HSBC	Woori

HISTORICAL FINANCIALS

Company Type: Public

Income Statement

FYE: December 31

	ASSETS ($ mil.)	NET INCOME ($ mil.)	INCOME AS % OF ASSETS	EMPLOYEES
12/13	674,380	4,090	0.6%	86,640
12/12	636,518	4,887	0.8%	89,058
12/11	599,070	4,849	0.8%	86,865
12/10	516,542	4,332	0.8%	85,231
12/09	436,653	3,380	0.8%	77,326
Annual Growth	**11.5%**	**4.9%**	**—**	**2.9%**

2013 Year-End Financials

Return on assets: 0.6%
Return on equity: 8.9%
Long-term debt ($ mil.): —
No. of shares (mil.): —
Sales ($ mil): 25,920

Dividends
Yield: —
Payout: —
Market value ($ mil.): —

Standard Life Assurance Co. (United Kingdom)

LOCATIONS

HQ: Standard Life Assurance Co. (United Kingdom)
Standard Life House, 30 Lothian Road, Edinburgh EH1 2DH
Phone: (44) 131 225 2552
Web: www.standardlife.com

HISTORICAL FINANCIALS

Company Type: Public

Income Statement

FYE: December 31

	ASSETS ($ mil.)	NET INCOME ($ mil.)	INCOME AS % OF ASSETS	EMPLOYEES
12/13	305,074	770	0.3%	8,224
12/12	280,627	1,125	0.4%	8,458
12/11	247,366	460	0.2%	8,789
12/10	239,286	670	0.3%	9,254
12/09	237,451	344	0.1%	9,752
Annual Growth	**6.5%**	**22.2%**	**—**	**(4.2%)**

2013 Year-End Financials

Return on assets: 0.2%
Return on equity: 10.8%
Long-term debt ($ mil.): —
No. of shares (mil.): —
Sales ($ mil): 33,993

Dividends
Yield: —
Payout: —
Market value ($ mil.): —

Standard Life Plc

Trying to set the standard for life insurance and financial services both at home and abroad Standard Life plc is a leading UK insurance asset management and pension firm. The holding company does business through subsidiaries including Standard Life Assurance Limited which provides life and pension products to 4 million customers in the UK market. Other divisions include Standard Life Investments (retail and institutional investment management). Standard Life established in 1825 has 6 million customers in the UK and abroad. In Canada its second largest market the company offers insurance pensions and asset management.

Geographic Reach

Standard Life's operations cover markets in North America Europe Asia and the Middle East. In addition to the UK (65% of sales) and Canada other international operations include subsidiaries and offices in Austria Australia Bermuda Germany Hong Kong Korea Ireland Singapore the United Arab Emirates and the US. It operates joint ventures in China and India. In all of these markets Standard Life offers life insurance and pension products to individuals and corporate clients.

Operations

The company's operating divisions provide investment protection and savings products; benefit and pension plans; and asset management services to corporations and individuals. Its Standard Life Investments division manages some Ã180 billion in assets around the globe. Altogether Standard

Life's subsidiaries administer some Â230 billion in assets (as of mid-2013). Due to the nature of the company's businesses investment returns often account for a larger percent of annual revenues than do insurance premiums and product fees and commissions.

Sales and Marketing

Standard Life distributes products directly to customers as well as through partnerships with banks. It formed a new partnership with RBS in 2012 to provide investment solutions to RBS banking customers.

Financial Performance

Revenue increased 111% in 2012 due to higher investment returns premiums and fee and commission income. Investment returns were up on equity security gains while fee and commission income received a boost from reclassified income. Net income rose 134% on higher revenues.

Strategy

The company is focused on maximizing profits to provide dividend growth and to reinvest in business growth. In the Standard Life Investments business the firm is focused on growing geographically and increasing investment capabilities. It opened new offices in Singapore and the Middle East and launched a new savings product in Germany in 2012. The company is also expanding its Standard Life Wealth division in the domestic market. In addition the Standard Life organization aims to increase customer and shareholder value and provide long-term savings and investment propositions.

Standard Life at one time had a few more eggs in its basket but pressures from the global economic downturn induced the company to simplify its holdings and focus more carefully on insurance long-term savings and investment management. The company sold off its Standard Life Bank (mortgages and savings products) subsidiary to Barclays in early 2010 for in Â226 million ($369 million); Standard Life and Barclays entered a partnership to offer retail investment offerings following the deal. Also in 2010 the company sold its Standard Life Healthcare (now part of PruHealth) to South African insurance and finance firm Discovery Holdings for Â138 million ($205 million).

Mergers and Acquisitions

To enhance its wealth management operations in 2011 the company acquired financial software and consulting firm Focus Solutions. In 2013 the Standard Life Wealth division further widened its operations through the purchase of the Newton Private Clients division of Newton Management.

HISTORY

The Life Insurance Company of Scotland opened in Edinburgh in 1825 as a subsidiary of The Insurance Company of Scotland a fire insurance firm. In 1832 the subsidiary became a separate business received a royal charter and began anew as The Standard Life Assurance Company. In 1833 Standard Life opened its first overseas agency in Canada and continued to grow by acquisitions.

Company executives established Colonial Life Assurance as a sister company in 1846 to insure clients across the far-flung British empire. When Colonial's success became a threat to Standard Life's own business at home Standard bought Colonial.

In 1869 Standard Life moved into India and China (although only to insure Europeans). It moved into Scandinavia Argentina and South Africa in the 1890s.

After the turn of the century however the company began to spin off foreign offices and focus on its domestic business. Standard Life became a customer-owned mutual company in 1925.

The company was expanding again by the 1990s. It bought health insurer Prime Health (now Standard Life Healthcare) in 1994. The next year it formed a joint venture with India-based Housing Development Finance Corporation to sell insurance. In 1998 it expanded its financial services with the opening of Standard Life Bank and Standard Life Investments.

Expanding globally Standard Life was granted a license in 2000 to sell policies in the huge Indian market. The company opened up an office in Hong Kong in 2001. Just like many other companies Standard Life wanted to do business in China so it set up a joint venture and was granted a license to sell there in 2005.

After long resisting the worldwide trend for demutualization Standard Life's board eventually succumbed to the necessity of such an action. Faced with lackluster equity markets and regulatory criticism of its capital-reserves accounting in 2004 the company announced plans to restructure. The firm's transformation from a mutual organization into a holding company was completed through a public offering in mid-2006; the IPO was the London Stock Exchange's biggest in five years. The company's name was changed from The Standard Life Assurance Company to Standard Life plc.

In 2007 the company made a failed attempt to take over fellow UK insurance firm Resolution plc.

To enhance growth back home the company formed a UK wealth management unit in 2008 and launched additional initiatives to strengthen its corporate offerings and online services. To further this goal it acquired employee benefits management software maker Vebnet in 2008.

At the start of 2010 long-time executive Sir Sandy Crombie stepped down from his post as CEO of Standard Life. Crombie led the company through many challenges including its successful demutualization. David Nish who previously held the title of finance director at Standard Life took over the role of CEO.

EXECUTIVES

Group Chief Executive, David Nish, age 57
Chairman, Gerry E. Grimstone, age 64
Managing Director Information Systems, Keith Young
President and CEO Standard Life Canada, Charles Guay
Executive Director and Chief Executive Standard Life Investments Limited, Keith Skeoch, age 68
Group Company Secretary; General Counsel, Malcolm Wood
Chief Executive Europe, Nathan Parnaby
Head Media Relations, Barry Cameron
Public Relations Manager, Nicola McGowan
Chief Marketing Officer, Simon Gulliford
Group Human Resources Director, Mike Conway
Chief Executive U.K., Paul Matthews
Chief Financial Officer, Jackie Hunt, age 46
Affairs Manager, Claire Burston
Affairs Manager, Nicki Lundy
Senior Non-Executive Independent Director, John John Paynter Paynter
UK Chief Information Officer, Mark Dixon
Group Marketing Director, Bruce Kelsall
Director, Crawford Gillies
Board Member, Colin Buchan, age 59
Group Chief Executive, David Nish, age 57
Director, Sheelagh D. Whittaker, age 67
Board Member, Lord Norman Blackwell, age 61
Board Member, Kent Atkinson, age 69
Executive Director and Chief Executive Standard Life Investments Limited, Keith Skeoch, age 68
Board Member, Baroness Margaret J. McDonagh, age 53
Independent Non-Executive Director, David David Grigson Grigson

Non-Executive Director, Lynne Lynne Peacock Peacock
Non-Executive Director, Noel Noel Harwerth Harwerth
Non-Executive Director, Pierre Pierre Danon Danon
Auditors: PricewaterhouseCoopersLLP

LOCATIONS

HQ: Standard Life Plc
Standard Life House, 30 Lothian Road, Edinburgh EH1 2DH
Phone: (44) 131 225 2552
Web: www.standardlife.com

2012 Premiums

	% of total
UK	65
Canada	18
International	17
Total	**100**

PRODUCTS/OPERATIONS

2012 Revenues

	% of total
Investment	73
Earned	22
Fee & commission	5
Total	**100**

Selected Products

Life insurance
Pension products
  Active Money Personal Pension (AMPP)
  Self Invested Personal Pension (SIPP)
  Stakeholder pension
  Starting a pension for a child
Retirement products
  Compulsory Purchase Annuity
  Immediate Vesting Personal Pension
  Immediate Vesting Personal Pension Select
  Impaired Life Annuity
  Income Drawdown
Savings and investment products
  International Bond
  Investment funds
  Other Onshore Bonds
  Stocks and Shares ISA
  Tailored Investment Bond

COMPETITORS

AXA UK	Power Financial
Aviva	Prudential plc
Canada Life	ReAssure
Equitable Life	Royal London Mutual
Friends Provident	Schroders
Great-West Lifeco	Scottish Equitable
Legal & General Group	Skandia UK
Liverpool Victoria	St. James' s Place plc
Phoenix Group	Sun Life
	permanent tsb

HISTORICAL FINANCIALS

Company Type: Public

Income Statement

FYE: December 31

	REVENUE ($ mil.)	NET INCOME ($ mil.)	NET PROFIT MARGIN	EMPLOYEES
12/13	33,952	770	2.3%	8,224
12/12	30,923	1,125	3.6%	8,458
12/11	14,036	460	3.3%	8,789
12/10	28,830	670	2.3%	9,254
12/09	28,237	344	1.2%	9,752
Annual Growth	4.7%	22.2%	—	(4.2%)

2013 Year-End Financials

Debt ratio: —	No. of shares (mil.): —
Return on equity: 10.8%	Dividends
Cash ($ mil.): 15,045	Yield: —
Current ratio: —	Payout: —
Long-term debt ($ mil.): —	Market value ($ mil.): —

Statoil ASA

The status of Statoil is that it is Norway's top integrated oil and gas company. Statoil operates in 40 countries focusing its upstream activities in more than 10 of them primarily on the Norwegian continental shelf the North Sea the Caspian Sea Western Africa North America and South America. In 2010 Statoil reported proved reserves of 5.3 billion barrels of oil equivalent. It indirectly operates a network of more than 2280 gas stations in Russia Scandinavia Poland and the Baltic States. (77% of these stations are in Scandinavia). Statoil also operates natural gas pipelines supplies electricity in Norway and Sweden and is engaged in green energy development (wind and biofuels).

Statoil manages the Norwegian state's direct financial interest (known as SDFI) in oil and gas partnerships active on the Norwegian continental shelf. It also owns the world's largest offshore gas platform the Aasgard B off Norway's west coast.

The company's strategy is to develop new oil and gas assets (based on its ongoing success in the Norwegian Continental Shelf) in four focus areas: deepwater harsh environment gas value chains and heavy oil.

Beefing up its global infrastructure in 2009 the company bought a crude oil terminal in the Bahamas (and a 50% interest in a related tugboat business) from World Point Terminals for $263.2 million.

The company reported a downturn in revenues and income in 2009 primarily as the result of the impact of the global recession on lowering commodity prices and weakening oil and gas demand.

In 2010 in a move to generate cash to pay down debt and to invest in its higher-return core exploration and production assets Statoil spun off its retail network of gas stations (including a chain of 200 automated outlets) in eight north European countries. Statoil retained more than 50% of the unit (Statoil Fuel and Retail) following the spin off. It also sold a 40% stake in its Peregrino oil field (offshore Brazil) to Sinochem for $3 billion and a 40% stake in its Canadian oil sands project to PTT Exploration and Production for $2.3 billion. In 2011 it also sold its 24% stake in the Gassled Pipeline joint venture to investment firms for $3.3 billion. That year it increased its presence in Alaska (where it is the fourth largest explorer) by acquiring a 25% stake in 50 Conoco Phillips oil leases located in the Chukchi Sea.

Higher oil and gas price and increased demand coupled with its strategic acquisitions divestments and reorganizations helped to lift Statoil's revenue sand net income in 2010.

Building its exploration and production position in the US in 2011 the company expanded its holdings in shale assets buying Brigham Exploration in a $4.4 billion deal. Thanks to new drilling technologies US gas shale has emerged as a lucrative growth market and Brigham Exploration had well-established shale plays in the Rockies.

To raise cash and focus on its core exploration and production activities in 2012 the company agreed to sell its 54% stake in Statoil Fuel and Retail to Alimentation Couche-Tard for $2.8 billion.

The Norwegian government owns 67% of Statoil.

HISTORY

To exert greater control over exploration and production of the Norwegian continental shelf (NCS) the government of Norway set up Den norske stats oljeselskap (Statoil) in 1972.

A decade earlier three geologists had visited Norway on behalf of Phillips Petroleum (later renamed ConocoPhillips) to apply for sole rights to explore on the NCS. The government initially refused drilling rights to foreign companies and in 1963 Norway claimed sovereignty over the NCS. Two years later the government began allowing exploration. Phillips' major discovery in the Ekofisk field in 1969 prompted Norway to set up its own oil company. After Statoil's formation in 1972 the company garnered funds to expand through taxation of multinationals production limits leasing contracts and other measures.

In 1974 a giant discovery was made in the North Sea's Statfjord field and Statoil was given a 50% stake. A year later Statoil began exploring for oil and gas exporting oil and commissioning its first subsea oil pipeline the Norpipe which extended to the UK. In 1986 Statoil's gas pipeline system the Statpipe began transporting gas from the North Sea to the mainland.

Moving into retailing Statoil acquired Esso's service stations and other downstream operations in Sweden and Denmark in 1985 and 1986. The next year cost overruns stemming from the extension of Statoil's Mongstad oil refinery led to the ousting of the company's first president Arve Johnsen and many of his deputies. Harald Norvik was appointed CEO in 1988.

In 1990 Statoil and BP teamed up to develop international operations and in 1992 Statoil acquired BP's service stations in Ireland. Statoil and Neste Chemicals (later part of Industri Kapital) formed the Borealis petrochemicals group in 1994.

The company in 1995 acquired Aran Energy moving into exploration of offshore Ireland and the UK. Statoil brought its field projects in China and Azerbaijan onstream in 1997. That year Statoil spun off its shipping operations as Navion partly owned by Norway's Rasmussen group. It also contracted with Kvaerner to build a giant offshore gas platform for the Aasgard field in the Norwegian Sea.

The Aasgard field project resulted in cost overruns in 1999 again leading to a Statoil board shakeup and CEO resignation. Norvik who had advocated partial privatization of Statoil was replaced by Olav Fjell former head of Norway's Postbanken (who resigned in 2003). That year Statoil helped Norsk Hydro take over rival Saga in return for some of Saga's assets.

As part of a major restructuring in 2000 Statoil sold most assets of US unit Statoil Energy. Political opposition that year postponed Statoil's plans for partial privatization but the government proceeded with an IPO in 2001 raising about $3 billion.

In 2002 Statoil sold its oil and gas assets in the Danish North Sea to Dong the Danish state oil company for about $120 million. That year the company also acquired the Polish unit of Sweden's Preem Petroleum which owned 79 gas stations in Poland.

In 2003 Statoil sold its Navion unit to shipping group Teekay for about $800 million. That year it also acquired two Algerian natural gas projects from BP for $740 million. A bribery scandal involving an Iranian oil contract forced the resignation of the chairman CEO and another top executive in 2003.

Statoil sold its 50% stake in petrochemicals venture Borealis in 2005.

In 2006 the company acquired three oil prospects in the Gulf of Mexico from Plains Exploration & Production for $700 million. It also acquired offshore assets in the Gulf of Mexico from Anadarko Petroleum for $901 million.

Expanding its upstream midstream and downstream assets in 2007 the company acquired $4.2 billion of subsea equipment from Aver Kvaerner Canada's North American Oil Sands Corporation for $1.96 billion and 274 gas stations in Scandinavia from ConocoPhillips.

In a major expansion that gave it a major international profile (including a strong presence in the deepwater Gulf of Mexico) in 2007 Statoil acquired the oil and gas exploration and production operations of Norsk Hydro in a $30 billion deal and became StatoilHydro.

In 2008 Statoil acquired ConocoPhillips' Jet gas station chain in Norway Sweden and Denmark.

Growing its exploration and production asset base in 2008 paid about $1.8 billion to acquire holdings in heavy-oil and deep-water projects in Brazil and the Gulf of Mexico from Anadarko Petroleum. That year it also teamed up with Chesapeake Energy to jointly explore unconventional gas opportunities around the world including in the Marcellus Shale play in the US.

EXECUTIVES

VP Media Relations North America, Jannik Lindb?k, age 74
EVP Development and Production International, Peter Mellbye, age 64, $631,293 total compensation
President; Chief Executive Officer, Helge Lund, age 51, $1,072,974 total compensation
SVP Corporate Human Resources, Jens R. Jenssen, age 60
Chairman, Svein Rennemo, age 66
EVP Exploration, Tim Dodson, age 54
Deputy Chairman, Marit Arnstad, age 51
SVP Investor Relations, Lars Troen S?rensen
VP Media Relations, Ola M. Aanestad
President StatoilHydro Brazil, Kjetil Hove
Public Affairs Manager, Kai Nielsen
Investor Relations, Morten S. Johannessen
EVP Development and Production International, Lars C. Bacher
EVP Development and Production North America, Bill Maloney, age 59
EVP Global Strategy and Business Development, John Knight, age 56
EVP and CFO, Torgrim Reitan
EVP and Chief Staff Officer, Tove Stuhr Sj?blom, age 48
President Canada, Stale Tungesvik
Executive Vice President; Marketing; Processing and Renewable Energy, Eldar Saetre
Executive Vice President; Technology; Projects and Drilling, Margareth Ovrum
Director, Lady Barbara T. Judge, age 67
Director, Lill-Heidi Bakkerud, age 50
Director, Grace Reksten Skaugen, age 60
Director, Morten Svaan, age 57
Deputy Chairman, Marit Arnstad, age 51
Director, Roy Franklin, age 60
Director, Jakob Stausholm, age 46
Director, Einar A. Iversen, age 52
Director, Bjorn T. Godal
Auditors: Ernst&YoungAS

LOCATIONS

HQ: Statoil ASA
Forusbeen 50, Stavanger N-4035
Phone: (47) 51 99 00 00 **Fax:** (47) 51 99 00 50
Web: www.statoil.com

Sales

	% of total
Norway	78
US	10
Sweden	4
Denmark	3
Other	5
Total	**100**

PRODUCTS/OPERATIONS

Sales

	% of total
Manufacturing &	52
Exploration &	28
Natural	11
Fuel &	9
Total	**100**

COMPETITORS

BP	Royal Dutch Shell
Exxon Mobil	TOTAL
OMV	

HISTORICAL FINANCIALS

Company Type: Public

Income Statement

FYE: December 31

	REVENUE ($ mil.)	NET INCOME ($ mil.)	NET PROFIT MARGIN	EMPLOYEES
12/13	104,898	6,566	6.3%	23,413
12/12	129,328	12,317	9.5%	23,028
12/11	111,467	13,103	11.8%	31,715
12/10	90,766	6,526	7.2%	30,344
12/09	80,787	3,178	3.9%	28,739
Annual Growth	**6.7%**	**19.9%**	**—**	**(5.0%)**

2013 Year-End Financials

Debt ratio: 3.3%
Return on equity: 11.8%
Cash ($ mil.): 14,038
Current ratio: 1.43
Long-term debt ($ mil.): 27,236
No. of shares (mil.): —
Dividends
Yield: 4.7%
Payout: 57.5%
Market value ($ mil.): —

	STOCK PRICE ($) FY Close	P/E High/Low		PER SHARE ($) Earnings	Dividends	Book Value
12/13	24.13	0	0	2.06	1.15	18.40
12/12	25.04	0	0	3.86	1.07	17.95
12/11	25.61	0	0	4.11	0.03	14.58
12/10	23.77	0	0	2.05	0.92	11.83
12/09	24.91	0	0	1.00	1.14	10.82
Annual Growth	**(0.8%)**	**—**	**—**	**19.8%**	**0.1%**	**14.2%**

Storebrand ASA

If you're planning for your golden years in Norway you may want to shop with Storebrand. The firm provides insurance and financial services to 1.8 million customers in Norway and Sweden. Products include life insurance policies property/casualty coverage health insurance asset management and banking. Its largest unit Storebrand Life offers pension savings occupational pension and life insurance products while its Storebrand P&C division provides property protection policies to individuals and businesses. The Storebrand Bank unit is a commercial bank that serves retail and corporate markets. The Storebrand Asset Management unit manages mutual funds and client portfolios.

EXECUTIVES

Chairman, Birger Magnus, age 59, $44,918 total compensation
CEO and Managing Director, Odd Arild Grefstad, age 49, $471,038 total compensation
Executive Vice President Corporate Communications, Egil Thompson, age 50, $338 total compensation
EVP Operative Processes, Roar Thoresen, age 57, $502,876 total compensation
Chief Marketing Officer, Anders R?ed, age 46, $308,299 total compensation
EVP SPP, Sarah McPhee, age 60, $511,653 total compensation
EVP Insurance and Risk, Gunnar Rogstad, age 59, $336,283 total compensation
Executive Vice President Corporate Responsibility, Elin M. Myrmel-Johansen, age 41
Head Investor Relations, Trond Finn Eriksen
EVP Bank, Truls Nergaard
Chief Operating Officer, Heidi Skaaret, age 54
Managing Director of Storebrand Livsforsikring AS, Geir Holmgren
Managing Director; Storebrand Asset Management, Hans Aasnaes
Chief Financial Officer, Lars Loddesol
Director, Halvor Stenstadvold, age 70
Director, Birgitte Nielsen, age 51
Director, Jon Arnt Jacobsen, age 57
Director, John Staunsbjerg Dueholm, age 64
Director, Camilla Marianne Grieg, age 49
Director, Annika Lundius, age 61
Director, Knut Dyre Haug, age 59
Director, Erik Haug Hansen, age 58
Director, Ann-Mari Gj?stein, age 50
Director; Employee Representative, Ann-Mari Gjostein
Director; Employee Representative, Kirsti Valborgland
Auditors: DeloitteAS

LOCATIONS

HQ: Storebrand ASA
Professor Kohtsvei 9, Lysaker NO-1327
Phone: (47) 22 31 50 50 **Fax:** (47) 22 48 98 90
Web: www.storebrand.no

COMPETITORS

AXA	SEB AB
Allianz	Skandia
Danske Bank	Swedbank AB
Eureko	Zurich Insurance Group
ING	ageas SA/NV
Nordea Bank	

HISTORICAL FINANCIALS

Company Type: Public

Income Statement

FYE: December 31

	ASSETS ($ mil.)	NET INCOME ($ mil.)	INCOME AS % OF ASSETS	EMPLOYEES
12/13	74,120	324	0.4%	2,138
12/12	75,119	179	0.2%	2,250
12/11	66,767	112	0.2%	2,221
12/10	66,905	252	0.4%	2,206
12/09	63,555	161	0.3%	2,280
Annual Growth	**3.9%**	**19.1%**	**—**	**(1.6%)**

2013 Year-End Financials

Return on assets: 0.4%
Return on equity: 9.3%
Long-term debt ($ mil.): —
No. of shares (mil.): 447
Sales ($ mil.): 8,703
Dividends
Yield: —
Payout: —
Market value ($ mil.): 5,256

	STOCK PRICE ($) FY Close	P/E High/Low		PER SHARE ($) Earnings	Dividends	Book Value
12/13	11.75	0	0	0.73	0.00	8.25
12/12	9.50	0	0	0.40	0.00	7.88
12/11	12.05	0	0	0.25	0.01	6.89
12/10	14.16	0	0	0.57	0.19	6.95
12/09	11.05	0	0	0.36	0.00	6.58
Annual Growth	**1.6%**	**—**	**—**	**19.1%**	**—**	**5.8%**

Sumitomo Corp. (Japan)

Sumitomo Corporation specializes in the general. A Japanese "sogo shosha" (general trading company) Sumitomo is active in a wide range of commercial ventures. Through some 800 subsidiaries and affiliates it imports and exports raw materials and goods including metals machinery electronics fuels chemicals and food products. It also participates in finance logistics and real estate development. The group's auto finance and media holdings are among its fastest-growing operations. Sumitomo Corporation is part of the Sumitomo "keiretsu" a group of companies loosely linked by cross-ownership. Other group companies include Sumitomo Mitsui Banking Sumitomo Life Insurance and electronics maker NEC.

Never one to sit still Sumitomo occupies much of its time trading on its own behalf. The company searches for opportunities to take advantage of market trends and secure new lines of revenue. The company in 2014 increased its 20% stake in major Malaysian fertilizer producer Union Harvest to 60%.

It was one of a number of foreign groups to move into Australia's agricultural sector when it bought half of Emerald Group in 2010. (It acquired the remaining 50% in 2014.) Emerald Group is one of Australia's largest grain trading firms; Japan also happens to be a major importer of Australian wheat. Also that year the company increased its stake in Jupiter Telecommunications (J:COM) Japan's largest cable television operator from 27% to 40%. It had tried unsuccessfully to buy out J:COM's largest owner Liberty Media. Instead Liberty sold its 38% stake to KDDI Corporation one of Japan's largest telecommunications companies.

In late 2012 KDDI and Sumitomo agreed to acquire all outstanding shares of J:COM and merge it with Japan's #2 cable operator Japan Cablenet (owned by KDDI); the resulting entity will control half of Japan's cable market.

Sumitomo has been building up its metals and mining business. In 2010 Sumitomo bought a 30% stake in the iron ore unit of Brazilian steelmaker Usiminas. Due to increasing copper demand especially from China Sumitomo has increased its copper mining operations in Indonesia. The company has also invested in a nickel mine in Madagascar with partners Korea Resources Sherritt International and SNC Lavalin. In 2011 Sumitomo and its Sumitomo Metal unit acquired Standard Steel in the US. The deal allowed Sumitomo to expand its railway business by tapping into the growing demand for train wheels in North America.

As part of a consortium Sumitomo purchased an oil and gas operation in the UK North Sea from Paris-based Wendel in 2009. The company Oranje-Nassau Energie owns six oil blocks capable of producing some 7000 barrels worth of oil and gas a day through 2030. The deal was worth about $900 million. Also that year Sumitomo acquired a 42%-stake in a US wind farm from American International Group; the group already had wind farms in Japan and China in its fold.

In 2008 Sumitomo took full control over its 24-hour home shopping network Jupiter Shop Channel when it bought a 30% equity stake from IAC for Å46 billion ($493 million). The acquisition provided the company with more flexibility in running the retail business and to implement a multi-channel strategy. Sumitomo also plans to leverage its existing media and lifestyle business portfolio via the channel.

HISTORY

Around 1630 Masatomo Sumitomo a Buddhist priest from the Kyoto area opened a medicine shop/bookstore after the dissolution of his sect. His descendants preserved his writings on business ethics and he is considered the spiritual founder of the Sumitomo Group. The commercial founder of the "keiretsu" however was Riemon Soga Sumitomo's brother-in-law. Soga researched and duplicated a Western copper-smelting technique that enabled him to build a prosperous copper company. After Soga died in 1636 his son Tomomochi married into the Sumitomo family and became its head.

Tomomochi Soga combined the families' businesses and moved to Osaka. By 1693 the family had turned a dilapidated copper mine into one of Japan's top producers. By the mid-1800s however the company's biggest mine was aging and output had dropped. The family mortgaged its assets to modernize the mine imported French technology and bought ships for copper transport. Production soared.

Sumitomo Bank was created from existing family operations in 1895. A copper wire business founded in 1897 evolved into Sumitomo Electric and Sumitomo Metal Industries. The family formed Sumitomo Chemical in 1913 and in 1925 began selling life insurance.

Nippon Electric Company (NEC) was managed by Sumitomo from 1932 until post-WWII occupation forces split the "zaibatsu" (family-run conglomerate) into numerous independent pieces. Employees of the old Sumitomo group migrated to a real estate and trading company today's Sumitomo Corporation. Sumitomo companies began regrouping in the 1950s at the behest of the Japanese government.

Sumitomo companies went on a buying spree during the "bubble economy" of the 1980s and early 1990s. Purchases included Dunlop's tire operations investments in Phelps Dodge's (now Freeport-McMoRan) Candelaria copper and gold mine in Chile and one-third of Satellite Japan. The Sumitomo Bank bought 13% of US investment house Goldman Sachs. In 1990 however bank chairman Ichiro Isoda resigned in an illegal-loan scandal.

Sumitomo Metal Industries invested about $200 million in LTV in 1993 to shore up its US supply of high-quality steel. Ironically LTV was one of several US steel companies that campaigned against Japanese steel imports in 1998.

In its first loss in 50 years Sumitomo Bank took a $2.8 billion hit in 1995 because of bad loans (the legacy of the economy's bubble burst of 1992). The next year Sumitomo Corporation announced

that its head copper-trader Yasuo Hamanaka had engaged in unauthorized trading over the previous decade –first attempting to corner the market then trying to cover his own deficit. Hamanaka pleaded guilty and went to jail. Sumitomo Corporation chairman Tomiichi Akiyama resigned in 1997. By 1998 the company had suffered $3 billion in trading losses fines and restitutions. (Sumitomo Corporation sued four investment banks alleging they had aided Hamanaka; separately Merrill Lynch settled a dispute over its role in the scandal by agreeing in 2000 to pay the company $275 million.)

In 1999 Sumitomo Rubber Industries and Goodyear Tire formed an alliance: Sumitomo Rubber got cash and control of Goodyear's Japanese operations and Goodyear gained control of Sumitomo Rubber's business in the US and Europe. Sumitomo Bank in 1999 announced plans to merge with Sakura Bank; the deal was completed in 2001.

That year Sumitomo Corporation agreed to buy Nomura Trading's steel-related operations; the deal was completed in 2002. Adding to one of its core businesses that year Sumitomo bought the steel products businesses of Nichimen (now Sojitz). Also in 2002 Sumitomo Corporation moved to expand its activities in China.

The year 2004 was a big one for the company: Sumitomo purchased US-based life science venture capital firm Oxford Finance embarked upon a joint venture with Australia-based glove manufacturer Ansell and fabric manufacturer Shinwa to make gloves and other products launched a credit-card subsidiary and acquired Nissin Sugar Manufacturing. In other deals it purchased US pet care products maker Hartz Mountain for $364 million; acquired Kiriu Corp a disc and drum brake-maker with operations in Asia and North America; and took controlling stakes of Sumisho Computer Systems Corp and movie theater chain United Cinemas.

Late in 2005 Sumitomo expanded its retailing operations again when its Sumitomo Corporation of America subsidiary acquired tire distributor TBC Corporation in a $1.1 billion deal. TBC's operations included National Tire & Battery Tire Kingdom and Merchant's Tire & Auto. It also owned the Big O Tires franchise business.

In 2008 the company increased its focus on upstream oil development and the trading of crude oil and petroleum products. To that end it sold its shares in domestic oil distribution unit Sumisho Oil to Idemitsu Kosa. The group also acquired 20% of Abu Dhabi-based energy and desalinated water supplier Shuweihat CMS International Power Company. The deal included a 50% stake in the company's operation and maintenance partnership.

Sumitomo exits or sells divisions that are less profitable. In 2008 it dissolved diamond distribution company FB Jewelry and began the dissolution of GeoFocus a developer of communication systems. The group cited poor performances of both units for the closures.

EXECUTIVES

Chairman, Motoyuki Oka
President and CEO, Susumu Kato
Senior Managing Executive Officer and General Manager Transportation & Construction Systems Business Unit, Naoki Hidaka
Executive Officer; General Manager Internal Auditing, Makoto Nakamura
Senior Managing Executive Officer and President Sumitomo Corporation of America, Kazuhiro Takeuchi
Chairman, Kazuo Ohmori

CFO Senior Managing Executive Officer and Director; General Manager Financial Resources Management Group, Toyosaku Hamada
Senior Managing Executive Officer and General Manager Americas; President and CEO Sumitomo Corporation North America Group; Director & President Sumitomo Corporation of America, Takashi Kano
President and CEO, Kuniharu Nakamura
EVP and General Manager Media Network Lifestyle Related Goods & Services Business Unit, Shinichi Sasaki
EVP and General Manager Human Resources General Affairs & Legal Group, Takuro Kawahara
Senior Managing Executive Officer and Director; General Manager Media Network and Lifestyle Retail Business Unit, Yoshio Osawa
EVP and General Manager Metal Products Business Unit, Kazuhisa Togashi
Senior Managing Executive Officer and General Manager Mineral Resources Energy Chemical & Electronics Business Unit, Toru Furihata
Managing Executive Officer and Director; General Manager Corporate Planning and Coordination, Masayuki Doi
Senior Managing Executive Officer and CFO, Hiroyuki Inohara
Senior Managing Executive Officer and General Manager Kansai Regional Business Unit, Masaru Nakamura
Managing Executive Officer and President and CEO Sumitomo Corporation Asia & Oceania Group, Kohei Hirao
Senior Managing Executive Officer and General Manager Corporate Planning & Coordination Group, Yasuyuki Abe
Senior Managing Executive Officer and General Manager Environment & Infrastructure Business Unit, Michihiko Kanegae
Executive Officer; General Manager Automotive Division No.2, Kiyomi Machida
Executive Officer; Assistant General Manager Financial Resources Management Group; General Manager Corporate Risk Management, Hideki Iwasawa
Executive Officer; EVP and CFO Sumitomo Corporation North America Group; General Manager Corporate Coordination Group Sumitomo Corporation North America Group; EVP and CFO Sumitomo Corporation of America; Assistant General Manager Americas, Masato Sugimori
Executive Officer; General Manager Mineral Resources Division No.1, Akira Takeuchi
Executive Officer; General Manager Accounting Controlling, Koichi Takahata
Executive Officer; General Manager Legal, Kiyoshi Ogawa
Executive Officer and President and CEO Sumitomo Corporation Kyushu Co. Ltd., Hiroaki Mizobuchi
Executive Officer; General Manager Non-Ferrous Products and Metals, Masao Sekiuchi
Executive Officer; General Manager Planning and Administration and Transportation and Construction Systems, Yutaka Sekine
Executive Officer and President and CEO Sumitomo Corporation (Shanghai) Limited, Fumihiro Koba
President and CEO, Susumu Kato
EVP and Director; General Manager Transportation and Construction Systems Business Unit, Kazuo Ohmori
CFO Senior Managing Executive Officer and Director; General Manager Financial Resources Management Group, Toyosaku Hamada
EVP and Director; General Manager Infrastructure Business Unit, Takahiro Moriyama
EVP and Director; General Manager Metal Products Business Unit, Shunichi Arai

Senior Managing Executive Officer and Director; **General Manager Mineral Resources Energy Chemical & Electronics Business Unit,** Kuniharu Nakamura

Senior Managing Executive Officer and Director; **General Manager General Products and Real Estate,** Shinichi Sasaki

Senior Managing Executive Officer and Director; **General Manager Human Resources General Affairs and Legal Group,** Takuro Kawahara

Senior Managing Executive Officer and Director; **General Manager Media Network and Lifestyle Retail Business Unit,** Yoshio Osawa

Managing Executive Officer and Director; General Manager Corporate Planning and Coordination, Masayuki Doi

Senior Managing Executive Officer Director and **General Manager New Industry Development and Cross-function Business Unit,** Yasuyuki Abe
Auditors: KPMGAZSA&Co.

LOCATIONS

HQ: Sumitomo Corp. (Japan)
1-8-11 Harumi, Chuo-ku, Tokyo 104-8610
Phone: (81) 3 5166 5000   **Fax:** (81) 3 5166 6203
Web: www.sumitomocorp.co.jp

PRODUCTS/OPERATIONS

Sales by Segment

	% of total
Media Network & Lifestyle	21
Overseas Subsidiaries &	20
Transportation & Construction	17
Mineral Resources Energy Chemical &	13
General Products & Real	11
Metal	8
Domestic Regional Business Units &	4
New Industry Development &	3
Infrastructure	3
Total	**100**

Selected Subsidiaries

General Poducts & Real Estate
 S.C. Cement Co. Lt.
 TBC Corporation (US wholesale and retail tires)
Infrastructure
 MobiCom Corporation (34% telecommunications in Mongolia)
Media Network & Lifestyle Retail
 Jupiter Telecommunications Co. Ltd. (28%)
 Montrive Corporation (luxury fabrics)
Metal Products
 Asian Steel Company Ltd. (steel plates)
 SC Pipe Services Inc. (US)
Mineral Resources Energy Chemical and Electronics
 Cantex Inc. (pipes)
 The Hartz Mountain Corporation (US pet products)
 LNG Japan Corporation (50%)
 Nusa Tenggara Mining Corporation (Indonesia 74%)
 Sumisho Coal Australia Pty. Ltd.
 Sumitronics Corporation (electronics)
New Industry Development and Cross-Function
 Bluewell Corporation (insurance agency)
Overseas
 Sumitomo Corporation Europe Holding Ltd.
 Sumitomo Corporation of America
Transportation and Construction Systems
 P.T. Summit Oto Finance (99.6% motorcycle financing)
 Sumisho Mitsui Auto Service Company Limited (60%)

COMPETITORS

ITOCHU	Samsung C&T
Kanematsu	America
Komatsu	Samsung Group
Marubeni	Sojitz
Mitsubishi Corp.	TOTAL
Mitsui	

HISTORICAL FINANCIALS

Company Type: Public

Income Statement

FYE: March 31

	REVENUE ($ mil.)	NET INCOME ($ mil.)	NET PROFIT MARGIN	EMPLOYEES
03/14	32,139	2,161	6.7%	64,886
03/13	32,056	2,470	7.7%	73,953
03/12	39,753	3,055	7.7%	72,087
03/11	37,438	2,417	6.5%	64,886
03/10	30,877	1,661	5.4%	93,774
Annual Growth	**1.0%**	**6.8%**	**—**	**(8.8%)**

2014 Year-End Financials

Debt ratio: 0.4%
Return on equity: 10.0%
Cash ($ mil.): 10,765
Current ratio: 1.66
Long-term debt ($ mil.): 32,576

No. of shares (mil.): 1,247
Dividends
 Yield: 3.4%
 Payout: 0.0%
Market value ($ mil.): 15,969

	STOCK PRICE ($) FY Close	P/E High/Low		PER SHARE ($) Earnings	Dividends	Book Value
03/14	12.80	0	0	1.73	0.44	18.67
03/13	12.61	0	0	1.97	0.00	17.45
03/12	14.52	0	0	2.44	0.00	16.47
03/11	14.33	0	0	1.93	0.36	15.17
03/10	11.53	0	0	1.33	0.26	13.56
Annual Growth	**2.6%**	**—**	**—**	**6.8%**	**14.2%**	**8.3%**

Sumitomo Life Insurance Co. (Japan)

Sumitomo Life is one of Japan's biggest mutual life insurers (along with Nippon Life). The firm sells individual group life and specialized health policies through about 70 branch offices and 1500 district offices. Along with its sales force Sumitomo Life sells its products through a network of financial institutions and affiliates. It also administers pension and employee benefit plans and offers brokerage and consulting. The company has a total of some 7 million policyholders. Sumitomo Life which has operations in other Asian and North American countries is part of the Sumitomo Mitsui keiretsu –a group of firms linked by cross-ownership.

Geographic Reach

In addition to Japan Sumitomo Life has operations in China and the US.

Sales and Marketing

The company's principal selling channels are its sales force of 30000 representatives banks and a third party distribution channel formed through sales agreements with Japan Post Group. It also has some online and retail sales operations.

Strategy

As part of the company's push into Southeast Asia Sumitomo Life has agreed to buy a 40% stake in PT BNI Life Insurance the life insurance unit of Bank Negara Indonesia. The move valued at more than 4 trillion rupiah ($351 million) makes Sumitomo Life the second-largest shareholder in BNI Life.

Financial Performance

Sumitomo Life reported decreased revenues in fiscal 2012 through 2010 due to decreased new business. The decrease in 2012 was attributed to intentional decreased sales of new single-premium

life insurance policies as well as lower levels of investment income.

EXECUTIVES

Chairman, Shinichi Yokoyama
President and CEO, Yoshio Sato
Senior Managing Executive Officer, Koichi Suzaki
Senior Managing Executive Officer, Haruo Urata
Senior Managing Executive Officer, Masahiro Hashimoto
President CEO and Director, Yoshio Sato
Senior Executive Officer and Director, Fumio Tokubutsu
Senior Executive Officer and Director, Ikunori Kato
Senior Executive Officer and Director, Norio Takamatsu
Managing Executive Officer and Director, Yutaka Amino
Senior Executive Officer and Director, Koichi Suzaki
Managing Executive Officer and Director, Haruo Urata
Managing Executive Officer and Director, Michihisa Tanimoto
Managing Executive Officer and Director, Masahiro Hashimoto
Director, Tsuguoki Fujinuma
Managing Executive Officer and Director, Yukio Noro
Managing Executive Officer and Director, Masaya Honjo
Director, Yosaku Fuji
Director, Hiroyuki Kamano
Auditors: KPMGAZSA&Co.

LOCATIONS

HQ: Sumitomo Life Insurance Co. (Japan)
1-4-35 Shiromi, Chuo-ku, Osaka 540-8512
Phone: (81) 6 6937 1435   **Fax:** 212 750-7930
Web: www.sumitomolife.co.jp

COMPETITORS

AIG	Fukoku Mutual
AXA	Gibraltar Life
AXA Life Insurance	Insurance
American Life	Meiji Yasuda Life
Insurance	Mitsui Life
Asahi Mutual Life	Nippon Life Insurance
Dai-ichi Life	T&D Holdings
Daido Life	Taiyo Life

HISTORICAL FINANCIALS

Company Type: Public

Income Statement

FYE: March 31

	ASSETS ($ mil.)	NET INCOME ($ mil.)	INCOME AS % OF ASSETS	EMPLOYEES
03/14	257,612	1,188	0.5%	42,109
03/13	282,347	1,146	0.4%	42,098
03/12	292,984	1,316	0.4%	42,953
03/11	286,871	1,315	0.5%	42,366
03/10	247,005	1,197	0.5%	45,281
Annual Growth	**1.1%**	**(0.2%)**	**—**	**(1.8%)**

2014 Year-End Financials

Return on assets: 0.4%
Return on equity: 9.5%
Long-term debt ($ mil.): —
No. of shares (mil.): —
Sales ($ mil): 34,801

Dividends
 Yield: —
 Payout: —
Market value ($ mil.): —

Sumitomo Mitsui Financial Group Inc Tokyo

Sumitomo Mitsui Financial Group (SMFG) is the holding company for Sumitomo Mitsui Banking one of Japan's largest banks. Its operations include retail corporate and investment banking; asset management; securities trading; and lending. Sumitomo Mitsui Banking has some 439 domestic branches and another 20 branches abroad. Other units of SMFG include credit card firm Sumitomo Mitsui Card brokerage SMBC Friend Securities management consulting firm Japan Research Institute and Sumitomo Mitsui Finance and Leasing. SMFG also operates the California-based Manufacturers Bank. In late 2014 the SMFG purchased Citigroup's Japanese consumer-banking business for 40 billion yen ($330 million) in a private deal.

EXECUTIVES

Chairman Sumitomo Mitsui Banking Corporation, Teisuke Kitayama
Chairman, Masayuki Oku, age 70
Head of Corporate Banking Unit International Banking Unit Global Advisory Department Sumitomo Mitsui Banking Corporation, Yoshinori Kawamura
Director; President Sumitomo Mitsui Banking, Takeshi Kunibe
Director; Senior Managing Director Human Resources Dept. Human Resources Development Dept. Quality Management Dept. General Affairs Dept. Legal Dept. and Administrative Services Dept. Sumitomo Mitsui Banking Corporation, Junsuke Fujii
Senior Managing Director IT Planning; Senior Managing Director IT Planning Dept. IT Business Promotion Dept. Operations Planning Dept. and Operations Support Dept. Sumitomo Mitsui Banking Corporation, Hideo Shimada
Senior Managing Director Investment Banking Planning; Senior Managing Director Sumitomo Mitsui Banking Corporation, Tetsuya Kubo
Senior Managing Director Consumer Planning Department; Senior Managing Director Consumer Banking Unit Sumitomo Mitsui Banking Corporation, Satoru Nakanishi
Corporate Auditor, Yoji Yamaguchi
Corporate Auditor Sumitomo Mitsui Financial Group and Sumitomo Mitsui Banking Corporation, Ikuo Uno
President, Koichi Miyata
Director, Ken Kubo
Director, Yujiro Ito
Managing Director, Jun Ohta
Managing Director, Yasuyuki Kawasaki
Managing Director, Fumiaki Kurahara
Director, Yoshinori Yokoyama, age 72
Director, Hiroki Nishio
Director, Yoshiaki Yamauchi, age 76
Director, Yoichiro Yamakawa
Deputy President Corporate Risk Management and Director Sumitomo Mitsui Financial Group and Sumitomo Mitsui Banking Corporation, Wataru Ohara
Senior Managing Director IT Planning; Senior Managing Director IT Planning Dept. IT Business Promotion Dept. Operations Planning Dept. and Operations Support Dept. Sumitomo Mitsui Banking Corporation, Hideo Shimada
Senior Managing Director Investment Banking Planning; Senior Managing Director Sumitomo Mitsui Banking Corporation, Tetsuya Kubo
Senior Managing Director Audit Department, Fumihiko Tanizawa
Senior Managing Director Consumer Planning Department; Senior Managing Director Consumer Banking Unit Sumitomo Mitsui Banking Corporation, Satoru Nakanishi
Managing Director Card Business Department; Managing Director Sumitomo Mitsui Banking Corporation; President SMFG Card and Credit, Kazuya Jono
Auditors: KPMGAZSA&Co.

LOCATIONS

HQ: Sumitomo Mitsui Financial Group Inc Tokyo
1-1-2 Marunouchi, Chiyoda-ku, Tokyo 100-0005
Phone: (81) 3 3282 8111
Web: www.smfg.co.jp

PRODUCTS/OPERATIONS

Sales

	% of total
Interest	
Loans &	46
Investment	5
Other	1
Noninterest	
Fees &	24
Trading	10
Other	14
Total	**100**

COMPETITORS

Bank of Yokohama	Mizuho Financial
Chuo Mitsui Trust	Norinchukin Bank
Citigroup	Resona
Credit Saison	Shinsei Bank
Mitsubishi UFJ	
Financial Group	

HISTORICAL FINANCIALS

Company Type: Public

Income Statement
FYE: March 31

	ASSETS ($ mil.)	NET INCOME ($ mil.)	INCOME AS % OF ASSETS	EMPLOYEES
03/14	1,564,961	8,093	0.5%	66,475
03/13	1,580,333	8,439	0.5%	64,635
03/12	1,743,755	6,321	0.4%	64,225
03/11	1,664,157	5,747	0.3%	61,555
03/10	1,318,519	2,907	0.2%	57,888
Annual Growth	4.4%	29.2%	—	3.5%

2014 Year-End Financials

Return on assets: 0.5%
Return on equity: 12.2%
Long-term debt ($ mil.): —
No. of shares (mil.): 1,367
Sales ($ mil): 45,021
Dividends
Yield: 2.8%
Payout: —
Market value ($ mil.): 11,827

	STOCK PRICE ($) FY Close	P/E High/Low	PER SHARE ($) Earnings	Dividends	Book Value
03/14	8.65	— —	5.92	0.25	63.81
03/13	8.16	— —	6.23	0.00	66.28
03/12	6.64	— —	4.56	0.00	65.46
03/11	6.25	— —	4.07	0.00	62.35
03/10	3.25	— —	2.61	0.00	53.65
Annual Growth	27.7%	— —	22.7%	—	4.4%

Sumitomo Mitsui Trust Holdings Inc

Chuo Mitsui Trust Holdings entailed Chuo Mitsui Trust and Banking (retail trust banking real estate and stock transfer services) and Chuo Mitsui Asset and Banking Company (pension and securities trusts) which also owned investment trust and private equity managers Chuo Mitsui Asset Management and Chuo Mitsui Capital. The group spans the US the UK Singapore the Cayman Islands and China. It offers consulting to individuals and large corporations alike specializing in brokerage securitization and investment advice related to real estate deals. Chuo Mitsui Trust Holdings and Sumitomo Trust and Banking merged in 2012 to form Sumitomo Mitsui Trust Bank one of Japan's largest asset management groups.

HISTORY

Before world markets were rocked by the shock waves of the US real estate and financial markets crash CMHD received about Y430 billion ($4.4 billion) in government support. The company had been making steady payments since 2006 and planned to pay the remaining Y200 before the August 2009 deadline for the conversion of the government's preferred shares into ordinary shares. But mid-year the bank along with several of its Japanese mid-level peers announced it would be unable to meet the goal due to poor earnings.

Once the crisis passes the company's strategy includes a focus on real estate lending long a mainstay of business and improving its position in the investment trust and real estate investing markets.

EXECUTIVES

Chairman, Hitoshi Tsunekage, age 60
Managing Executive Officer and Director, Shinji Ochiai, age 59
Managing Executive Officer and Director, Tetsuo Ohkubo, age 58
President and Representative Director, Kazuo Tanabe
Director, Jun Okuno, age 63
Deputy President and Representative Director, Kiyoshi Mukohara, age 61
Senior Managing Executive Officer and Director, Nobuo Iwasaki, age 58
Managing Executive Officer and Director, Junichi Sayato, age 58
Deputy President and Representative Director, Kunitaro Kitamura, age 61
Managing Executive Officer and Director, Shinji Ochiai, age 59
Managing Executive Officer and Director, Tetsuo Ohkubo, age 58
Auditors: DeloitteToucheTohmatsu

LOCATIONS

HQ: Sumitomo Mitsui Trust Holdings Inc
1-4-1 Marunouchi, Chiyoda-ku, Tokyo 100-6611
Phone: (81) 3 6256 6000
Web: www.smth.jp

COMPETITORS

Aozora Bank	Resona
Mitsubishi UFJ	Sumitomo Trust and
Financial Group	Banking
Mizuho Trust &	
Banking Ltd	

Company Type: Public

Income Statement
FYE: March 31

	ASSETS ($ mil.)	NET INCOME ($ mil.)	INCOME AS % OF ASSETS	EMPLOYEES
03/14	405,828	1,333	0.3%	20,890
03/13	400,714	1,421	0.4%	20,189
03/12	419,068	2,007	0.5%	20,305
03/11	171,859	570	0.3%	8,846
03/10	160,350	501	0.3%	8,872
Annual Growth	26.1%	27.7%	—	23.9%

2014 Year-End Financials

Return on assets: 0.3%
Return on equity: 6.9%
Long-term debt ($ mil.): —
No. of shares (mil.): —
Sales ($ mil): 11,511

Dividends
Yield: 2.1%
Payout: —
Market value ($ mil.): —

	STOCK PRICE ($) FY Close	P/E High/Low	PER SHARE ($) Earnings	Dividends	Book Value
03/14	4.50	— —	0.33	0.10	6.06
03/13	4.67	— —	0.33	0.00	6.72
03/12	3.14	— —	0.47	0.00	6.86
Annual Growth	19.7%	— —	(8.2%)	—	(3.1%)

Sun Life Assurance Company of Canada

LOCATIONS

HQ: Sun Life Assurance Company of Canada
150 King Street West, Toronto, Ontario M5H 1J9
Phone: 416 979-9966   Fax: 416 979-3209
Web: www.sunlife.com

HISTORICAL FINANCIALS
Company Type: Public

Income Statement
FYE: December 31

	ASSETS ($ mil.)	NET INCOME ($ mil.)	INCOME AS % OF ASSETS	EMPLOYEES
12/13	180,494	(4)	—	0
12/12	179,026	7	0.0%	0
12/11	164,808	6	0.0%	0
12/10	95,546	1,583	1.7%	0
12/09	88,844	690	0.8%	0
Annual Growth	19.4%	—	—	—

Sun Life Financial Inc

Sun Life tries to stay on the sunny side of life and life insurance. The company offers insurance and wealth management products to individuals and business entities primarily in Canada and the US. It also has operations in Asia Europe and the UK. Sun Life's products include individual and group life and health insurance individual annuities group pensions mutual funds and asset management services. The US subsidiaries include Massachusetts Financial Services (or MFS Investment Management). Sun Life's products and services are distributed through direct and independent sales agents as well as banks and consultants.

In its home market Sun Life is a key player in individual life insurance employee benefits products as well as mutual funds. Its Asian operations are focused on the growing middle class customers in China India and the Philippines.

Having developed an allergy to equity volatility and low interest rates in late 2011 the company decided to reduce its exposure in its US operations. It announced that it would quit selling variable annuities and individual life insurance products in the US and instead is choosing to focus on its employee benefits and voluntary benefits business. Sun Life had already quit selling plain vanilla universal life insurance products in the US citing their status as commodities with low margins. In late 2012 it agreed to sell its US annuity business to Delaware Life Holdings for some $1.35 billion.

In the wake of the global financial crisis Sun Life has steadily adjusted its goals and worked to "derisk" its products. It made an effort to build up its sales to individual customers in Canada tightened up its distribution system and expanded direct sales channels in Asia including China and its joint venture in India. To perk up its branding the company purchased the naming rights to the sports stadium in Miami and rolled out fresh ad campaigns in key markets.

The company is slowly regaining its acquisition groove after the financial crisis. It paid some C$359 million to buy up Lincoln National (UK) from Lincoln National in 2009. It merged the business with its existing UK operations doubling the number of policies the company holds there. In 2011 it agreed to acquire 49% of Grepalife Financials a bancassurance insurance provider in the Philippines for an undisclosed sum.

Sun Life demutualized in 2000 and the money it raised as a publicly traded company helped finance growth. During the first ten years of its public status it grew through a steady pace of acquisitions beginning with its buy of Clarica Life in 2002. Clarica's products were later rebranded with the Sun Life name. International acquisitions have included Genworth's US employee benefits group (2007) and insurance and pension operations in Hong Kong from Commonwealth Bank of Australia (2005).

Sun Life has disposed of businesses including the 2008 sale of Sun Life Retirement Services unit a US business that provided 401k administrative services to Hartford Financial Services. At the close of 2010 the company sold off its life reinsurance business to Berkshire Hathaway for an undisclosed sum. Proceeds from the asset sale were earmarked to fund growth efforts in other business areas.

After selling off a minority ownership in a Canadian mutual fund provider in 2008 Sun Life did an about-face and reentered the Canadian mutual fund market in 2010 by forming a new standalone mutual fund company: Sun Life Global Investments (Canada). Sun Life launched the new company and a family of funds in 2010 sold through Sun Life Financial advisers. The new funds came from the company's MFS affiliate in the US McLean Budden in Canada and Biria Sun Life Asset Management in India.

EXECUTIVES

EVP Corporate Development and General Counsel, Thomas A. Bogart
President Sun Life Financial US, Westley V. (Wes) Thompson, age 60
Senior Managing Director and Head of North American Private Fixed Income, Thomas J. Robinson
Chairman, James H. (Jim) Sutcliffe, age 57
SVP Group Retirement Services Sun Life Financial Canada, Thomas G. Reid
SVP and General Manager Individual Insurance Sun Life Financial U.S. and International, Janet V. Whitehouse
President Sun Life Financial Canada and Sun Life Global Investments, Kevin P. Dougherty, $1,019 total compensation
SVP and Chief Credit Risk Officer, Candace G. Shaw
Chairman and CEO MFS Investment Management Sun Life Global Investments, Robert J. (Rob) Manning
EVP and CFO, Colm J. Freyne, $318,598 total compensation
SVP and General Counsel Sun Life Financial Canada, William R. Minucci
EVP Actuarial and Risk Management, Claude A. Accum
Vice-President Human Resources, Sean N. Woodroffe
EVP and Chief Investment Officer, Stephen C. Peacher, $106,187 total compensation
SVP Client Solutions Sun Life Financial Canada, Brigitte Parent
SVP and General Counsel Sun Life Financial US and International, Scott M. Davis
Chairman and CEO MFS McLean Budden Limited Sun Life Global Investments, Martin E. (Marty) Beaulieu
President CEO and Director, Dean A. Connor, $538,354 total compensation
SVP Individual Insurance and Investments Sun Life Financial Canada, Kevin D. Strain
SVP and CFO Sun Life Financial Canada, Paul O. Petrelli
Media Contact Philippines, Mariquit Lintag
SVP Tax, Michael J. O'Connor
VP Human Resources Sun Life Financial Canada, Sandra L. Delamere
SVP Operations Sun Life Financial Canada, Jim Giesinger
SVP Group Benefits Sun Life Financial Canada, Stuart Monteith
Head of Human Resources Sun Life Financial Asia, Michelle Li
President Sun Life Global Investments (Canada), Rick Headrick
VP Investor Relations, Philip G. (Phil) Malek
EVP and CIO, Mark S. Saunders
SVP Enterprise Infrastructure and CTO, Stevan Lewis
VP Corporate Communications, Frank T. Switzer
SVP Application Services, Philip Armstrong
President Sun Life Financial Quebec, Isabelle Hudon
VP Associate General Counsel and Corporate Secretary, Dana J. Easthope
VP Voluntary Benefits Sun Life Financial U.S. and International, Robert E. Klein
Media Contact Canada, Andrea Zviedris
Media Contact United Kingdom, James Terry
Executive Vice-President Human Resources, Carolyn Blair
Executive Vice President; Chief Marketing Officer and Public & Corporate Affairs, Mary Paoli
Director, Mitchell M. (Mitch) Merin, age 61
Director, William D. (Bill) Anderson, age 65
Director, Jon A. Boscia, age 60
Director, David W. Kerr, age 71
Director, Hugh D. Segal, age 63
Director, Martin J. G. Glynn, age 62
Director, Prof Idalene F. (Idie) Kesner, age 57
Director, David A. Ganong, age 71
Director, Krystyna T. Hoeg, age 64
Director, Bertin F. Nadeau, age 72

President CEO and Director, Dean A. Connor
Director, John H. Clappison, age 68
Independent Director, Richard Booth
Auditors: Deloitte&ToucheLLP

LOCATIONS

HQ: Sun Life Financial Inc
150 King Street West, Toronto, Ontario M5H 1J9
Phone: 416 979-9966   Fax: 416 979-3209
Web: www.sunlife.com

PRODUCTS/OPERATIONS

Revenues

Premiums	
Health insurance	18
Net investment income	32
Total	**100**

2010 Revenues

	% of total
SLF	46
SLF	33
SLF	7
MFS	6
Corporate	8
Total	**100**

COMPETITORS

AGF Management
AIA Group
Aviva
Canada Life
China Life Insurance
Fairfax Financial Holdings
Great-West Life Assurance
Great-West Lifeco
Industrial Alliance Insurance and Financial Servic
Manulife Financial
MetLife
Prudential
Standard Life
The Hartford

HISTORICAL FINANCIALS

Company Type: Public

Income Statement   FYE: December 31

	ASSETS ($ mil.)	NET INCOME ($ mil.)	INCOME AS % OF ASSETS	EMPLOYEES
12/14	192,880	4,660	2.4%	16,275
12/13	187,646	3,477	1.9%	0
12/12	227,013	4,627	2.0%	14,880
12/11	213,730	(196)	—	15,000
12/10	210,695	1,502	0.7%	14,755
Annual Growth	(2.2%)	32.7%	—	2.5%

2014 Year-End Financials

Return on assets: 2.5%	Dividends
Return on equity: 29.8%	Yield: 3.9%
Long-term debt ($ mil.): —	Payout: 54.5%
No. of shares (mil.): 613	Market value ($ mil.): 22,105
Sales ($ mil): 22,248	

	STOCK PRICE ($) FY Close	P/E High/Low		PER SHARE ($) Earnings	Dividends	Book Value
12/14	36.06	11	9	2.47	1.30	26.59
12/13	35.33	21	15	1.46	1.38	26.80
12/12	26.53	11	7	2.60	1.44	28.65
12/11	18.52	—	—	(0.51)	1.41	26.23
12/10	30.10	13	9	2.40	1.39	28.02
Annual Growth	4.6%	—	—	0.8%	(1.5%)	(1.3%)

Suncor Energy Inc.

Suncor Energy takes a shine to the cold of Canada. That country's largest energy company explores for processes and markets oil and natural gas. In 2012 it reported net proved and probable reserves of 1.8 billion barrels of synthetic oil 163 million barrels of bitumen 159 million barrels of oil and 619 billion cu. ft. of natural gas. Suncor Energy was first company to produce commercial crude oil from Canada's Athabasca oil sands. It also holds 12% of Syncrude. Its Sunoco unit refines crude oil and processes and distributes fuels petrochemicals and heating oils and invests in renewable energy. Suncor Energy also operates a nationwide network of gas stations primarily under the Petro-Canada brand.

Geographic Reach

The company has operations in Canada Germany Libya the Netherlands Norway Syria the UK and the US. In 2012 Canada accounted for 79% of Suncor Energy's revenues.

Operations

Suncor Energy is one of Canada's largest oil sands producers. It oil sands assets include a 36% interest in the Joslyn North mine 41% in the Fort Hills mine and 51% of the Voyageur upgrader project as well as a 12% stake in the Syncrude oil sands mining venture.

The company also has conventional natural gas assets as well as international and offshore oil exploration and production holdings. In addition to its production refining and marketing operations across Canada (and in Colorado) the company has exploration assets in Libya Norway Syria and the UK. (In 2011 Suncor Energy suspended its operations in Syria in light of international sanctions imposed against that country.)

The company has four refineries (in Alberta Ontario Quebec and Colorado —460000 barrels of combined capacity per day) and a network of 1460 Petro-Canada retail gas stations.

To meet clean air regulations the company is also investing in green energy. It has six wind power projects (255 MW) and operates Canada's largest biofuel plant (412 million liters of ethanol per day) at St.Clair Ontario.

Financial Performance

Suncor Energy's revenues declined by $176 million in 2012 as a result of lower product stemming from planned off-station maintenance programs at Terra Nova and related delays in get back online planned maintenance at White Rose oilfield in Nova Scotia the suspension of oil and gas operations in Syria and declines in production from the North America Onshore segment. These factors were partially offset by the resumption of operations in Libya. Oil Sands oil prices declined in 2012 due primarily to lower premiums for sweet crude oil and wider light/heavy differentials that impacted prices for sour crude oil and bitumen.The company reported a $35% drop in net income in 2012 due to lower reveneus and an increase in operating expenses.

Strategy

Oil sands which hold deposits of heavy bitumen make up nearly a third of Canada's oil production and Suncor Engery's long term business focus is developing synthetic oil from its oil sands holdings in Alberta. Suncor Energy plans to produce 1 million barrels per day of oil equivalent from its oil sands holdings by 2020.

To focus on its growth markets and to pay down debt in 2013 the company agreed to sell its conventional natural gas business in Western Canada to a Centrica and Qatar Petroleum partnership for $1 billion.

Company Background

To further develop its oil sands assets in 2010 the company formed a strategic alliance with TOTAL. As part of the deal France-based TOTAL paid Suncor Energy about $1.7 billion to acquire 19% of Suncor Energy's 60% interest in the Fort Hills mining project and a 49% stake in the Voyageur Upgrader project near Fort McMurray. Suncor Energy acquired about 37% of TOTAL's stake in the Joslyn project.

Boosting its profile as an integrated energy company in 2009 the company acquired Petro-Canada in a $15 billion deal. The acquisition created an energy behemoth with extensive holdings in oil sands solid conventional exploration and production assets and a major refining and retailing network. Following the Petro-Canada deal the company divested about $1.5 billion of non-core assets in Western Canada the US Trinidad and Tobago and the North Sea. In 2010 Suncor Energy sold its North Sea exploration assets (of Petro Canada Netherlands) to Dana Petroleum for $393 million. Later that year it sold a pair of natural gas properties in Alberta to a subsidiary of Abu Dhabi National Energy Company for $285 million. It also sold its Wildcat Hills assets which produce some 80 million cu. ft. of natural gas per day to Direct Energy for about $360 million.

EXECUTIVES

Senior Vice President General Counsel Corporate Secretary, Janice B. Odegaard
CEO and Director, Richard L. (Rick) George, age 62, $1,115,708 total compensation
Executive Vice President - Refining and Marketing, Boris J. Jackman, $711,926 total compensation
Chairman, John T. Ferguson, age 73
President; Chief Executive Officer; Non-independent Director, Steven W. (Steve) Williams, $698,514 total compensation
SVP Exploration and Production, Francois Langlois
CFO, Bart W. Demosky, $288,472 total compensation
Executive Vice President - Oil Sands Ventures, Steve D. L. Reynish
Executive Vice President - Major Projects, Mike MacSween
EVP Oil Sands and In Situ, Mark Little
Executive Vice President - Business Services, Eric Axford
SVP Human Resources, Paul Gardner
SVP Supply Trading and Corporate Development, Kris Smith
Director, Michael W. (Mike) O'Brien, age 70
CEO and Director, Richard L. (Rick) George, age 62
Director, Dominic D'Alessandro, age 66
Director, Jacques Lamarre, age 71
Director, Paul Haseldonckx, age 66
Director, Mel E. Benson, age 66
Director, W. Douglas (Doug) Ford, age 70
President COO and Director, Steven W. (Steve) Williams
Director, Maureen McCaw, age 60
Director, James W. (Jim) Simpson, age 70
Independent Director, Dominic Alessandro
Independent Director, Michael Brien
Auditors: PricewaterhouseCoopersLLP

LOCATIONS

HQ: Suncor Energy Inc.
150 - 6th Avenue S.W., Calgary, Alberta T2P 3E3
Phone:
Web: www.suncor.com

Sales

	% of total
Canada	79
Other	21
Total	**100**

PRODUCTS/OPERATIONS

Sales

Refining & marketing	63
Exploration & production	11

COMPETITORS

Anadarko Petroleum	Husky Energy
BP NGL	Imperial Oil
Canadian Natural	Murphy Oil
Devon Energy	Nordex
Dominion Resources	Shell Canada
Encana	Talisman Energy

HISTORICAL FINANCIALS

Company Type: Public

Income Statement

FYE: December 31

	REVENUE ($ mil.)	NET INCOME ($ mil.)	NET PROFIT MARGIN	EMPLOYEES
12/13	37,896	3,678	9.7%	13,946
12/12	38,826	2,798	7.2%	13,932
12/11	39,005	4,219	10.8%	13,026
12/10*	32,673	3,837	11.7%	12,076
01/10	0	0	—	0
Annual Growth	—	—	—	—

*Fiscal year change

2013 Year-End Financials

Debt ratio: 13.7%
Return on equity: 9.7%
Cash ($ mil.): 4,892
Current ratio: 1.39
Long-term debt ($ mil.): 9,595

No. of shares (mil.): 1,478
Dividends
  Yield: 2.0%
  Payout: 29.8%
Market value ($ mil.): 51,815

	STOCK PRICE ($) FY Close	P/E High/Low		PER SHARE ($) Earnings	Dividends	Book Value
12/13	35.05	13	9	2.45	0.70	26.20
12/12	32.98	21	14	1.80	0.50	25.89
12/11	28.83	18	8	2.62	0.42	24.28
12/10*	38.29	16	11	2.44	0.38	22.53
01/10	35.31	—	—	(0.00)	0.19	(0.00)
Annual Growth	(0.2%)	—	—	—	38.5%	—

*Fiscal year change

Suncorp Group Ltd.

Suncorp-Metway (aka Suncorp Group) wants to be a rising star in Australia's insurance and banking sectors. The group owns Suncorp Insurance which operates one of the country's largest general insurance companies as well as a small but growing life insurance and wealth management business. The general insurance business sells personal and commercial property/casualty insurance under its Suncorp AAMI GIO Vero and Shannons brands. In addition to its insurance business Suncorp also runs Suncorp Bank an operator of some 200 branches in eastern Australia. Among other products the bank offers personal and commercial banking accounts financial planning and loans to consumers and small to midsized businesses.

EXECUTIVES

CEO and Director, Patrick Snowball, age 63
Chairman, John D. Story, age 67
Group Executive Banking, David Foster
Group Executive Personal Insurance, Mark Milliner

CEO and Director, Patrick Snowball, age 63
Auditors: KPMG

LOCATIONS

HQ: Suncorp Group Ltd.
  Level 28, 266 George Street, Brisbane, Queensland 4000
Phone: (61) 7 3362 1222   **Fax:** (61) 7 3135 2940
Web: www.suncorpgroup.com.au

PRODUCTS/OPERATIONS

Sales

	% of total
General Insurance	
Personal	31
Commercial	24
Banking	28
Life and Wealth	13
New Zealand General	4
Total	**100**

Selected Subsidiaries

Asteron Group Ltd. (life insurance)
GIO General Ltd (general insurance products)
Suncorp Life & Superannuation Limited life (insurance products)
Suncorp Metway Insurance Ltd (general insurance products)
Suncorp Metway Investment Management Limited (investment schemes and provides investment management services)
Vero Insurance Ltd. (New Zealand general insurance)

COMPETITORS

AMP Limited	Insurance Australia
AXA Asia Pacific	Macquarie Group
Australia and New Zealand Banking	National Australia Bank
Commonwealth Bank of Australia	Westpac Banking

HISTORICAL FINANCIALS

Company Type: Public

Income Statement

FYE: June 30

	ASSETS ($ mil.)	NET INCOME ($ mil.)	INCOME AS % OF ASSETS	EMPLOYEES
06/14	88,728	685	0.8%	0
06/13	88,481	452	0.5%	0
06/12	97,829	737	0.8%	0
06/11	102,355	485	0.5%	0
06/10	81,266	664	0.8%	0
Annual Growth	2.2%	0.8%	—	—

2014 Year-End Financials

Return on assets: 0.7%
Return on equity: 5.2%
Long-term debt ($ mil.): —
No. of shares (mil.): 1,286
Sales ($ mil): 15,381

Dividends
  Yield: 2.3%
  Payout: 47.4%
Market value ($ mil.): 16,456

	STOCK PRICE ($) FY Close	P/E High/Low		PER SHARE ($) Earnings	Dividends	Book Value
06/14	12.79	20	15	0.54	0.30	10.06
Annual Growth	—	—	—	—	—	—

Suzuki Motor Corp. (Japan)

Suzuki Motor Corporation is a leading Japanese carmaker and a global motorcycle manufacturer competing head-to-head with rivals Honda and Yamaha. Suzuki's passenger car models include the Alto Grand Vitara Swift Splash and SX4. Its motorcycle products include cruiser motocross offroad scooter street and touring models as well as ATVs. Suzuki Motor's non-vehicle products include outboard motors for boats and motorized wheelchairs. It builds its lineup on its own and through numerous subsidiaries and joint ventures overseas. Japan accounts for nearly 45% of sales. Suzuki entered the US car market in 1985 with the Samurai the country' first compact SUV.

Geographic Reach

The company has man production facilities in 22 countries and serves more than 200 countries. Outside of Japan (around 45% of its total sales) Asian consumers represent nearly 35% of its sales whereas North American and European purchases combined account for nearly 15%. Suzuki subsidiary Maruti Suzuki India is India's largest passenger car company.

Operations

Suzuki divides its operations into four reportable segments. The Automobile segment generated 88% of the company's total sales for 2012 while its motorcycle operations accounted for 10%. The other segments —marine and power products; and financial services —accounted for the remaining 2%.

Financial Performance

Suzuki's balance sheet has been up and down over the years. After posting increases in both revenue and net income in 2011 the company saw its revenues decrease by 4% in 2012. The lower revenue was attributed to a 1% decrease in its motorcycle segment and a 4% dip in its automobile segment. The company however did recognize a 19% increase in its net income for 2012 due to lower expenses related to sales marketing and promotions.

Strategy

Suzuki is expanding its vehicle lineup in China through Suzuki China which imports and sells Japanese-made cars. The company imports and exports Suzuki-brand vehicles through Suzuki Automobile (Thailand) a joint venture with Siam International Corp. Demand in Vietnam the Philippines and Malaysia has continued to grow modestly too.

In 2012 Suzuki began construction of a new motorcycle plant in Rohtak Haryana of India and a second plant through Chongqing Changan Suzuki Automobile Co. Ltd. (Changan Suzuki) an automobile manufacturing and sales joint venture company in China. The Indian motorcycle market in 2011 exceeded 13 million units and Suzuki expects continuous growth in the region. To capitalize on the expanding Chinese automobile market and to establish an annual capacity of 500000 units Suzuki has decided to construct its second plant in the area next to its current plant.

HISTORY

In 1909 Michio Suzuki started Suzuki Loom Works in Hamamatsu Japan. The company went public in 1920 and continued producing weaving equipment until the onset of WWII when it began to make war-related products.

Suzuki began developing inexpensive motor vehicles in 1947 and in 1952 it introduced a 36cc engine to motorize bicycles. The company changed its name to Suzuki Motor and launched its first motorcycle in 1954. Suzuki's entry into the minicar market came in 1955 with the Suzulight followed by the Suzumoped (1958) a delivery van (1959) and the Suzulight Carry FB small truck (1961).

Suzuki's triumph in the 1962 50cc-class Isle of Man TT motorcycle race started a string of racing successes that brought international prominence to the Suzuki name. The company established its first overseas plant in Thailand in 1967.

In the 1970s Suzuki met market demand for motorcycles with large engines. Meanwhile a mid-1970s recession and falling demand for low-powered cars in Japan led the minicar industry there to produce two-thirds fewer minicars in 1974 than in 1970. Suzuki responded by pushing overseas beginning auto exports and expanding foreign distribution. In 1975 it started producing motorcycles in Taiwan Thailand and Indonesia.

Suzuki boosted capacity internationally throughout the 1980s through joint ventures. Motorcycle sales in Japan peaked in 1982 then tapered off but enjoyed a modest rebound in the late 1980s. In 1988 the company agreed to handle distribution of Peugeot cars in Japan.

Suzuki and General Motors began their longstanding relationship in 1981 when GM bought a small stake in Suzuki. The company began producing Swift subcompacts in 1983 and sold them through GM as the Chevy Sprint and later the Geo Metro. In 1986 Suzuki and GM of Canada jointly formed CAMI Automotive to produce vehicles including Sprints Metros and Geo Trackers (Suzuki Sidekicks) in Ontario; production began in 1989.

Although sales via GM increased through 1990 US efforts with the Suzuki nameplate faltered shortly after Suzuki formed its US subsidiary in Brea California in 1986. A 1988 "Consumer Reports" claim that the company's Samurai SUV was prone to rolling over devastated US sales. The next year Suzuki's top US executives quit apparently questioning the company's commitment to the US market.

Suzuki established Magyar Suzuki a joint venture with Hungarian automaker Autokonszern Rt. C. Itoh & Co. and International Finance Corporation in 1991 to begin producing the Swift sedan in Hungary. The company expanded a licensing agreement with a Chinese government partner in 1993 becoming the first Japanese company to take an equity stake in a Chinese carmaking venture. The next year Suzuki introduced the Alto van Japan's cheapest car at just over $5000 and the Wagon R miniwagon which quickly became one of Japan's top-selling vehicles.

In a case that was later overturned a woman was awarded $90 million from Suzuki after being paralyzed in a Samurai rollover in 1990. The company sued Consumers Union publisher of "Consumer Reports" in 1996 charging it had intended to fix the results in the 1988 Samurai testing.

GM raised its 3% stake in Suzuki to 10% in 1998. The company teamed up with GM and Fuji Heavy Industries (Subaru) in 2000 to develop compact cars for the European market. It was also announced that GM would spend about $600 million to double its stake in Suzuki to 20%. In 2001 Suzuki announced that it had agreed to cooperate with Kawasaki in the development of new motorcycles scooters and ATVs.

The following year Suzuki agreed to take control of Maruti Udyog Ltd. the state-owned India-based car manufacturer in an $80 million rights issue deal.

GM sold almost all of its 20% stake in Suzuki in early 2006 to raise cash for its own beleaguered

operations. GM divested the remaining 3% stake in late 2008 for about $230 million as it endured a dire cash crisis.

EXECUTIVES

Chairman and CEO, Osamu Suzuki
EVP, Toshihiro Suzuki
EVP, Minoru Tamura
EVP, Osamu Honda
EVP, Yasuhito Harayama
Managing Officer, Takashi Iwatsuki
EVP and Director, Toshihiro Suzuki
Senior Managing Officer and Director, Masanori Atsumi
Senior Managing Officer and Director, Shinzo Nakanishi
EVP and Director, Minoru Tamura
Senior Managing Officer and Director, Naoki Aizawa
Senior Managing Officer and Director, Eiji Mochizuki
Senior Managing Officer and Director, Toyokazu Sugimoto
EVP and Director, Osamu Honda
EVP and Director, Yasuhito Harayama
Auditors: SeimeiAuditCorporation

LOCATIONS

HQ: Suzuki Motor Corp. (Japan)
300 Takatsuka-cho, Hamamatsu, Shizuoka 432-8611
Phone: (81) 53 440 2030
Web: www.suzuki.co.jp

Sales

Asia	
Other countries	34
North America	4
Total	**0**
	100

PRODUCTS/OPERATIONS

Sales

Automobiles	88
Other products	2

List of Items
Automobiles
Alto/CELERIO
APV
Grand Vitara SUV
Jimny
Kizashi sport sedan
Splash
Swift
SX4 Crossover Sport SportBack
Motorcycles/ATV
Cruiser
Dual purpose
Motocross
Offroad
Scooter
Sport Enduro Tourer
Street
Supersport
Outboard motors
Carburetor series (4-stroke)
Electronic fuel injection series (4-stroke)
Kerosene Outboards (2-stroke)

COMPETITORS

BMW	Kawasaki Heavy
Bajaj Auto	Industries
Brunswick Corp.	Mahindra
Chrysler	Mazda
Daimler	Nissan
Ducati	Piaggio & Co.
Ek Chor China	Polaris Industries
Motorcycle	Renault
Ford Motor	Tata Motors
General Motors	Toyota
Harley-Davidson	Triumph Motorcycles
Honda	Volkswagen
Hyundai Motor	Yamaha Motor

HISTORICAL FINANCIALS

Company Type: Public

Income Statement

FYE: March 31

	REVENUE ($ mil.)	NET INCOME ($ mil.)	NET PROFIT MARGIN	EMPLOYEES
03/14	28,466	1,041	3.7%	57,749
03/13	27,402	854	3.1%	55,948
03/12	30,625	656	2.1%	54,484
03/11	31,497	545	1.7%	52,731
03/10	26,433	309	1.2%	51,503
Annual Growth	**1.9%**	**35.4%**	**—**	**2.9%**

2014 Year-End Financials

Debt ratio: 0.1%	No. of shares (mil.): 560
Return on equity: 8.6%	Dividends
Cash ($ mil.): 3,476	Yield: —
Current ratio: 1.69	Payout: —
Long-term debt ($ mil.): 2,026	Market value ($ mil.): 61,390

	STOCK PRICE ($) FY Close	P/E High/Low	PER SHARE ($) Earnings	Dividends	Book Value
03/14	109.45	— —	1.86	0.00	25.81
03/13	90.52	— —	1.40	0.00	24.61
03/12	96.10	— —	1.08	0.00	24.16
03/11	85.50	— —	0.89	0.00	23.83
03/10	87.20	— —	0.59	0.00	20.94
Annual Growth	**5.8%**	—	**33.1%**	**—**	**5.4%**

Svenska Handelsbanken

Svenska Handelsbanken is Swedish for universal banking. The group provides corporate and individual clients with deposit products loans credit cards and other banking services. Subsidiaries operate in several related areas including life insurance mortgages pensions fund management and Internet banking. The bank boasts more than 810 branches located mostly in Sweden and the rest of Scandinavia the UK Denmark Finland Norway and other countries. It has a presence in countries including Austria China Hong Kong Russia and the US. Subsidiaries include corporate financing unit Handelsbanken Finans Handelsbanken Asset Management and Handelsbanken Liv. It bought Heartwood in the UK in 2013.

The bank has been growing its retail operations both at home and overseas; it has opened some 150 new branches in the past few years. Handelsbanken usually opts for organic growth as a basic strategy. However it does make some acquisitions. It also recently launched operations in Lithuania; it already had a presence in the Balkans in Estonia and Latvia.

As it grows the company also is reconfiguring its nonbank operations selling some and in the case of its Internet bank Stadshypotek Bank merging it into the parent so as to streamline its brands. It also sold its SPP occupational pensions subsidiary to Storebrand of Norway.

HISTORY

Svenska Handelsbanken (roughly translated as The Swedish Commercial Bank) was founded as Stockholms Handelsbank in 1871 by former directors of Stockholms Enskilda Bank who lost an internal power struggle. Industrialization in the latter stages of the 19th century saw Stockholms Handelsbank expand nationwide with the bank pursuing an aggressive lending policy. Larger companies required larger financing resulting in smaller local banks running into trouble and forcing them to merge with bigger ones. Through a series of mergers of this kind Stockholms Handelsbank exploded in size and branches increased from seven (all Stockholm-based) to 250 nationwide by 1919. To reflect this growth the company changed its name to Svenska Handelsbanken the same year.

Sweden remained neutral during WWI allowing business to prosper but the depression hit hard. The bank had to write off millions in bad loans and additions to its reserves. During the 1930s Handelsbanken regained stability largely thanks to its geographical diversity; operations in areas with high economic activity made up for struggling regions.

Sweden once again remained neutral during WWII but political uncertainty kept deposits high and it became difficult to maintain profitable loan volumes. In the 1940s Svenska Handelsbanken divested many of its industrial holdings and began to rededicate itself to small- and medium-scale lending.

Through a string of purchases in the 1950s and 1960s the bank became the largest bank in Scandinavia and began looking to expand internationally. Joint ventures and acquisitions saw the company move into other parts of Europe and the US in the 1970s. Nordic American Banking a US subsidiary was set up to handle import and export financing for North and South American clients doing business with Scandinavian countries. The 1980s saw the company establish a merchant-banking subsidiary in London and enter the Asian market forming Svenska Handelsbanken Asia (based in Singapore).

The bank remained acquisitive during the first half of the 1990s including a purchase of life insurance company RKA (later renamed Handelsbanken Liv) and parts of the Finnish Skopbank. In 1996 Handelsbanken acquired Swedish mortgage company Stadshypotek.

During the latter half of the 1990s it ventured into e-business and increased its presence in the Nordic countries and the UK. In 1999 the company acquired the Norwegian Bergensbanken after having been beaten by MeritaNordbanken in the chase for Christiania Bank (which was Norway's second-largest at the time). The next year Handelsbanken acquired Spartacus a Danish consumer finance company. In 2001 it made another Danish purchase Midtbank making it one of Denmark's largest bankers. That year it also acquired Swedish life insurance company SPP.

In 2004 Handelsbanken bought Swedish fund manager XACT Fonder from OMHEX (now OMX).

The company bought Lokallbanken in Denmark in 2008. The deal added about 15 branches to Handelsbanken's network.

EXECUTIVES

Vice Chairman, Fredrik Lundberg, age 62
Director, Goran Ennerfelt, age 73
Director, Jon F. Baksaas, age 59
Director, Bente Rathe, age 59
Director, Jan C. Johansson, age 59
Director, Sverker Martin-Lof, age 70
Vice Chairman, Anders Nyren, age 59
President and Group CEO, Par Boman, age 52
Director, Ulrika Boethius, age 52
Director, Tommy Bylund, age 54
Director, Lone F. Schroeder, age 53
Auditors: KPMGBohlinsAB

LOCATIONS

HQ: Svenska Handelsbanken
Kungstradgardsgatan 2, Stockholm SE-106 70
Phone: (46) 8 701 10 00
Web: www.handelsbanken.com

PRODUCTS/OPERATIONS

Sales by Segment

	% of total
Branch operations	
Sweden	56
Other	28
Capital	15
Other	1
Total	**100**

COMPETITORS

BNP Paribas	Deutsche Bank
Citigroup	Nordea Bank
Credit Agricole	SEB AB
Danske Bank	Societe Generale

HISTORICAL FINANCIALS

Company Type: Public

Income Statement

FYE: December 31

	ASSETS ($ mil.)	NET INCOME ($ mil.)	INCOME AS % OF ASSETS	EMPLOYEES
12/13	388,352	2,229	0.6%	11,503
12/12	366,543	2,233	0.6%	11,192
12/11	355,859	1,786	0.5%	11,184
12/10	321,154	1,644	0.5%	10,850
12/09	298,066	1,438	0.5%	10,821
Annual Growth	**6.8%**	**11.6%**	**—**	**1.5%**

2013 Year-End Financials

Return on assets: 0.5%
Return on equity: 13.1%
Long-term debt ($ mil.): —
No. of shares (mil.): 635
Sales ($ mil): 10,236

Dividends
Yield: 3.3%
Payout: 0.5%
Market value ($ mil.): 15,688

	STOCK PRICE ($) FY Close	P/E High/Low		PER SHARE ($) Earnings	Dividends	Book Value
12/13	24.68	0	0	3.47	0.82	27.32
12/12	18.03	0	0	3.47	0.72	25.93
12/11	13.43	0	0	2.81	0.02	21.96
12/10	16.30	0	0	2.60	0.01	21.14
12/09	14.15	0	0	2.24	1.12	18.72
Annual Growth	**14.9%**	**—**	**—**	**11.5%**	**(7.5%)**	**9.9%**

Sveriges Riksbank (Sweden)

LOCATIONS

HQ: Sveriges Riksbank (Sweden)
Brunkebergstorg 11, Stockholm SE-103 37
Phone: (46) 8 787 00 00   **Fax:** (46) 8 21 05 31
Web: www.riksbank.se

HISTORICAL FINANCIALS

Company Type: Public

Income Statement

FYE: December 31

	ASSETS ($ mil.)	NET INCOME ($ mil.)	INCOME AS % OF ASSETS	EMPLOYEES
12/13	67,323	(313)	—	341
12/12	53,071	296	0.6%	351
12/11	50,444	569	1.1%	332
12/10	48,754	81	0.2%	339
12/09	99,527	1,994	2.0%	351
Annual Growth	**(9.3%)**	**—**		**(0.7%)**

Swedbank A B

From Scandinavia to the Baltics one common denominator might be the institution with which people entrust their money. Swedbank serves more than 10 million private and corporate customers through 315 branches in Sweden and more than 200 branches in the Baltic countries. The bank also has an international presence in countries such as China Russia and Ukraine. Swedbank offers the usual banking staples —checking savings accounts credit cards electronic banking and loans —but also runs the gamut from investment business in the commodity stock and money markets to real estate brokerage and life insurance. The bank was formed by the 1997 merger of Foreningsbanken and Sparbanken Sverige.

After enduring some rather big losses as a result of the global economic crisis and (more specifically) bad loans in the Baltics Swedbank is trying to pick up the pieces and move forward. The company was able to recover in 2010 and reported a profit. The improvement was due to economic growth in Sweden and improving financial conditions in the Baltics. Swedbank also received backing from the Swedish government and moved to reduce costs. Conditions continued to improve (along with higher interest rates) in 2011 and net interest income rose by 17%. However profit dipped drastically in the final quarter of 2011 (down 65%) prompting the company to continue cutting costs.

Despite the stumbling block created by the global crash Swedbank maintains its vision to become an international banking group with a Swedish base. The bank is looking to build its business in Estonia Latvia and Lithuania. Estonia entered the eurozone at the end of 2010 which will help reduce business risk and boost the country's economy.

However the European debt crisis which struck in 2011 impacted growth prospects. Swedbank is scaling back some of its international ambitions and is focusing more on its home markets. The company had positioned itself for growth in Russia and Ukraine. However in 2010 Swedbank chose to shift its focus in Russia and Ukraine away from private customers and to target only corporate customers in the bank's home markets. The private customer offering will be gradually phased out and the number of branches reduced.

Swedbank is placing more emphasis on its corporate customers. Large corporates and institutions is a major contributor to Swedbank's income and the company's goal is to be the primary provider of financial advice and capital market products in its core markets. The company is working to broaden customer relations and attract new corporate and institutional clients. One way it is doing this is by growing its Norwegian brokerage First Securities which offers equity trading and research corporate finance and fixed-income trading. In 2010 Swedbank bought the half of First Securities it already didn't own.

Swedbank's smallest business segment is also its newest. Born out of the global economic meltdown Ektornet manages and develops Swedbank's repossessed assets and tries to recover as much value as possible. The real estate segment seeks to reduce costs and minimize impairment losses for the company.

EXECUTIVES

Head of Group Human Resources, Marie Hallander Larsson, age 53
Chairman, Anders Sundstrom, age 62
Head of Retail, Catrin Fransson, age 51
Deputy Chair, Lars Idermark, age 58
President and CEO, Michael Wolf, age 51
Head of Corporate Affairs, Thomas Backteman, age 49
Chief Risk Officer, H?kan Berg, age 59
Head of Group Business Support, Mikael Bjorknert, age 49
Head Baltic Banking, Birgitte Bonnesen, age 59
CFO, Goran Bronner, age 53
President CEO, Ulrika Born
Head of Baltic Institutes for Private Finances, Erika Pahne
Independent Vice Chairman of the Board, Anders Anders Sundstrom Sundstrom
Head of Russia & Ukraine, Annika Annika Wijkstrom Wijkstrom
Member of the Board of Directors, Charlotte Charlotte Stromberg Stromberg
Head of Large Corporates & Institutions, Magnus Geeber, age 45
Head of Group Human Resources, Marie Marie Hallander Larsson Larsson
Head of Group Business Support, Mikael Mikael Bjorknert Bjorknert
Head of Group HR, Lars Friberg
Head of South region, Stojko Gjurovski, age 52
Head of North region, Ulf Ejelov
Head of East region, Marie Halling, age 51
Head of Region Stockholm, Bjorn Elfstrand, age 50
CIO, Mats Engstrand, age 50
Chief Risk Officer, Anders Karlsson, age 48
Head of Group Treasury, Jonas Erikson
Head of West region, Lena Smeby-Udesen
Head of Central Region, Johan Smedman, age 50
Director, Ulrika Francke, age 57
Independent Director, Anders Anders Igel Igel
Independent Director, Helle Helle Kruse Nielsen Nielsen
Director; Employee Representative, Jimmy Jimmy Johnsson Johnsson
Independent Director, Karl-Henrik Karl-Henrik Sundstrom Sundstrom
Director; Employee Representative, Kristina Kristina Janson Janson
Independent Director, Olav Olav Fjell Fjell
Independent Director, Pia Pia Rudengren Rudengren
Independent Director, Siv Siv Svensson Svensson
Auditors: DeloitteAB

LOCATIONS

HQ: Swedbank A B
Brunkebergstorg 8, Stockholm SE-105 34
Phone: (46) 8 585 900 00   **Fax:** (46) 8 796 80 92
Web: www.swedbank.se

PRODUCTS/OPERATIONS

2011 Income

	% of total
Retail	54
Large corporations and	20
Baltic	17
Asset	5
Russia and	2
Other	2
Total	**100**

COMPETITORS

Danske Bank	Sberbank
Jyske	Sistema
MDM Bank	Storebrand ASA
Nordea Bank	Svenska Handelsbanken
SEB AB	ZAO Citibank

HISTORICAL FINANCIALS

Company Type: Public

Income Statement

FYE: December 31

	ASSETS ($ mil.)	NET INCOME ($ mil.)	INCOME AS % OF ASSETS	EMPLOYEES
12/13	284,004	2,012	0.7%	14,265
12/12	283,511	2,216	0.8%	16,088
12/11	269,256	1,702	0.6%	18,716
12/10	255,858	1,110	0.4%	20,639
12/09	251,990	(1,475)	—	23,696
Annual Growth	**3.0%**	**—**	**—**	**(11.9%)**

2013 Year-End Financials

Return on assets: 0.7%
Return on equity: 11.9%
Long-term debt ($ mil.): —
No. of shares (mil.): 1,097
Sales ($ mil): 10,061

Dividends
  Yield: 5.3%
  Payout: 2.3%
Market value ($ mil.): 31,068

	STOCK PRICE ($) FY Close	P/E High/Low		Earnings	PER SHARE ($) Dividends	Book Value
12/13	28.31	0	0	1.58	1.52	15.57
12/12	19.80	0	0	1.87	0.78	17.75
12/11	12.85	0	0	1.38	0.01	15.66
12/10	14.06	0	0	0.96	1.99	14.87
12/09	10.00	—	—	(1.50)	2.26	13.39
Annual Growth	**29.7%**	**—**	**—**	**—**	**(9.5%)**	**3.8%**

Swiss Life (UK) plc (United Kingdom)

LOCATIONS

HQ: Swiss Life (UK) plc (United Kingdom)
General-Guisan-Quai 40, P.O. Box 2831, Zurich CH-8022
Phone: (41) 43 284 33 11
Web: www.swisslife.com

HISTORICAL FINANCIALS

Company Type: Public

Income Statement

FYE: December 31

	ASSETS ($ mil.)	NET INCOME ($ mil.)	INCOME AS % OF ASSETS	EMPLOYEES
12/13	191,380	876	0.5%	6,992
12/12*	179,406	106	0.1%	7,046
01/12	161,771	0	—	0
12/01	2,814	(6)	—	12,265
12/00	2,706	7	0.3%	0
Annual Growth	**38.8%**	**44.6%**		

*Fiscal year change

2013 Year-End Financials

Return on assets: 0.4%
Return on equity: 8.1%
Long-term debt ($ mil.): —
No. of shares (mil.): 31
Sales ($ mil): 21,841

Dividends
  Yield: —
  Payout: —
Market value ($ mil.): —

Swiss Re Ltd.

LOCATIONS

HQ: Swiss Re Ltd.
Mythenquai 50/60, PO Box, Zurich 8022
Phone: (41) 43 285 2121   **Fax:** (41) 43 285 2999
Web: www.swissre.com

HISTORICAL FINANCIALS

Company Type: Public

Income Statement

FYE: December 31

	REVENUE ($ mil.)	NET INCOME ($ mil.)	NET PROFIT MARGIN	EMPLOYEES
12/13	36,902	4,511	12.2%	11,574
12/12	33,624	4,257	12.7%	11,193
12/11	28,083	2,626	9.4%	10,788
12/10	28,835	1,980	6.9%	10,362
Annual Growth	**8.6%**	**31.6%**		**3.8%**

2013 Year-End Financials

Debt ratio: 8.6%
Return on equity: 13.4%
Cash ($ mil.): 8,072
Current ratio: 10.86
Long-term debt ($ mil.): 14,722

No. of shares (mil.): 342
Dividends
  Yield: 8.6%
  Payout: 67.5%
Market value ($ mil.): 31,612

	STOCK PRICE ($) FY Close	P/E High/Low		Earnings	PER SHARE ($) Dividends	Book Value
12/13	92.38	7	6	11.89	8.03	96.30
12/12	72.30	6	4	11.06	3.29	99.08
12/11	50.55	8	5	7.49	0.00	86.33
12/10	0.00	—	—	2.43	0.00	73.97
Annual Growth	**—**	**—**	**69.8%**		**—**	**9.2%**

T&D Holdings Inc

No mystery in a name here: T&D Holdings serves as the holding company for Japanese insurance companies Taiyo Life and Daido Life. Combined the companies constitute one of Japan's top life insurers. Taiyo Life gears its products to individuals while Daido Life's products are targeted toward small businesses. Another subsidiary T&D Financial Life sells whole life policies through financial institutions the likes of banks securities firms and insurance shop agents. Other businesses under the T&D umbrella include T&D Asset Management T&D Customer Services (administrative services) and Pet & Family (pet insurance) and T&D Information Systems (computer processing).

Operations

T&D Holdings' Taiyo Life division which accounts for half of the holding company's annual revenues serves households with comprehensive life products including death benefits and medical or nursing care coverage. Meanwhile the Daido Life unit (39% of sales) focuses on the sale of term life insurance and illness policies through business accounts. The third-largest business unit T&D Financial Life sells whole life policies.

Sales and Marketing

The operating units of T&D Holdings use targeted sales techniques. With a focus on selling to housewives and middle-aged women Taiyo Life employs a sales force made up of women (similar in age to their target market base) who visit homes to present tailor-made coverage options. Daido Life gears its marketing efforts towards small and midsized businesses by partnering with enterprise associations (such as the National Federation of Corporate Taxpayers Association). The company's T&D Financial Life unit markets through a network of some 80 agencies including financial institutions.

Strategy

T&D Holdings is seeking to grow by branching out beyond its traditional market segments. Its Taiyo Life unit is working to expand policy sales by marketing policies geared at men and children. Daido Life is adding products for business owners such as living protection coverage while T&D Financial Life is introducing new products for bereaved families and retirees.

T&D Holdings is also growing its operations into the provision of short-term small-amount policies for pet shops. The company seeks to expand in new and existing business fields through alliances and acquisitions as well.

Company Background

T&D Holdings was formed through the merger of Taiyo Life and Daido Life in 2004. The companies first began working together through an alliance formed in 1999.

EXECUTIVES

Chairman, Naoteru Miyato, age 71
President and Representative Director, Kenji Nakagome, age 61
Senior Executive Officer and Director, Tamiji Matsumoto, age 60
Senior Executive Officer and Director, Tsutomu Igarashi, age 63
EVP and Director, Sonosuke Usui
Director; President Daido Life, Tetsuhiro Kida, age 61
Managing Executive Officer and Director T&D Holdings and Taiyo Life, Terunori Yokoyama, age 61
Executive Officer, Hirohisa Uehara, age 53
President and Representative Director, Kenji Nakagome, age 61
Senior Executive Officer and Director, Tamiji Matsumoto, age 60
Senior Executive Officer and Director, Tsutomu Igarashi, age 63
EVP and Director, Sonosuke Usui
Director; President Daido Life, Tetsuhiro Kida, age 61

Managing Executive Officer and Director T&D Holdings and Taiyo Life, Terunori Yokoyama, age 61
Auditors: Ernst&YoungShinNihon

LOCATIONS

HQ: T&D Holdings Inc
1-2-3 Kaigan, Minato-ku, Tokyo 105-0022
Phone: (81) 3 3434 9151   **Fax:** (81) 3 3434 9055
Web: www.td-holdings.co.jp

PRODUCTS/OPERATIONS

Sales

Taiyo Life	51
T&D Financial Life	5
Other	1

COMPETITORS

Aflac	Gibraltar Life
American Life	Insurance
Insurance	Meiji Yasuda Life
Asahi Mutual Life	Mitsui Life
Dai-ichi Life	Nippon Life Insurance
Fukoku Mutual	Sumitomo Life

HISTORICAL FINANCIALS

Company Type: Public

Income Statement

	ASSETS ($ mil.)	NET INCOME ($ mil.)	INCOME AS % OF ASSETS	EMPLOYEES
03/14	133,736	765	0.6%	19,868
03/13	145,269	677	0.5%	20,497
03/12	156,784	326	0.2%	20,982
03/11	153,861	288	0.2%	21,732
03/10	137,877	260	0.2%	21,975
Annual Growth	(0.8%)	31.0%	—	(2.5%)

FYE: March 31

2014 Year-End Financials

Return on assets: 0.5%
Return on equity: 8.1%
Long-term debt ($ mil.): —
No. of shares (mil.): 672
Sales ($ mil): 20,210

Dividends
  Yield: —
  Payout: —
Market value ($ mil.): 4,175

	STOCK PRICE ($) FY Close	P/E High/Low	Earnings	PER SHARE ($) Dividends	Book Value
03/14	6.21	— —	1.14	0.00	14.70
03/13	5.90	— —	1.00	0.00	14.50
03/12	5.43	— —	0.48	0.00	12.39
03/11	12.21	— —	0.42	0.00	11.03
Annual Growth	(20.2%)	— —	28.0%	—	7.4%

Taiwan Cooperative Bank

Taiwan Cooperative Bank is Taking Care of Business. Known as TCB for short the bank was founded in 1946 during the Japanese occupation of Taiwan to foster the country's burgeoning cooperative system. Today the bank still provides financing for economic development particularly for cooperative enterprises and small and middle-market businesses with a focus on the fishing and farming sectors. It also provides standard banking services such as deposits and financial manage-

ment to businesses and consumers. TCB has more than 300 branches in its home country plus six offices in the US China Belgium and Philippines. The Taiwanese government owns nearly 40% of the bank.

In late 2009 TCB formed a life insurance joint venture with BNP Paribas. The program strengthened the bank's foothold in the insurance market by taking advantage of its branch network. The deal expanded TCB's offerings to include savings-linked insurance products and mortgage insurance. Shortly afterwards TCB and BNP announced plans for another joint venture —this time focused on asset management services. TCB's stake in both ventures is 51% to BNP's 49%.

EXECUTIVES

EVP, Chung-Dea Hsieh
EVP, Shu-Chang Chou
SVP and General Manager Information Technology Division, Hsiang Hu
President, Chiu-Jung Tsai
EVP, Yang-Jan Fan
VP and General Manager Treasury Department, Pe-Chu Wu
SVP and General Manager Electronic Banking Department, Chun-Lung Chou
SVP and General Manager Loan Assets Management Department, Cheng-Kang Chen
SVP and General Manager Secretariat Department, Fei-Ling Hu
SVP and General Manager Accounting Division, Chen-Tsai Chou
SVP and General Manager Risk Management Division, Shiaw-Yen Lun
SVP and General Manager Human Resources Division, Sue-Chuan Wang
Auditors: Deloitte&Touche

LOCATIONS

HQ: Taiwan Cooperative Bank
No. 77, Guan Qian Road, Jhongjheng District, Taipei 100
Phone: (886) 2 2311 8811   **Fax:** (886) 2 2375 2954
Web: www.tcb-bank.com.tw

COMPETITORS

Chang Hwa Bank	SinoPac Holdings
Fubon Financial	Taiwan Business Bank
Hua Nan Financial	

HISTORICAL FINANCIALS

Company Type: Public

Income Statement

	ASSETS ($ mil.)	NET INCOME ($ mil.)	INCOME AS % OF ASSETS	EMPLOYEES
12/13	97,967	269	0.3%	8,444
12/12*	98,462	254	0.3%	8,563
01/12	90,991	0	—	0
12/11	90,932	250	0.3%	8,697
12/10	91,985	264	0.3%	8,803
Annual Growth	2.1%	0.6%	—	(1.4%)

FYE: December 31

*Fiscal year change

2013 Year-End Financials

Return on assets: 0.2%
Return on equity: 5.9%
Long-term debt ($ mil.): —
No. of shares (mil.): —
Sales ($ mil): 1,729

Dividends
  Yield: —
  Payout: —
Market value ($ mil.): —

Talanx AG

Talanx Group offers its customers an army of protection. The Germany-based insurance group is the third-largest in the country. Talanx operates in property/casualty insurance life insurance and financial services as well as reinsurance in both the property/casualty and life categories. Brands include HDI and HDI Direkt which provides insurance policies to both private and industrial customers; Aspecta a provider of individual insurance and investment products; Hannover Re one of the world's largest reinsurers; and fund guarantor and asset manager AmpegaGirling among others. Talanx has operations in 150 countries worldwide. Talanx is part of HDI Haftpflichtverband der Deutschen Industrie.

IPO

In 2012 the company completed its IPO and began trading on Germany's Frankfurt Stock Exchange. The company raised about Å817 million which it is using to grow its business. Post-IPO HDI Haftpflichtverband der Deutschen Industrie maintained Talanx.

Operations

The company reports its business in five segments: industrial lines retail Germany retail international non-life reinsurance and life/health reinsurance. Non-life reinsurance leads the pack with 31% of revenue; retail Germany and life/health reinsurance share the #2 spot.

Geographic Reach

Europe accounts for about 67% of premiums written with Germany holding the majority across the board. The US is the company's largest non-European region.

Major operations outside of Germany are located in Austria Hungary Italy Spain Poland Russia and Turkey. The company also has operations in the Americas Africa and the Asia/Pacific region. Talanx prefers to operate semi-independent businesses in local markets and expands by acquiring or opening divisions in new territories. It operates in 150 countries.

Japanese insurer Meiji Yasuda Life Insurance has been expanding into Europe using Talanx as a springboard; it took a 7% stake in Talanx during the company's IPO. The two companies use a joint venture with a Talanx subsidiary as the framework to grow in Central and Eastern European markets.

Sales and Marketing

Talanx uses both its own sales agents and offices and brokers and independent agents as well as specialized cooperatives in its various markets.

Financial Performance

Revenue improved about 13% in 2012 as nearly every segmented reported increased sales. Net income also grew 22% as most segments reported large increases in investment income offset by claim expenses and administrative costs. The improved revenue and net income lead to higher cash flow.

Strategy

Growth is the name of the game at Talanx and the company plans to accomplish by organic and acquisitive means. Key target areas include Central and Eastern Europe (CEE) and Latin America. It also focuses on improving profitability and customer relations especially in its retail divisions. In 2012 Talanx expanded into Canada Singapore and Bahrain.

Mergers and Acquisitions

In 2012 Talanx scooped up Polish insurer TuiR Warta in conjunction with its Japanese partner Meiji Yasuda which took 30%.

Background

The company traces its roots back over a century but began operating as a holding company under the name HDI Beteilgung AG in 1996. In 1998 it was renamed Talanx which is a blend of the words "talent" and "phalanx" (a Greek word referring to a battle formation).

EXECUTIVES

Chairman Management Board, Herbert K. Haas, age 60

Member Management Board, Immo Querner

Member Management Board Reinsurance, Ulrich Wallin, age 53

Chairman Supervisory Board, Wolf-Dieter Baumgartl, age 71

Deputy Chairman Management Board, Christian Hinsch, age 59

Deputy Chairman Supervisory Board, Prof Eckhard Rohkamm

Head Communications, Thomas von Mallinckrodt

Head Investor Relations, Wolfram Schmitt, age 56

Member Management Board, Thomas Noth

Deputy Chairman Supervisory Board, Ralf Rieger

Member Management Group Retail Germany, Heinz-Peter Ro?

Member Supervisory Board, Michael Rogowski, age 75

Member Supervisory Board, Hans-Dieter Petram, age 71

Member Supervisory Board, Erhard Schipporeit, age 66

Deputy Chairman Supervisory Board, Prof Eckhard Rohkamm

Member Supervisory Board, Gerald Herrmann

Member Supervisory Board, Thomas Lindner

Member Supervisory Board, Otto Muller

Deputy Chairman Supervisory Board, Ralf Rieger

LOCATIONS

HQ: Talanx AG
Riethorst 2, Hannover 30659
Phone: (49) 511 3747 0   **Fax:** (49) 511 3747 2525
Web: www.talanx.com

PRODUCTS/OPERATIONS

2008 Premiums

	% of total
Property/casualty	31
Life	30
Non-life	24
Life/health	15
Total	**100**

COMPETITORS

AEGON	Generali
AXA	ING
Allianz	Munich Re Group
ERGO	Swiss Re
General Re	Zurich Insurance Group

HISTORICAL FINANCIALS

Company Type: Public

Income Statement   FYE: December 31

	REVENUE ($ mil.)	NET INCOME ($ mil.)	NET PROFIT MARGIN	EMPLOYEES
12/13	38,956	1,049	2.7%	21,529
12/12	35,406	830	2.3%	22,180
12/11	31,411	672	2.1%	18,314
12/10	31,363	294	0.9%	18,006
12/09	30,534	757	2.5%	18,038
Annual Growth	6.3%	8.5%	—	4.5%

2013 Year-End Financials
Debt ratio: —   No. of shares (mil.): 252
Return on equity: 10.3%   Dividends
Cash ($ mil.): 2,566   Yield: —
Current ratio: —   Payout: —
Long-term debt ($ mil.): —   Market value ($ mil.): —

Tata Motors Ltd

Tata Motors enjoys giant-sized growth thanks to its Nano cars. The company —India's largest automobile maker by sales —makes buses trucks tractor-trailers passenger cars (Indica Indigo Jaguar Land Rover Safari Sumo and the popular micro car Nano) light commercial vehicles and utility vehicles. It also makes construction equipment and provides IT services. Tata Motors sells through more than 1000 dealers in India as well as exports vehicles to countries in Africa Asia Europe the Middle East and South America. In addition the company distributes Fiat-brand cars in India through its Tata-Fiat dealer network.

Geographic Reach

Through subsidiaries and affiliated companies Tata Motors has operations in India the UK South Korea Thailand Spain and South Africa. India is its largest market representing 34% of its total sales. China the UK and the US follow with 18% 11% and nearly 10% of total sales respectively. Other European countries account for nearly 12% of total sales while the rest of the world contributes roughly 18%.

Operations

Tata Motors' business segments are primarily its automotive operations which develop design manufacture assemble and sell vehicles and provide financing. The automotive segment is divided into Tata and other brand vehicles as well as Jaguar Land Rover. Other operations include information technology or IT services and machine tools and factory automation products and services.

Tata Motors also has franchisee and joint venture assembly operations in Bangladesh Ukraine and Senegal.

Sales and Marketing

Tata Motors' vehicles are sold through a network of authorized dealers and service centers across the Indian market and a network of distributors and local dealers in international markets.

Financial Performance

Tata Motors has seen significant growth over the last four years with 2012 representing its best year to date. From 2011 to 2012 its total revenues in rupees increased by 35% (or 18% when converted into US dollar) and its net income skyrocketed by 58% (37% in US dollar).

The company has been helped by increases in volumes across all its markets particularly a 29% surge in the premium car segment and impressive growth in the Chinese market. Revenues in China increased 155% and accounted for 18% of the company's net revenues in 2012.

Strategy

Tata Motors is a leader in one of the only growth areas for the automotive market in recent years — India —which gives it a slight edge over competitors in the region. It is also extending its commercial vehicles penetration into countries like Bangladesh Nepal Sri Lanka and Bhutan.

During the Great Recession the Jaguar and Land Rover lines created financial pressure for Tata Motors as consumers bought smaller more fuel efficient cars. However by mid-2010 interest in luxury cars returned spurring the company to secure some $1.5 billion to support the expansion of Jaguar and Land Rover manufacturing facilities over the next four years. This allowed the luxury brands to remain in the UK and quickly cut costs tightened up efficiencies and improved its cash management. Now the well-known British brands are recapturing some of their lost luster generating rising sales from important markets like Shanghai to London.

Company Background

In 2008 Tata Motors bought the Jaguar and Land Rover brands from Ford for about $2.3 billion. It took over the two struggling businesses in an effort to diversify its customer base by expanding its product portfolio from commercial and small passenger vehicles to premium cars.

Ownership

Tata Sons Limited and Subsidiaries own 26% of the company while Citibank N owns 16%.

EXECUTIVES

Director; CEO Jaguar and Land Rover, Ralf Speth, age 58

Managing Director, Karl Slym, age 52

President and Head Engineering Research Centre, Tim Leverton

Vice Chairman, Ravi Kant, $625,903 total compensation

President and CFO, C. Ramakrishnan, $326,378 total compensation

Executive Director and Head Commercial Vehicles Business Unit, Ravindra Pisharody, $154,989 total compensation

Executive Director and Head Quality, Satish B. Borwankar, $164,951 total compensation

Chairman, Cyrus P. Mistry

President and Head Passenger Vehicles Business Unit, Ranjit Yadav

SVP and Head Purchasing and Supply Chain, Venkatram Mamillapalle

Sr. Vice President Chief Human Resources Officer, Prabir Jha

SVP and Head Commercial Passenger Vehicle Business Unit, Ankush Arora

Director; CEO Jaguar and Land Rover, Ralf Speth, age 58

Vice Chairman, Ravi Kant, age 70

Managing Director Indian Operations and Board Member, Prakash M. Telang, age 59

Director, Subodh Bhargava, age 71

Director, Nusli N. Wadia, age 70
Director, S. M. (Sam) Palia, age 75
Director, Jamshed J. (JJ) Irani, age 77
Director, Ramesh A. Mashelkar, age 70
Director, Nasser M. Munjee, age 61
Director, V. K. Jairath, age 55
Director, Ranendra Sen, age 69
Auditors: DeloitteHaskins&Sells

LOCATIONS

HQ: Tata Motors Ltd
Bombay House, 24, Homi Mody Street, Mumbai, Maharashtra 400 001
Phone: (91) 22 6665 8282   **Fax:** (91) 22 6665 7799
Web: www.tatamotors.com

Sales

	% of total
India	34
China	18
UK	11
US	9
Total	**100**

Selected Subsidiaries

Concorde Motors (India) Limited
Jaguar Land Rover PLC-UK
PT Tata Indonesia
Sheba Properties Ltd-India

TAL Manufacturing Solutions Ltd-India
Tata Daewoo Commercial Vehicle Co Ltd- South Korea
Tata Hispano Motors Carrocera SA- Spain
Tata Marcopolo Motors Ltd-India.
Tata Motors (SA) Proprietary Ltd South Africa.
Tata Motors European Technical center PLC UK
Tata Motors Finance Ltd India
Tata Motors Insurance Broking and Advisory Services Ltd-India
Tata Motors(Thailand) Ltd
Tata Precision Industries Pts Ltd-Singapore
Tata Technologies Ltd-India
TML Distribution Company Ltd-India
TML Drivelines Ltd-India
TML Holdings Pte Ltd- Singapore

PRODUCTS/OPERATIONS

Selected Products and Services

Light commercial vehicles
  Ace
  Magic
  Winger
Medium and heavy commercial vehicles
  Paradiso
  Prima
Passenger cars
  Indica
  Indica Vista
  Indigo eCS
  Indigo Manza
  Jaguar
  Nano
Utility vehicles
  Aria
  Land Rover
  Range Rover
  Sumo
  Safari
  Venture
  Xenon XT

COMPETITORS

BMW	Isuzu
Bajaj Auto	Kia Motors
Caterpillar	Komatsu
Chrysler	Mahindra
Daimler	Mazda
Fiat	Nissan
Ford Motor	Renault
Fuji Heavy Industries	Saab Automobile
General Motors	Suzuki Motor
Hindustan Motors	Toyota
Honda	Volkswagen
Hyundai Motor	Volvo

HISTORICAL FINANCIALS

Company Type: Public

Income Statement

FYE: March 31

	REVENUE ($ mil.)	NET INCOME ($ mil.)	NET PROFIT MARGIN	EMPLOYEES
03/14	39,000	2,176	5.6%	68,889
03/13	34,813	1,633	4.7%	62,716
03/12	32,724	2,273	6.9%	58,618
03/11	27,635	1,646	6.0%	26,214
03/10	20,631	847	4.1%	0
Annual Growth	**17.3%**	**26.6%**	**—**	**—**

2014 Year-End Financials

Debt ratio: 0.4%
Return on equity: 26.2%
Cash ($ mil.): 4,747
Current ratio: 1.05
Long-term debt ($ mil.): 7,563
No. of shares (mil.): —
Dividends
  Yield: 0.3%
  Payout: 0.0%
Market value ($ mil.): —

	STOCK PRICE ($) FY Close	P/E High/Low		PER SHARE ($) Earnings	Dividends	Book Value
03/14	35.41	0	0	0.68	0.13	3.25
03/13	24.41	0	0	0.51	0.00	2.14
03/12	26.97	0	0	0.71	0.00	2.03
03/11	27.79	0	0	0.11	0.30	1.48
03/10	18.46	0	0	0.06	0.10	(0.00)
Annual Growth	**17.7%**	**—**		**80.2%**	**7.2%**	**—**

Telecom Italia SPA

Telecom Italia's wireline unit is Italy's #1 telephone operator with some 4.1 million fixed access lines. It serves Italian customers through millions of broadband and wireless connections. While Telecom Italia does most of its business in Italy Latin America is a key international market. The company provides wholesale network access in South America as well as Italy. Its TIM Brasil subsidiary is a leader in the Brazilian wireless market with more than 64.1 million subscribers; its Argentina subsidiaries cater to 1.6 million broadband subscribers and 18.2 million mobile subscribers.

Geographic Reach

Telecom Italia has a presence in Italy Latin America North America Europe Africa and Asia. It generates about 64% of its revenue from its domestic market (Italy) and the remaining 36% derive from Brazil and Argentina.

Operations

The operating segments of Telecom Italia are organized according to the relative geographical location for the telecommunications business and relative to the specific businesses for the other segments. The market of its main business unit is focused mainly in serving customers in Europe Asia and South America.

In addition subsidiary Telecom Italia Media produces and distributes TV and Web content and Olivetti provides office equipment such as ink-jet printer heads mostly for the banking industry.

Financial Performance

Thanks to growth in foreign markets the company's revenues increased by 9% from 2010 to 2011. Revenues from Brazil were up by 18% as a result of a 26% increase in the market share of mobile lines. Revenue from Argentina increased by 27% in 2011 due to the growth of customers in the fixed and broadband businesses as well as mobile businesses.

Despite this growth Telecom Italia recorded a net loss for 2011 due to the acquisition of goods and services and net impairment losses on noncurrent assets.

Strategy

Over the last few years the company has been selling off interests not related to its businesses in Italy or Brazil. These deals were also part of Telecom Italia's ongoing effort to sell non-core businesses in order to reduce debt.

Outside Italy the company is focused on bolstering its operations only in Brazil an emerging market that now accounts for almost 20% of revenue. In 2011 it bought AES Atimus a Brazilian subsidiary of US power company AES. AES Atimus operates a 3400-mile fiber optic network in Rio de Janeiro and Sao Paulo. The deal Â700 million ($1 billion) was Telecom Italia's largest acquisition in a decade.

In another 2011 acquisition that boosted its Latin American holdings Telecom Italia paid about

$145 million to raise its ownership stake in Sofora Telecomunicaciones the holding company which owns Telecom Argentina from 58% to 68%. Closer to home Telecom Italia bought 71% of Italian mobile phone retailer 4G Holding from GIR Srl a company controlled by 4G's CEO 2011. The deal boosted the company's domestic retail presence by 200 shops as it works to get its brand out in front of more wireless customers in a saturated market. GIR retained 29% of 4G Holding.

Ownership

The former state-owned monopoly has one major institutional shareholder. An investment group made up primarily of Italian financial backers known as Telco SpA owns a 22% stake. Telco is made up of Telefonica (46%) Italian insurance giant Generali (31%) investment bank Mediobanca (12%) and commercial bank Intesa Sanpaolo (11%).

HISTORY

After gaining political power in Italy Benito Mussolini began a program of nationalization focusing first on three major banks and their equity portfolios. Included were three local phone companies that became the core of Societa Finanziaria Telefonica (STET) created in 1933 to handle Italy's phone services under the state's industrial holding company Istituto per La Ricostruzione Industriale (IRI).

Germany and Italy grew closer in the years leading up to WWII and Italian equipment makers entered a venture with Siemens to make phone equipment. STET came through the war with most of its infrastructure intact and a monopoly on phone service in Italy. Siemens' properties along with those of other equipment makers were taken over by another company TETI which was nationalized and put under STET's control in 1958. This expanded STET's monopoly to include equipment manufacturing.

Italy's industries were increasingly nationalized under IRI. Companies within the IRI family forged alliances with each other and with independent companies which frequently were absorbed into STET.

STET's scope expanded during the 1960s and 1970s to include satellite and data communications but its monopoly was undermined by new technologies such as faxes PCs and teleconferencing. In the technology race among equipment makers STET fell behind. And in a satellite communications era STET's status as a necessary long-distance carrier was threatened. Despite these pressures change did not come easily to STET. State monopolies maintained popular support not only on nationalistic grounds but also because of labor's strong anticompetitive stance.

Anticipating privatization however IRI reorganized STET in 1994 and poured new capital into the company. STET's five telecom companies —SIP (domestic phone operator) Italcable (intercontinental) Telespazio (satellite) SIRM (maritime) and Iritel (domestic long distance) —were merged into one Telecom Italia. Its mobile phone business was spun off as Telecom Italia Mobile (TIM) in 1995.

To end political feuding the government abruptly replaced the heads of STET and Telecom Italia in 1997. Telecom Italia was merged with STET which took the Telecom Italia name and was privatized that year. Berardino Libonati became chairman and Franco Bernabe formerly CEO of oil company ENI took the helm as CEO. The company began taking stakes in foreign telecom companies including mobilkom austria Spanish broadcaster Retevision and —as European Union competition began in 1998 —Telekom Austria.

Erstwhile rival Olivetti launched a hostile takeover bid for Telecom Italia in 1999. Though

Telecom Italia tried to fend off the smaller firm with various maneuvers including a proposed merger with Deutsche Telekom Olivetti gained 55% of Telecom Italia. Olivetti CEO Roberto Colaninno took over as chairman and CEO.

That year Telecom Italia sold 50% of Stream its pay TV unit to an investor group led by News Corp. The company also announced plans to spin off and sell a stake in its ISP Tin.it. In 2000 however Telecom Italia instead combined Tin.it with SEAT Pagine Gialle a yellow pages directory publisher and Internet portal operator (spun off from the parent company and sold in 2003). Also that year the company sold off 81% of its telecom equipment unit Italtel and its 49% stake in installations firm Sirti.

In 2001 Colaninno and several other Telecom Italia officials were named as suspects in an investigation of whether the company had violated accounting conflict of interest and share manipulation laws. Colaninno was replaced when tire maker Pirelli and Edizione Holding the parent company of the Benetton Group acquired a 23% stake in Olivetti.

Telecom Italia teamed up with News Corp. to develop the Stream pay TV joint venture renamed Sky Italia. The venture gained a kick-start when the two companies teamed to buy Italian pay-TV business Telepiu from Vivendi Universal in a cash and debt assumption deal that was valued at $871 million. The deal included agreements to drop disputes between Telepiu and Stream. Telecom Italia then sold a 30% stake in the venture to News Corp. It retained a 20% share with News Corp. controlling 80%.

In 2003 the company abandoned plans to acquire phone directories group Pagine Utili from Fininvest in a deal that would have been worth more than $130 million because of protests by Italian regulators who claimed the deal would breach competition laws. It also spun off its international services division starting in 2003 into a separate company Telecom Italia Sparkle which concentrated on services to other fixed-line operators ISPs and international corporations and sold its nearly 62% stake in SEAT Pagine Gialle to an investor group for $3.55 billion.

Once the subsidiary Telecom Italia became the parent company after the 2003 merger with former parent Olivetti. The reorganization simplified a corporate structure that was at best confusing: Olivetti through its Tecnost unit had acquired a controlling 55% stake in Telecom Italia in 1999. Two years later tire maker Pirelli and the Benetton family teamed up to take control of Olivetti. Olivetti's largest shareholder was Olimpia a company owned by Pirelli and the Benetton Group among others.

Because Telecom Italia accounted for more than 95% of the revenues of Olivetti the reorganization also kept the focus on the core business. The merger was met with favor among market watchers and some shareholders although a group of international investors opposed the restructuring.

Reorganization continued at the company and it began selling some international fixed-line assets and putting some wireless operations outside Italy on the market. Disposals included Digitel the Venezuelan wireless carrier to Oswaldo Cisneros' Telvenco in a deal valued at about $425 million. It also sold its 81% stake in Greek wireless carrier Hellas Telecommunications to US-based private equity firms Texas Pacific Group and Apax Partners in a deal valued at $1.4 billion; stakes in Spanish joint venture Auna and satellite unit Telespazio (to Finmeccanica); and in 2005 it sold its holdings in IT services and consulting company Finsiel to Italian outsourcing firm Gruppo COS.

After spurning an offer from AT&T to buy the company Telecom Italia named Pasquale Pistorio

chairman in 2007 replacing Guido Rossi who had held the position for only seven months. Telefonica subsequently won control of the company. Later that year Pistorio was replaced by Gabriele Galateri as chairman; Galateri was nominated by another top shareholder Mediobanca.

In 2010 the company began selling off interests not related to its businesses in Italy or Brazil. It sold its 70% stake in Elettra which specialized in laying submarine cables to France Telecom (later renamed Orange) for Â20 million ($27 million); its Netherlands fixed-line provider BBNed to Tele2 for Â50 million ($64 million); and its German broadband unit HanseNet to Telefonica for the tidy sum of Â900 million ($1.2 billion) in cash. The following year Telecom Italia sold its 27% stake in the state-run Cuban phone company ETECSA for $706 million to Rafin SA a financial services firm in that country. Also in 2011 the company sold subsidiary Loquendo to US-based Nuance Communications. The sales were part of Telecom Italia's ongoing effort to sell non-core businesses in order to reduce debt.

EXECUTIVES

Head Disposals; EVP of Telecom Italia Media and Head of the Media Business Unit, Giovanni Stella, age 66
Manager Consumer, Fabrizio Bona
Chairman, Gabriele Galateri di Genola, age 67
Head External Relations, Carlo Fornaro, age 54
Managing Director COO, Marco Patuano, age 50
Head Purchasing, Stefano Ciurli, age 52
Investor Relations Officer, Elisabetta Ripa, age 48
Manager Public Affairs Department, Paolo Annunziato, age 53
Head Audit and Compliance Services, Frederico M. D'Andrea
Head Human Resources Organization and Industrial Relations, Antonio Migliardi, age 55
Head Domestic Legal Affairs and Board Secretary, Antonino Cusimano, age 49
Head Quality of Service, Paolo D'Andrea
Head Administration Finance Control and International Business, Andrea Mangoni
CEO Assistant, Franco R. Brescia
Head Strategy and Innovation, Cesare Sironi
Chief Regulatory Officer, Alessandro Talotta
Head Security, Damiano Toselli, age 61
Head National Wholesale Services, Riccardo Delleani, age 54
CEO TIM Brasil, Luca Luciani, age 46
Manager Broadband Content, Luca Tomassini
Head International Operations, Francesco Armato
Manager Business, Pietro Labriola
Manager Top Clients Market and Networked IT Services, Gianfilippo D'Agostino, age 53
Investor Relations Contact Domestic Operations, Helen Mainardi-Rosenthal
Investor Relations Contact Internal Operations - Credit Analysts and Bondholders, Paolo Germiniani
Investor Relations Contact Sustainability Retail Investors and Benchmarking, Alessandra Cantu
Investor Relations Contact Sustainability Retail Investors and Benchmarking, Maria A. Ruggieri
Investor Relations Contact Sustainability Retail Investors and Benchmarking, Giorgio Tavolini
Press Office Assistant, Rita Carboni
Head Market Press Office, Marco Rosatella
Head Regulation Press Office, Marco Signoretti
IR Contact Officer, Alex Alex Bolis Bolis
Head of Domestic Media, Carlotta Carlotta Ventura Ventura
Head of TI Audit & Compliance Services, Federico Federico DAndrea DAndrea
Group Compliance Officer, Francesca Francesca Petralia Petralia

Chairman of the Board, Franco Franco Bernabe Bernabe
Chief Executive Officer of Telecom Argentina; Chairman of Telecom Personal, Franco Franco Bertone Bertone
Information Technology Director, Gianluca Gianluca Pancaccini Pancaccini
Head of Quality, Giuseppe Giuseppe Zaza Zaza
Head of Administration; Finance and Control; Financial Reporting Officer, Piergiorgio Piergiorgio Peluso Peluso
Head of IT & Security Compliance, Roberto Roberto Mazzilli Mazzilli
Head of Top Clients and Public Sector, Simone Simone Battiferri Battiferri
Director, Aldo Minucci, age 67
Director, Mauro Sentinelli, age 67
Director, Stefano Cao, age 63

Director, Elio Cosimo Catania, age 67
Director, Roland Berger, age 76
Chairman, Gabriele Galateri di Genola, age 67
Director, Renato Pagliaro, age 57
Director, Paolo Baratta, age 75
Director, Jean-Paul Fitoussi, age 72
Director, Tarak Ben Ammar, age 65
CEO and Director, Franco Bernabe, age 65
Director, Julio L. Lopez, age 69
Director, Gaetano Micciche, age 63
Director, Cesar Alierta
Non-Executive Director, Cesar Cesar Alierta Izuel Izuel
Non-Executive Director, Gabriele Gabriele Galateri di Genola Genola
Non-Executive Director, Gaetano Gaetano Micciche Micciche
Non-Executive Director, Julio Julio Linares Lopez Lopez
Non-Executive Independent Director, Lucia Lucia Calvosa Calvosa
Non-Executive Independent Director, Massimo Massimo Egidi Egidi
Non-Executive Director, Tarak Tarak Ben Ammar Ammar
Auditors: RecontaErnst&YoungS.p.A.

LOCATIONS

HQ: Telecom Italia SPA
Corso d?Italia, 41, Rome 00198
Phone: (39) 06 36 88 1
Web: www.telecomitalia.com

Sales

	% of total
Italy	64
Other	36
Total	**100**

PRODUCTS/OPERATIONS

Sales

	$ mil.	% of total
Services		93
Equipment sales		7
Total		**100**

COMPETITORS

America Movil	Orange
BT	Ricoh Company
Cable & Wireless	SFR
Canon	Swisscom
Deutsche Telekom	Tele2
FastWeb	Telefonica
Hewlett-Packard	Tiscali
Hutchison Whampoa	Vivo Participac?es
IBM	Vodafone Omnitel
KPN	Wind Telecomunicazioni
Millicom	Xerox

HISTORICAL FINANCIALS

Company Type: Public

Income Statement

FYE: December 31

	REVENUE ($ mil.)	NET INCOME ($ mil.)	NET PROFIT MARGIN	EMPLOYEES
12/13	33,418	(927)	—	65,623
12/12	40,044	(2,144)	—	83,184
12/11	39,870	(6,112)	—	84,154
12/10	37,973	4,177	11.0%	84,200
12/09	40,278	2,277	5.7%	71,384
Annual Growth	**(4.6%)**	**—**		**(2.1%)**

2013 Year-End Financials

Debt ratio: 72.9%
Return on equity: (-3.7%)
Cash ($ mil.): 7,907
Current ratio: 1.03
Long-term debt ($ mil.): 42,794

No. of shares (mil.): —
Dividends
Yield: 6.4%
Payout: —
Market value ($ mil.): —

	STOCK PRICE ($) FY Close	P/E High/Low		PER SHARE ($) Earnings	Dividends	Book Value
12/13	9.96	—	—	(0.04)	0.64	1.77
12/12	9.05	—	—	(0.11)	0.43	1.93
12/11	10.65	—	—	(0.31)	1.14	2.22
12/10	12.94	189	105	0.21	0.45	2.91
12/09	15.43	489	218	0.12	0.48	2.83
Annual Growth	**(10.4%)**	**—**	**—**	**—**	**7.7%**	
(11.0%)						

Telefonaktiebolaget LM Ericsson (Sweden)

LOCATIONS

HQ: Telefonaktiebolaget LM Ericsson (Sweden)
Torshamnsgatan 23, Stockholm SE-164 83
Phone: (46) 10 719 0000
Web: www.ericsson.com

HISTORICAL FINANCIALS

Company Type: Public

Income Statement

FYE: December 31

	REVENUE ($ mil.)	NET INCOME ($ mil.)	NET PROFIT MARGIN	EMPLOYEES
12/13	35,465	1,872	5.3%	114,340
12/12	34,964	886	2.5%	110,255
12/11	32,901	1,768	5.4%	0
12/10	30,325	1,662	5.5%	0
Annual Growth	**5.4%**	**4.1%**	**—**	**—**

2013 Year-End Financials

Debt ratio: 1.7%
Return on equity: 8.6%
Cash ($ mil.): 6,565
Current ratio: 2.09
Long-term debt ($ mil.): 3,441

No. of shares (mil.): —
Dividends
Yield: —
Payout: —
Market value ($ mil.): —

	STOCK PRICE ($) FY Close	P/E High/Low		PER SHARE ($) Earnings	Dividends	Book Value
12/13	0.00	—	—	0.58	0.00	(0.00)
Annual Growth	**—**	**—**	**—**	**—**		

Telefonica, S.A.

Telefonica calls Spain home but customers in 25 countries call home with Telefonica. The company provides fixed and mobile phone service across Europe (55% of sales) and Latin America (45%). Its fixed-line portfolio includes voice Internet access cable and satellite television enterprise networking and hosting and wholesale services. Its mobile business encompasses voice messaging and corporate infrastructure services. Telefonica divides its business into three segments —Telefonica Espana Telefonica Europe and Telefonica LatinoAmerica. Telefonica Espana has 24 million mobile customers and 13 million access lines and Telefonica LatinoAmerica has almost 145 million mobile subscribers.

As the incumbent carrier in Spain Telefonica Espana is the leading fixed-line operator in Spain with more than 13 million access lines in service. Like other landline providers the company has seen its number of subscribers drop by about 1 million a year over the past couple of years as more people switch to cellular phones for their primary service. Mobile data and pay TV users continue to rise. The company counts almost 6 million Internet users and more than 775000 pay TV viewers. Telefonica Espana accounted for abouth 30% of the group's revenues in 2010.

Telefonica Europe oversees the group's operations in the Czech Republic Germany Ireland Slovakia and the UK; its services are marketed under the O2 brand. Altogether it has more than 3.5 million fixed-line customers 4.4 million Internet and data access users about 200000 pay TV viewers and almost 46 million mobile subscribers. Again while the number of fixed-line customers drop mobile data and pay TV users are on the rise. Telefonica Europe accounted for about 25% of the group's revenues in 2010.

Telefonica LatinoAmerica is a top carrier in Argentina Brazil (with Portugal Telecom) Chile Colombia and Peru; the company also has substantial operations in Ecuador El Salvador Guatemala Mexico Nicaragua Panama Puerto Rico Uruguay and Venezuela. In these countries the company has 24 million fixed-line customers 8 million Internet and data access users 1.7 million pay TV viewers and almost 150 million mobile subscribers. Up against regional wireless leader America Movil the company is the dominant carrier in some markets. Telefonica LatinoAmerica accounted for more than 40% of the group's revenues in 2010.

With the market cornered on traditional voice services Telefonica's acquisitions and divestures are centered around auxiliary services. In early 2010 it bought broadband service provider Hansenet from Telecom Italia for E900 million ($1.2 billion). The deal added about 2 million high-speed Internet customers to Telefonica's books and gave it a better foothold in Germany where its Telefonica O2 Germany struggles to gain ground on rivals Vodafone and United Internet not to mention incumbent provider Deutsche Telekom.

Later that year Telefonica got the green light from Spanish anti-trust regulators to acquire a 22% stake in Sogecable's Digital+ satellite TV service. Telefonica had originally wanted to make strategic decisions on Digital+'s business plan and govern its management; in the end regulators agreed to also give broadcaster Mediaset Espana (formerly Telecinco) a 22% stake and leave parent Prisa with the 56% majority control. Upon completion of the deal including financial terms Telefonica will likely strengthen its presence in the pay-TV market.

Telefonica has numerous stakes in companies outside of its core operating countries. It owns 100% of 3G Mobile AG Switzerland (inactive) call center Atento Brasil and media distributor Telefonica de Contenidos; 46% of Telco S.p.A. a holding company that controls more than 20% of Telecom Italia; 32% of Lycos Europe; and a 5% stake in China Unicom. The company is looking to reduce its debt load however by selling non-core operations. In late 2012 it agreed to sell Atento to private equity group Bain Capital for some E1 billion ($1.3 billion).

In 2013 it formed a mobile advertising network with US telecom giant Sprint Nextel that will offer advertisers access to more than 370 million customers in the Americas and Europe.

HISTORY

When a 1923 military coup brought General Miguel Primo de Rivera to power in Spain the government-run phone system was in shambles. More than half of the country's 90000 lines did not work. With little cash in the government coffers Primo de Rivera sought foreign assistance.

Supported by National City Bank (now Citigroup) US-based ITT bought three private Spanish phone companies later combining them to form Compania Telefonica Nacional de Espana. The ITT unit gained the state phone concession in 1924 and the government agreed not to reclaim the system for 20 years. But when Franco came to power in 1939 he froze Telefonica's assets. ITT tried to sell the company to German buyers in 1941 but backed out when the US State Department objected. The Spanish government nationalized Telefonica in 1945 keeping 41% of its shares.

Long-distance service was introduced in 1960 satellite communications in 1967 and international service in 1971. Still when Spain entered the European Union (EU) in 1986 Telefonica was unprepared for the increase in demand for services and complaints rose.

The firm purchased a minority stake in Compania de Telefonos de Chile in 1990 and a Telefonica-led consortium won a bid to manage the southern half of ENTEL Argentina's former state phone system. The company acquired a majority stake in Peru's telecom monopoly in 1994 and a year later joined Unisource a European telecom consortium.

The Spanish government at first defied the EU's directive to break up its telecom monopoly. But in 1994 the government announced it would meet the EU's 1998 deadline for opening telecom markets; in exchange Telefonica won permission to begin new businesses when competition arrived.

Flamboyant former investment banker Juan Villalonga took over as chairman in 1996. The boyhood friend of Spain's prime minister began expanding Telefonica's presence in Latin America with several acquisitions in 1997. They included 35% of Brazil's Companhia Riograndense de Telecomunicacies (CRT); a large stake in Multicanal Argentina's #1 cable company (sold in 1998 to Grupo Clarin); and 35% of satellite TV service Via Digital.

That year Telefonica broke off with Unisource and allied with British Telecom (now BT Group) and MCI only to have the alliance break up when MCI agreed to be bought by WorldCom in 1998. Meanwhile the Spanish government had finished divesting its interest in the company in 1997 (retaining a golden share) and competition came to Spain the next year. The company revamped its corporate structure cut 10000 jobs and became Telefonica S.A. It also won fixed-line phone company Telesp and a cellular company in Brazil's auction of the former national phone company Telebras.

In 1999 Telefonica sold to the public a part of its Internet unit Terra Networks (formerly Telefonica Interactiva). The next year it took near-total ownership of four of its Latin American units: Telefonica de Argentina Telefonica del Peru Telesp and Tele Sudeste Celular (it later sold its stake in CRT to meet regulatory approval) and separated the mobile and data operations to reorganize by business units.

To expand its multimedia offerings Telefonica bought Netherlands-based independent TV producer Endemol for $5.3 billion in 2000 and formed Telefonica Media (it agreed to sell the stake back to a consortium including the company's founder John de Mol in 2007 for $3.65 billion). After dropping out of the UK wireless license auction the company teamed up with Finland's Sonera (later acquired by Telia) to win a license in the German auction. But when merger talks with Dutch telecom carrier KPN broke down Villalonga resigned over disagreements on the direction of the company.

In 2001 Telefonica combined its Brazilian mobile telephone holdings with those of Portugal Telecom to form market leader Brasilcel. It then spent $2.7 billion in Mexico in 2001 and 2002 to buy four wireless operators and a 65%-stake in a fifth (Pegaso PCS) to achieve #2 in that market.

Telefonica acquired the assets of BellSouth Latin America Group which had holdings in 10 South and Central American countries in a $5.8 billion deal in 2005.

The company sold its stake in phone directory business Telefonica Publicidad e Informacion (TPI) to Yell Group in 2006. Also that year Telefonica purchased the remaining 7% stake of its Telefonica Moviles wireless arm that it did not already own and integrated those operations. The company's 2006 acquisition of UK-based mobile phone operator O2 for more than $31 billion gave Telefonica a strong presence in the UK and Germany. The Spanish operator previously had no operations in those regions.

In partnership with a coalition of Italian financial backers the company bought a stake in Telecom Italia for about $5.58 billion in mid-2007. Telefonica also sold its 75% stake in Dutch TV producer Endemol for $3.65 billion in 2007.

Telefonica exited Morocco in 2009 when it sold its 32% stake in Medi Telecom for E400 million ($572 million). Later that year it bought California-based communications software developer JAJAH Inc. for E145 million ($207 million) in cash to enhance its ability to offer computer telephony services to customers regardless of their location. JAJAH specializes in applications that allow interoperability between wired and wireless IP-based communications systems.

EXECUTIVES

Vice-Chairman, Isidro Faine Casas, age 71
Director, Sir David G. Arculus, age 67
Director, Peter Erskine, age 62
Vice-Chairman, Vitalino M. Nafria Aznar, age 63
Director, Pablo Isla Alvarez de Tejera, age 49
Director, Gonzalo Hinojosa Fernandez de Angulo, age 68
Director, Alfonso Ferrari Herrero, age 71
Director, Carlos Colomer Casellas, age 69
Director, Jose M. Abril Perez, age 61
Director, Antonio Massanell Lavilla, age 59
Legal and Board Secretary and Director, Ramiro Sanchez de Lerin Garcia-Ovies
Director, Jose Fernando de Almansa Moreno-Barreda, age 65
COO and Director, Julio Linares Lopez
Director, Javier de Paz Mancho, age 55
Chairwoman and CEO Telefonica Europe and Director, Eva Castillo Sanz, age 51

Director, Luiz Fernando Furlan, age 67
Auditors: Ernst&YoungS.L.

LOCATIONS

HQ: Telefonica, S.A.
Distrito Telefonica, Ronda de la Comunicacion, s/n, Madrid 28050
Phone: (34) 91 482 8700   **Fax:** (34) 91 482 8600
Web: www.telefonica.com

Sales

	% of total
Telefonica Latin	44
Telefonica	31
Telefonica	25
Total	**100**

PRODUCTS/OPERATIONS

Selected Subsidiaries

Atento Brasil S.A.
Brasilcel (Brazil)
Colombia Telecomunicaciones S.A. ESP.
Otecel S.A. (Ecuador)
Telcel S.A. (Venezuela)
Telecomunicac?es de S?o Paulo S.A (Brazil)
Telefonica Chile S.A.
Telefonica de Argentina S.A.
Telefonica del Peru S.A.A.
Telefonica Moviles Argentina S.A.
Telefonica Moviles Chile S.A.
Telefonica Moviles Colombia S.A.
Telefonica Moviles El Salvador S.A. de C.V.
Telefonica Moviles Guatemala S.A.
Telefonica Moviles Mexico S.A. de C.V.
Telefonica Moviles Nicaragua S.A.
Telefonica Moviles Panama S.A.
Telefonica Moviles Peru S.A.C.
Telefonica Moviles Uruguay S.A.
Telefonica O2 Czech Republic a. s.
Telefonica O2 Germany
Telefonica O2 Ireland Limited
Telefonica O2 Slovakia S R O
Telefonica O2 UK Limited

COMPETITORS

America Movil	Orange
BT	Orange Espa?a
Brasil Telecom	Portugal Telecom
COLT Group	Telecom Italia
Cableuropa	Telemar Norte Leste
Carphone Warehouse	TeliaSonera
Hutchison	Telmex
Telecommunications	Virgin Mobile
Jazztel	Vodafone
KPN	Vodafone Espa?a

HISTORICAL FINANCIALS
Company Type: Public

Income Statement
FYE: December 31

	REVENUE ($ mil.)	NET INCOME ($ mil.)	NET PROFIT MARGIN	EMPLOYEES
12/13	78,557	6,323	8.0%	291,027
12/12	82,188	5,177	6.3%	133,186
12/11	81,276	6,988	8.6%	291,027
12/10	81,288	13,607	16.7%	285,106
12/09	81,724	11,201	13.7%	257,426
Annual Growth	(1.0%)	(13.3%)	—	3.1%

2013 Year-End Financials

Debt ratio: 70.3%	No. of shares (mil.): —
Return on equity: 22.0%	Dividends
Cash ($ mil.): 13,735	Yield: 2.8%
Current ratio: 1.00	Payout: 63.0%
Long-term debt ($ mil.): 70,450	Market value ($ mil.): —

	STOCK PRICE ($)	P/E	PER SHARE ($)		
	FY Close	High/Low	Earnings	Dividends	Book Value
12/13	16.34	34 22	1.39	0.47	6.45
12/12	13.49	36 19	1.15	2.08	5.99
12/11	17.19	108 24	1.53	3.93	6.25
12/10	68.42	75 39	2.96	1.72	7.26
12/09	83.52	113 55	2.46	1.42	6.86
Annual Growth(33.5%) (1.5%)		—	—(13.3%)	(24.1%)	

Tesco PLC (United Kingdom)

Tesco is the #1 retailer in the UK and one of the top retailers in the world by annual sales behind Wal-Mart and Carrefour. Tesco and its subsidiaries have more than 6200 stores in 14 countries in Europe Asia and North America with about half located in the UK. Although built on the "pile it high sell it cheap" creed of founder Sir Jack Cohen Tesco abandoned its discount format to become a multi-format retailer in stores and online. Among its banners are Tesco Extra superstores; Tesco Express Tesco Metro and One Stop convenience stores; Homeplus hypermarket small express and virtual stores in South Korea; and Dobbies gardening stores in the UK Scotland and northern Ireland.

Geographic Reach

Tesco's presence spans about a dozen countries worldwide. Outside of the UK which is its largest market the company's other European-based stores are located in the Czech Republic Hungary Ireland Poland Slovakia and Turkey. In Asia it operates in China India Malaysia South Korea and Thailand. It is exiting the US market with the sale of its Fresh & Easy banner.

Operations

As a multi-format multi-channel retailer Tesco's various physical retail store operations are complemented by its online retailing operations including tesco.com (the world's largest online grocery retailer) and Tesco Direct. As a provider of financial services Tesco is the UK's largest supermarket bank through Tesco Personal Finance (which does business as Tesco Bank). Through wholly owned dunnhumby Tesco offers data analytics and customer insight to such clients as Coca-Cola Kroger and Procter & Gamble. The dunnhumby group includes marketing expert BzzAgent and price optimization company KSS Retail.

Tesco boasts an impressive presence in Asia. Homeplus in South Korea is the company's largest international business with some 475 stores consisting of large hypermarkets and small Tesco Express stores an online business and virtual stores in subway and bus stops where customers can buy products via their mobile devices and get them delivered to their homes. In Southeast Asia Tesco is a market leader in Thailand where it operates locally as Tesco Lotus. It operates in Malaysia with conglomerate partner Sime Darby while in India the company has an exclusive franchise agreement with the retail arm of Tata Group to develop Star Bazaar hypermarkets there.

In China Tesco is playing catch up to global rivals Wal-Mart and Carrefour which entered that market nearly a decade before Tesco. There it has more than 100 stores along the eastern seaboard provinces and it is developing shopping malls

under the Lifespace brand that are anchored by Tesco hypermarkets. China is also a major sourcing market for Tesco; it has international sourcing headquarters in Hong Kong and a hub in Singapore.

Financial Performance

Tesco is under pressure to reverse a slide in its core UK business after 20 years of solid growth and profitability. In early 2012 the company issued its first earnings warning in two decades. While group sales rose about 5% in fiscal 2012 (ends February) compared to the previous year and group profit rose modestly Tesco lost money at home. The UK lagged Asia Europe and the US in sales growth and profitability.

Strategy

After being criticized for allowing its UK business to deteriorate while it focused on expansion abroad Tesco is refocusing its strategy on core UK growth which is still a key driver of sales and profit. In fiscal 2013 it is investing Â1 billion (roughly $1.6 billion) to improve the shopping experience for its UK customers in stores and online. The retailer will overhaul its existing UK stores by adding more staff and improving in-store service accelerating its remodeling schedule and offering better prices and more personalized promotions. It will also add about 38% less retail space in Britain this year than last as it moves away from big stores in favor of smaller shops and the Internet. To that end Tesco will ramp up investment in its online operations and accelerate the roll out of its Click and Collect program which allows shoppers to pick up orders placed online.

Tesco has seen its market share decline in recent years as rival Wal-Mart-owned ASDA and deep discounters such as ALDI and Lidl increase their share of the fiercely competitive UK grocery market. To win the hearts of cash-strapped consumers and keep them in its stores Tesco has expanded its own Tesco Value line of discount products and its Tesco Finest brand —both of which exceed Â1 billion in annual sales. Also Tesco is facing even stronger competition from its chief UK rival ASDA which recently acquired the Netto chain of discount stores in the UK. To bolster its One Stope Stores convenience chain Tesco acquired more than 75 stores from privately owned Mills Group (boosting its store count to more than 600 across England and Wales) in 2011.

Outside of the UK Tesco is strategically reviewing certain underperforming international operations including its US-based Fresh & Easy business a chain of 200 unprofitable stores launched in 2007. Indeed Tesco has struck a deal to exit the US with the sale of about 150 Fresh & Easy stores to The Yucaipa Cos. (It will close the remaining 50 stores). Across the Pacific in a two-stage process Tesco is selling its 50% stake in its loss-making Tesco Japan business to AEON for a nominal sum after after nine years of struggling in that market.

HISTORY

With WWI behind him in 1919 Jack Cohen invested his serviceman's gratuity in a grocery stall in London's East End. He introduced his first private-label product Tesco Tea in 1924 —the name was the combination of the initials of his tea supplier (T. E. Stockwell) and the first two letters of Cohen's last name. By the late 1920s Cohen had several stalls and in 1929 he opened his first store under the Tesco name in Edgeware London.

Cohen founded Tesco Stores Limited in 1932. During the rest of the decade the company added more than 100 stores mainly in London. Cohen visited the US in 1935 studying its self-service supermarkets and returned to England with a plan of using a similar "pile it high and sell it cheap" format. Delayed by WWII Tesco opened its first Amer-

ican-styled store in 1947 and went public that year as Tesco Stores Holdings. By 1950 the company ran 20 self-service stores.

Tesco grew primarily through acquisitions during the 1950s and 1960s adding about 600 stores. By the early 1970s however competition and a recession battered Tesco. Managing director Ian MacLaurin initiated radical changes including abandoning trading stamps and to shed its downmarket image refurbishing stores with a more upscale decor. A price-slashing initiative in 1977 dramatically increased Tesco's market share within a year. Because cheap brands were best-sellers Tesco began creating its own private-label brands. The company also started closing unprofitable stores while opening superstores some with gas stations.

In 1979 the year Sir Jack Cohen died Tesco entered Ireland by buying Three Guys (abandoning the effort in 1986). In 1983 the company became Tesco and two years later it named MacLaurin as chairman. By 1991 Tesco was the UK's largest independent gasoline retailer.

Looking for new opportunities in 1992 Tesco introduced small urban stores called Tesco Metro and the next year began expanding outside England acquiring stores in France and Scotland. In 1994 it acquired an initial 51% stake in Global a 43-store grocery chain in Hungary. That year it also opened Tesco Express (combination convenience stores and gas stations).

Tesco acquired 31 Stavia stores in Poland in 1995; a year later it added 13 Kmart stores in the Czech Republic and Slovakia. Tesco returned to Ireland in 1997 by acquiring 109 Associated British Food stores. It also launched its financial services division —Tesco Personal Finance —that year and named John Gardiner as chairman (replacing the retiring MacLaurin) and Terry Leahy as CEO. In 1998 the retailer purchased 75% of food retailer Lotus with 13 stores in Thailand. The following year Tesco partnered with Samsung to develop Homeplus hypermarkets in South Korea.

By 2000 Tesco's profitable online shopping business was one of the world's most successful and the company made it a separate subsidiary Tesco.com. To build on that success Tesco bought a 35% stake in GroceryWorks a subsidiary of the US Safeway grocery chain in June 2001.

Tesco acquired the travel company First Class Leisure in March 2002 and renamed the business Tesco Freetime. The acquisition was yet another move by the supermarket chain to expand beyond groceries. Tesco became the market leader in the fragmented Polish food retailing arena by acquiring German hypermarket operator HIT in July 2002. In January 2003 Tesco completed the acquisition of the British convenience store chain T&S Stores for Â519 million. In July it acquired a 95% stake in Japanese convenience store operator C Two-Network for about Â139 million. In November Tesco acquired Kipa a small hypermarket operator in Turkey for Â96 million.

To strengthen its presence in the convenience market Tesco bought T&S Stores (now One Stop Stores) in 2003 and has converted many of its 800-plus shops to its Express banner.

In April 2004 David Reid became non-executive chairman replacing Gardiner who retired from Tesco. In August Tesco sold the Dillons chain of newsstands to TM Retail for an undisclosed amount. Tesco had acquired Dillons when it purchased T&S Stores.

Tesco transferred some 770 back office jobs in January 2005 from the UK to Bangalore India where it opened a software development and accounting office. In mid-year Tesco opened its first Kipa store in Turkey since it acquired the Turkish chain in 2003. The 50000-sq.-ft. store brought Tesco's store count in Turkey to six.

In 2006 the company bought 27 small stores from Edeka in the Czech Republic. In the fall it launched a higher-end 30-piece apparel line for men and women called F&F Collection by Lee Rees-Oliviere (Tesco's head designer recruited in 2005 from Marks and Spencer). In October Tesco sold its 38% stake in Internet grocer Grocery-Works to Safeway its partner in the venture. In December Tesco increased its stake in China's Ting Hsin Holding Corp. to 90% from 50% in a deal valued at about $352 million. (Tesco entered China in 2004 paying approximately $275 million for 50% in Ting Hsin's subsidiary Ting Cao.)

Tesco increased its international selling space by 25% in the fiscal year ending in February 2007. In early November the British retailer opened its first US store: a Fresh & Easy Neighborhood Market in Hemet California (outside Los Angeles). Also in 2007 Tesco acquired nearly a two-thirds ownership stake in the Scottish garden center operator Dobbies Garden Centers PLC. (It increased its ownership to 100% in July 2008).

In August 2008 Tesco bought the UK operation of Handleman a leading UK-based distributor and store merchandiser of books music computer games and other products for about Â9.4 million (about $16 million). Tesco retained a substantial portion of Handleman's UK workforce. Also that year Tesco made a major acquisition of a chain of hypermarkets in South Korea from E-Land Group for about $2 billion.

Tesco bought out its joint venture partner — Royal Bank of Scotland —in Tesco Personal Finance (TPF) for about $1.9 billion in 2008. TPF which was formed in 1997 has grown to serve more than 6 million customer accounts and offers insurance credit cards loans mortgages and savings products. The purchase is part of Tesco's strategy to expand into the service sector which is outpacing food in terms of growth. The timing of its push into retail banking —just ahead of the banking crisis in the UK —was auspicious. Tesco is enjoying increased demand for its banking services as distrust of traditional banks has grown in the aftermath of big bank bailouts in the UK during the financial crisis. TPF is also getting into the auto and home insurance markets via a partnership with the UK arm of Fortis Insurance.

In early 2011 international executive Philip Clarke replaced retiring longtime chief executive Terry Leahy.

Also that year Tesco acquired an 80% stake in the British video-on-demand (VoD) service Blinkbox which competes with Amazon.com's LoveFilm. Tesco entered the VoD market to position itself for the next phase of Internet-driven home entertainment even though the retailer is a huge seller of DVDs.

EXECUTIVES

Deputy Chairman, Patrick J. Cescau, age 65
CEO Tesco Personal Finance Limited (Tesco Bank), Benny Higgins, age 53
Board Member; CEO Retail Services, Andrew T. Higginson, age 56, $1,597,200 total compensation
Board Member; Deputy CEO and Chief Marketing Officer; President and CEO Fresh & Easy Neighborhood Market, Tim J. R. Mason, age 56, $1,995,322 total compensation
Marketing Director UK, Carolyn Bradley
Director Investor Relations, Steve Webb, age 53
Board Member; Corporate and Legal Affairs Director, Lucy Neville-Rolfe, age 61, $1,025,626 total compensation
Commercial Director Clothing Electronics and General Merchandise, Laura Wade-Gery, age 48
Head Retail Operations and Logistics UK, Noel W. Robbins
Chairman, Sir Richard Broadbent, age 60

Chief Clothing, Richard Jones
Board Member; Company Secretary, Jonathan Lloyd, age 48
CEO and Board Member, Philip (Phil) Clarke, age 53, $1,503,821 total compensation
CEO Tesco Mobile and Tesco Telecoms, Lance Batchelor
CFO and Board Member, Laurie McIlwee, age 51, $838,312 total compensation
Buyer Tea, Paul Grigg
Tesco Salad Food Buyer, Sam Wright
Senior Buying Manager, Dryell Simon
CEO Asia, Trevor Masters
Director Media Relations, Trevor Datson
Online Food and Internet Retailing Director, Ken Towle, age 49
COO UK, Bob Robbins
Director Finance UK, Mike Iddon
Group Director Digital and Marketing, Matt Atkinson
CIO, Mike McNamara, age 49
Group Chief Financial Officer; Executive Director, Laurie McIlwee
Senior Independent Director, Patrick J. Cescau, age 66
Board Member, Kenneth J. (Ken) Hydon, age 69
Board Member; CEO Retail Services, Andrew T. Higginson, age 56
Board Member; Deputy CEO and Chief Marketing Officer; President and CEO Fresh & Easy Neighborhood Market, Tim J. R. Mason, age 56
Board Member, Stuart Chambers, age 58
Board Member; Corporate and Legal Affairs Board Member, Karen Cook, age 60
Board Member; Company Secretary, Jonathan Lloyd, age 48
CEO and Board Member, Philip (Phil) Clarke, age 53
CFO and Board Member, Laurie McIlwee, age 51
Board Member, Jacqueline Tammenoms Bakker, age 60
Non-Executive Independent Director, Deanna Oppenheimer
Auditors: PricewaterhouseCoopersLLP

LOCATIONS

HQ: Tesco PLC (United Kingdom)
Tesco House, Delamare Road, Cheshunt, Hertfordshire EN8 9SL
Phone: (44) 1992 632222   **Fax:** (44) 1992 630794
Web: www.tescoplc.com

2012 Retail Sales

	% of total
Europe	
UK	67
Other	16
Asia	16
US	1
Total	**100**

2012 Stores

	No.
UK	2,979
Asia	1,719
Rest of	1,351
US	185
Total	**6,234**

PRODUCTS/OPERATIONS

2012 UK Stores

	No.
Tesco	1,427
One	613
Tesco	471
Tesco	230
Tesco	190
Dobbies	31
Tesco Home	13
Other	4
Total	**2,975**

Selected Subsidiaries and Joint Ventures

Dobbies Garden Centres PLC (100% Scotland)
dunnhumby Ltd. (100% data analysis England)
Ek-Chai Distribution System Co. Ltd. (86% Lotus stores Thailand)
One Stop Stores Ltd. (100% convenience stores England and Wales)
Tesco Ireland Ltd. (100% Republic of Ireland)
Tesco Japan Co. Ltd. (100% Japan)
Tesco Kipa (93% hypermarkets Turkey)
Tesco Mobile Ltd. (50% telecommunications)
Tesco Personal Finance Group Limited (50%; credit cards savings accounts loans online banking insurance)
Tesco Polska Sp. Z o.o. (100% Czestochowa stores Poland)
Tesco Stores CR a.s. (100% Czech Republic)
Tesco Stores SR a.s. (100% Slovakia)
Tesco Qinhuangdo Property Ltd. (50% PRC)

COMPETITORS

A.S. Watson	METRO AG
ALDI	Marks & Spencer
ASDA	Matalan
Alliance Boots	Musgrave Retail
BP	Partners
Carphone Warehouse	NEXT plc
Carrefour	Primark
Co-operative Group	Royal Dutch Shell
Convenience Retail	SPAR Handels
Asia	Seven & i
Dairy Farm	Stater Bros.
International	T.K. Maxx
Dunnes Stores	The Gap
Exxon Mobil	Virgin Money
Iceland Foods	Vons
J Sainsbury	Waitrose
John Lewis	Wal-Mart
LAWSON	Wm Morrison
LOVEFiLM	Supermarkets
Lidl	Wyevale Garden

HISTORICAL FINANCIALS

Company Type: Public

Income Statement

FYE: February 22

	REVENUE ($ mil.)	NET INCOME ($ mil.)	NET PROFIT MARGIN	EMPLOYEES
02/14	105,931	1,623	1.5%	902,312
02/13	98,950	189	0.2%	954,225
02/12	101,973	4,433	4.3%	925,759
02/11	98,061	4,272	4.4%	877,103
02/10	86,770	3,547	4.1%	844,432
Annual Growth	5.1%	(17.8%)	—	1.7%

2014 Year-End Financials

Debt ratio: 37.2%
Return on equity: 6.2%
Cash ($ mil.): 4,176
Current ratio: 0.77
Long-term debt ($ mil.): 15,505
No. of shares (mil.): —
Dividends
Yield: 0.0%
Payout: 839.5%
Market value ($ mil.): —

	STOCK PRICE ($) FY Close	P/E High/Low		PER SHARE ($) Earnings	Dividends	Book Value
02/14	16.76	407319		0.20	1.69	3.03
02/13	17.14	27452127		0.02	1.62	3.15
02/12	15.24	155101		0.55	1.72	3.50
02/11	20.03	164118		0.53	1.44	3.31
02/10	19.21	190 90		0.45	1.29	2.79
Annual Growth	(3.4%)	—	(18.0%)		7.0%	2.1%

Thyssen Krupp Steel AG (Germany)

LOCATIONS

HQ: Thyssen Krupp Steel AG (Germany)
ThyssenKrupp Allee 1, Essen D-45143
Phone: (49) 201 844 0   **Fax:** (49) 201 844 536000
Web: www.thyssenkruppl.com

HISTORICAL FINANCIALS

Company Type: Public

Income Statement

FYE: September 30

	REVENUE ($ mil.)	NET INCOME ($ mil.)	NET PROFIT MARGIN	EMPLOYEES
09/13	52,044	(1,884)	—	156,856
09/12	53,706	(5,483)	—	167,961
09/99	10,472	85	0.8%	54,388
Annual Growth	12.1%	—	—	7.9%

2013 Year-End Financials

Debt ratio: 33.9%
Return on equity: (-44.8%)
Cash ($ mil.): 5,146
Current ratio: 1.11
Long-term debt ($ mil.): 9,387

No. of shares (mil.): 514
Dividends
  Yield: —
  Payout: —
Market value ($ mil.): —

	STOCK PRICE ($) FY Close	P/E High/Low	PER SHARE ($) Earnings	Dividends	Book Value
09/13	0.00	— —	(3.66)	0.00	5.88
09/12	0.00	— —	(10.65)	0.00	10.02
Annual Growth	—	— —	—	—	(3.7%)

ThyssenKrupp AG

How do you say "giant engineering and steel company" in German? Try ThyssenKrupp and pronounce it "TISS-in kroop." The company is one of the world's largest steel producers and operates worldwide in two business areas: Materials and Technologies. The first comprises the company's steel (carbon and stainless steel) and materials services businesses. ThyssenKrupp's Technologies group consists of its elevators unit marine systems components technology (for the auto and engineering markets) and plant technology (construction and environmental services) segments. Although its combined interests range from elevators to shipbuilding the company has historically relied upon the steel market.

ThyssenKrupp's diversified industrial operations are split into seven operating business areas plus Inoxum (formerly Stainless Global) as a discontinued operation. The Materials division consists of the Steel Europe Steel Americas and Materials Services units. The Technologies division comprises the company's Elevator Technology Plant Technology Components Technology and Marine Systems units.

In 2011 ThyssenKrupp's revenues increased 15% from the previous year (for both continuing operations and before Stainless Global carve-out sales figures). Although growth continued to be weak in Europe and the US during 2011 the Ger-

man economy was positive and the group's rise in orders and sales increased in most business areas. That year the company received strong demand for its flat carbon steel auto components and naval shipbuilding operations. Five business areas increased earnings from the previous year with Steel Europe being the largest contributor. The company's net loss of Â1.8 billion ($2.3 billion) in 2011 compared with a net income of Â927 million ($1.2 billion) in 2010 resulted from impairment charges for the discontinued operations of its Stainless Global business and its Steel Americas unit (from cost overruns in the build of its plant in Brazil and the weakness of markets in the US and Europe).

To pay down debt the company decided in 2011 to divest Â10 billion ($14.4 billion) worth of noncore assets. Stainless Global its stainless steel business was the largest asset on the chopping block. At 3 million tons a year Stainless Global was Europe's largest stainless steel producer. ThyssenKrupp followed in the footsteps of rival ArcelorMittal which spun off its stainless unit into a new company Aperam earlier in 2011.

ThyssenKrupp split off Stainless Global from its other operations and renamed it Inoxum. Inoxum's operations include the manufacture of stainless steel flat products and materials such as nickel alloys titanium and zirconium. Early in 2012 ThyssenKrupp agreed to sell Inoxum to Finnish company Outokumpu for Â2.7 billion ($3.54 billion). The deal awaits approval by the European Commission after Outokumpu divests some of its combined operations with Inoxum.

In 2012 the company also offloaded ThyssenKrupp Steel Europe's lightweight steel construction elements group to Irish company Kingspan.

In 2013 ArcelorMittal formed a joint venture with Nippon Steel & Sumitomo Metal to buy ThyssenKrupp Steel USA from ThyssenKrupp for $1.5 billion. The deal is expected to deliver $60 million in annual savings.

ThyssenKrupp sold its metal forming unit which supplies the automotive industry to Spain's Gestamp Automocion in 2011. The metals unit was no longer part of ThyssenKrupp's core business of Steel Europe. In another move to unload noncore businesses and pay down debt that year ThyssenKrupp sold Xervon a service provider for the processing construction and energy and power industries to German water and recycling services company Remondis.

In another exit that year ThyssenKrupp terminated its submarine sales joint venture with Ferrostaal which is owned by Germany's MAN group and Abu Dhabi's International Petroleum Investment Co. (IPIC). The company is reorganizing its Marine Systems business unit.

While continuing to divest noncore operations the group is making selective investments in key growth areas. It is making major investments in projects in Brazil and the US. Its Elevator Technology has made strategic acquisitions in the US and Canada as well as smaller buys in the Benelux countries France Italy and Spain. The Plant Technology unit has expanded its coke plant activities by acquiring Tokyo-based Otto Corporation. Through its Components Technology unit ThyssenKrupp has invested in crankshaft factories in Nanjing China.

ThyssenKrupp is a product of the 1999 merger of Thyssen AG and Fried. Krupp AG Hoesch-Krupp. The Alfried Krupp von Bohlen und Halbach Foundation owns 25% of the company.

HISTORY

Formed separately in the 1800s both Thyssen and Krupp flourished in their early years under family control. Friedrich Krupp opened his steel factory in 1811. He died in 1826 and left the nearly

bankrupt factory in the hands of his 14-year-old son Alfred who turned the business around. At the first World's Fair in 1851 Alfred unveiled a steel cannon far superior to earlier bronze models.

Twenty years later August Thyssen founded a puddling and rolling mill near Mulheim. He bought small factories and mines and by WWI he ran Germany's largest iron and steel company. During the world wars the resources of both companies were turned toward military efforts.

Post-WWII years were tough for both companies. Thyssen was split up by the Allies and when it began production again in 1953 it consisted of one steel plant. In the Krupp camp Alfred's great-grandson Alfried was convicted in 1948 of using slave labor during WWII. Released from prison in 1951 Alfried rebuilt Krupp. After near ruin following WWII both companies emerged and enjoyed a resurgence along with the German economy in which they prospered and expanded during the 1950s.

By the 1980s Thyssen's businesses included ships locomotives offshore oil rigs specialty steel and metals trading and distribution. Krupp continued to grow and in 1992 it took over engineering and steelmaking concern Hoesch AG. (Eberhard Hoesch had begun making railroad tracks in the 1820s. The company grew and expanded into infrastructure and building products.)

The new Fried. Krupp AG Hoesch-Krupp bought Italian specialty steelmaker Acciai Speciali Terni chemical-plant builder Uhde and South African shipper J.H. Bachmann. Its automotive division formed a joint venture in Brazil and added production sites in China Mexico Romania and the US.

In 1997 Thyssen expanded in North America with its $675 million acquisition of Giddings & Lewis (machine tools US) and the purchase of Copper & Brass Sales (metals processing and distributing).

Krupp attempted a hostile takeover of Thyssen in 1997. The takeover failed but the companies soon agreed to merge their steel operations to form Thyssen Krupp Stahl. Bigger plans were in the works and in 1998 the two companies agreed to merge. That year Thyssen sold its Plusnet fixed-line phone business to Esprit Telecom Group.

In 1999 Krupp's automotive division (Krupp Hoesch Automotive) bought Cummins' Atlas Crankshaft subsidiary. Thyssen also bought US-based Dover's elevator business for $1.1 billion. Krupp and Thyssen completed their merger in 1999. The company planned to spin off its steel operations but held off due to its success in 2000. ThyssenKrupp did however sell its Krupp Kunststofftechnik unit (plastic molding machines) for about $183 million. To speed corporate decision-making the company made plans to scrap its dual-management structure in 2001.

Early in 2001 ThyssenKrupp agreed to buy 51% of Fiat unit Magneti Marelli's suspension-systems and shock-absorbers business. It also had the option of buying the remainder after 2004. In 2002 the company formed alliances with NKK and Kawasaki Steel to share its steel sheet making technologies while expanding its business with Japanese automotive makers in Europe. ThyssenKrupp's joint venture with Chinese steelmaker ANSC Angang New Steel known as TAGAL began producing galvanized coil of which about 80% will be used in China's burgeoning automotive industry.

In 2004 ThyssenKrupp sold its residential real estate unit for around $2.8 billion to a consortium of real estate funds operated by Morgan Stanley and Corpus-Immobiliengruppe. It divested the automotive segment of the capital goods unit in 2006 selling it off in pieces.

ThyssenKrupp opened three major new steel facilities in the Americas in 2010. A new integrated steel mill in Santa Cruz Brazil started production in mid-year. The $7 billion plant the company's biggest project ever is a partnership with South American giant Vale SA which owns a 25% stake in the venture. The company also began production at two plants in Calvert Alabama: a $3.6 billion carbon steel plant and a $1.4 billion stainless steel rolling plant. The company also constructed —and consolidated its corporate staff in —a new headquarters building in Essen Germany in 2010.

In 2010 ThyssenKrupp sold its Hamburg-based mega-yacht and shipbuilding operations to Abu Dhabi MAR Group. ThyssenKrupp is exiting the civil shipbuilding business to focus on constructing military vessels. The company also sold its interest in Hellenic Shipyards to Abu Dhabi MAR following difficulties related to the Greek government's financial problems.

Heinrich Hiesinger was named CEO of ThyssenKrupp in 2011. He replaced Ekkehard Schulz who retired. Hiesinger was previously an executive of German engineering company Siemens AG.

EXECUTIVES

Member Executive Board Technologies; CEO Elevator Technology, Olaf Berlien, age 52, $556,512 total compensation
Head Corporate Investor Relations, Claus Ehrenbeck
Chairman Executive Board, Heinrich Hiesinger, age 54
Vice Chairman, Bertin Eichler, age 62
Member Executive Board Materials; CEO Steel Europe and Steel Americas, Edwin Eichler, age 56, $700,320 total compensation
Member Executive Board Human Resources, Ralph Labonte, age 61, $653,280 total compensation
Member Executive Board Controlling and Risk, Guido Kerkhoff, age 46
Corporate Center Communications Strategy and Technology, Stefan Ettwig
Member Supervisory Board, M. Christian Streiff, age 58
Honorary Chairman, Gunter Vogelsang
Member Supervisory Board, Hans-Peter Keitel, age 67
Honorary Chairman, Berthold Beitz, age 71
Member Supervisory Board, Kersten von Schenck, age 64
Vice Chairman, Bertin Eichler, age 61
Member Supervisory Board, Prof Bernard Pellens, age 58
Member Supervisory Board, Wilhelm Segerath, age 62
Member Supervisory Board, Prof Ulrich Lehner, age 69
Member Supervisory Board, Peer Steinbruck, age 66
Member Supervisory Board, Jurgen R. Thumann, age 72
Member Supervisory Board, Prof Beatrice Weder di Mauro, age 50
Auditors: KPMGDeutscheTreuhand-GesellschaftAG

LOCATIONS

HQ: ThyssenKrupp AG
ThyssenKrupp Allee 1, Essen D-45143
Phone: (49) 201 844 0   **Fax:** (49) 201 844 53600
Web: www.thyssenkrupp.com

Sales

	% of total
EU	
Other countries	29
Asia/Pacific	12
Total	**100**

PRODUCTS/OPERATIONS

Sales (Continued Operations)

	% of total
Materials	
Materials Services	32
Steel	
Steel Europe	28
Steel America	2
Components Technology	15
Elevator Technology	11
Plant Technology	9
Marine Systems	3
Total	**100**

COMPETITORS

Acerinox
ArcelorMittal
Bechtel
Descours & Cabaud
GEA Group
ITOCHU
Ingersoll-Rand
JFE Holdings
Kobe Steel
MAN
Magna International
Marubeni
Nippon Steel & Sumitomo Metal Corporation
POSCO
Qingdao Iron and Steel
Schindler Holding
Sumitomo Metal Industries
Tata Europe
United States Steel
United Technologies

HISTORICAL FINANCIALS
Company Type: Public

Income Statement
FYE: September 30

	REVENUE ($ mil.)	NET INCOME ($ mil.)	NET PROFIT MARGIN	EMPLOYEES
09/13	52,044	(1,884)	—	156,856
09/12	51,880	(6,035)	—	167,961
09/11	58,490	(1,741)	—	180,050
09/10	58,084	1,122	1.9%	177,346
09/09	59,373	(2,718)	—	187,495
Annual Growth	**(3.2%)**	**—**	**—**	**(4.4%)**

2013 Year-End Financials

Debt ratio: 33.9%
Return on equity: (-48.1%)
Cash ($ mil.): 5,146
Current ratio: 1.11
Long-term debt ($ mil.): 9,387
No. of shares (mil.): 514
Dividends
  Yield: —
  Payout: —
Market value ($ mil.): 12,317

	STOCK PRICE ($) FY Close	P/E High/Low	PER SHARE ($) Earnings	Dividends	Book Value
09/13	23.94	— —	(3.66)	0.00	5.88
09/12	21.50	— —	(11.73)	0.00	8.94
09/11	24.60	— —	(3.66)	0.00	23.63
09/10	31.95	45 23	2.41	0.00	27.96
09/09	34.47	— —	(5.87)	0.00	25.04
Annual Growth	**(8.7%)** (30.4%)		**—**	**—**	**—**

Toho Bank, Ltd. (The)

The Toho Bank is a regional bank serving the Fukushima Prefecture in Japan. Armed with more than 115 branches and ATMs installed at more than 230 locations the bank offers local customers businesses and public institutions the traditional array of banking services including savings lending real estate venture firm support and financing and foreign and domestic exchange products. Toho Bank was established in 1941 and owns subsidiaries and affiliated companies such as The Toho Real Estate Service Co. The Toho Card Co. and The Toho Staff Service Co.

EXECUTIVES

Managing Director, Akira Kondo
Chairman, Toshio Seya
President, Seishi Kitamura
Managing Director Chief Director of Sales, Hiroyuki Motoyanagi
Managing Director Director of Main Store Sales, Tadashi Uchiyama
Manager of Koriyama Office, Kensuke Abe
Managing Director, Hiroshi Endo
Managing Director Chief Director of Business Director of Marketing and Finance, Tsugunobu Amano
Managing Director, Mamoru Sakuma
Manager of Tokyo Office, Toshikatsu Takaara
Director of Audit, Masahiko Watanabe
Manager of Aizu Office, Satoshi Saito
Director of Funds, Shoichi Kushiya
Auditors: Ernst&YoungShinNihon

LOCATIONS

HQ: Toho Bank, Ltd. (The)
3-25 Ohmachi, Fukushima 960-8633
Phone: (81) 24 523 3131   **Fax:** (81) 24 524 1583
Web: www.tohobank.co.jp

COMPETITORS

Aozora Bank
Iyo Bank
Mitsubishi UFJ Financial Group
Miyazaki Bank
Shizuoka Bank
Towa Bank

HISTORICAL FINANCIALS
Company Type: Public

Income Statement
FYE: March 31

	ASSETS ($ mil.)	NET INCOME ($ mil.)	INCOME AS % OF ASSETS	EMPLOYEES
03/14	52,170	88	0.2%	1,923
03/13	49,604	67	0.1%	1,925
03/12	51,716	57	0.1%	1,934
03/11	39,387	54	0.1%	1,963
03/10	33,811	70	0.2%	1,945
Annual Growth	**11.5%**	**6.1%**	**—**	**(0.3%)**

2014 Year-End Financials

Return on assets: 0.1%
Return on equity: 5.5%
Long-term debt ($ mil.): —
No. of shares (mil.): 252
Sales ($ mil): 601
Dividends
  Yield: —
  Payout: —
Market value ($ mil.): —

Tokio Marine Holdings Inc

Tokio Marine Holdings might have old roots but it still knows how to learn new tricks. Japan's oldest property/casualty insurance company the firm has one of the largest insurance sales networks in Japan and has expanded its insurance operations to about 40 additional countries in Asia Europe and North America. Through Tokio Marine & Nichido Fire (TMNF) Nisshin Fire Philadelphia Insurance Companies Kiln and other subsidiaries Tokio Marine Holdings provides marine property/casualty personal accident fire auto and life insurance as well as reinsurance. It also offers asset management pension plans and other services.

Geographic Reach

The firm has insurance operations in about 40 countries throughout Asia Europe and North America. The majority of Tokio Marine's revenue comes from Japan (about 85% in fiscal 2012).

Financial Performance

Tokio Marine's revenue has been trending upward during recent fiscal years. The firm claimed about $41.5 billion in revenue for fiscal 2012 up from the $39.7 billion it reported for fiscal 2011 and the $38.5 billion it brought in during fiscal 2010.

Mergers and Acquisitions

In mid-2012 Tokio Marine made another large US acquisition this time of property/casualty and specialty life insurer Delphi Financial Group. The $2.7 billion acquisition enhanced Tokio Marine's property/casualty offerings by adding Safety National Casualty's workers' compensation offerings and Matrix Absence Management's disability offerings; it will brought the company into the US life insurance market through the addition of Delphi's Reliance Standard Life unit which provides group employee benefits and individual annuities.

In 2011 TMNF bought up CNA Financial Corporation's 50% interest in First Insurance Company of Hawaii the state's largest property/casualty insurance firm. TMNF had held the other 50% of the company since 1999 and buying up the balance of First Insurance Company of Hawaii sped up its US expansion efforts.

Other potential countries targeted for growth efforts include China and India.

HISTORY

After the US forced Japan to open to trade in 1854 Western marine insurers began operating there. In 1878 Japan's government organized backers for a Japanese marine insurance firm. Tokio Marine and Fire Insurance was founded the next year.

Tokio grew quickly insuring trading companies like Mitsubishi and Mitsui; it soon had offices in London Paris and New York. Increased competition in the 1890s forced it to curtail its foreign operations and begin using brokers in most other countries.

Victory in the Russo-Japanese War of 1904-05 buoyed the country but the economy slowed as it demobilized. Businesses responded by forming cooperative groups known as "zaibatsu". Tokio Marine and Fire was allied with the Mitsubishi group.

Before WWI Tokio expanded by adding fire personal accident theft and auto insurance and it continued to buy foreign sales brokers. Japan's insurance industry consolidated in the 1920s and the company bought up smaller competitors. The 1923 Tokyo earthquake hit the industry hard but Tokio's new fire insurance operations had little exposure.

Most of Tokio's foreign operations were seized during WWII. In 1944 Tokio merged with Mitsubishi Marine Insurance and Meiji Fire Insurance. Business grew in WWII but wartime destruction left Tokio with nothing to insure and no money to pay claims.

After the war Tokio slowly recovered and resumed overseas operations. Although the US had

dismantled the "zaibatsu" during occupation Tokio allied once again with Mitsubishi when Japan's government rebuilt most of the old groups as "keiretsu".

During the 1950s and 1960s the company grew its personal lines adding homeowners coverage. Domestic business slowed during the 1970s and 1980s and Tokio boosted operations overseas. It added commercial property/casualty insurer Houston General Insurance (a US company sold in 1997) Tokio Reinsurance and interests in insurance and investment management firms.

In the 1980s the firm invested heavily in real estate through "jusen" (mortgage companies). Japan's overheated real estate market collapsed in the early 1990s dumping masses of nonperforming assets on "jusen" and their investors (the country's major banks and insurers including Tokio).

Deregulation began in 1996 and economic recession soon followed. In 1998 Tokio joined other members of the Mitsubishi group including Bank of Tokyo-Mitsubishi and Meiji Life Insurance to form investment banking pension and trust joint ventures. The firm also formed its own investment trust and allied with such foreign financial companies as BANK ONE and United Asset Management to develop new investment products. Brokerage firm Charles Schwab Tokio Marine Securities a joint venture was launched in 1999. That year Tokio consolidated its foreign reinsurance operations into Tokio Marine Global Re in Dublin Ireland and kicked off a business push that included reorganizing its agent force and planning for online sales.

Millea Holdings was created in 2002 as the holding company for the merger between Tokio Marine and Fire and Nichido Fire and Marine. The two were combined and renamed Tokio Marine & Nichido Fire Insurance a subsidiary of Millea Holdings.

The company's 2005 acquisition of Real Seguros allowed the company to bring its life insurance products to Brazil (renamed Tokio Marine Seguradora). In 2006 Millea acquired Nisshin Fire and Marine Insurance Company as a separately operated subsidiary. In 2007 the firm purchased Asia General Holdings and its life insurance subsidiaries which operated in Singapore and Malaysia. It also purchased Japanese fire insurance provider Nihon Kousei Kyousaikai.

In 2008 Millea Holdings changed its name to Tokio Marine Holdings to reflect the positive brand recognition associated with the Tokio Marine name.

EXECUTIVES

Chairman, Kunio Ishihara, age 71
EVP, Takaaki Tamai, age 64
EVP, Hiroshi Amemiya, age 64
President Nisshin Fire, Hiroshi Miyajima, age 64
Chairman, Shuzo Sumi
Senior Managing Executive Officer International Business Development, Hiroshi Endo
President and CEO, Tsuyoshi Nagano
Managing Executive Officer, Masashi Oba
General Manager Personnel Planning Dept., Takefumi Horiuchi
General Manager of Domestic Business Development Dept, Mitsuhiko Uehira
Managing Director General Manager of Corporate Accounting Dept, Hirokazu Fujita
General Manager of International Business Development Dept, Ichiro Ishii
President Tokio Marine & Nichido Life, Toshifumi Kitazawa
EVP, Kazuo Kouduki
Auditors: ChuoAoyamaPricewaterhouseCoopers

LOCATIONS

HQ: Tokio Marine Holdings Inc
1-2-1 Marunouchi, Chiyoda-ku, Tokyo 100-0005
Phone: (81) 3 6212 3333
Web: www.tokiomarinehd.com/en/

Sales

	% of total
Japan	85
Other	15
Total	**100**

PRODUCTS/OPERATIONS

Sales

	% of total
Property/casualty	78
Life	13
Other	9
Total	**100**

Selected Mergers and Acquisitions

FY2012
Delphi Financial Group ($2.7 billion; Wilmington DE; specialty life insurer)

COMPETITORS

AIG	Hiscox
Allianz	ING
Aviva	MS&AD Holdings
Brit Insurance	Markel
Chubb Corp	NKSJ Holdings
Dai-ichi Life	Nippon Life Insurance
Daido Life	Prudential plc
Equity Insurance	Sumitomo Life
Fuji Fire and Marine	Travelers Companies
HCC Insurance	Zurich Insurance Group

HISTORICAL FINANCIALS

Company Type: Public

Income Statement

FYE: March 31

	ASSETS ($ mil.)	NET INCOME ($ mil.)	INCOME AS % OF ASSETS	EMPLOYEES
03/14	183,570	1,783	1.0%	33,310
03/13	191,614	1,377	0.7%	33,006
03/12	199,176	73	0.0%	30,831
03/11	199,605	868	0.4%	29,758
03/10	184,844	1,374	0.7%	29,578
Annual Growth	(0.2%)	6.7%	—	3.0%

2014 Year-End Financials

Return on assets: 1.0%	Dividends
Return on equity: 7.2%	Yield: 2.8%
Long-term debt ($ mil.): —	Payout: —
No. of shares (mil.): 767	Market value ($ mil.): 23,142
Sales ($ mil): 40,393	

	STOCK PRICE ($) FY Close	P/E High/Low	PER SHARE ($) Earnings	Dividends	Book Value
03/14	30.16	— —	2.32	0.87	34.59
03/13	28.72	— —	1.79	0.00	32.74
03/12	27.66	— —	0.10	0.00	29.53
03/11	26.78	— —	1.12	0.59	29.99
03/10	28.20	— —	1.74	0.52	29.70
Annual Growth	1.7%	— —	7.4%	13.6%	3.9%

Tokyo Electric Power Co. Inc. (The) (Japan)

Japan Inc. would grind to a halt without Tokyo Electric Power Company (TEPCO) which supplies power to 28.8 million customers in Tokyo Yokohama and the rest of the Kanto region. As one of the world's largest electric utilities TEPCO's 190 power plants have the generating capacity of approximately 64500 MW primarily produced by thermal nuclear and hydroelectric power sources. In 2011 it faced a major crisis when its Fukushima Dai-ichi nuclear plant complex experienced a partial meltdown at three reactors and radioactive material was released in the wake of a major earthquake and tsunami. The disaster could lead to multi-billion dollar losses which it has been selling assets to cover.

Public confidence had already been shaken by a rash of accidents within Japan's nuclear industry. The company had struggled to restore its credibility after the Japanese government shut down TEPCO's 17 nuclear reactors due to safety concerns prompted by the company's admittance of falsifying safety data to cover up faults at several of its nuclear facilities in 2002. In 2009 it reopened the Kashiwazaki-Kariwa Nuclear Power Station which was closed in 2007 due to a major earthquake in the region.

Through affiliates TEPCO also offers cable TV and Internet services international consulting and investing in non-Japan-based independent power producers. Other businesses include construction real estate and transportation companies.

The company is developing new green energy sources such as wind and solar in order to meet carbon emission reduction targets. In 2009 the company agreed to build a major solar project in Kawasaki Kanagawa to serve about 5900 households. In 2010 it teamed up with Toyota Tsusho to fund wind power company Eurus Energy Holdings which acquired solar power company Jindosun Park in 2011. Jindosun oversees the generation of 2974KW of electricity mostly in South Korea and will activate a 45000KW plant in the US in mid-2011.

Broadening its international power assets in 2011 the company agreed to buy 12% of Thailand-based independent power producer Electricity Generating PCL for about $274 million. However the daunting financial impact of the Fukushima disaster has cast a pall over the company's international expansion plans.

The company is selling assets to pay off its massive debt. In 2012 it agreed to sell its 67.5% stake in Australian power station Loy Yang A to the plant's minority owner AGL Resources for $1.6 billion.

HISTORY

The Tokyo Electric Power Company (TEPCO) descended from Tokyo Electric Light which was formed in 1883. In 1887 the company switched on Japan's first power plant a 25-KW fossil fuel generator. Fossil fuels were the main source of electricity in Japan until 1912 when long-distance transmission techniques became more efficient making hydroelectric power cheaper.

In 1938 Japan nationalized electric utilities despite strong objections from Yasuzaemon Matsunaga a leader in Japan's utility industry and former president of the Japan Electric Association. After WWII Matsunaga championed public ownership of Japan's power companies which helped in

1951 to establish the current system of 10 regional companies each with a service monopoly. Tokyo Electric Power was the largest. That year it was listed on the Tokyo Stock Exchange and was regulated by the Ministry of International Trade and Industry. (The ministry has regulated electric utilities since 1965.)

Fossil fuel plants made a comeback in Japan in the postwar era because they could be built more economically than hydroelectric plants. When the OPEC oil embargo of the 1970s demonstrated Japan's dependence on foreign oil TEPCO increased its use of liquefied natural gas (LNG) and nuclear energy sources. (It brought its first nuke online in 1971.) In 1977 it formed the Energy Conservation Center to promote conservation and related legislation.

To further reduce its oil dependence TEPCO joined other US and Japanese firms in building a coal gasification plant in California's Mojave Desert in 1982. Two years later TEPCO announced it would begin building its first coal-burning generator since the oil crisis. It established Tokyo Telecommunication Network (TTNet) a partnership to provide telecommunications services in 1986 and TEPCO Cable TV in 1989.

As part of its interest in alternative energy systems TEPCO established a global environment department in 1990 to conduct R&D on energy and the environment. Its environmental program has included reforestation and fuel cell research.

Liberalization in 1995 allowed Japan's electric utilities to buy power from independent power producers; TEPCO quickly lined up 10 suppliers. The company proceeded with energy experimentation in 1996 trying a 6000-KW sodium-sulfur battery at a Yokohama transformer station. The next year the company announced that it would become the first electric utility to sell liquefied natural gas as part of its energy mix and finished building the world's largest nuclear plant.

To gain experience in deregulating markets TEPCO invested in US power generating company Orion Power in 1999. (It agreed to sell its 5% stake to Reliant Energy in 2001.) At home the firm joined Microsoft and SOFTBANK to form SpeedNet which provides Internet access over TTNet's network. In 2000 TEPCO got its first taste of deregulation when large customers (accounting for about a third of the market) began choosing their electricity suppliers. Also in 2000 TEPCO joined a group of nine Japanese electric companies to create POWEREDCOM. (In 2005 TEPCO sold its stake in POWEREDCOM to KDDI in order to focus on its core power business).

In 2001 TEPCO joined up with Sumitomo and Electricite de France to build Vietnam's first independent power plant.

To raise cash in 2006 Mirant (now GenOn Energy) sold its power plants in the Philippines to TEPCO and Marubeni for $3.4 billion.

EXECUTIVES

Chairman, Tsunehisa Katsumata
EVP, Norio Tsuzumi
EVP, Hiroshi Yamaguchi
Managing Director and General Manager Business Development Division, Makio Fujiwara
Managing Director; Deputy General Manager Nuclear Power Plant Siting Division, Sakae Muto
Managing Director, Yoshihiro Naito
President, Toshio Nishizawa
EVP, Zengo Aizawa
Chairman, Kazuhiko Shimokobe
President, Naomi Hirose
EVP, Yoshiyuki Ishizaki

Director, Yoshihisa Morimoto
EVP and Director, Susumu Shirakawa
EVP General Manager Marketing and Sales and Director, Shigeru Kimura
EVP General Manager Engineering Research and Development and Director, Hiroyuki Ino
Director, Tomijirou Morita
Director, Yasushi Aoyama
Auditors: Ernst&YoungShinNihon

LOCATIONS

HQ: Tokyo Electric Power Co. Inc. (The) (Japan)
1-1-3 Uchisaiwai-cho, Chiyoda-Ku, Tokyo 100-8560
Phone: (81) 3 6373 1111
Web: www.tepco.co.jp

PRODUCTS/OPERATIONS

Sales

	% of total
Electricity	89
Energy &	7
Living environment &	2
Information &	2
Total	**100**

Selected Subsidiaries

TEPCO CABLE TELEVISION Inc. (85% cable television)
TEPCO SYSTEMS CORPORATION (information software and services)
Toden Kogyo Co. Ltd. (facilities construction and maintenance)
Toden Real Estate Co. Inc. (property management)
Tokyo Densetsu Service Co. Ltd. (facilities construction and maintenance)
Tokyo Electric Power Environmental Engineering Company Incorporated (facilities construction and maintenance)
Tokyo Electric Power Services Company Limited (facilities construction and maintenance)

COMPETITORS

Chubu Electric Power	KDDI
Chugoku Electric Power	KEPCO
Hokkaido Electric Power	Korea Electric Power
Hokuriku Electric Power	Kyushu Electric Power
	NTT
Internet Initiative Japan	Osaka Gas
	Shikoku Electric
Jinpan International	Tohoku Electric Power
	Tokyo Gas

HISTORICAL FINANCIALS

Company Type: Public

Income Statement

FYE: March 31

	REVENUE ($ mil.)	NET INCOME ($ mil.)	NET PROFIT MARGIN	EMPLOYEES
03/14	64,245	4,249	6.6%	45,744
03/13	63,514	(7,283)	—	48,757
03/12	65,213	(9,528)	—	52,046
03/11	64,832	(15,063)	—	52,970
03/10	53,702	1,432	2.7%	52,452
Annual Growth	**4.6%**	**31.2%**	**—**	**(3.4%)**

2014 Year-End Financials

Debt ratio: 0.5%
Return on equity: 32.9%
Cash ($ mil.): 16,034
Current ratio: 1.38
Long-term debt ($ mil.): 64,739

No. of shares (mil.): 1,600
Dividends
  Yield: —
  Payout: —
Market value ($ mil.): 6,593

STOCK PRICE ($) FY Close	P/E High/Low	PER SHARE ($) Earnings	Dividends	Book Value
03/14	4.12	— —	0.86	0.00	9.55
03/13	2.01	— —	(4.54)	0.00	7.56
03/12	2.40	— —	(5.95)	0.00	6.19
03/11	5.82	— —	(10.22)	0.68	12.09
Annual Growth	(10.9%)	— —	—	—	(5.7%)

TonenGeneral Sekiyu K.K.

TonenGeneral Sekiyu is a leading Japanese refiner that came into being in 2000 as the result of the merger of Japanese refiners Tonen and General Sekiyu both affiliates of global oil and gas behemoth Exxon Mobil. TonenGeneral Sekiyu (50.02%-owned by Exxon Mobil) combines Tonen's 505000 barrels a day of refining capacity in Kawasaki and Wakayama with General Sekiyu's 156000 barrels a day of capacity at Sakai. The oil producing company also operates a 100000 barrels-a-day refinery at Nishihara (in Okinawa) through its 87.5%-owned Nansei Sekiyu subsidiary. TonenGeneral Sekiyu operates a chain of gas stations across Japan under the Esso General and Mobil brands.

The company is trying to diversify its sources of crude oil supply (about 70% comes from the Middle East) and upgrade its refineries in order to reduce costs.

EXECUTIVES

Managing Director and Representative Director, Jun Mutoh
Auditor, Tetsuro Yamamoto
Auditor, Masaaki Ayukawa
President and Director, Kazuo Suzuki
Managing Director and Representative Director, W. J. Bogarty
Managing Director and Representative Director, Jun Mutoh
Director, Kyoji Yoshida
Director, S.K. Arnet
Director, D.R. Csapo
Director, P.P. Ducom
Auditors: PricewaterhouseCoopersLLP

LOCATIONS

HQ: TonenGeneral Sekiyu K.K.
1-8-15 Kohnan, Minato-ku, Tokyo 108-8005
Phone: (81) 3 6713 4400
Web: www.tonengeneral.co.jp

PRODUCTS/OPERATIONS

Sales

	% of total
Oil	89
Chemical	11
Total	**100**

COMPETITORS

Idemitsu Kosan
JX Nippon Mining & Metals

JX Nippon Oil & Energy
Showa Shell Sekiyu

HISTORICAL FINANCIALS

Company Type: Public

Income Statement

FYE: December 31

	REVENUE ($ mil.)	NET INCOME ($ mil.)	NET PROFIT MARGIN	EMPLOYEES
12/13	30,876	218	0.7%	2,921
12/12	32,566	635	2.0%	2,805
12/11	34,594	1,715	5.0%	2,171
12/10	29,490	527	1.8%	2,178
12/09	22,856	(235)	—	2,354
Annual Growth	**7.8%**	**—**	**—**	**5.5%**

2013 Year-End Financials

Debt ratio: 0.2%
Return on equity: 7.8%
Cash ($ mil.): 177
Current ratio: 1.00
Long-term debt ($ mil.): 1,678

No. of shares (mil.): 364
Dividends
Yield: —
Payout: —
Market value ($ mil.): —

Toronto Dominion Bank

The Toronto-Dominion Bank wants to score financial TDs at home and abroad. Also known as TD Bank or TD Financial the company ranks among the world's top online financial services firms and is one of the largest banks in Canada where it operates more than 1100 branches under the TD Trust banner. US subsidiary TD Bank N.A. has another 1300 branches in about 15 eastern states. TD also offers commercial financial and advisory services. Other units include TD Insurance TD Asset Management (mutual funds) and TD Securities (investment banking equities and foreign exchange). Its TD Waterhouse is the largest online brokerage in the UK and Canada; TD Bank also owns 45% of US discount brokerage TD Ameritrade.

Over the years TD Bank has been building its US operations to increase its earnings beyond Canada –a mature market with limited growth potential and several large competitors. As US banks fell in record amounts as a result of the global financial crisis TD Bank and other Canadian firms took the opportunity to further boost their US holdings. To this end TD Bank and Target Corporation inked a deal in late 2012 for the purchase of the retailer's existing US Visa and private label credit card portfolio (with a gross outstanding balance of $5.9 billion). As part of an associated seven-year program agreement TD was granted exclusive rights as the issuer of the Target-branded Visa and private label credit cards to Target's US customers. TD benefits by taking over the established card program that enjoys one of the industry's leading rewards programs.

In 2010 TD Bank N.A. added more than 60 branches in Florida by acquiring three failed banks. It also bought The South Financial Group to further expand in the Sunshine State and establish a presence in the Carolinas; that deal added about 70 locations.

In 2011 TD Bank bought most of auto lender Chrysler Financial from Cerberus in a $6.3 billion deal. The acquisition provided a significant boost to the company's loan portfolio as well as some one million customers in the US and Canada. TD Bank rebranded the lender TD Auto Finance. It later expanded another segment of its consumer lending operations when it bought Bank of America's MBNA Canada credit card business adding some 1.8 million active accounts.

TD Bank sold the US operations of online discount brokerage TD Waterhouse to Ameritrade (now TD Ameritrade) in 2006. (TD Waterhouse continues to operate in Canada.) As part of the deal TD Bank acquired a 40% stake in TD Ameritrade. It upped its stake to 45% in 2009 and bought the operations of online broker thinkorswim Group in Canada. Also that year TD increased its stake in Luxembourg-based Internaxx to 75%; the move has helped it expand its online brokerage business in Europe. As of late 2012 TD boasted some 8.5 million online customers.

On the other side of the ledger TD Bank sold fund of funds manager TD Capital Private Equity Investors (now Northleaf Capital Partners) to the unit's management team in 2009. The move was designed to allow TD Bank to focus on its core operations.

HISTORY

The Bank of Toronto was established in 1855 by flour traders who wanted their own banking facilities. Its growth encouraged another group of businessmen to found the Dominion Bank in 1869. Dominion emphasized commercial banking and invested heavily in railways and construction.

As the new nation expanded westward both banks established branch networks. They helped fund Canada's primary industries –dairy mining oil pulp and textiles. True to its pioneering spirit a Bank of Toronto official claimed to be the first to have set up a branch office with the help of aviation (in Manitoba in the 1920s).

The demand for agricultural products and commodities dropped after WWI but production continued full throttle creating a world grain glut that helped trigger the stock market crash of 1929. Both the Bank of Toronto and Dominion Bank contracted during the 1930s. After growing during and subsequent to WWII The Bank of Toronto and Dominion Bank decided to increase their capital base merging into a 450-branch bank in 1955.

In the 1970s TD Bank opened offices in Bangkok Beirut and Frankfurt among other cities abroad. During the 1980s it was active in making loans to less-developed countries. After the deregulation of the Canadian securities industry in 1987 then-CEO Richard Thomson reduced international lending and began focusing on brokerage activities. The strategy paid off when several Latin American countries fell behind on their loans in the late 1980s.

As the North American economy slowed in the early 1990s TD Bank's nonperforming loans increased and with it its loan loss reserves. The bank still made acquisitions including Central Guaranty Trust (1993) and Lancaster Financial Holdings (1995 investment banking). It worked to build its financial services expanding its range of service offerings and geographic coverage and buying New York-based Waterhouse Investor Services (1996); 97% of Australia-based Pont Securities (1997); and California-based Kennedy Cabot & Co. (1997). In 1998 the bank sold its payroll services to Ceridian and its Waterhouse Securities unit bought US discount brokerage Jack White & Co.

That year the government nixed TD Bank's merger with Canadian Imperial on the same day it voided the Royal Bank of Canada/Bank of Montreal deal. The banks believed the consolidation was necessary to stave off foreign banks' encroachment into Canada but the government had domestic antitrust concerns: Though Canada has one-tenth the population of the US its five top banks all ranked in the top 15 in North America.

In 1999 TD Bank bought Trimark Financial's retail trust banking business and spun off part of Waterhouse Investor Services which would become part of TD Waterhouse Group. That year the bank ramped up its focus on Internet banking.

Not giving up on acquisition-fueled growth in 2000 the company bought CT Financial Services (now TD Canada Trust) from British American Tobacco. As a condition for government approval TD Bank had to sell its MasterCard credit portfolio (sold to Citibank Canada) and a dozen southern Ontario branches (to Bank of Montreal).

The company's plans to hitch a ride on the Wal-Mart gravy train derailed in 2001. Arrangements to open bank branches in some US-based Wal-Mart stores were squelched by regulators enforcing the banking and commerce barrier. TD Bank later closed all of its existing branches (more than 100 in all) inside Canadian Wal-Marts as part of a broader restructuring.

TD Bank suffered its first-ever annual loss during fiscal year 2002. Write-downs on loans to telecommunications technology and energy firms contributed mightily to the dismal results.

Frustrated by limited growth opportunities at home in 2005 TD Bank ventured south of the border with its purchase of a stake in Banknorth. TD Bank paid about $4.8 billion in cash and stock for its original 51% stake (it bought the rest in 2007). Additionally in 2006 the company assumed about a 40% ownership in TD AMERITRADE as part of the sale of TD Waterhouse.

In 2008 the company acquired New Jersey-based Commerce Bancorp. The $8.5 billion acquisition deal added some 450 branches along the eastern seaboard to TD Bank's US network and exemplified the company's plans to expand abroad. TD merged Commerce with its TD Banknorth unit to create TD Bank.

EXECUTIVES

Group Head Wealth Management Direct Channels and Corporate Shared Services, Mike Pedersen
Chairman, Brian M. Levitt, age 67
Group President and Chief Executive Officer, W. Edmund (Ed) Clark, age 67, $1,337,850 total compensation
Group Head Insurance Credit Cards and Enterprise Strategy, Riaz E. Ahmed
Deputy Chair, Frank J. McKenna, age 66
EVP; Head Regional Retail Banking and Direct Channels TD Bank, Brian J. Haier
Group Head Wholesale Banking; Chairman President and CEO TD Securities, Robert E. (Bob) Dorrance, age 58, $445,950 total compensation
EVP Senior Client Relationships and Shared Services Wealth Management, John G. See
Group Head Canadian Banking Auto Finance and Credit Cards; President and CEO TD Canada Trust, Timothy D. (Tim) Hockey, age 50, $490,250 total compensation
Chief Operating Officer, Bharat B. Masrani, age 57, $521,449 total compensation
EVP and Chief Risk Officer Risk Management, Mark R. Chauvin
Group Head Finance Sourcing and Corporate Communications and Chief Financial Officer, Colleen M. Johnston, $416,488 total compensation
Group Head Marketing Corporate and People Strategies TD Bank Group, Theresa L. (Teri) Currie
SVP Wealth Management, David P. (Dave) Pickett
EVP; Chief Operating Officer TD Securities, Paul M. Clark
Group Head Legal Compliance and Anti Money Laundering and General Counsel, Norie C. Campbell
SVP Wealth Management, Michael E. (Mike) Reilly
SVP Wealth Management, Kevin J. Whyte
SVP Wholesale Banking, Brian Smith
Vice President - Legal; Corporate Secretary, Kevin Thompson

Executive Vice President; Head - Retail Distribution and Products, Nandita Bakhshi
Group Head - Corporate Development; Enterprise Strategy and Treasury; Corporate Office, Raiz Ahmed
Group President and Chief Executive Officer, W. Edmund (Ed) Clark, age 67
Independent Director, Karen E. Maidment
Director, Nadir H. Mohamed, age 57
Director, Wilbur J. (Bill) Prezzano Jr., age 73
Director, Harold H. MacKay, age 73
Director, Irene R. Miller, age 61
Director, Carole S. Taylor, age 66
Deputy Chair, Frank J. McKenna, age 66
Director, John L. Bragg, age 73
Director, Colleen A. Goggins, age 59
Director, Wendy K. Dobson, age 71
Director, Henry H. Ketcham, age 64
Director, Pierre H. Lessard, age 70
Director, Helen K. Sinclair, age 62
Director, Hugh J. Bolton, age 75
Director, William E. Bennett, age 67
Director, John M. Thompson, age 70
Director, Amy W. Brinkley, age 58
Auditors: Ernst&YoungLLP

LOCATIONS

HQ: Toronto Dominion Bank
Toronto-Dominion Centre, King Street West & Bay Street, Toronto, Ontario M5K 1A2
Phone: 416 944-6367   **Fax:** 416 982-6166
Web: www.td.com

PRODUCTS/OPERATIONS

Sales

	% of total
Interest	
Deposits with	41
Loans	30
Securities	9
Noninterest	
Investments & securities	6
Service	4
Other	10
Total	**100**

Selected Canadian Subsidiaries

CT Financial Assurance Company (99.9%)
Meloche Monnex Inc.
 Security National Insurance Company
  Primmum Insurance Company
  TD Direct Insurance Inc.
  TD General Insurance Company
  TD Home and Auto Insurance Company
TD Asset Finance Corp.
TD Asset Management Inc.
 TD Waterhouse Private Investment Counsel Inc.
TD Investment Services Inc.
TD Life Insurance Company
TD Mortgage Corporation
 The Canada Trust Company
 TD Pacific Mortgage Corporation
 TD Mortgage Investment Corporation
TD Nordique Investments Limited
TD Parellel Private Equity Investors Ltd.
TD Securities Inc.
TD Timberlane Investments Limited
 TD McMurray Investments Limited
 TD Redpath Investments Limited
 TD Riverside Investments Limited
TD Vermillion Holdings ULC
 TD Financial International Ltd. (Bermuda)
  Canada Trustco International Limited (Barbados)
  TD Reinsurance (Barbados) Inc.
 Toronto Dominion International Inc. (Barbados)
TD Waterhouse Canada Inc.
 thinkorswim Canada
Truscan Property Corporation

Selected US Subsidiaries

TDAM USA Inc.
Toronto Dominion Holdings (U.S.A.) Inc.

TD Holdings II Inc.
 TD Securities (USA) LLC
 Toronto Dominion (Texas) LLC
Toronto Dominion Capital (U.S.A.) Inc.
Toronto Dominion Investments Inc.

Selected Other International Subsidiaries

Internaxx Bank S.A. (Luxembourg)
NatWest Personal Financial Management Limited (50% UK)
 NatWest Stockbrokers Limited
TD Ireland
 TD Global Finance
TD Waterhouse Bank N.V. (The Netherlands)
TD Waterhouse Investor Services (UK) Limited
 TD Waterhouse Investor Services (Europe) Limited (UK)
Toronto Dominion (South East Asia) Limited (Singapore)

COMPETITORS

BMO Financial Group	Edward Jones
Bank of America	FMR
Berkshire Hills	KeyCorp
Bancorp	Laurentian Bank
CI Financial	Morgan Stanley
CIBC	National Bank of
Caisses centrale	Canada
Desjardins	RBC Financial Group
Charles Schwab	Scotiabank
E*TRADE Financial	Sovereign Bank

HISTORICAL FINANCIALS

Company Type: Public

Income Statement

FYE: October 31

	ASSETS ($ mil.)	NET INCOME ($ mil.)	INCOME AS % OF ASSETS	EMPLOYEES
10/14	844,306	6,821	0.8%	81,137
10/13	824,651	6,092	0.7%	78,748
10/12	813,315	6,187	0.8%	78,397
10/11	738,424	5,783	0.8%	75,631
10/10	608,172	4,558	0.7%	68,725
Annual Growth	**8.5%**	**10.6%**	**—**	**4.2%**

2014 Year-End Financials

Return on assets: 0.8%
Return on equity: 14.5%
Long-term debt ($ mil.): —
No. of shares (mil.): 1,844
Sales ($ mil): 32,731
Dividends
 Yield: 3.7%
 Payout: 49.4%
Market value ($ mil.): 90,865

	STOCK PRICE ($) FY Close	P/E High/Low		PER SHARE ($) Earnings	Dividends	Book Value
10/14	49.26	19	8	3.70	1.69	26.49
10/13	91.72	24	20	3.30	1.59	26.29
10/12	81.34	26	18	3.39	1.44	26.01
10/11	75.28	29	20	3.23	1.32	23.69
10/10	72.20	29	21	2.50	1.20	23.63
Annual Growth	**(9.1%)**	**—**	**—**	**10.3%**	**9.0%**	**2.9%**

Toshiba Corp

Toshiba products play an active role be it in computing controlling powering or communicating —transporting playing or even just chillin'. The company's portfolio includes personal and professional computers (PCs point-of-sale systems) telecommunications and medical equipment (LCDs for mobile devices X-ray machines) industrial machinery (power plant reactors elevators) consumer appliances (air conditioners Blu-ray Disc recorders) electronic components (electron tubes batteries) and semiconductors. Its portfolio also includes air traffic control and railway transportation systems. Customers outside Japan account for 55% of Toshiba's revenues.

In 2009 the company announced its biggest ever annual loss. The global recession took its toll across all of Toshiba's primary product groups — digital products social infrastructure electronic devices and home appliances —with each experiencing a drop in revenues and only social infrastructure reporting positive operating income.

As the global recession eased in 2009 and 2010 Toshiba saw strengthening sales and better financial results in some segments such as digital products electronic devices and home appliances. Revenue rose 1% year-over-year in the fiscal year that ended in March 2011. The company also recorded net income in 2010 and 2011.

By segment sales of digital products (about 33% of sales) decreased by 3% in fiscal 2011. Social infrastructure (also 33%) was down 2%. Electronic devices (20%) rose 6%. Home appliances (9%) increased 3%.

By 2013 the company plans to increase sales of digital products by 10% electronic devices by 13% social infrastructure by 10% and home appliances by 4%. Geographically Toshiba wants to increase its proportion of international sales from 55% to more than 65% during the same time period. While increasing sales and improving profitability remain top strategic goals Toshiba also aspires to becoming a greener company reducing its CO2 emissions and promoting more environmentally friendly products and technologies.

Digital products includes personal computers visual products hard disk drives (HDDs) and multifunction peripherals. Social infrastructure consists of energy-related equipment medical equipment IT products and elevators. Under electronic devices are semiconductors and liquid crystal displays. The home appliance segment comprises refrigerators washing/drying machines light fixtures and air conditioners. Included in the other segment is logistics services.

In 2012 Toshiba made a move to increase the scope of its storage device portfolio specifically HDDs when it bought certain of Western Digital's 3.5 inch HDD assets. The deal gives Toshiba the ability to provide products covering all aspects of the HDD market and increase its capacity to supply nearline HDDs. Demand for nearline HDDs is growing along with continued expansion in the server market. As part of the sale Western Digital acquired Toshiba Storage Device (Thailand) a disk drive manufacturer that has not resumed operations since the Thailand flooding in 2011. The sale of the HDD assets were required for Western Digital to get regulatory approval for its purchase of Hitachi Global Storage Technologies.

In 2010 the company combined its wireless handset business with that of archrival Fujitsu to create Fujitsu Toshiba Mobile Communications Limited the largest cell phone maker in Japan. The companies hope to better compete with market leader Nokia and a number of key players from Asia and North America; Fujitsu owns an 80% stake in the new company while Toshiba owns around 20%. Fujitsu is now looking to acquire Toshiba's interest in the JV in an effort to boost its smartphone operations.

In 2011 the company announced a deal that would both increase its overseas sales and provide entry into the smart grid market. Toshiba bought Swiss smart meter hardware and communications module maker Landis+Gyr for $2.3 billion including debt. Founded in 1896 Landis+Gyr boasted more than 8000 utility customers worldwide and operations in more than 30 countries; it was selected to supply 10000 smart meters to the State Grid Corporation of China as that country constructs the world's largest smart grid. Toshiba is eager to enter the burgeoning smart grid market especially as concerns about the safety of nuclear power overshadow growth plans for its nuclear power division.

Toshiba which holds a 67% stake in Westinghouse Electric shares ownership with The Shaw Group (20%) and IHI (3%). The remaining 10% is held by Kazatomprom a state-owned uranium supplier based in Kazakhstan which acquired the stake from Toshiba for $540 million in 2007. In 2011 Toshiba announced that it would acquire Shaw's stake.

In 2011 Toshiba Medical Systems bought longtime partner Vital Images a developer of visualization and analysis software used in computed tomography (CT) scanners and magnetic resonance imaging (MRI) equipment. Toshiba Medical Systems paid about $273 million in cash for the company in an effort to further expand its global imaging business.

Toshiba has used partnerships (often with competitors) to fuel product development and reduce costs. The company has worked with rivals such as Fujitsu and NEC on semiconductor development. It has a strategic relationship with SanDisk for the production of NAND flash memories.

Toshiba bought out Panasonic's stake in another joint venture Toshiba Matsushita Display Technology in 2009. Toshiba took full ownership of the unit so it can more quickly implement restructuring measures. Renamed Toshiba Mobile Display the company is a leading provider of LCDs used in mobile phones in-vehicle displays and portable computers.

In 2012 Toshiba became part of a joint venture named Japan Display Inc. (JDI) that combined its small- and medium-sized LCD panel business with those of Hitachi and Sony along with investment by a Japanese government-backed fund. The government owns 70% of JDI while the three companies each hold 10%. Also that year subsidiary Toshiba TEC which offers point-of-sale systems for retailers bought IBM's retail store solutions business for about $850 million. The initial stage of the deal will be a joint venture Toshiba Global Commerce Solutions Holdings Corporation with IBM owning just shy of 20% and Toshiba TEC owning the rest and then buying out IBM three years later. The joint venture began operations in the US Canada Mexico and Australia. Late in 2011 Toshiba and OJSC Power Machines announced a joint venture for electrical power transformer manufacturing slated for a 2013 start. The plant is to be built in St. Petersburg with Toshiba holding a nearly 50/50 ownership with OJSC Power Machines.

HISTORY

Two Japanese electrical equipment manufacturers came together in 1939 to create Toshiba. Tanaka Seizo-sha Japan's first telegraph equipment manufacturer was founded in 1875 by Hisashige Tanaka the so-called Edison of Japan. In the 1890s the company started making heavier electrical equipment such as transformers and electric motors adopting the name Shibaura Seisakusho Works in 1893. Seisakusho went on to pioneer the production of hydroelectric generators (1894) and X-ray tubes (1915) in Japan.

The other half of Toshiba Hakunetsusha & Company was founded by Ichisuke Fujioka and Shoichi Miyoshi as Japan's first incandescent lamp maker (1890). Renamed Tokyo Electric Company (1899) the company developed the coiled filament lightbulb (1921) Japan's first radio receiver and cathode-ray tube (1924) and the internally frosted glass lightbulb (1925). In 1939 it merged with Shibaura Seisakusho to form Tokyo Shibaura Electric Company (Toshiba).

Toshiba was the first company in Japan to make fluorescent lamps (1940) radar systems (1942) broadcasting equipment (1952) and digital computers (1954). Production of black-and-white televisions began in 1949. Even so through the 1970s the company was considered an also-ran trailing other Japanese business groups known as keiretsu partly because of its bureaucratic management style.

Electrical engineer Shoichi Saba became president in 1980. Saba invested heavily in Toshiba's information and communications segments. The company became the first in the world to produce the powerful one-megabit DRAM chip (1985). That year it unveiled its first laptop PC. In the meantime Saba (named chairman 1986) pushed Toshiba into joint ventures to exchange technology with companies such as Siemens and Motorola.

But in 1987 Toshiba incurred the wrath of the US government. A subsidiary sold submarine sound-deadening equipment to the USSR resulting in threats of US sanctions and a precipitous decline in its stock price and in US sales. Chairman Saba and president Sugichiro Watari resigned in shame.

Toshiba in 1992 bought a $500 million stake in Time Warner (the stake was reduced in 1998). In 1996 the company appointed marketing and multimedia specialist Taizo Nishimuro as president breaking its tradition of filling the position with an engineer from its heavy electrical operations.

In 1997 Toshiba and IBM formed joint venture Dominion Semiconductor to develop memory chips. (IBM sold its stake to Toshiba in 1999.) The next year the company looked to boost earnings by cutting its workforce and allying with other manufacturers such as Fujitsu and General Electric in development deals. But continued semiconductor price declines and sluggish demand in Japan caused the company to record its first annual loss in more than two decades.

Nishimuro made plans to cut 5000 jobs and streamline Toshiba's 15 divisions to eight inhouse companies. Toshiba in 1999 agreed to take a $1 billion charge to settle a class-action lawsuit alleging some manufacturers supplied potentially corrupt disk drives in its portable computers —even though no Toshiba customer complaints were filed.

In 2000 Nishimuro stepped down as CEO. SVP and Information and Industrial Systems and Services subsidiary president Tadashi Okamura assumed the post. Nishimuro filled the vacant chairman's seat. Toshiba announced another restructuring effort in 2001 which included plans to reduce its workforce shift manufacturing to overseas plants and withdraw from unprofitable businesses. The following year it sold its DRAM manufacturing plant Dominion Semiconductor to Micron Technology.

In 2004 Toshiba partnered with Canon to develop surface conduction electron emitter display (SED) panels an alternative technology to LCD televisions. In 2005 Atsutoshi Nishida an executive that led the company's PC operations succeeded Okamura as CEO.

In 2006 Toshiba acquired nuclear power plant equipment and service provider Westinghouse Electric for $5.4 billion. Canon purchased Toshiba's stake in the SED joint venture in 2007.

The company acknowledged a setback for its consumer electronics business in 2008 when it announced the discontinuation of HD-DVD development. Toshiba was the primary backer of the HD-DVD format for high-definition DVD players and recorders —a market where it battled with Sony the primary backer of the competing Blu-ray format for support among manufacturers media companies and consumers.

In 2009 Norio Sasaki became CEO of Toshiba; Nishida was named chairman.

Toshiba acquired the hard-disk drive business of Fujitsu in 2009. In addition to augmenting Toshiba's consumer product-oriented disk drive line the purchase moved the company into the enterprise disk drive business. Toshiba formed three new subsidiaries with the purchase including Toshiba Storage Device Corp. The company also bought the Advanced Visual Imaging Systems division of imaging and graphics systems maker Barco that year. The purchase augmented its Toshiba Medical Systems unit which develops diagnostic medical imaging systems.

EXECUTIVES

Chairman, Atsutoshi Nishida, age 71
EVP, Hiroshi Saito
SEVP and Director, Fumio Muraoka, age 66
EVP, Shozo Saito
Vice Chairman, Norio Sasaki, age 65
President and CEO, Hisao Tanaka, age 64
SEVP, Hidejiro Shimomitsu, age 62
EVP, Toshiharu Watanabe
SEVP, Hideo Kitamura, age 62
VP, Shoji Yoshioka
EVP, Masahiko (Masa) Fukakushi, age 60
SEVP, Akira Sudo, age 63
SEVP, Makoto Kubo, age 63
EVP, Yasuharu Igarashi
EVP, Kiyoshi Kobayashi
VP, Masakazu Kakumu
VP, Hiroshi Igashira
VP, Munehiko Tsuchiya
VP, Takaaki Tanaka
VP, Hironobu Nishikori
VP, Yasuhiro Shimura
EVP, Toshio Masaki
General Manager Human Resources And Administration Division and Director, Hiroshi Horioka, age 61
Managing Executive Officer, Fumiaki Fumiaki Ushio Ushio
Managing Executive Officer; Director of Nuclear Power Business in Electric System Company, Kiyoshi Kiyoshi Okamura Okamura
Managing Executive Officer; Vice President of Semiconductor & Storage Company, Makoto Makoto Hideshima Hideshima
Managing Executive Officer; Senior Executive Officer; Chairman of Subsidiary, Masaaki Masaaki Ohsumi Ohsumi
Managing Executive Officer; Senior Executive Officer; President of Subsidiary, Masayasu Masayasu Toyohara Toyohara
Managing Executive Officer; President of Kansai Office, Naoki Naoki Takenaka Takenaka
Managing Executive Officer; Senior Executive Officer; Manager of Electric Power & Social System Technology Development Center, Osamu Osamu Maekawa Maekawa
Senior Managing Executive Officer; Vice President of Electric System Company; President of Subsidiary, Shigenori Shigenori Shiga Shiga
Managing Executive Officer; Senior Executive Officer; Vice President of Digital Products & Service Company, Shigenori Shigenori Tokumitsu Tokumitsu
Managing Executive Officer; Senior Director of Cloud & Solution Business, Shigeyoshi Shigeyoshi Shimotsuji Shimotsuji
Managing Executive Officer; Vice President of Social Infrastructure System Company, Takemi Takemi Adachi Adachi

Managing Executive Officer; Director of Electric Power Distribution System Business in Social Infrastructure System Company, Takeshi Takeshi Yokota Yokota
Managing Executive Officer; Chairman of the Board in Subsidiary, Teruo Teruo Kiriyama Kiriyama
Managing Executive Officer; Director of Memory Business in Semiconductor Company, Yasuo Yasuo Naruke Naruke
Managing Executive Officer; Director of Thermal Power and Water Power Business in Electricity System Company, Yoshihiro Yoshihiro Aburatani Aburatani
Director, Kiichiro Furusawa, age 74
Director, Shigeo Koguchi, age 68
SEVP and Director, Yoshihiro Maeda, age 65
SEVP and Director, Fumio Muraoka, age 66
SEVP and Director, Ichiro Tai, age 65
SEVP and Director, Masao Namiki, age 64
EVP and Director, Kazuo Tanigawa, age 64
SEVP and Director, Masashi Muromachi, age 63
Vice Chairman, Norio Sasaki, age 65
Director, Hiroshi Hirabayashi, age 73
Director, Takeshi Sasaki, age 71
General Manager Human Resources And Administration Division and Director, Hiroshi Horioka, age 61
Director, Takeo Kosugi, age 72
Independent Director, Hiroyuki Itami
Independent Director, Ken Shimanouchi
Auditors: Ernst&Young

LOCATIONS

HQ: Toshiba Corp
1-1-1 Shibaura, Minato-ku, Tokyo 105-8001
Phone: (81) 3 3457 4511   **Fax:** (81) 3 3456 1631
Web: www.toshiba.co.jp

Sales

	% of total
Asia	
Japan	45
Other	20
North	18
Europe	13
Other	4
Total	**100**

PRODUCTS/OPERATIONS

Sales

	% of total
Digital	33
Social	33
Electronic	20
Home	9
Other	5
Total	**100**

Selected Products

Digital products
  Digital Media Network Company
    Digital cameras
    Digital tuners
    DVD players and recorders
    Hard disk drives
    Industrial and surveillance cameras
    Optical disk drives
    Projectors
    Televisions
  Mobile Communications Company
    Mobile phones
  Personal Computer & Network Company
    Handheld computers
    Notebook computers
    Servers
Social infrastructure
  Industrial and Power Systems & Services Company
    Boiling water reactor plants
    Building energy management systems
    Control and measurement system devices
    Industrial computers

Nuclear fuel reprocessing plants
Power generating equipment (hydroelectric thermal geothermal)
Railway station service systems
Superconducting magnets
Transportation management systems
Water supply and sewage monitoring systems
Social Network & Infrastructure Systems Company
  Air traffic control and navigation aid systems
  Automatic letter processing systems
  Banknote processing machines
  Broadcasting systems
  Face recognition security systems
Electronic devices
Semiconductor Company
  LSI systems
  Memory
  Microprocessors
Home appliances
  Air conditioners
  Batteries
  Lighting
  Microwaves
  Refrigerators
  Washing machines

COMPETITORS

ABB	Mitsubishi Electric
ALSTOM	NEC
AREVA	NTT DATA
Acer	Nokia
Alcatel-Lucent	Oki Electric
Apple Inc.	Panasonic Corp
CASIO COMPUTER	Philips Electronics
Canon	Pioneer Corporation
Dell	Ricoh Company
Electrolux	STMicroelectronics
Emerson Electric	Samsung Electronics
Ericsson	Schindler Holding
FUJIFILM	Seagate Technology
Fujitsu	Seiko
GE	Sharp Corp.
Hewlett-Packard	Siemens AG
Hitachi	Sony
IBM	Sony Mobile
Ingersoll-Rand	Spansion
Intel	Texas Instruments
KONE	Unisys
Kyocera	Western Digital
Lenovo	Xerox

HISTORICAL FINANCIALS

Company Type: Public

Income Statement

FYE: March 31

	REVENUE ($ mil.)	NET INCOME ($ mil.)	NET PROFIT MARGIN	EMPLOYEES
03/14	63,811	492	0.8%	200,260
03/13	63,079	824	1.3%	206,087
03/12	75,639	898	1.2%	209,784
03/11	78,417	1,664	2.1%	202,638
03/10	68,349	(211)	—	203,889
Annual Growth	**(1.7%)**	**—**	**—**	**(0.4%)**

2014 Year-End Financials

Debt ratio: 0.2%	No. of shares (mil.): —
Return on equity: 4.4%	Dividends
Cash ($ mil.): 1,659	Yield: 1.8%
Current ratio: 1.24	Payout: 0.0%
Long-term debt ($ mil.): 11,479	Market value ($ mil.): —

	STOCK PRICE ($) FY Close	P/E High/Low		PER SHARE ($) Earnings	Dividends	Book Value
03/14	25.41	0	0	0.12	0.47	2.81
03/13	30.40	0	0	0.19	0.00	2.60
03/12	26.57	0	0	0.21	0.00	2.50
03/11	29.60	0	0	0.38	0.14	2.48
03/10	30.80	—	—	(0.05)	0.00	2.02
Annual Growth	**(4.7%)**	**—**	**—**	**—**	**—**	**8.7%**

Total S.A.

TOTAL does it all. With operations in more than 130 countries TOTAL engages in all aspects of the petroleum industry including Upstream operations (oil and gas exploration development and production LNG) and Downstream operations (refining marketing and the trading and shipping of crude oil and petroleum products). TOTAL also produces base chemicals (petrochemicals and fertilizers) and specialty chemicals for the industrial and consumer markets (rubber processing adhesives resins and electroplating). In addition TOTAL has interests in power generation.

Geographic Reach

TOTAL has operations in 130 countries. European countries excluding France generate the most revenues for TOTAL —51% in 2013.

Operations

The company's business is divided into three main segments: Upstream Downstream and Chemicals. Its Downstream operations has two divisions: Refining and Chemicals and Supply and Marketing (of petroleum products).

Upstream TOTAL explores for and produces oil and gas in 40 countries and had reserves of 11.5 billion barrels of oil equivalent (49% of which were proved developed reserves) in 2013. Liquids (crude oil condensates natural gas liquids and bitumen) represented 47% of these reserves; natural gas the remaining 53%. It is a major player in the global natural gas market with more than 60 years of experience in the field. Its expertise covers natural gas as well as liquid natural gas (LNG) and liquefied petroleum gas (LPG).

Downstream it has a refining capacity of 2 million barrels a day and some 14820 gas stations mostly in Europe and Africa.

TOTAL is also one of the world's largest integrated chemical producers and a leader in each of its markets —Petrochemicals and Fertilizers and Specialties.

Financial Performance

After experiencing strong revenue growth over the last few years in 2013 TOTAL's revenues declined by 5%. There was a 10% sales drop in the Upstream segment 5% in the Refining & Chemicals segment and 4% in the Marketing & Services segment. Upstream revenues decreased due to a less favorable production mix higher technical costs (particularly for exploration) and a higher tax rate. TOTAL's net income dropped by 20% in 2013 mainly due to lower Upstream sales partially offset by a higher contribution from Marketing & Services. The after-tax inventory valuation effect had a negative impact on net income of Ä549 million in 2013.Cash flow from operations decreased by 4% in 2013 reflecting the decrease in net income partially offset by the change in working capital.

Strategy

In 2014 TOTAL teamed up with DONG to develop the Edradour gas field in the West of Shetland area and a 60% stake in the neighboring Glenlivet discovery. The field are expected to more than 65 million barrels of oil equivalent of reserves. That year it also sign an LNG Cooperation Agreement strengthening the partnership between TOTAL and CNOOC. Under the terms of an existing 15 year contract TOTAL has been supplying China with up to 1 million tons per year of LNG since 2010. The new deal sets a framework for an additional supply of 1 million tons per year of LNG as well as further cooperation throughout the LNG value chainTo raise cash and to focus on its core businesses in 2014 TOTAL sold Total Coal South Africa its coal-producing affiliate to Exxaro Resources for $472 million.

In 2013 the Upstream segment launched major projects in Congo Nigeria Canada and Russia and acquired 20% of the high-potential Libra field in Brazil. TOTAL continued to extend its oil and gas acreage that year by obtaining licenses in promising exploration areas particularly in Iraq Brazil Bolivia and South Africa. It made large discoveries in Iraq and Argentina in 2013.

Over the long term the company is committed to building its leading position in all three segments of its business through acquisitions divestitures and investments. It is investing heavily in refinery expansion in Jubail Saudi Arabia and in Port Arthur Texas. Other long-term growth initiatives include teaming up with Gazprom and Statoil to develop the vast Shtokman gas field in the Barents Sea.

TOTAL is also expanding its energy offerings and developing complementary next generation energy activities (solar biomass nuclear).

HISTORY

A French consortium formed the Compagnie Fransise des Petroles (CFP) in 1924 to develop an oil industry for the country. Lacking reserves within its borders France had a 24% stake in the Turkish Petroleum Company (TPC) acquired from Germany in 1920 as part of the spoils from WWI. When oil was discovered in Iraq in 1927 the TPC partners (CFP; Anglo-Persian Oil later BP; Royal Dutch Shell; and a consortium of five US oil companies) became major players in the oil game.

In 1929 France acquired a 25% stake in CFP (raised to 35% in 1931) but ensured the company's independence from government control. CFP began establishing refining and transporting capabilities and by the start of WWII it was a vertically integrated petroleum company.

With France's occupation by Germany during WWII CFP was effectively blocked from further expansion and its stake in Iraq Petroleum (formerly the TPC) was held by its partners until the end of the war. In 1948 over French protests the US partners ended the "Red Line" agreement a pact that limited members' competition in that Middle Eastern region.

After WWII CFP diversified its sources for crude opening a supply in 1947 from the Venezuelan company Pantepec and making several major discoveries in colonial Algeria in 1956. It also began supplying crude to Japan South Korea and Taiwan in the 1950s. To market its products in North Africa and France and other European areas it introduced the brand name TOTAL in 1954. It began making petrochemicals in 1956.

Algeria in 1971 became North Africa's first major oil-producing country to nationalize its petroleum industry. This was not as dire a blow to CFP as it could have been; by that time the company got only about 20% of its supplies from Algeria. Exploration had paid off with discoveries in Indonesia in the 1960s and the North Sea in the early 1970s.

CFP joined Elf Aquitaine in 1980 to buy Rhone-Poulenc's petrochemical segment. Ten years later it purchased state-owned Orkem's coating business (inks resins paints and adhesives).

In 1985 the company had adopted its brand name as part of its new name TOTAL Compagnie Francaise des Petroles shortened in 1991 to TOTAL. The firm was listed on the NYSE that year. The French government began reducing its stake in TOTAL in 1992 (ultimately to less than 1%). The company expanded reserves with stakes in fields in Argentina the Caspian Sea and Colombia.

In 1995 the year Thierry Desmarest became CEO TOTAL contracted to develop two large oil and gas fields in Iran despite US pressure not to do business there. The next year TOTAL led a consortium (including Russia's Gazprom and Malaysia's Petronas) in a $2 billion investment in Iran's gas sector just days after selling its 55% stake in its North American arm Total Petroleum to Ultramar Diamond Shamrock — insulating TOTAL from the threat of US sanctions.

TOTAL bought Belgium's Petrofina an integrated oil and gas company for $11 billion in 1999 and became TOTAL FINA. Within days the new TOTAL FINA launched a $43 billion hostile bid for rival Elf Aquitaine. Elf made a counterbid but TOTAL FINA wound up acquiring 95% of Elf in 2000 for $48.7 billion and became TOTAL FINA ELF. The new company gained control of the remainder of Elf later that year.

In 2001 the company in collaboration with Pertamina and Unocal Indonesia agreed to invest $500 million to boost its production of liquefied gas in Indonesia by 14%. That year the company also acquired generating assets in Argentina from AES for $370 million. Also that year an explosion in a TOTAL FINA ELF subsidiary's petrochemical and fertilizer plant in southern France killed 29 people and injured 2500. In 2003 a number of former Elf executives and state officials were named in a corruption scandal that implicated the former French oil giant in influence peddling and bribery in the early 1990s.

TOTAL FINA ELF was renamed TOTAL S.A. in 2003.

In 2006 the company spun off its Arkema unit which produces chlorochemicals intermediates and performance polymers.

With an eye to restructuring as a pure integrated oil business in 2007 TOTAL began to sell its then-18% stake in pharmaceutical manufacturer Sanofi. By mid-2009 the stake had fallen below 10%.

Oil sands has been a major source of growth. In 2008 it paid $470 million to buy Canada's Synenco Energy whose principal asset is a 60% stake in the Northern Lights oil sands project in the Athabasca region. Sinopec owns the remaining stake in the project. Again looking to expand its Canadian oil sands assets in 2009 TOTAL made a $617 million bid to acquire UTS Energy. That bid failed but TOTAL came back in 2010 with a $1.4 billion offer that led to an acquisition agreement for UTS. Following the acquisition it absorbed UTS's 20% stake in the Fort Hills oil sands project into its Canadian exploration and production unit and spun off the rump of UTS as a new oil sands explorer SilverBirch Energy.

To improve its cash flow in 2010 TOTAL merged its Italian retail operations with ERG's to create TotalERG the #3 gas station network in Italy with 3300 outlets and it sold two noncore oil fields in the Norwegian sector to BP for $991 million

In the US in early 2010 in a further expansion TOTAL also acquired 25% of Chesapeake Energy's Barnett Shale properties forming a $2.25 billion joint venture with that company.

Furthering its investment in Canada's oil sands in late 2010 the company formed a strategic alliance with Suncor Energy in which it paid Suncor about $1.7 billion to acquire 19% of Suncor's holdings in the Fort Hills mining project and a 49% stake in the Voyageur Upgrader project near Fort McMurray. Suncor bought about 37% of TOTAL's interest in the Joslyn project.

The company made a couple of notable divestitures in 2011. To reduce its financial exposure in the refining sector the company agreed to sell its 49% stake in Spain's CEPSA to joint venture partner Abu Dhabi-based IPC. In a move to refocus its

Chemicals segment TOTAL divested its coatings resins and photocure resins businesses to Arkema in a deal valued at $730 million.

It made a big move into renewable energy in 2011 buying 60% of solar company SunPower for $1.4 billion.

To raise $1 billion to pay down debt the company sold some mature assets in 2011 and 2012 including TEPMA BV (to Sinochem) a 5% stake in the Ocensa pipeline to Petrominerales and another 5% to Cepsa.

EXECUTIVES

Chairman and CEO, Christophe de Margerie, age 63, $1,310,000 total compensation
Chief Administrative Officer, Jean-Jacques Guilbaud, age 61
President Chemicals, Francois Cornelis, age 65
President Exploration and Production, Yves-Louis Darricarrere, age 63
SVP Overseas Downstream, Alain Champeaux
SVP Marketing France Refining and Marketing, Andre Tricoire
SVP Marketing Europe Refining and Marketing, Eric de Menten
SVP Industrial Safety, Jean-Marc Jaubert
Chief Purchasing Officer, Sonia Sikorav
President Marketing and Services and New Energies, Philippe Boisseau, age 51
CFO, Patrick de La Chevardiere, age 57
President Refining and Chemicals, Patrick Pouyanne
SVP Scientific Development, Jean-Francois Minster
General Counsel, Peter Herbel
SVP Exploration and Production Africa, Jacques Marraud des Grottes, age 61
General Secretary Total Refining and Marketing, Bertrand Deroubaix, age 58
VP Strategy and Planning, Jean-Jacques Mosconi
EVP Sustainable Development and Environment, Manoelle Lepoutre
SVP Geosciences Exploration and Production, Marc Blaizot, age 60
VP Corporate Communications, Yves-Marie Dalibard
General Secretary Chemicals, Francoise Leroy
CEO and Director, Christophe de Margerie, age 63
Director, Serge Tchuruk, age 76
Director, Anne Lauvergeon, age 55
Director, Paul Desmarais Jr., age 59
Director, Michel Pebereau, age 71
Director, Daniel Bouton, age 63
Director, Bertrand P. Collomb, age 71
Director, Claude Mandil, age 73
Director, Bertrand Jacquillat, age 68
Director, Pierre Vaillaud, age 77
Director, Patricia Barbizet, age 59
Director, Antoine Jeancourt-Galignani, age 76
Director, Thierry de Rudder, age 65
Director, Lord Peter Levene, age 71
Director Training and Skills Management Specialties Sector and Director, Daniel Boeuf, age 64
Director, Maj. Patrick Artus, age 55
Auditors: KPMGAudit

LOCATIONS

HQ: Total S.A.
2, place Jean Millier, La Defense 6, Courbevoie 92400
Phone: (33) 1 47 44 45 46   **Fax:** (33) 1 47 44 49 44
Web: www.total.com

Sales

	% of total
Europe	
France	23
Other	44
Africa	9
North	8
Other	16
Total	**100**

PRODUCTS/OPERATIONS

Sales

Downstream	65
Chemicals	10

COMPETITORS

Akzo Nobel	MOL
Ashland Inc.	Norsk Hydro ASA
BASF SE	Occidental Petroleum
BHP Billiton	PEMEX
BP	PETROBRAS
Chevron	Pakistan State Oil
ConocoPhillips	Petroleos de Venezuela
DuPont	Royal Dutch Shell
Eni	Statoil
Exxon Mobil	ZaZa Energy
Imperial Oil	

HISTORICAL FINANCIALS

Company Type: Public

Income Statement

FYE: December 31

	REVENUE ($ mil.)	NET INCOME ($ mil.)	NET PROFIT MARGIN	EMPLOYEES
12/13	236,323	11,619	4.9%	98,799
12/12	240,279	14,095	5.9%	97,126
12/11	215,424	15,878	7.4%	96,104
12/10	188,009	14,147	7.5%	92,855
12/09	161,564	12,168	7.5%	96,387
Annual Growth	10.0%	(1.1%)	—	0.6%

2013 Year-End Financials

Debt ratio: 26.3%
Return on equity: 11.6%
Cash ($ mil.): 20,165
Current ratio: 1.37
Long-term debt ($ mil.): 34,513

No. of shares (mil.): —
Dividends
  Yield: 5.0%
  Payout: 56.6%
Market value ($ mil.): —

	STOCK PRICE ($) FY Close	P/E High/Low	PER SHARE ($) Earnings	Dividends	Book Value
12/13	61.27	31 22	5.12	3.11	44.08
12/12	52.01	21 14	6.22	2.86	42.57
12/11	51.11	23 13	7.04	0.00	39.04
12/10	53.48	28 15	6.30	2.93	36.14
12/09	64.04	37 21	5.45	3.28	33.90
Annual Growth	(1.1%)	— —	(1.5%)	(1.3%)	6.8%

Toyota Motor Corp

Toyota Motor among the world's largest automotive manufacturers by auto sales (running a tight race with GM) designs and manufactures a diverse product line-up that ranges from subcompacts to luxury and sports vehicles to SUVs trucks minivans and buses. Its vehicles are produced either with combustion or hybrid engines as with the Prius. Toyota's subsidiaries also manufacture vehicles: Daihatsu Motor produces mini-vehicles while Hino Motors produces trucks and buses. Additionally Toyota makes automotive parts for its own use and for sale to others. Popular models include the Camry Corolla Land Cruiser and luxury Lexus line as well as the Tundra truck.

Major Toyota subsidiaries include Toyota Auto Body Co. Ltd. Toyota Motor Sales U.S.A. Toyota Motor North America Toyota Motor Engineering & Manufacturing North America Toyota Financial Services Corporation and Toyota Motor Credit Corporation.

Toyota divides its operations into the three segments of automotive (91% of total sales) financial services (6%) and other (3%). Automotive is obviously Toyota's bread and butter; the segment makes passenger and commercial vehicles minivans trucks and related parts. Its less known financial services segment provides financing to dealers and their customers for the lease or purchase of Toyota vehicles.

Toyota maintains a vast geographical reach selling to 170 countries and regions through more than 500 consolidated subsidiaries and some 210 affiliated companies. Almost 60% of its sales come from Asia (Japan counts for 48%) while North America generates around 20% of total sales. Countries in Europe Africa the Middle East Oceania and Latin America account for the remainder.

Toyota has been focused on regaining its financial footing after suffering through several economic disasters. From 2010 to 2011 its overall net revenue decreased by 2% due to the March 2011 Great East Japan Earthquake flood in Thailand and a shortage of parts supplies stemming from those disasters. Its geographical segments were also stung by volatile exchange rates. However despite these challenges the total number of overall vehicles sold in 2012 for Toyota was roughly 7.3 million vehicles up 0.6% compared to 2011.

Like its competitors Toyota is beefing up its Chinese operations by joining forces with local automotive players. With its partner China FAW Group Corporation Toyota builds nine models including Land Cruisers and Corollas in the country. The third factory operated by the JV began producing Corollas in May 2012.

Along with China India is generating a lot of interest in the automotive industry. Toyota in late 2010 opened a manufacturing plant near Bangalore through its Toyota Kirloskar Motor (TKM) joint venture with partner Kirloskar Group. The move established Toyota's presence in India's heartland by launching its compact Etios to the Indian market.

While Toyota shared the pain of its global competitors during the Great Recession it was spared the government-supervised bankruptcy reorganizations that Chrysler and GM endured. During the hard times Toyota focused on consolidating its North American operations shifting its resources and closing underperforming operations. In early 2010 it sold off Toyota Financial Services Securities Corp. (the brokerage unit of its financial arm Toyota Financial Services Corp.) to Tokai Tokyo Financial Holdings.

Toyota was met with massive recalls beginning in 2010 in regard to defective gas pedals faulty floor mats and problems with braking software. It recalled more than 8 million vehicles worldwide and halted production of the subject models including the top-selling Camry at US and Canadian plants. The recalls were the largest for Toyota in the US and the suspension of sales and production resulting from vehicle defects topped the industry's charts.

HISTORY

In 1926 Sakichi Toyoda founded Toyoda Automatic Loom Works. In 1930 he sold the rights to the loom he invented and gave the proceeds to his son Kiichiro Toyoda to begin an automotive business. Kiichiro opened an auto shop within the loom works in 1933. When protectionist legislation (1936) improved prospects for Japanese automakers Kiichiro split off the car department took it public (1937) and changed its name to Toyota.

During WWII the company made military trucks but financial problems after the war caused Toyota to reorganize in 1950. Its postwar commitment to R&D paid off with the launch of the four-wheel-drive Land Cruiser (1951); full-sized Crown (1955); and the small Corona (1957).

Toyota Motor Sales U.S.A. debuted the Toyopet Crown in the US in 1957 but it proved underpowered for the US market. Toyota had better luck with the Corona in 1965 and with the Corolla (which became the best-selling car of all time) in 1968. By 1970 Toyota was the world's fourth largest carmaker.

Toyota expanded rapidly in the US. During the 1970s the oil crisis caused demand for fuel-efficient cars and Toyota was there to grab market share from US makers. In 1975 Toyota displaced Volkswagen as the US's #1 auto importer. Toyota began auto production in the US in 1984 through NUMMI its joint venture with General Motors. The Lexus line was launched in the US in 1989.

Because of European restrictions on Japanese auto imports until 2000 Toyota's European expansion slowed. Toyota responded in 1992 by agreeing to distribute cars in Japan for Volkswagen and also by establishing an engine plant (later moved to full auto production) in the UK.

The SUV mania of the 1990s spurred Toyota's introduction of luxury minivans and light trucks. Hiroshi Okuda a 40-year veteran with Toyota and the first person from outside the Toyoda family to run the firm succeeded Tatsuro Toyoda as president in 1995. The next year Toyota consolidated its North American production units into Cincinnati-based Toyota Motor Manufacturing North America.

In 1997 Toyota introduced the Prius a hybrid electric- and gas-powered car. The next year Toyota boosted its stake in affiliate Daihatsu Motor (mini-vehicles) to about 51% and started Toyota Mapmaster (51% owned) to make map databases for car navigation systems. Okuda became chairman in 1999 replacing Shoichiro Toyoda and Fujio Cho became president (later vice chairman). Also that year Toyota agreed to form a joint venture with Isuzu Motors to manufacture buses.

In 2000 Toyota launched the WiLL Vi a sedan aimed at young people. It announced that it was building an online replacement parts marketplace with i2 Technologies and formed a financial services company (Toyota Financial Service) and a brokerage firm (Toyota Financial Services Securities Corp.). Toyota also bought a 5% stake in Yamaha Motor (the world's #2 motorcycle maker) and raised its stake in truck maker Hino Motors from about 20% to around 34%.

International developments included Toyota's agreement with the Chinese government to produce passenger cars for sale in China built by Tianjin Toyota Motor Corp. a joint venture between Chinese carmaker Tianjin Automobile Xiali and Toyota. In 2001 Toyota opened a plant in France. Later that year Toyota also increased its stake in Hino Motors to 50%. With partners Toyoda Gosei and Horie Metal Co. Ltd. Toyota formed a joint venture in 2002 to manufacture resin fuel tank systems. In 2004 Toyota forged a joint venture agreement with Guangzhou Automobile Group to build engines in China. The following year Toyota established 14 Lexus dealerships in China. The company began joint car production in Europe with Peugeot S.A. in 2005. Also in 2005 Toyota bought just under 9% of Fuji Heavy Industries –the Japanese maker of Subaru passenger vehicles. The two companies began production of Toyota Camrys at Fuji Heavy Industries' underutilized Subaru of Indiana plant in 2007.

After suffering through the Great Recession from 2008 to 2010 Toyota faced another unforeseen crisis. In March 2011 its business suffered unexpectedly from the Great East Japan Earthquake which triggered a deadly tsunami and subsequent nuclear crisis that forced Tokyo Electric Power (Tepco) to shut down reactors at two nuclear power plants and five other conventional power plants. The events forced manufacturers to reduce their output or move production to other regions. Toyota along with its rivals (Nissan Honda and Mazda) were forced to close their factories days after the devastation.

EXECUTIVES

Chairman, Fujio Cho, age 77
Vice Chairman, Katsuaki Watanabe, age 72
Vice Chairman, Kazuo Okamoto, age 70
Chairman, Takeshi Uchiyamada, age 68
Corporate Auditor, Masaki Nakatsugawa
VP Toyota Product Communications Toyota Motor Sales U.S.A., James H. (Jim) Colon
President and COO Toyota Motor North America; Chairman and CEO Toyota Motors Sales U.S.A., Yoshimi Inaba, age 68
President and Board Member, Akio Toyoda, age 58
EVP and Representative Director, Atsushi (Art) Niimi, age 66
EVP and Representative Director, Yukitoshi (Yuki) Funo, age 67
EVP and Representative Director, Shinichi Sasaki, age 67
Senior Managing Officer, Masanao Tomozoe
Managing Officer, Katsutada Masumoto
Managing Officer, James E. (Jim) Lentz III, age 58
Managing Officer; EVP Toyota Motor Engineering & Manufacturing North America; President Toyota Technical Center, Shigeki Terashi
Senior Managing Executive Officer, Takahiro Iwase, age 62
Senior Managing Officer, Yoshimasa Ishii, age 61
Senior Managing Officer, Takeshi Shirane
Chief Officer of the China Operations Group, Akira Sasaki, age 66
EVP and Board Member, Masamoto Maekawa
Senior Managing Executive Officer; Chief Director of Public Relations; Director, Mamoru Furuhashi, age 64
EVP and Representative Director, Satoshi Ozawa, age 65
EVP and Board Member, Seiichi Sudo
Senior Managing Officer, Tadashi Yamashina, age 63
EVP and Board Member, Yasumori Ihara, age 63
EVP and Board Member, Mitsuhisa Kato
President and COO Toyota Motor Engineering & Manufacturing North America, Tetsuo Agata, age 61
Managing Officer; EVP Toyota Motor Engineering & Manufacturing North America; Chief Quality Officer North American Quality Task Force; Chairman Toyota Motor Manufacturing Kentucky; Chairman Toyota Motor Manufactuing Mississippi, Steve St. Angelo, age 58
Managing Officer, Hiroyoshi Yoshiki
Managing Officer, Koichi Sugihara
Managing Officer, Osamu Nagata
Managing Officer, Shigeru Hayakawa
Senior Managing Officer, Hirofumi Muta
Managing Officer, Shigeki Suzuki
Managing Officer, Hisayuki Inoue
Managing Officer, Hiroji Onishi
Managing Officer, Keiji Masui
Managing Officer, Kenji Miura
Managing Officer Design Quality Innovation Sports Vehicle Management Product Development Management and LEXUS Development Center, Kiyotaka Ise
Managing Officer; Chief Quality Officer Europe, Didier Leroy
Managing Officer, Hiroyuki Yokoyama
Managing Officer, Koei Saga
Managing Officer, Takuo Matsui
Managing Officer, Soichiro Okudaira
Managing Officer, Hiroyuki Ochiai
Managing Officer, Yasuo Kawada
Managing Officer, Naoki Miyazaki
Managing Officer; VP Production Control Division and Corporate Strategy Division Toyota Motor Engineering & Manufacturing North America; Corporate Auditor Aisan Industry, Kazuhiro Miyauchi
VP Marketing, Bill Fay
VP Sales Administration, Randy Pflughaupt
Corporate Auditor, Kunihiro Matsuo
Corporate Auditor, Yoichi Morishita
Corporate Auditor, Akishige Okada
EVP and Board Member, Nobuyori Kodaira, age 65
Managing Officer, Shunichi Konishi
Managing Officer, Yoichi Inoue
Managing Officer, Yoshihiko Matsuda
Managing Officer, Satoru Mouri
Managing Officer, Moritaka Yoshida
Managing Officer, Johan van Zyl
Vice Chairman, Katsuaki Watanabe, age 72
Vice Chairman, Kazuo Okamoto, age 70
EVP and Representative Director, Takeshi Uchiyamada, age 67
President and Board Member, Akio Toyoda, age 58
EVP and Representative Director, Atsushi (Art) Niimi, age 66
EVP and Representative Director, Yukitoshi (Yuki) Funo, age 67
EVP and Representative Director, Shinichi Sasaki, age 67
EVP and Board Member, Masamoto Maekawa
Director; Chief Officer Government and Public Affairs Group, Mamoru Furuhashi, age 63
EVP and Representative Director, Satoshi Ozawa, age 65
EVP and Board Member, Seiichi Sudo
EVP and Board Member, Yasumori Ihara, age 63
EVP and Board Member, Mitsuhisa Kato
Director, Takahiko Ijichi, age 61
EVP and Board Member, Nobuyori Kodaira, age 65
Auditors: PricewaterhouseCoopersAarata

LOCATIONS

HQ: Toyota Motor Corp
1 Toyota-cho, Toyota, Aichi 471-8571
Phone: (81) 565 28 2121   **Fax:** (81) 565 23 5800
Web: www.toyota.co.jp

Sales

	$ mil.	% of total
Asia		
Other countries		14
Europe		9
Total		**100**

2012 Unit Sales

		% of total
Asia		
Other countries	1,326,829	18
Europe	797,993	11
Total	**7,351,929**	**100**

PRODUCTS/OPERATIONS

Sales

	$ mil.	% of total
Automotive		91
Other		3

Selected Products

Vehicles
  4Runner
  Allion (sold in Japan)
  Alphard (minivan sold in Japan)
  Aurus (hybrid)
  Avalon
  Camry (also hybrid)
  Corolla
  Corolla Rumion
  Crown
  FJ Cruiser
  Highlander (also hybrid)
  Land Cruiser
  Lexus

GX
LS600h (hybrid)
LX (SUV)
RX
SC
Mark X (sold in Japan)
Matrix
Premio (sold in Japan)
Prius (hybrid)
RAV4
Scion
Sequoia
Sienna (minivan)
Tacoma (truck)
Tundra (truck)
Vanguard
Vellfire (minivan)
Venza
Wish (minivan sold in Japan)
Yaris (marketed in Japan as the Vitz)
Other products
Factory automation equipment
Forklifts and other industrial vehicles
Housing products

Selected Investments

Daihatsu Motor (51% motor vehicles)
Hino Motors Ltd. (50% trucks)

COMPETITORS

BMW	Kia Motors
Brilliance China	Komatsu
Caterpillar	Kubota
Chery Automobile	Land Rover
Chrysler	Mazda
Daimler	Mitsubishi Motors
Deere	Nissan
Fiat	Peugeot
Ford Motor	Renault
Fuji Heavy Industries	Saab Automobile
General Motors	Shanghai Automotive
Global Diversified	Suzuki Motor
Industries	Tata Motors
Honda	Volkswagen
Hyundai Motor	Volvo
Isuzu	Volvo Car Corp.

HISTORICAL FINANCIALS

Company Type: Public

Income Statement

FYE: March 31

	REVENUE ($ mil.)	NET INCOME ($ mil.)	NET PROFIT MARGIN	EMPLOYEES
03/14	248,905	17,662	7.1%	338,875
03/13	234,495	10,225	4.4%	333,498
03/12	226,546	3,456	1.5%	325,905
03/11	229,374	4,929	2.1%	317,716
03/10	202,885	2,242	1.1%	320,590
Annual Growth	5.2%	67.5%	—	1.4%

2014 Year-End Financials

Debt ratio: 0.3%
Return on equity: 13.7%
Cash ($ mil.): 41,351
Current ratio: 1.07
Long-term debt ($ mil.): 82,803
No. of shares (mil.): —
Dividends
Yield: 2.2%
Payout: 55.4%
Market value ($ mil.): —

	STOCK PRICE ($) FY Close	P/E High/Low		PER SHARE ($) Earnings	Dividends	Book Value
03/14	112.90	0	0	5.57	2.54	44.22
03/13	102.64	0	0	3.23	0.00	40.76
03/12	86.82	0	0	1.10	0.00	40.61
03/11	80.25	0	0	1.57	1.03	39.79
03/10	80.42	0	0	0.72	1.18	35.37
Annual Growth	8.9%	—	—	67.1%	21.0%	5.7%

Toyota Tsusho Corp

Toyota Tsusho is the trading unit for the Toyota Group which includes Toyota Motor and auto parts maker DENSO. The company brokers a wide array of goods including metals such as steel and aluminum (comprising its largest division) machinery and electronics energy and chemicals and various consumer products. As its family relationship would imply Toyota Tsusho exports Toyota vehicles around the world but plenty of non-automotive consumer products also contribute to its business. Those other products include foodstuffs like produce and wine as well as personal nursing care equipment. Toyota Motor Corporation owns 22% of the company while Toyota Industries owns 11%.

With the global recession as a background Toyota Tusho's revenues fell almost 19% in 2010. The downturn was precipitated by an across-the-board drop in the company's sales led by a 28% dip in its Automotive division and 21% in its Metals unit. Correspondingly net income was off 32% over 2009.

In 2010 parent company Toyota Motor introduced a new low-carbon plastic material to be used in a number of its 2011 model vehicles. The "Ecological Plastic" developed by Toyota Tusho marks the world's first use of bio-polyethylene terephthalate derived from sugar cane. The new material is a second-generation bio-plastic that is more durable than earlier substances.

Also that year Eurus Energy Holdings a joint venture between Tokyo Electric Power and Toyota Tsusho acquired South Korean solar power company Jindosun Park Inc. Jindosun oversees the generation of 2974KW of electricity mostly in South Korea and will activate a 45000KW plant in the US in mid-2011.

In 2010 Toyota Tsusho acquired UK-based CalEnergy Gas's 5% stake in the Otway Gas Project and exploration rights in the Bass Straits in Australia. Toyota Tsusho considers Australia an important country for upstream investments in the gas value chain.

The company agreed in 2009 to separate its automotive fabrics business and join the unit with similar businesses of Toyota Boshoku and Kawashima Selkon. Toyota Tsusho own 30% of the resulting company. The move away from sole ownership of that business fits within Tsusho's general strategic plan to earn half of its revenue from the automotive sector by 2015.

The acquisition of TOMEN Corporation made Toyota Tsusho the sixth-largest trading company in Japan and it expanded the company's operations in the non-auto sector. Products under Tomen's purview include chemicals and plastics foodstuffs IT telecommunications and power supply equipment and textiles.

EXECUTIVES

Executive Officer; Deputy Chief Division Officer Automotive Division, Takashi Hattori
Executive Officer; Deputy Chief Division Officer Energy and Chemicals Division, Kuniaki Yamagiwa
Chairman, Junzo Shimizu, age 67
President Toyota Tsusho Asia Pacific, Jun Nakayama
Managing Executive Officer; President Toyota Tsusho America, Masanori Yamase
EVP, Mikio Asano
President and CEO, Jun Karube
Vice Chairman, Yoshio Shirai, age 63
Senior Managing Director, Hiroshi Takano
Managing Director, Takumi Shirai

Executive Officer; Deputy Chief Division Officer Machinery and Electronics Division, Soichiro Matsudaira
President of Toyota Tsusho Europe S.A, Seiichiro Adachi
President S.C. Toyota Tsusho do Brasil, Yoshifumi Araki
Executive Officer; President Toyota Tsusho Europe; President Toyota Tsusho (UK), Hiroki Sawayama
Executive Officer; Deputy Chief Division Officer Global Strategic Integration Division, Yuichi Oi
EVP, Akimasa Yokoi
President Toyota Tsusho America, Nobuyuki Minowa
Executive Officer; Deputy Chief Division Officer Metals Division, Minoru Murata
President Toyota Tsusho Europe, Kiyoshi Yamakawa
President Toyota Tsusho India, Shizuka Hayashi
President Toyota Tsusho (Thailand), Hirofumi Sato
Managing Director; Chief Division Officer Produce and Foodstuffs Division, Makoto Hyodo
Director, Hiroshi Kawakami, age 63
President and Representative Director, Junzo Shimizu, age 67
Senior Managing Director Chief Division Officer Energy and Chemicals Division and Representative Director, Yoshimasa Kondo
Vice Chairman, Yoji Toyohara, age 71
EVP Chief Representative of Tokyo Head Office and Representative Director, Kiyoshi Furubayashi, age 68
EVP and Representative Director, Katsunori Takahashi
Senior Managing Director Chief Division Officer Consumer Products Services and Materials Division and Representative Director, Koji Oshige, age 65
Managing Director; Chief Division Officer of Machinery & Electronics Division, Hisashi Yamamoto
Managing Director Chief Division Officer Administrative Division and Representative Director, Mikio Asano
Senior Managing Director; Chief Division Officer of Global Strategic Integration Division, Kenji Takanashi
Managing Director; Chief Division Officer Automotive Division, Seiichiro Adachi
Managing Director; Chief Division Officer Metals Division, Minoru Hayata
Auditors: PricewaterhouseCoopersAarata

LOCATIONS

HQ: Toyota Tsusho Corp
Century Toyota Bldg., 4-9-8 Meieki, Nakamura-ku, Nagoya, Aichi 450-8575
Phone: (81) 52 584 5482   **Fax:** 502 868 3355
Web: www.toyota-tsusho.com

Sales

	$ mil.	% of total
Asia & Oceania		

PRODUCTS/OPERATIONS

Sales

Metals	30
Energy & chemicals	22
Produce & foodstuffs	6

COMPETITORS

Daewoo International	Samsung C&T
Mitsui	Sojitz
Nippon Steel Trading	Sumitomo
Rieter Holding	Yamato Kogyo

HISTORICAL FINANCIALS

Company Type: Public

Income Statement

FYE: March 31

	REVENUE ($ mil.)	NET INCOME ($ mil.)	NET PROFIT MARGIN	EMPLOYEES
03/14	75,017	707	0.9%	50,423
03/13	67,001	716	1.1%	48,336
03/12	72,129	807	1.1%	33,845
03/11	69,362	569	0.8%	31,081
03/10	54,623	292	0.5%	29,832
Annual Growth	8.3%	24.7%	—	14.0%

2014 Year-End Financials

Debt ratio: 0.3%
Return on equity: 8.4%
Cash ($ mil.): 3,992
Current ratio: 1.30
Long-term debt ($ mil.): 7,951

No. of shares (mil.): 351
Dividends
  Yield: —
  Payout: —
Market value ($ mil.): —

	STOCK PRICE ($) FY Close	P/E High/Low	PER SHARE ($) Earnings	Dividends	Book Value
03/14	0.00	— —	2.01	0.00	31.87
03/13	23.04	— —	2.05	0.00	27.88
03/12	17.65	— —	2.31	0.00	26.18
03/11	19.05	— —	1.63	0.00	23.04
Annual Growth	—	— —	5.5%	—	8.5%

Turkiye Garanti Bankasi A.S.

Torkiye Garanti Bankasi (Garanti Bank Turkey) provides banking services from about 966 domestic branches and more than 3700 ATMs. Subsidiaries and branches can also be found in China Cyprus Germany Luxembourg Malta Russia and the UK. In addition to traditional deposit products Garanti Bank provides brokerage factoring insurance leasing personal pension plans portfolio management and other services. The bank serves more than 12.2 million customers and has assets of more than $106 billion. Banco Bilbao Vizcaya Argentaria owns 25% of the bank once owned by the Dou Group which now holds 24%. Torkiye Garanti Bankasi was founded in 1946.

EXECUTIVES

President CEO and Director, Ergun Ozen
EVP Financial Institutions and Corporate Banking, Tolga Egemen
Executive Vice President Financial Institutions and Corporate Banking, Ali Fuat Erbil
Chairman, Ferit Faik Sahenk
Vice Chairman, Suleyman Sozen
Executive Vice President Technology Operational Services and Central Marketing, Husnu Erel
Executive Vice President Domestic & Overseas Subsidiaries Coordination, Turgay Gonensin
Executive Vice President Support Services, Adnan Memis
EVP Loans, Ali Temel
Executive Vice President Strategic and Financial Planning, Murat Mergin
EVP Treasury, Uruz Ersozoglu
EVP Human Resources Training Treasury & Investment Banking, Gokhan Erun
Executive Vice President SME Banking, Nafiz Karadere

Executive Vice President Technology Operations Management & Central Marketing, Husnu Erel
Executive Vice President CFO, Afzal M. Modak
Executive Vice President, Onur Genc
Executive Vice President - Loans, Erhan Adali
Executive Vice President Delivery Channels Social Platforms Management Customer Satisfaction, Didem Dincer Baser
Executive Vice President General Accounting & Financial Reporting, Ibrahim Aydinli
Executive Vice President Commercial Banking, Recep Bastug
Executive Vice President Legal Services and Retail Risk Monitoring, Aydin Duren
Executive Vice President Project and Acquisition Finance Sustainability, Ebru Dildar Edin
Executive Vice President Retail and Private Banking Call Center Garanti Payment Systems CEO, Onur Genc
Executive Vice President SME Banking Corporate Brand Management and Marketing Communication, Nafiz Karadere
Executive Vice President Purchasing & Tax Management, Aydin Senel
President CEO and Director, Ergun Ozen
Vice Chairman, Suleyman Sozen
Auditors: KPMG

LOCATIONS

HQ: Turkiye Garanti Bankasi A.S.
  Levent, Nispetiye Mahallesi, Aytar Caddesi, No. 2, Besiktas, Istanbul, Istanbul Province 34340
Phone: (90) 212 318 18 18   **Fax:** (90) 212 216 59 02
Web: www.garantibank.com

COMPETITORS

Akbank	Sabanci
Finansbank	Sekerbank
Isbank	Turk Ekonomi Bankasi
Koc	Yapi Kredi

HISTORICAL FINANCIALS

Company Type: Public

Income Statement

FYE: December 31

	ASSETS ($ mil.)	NET INCOME ($ mil.)	INCOME AS % OF ASSETS	EMPLOYEES
12/13	101,791	1,669	1.6%	21,853
12/12	99,102	1,878	1.9%	20,287
12/11	85,900	1,789	2.1%	19,547
12/10	87,971	2,220	2.5%	19,497
12/09	77,183	2,056	2.7%	18,875
Annual Growth	7.2%	(5.1%)	—	3.7%

2013 Year-End Financials

Return on assets: 1.8%
Return on equity: 15.8%
Long-term debt ($ mil.): —
No. of shares (mil.): —
Sales ($ mil): 8,543

Dividends
  Yield: 1.8%
  Payout: 3.8%
Market value ($ mil.): —

	STOCK PRICE ($) FY Close	P/E High/Low	PER SHARE ($) Earnings	Dividends	Book Value
12/13	3.21	2 1	0.40	0.06	0.03
12/12	5.20	2 1	0.45	0.06	0.03
12/11	3.11	2 1	0.43	0.02	0.02
12/10	5.15	4 2	0.53	0.07	0.03
12/09	3.95	3 1	0.49	0.01	0.02
Annual Growth	(5.1%)	— —	(5.1%)	41.2%	4.3%

Turkiye Is Bankasi A.S.

Torkiye Bankasι A.. is banking in Turkey. Known as Isbank it's the country's largest publicly traded bank with 15 million customers. It provides standard banking services including commercial lending and retail banking through more than 1250 mostly domestic branches worldwide. It also offers its service through about 4850 ATMs more than 1000 kiosks and 65-plus Cash Receiving Systems machines. Isbank was founded in 1924 by mandate of the Turkish Republic's founding father Mustafa Kemal Atatork. Employees own about 40% of Isbank through the Private Pension Fund of Employees. Some 28% of the bank is owned in the name of Atatork by the Republican People's Party.

Isbank GmbH an Isbank subsidiary runs most of the banks European branches. It also directly operates branches in Cyprus and Bahrain as well as a representative office in China and an online only branch in Ireland.

Other Isbank operations are split into financial services including life insurance pension plans asset management brokerage and factoring and non-financial covering holdings in glassware telecom facilities management publishing and other businesses.

LOCATIONS

HQ: Turkiye Is Bankasi A.S.
  Is Kuleleri, Istanbul, Levent 34330
Phone: (90) 212 316 00 00   **Fax:** (90) 212 316 09 00
Web: www.isbank.com.tr

PRODUCTS/OPERATIONS

HISTORICAL FINANCIALS

Company Type: Public

Income Statement

FYE: December 31

	ASSETS ($ mil.)	NET INCOME ($ mil.)	INCOME AS % OF ASSETS	EMPLOYEES
12/13	112,508	1,724	1.5%	24,129
12/12	111,088	2,330	2.1%	24,411
12/11	96,960	1,303	1.3%	24,887
12/10	97,346	1,716	1.8%	23,944
12/09	87,262	1,424	1.6%	22,473
Annual Growth	6.6%	4.9%	—	1.8%

2013 Year-End Financials

Return on assets: 1.6%
Return on equity: 15.9%
Long-term debt ($ mil.): —
No. of shares (mil.): —
Sales ($ mil): 12,989

Dividends
  Yield: 0.0%
  Payout: 102.7%
Market value ($ mil.): —

	STOCK PRICE ($) FY Close	P/E High/Low	PER SHARE ($) Earnings	Dividends	Book Value
12/13	2.02	14 14	0.02	0.02	(0.00)
12/12	3.20	27 21	0.02	0.02	(0.00)
12/11	2.76	59 41	0.01	0.03	(0.00)
12/10	3.45	78 61	0.02	0.04	(0.00)
Annual Growth	(16.3%)	— —	0.1%	(20.3%)	

UBS AG (Switzerland)

If you be wealthy then UBS is for you. UBS is one of the world's largest private banks with operations in more than 50 countries. UBS also provides asset management and investment banking as well as traditional banking services in its home country of Switzerland. The group includes four primary segments: Wealth Management & Swiss Bank Wealth Management Americas Global Asset Management and UBS Investment Bank. Investment management clients include ultra-wealthy individuals corporations and institutional investors. Asset classes offered include internal and external mutual bonds money markets stocks and bonds. Investment banking options include securities underwriting advisory and foreign exchange.

After suffering billions in losses in the global recession UBS has been restructuring itself and cutting down its portfolio of businesses. It is also looking for ways to sharpen its focus on client-focused investment operations and move away from the proprietary trading business that contributed to its losses. The company plans to focus on its global wealth management and Swiss banking operations while utilizing its investment banking operations as a supporting partner to its core businesses. (Going forward it will report Wealth management and Retail & Corporate as separate divisions while its Wealth Management & Swiss Bank segment will go away.) Recent acquisitions that fall in line with that goal include Dutch wealth management firm VermogensGroep the French asset management operations of rival Commerzbank and ING Groep's investment management business in Australia. It also bought structured products boutique Luxembourg Financial Group boosting its global equities activities.

The group's corporate rejiggering and fiscal discipline along with the relative strength of the Swiss franc helped UBS return to profitability in 2010. Its investment bank operations provided the company with its greatest boost that year as it lessened its exposure to risky investments and turned around losses in fixed income currencies and commodities. However the lingering downturn and concerns over European sovereign debt have been a drain on the company. Investment banking activity slowed down in 2011 which was the primary reason profits slipped some 45% that year. On the other hand the company reported improved new client assets and wealth management revenues rose. UBS has a strong capital position with a core Tier 1 ratio ahead of many other European banks as they work to meet Basel III standards.

In 2011 the company reported a third-quarter loss after it discovered unauthorized trading in its London investment bank. The rogue trader was arrested under suspicion of fraud; losses from the speculative trading amounted to CHF 1.9 billion (more than $2 billion). Although UBS' risk system detected unauthorized trading the company did not investigate and controls were not put in place. The incident led to further declines in UBS' investment banking business.

HISTORY

Businessmen in Winterthur Switzerland formed the Bank of Winterthur in 1862 to serve trading interests finance railroads and operate a warehouse. In 1912 the bank merged with the Bank of Toggenburg (formed in 1863) to create Schweizerische Bankgesellschaft —Union Bank of Switzerland (UBS).

It expanded in Switzerland buying smaller banks and adding branches. After growing in the post-

WWI era it was hit hard by the Depression. UBS benefited from Switzerland's neutrality in WWII gaining deposits from both Jews and Nazis. In 1946 the bank opened an office in New York. Expansion in Switzerland continued after the war with the purchase of Eidgenossische Bank of Zurich.

UBS continued its acquisitions in the 1950s; by 1962 it had 81 branches. Other purchases included Interhandel a cash-rich Swiss financial concern (1967) and four savings banks (1968). In 1967 it opened a full-service office in London and during the 1970s established several securities underwriting subsidiaries abroad.

International financial markets became supercharged in the 1980s and UBS resolved to catch up with its domestic peers in international operations. As London prepared for financial deregulation in 1986 UBS bought brokerage house Phillips & Drew.

The firm's UK brokerage business was hit hard by the 1987 US stock market crash; over the next two years losses continued prompting an overhaul of the London operations. Then its US operations were jarred by the collapse of the junk bond market in 1990. The next year UBS set up offices in Paris Singapore and Hong Kong and took over Chase Manhattan's (now JPMorgan Chase) New York money management unit.

Meanwhile the firm continued to expand within Switzerland buying five more banks to boost market share and fill in gaps in its branch network. These buys left UBS with overlapping operations and a bloated infrastructure when recession hit. Falling real estate values left the bank with a heavy load of nonperforming loans.

In 1994 profits plummeted. Stockholder Martin Ebner dissatisfied with the performance of president Robert Studer tried to gain control of UBS; failing that he sought to have Studer charged with criminal fraud. In 1996 he almost thwarted Studer's election to the chairmanship.

UBS launched a multiyear reorganization in 1994 by consolidating its consumer credit operations. The next year it joined with Swiss Life/Rentenanstalt to offer insurance products through its bank network.

In 1996 after rebuffing Credit Suisse Group's merger bid UBS began an even more draconian reorganization cutting domestic branches and writing down billions of francs in bad loans leading to UBS' first-ever loss (with another the next year). In 1998 the company merged with Swiss Bank Corp. then cut 23% of its staff. Later that year the bank lost $1.6 billion in the stumbling Long-Term Capital Management hedge fund prompting chairman Mathis Cabiallavetta to resign.

As UBS struggled to swallow Swiss Bank in 1999 it retreated somewhat from riskier markets began selling some $2 billion in real estate and sold its 25% stake in Swiss Life/Rentenanstalt. Looking to bulk up the firm that year bought Bank of America's European and Asian private banking operations and Allegis Realty Investors a US real estate investment management firm.

In 2000 UBS reorganized yet again and bought US broker Paine Webber (now UBS Paine Webber). UBS's integration of Paine Webber continued into the next year. Also in 2001 chairman Marcel Ospel was criticized for UBS's handling of Swissair's cash crisis which resulted in the air fleet's grounding.

The bank came under computer attack in 2002 when a disgruntled PaineWebber employee set off a "logic bomb" in UBS's computer system. Despite the deletion of 1000 files across the company network and $3 million in damages UBS and its stock price weathered the attack.

Continuing to target the mass affluent around the planet UBS acquired the South American

wealth management operations of Dresdner Bank and the North American wealth management business of Julius Baer in 2004. It sold some of its private banking business in Switzerland to Julius Baer the following year.

In late 2004 UBS bought SoundView (renamed UBS Capital Markets) the capital markets and specialist business of US company Charles Schwab for $265 million in cash. UBS integrated the operations into the equities business of its investment bank making the unit one of the top market makers of Nasdaq stock.

UBS's 2006 acquisition of #2 Brazilian investment bank Banco Pactual for about $2.6 billion gave it a foothold in the volatile-yet-growing Brazilian private equity market (a market in which rival Credit Suisse was already active). Also that year with the commodities market at a fever pitch UBS bought ABN AMRO's futures and commodities trading business for an estimated $400 million. It bought the private client services business of Piper Jaffray Companies for $875 million and KeyCorp's McDonald Investments.

UBS suffered severe losses in 2007 and 2008 related to investments in the US subprime mortgage market. It was one of Europe's hardest-hit financial institutions and in late 2008 UBS received government bailout funds to the tune of CHF 68 billion ($60 billion). Ironically UBS' exposure to subprime mortgages had been undertaken as a way to play catch-up with competition in the bonds markets. UBS ended up writing down around $40 billion and closing its Dillon Read Capital Management operations (paying out some $300 million in the process).

In 2009 the company restructured to separate its struggling divisions into four autonomous units including splitting up the former Global Wealth Management & Business Bank segment to give each unit more accountability and flexibility. UBS cut costs as well including cutting some 12500 jobs (it cut 6000 jobs the previous year). In 2008 the company sold $15 billion in distressed mortgage assets to BlackRock shut down its municipal bond business and sold its 3.4 billion shares in Bank of China. It also sold UBS Fiduciary Trust to Wilmington Trust its mortgage servicing business to Impac Mortgage and its Canadian energy business to JPMorgan Chase.

The company ran into more trouble in 2009. To settle claims that it helped American clients avoid paying taxes to the US government the company paid a $780 million fine and turned over once-secret banking client records. It also exited the US cross-border banking business. Some UBS account-holders countered by suing the company in Swiss court. As the company cooperates with authorities to provide more transparency though UBS risks losing some of its ober-wealthy customers.

The turmoil was the final straw for CEO Marcel Rohrer who was replaced in 2009 by Oswald Grobel the former CEO of rival Credit Suisse. Grobel retired from Credit Suisse in 2007 and was credited with turning that company around after a period of poor performance. UBS continued to clear out its top management that year and brought in former Swiss finance minister Kaspar Villiger as its chairman.

EXECUTIVES

Head Wealth Management International, Juerg Haller
Chief Group Internal Audit Swiss Bank, Stephan Zimmermann
Secretary, Luzius Cameron
Chairman and CEO Global Asset Management; Chairman UBS Saudi Arabia, John A. Fraser, age 63

Chairman Americas; President UBS Investment Bank, Robert Wolf, age 52

Group COO; CEO Corporate Center and UBS Group Europe Middle East and Africa, Ulrich Korner, age 52

Vice Chairman Wealth Management Americas; Vice Chairman UBS Bank USA, Rosemary T. Berkery, age 60

Head Wealth Management Origination UBS Financial Services, Robert E. (Bob) Mulholland, age 62

Co-Head Investment Banking EMEA, Hermann Prelle, age 49

Co-Head Wealth Management Advisor Group US Global Wealth Management Americas, James D. (Jamie) Price

Executive Chairman Fixed Income Currencies and Commodities (FICC); Head Complex Structured Products UBS Investment Bank, Jeffrey (Jeff) Mayer, age 55

Group CEO, Sergio P. Ermotti, age 54

CFO, Thomas C. (Tom) Naratil

Global Head Equity Capital Markets, Matthew Koder

Chief Executive UBS Jersey, Thomas R. (Tom) Hill, age 52

COO UBS Switzerland, Markus Ronner

Head Wealth Management Asia Pacific, Kathryn Shih

COO Wealth Management Advisor Group US, Anton Stadelmann

CEO Americas and Wealth Management Americas, Robert J. (Bob) McCann, age 56

Vice Chairman Wealth Management Americas, James M. Pierce

Chairman Investment Banking Division, J. Richard (Rick) Leaman III

Head Wealth Management Partnership Wealth Management Americas, Brian P. Hull

Global Chief Risk Officer, Philip J. Lofts

Head Group Compliance, Neil R. Stocks

Vice Chairman Wealth Management and Swiss Bank, Carlo Grigioni

Head Products and Services Wealth Management Americas, Michael A. Weisberg

Global Head Alternative and Quantitative Investments Global Asset Management, Joseph (Joe) Scoby, age 49

Head Human Resources, John F. Bradley, age 53

CFO Wealth Management and Swiss Bank, William F. Widdowson

Global Head Human Resources UBS Investment Bank, Maria Bentley

Head Banking Products and Wealth Services, Bernhard Buchs

Member of the Executive Board; Group General Counsel, Markus U. Diethelm, age 57

Chief Investment Officer Private Bank, Alexander S. Friedman

Co-Head Investment Banking Division, Simon Warshaw

CEO Russia and the Commonwealth of Independent States, Steven Meehan

Vice Chairman Saudi Arabia, Mohammed Al Dhoheyan

CEO UBS Saudi Arabia, Mohamed Sammakia

Head Human Resources and Education Wealth Management and Swiss Bank, Gabriela Maria Payer

Head Wealth Management Greater China and Deputy Head Wealth Management Asia Pacific, Allen C. L. Lo

General Counsel Wealth Management Americas, Mark Shelton

Special Counsel Wealth Management and Swiss Bank, Ursula Suter

Chairman Global Markets Asia, Peter W. Burnett

CFO Global Asset Management, Paresh Sodha

Deputy Global Head Alternative and Quantitative Investments Global Asset Management, William J. (Bill) Ferri

Global Head Equities, John C. Leonard

Chief Communication Officer, Michael Willi

CEO UBS Investment Bank, Carsten Kengeter, age 46, $711,178 total compensation

President UBS Global Asset Management (Japan) Ltd., Susumu Okamura

Co-Head Securities, Yassine Bouhara

Chief Economist Swiss Business and Private Bank, Andreas Hoefert, age 46

Head Asia Equity Syndicate, James Fleming

Managing Director and Head Corporate Communications Americas, Mark Arena

Co-Chairman and Co-CEO Asia Pacific, Chi-Won Yoon, age 55

Media Relations Europe Middle East and Africa, Oliver (Ollie) Gadney

Co-Head Global Debt Capital Markets, David Soanes

Co-Head Global Debt Capital Markets, Mike Davidson

Media Relations Investment Bank, Kelly Smith

Media Relations Investment Bank, Doug Morris

Media Relations Wealth Management US, Allison Chin-Leong

Media Relations Global Asset Management and Wealth Management US, Kris Kagel

Media Relations Canada, Graeme Harris

Global Head Securities UBS Investment Bank, Neal Shear

Co-Head Securities, Francois Gouws

Head Wealth Management Solutions Wealth Management Americas, John Brown

COO UBS Financial Services, Anita Sands

Head Wealth Management Germany, Axel Hoerger

Head Prime Broking Singapore, David Forsyth

COO UBS Investment Bank, Sam Molinaro

Co-Head Investment Banking Division, Matthew Grounds

Member of the Executive Board; Co-CEO of UBS Investment Bank, Andrea Orcel

Chairman of the Board of Directors, Beatrice Mauro

Member of the Board of Directors, Isabelle Romy

Member of the Executive Board; CEO of UBS Switzerland; CEO of UBS Retail & Corporate, Lukas Gaehwiler

Independent Vice Chairman of the Board, Michel Demare

Member of the Executive Board; Group Chief Operating Officer; CEO of Corporate Center; CEO of UBS Europe; Middle East and Africa, Ulrich Koerner

Account Vice President, Jeffrey C. Mull

Corporate Vice President, Timothy L. Andrews

Vice President Wealth Management, Dax P. McCracken

Director, Wolfgang Mayrhuber, age 67

Director, David H. Sidwell, age 60

Director, Helmut Panke, age 68

Director, Axel P. Lehmann, age 55

Director, Prof Bruno Gehrig, age 68

Director, Ann F. Godbehere, age 58

Director, William G. (Bill) Parrett, age 68

Vice Chairman, Michel Demare, age 57

Director, Rainer-Marc Frey, age 52

Director, Joseph Yam

Auditors: Ernst&YoungLtd.

LOCATIONS

HQ: UBS AG (Switzerland)
Bahnhofstrasse 45, Zurich CH-8001
Phone: (41) 44 234 11 11
Web: www.ubs.com

Sales

	% of total
Europe	
Switzerland	41
UK	5
Other	6
US	34

Asia/Pacific	13
Other	1
Total	**100**

PRODUCTS/OPERATIONS

Sales

	% of total
Interest	46
Net fees &	39
Net trading	11
Other	4
Total	**100**

Sales by Segment

	% of total
Wealth Management & Bank	
Wealth	27
Retail &	15
Investment	32
Wealth Management	19
Global Asset	7
Total	**100**

COMPETITORS

Bank of America	Julius Baer
Barclays	Mitsubishi UFJ
CIBC	Financial Group
Citigroup	Mizuho Financial
Coutts Group	Morgan Stanley
Credit Suisse	RBC Financial Group
Goldman Sachs	UniCredit
HSBC	Wells Fargo Advisors
JPMorgan Chase	

HISTORICAL FINANCIALS

Company Type: Public

Income Statement

FYE: December 31

	ASSETS ($ mil.)	NET INCOME ($ mil.)	INCOME AS % OF ASSETS	EMPLOYEES
12/13	1,133,332	3,559	0.3%	60,205
12/12	1,373,662	(2,739)	—	62,628
12/11	1,508,470	4,420	0.3%	64,820
12/10	1,407,629	8,050	0.6%	64,617
12/09	1,301,498	(2,656)	—	67,518
Annual Growth	**(3.4%)**	**—**		**(2.8%)**

2013 Year-End Financials

Return on assets: 0.2%
Return on equity: 6.6%
Long-term debt ($ mil.): —
No. of shares (mil.): —
Sales ($ mil): 39,429

Dividends
Yield: —
Payout: —
Market value ($ mil.): —

	STOCK PRICE ($) FY Close	P/E High/Low	PER SHARE ($) Earnings	Dividends	Book Value
12/13	19.25	32 21	0.93	0.00	14.86
12/12	15.74	— —	(0.73)	0.00	13.36
12/11	11.83	22 11	1.15	0.00	15.16
12/10	16.47	10 6	2.09	0.00	13.19
12/09	15.51	— —	(0.73)	0.00	11.31
Annual Growth	**5.5%**	**— —**	**—**	**—**	**7.1%**

Unicredito S.p.A. Roma

Let's give credit where credit is due: UniCredit (formerly UniCredito Italiano) is a giant among Europe's banking giants. The financial services group and its units operate in some 22 European countries with more than 9290 branches in about 50 markets. UniCredit is also the largest foreign bank in Central and Eastern Europe (CEE) with 4295 branches and units. It is organized into several divisions including retail banking (targeting families and small- to mid-sized businesses) corporate and investment banking private banking and CEE. UniCredit's retail banking operations are led by its bank of the same name in Italy UniCredit Bank in Germany UniCredit Bank Austria and Bank Pekao in Poland.

HISTORY

UniCredito Italiano's ancestor Banca di Genova was formed in 1870 just after Italy unified. Within a year the bank was in a South American banking venture Banco de Italia y Rio de la Plata. A banking crisis beginning in the late 1880s threatened the company which was saved and reorganized with the aid of German banking interests. The changes gave the bank —which was renamed Credito Italiano —an advantage over home-grown rivals and pointed it in the direction of German-style universal banking including making direct investments in Italy's late-blooming industrial sector.

In the early 20th century Credito Italiano joined other banks in foreign ventures in Albania Brazil and China and opened offices in London and New York.

After the 1929 crash Credito Italiano acquired several failed banks. But Credito Italiano itself was none too healthy: Government attempts in the 1920s to peg the lira to the pound led to industrial stagnation leaving the bank holding highly illiquid industrial investments and by the early 1930s it was essentially an industrial holding company.

Credito Italiano's existence was threatened when the Depression hit in earnest. To save the bank and its peers Mussolini established the Istituto per la Ricostruzione Industriale (IRI) in 1933 as a "temporary" Resolution Trust-style holding company (IRI was finally liquidated in 2000) to take over the industrial assets of Credito Italiano and several other banks. IRI was instantly a major shareholder in Credito Italiano. IRI-held banks were designated "banks of national interest" three years later and were allowed to provide only short-term commercial banking services a limit that remained in effect for more than 50 years.

In 1946 to fill the need for long-term industrial credit to rebuild war-torn Italy Credito Italiano joined with Banca Commerciale Italiana (now part of IntesaBci) and Banco di Roma to form Mediobanca.

Credito Italiano went public in 1969 (IRI sold its interest in the bank in 1993). As a bank of national interest Credito Italiano was called upon to help bail out several of the country's industrial groups in 1979 (it did so reluctantly).

Changing laws allowed the company to expand its branch network in 1980 and in 1982 IRI allowed Credito Italiano to raise capital (although it was still obliged to prop up struggling state industries). But the 1987 US stock market crash caused Credito Italiano's earnings to plunge 33%. Two years later it bought a stake in Banca Nazionale dell'Agricoltura then Italy's largest private bank.

In 1995 the company joined forces with Rolo Banca 1473 (named for the year its progenitor was founded) to form Credito Italiano Group. Two years later Alessandro Profumo became CEO. He would usher in more than a decade of rapid and agressive expansion.

Credito Italiano merged in 1998 with UniCredito a collection of several northern Italian banks. One Cassa di Risparmio di Verona Vicenza Belluno e Ancona (Cariverona) began in 1501 as a pawnshop operated by monks.

Foreshadowing the bank's shift to an Internet growth strategy (announced after talks with Spain's Banco Bilbao Vizcaya Argentaria fell through) UniCredito in 1999 announced plans for an electronic stock market to include after-hours trading. It also continued to boost holdings in Eastern European banks. In 2000 the company entered into securities brokerage and mutual fund administration with its purchase of US-based Pioneer Investment Management.

In 2001 UniCredito bought 10% of the Pirelli/Benetton-owned holding company formed to control Italian telecommunications company Olivetti. The following year the company partnered with Koc Holding to take a majority stake in Yapi Kredi.

The bank acquired HVB and Bank Austria in 2005 in an $18 billion cross-border deal one of the largest such deals ever seen in Europe. The bank strengthened its hold at home in 2007 with the nearly $30 billion purchase of Italian bank Capitalia. Antitrust authorities ordered UniCredit to sell its stake in Assicurazioni Generali following the Capitalia transaction.

EXECUTIVES

Chairman, Dieter Rampl, age 67
Vice Chairman, Fabrizio Palenzona, age 61
Vice Chairman, Vincenzo C. Buonaura, age 68
Deputy General Manager and Head Corporate and Investment Banking, Jean-Pierre Mustier, age 53
Vice Chairman, Farhat O. Bengdara, age 49
COO, Paolo Fiorentino, age 59
General Manager, Roberto Nicastro, age 50
CEO, Federico Ghizzoni, age 59
Vice Chairman of the Board, Candido Fois
CFO, Marina Natale
Secretary, Lorenzo Lampiano

General Counsel and Group Compliance Officer, Nadine Faruque, age 54
Head Group Human Resources, Paolo Cornetta
Head Group Investor Relations, Simone Concetti
Chief Risk Officer, Alessandro Decio
Investor Relations Officer, Andrea Pavoncello
Chairman of the Board, Giuseppe Vita
Vice Chairman of the Board, Luca Montezemolo
Head of Internal Audit, Ranieri Marchis
Director, Manfred Bischoff, age 72
Director, Piero Gnudi, age 76
Director, Luigi Maramotti, age 57
Director, Hans-Jurgen Schinzler, age 74
Director, Anthony B. Wyand, age 71
Vice Chairman, Fabrizio Palenzona, age 61
Vice Chairman, Vincenzo C. Buonaura, age 68
Director, Carlo Pesenti, age 51
Director, Friedrich Kadrnoska, age 63
Director, Antonio M. Marocco, age 79
Director, Enrico T. Cucchiani, age 64
Vice Chairman, Farhat O. Bengdara, age 49
Director, Donato Fontanesi, age 72
Director, Francesco Giacomin, age 63
Director, Franz Zwickl, age 61
Vice Chairman of the Board, Candido Fois
Deputy Vice Chairman, Luigi Castelletti, age 58
Director, Giovanni Belluzzi, age 69
Director, Marinna Li Calzi, age 64
Director, Lucrezia Reichlin, age 60
Director, Theodore Waigel, age 74
Independent Director, Alessandro Caltagirone
Chairman of the Board, Giuseppe Vita
Non-Executive Director, Helga Jung
Independent Director, Henryka Bochniarz
Independent Director, Lorenzo Bianchi
Non-Executive Independent Director, Marianna Calzi
Independent Director, Mohamed Fahim
Auditors: KPMGS.p.A.

LOCATIONS

HQ: Unicredito S.p.A. Roma
Piazza Cordus, Milano 20123
Phone: (39) 2 88 621   **Fax:** (39) 2 8862 3463
Web: www.unicreditgroup.eu

Sales

	% of total
Europe	
Italy	38
Germany	17
Austria	9
Other	34
Asia	1
Americas	1
Total	**100**

PRODUCTS/OPERATIONS

Sales

	% of total
Retail	48
Corporate & investment	28
Central & Eastern	18
Private	3
Asset	3
Total	**100**

COMPETITORS

ABN AMRO Group	Banco Popolare
Antonveneta	Credit Suisse
BNL bc	Deutsche Bank
BNP Paribas	Intesa Sanpaolo
Banca Popolare di Milano	UBS

HISTORICAL FINANCIALS

Company Type: Public

Income Statement
FYE: December 31

	ASSETS ($ mil.)	NET INCOME ($ mil.)	INCOME AS % OF ASSETS	EMPLOYEES
12/13	1,164,495	(19,225)	—	153,449
12/12	1,221,604	1,139	0.1%	162,864
12/11	1,198,730	(11,908)	—	167,014
12/10	1,244,000	1,771	0.1%	167,914
12/09	1,337,942	2,452	0.2%	170,017
Annual Growth	**(3.4%)**	**—**		**(2.5%)**

2013 Year-End Financials

Return on assets: (-1.5%)	Dividends
Return on equity: (-25.4%)	Yield: 1.2%
Long-term debt ($ mil.): —	Payout: —
No. of shares (mil.): —	Market value ($ mil.): —
Sales ($ mil): 53,655	

	STOCK PRICE ($) FY Close	P/E High/Low		PER SHARE ($) Earnings	Dividends	Book Value
12/13	7.46	— —		(3.39)	0.12	11.14
12/12	4.89	71 30		0.20	0.00	14.30
Annual Growth	**52.7%**	**— —**		**—**	**—**	**(6.1%)**

Unilever N.V.

Unilever N.V. is the numero uno Unilever. It has joint custody of food and personal care products giant Unilever. Along with Unilever PLC the Netherlands-based firm operates Unilever as a joint venture. The three companies operate as the Unilever Group which has a single board of directors and one set of financial statements. Unilever holds the No. 1 spot in manufacturing dressings savory and spreads with brand names Hellmann's Knorr Wish-Bone and Ragu. Its other top products include ice cream (Breyers Ben & Jerry's) tea (Lipton) soaps (Dove Lux) and Sunsilk (hair care). The company holds a leading position in laundry detergents. Unilever also operates tea and oil plantations.

The company boasts a vast products portfolio. In 2008 13 of its brands logged $1 billion or more in revenue. These were Knorr Hellmann's Lipton Becel/Flora (Healthy Heart) Rama/Blue Band (Family Goodness) Wall's/Algida (Heartbrand) Omo Surf Dove Lux Rexona (including Sure and Degree) Axe/Lynx and Sunsilk (including Seda and Sedal).

Unilever's primarily a food maker that participates in other niches to diversify. It generated 54% of its 2008 sales from food items while home and personal care products brought in the remaining 46%. The manufacturer's savory dressings and spreads segment (35%) logged the most revenue in 2008 followed by personal care (28%) ice cream and beverages (19%) and home care (18%).

Building upon its non-food offerings the company agreed to acquire Sara Lee's body care products and European detergents business for about Â1.3 billion (nearly $2 million) in cash. The deal which includes the Sanex Radox and Duschdas brands is subject to regulatory approval by the European Commission which is expected to rule on transaction by October 2010. The brands earned Sara Lee about Â750 million ($1 billion) in revenue in 2009. Unilever looks poised to expand the market of its new goods in developing countries where Sara Lee cultivated about 15% of personal care product sales.

During the past few years Unilever has felt intense heat on the competitor front despite its leader status in the consumer products arena for many years. When The Procter & Gamble Company (P&G) acquired The Gillette Company —overnight making P&G the largest consumer products maker in the world ahead of Unilever —Unilever launched a restructuring. The company also made sweeping changes to its leadership organization and abandoned its dual chairman/CEO structure that had been in place for decades. Antony Burgmans chairman stepped down and was replaced by Ericsson chairman Michael Treschow in 2007. Patrick Cescau the company's CEO retired at the end of 2008 and was replaced by Paul Polman an executive at Nestle USA who strategically had logged 26 years of experience at P&G.

To compete with rival P&G and climb back on top Unilever in mid-2007 implemented a four-year plan that involved slashing some 20000 jobs (or a tenth of its workforce) and selling off slow-growth businesses. Its job cuts were to be focused on Europe.

As part of its strategy to dispose of non-strategic brands Unilever is clearing its pantry. The company sold its Boursin cheese-making business in early 2008. In August 2008 Unilever sold its Lawry's and Adolph's seasoning brands to McCormick & Company for about $604 million in cash. It sold off of its North American laundry business which includes the All Wisk Sunlight Surf and Snuggle brands to private-equity firm Vestar Capital Partners in September 2008 in return for about $1.45 billion in cash and preferred stock in Sun Products (a new company formed by the integration of the Unilever laundry business and Vestar's Huish Detergents). Unilever made the move to focus on its laundry business in Europe Asia Africa and Latin America. The transaction includes the fabric-cleaning brands as well as Unilever's manufacturing plant in Baltimore. Unilever also sold its Bertolli olive oil and vinegar business to SOS

Group for some $1 billion in December 2008. The deal is structured as a perpetual brand license by Unilever. The firm retained the Bertolli brand for other foods such as pasta and frozen meals until mid-2012 when it sold the brand (alongside its P.F. Chang's frozen food business) to ConAgra for $267 million.

Additionally in some cases Unilever has rewritten its expansion plans into certain countries. Despite efforts to expand its reach into the European chilled-products market in recent years Unilever announced in 2007 that due to stalled growth it planned to divest its European frozen foods unit while retaining its similar business in Italy. Its decision to keep a foothold in Italy is due in part a need to maintain a presence in the country to promote future trade relations there. Unilever also sold its Spanish frozen foods business to Bonduelle for several million euros in 2006 and sold the majority of its Western European frozen foods business to private-equity firm Permira for more than $2.2 billion. (The transaction included the Iglo and Birds Eye brands in Austria Belgium France Germany Greece Ireland the Netherlands Portugal and the UK.)

The company has earlier purged a handful of hair care brands signaling that it's not very interested in maintaining a portfolio rich in the hair care niche. Unilever sold its Finesse and Aqua Net brands in 2006 for some $130 million. (The two brands had generated more than $85 million in 2005 for Unilever which retained the Aqua Net brand in Mexico.) Lornamead picked up the two hair care products to breath new life into the "heritage" brands through rebranding and increased marketing. The company also sold its Unilever Cosmetics International business to Coty in 2005 for some $800 million.

Shares of Unilever N.V. trade in France Germany the Netherlands Switzerland the UK and the US. Unilever N.V. has an 85% stake in Unilever Indonesia.

EXECUTIVES

Chairman, Michael Treschow, age 71
Non-Executive Vice-Chairman of the Board and Senior Independent Director, Kornelis J. (Kees) Storm, age 72
Chief Operating Officer, Harish Manwani, age 62
Chief Human Resources Officer, Douglas A. (Doug) Baillie, age 59
CEO and Director, Paul Polman, age 57, $1,456,014 total compensation
Chief Marketing and Communication Officer, Keith Weed, age 52
Chief Human Resources Officer, Sandy Ogg, age 60
President Americas, David (Dave) Lewis, age 49
Chief Auditor, Alan Johnson, age 60
Chief Research and Development Officer, Prof Genevieve B. Berger, age 59
Group Controller, Charles Nichols, age 54
Chief Supply Chain Officer, Pier Luigi Sigismondi, age 48
EVP Global Skin, Antoine De-Saint-Affrique
VP IT Services Europe, Paulo de Sa
VP Nutrition and Health, Gert Meijer
Global Corporate Communications Manager, Lucila Zambrano
Chief Legal Officer and Group Secretary, Tonia Lovell, age 45
Corporate Media Relations Manager, Flip Dotsch
President; North Asia, Alan Jope
President - Foods, Antoine Saint-Affrique
President; Europe, Jan Zijderveld
Chief Financial Officer; Executive Director, Jean-Marc Huet
President; North America, Kees Kruythoff
President - Refreshment, Kevin Havelock

Director, Paul S. Walsh, age 59
Director, Charles E. Golden, age 67
Director, Ann M. Fudge, age 62
Director, Byron E. Grote, age 65
Vice Chairman, Kornelis J. (Kees) Storm, age 71
Non-Executive Independent Director, Sir Malcolm L. Rifkind, age 67
CEO and Director, Paul Polman, age 57
Director, T. Hixonia Nyasulu, age 60
CFO and Director, Jean-Marc Huet, age 44
Director, Louise O. Fresco, age 63
Director, Sunil Bharti Mittal, age 57
Non-Executive Independent Director, Sunil Mittal
Auditors: PricewaterhouseCoopersN.V.

LOCATIONS

HQ: Unilever N.V.
  Weena 455, Rotterdam 3013 AL
Phone: (31) 10 217 4000   **Fax:** (31) 10 217 4798
Web: www.unilever.com

Sales

	% of total
Asia Africa & Central & Eastern	40
The	33
Western	27
Total	**100**

PRODUCTS/OPERATIONS

Sales

	% of total
Savory dressings &	32
Personal	31
Ice cream &	19
Home care &	18
Total	**100**

COMPETITORS

Alticor	Kao
Atkins Nutritionals	L' Oreal
Avon	LVMH
Beiersdorf	Mars Incorporated
Boulder Brands	McBride plc
Campbell Soup	Meda Pharmaceuticals
Church & Dwight	Mondelez International
Clorox	Nestle
Coca-Cola	Procter & Gamble
Colgate-Palmolive	R.C. Bigelow
ConAgra	Reckitt Benckiser
Dairy Farmers of	Republic of Tea
America	Revlon
Danone	S.C. Johnson
Del Monte Foods	Shiseido
Estee Lauder	Tata Global Beverages
General Mills	The Dial Corporation
Henkel	Uniq
Johnson & Johnson	

HISTORICAL FINANCIALS

Company Type: Public

Income Statement

FYE: December 31

	REVENUE ($ mil.)	NET INCOME ($ mil.)	NET PROFIT MARGIN	EMPLOYEES
12/13	68,557	6,666	9.7%	174,000
12/12	67,647	5,904	8.7%	172,000
12/11	60,102	5,499	9.2%	169,000
12/10	59,239	5,680	9.6%	165,000
12/09	57,367	4,854	8.5%	168,000
Annual Growth	4.6%	8.3%	—	0.9%

2013 Year-End Financials

Debt ratio: 34.7%   No. of shares (mil.): 1,573
Return on equity: 32.8%   Dividends
Cash ($ mil.): 3,145   Yield: 3.4%
Current ratio: 0.70   Payout: 112.3%
Long-term debt ($ mil.): 10,313   Market value ($ mil.): 63,289

	STOCK PRICE ($) FY Close	P/E High/Low		PER SHARE ($) Earnings	Dividends	Book Value
12/13	40.23	45 40		2.29	1.40	12.55
12/12	38.30	43 32		2.03	1.23	11.71
12/11	34.37	43 33		1.89	2.25	10.78
12/10	31.40	42 29		1.95	1.11	11.31
12/09	32.33	58 26		1.69	1.09	10.14
Annual Growth	5.6%	—		7.9%	6.5%	5.5%

Unilever Plc (United Kingdom)

It takes two parents –one Dutch and one British –to make one Unilever. Unilever N.V. and Unilever PLC together with their group companies constitute a global food personal care and household products powerhouse. The group's vast portfolio of consumer products includes a dozen global brands including Hellmann's (mayonnaise) Knorr (soups) Lipton (tea) and Dove and Lux (soaps) that each ring up more than Â1 billion ($1.4 billion) in sales. Unilever's consumer goods are sold in more than 190 countries. The company was the world's #1 consumer products maker until Procter & Gamble purchased Gillette in 2005. Based in England Unilever PLC trades on the London and New York stock exchanges.

Unilever acquired salon hair care products maker TIGI in 2009. The more than $410 million purchase which includes the firm's hair styling academies adds the Bed Head Catwalk and S-factor brands among others to Unilever's hair care products offering. TIGI remains headquartered in Dallas and operates as a stand-alone global business unit within Unilever.

The company has seen revenue gains in recent years despite rising commodity costs. Unilever points to several countries for its notable yet steady growth. These include Africa the Americas (including Brazil and Mexico) China Europe India and Russia. China Russia and Brazil are three of the company's biggest hair care markets in the world.

CEO Patrick Cescau retired at the end of 2008 and was replaced by Paul Polman an executive at Nestle USA who has some 25 years of experience at P&G.

EXECUTIVES

Chairman, Michael Treschow, age 71
President Asia Africa and Central & Eastern Europe, Harish Manwani, age 61
Group Controller and SVP Finance Categories, Howard Green
Innovation Project Leader Unilever Research Colworth UK, Shelagh Muir
Manager Product Design Global Research Center Vlaardingen Netherlands, Ingeborg van Heetvelde
Chief HR Officer, Douglas A. (Doug) Baillie, age 58
SVP Communications and Sustainability, Gavin Neath
Group VP; President Unilever U.S., Kevin Havelock, age 57
CEO and Director, Paul Polman, age 57
Chief Marketing and Communication Officer, Keith Weed, age 52
President Americas, David (Dave) Lewis, age 49
Managing Director and CEO Hindustan Unilever, Nitin Paranjpe, age 50

Group Secretary, Sven Dumoulin
VP Finance, Philip de Klerk
Chief Research and Development Officer, Prof Genevieve B. Berger, age 59
Brand Manager Domex Philippines, Patricia Niles
Director Customer Management Ghana, Cynthia Ifeagwu
Director Customer Development Argentina, Tomas Jans
Manager European Operations Kingston UK, Jane Mackie
Personal Assistant Jakarta Indonesia, Arif Hudaya
Manager Regional Management Development Home and Personal Care Categories Latin America Chile and South America, Katia Cuellar
Life sciences Colworth UK, Steve Colliver
Ice cream Colworth UK, Andrew Cox
Manager Research Unilever Research China Shanghai, David Liu
Beverages Colworth UK, Stella Peace
Director Customer and Channel Marketing Unilever Foodsolutions North America, Ted Skodol
Chief Supply Chain Officer, Pier Luigi Sigismondi, age 48
Chief Legal Officer and Secretary, Tonia Lovell, age 45
General Counsel, Steve Williams
Chief Auditor, Akhter Mateen
President; North Asia, Alan Alan Jope Jope
President - Foods, Antoine Antoine de Saint-Affrique Saint-Affrique
President; Europe, Jan Jan Zijderveld Zijderveld
Chief Financial Officer; Executive Director, Jean-Marc Jean-Marc Huet Huet
President; North America, Kees Kees Kruythoff Kruythoff
Chief Supply Chain Officer, Pier Sigismondi
Director, Paul S. Walsh, age 59
Director, Charles E. Golden, age 66
Director, Ann M. Fudge, age 62
Director, Byron E. Grote, age 65
Director, Kornelis J. (Kees) Storm, age 72
Non-Executive Independent Director, Sir Malcolm L. Rifkind, age 67
CEO and Director, Paul Polman, age 57
CFO and Director, Jean-Marc Huet, age 43
Director, Hixonia Nyalsulu, age 58
Director, Louise O. Fresco, age 62
Non-Executive Independent Director, Hixonia Hixonia Nyasulu Nyasulu
Non-Executive Independent Director, Sunil Sunil Mittal Mittal
Auditors: PricewaterhouseCoopersLLP

LOCATIONS

HQ: Unilever Plc (United Kingdom)
  Unilever House, Blackfriars, London EC4Y 0DY
Phone: (44) 20 7822 5252   **Fax:** (44) 20 7822 6108
Web: www.unilever.com

PRODUCTS/OPERATIONS

Selected Global Brands
Axe/Lynx (male grooming)
Blue Band (margarine)
Dove (personal care)
Heartbrand ice creams
Hellmann's (mayonnaise)
Knorr (soup)
Lipton (tea)
Lux (soap)
Omo (detergent)
Rexona (deodorant)
Sunsilk (hair care)

COMPETITORS

Church & Dwight	Premier Foods
Canada	Procter & Gamble

Henkel
Mondelez International
Nestle
R&R Ice Cream
Reckitt Benckiser

HISTORICAL FINANCIALS
Company Type: Public

Income Statement
FYE: December 31

	REVENUE ($ mil.)	NET INCOME ($ mil.)	NET PROFIT MARGIN	EMPLOYEES
12/13	68,557	6,666	9.7%	174,000
12/12	67,647	5,904	8.7%	172,000
12/11	60,102	5,499	9.2%	169,000
12/10	59,239	5,680	9.6%	165,000
12/09	57,367	4,854	8.5%	168,000
Annual Growth	4.6%	8.3%	—	0.9%

2013 Year-End Financials
Debt ratio: 34.7%
Return on equity: 32.8%
Cash ($ mil.): 3,145
Current ratio: 0.70
Long-term debt ($ mil.): 10,313
No. of shares (mil.): 1,283
Dividends
  Yield: 3.3%
  Payout: 112.3%
Market value ($ mil.): 52,879

	STOCK PRICE ($) FY Close	P/E High/Low		PER SHARE ($) Earnings	Dividends	Book Value
12/13	41.20	46 40		2.29	1.40	15.39
12/12	38.72	44 32		2.03	1.23	15.57
12/11	33.52	43 33		1.89	2.25	14.11
12/10	30.88	41 28		1.95	1.11	14.80
12/09	31.90	55 26		1.69	1.00	13.27
Annual Growth	6.6%	—		7.9%	8.6%	3.8%

Unione Di Banche Italiane S.c.p.a.

Unione di Banche Italiane known as UBI Banca serves individuals and businesses through nine subsidiary banks with some 1720 branches in Italy (concentrated in the Lombardy region). It also operates offices in about a dozen other countries across Europe Asia and South America and boasts some 3.7 million customers worldwide. The banks offer such standard deposit products as savings and checking accounts and CDs. They also provide asset management leasing operations private banking insurance corporate banking and mortgage and other types of lending. The group was formed in 2007 when Banche Popolari Unite acquired rival Banca Lombarda e Piemontese and changed its name to UBI Banca.

EXECUTIVES

Chairman Management Board, Emilio Zanetti, age 83
Deputy Chairman Supervisory Board, Alberto Folonari, age 77
General Manager, Riccardo Sora, age 64
Joint General Manager and Head Human Resources and Organization, Graziano Caldiani, age 64
Chief Executive Officer, Victor Massiah, age 56
General Manager UBI Banca Group, Francesco Iorio, age 46
Deputy General Manager and Operational Chairman UBI Sistemi e Servizi, Pierangelo Rigamonti
Head Investor Relations, Laura Ferraris

Senior Deputy Chairman Supervisory Board,
Giuseppe Calvi, age 83

Deputy Chairman Supervisory Board, Mario
Mazzoleni, age 71

Chairman Supervisory Board, Andrea Moltrasio, age
59

Deputy Chairman Management Board, Flavio
Pizzini, age 59

Deputy General Manager Chief of Business,
Rossella Leidi

**Deputy General Manager and Head Credit and
Credit Recovery,** Giovanni Lupinacci

**Deputy General Manager and Chief of General
Affairs and Subsidiaries,** Ettore Medda

**Senior Deputy General Manager Chief Operating
Officer,** Elvio Sonnino

Senior Deputy Chairman, Mario Cera

Director, Carlo Garavaglia

Director, Pietro Gussalli Beretta, age 52

Director, Giovanni Bazoli, age 82

Deputy Chairman Supervisory Board, Alberto
Folonari, age 76

Director, Mario G. Cattaneo, age 83

Director, Italo Lucchini

Director, Giuseppe Lucchini

Director, Alessandro (Att) Pedersoli, age 85

Senior Deputy Chairman Supervisory Board,
Giuseppe Calvi, age 83

Director, Enio Fontana

Director, Giorgio Perolari

Director, Sergio Orlandi

Deputy Chairman Supervisory Board, Mario
Mazzoleni, age 71

Director, Salvatore Toti Musumeci

Director, Roberto Sestini

Director, Sergio Pivato

Director, Federico Manzoni

Director, Virginio Fidanza

Director, Luigi Bellini

Director, Battista Albertani

Auditors: KPMGS.p.A.

LOCATIONS

HQ: Unione Di Banche Italiane S.c.p.a.
Piazza Vittorio Veneto 8, Bergamo 24122
Phone: (39) 035 392111
Web: www.ubibanca.it

PRODUCTS/OPERATIONS

Selected Subsidiaries

Aviva Assicurazioni Vita Spa (49.9%)
Banco di San Giorgio Spa (93%)
Banca Populare Commercio e Industria Spa (84%)
Banca Populare di Bergamo Spa
Banca Regionale Europea Spa (60%)
Capitalgest Alternative Investments SGR Spa
Centrobanca Spa (98%)
FinanzAttiva Servizi Srl
IW Bank Spa (80%)
Mercato Impresa Spa (99%)
Prestitalia Spa (23%)
S.B.I.M. Spa
UBI Assicurazioni Spa
UBI Banca Private Investment Spa
UBI Gestioni Fiduciarie Sim Spa
UBI Leasing Spa (99%)
UBI Pramerica SGR Spa (65%)

COMPETITORS

Antonveneta	Banco Popolare
BNL bc	HSBC
BPER-Emilia Romagna	Intesa Sanpaolo
Banca Carige	Monte dei Paschi di
Banca Popolare di	Siena
Milano	UniCredit

HISTORICAL FINANCIALS

Company Type: Public

Income Statement
FYE: December 31

	ASSETS ($ mil.)	NET INCOME ($ mil.)	INCOME AS % OF ASSETS	EMPLOYEES
12/13	171,048	345	0.2%	18,337
12/12	174,554	109	0.1%	19,114
12/11	167,894	(2,381)	—	19,405
12/10	174,735	230	0.1%	19,699
12/09	176,200	389	0.2%	20,285
Annual Growth	(0.7%)	(2.9%)	—	(2.5%)

2013 Year-End Financials

Return on assets: 0.2%	Dividends
Return on equity: 2.5%	Yield: —
Long-term debt ($ mil.): —	Payout: —
No. of shares (mil.): 900	Market value ($ mil.): —
Sales ($ mil): 6,899	

Unipol Gruppo Finanziaro SPA Bologna

LOCATIONS

HQ: Unipol Gruppo Finanziaro SPA Bologna
Via Stalingrado, 45, Bologna 40128
Phone: (39) 051 507 61 11   **Fax:** (39) 051 507 66 66
Web: www.unipolgf.it

HISTORICAL FINANCIALS

Company Type: Public

Income Statement
FYE: December 31

	REVENUE ($ mil.)	NET INCOME ($ mil.)	NET PROFIT MARGIN	EMPLOYEES
12/13	27,056	(108)	—	15,230
12/12	18,905	393	2.1%	15,212
12/11	12,895	(140)	—	7,638
12/10	14,020	42	0.3%	7,529
12/09	14,864	(1,111)	—	7,157
Annual Growth	16.2%	—	—	20.8%

2013 Year-End Financials

Debt ratio: —	No. of shares (mil.): 437
Return on equity: (-1.4%)	Dividends
Cash ($ mil.): 1,152	Yield: 0.6%
Current ratio: —	Payout: —
Long-term debt ($ mil.): —	Market value ($ mil.): 48

	STOCK PRICE ($) FY Close	P/E High/Low		PER SHARE ($) Earnings	Dividends	Book Value
12/13	0.11	—	—	(0.15)	0.12	17.05
12/12	10.77	17	0	1.67	1.82	16.59
12/11	0.08	—	—	(0.04)	0.00	1.88
12/10	0.23	129	37	0.01	0.00	2.31
12/09	0.62	—	—	(0.48)	0.00	3.49
Annual Growth	(35.2%)	—	—	—	—	48.7%

United Overseas Bank Ltd. (Singapore)

One of Singapore's top financial institutions
United Overseas Bank (UOB) provides a range of
commercial banking and personal financial services. Offerings include checking and savings accounts private banking loans investment banking
commodities trading and asset management. It is
also one of the largest issuers of credit cards in the
Asia-Pacific region. Altogether the bank has about
500 branches and 1300 ATMs across Asia (its
largest markets are in Singapore Thailand and Indonesia) and a handful of representative offices in
Europe and North America.

Operations

UOB is organized into three businesses - Retail
Wholesale and Global Markets and Investment
Management. Its retail business covers personal accounts private banking and small businesses. It
accounts for about 35% of revenue. The wholesale
division serves large corporations and financial institutions; it also accounts for about 35% of revenue. Global markets and investment management
which provides asset management foreign exchange money market funds derivatives and other
capital market activities accounts for 20% of revenue.

Geographic Reach

Altogether the bank has operations in about 15
Asian countries. While it's headquartered in Singapore it only has about 75 branches in that country of 5 million people. The more populated countries of Indonesia (246 million people) has some
215 branches while Thailand with 67 million people has more than 160 branches. Outside Asia
UOB has branches in London Los Angeles New
York City Paris and Vancouver.

Company Background

UOB was founded in 1935 as the United Chinese
Bank and catered mainly to the Fujian community
in Singapore. The bank changed its name to
United Overseas Bank in 1965.

EXECUTIVES

Chairman, Cho Yaw Wee, age 85
Head Group Retail, Francis Chin Yong Lee
Head Commercial Banking, Eng Cheong Yeo
**Head Group Global Markets and Investment
Management,** Terence Sea Eng Ong
Head Corporate Banking, Joo Yeow Wee
Head Group Institutional Financial Services, Kie
Cheong Chong
CFO and Head Group Corporate Services, Wai Fai
Lee
Head Personal Financial Services, Eddie Boo Jin
Khoo
Head Investment Banking, Tong Poh Tay
Head Risk Management, Ming Soong Tham
Head Group Compliance, Mei Lee Chew
Senior Vice President Group Audit, Victor Ngo
Executive Vice President Human Resources, Jenny
Mei Leng Wong
Chief Executive Officer, Chan Seong
Executive Vice President Information Technology,
Hwee Susan
Chief Financial Officer, Lee Fai
Executive Vice President Investment Banking,
Tay Poh
Executive Vice President Risk Management, Tham
Soong
Executive Vice President Corporate Banking, Wee
Yeow
Deputy Chairman and CEO, Wee Ee Cheong, age
60

Director, Reggie Thein, age 73
Director, Tong Dow Ngiam, age 76
Director, Cham Tao Soon, age 74
Director, Philip Liat Kok Yeo, age 66
Director, Meng Meng Wong, age 65
Director, Pin Lim, age 77
Auditors: Ernst&YoungLLP

LOCATIONS

HQ: United Overseas Bank Ltd. (Singapore)
  80 Raffles Place, UOB Plaza, 048624
Phone: (65) 6533 9898   **Fax:** (65) 6534 2334
Web: www.uobgroup.com

PRODUCTS/OPERATIONS

Sales

	% of total
Interest	69
Noninterest	
Fees &	16
Rental	2
Dividends	1
Other	12
Total	**100**

COMPETITORS

Bangkok Bank	Hang Seng Bank
Bank of China	Hong Leong Finance
DBS Group Holdings	Maybank
Edaran Otomobil	OCBC Bank
HSBC	Standard Chartered

HISTORICAL FINANCIALS
Company Type: Public

Income Statement
FYE: December 31

	ASSETS ($ mil.)	NET INCOME ($ mil.)	INCOME AS % OF ASSETS	EMPLOYEES
12/13	224,984	2,380	1.1%	0
12/12	206,769	2,291	1.1%	0
12/11	182,320	1,790	1.0%	0
12/10	166,717	2,102	1.3%	0
12/09	132,402	1,356	1.0%	0
Annual Growth	14.2%	15.1%	—	—

2013 Year-End Financials

Return on assets: 1.1%	Dividends
Return on equity: 11.6%	Yield: 3.3%
Long-term debt ($ mil.): —	Payout: 48.2%
No. of shares (mil.): 1,576	Market value ($ mil.): 52,999
Sales ($ mil): 7,361	

	STOCK PRICE ($) FY Close	P/E High/Low		PER SHARE ($) Earnings	Dividends	Book Value
12/13	33.62	13	10	1.46	1.11	13.25
12/12	32.85	13	9	1.40	0.95	13.02
12/11	23.56	16	9	1.09	0.71	11.23
12/10	28.36	10	8	1.32	0.84	10.86
12/09	27.94	13	4	0.85	0.83	8.99
Annual Growth	4.7%	—	—	14.4%	7.6%	10.2%

Vale S.A.

Vale has more than just one iron in the fire. Iron ore and pellets account for more than two-thirds of Vale's sales and the company accounts for a third of the world's ocean-shipped iron ore. Vale also mines for bauxite nickel kaolin and potash.

Other products include steel copper and aluminum. It has holdings in hydroelectric power generation and in the rail and shipping businesses mainly to support its mining activities in Brazil. The company is the world's second-largest iron ore miner having grown dramatically with the 2006 acquisition of Vale Limited (formerly Vale Inco). To keep all of its materials coming out of the ground Vale maintains its exploration efforts in 24 countries around the world.

Vale's revenues almost doubled in 2010 growing more than 94% as a result of increased production and higher prices for its major products particularly metals including iron ore nickel and copper. Net income grew 223% for the year on the strength of higher sales volumes and profit on the sale of assets.

In early 2012 the company declared force majeure on a number of its iron ore sales contract after high rainfall in three Brazilian states curtailed Vale's operations. The company estimated a loss of 2 million metric tons in iron ore shipments.

In 2011 Vale agreed to buy out minority shareholders of its Vale Fertilizantes SA subsidiary in a $1.4 billion move to consolidate its fertilizer business. Vale sought to buy the 16% of Fertilizantes it did not already own. The subsidiary is a small part of Vale's overall fertilizer business which the company had planned to spin off in 2011 but canceled those plans when it proved to be more profitable than Vale had projected.

Vale spent much of 2010 acquiring fertilizer companies and forming ventures. Mitsui teamed up with US fertilizer company Mosaic in 2010 for a joint venture investing in a Vale phosphorus ore development project in Peru. Mitsui spent $275 million to acquire a 25% stake and voting rights in a Vale subsidiary while Mosaic holds a 24% stake. The project is located in northwestern Peru's Piura province. Vale also completed a $4.7 billion deal for Brazil's Fosfertil and US-based agribusiness Bunge Co. to create Vale Fertilizantes.

Also in 2011 Vale announced plans to acquire South Africa-based copper and cobalt miner Metorex Ltd. for about $1.1 billion. However prior to the deal's close China's Jinchuan Group countered Vale's bid for Metorex with a $1.34 billion offer. Vale subsequently dropped its offer refusing to engage in a bidding war.

In 2010 Vale sold its Brazilian aluminum operations to Norwegian aluminum producer Norsk Hydro for $5.7 billion. Norsk Hydro paid Vale a combination of cash and a 22% stake in Norsk Hydro. Vale said it divested Paragominas one of the world's largest bauxite mines because it did not see enough growth potential in the operation.

Remaining active in the mining sector Vale is developing a copper mine in Zambia in a $400 million joint venture with African Rainbow Minerals. The Konkola North project is expected to begin production in 2013. In 2010 Vale acquired a 51% stake in Guinea iron-ore mining firm BSG Resources for $2.5 billion. The acquisition expands Vale's presence in Africa where it is also developing the Moatize coal deposit in Mozambique in a $6 billion joint venture with South Korean steelmaker POSCO.

In 2011 Vale resumed work on a $6.2 billion steelworks operation in Espirito Santo in southeast Brazil. The project part of a network of five mills planned around the country was dropped in 2009 after local authorities refused to issue an environmental permit. Now with permit in hand Vale is going forward with the redesigned project which is expected to produce about 5 million tons of slab steel a year beginning in 2014. Vale which had originally partnered with China's Baosteel Group is seeking another partner for the project.

To complement its rail port and shipping facilities Vale created a new logistics company for cargo

transport in 2011. Vale Logistics Integrada will handle the company's general cargo assets including its operations for moving iron ore and other minerals from its mines to its customers. The company received $1.5 billion in sales from logistics services in 2010 primarily from the shipping of agricultural and steel products fuel and construction materials.

Murilo Pinto de Oliveira Ferreira was named president and CEO of Vale in 2011. He succeeds Roger Agnelli who completed his 10-year term in the position. Ferreira was previously the CEO of Vale Canada and Executive Director of Vale's Nickel and Base Metals Sales.

Investment group Valepar controls a third of Vale. The Brazilian government holds limited veto power on any permanent company changes.

HISTORY

During the 1890s as land reforms opened the way for foreign investments in Brazil the mineral-rich state of Minas Gerais caught the attention of mining companies from Europe and the US. British engineers founded the Itabira Iron Ore Company and took over the Doce River Valley's Vitoria-Minas Railroad. After Brazil's revolution (1930) Itabira was split up. One of the new companies Itabira Mineraco began shipping iron ore in 1940.

A 1942 agreement prompted by the outbreak of WWII established iron export regulations from Brazil to the US and the UK. Later that year the Companhia Vale do Rio Doce (CVRD) was formed with the Brazilian government owning 80%. The new company received the assets of Itabira including Brazil's "iron mountain" Caue Peak. By the end of the 1940s 80% of Brazil's iron ore exports were mined by CVRD. During the 1950s CVRD invested in land holdings and shipping operations. The company set up a shipping and logistics subsidiary in 1962.

CVRD teamed up with US Steel in 1970 to mine iron ore at Carajas in Amazonian Brazil; two years later the site was found to hold the world's largest iron ore reserves (18 billion tons). By 1975 CVRD had become the world's largest iron ore exporter. A year later the company finished doubling the tracks of the Vitoria-Minas Railroad. It also set up a manganese mining company (Urucum Mineracio) and an alumina production facility (Alumina do Norte do Brasil or Alunorte).

To support its Carajas mining operations CVRD added the Estrada de Ferro de Carajas railway (finished 1985) and a hydroelectric project. In all the giant Carajas project involved investments from the US Japan France the European Economic Community and the World Bank. (The Carajas area like many mining sites in Brazil has been the site of intense controversy because it attracts subsistence miners including children who work under dangerous circumstances.) By the late 1980s the company had become a major supplier of pelletized iron used as feed for steel mill blast furnaces.

In 1992 CVRD expanded into the production of chemicals (Rio Capim Quimica now Para Pigmentos SA). The company acquired stakes in two steel mills —Siderurgica de Tubarao and Aco Minas Gerais SA —in 1993. In 1996 it invested in gold finds in Para state. CVRD was privatized in 1997 and the next year set the sales record for a private Brazilian company.

The company listed ADR shares on the NYSE in 2000. Acquisitions that year included Brazilian iron ore companies SOCOIMEX and SAMITRI (73%). CVRD sold its 50% stake in pulp and paper group Bahia Sul to Suzano for $320 million in 2001. It also sold its 51% share of pulp maker Cenibra and its share of steelmaker Companhia Siderurgica Nacional (CSN).

In 2002 the Brazilian Treasury and the National Social and Economic Bank (BNDES) sold 33% of CVRD's shares further privatizing the company. CVRD disposed of its last gold mine (Fazenda Brasileiro) in 2003. It also exited the dry bulk-shipping business that year.

Under pressure from increasing globalization Vale had been forced to trim some of its operations (including its stake in CSN) to focus on mining and bulk transport. Those asset sales helped fund Vale's win over Australian mining giant BHP Billiton the world's #2 iron ore producer in a battle for Brazil's iron miner Caemi Mineracao e Metalurgia #4 worldwide. (From 2001 through 2006 the company picked up stakes in Caemi until it owned it fully.) The deal for Inco trumped offers from Canadian miner Teck and US copper producer Phelps Dodge.

Toward the end of 2007 the company —then called Companhia Vale do Rio Doce —decided that it wanted a new brand identity and so ditched its longtime nickname CVRD in favor of Vale. Two years later it changed its name legally dropping the more formal Companhia Vale do Rio Doce.

EXECUTIVES

Executive Officer Human Resources and Corporate Services, Carla Grasso, age 53
President and CEO, Roger Agnelli, age 55
Executive Officer Non-Ferrous Minerals and Basic Metals Operations; President and CEO Vale Inco, Tito Botelho Martins Jr., age 52
Vice Chairman, Mario da Silveira Teixeira Jr., age 69
Executive Officer Ferrous Minerals Marketing Sales and Strategy, Jose Carlos Martins, age 65
CFO, Guilherme Perboyre Cavalcanti
President Chief Executive Officer CEO, Murilo Pinto de Oliveira Ferreira
Executive Officer Integrated Operations Logistics Project Management and Sustainability, Eduardo de Salles Bartolomeo, age 51
Executive Officer Fertilizers, Mario Alves Barbosa Neto
Press Manager, Monica Ferreira
Media Contact National Press and Steel Mill, Marcos Henrique Almeida
Media Contact International, Fatima Cristina
Media Contact Research and Development Innovation and Technology, Murilo Fiuza
Media Contact Logistics Energy and Fertilizers, Renata Bellozi
Media Contact Financial Investor Relations and Human Resources, Patricia Malavez
Chairman of the Board, Dan Conrado
Member of the Board of Directors, Fuminobu Kawashima
Capital Projects Implementation Officer; Member of the Executive Board, Galib Chaim
Logistics and Mineral Research Officer; Member of the Executive Board, Humberto Freitas
Member of the Board of Directors, Jose Cunha
Chief Finan.; Investor Rel.; Supplies and Shared Services Officer; Member of the Exec. Board, Luciano Pires
Vice Chairman of the Board, Mario Teixeira
Member of the Board of Directors, Nelson Barbosa
Member of the Board of Directors, Oscar Camargo
Member of the Board of Directors, Paulo Souza
Member of the Board of Directors, Renato Gomes
Member of the Board of Directors, Robson Rocha
Human Resources; Health & Safety; Sustainability & Energy Officer; Member of the Executive Board, Vania Somavilla
Director, Renato da Cruz Gomes, age 62
Director, Oscar Augusto de Camargo Filho, age 77
Vice Chairman, Mario da Silveira Teixeira Jr., age 69
Director, Ken Abe, age 65
Director, Eduardo Fernando Jardim Pinto, age 50
Director, Jorge Luiz Pacheco, age 60

Director, Jose Ricardo Sasseron, age 58
Director, Sandro Kohler Marcondes, age 51
Director, Luciano Galv?o Coutinho, age 68
Auditors:
PricewaterhouseCoopersAuditoresIndependentes

LOCATIONS

HQ: Vale S.A.
Av. Graca Aranha 26, 18 Andar, Centro, Rio de Janeiro, RJ 20030-900
Phone: (55) 21 3814 4477   **Fax:** (55) 21 3814 9935
Web: www.cvrd.com.br

Sales

	$ mil.	% of total
Asia	24,791	53
South America	8,960	19
Europe	8,912	19
North America	2,028	5
Other	1,790	4
Adjustments	(1188)	-
Total	**45,293**	**100**

PRODUCTS/OPERATIONS

Sales

	$ mil.	% of total
Ores & minerals	39,422	85
Aluminum	2,554	5
Fertilizers	1,845	4
Other products	1,195	3
Adjustments	(1188)	-

COMPETITORS

AHMSA	Freeport-McMoRan
Alcoa	Kumba Iron Ore
Anglo American	Norilsk Nickel
BHP Billiton	Rio Tinto Limited
BHP Billiton Plc	Rio Tinto plc
Cliffs Natural Resources	Teck
	Xstrata
Exxaro	

HISTORICAL FINANCIALS

Company Type: Public

Income Statement

FYE: December 31

	REVENUE ($ mil.)	NET INCOME ($ mil.)	NET PROFIT MARGIN	EMPLOYEES
12/13	46,767	990	2.1%	83,286
12/12	47,694	5,511	11.6%	70,785
12/11	58,990	22,885	38.8%	79,646
12/10	45,293	17,264	38.1%	70,785
12/09	23,311	5,349	22.9%	60,036
Annual Growth	**19.0%**	**(34.4%)**	**—**	**8.5%**

2013 Year-End Financials

Debt ratio: 25.0%	No. of shares (mil.): —
Return on equity: 1.4%	Dividends
Cash ($ mil.): 5,321	Yield: 4.7%
Current ratio: 2.14	Payout: 146.5%
Long-term debt ($ mil.): 29,445	Market value ($ mil.): —

	STOCK PRICE ($) FY Close	P/E High/Low	PER SHARE ($) Earnings	Dividends	Book Value
12/13	15.25	195115	0.11	0.72	12.29
12/12	20.96	25 15	1.07	0.99	14.41
12/11	21.45	9 5	4.33	1.56	15.25
12/10	34.57	11 7	3.23	0.45	13.24
12/09	29.03	30 12	0.97	0.45	10.92
Annual Growth	**(14.9%)**	**—**	**(42.0%)**	**12.5%**	**3.0%**

Veolia Environnement

Voila! Veolia Environnement holds water —as well as wastewater waste management energy and passenger transportation —operations. The company provides more than 90 million people with drinking water. One of the world's leading wastewater companies it serves more than 62 million people a year. It also provides waste management services managing some 54 million metric tons of waste and provides energy at 120000 facilities. Energy unit Dalkia (Veolia Energy Services) operates global cogeneration facilities and heating and cooling systems. Joint venture Veolia Transdev (up for sale) is a top European provider of bus light-rail and rail transport and operates in about 30 countries.

Geographic Reach
The company has a strong presence in the European Union North America and northern Asia.

Operations
Veolia Environnement offers a broad range of utility services: supplying water and recycling wastewater; collecting and treating waste; supplying heat and cooled air; and optimizing industrial processes. It provides technical services to its municipal and industrial customers in the water services market. The company's operations are conducted through three divisions each specializing in a single business sector: Veolia Eau (Water) Veolia Energie (Dalkia Energy Services) and Veolia Proprete (Environmental Services). The Group designs and provides water waste and energy management solutions that contribute to the sustainable development of communities and industries.

Veolia Environnement's expertise includes securing water and wastewater management contracts from large cities and industrial companies. In waste management it focuses on treating and recycling hazardous waste and on large concession contracts in the UK. Through its Dalkia unit it manages large public networks and local energy cycles. It plans to concentrate on high added-value services and technologies to attain more profitable growth.

Sales and Marketing
The company provides more than 100 million people with drinking water. One of the world's leading wastewater companies it serves more than 70 million people a year. It also provides waste management services managing some 60 million metric tons of waste and provides energy at 120000 facilities.

Financial Performance
Veolia Environnement's revenues decreased by 4% in 2013 due to changes in the Environmental Services division primarily related to the divestiture of activities in Switzerland the Baltic States the disposal of Energonut in Italy and Pinellas in 2012 as well as the divestiture of Marine Services Offshore in the US in 2013. This was partially offset by the acquisition of the 50% stake held by the Fomento de Construcciones y Contratas (FCC) Group in Proactiva Medio Ambiente in 2013.In 2013 the company posted a net loss of $186.3 million (compared to net income of $530.4 million in 2012) due to lower revenues reduced operating income and decreased income from the discontinued operations.Operating cash inflow decreased by 11% in 2013 due to a decrease in the working capital as the result of measures to manage customer receivables and Days Sales Outstanding despite an extension in certain businesses/countries of days sales outstanding for customer receivables due from public authorities; and Advances received at the end of December 2013 for new major projects in the Technologies and Networks activity.

Strategy

The company's strategy is refocusing the Group geographically and concentrating on areas where it can seize less capital intensive opportunities. To reduce debt in 2014 Veolia Environnement sold its 65% stake in Marius Pedersen Group which provides solid waste management services in Denmark the Czech Republic and Slovakia to Entreprenør Marius Pedersens Fond (Marius Pedersen Foundation) for Â240 million ($325.3 million). It also agreed to sell its water waste and energy activities in Israel in a deal that will contribute to Veolia's debt reduction by around Â250 million ($338.8 million).

In addition in 2013 Veolia was looking to sell its 50% stake in Veolia Transdev its transportation joint venture with French state bank Caisse des Depots et Consignations (CDC) in order to focus on its core businesses.In 2014 Masdar (Abu Dhabi Future Energy Company) selected Veolia Environnement to collaborate on the ambitious Renewable Energy Water Desalination Program in Abu Dhabi.

Mergers and Acquisitions

In 2014 the company signed an agreement to acquire EDF's interest in the international activities of Dalkia and to transfer to EDF Veolia Environnement's interest in Dalkia's French activities.In 2013 Veolia Environnement acquired the 50% stake it did not own (held by the Fomento de Construcciones y Contratas) in Proactiva Medio Ambiente. The deal allow the company to consolidate its positions in Latin America in waste management and water treatment and support its development strategy in this high-growth region.

Company Background

Veolia Environnement was formed from the water waste energy and transport businesses of the former Vivendi group. (The name Veolia is derived from Aeolus the keeper of the winds in Greek mythology). The group spun off Veolia Environnement (then called Vivendi Environnement) sold a minority stake to the public and renamed itself Vivendi Universal in 2000 (and Vivendi in 2006).

HISTORY

What is now Veolia Environnement originated in 1853 as Compagnie Generale des Eaux in Paris. The company irrigated farmlands and subsequently supplied water. By 1860 Paris had granted the company a 50-year contract to provide the city's water. In 1880 it moved beyond France to provide water in Venice Italy. Operations in Turkey (Istanbul) and Portugal (Oporto) followed.

Compagnie Generale des Eaux extended its water network in 1924 and by WWII it supplied half of all urban households in France. After the war the company expanded into household waste collection (1953) and operation of household waste incineration and compost plants (1967). Wastewater treatment activities began in 1972.

In the next decade Compagnie Generale des Eaux dove into diversification. It increased its holding in energy-conversion systems operator Compagnie Generale de Chauffe to 100% (making it France's leading energy company) in 1980. That year it merged its wastewater treatment subsidiaries to create Omnium de Traitement et de Valorisation (OTV). Its waste operations were further augmented through the takeover of Compagnie Generale d'Entreprises Automobiles (CGEA) a transport and waste management firm. The company also ventured into telecommunications pay-TV and construction (it gained a controlling stake in builder SGE in 1988 but disposed of its interest in the firm later known as VINCI in 2000).

CGEA bid for and won control of several former British Rail lines in 1996 when the UK's railway system was privatized. Operating under the name Connex the company began to run trains through-out southeastern England the UK's largest commuting area.

In 1998 CGEA changed its name to Vivendi. The group (which came to include mobile phone provider Cegetel and a stake in the Havas media company) transferred the Compagnie Generale des Eaux name to its water business. Vivendi also organized its Compagnie Generale de Chauffe and Sithe Energies (now a part of Dynergy) subsidiaries into a single energy division named Dalkia. In 1999 Sithe Energies bought 23 thermal power plants from US utility GPU (later FirstEnergy) and became the leading independent power producer in the northeastern US.

Vivendi continued its charge into the US that year. The group acquired waste services company Superior Services (then the US's fourth-biggest solid waste company). Its purchase of USFilter transformed Vivendi into the world's largest water company and marked the biggest acquisition of a US firm by a French company.

The ever-evolving Vivendi transformed into a global media company and renamed itself Vivendi Universal in 2000. It bought Seagram and French pay-TV provider CANAL+ and spun off its water waste management transportation and energy operations (Vivendi Environnement) after turning down German utility RWE's $28 million offer to buy the business.

Vivendi Environnement's waste operations grew after snapping up operations in Brazil Hong Kong and Mexico from Waste Management. In 2001 the company merged its Dalkia energy operations with the energy services operations of Electricite de France (EDF).

In 2002 Vivendi Universal reduced its stake in Vivendi Environnement from 63% to about 20%; the following year Vivendi Environnement changed its name to Veolia Environnement. Vivendi finally divested all of its interest in Veolia in the middle of 2006.

In 2007 the company acquired Thermal North America Inc. the largest portfolio of district heating and cooling networks in the US.

Late in 2009 the company named Antoine Frerot as CEO. He had been in charge of Veolia's water division previously.

To generate cash in 2010 Veolia Environnement sold US waste-to-energy contractor Montenay International (which held its North American waste-to-energy assets) to Covanta Holding for $450 million. Marking a push for more green energy projects in Europe that year the company opened France's largest biomass-fueled boiler plant serving a district heating system in Val d'Oise.

In 2011 Veolia Transport merged with Transdev to create the world's largest private-sector transportation business jointly owned by Veolia Environnement and Caisse des Depots. Although the joint venture announced plans to seek a public listing when market conditions permitted by the end of 2011 Veolia Environnement had decided to sell its half of the venture.

After binging on acquisitions from 2006 to 2008 Veolia started slimming down its operations in 2012 to combat worsening economic conditions. In late 2011 it presented a strategy to restructure its portfolio and cut debt streamline its organization and reduce costs. Its plan for 2012-2013 called for generating $6.6 billion (Â5 billion) from asset sales. As part of that plan in 2012 the company sold its US solid waste operations part of its Veolia Environmental Services North America unit to US investment firm Highstar Capital for $1.9 billion (Â1.5 billion).

The company also sold a majority stake in its UK regulated water businesses —Veolia Water Central Veolia Water East and Veolia Water Southeast — for $1.9 billion (Â1.5 billion) to Infracapital Partners an investment fund managed by the European investment arm of Prudential plc (M&G) and Morgan Stanley Infrastructure Partners.

EXECUTIVES

Vice Chairman, Louis Schweitzer, age 72
COO and SEVP, Denis Gasquet, age 60
CEO VeoliaTransdev, Jerome Gallot, age 54
EVP Human Resources, Jean-Marie Lambert
EVP Water, Jean-Michel Herrewyn, age 53
EVP Energy, Franck LaCroix
EVP and CFO, Pierre-Francois Riolacci, age 46
EVP and Secretary General, Olivier Orsini
EVP Public Entities and European Affairs, Jean-Pierre Fremont
Chairman of the Board; Chief Executive Officer; Member of the Executive Committee, Antoine Antoine Frerot Frerot
Senior Executive Vice President; Secretary General; Member of the Eecuvive Committee, Helman Helman le Pas de Secheval Secheval
Senior Executive Vice President - Environmental Services Division; Member of the Executive Committee, Jerome Jerome Le Conte Conte
Independent Director - Representative of Groupe Industriel Marcel Dassault, Olivier Olivier Costa de Beauregard Beauregard
Secretary of the Executive Committee, Sylvain Sylvain Boucher Boucher
Chief Operating Officer; Member of the Executive Committee, Francois Bertreau
Senior Executive Vice President; Secretary General; Member of the Executive Committee, Helman le Pas de Secheval
Chairman and Chief Executive Officer of Veolia Transdev; Member of the Executive Committee, Jean-Marc Janaillac
Senior Executive Vice President - Environmental Services Division; Member of the Executive Committee, Jerome Le Conte
Vice Chairman, Louis Schweitzer, age 71
Director, Paolo Scaroni, age 68
Director, Jean-Francois Dehecq, age 74
Director, Baudouin Prot, age 62
Director, Daniel Bouton, age 63
Director, Pierre-Andre de Chalendar, age 55
Director, Henri Proglio, age 65
Director, Georges Ralli, age 65
Director, Serge Michel, age 87
Director, Paul-Louis Girardot, age 79
Director, Esther Koplowitz, age 61
Director, Philippe Kourilsky, age 71
Director, Olivier Costa de Beauregard
Director, Thierry Dassault, age 57
Director, Mohd Alhamadi, age 51
Director - Representative of Caisse des depots et consignations, Olivier Olivier Mareuse Mareuse
Independent Director, Pierre-Andre Pierre-Andre de Chalendar Chalendar
Auditors: KPMGAudit

LOCATIONS

HQ: Veolia Environnement
36/38, avenue Kleber, Paris 75116
Phone: (33) 1 71 75 00 00
Web: www.veolia.com

Sales

	% of total
Europe	
France	39
Germany	9
UK	9
Other	19
North	8
Asia	6
Oceania	3
Other	7
Total	**100**

PRODUCTS/OPERATIONS

Sales

	% of total
Water	42
Environmental	33
Energy	25
Transportation —	
Total	**100**

Selected Operations

Selected Operations

Water
  Veolia Eau - Compagnie Generale des Eaux
    Veolia Water S.A.
Environmental Services
  Veolia Environmental Services North America Corp.
Energy
  Dalkia (66%)
Transport
  Veolia Transdev (50%)

COMPETITORS

Alpheus	SNCF
American States Water	SUEZ Environnement
Anglian Water Group	Severn Trent
Bouygues	Shanks
COFELY	Stagecoach
Electricite de France	Thames Water
Electricite de	ThermoEnergy
Strasbourg	United Utilities
Kelda	Vattenfall
Northumbrian Water	Waste Management
Pennon	Waste Recycling
RWE	Welsh Water
SABESP	

HISTORICAL FINANCIALS

Company Type: Public

Income Statement
FYE: December 31

	REVENUE ($ mil.)	NET INCOME ($ mil.)	NET PROFIT MARGIN	EMPLOYEES
12/13	30,721	(186)	—	202,800
12/12	38,801	519	1.3%	219,739
12/11	38,347	(633)	—	231,477
12/10	46,557	777	1.7%	317,034
12/09	49,773	841	1.7%	312,590
Annual Growth (11.4%)	—	—	(10.3%)

2013 Year-End Financials

Debt ratio: 47.9%
Return on equity: (-1.7%)
Cash ($ mil.): 5,884
Current ratio: 1.19
Long-term debt ($ mil.): 13,074

No. of shares (mil.): 534
Dividends
  Yield: 0.0%
  Payout: —
Market value ($ mil.): 8,747

	STOCK PRICE ($) FY Close	P/E High/Low	PER SHARE ($) Earnings	Dividends	Book Value
12/13	16.36	— —	(0.40)	1.65	21.13
12/12	12.24	38 20	1.03	1.48	18.56
12/11	11.05	— —	(1.28)	3.20	18.09
12/10	29.36	60 32	1.62	2.46	21.99
12/09	32.88	68 29	1.79	3.27	22.44
Annual Growth (16.0%)	— —		(15.7%)	(1.5%)

Vinci SA

Veni vidi vici ...VINCI. Through its VINCI Construction division this company conquers the world as one of the largest building civil engineering and maintenance contractors. VINCI operates in two divisions: concessions and contracting (85% of sales). Its concessions business which builds and operates motorways parking garages rail infrastructure stadiums and airports includes motorway operator VINCI Autoroutes and parking manager VINCI Park. Under the contracting umbrella VINCI provides electrical engineering maintenance and facilities management. Roadworks and transportation infrastructure is handled by Eurovia. VINCI is active in some 100 countries with France accounting for the majority of its sales.

Geographic Reach

VINCI is Europe's biggest construction and concessions company. France is the company's largest market accounting for more than 60% of its annual revenue. Other important markets for the firm include Germany and the UK. Beyond Europe the group is active in Asia Africa the Americas and the Middle East.

Operations

VINCI divides its business into two segments: Contracting (86% of 2013 revenue) and Concessions which accounts for the remainder. VINCI Immobilier the group's real estate unit accounts for about 2% of sales.

VINCI's Eurovia subsidiary builds roads motorways airports rail and light rail infrastructure and has been investing heavily in raw building materials. It has bought several European gravel quarry operations and road construction companies over the last several years. In 2010 it bought about 100 quarries from Tarmac. The deal helped expand operations in Central Europe where road construction is growing. Eurovia now operates a network of about 430 quarries.

Not to be left out of the growth spurt VINCI Park has been busy making acquisitions in the US Canada and Europe in efforts to make it one of the largest parking operators in the world. VINCI Park (and subsidiaries such as LAZ Parking in the US) manages more than a million on-street and off-street parking spaces in Europe North America and Asia.

Financial Performance

VINCI reported Â40.3 billion ($56 billion) in revenue in 2013 a 4% increase versus the prior year. The firm's main Contracting business posted a 5% increase in annual sales due primarily to growth at VINCI Construction partially offset by a decline in sales by Eurovia. The Concessions unit saw its revenues rise 5% on gains by VINCI Autoroutes due to a 3% increase in intercity network traffic and strong growth at VINCI Airports. Net income rose 7% in 2013 versus the prior year to $2.7 billion. Cash flow decreased by Â26 million ($36 million) in 2013 from 2012 due to cash used in the acquisition of ANA (a holder of concessions at 10 airports in Portugal) and the purchase of an additional 4.7% stake in Aeroports de Paris.

Strategy

Like other builders VINCI has seen construction slow since the 2008 crisis and as a result has been expanding into higher-growth higher-margin concessions such as airports and motorways. It recently agreed to sell the bulk of its parking lot business to free up cash for acquisitions.

VINCI is pursuing an aggressive growth strategy as it continues to increase revenues and grow organically and through acquisitions. Despite continuing economic weakness in the Europe and other parts of the world VINCI has managed grow experiencing a revival in revenue since 2010. VINCI also is expanding internationally in regions experiencing economic growth such as central and eastern Europe the Middle East and India. The company also sees opportunities in North America where aging infrastructure needs to be replaced. Indeed VINCI in 2014 won major contracts to expand or upgrade roads and transportation infrastructure in California Indiana and Georgia. In Qatar the French firm is partnering with Qatari Diar which holds shares in VINCI to design and build a new motorway on the outskirts of Doha. The project is an outgrowth of an effort by VINCI to establish local roots in Qater through the formation of subsidiary QDVC which has positioned itself in seven years as a major player in the Qatari construction market. Previously VINCI and Quatri Diar announced plans for a parking lot joint venture which will run lots in Qatar and are working on a Â2.2 billion ($3 billion) bridge linking Qatar and Bahrain.

Mergers and Acquisitions

VINCI has an ongoing strategy to acquire specialty companies that have a global reach. Specific target areas include ground technologies oil and gas infrastructure and nuclear engineering. VINCI is aligning its growth areas with marketplace trends such as urban development mobility needs and growing demand for new energy infrastructure.

In 2014 the company added to its holdings in Confiroute taking 100% ownership. The deal was priced in the range of Â780 million to Â800 million. It also acquired Imtech ICT the information and communication technologies division of Imtech as well as the Electrix company from McConnell Dowell a subsidiary of South African group Aveng.

In 2013 the company acquired ANA the company holding the 50-year concession for Portugal's 10 airports in a transaction valued at about Â3.1 billion ($4.3 billion). The purchase furthered VINCI's strategy of making VINCI Airports a leading international players in airport concessions. With the addition of ANA'S airports VINCI now manages concessions at 23 airports in Portugal France and Cambodia. The French firm in July 2013 acquired an additional 5% stake in Aerports de Paris in July for Â365 million ($504.5 million) bringing its holding to 8%. Also in 2013 VINCI purchased London-based Mentor IMC Group Ltd. a global oil and gas project resource specialist thereby broadening the customer base of its Energies' oil and gas business.

HISTORY

VINCI's origins lie with French conglomerate Vivendi (now Vivendi Universal) which was founded in 1853 as Compagnie Generale des Eaux. Its mission was to irrigate French farmland and supply water to towns. The company won contracts to serve Lyons (1853) Nantes (1854) Paris (1860) and Venice (1880). Generale des Eaux moved into construction in 1972 building an office tower (and later hotels and houses) in Paris. The company also entered communications in the 1980s.

In 1988 Generale des Eaux acquired control of construction and civil engineering giant Societe Generale d'Entreprises. SGE subsidiaries included Campenon Bernard SGE (part of Generale des Eaux since 1981) Sogea Freyssinet Cochery Bourdin Chausse Saunier Duval Tunzini Lefort Francheteau and Wanner. SGE traces its construction roots to 1910. It became a subsidiary of Generale d'Electricite in 1966. Glassmaker Saint-Gobain acquired control of SGE in 1984. Under Generale des Eaux SGE enhanced its European profile through acquisitions including British builder Norwest Holst (1989) German road builder VBU (1991) and German pipe and duct maker MLTU (1992).

Generale des Eaux acquired publisher Havas in 1998 and took the name Vivendi –representing vivacity and mobility. Its purchase of USFilter in 1999 made Vivendi the world's largest water company. Vivendi's SGE unit (renamed VINCI) agreed to acquire the construction arm of rival conglomerate Suez's GTM unit in 2000.

Groupe GTM traces its roots to Societe Lyonnaise des Eaux et de L'Eclairage a leading French water utility. Formed in 1880 Lyonnaise des Eaux built up its French and international operations to include water distribution as well as gas and electricity production and distribution. A century later the company had diversified into such businesses as heating (Cofreth) waste management (Sita) and communications acquiring a stake in Lyonnaise Communications (now Lyonnaise Cable) in 1986.

In 1990 Lyonnaise des Eaux acquired construction firm Dumez whose subsidiary GTM-Entrepose was France's largest car park manager. Four years later Dumez-GTM was formed to consolidate the construction and civil engineering businesses of Dumez and GTM-Entrepose. In 1997 Lyonnaise des Eaux and Compagnie de Suez merged to create a leading provider of private infrastructure services Suez Lyonnaise des Eaux (which shortened its name to SUEZ in 2001). Compagnie Universal du Canal Maritime de Suez the builder of the Suez Canal was founded in 1858 and became Financiere de Suez in 1958. In 1967 Financiere de Suez acquired control of Lyonnaise des Eaux.

SGE changed its name to VINCI in 2000. That year as part of their strategy to rationalize operations and focus on core businesses Vivendi and SUEZ agreed to a friendly takeover of GTM by VINCI. SUEZ emerged as the combined company's largest shareholder but by the following year both SUEZ and Vivendi Universal had exited most of VINCI's capital leaving no core stockholder.

To better control its car park management operations the company in 2001 created VINCI Park to operate as an umbrella of its VINCI Concessions unit. It expanded its concessions holdings even more in 2002 by hooking up with construction group Eiffage to grab a 17% stake in Europe's second-largest toll road operator ASF which was floated that year by the French government.

In 2003 the group won the contract to manage the restoration of the historic Hall of Mirrors. It also won the concession contract to operate along with joint venture partner Keolis the International Airport of Grenoble.

VINCI completed its acquisition of ASF in 2005. The deal was part of a government program to privatize motorway companies.

The company has had volatile internal struggles. There was unrest in the board room during 2006 as chairman Antoine Zacharias reportedly wanted to oust CEO Xavier Vuillard in favor of Nexity CEO Alain Dinin. Zacharias was the one who ended up resigning and at the end of 2006 Dinin resigned from VINCI's board.

In 2007 VINCI's top French construction businesses Sogea Construction and GTM Construction merged to create VINCI Construction France its domestic construction giant.

The company strengthened its position in the UK in 2008 when it bought British construction and facilities management firm Taylor Woodrow from Taylor Wimpey. The deal consolidated VINCI's position in UK facilities management and public-private partnership projects such as rail airports and energy infrastructure. In 2009 VINCI Construction acquired the troubled UK builder Haymills Group as that company teetered on the brink of collapse.

In 2008 Eurovia branched out from the road to the rails when it acquired rail infrastructure firm Vossloh Infrastructure Services (now ETF-Eurovia Travaux Ferroviaires) from Vossloh. The division specializes in rail track maintenance and installation.

EXECUTIVES

COO Energy Business Line, Yves Meignie, age 59
Chairman VINCI Autoroutes, Pierre Coppey, age 51
Executive Vice-President and Chief Financial Officer, Christian Labeyrie, age 58
Deputy Managing Director Eurovia, Dominique Collomp
VP Business Development, Jean-Luc Pommier, age 61
Chairman and Chief Executive Officer, Xavier Huillard, age 60
VP Human Resources and Sustainable Development, Franck Mougin, age 55
Chairman VINCI Construction, Jean Rossi, age 65
COO VINCI Construction, Bruno Dupety, age 58
Chairman VINCI PLC, John Stanion
Managing Director CFE, Renaud Bentegeat, age 60
Chairman Energy Business Line, Jean-Yves le Brouster, age 66
COO Eurovia, Guy Vacher
Executive Vice-President Contracting, Richard Francioli, age 55
Senior Vice-President International Development, Pascale Sourisse
Chairman Soletanche Freyssinet; Director, Jean-Pierre Lamoure
Chairman Chief Executive Officer, Dominique Bouvier
COO Eurovia, Pierre Anjolras
Chairman and Chief Executive Officer Eurovia, Jacques Tavernier, age 64
CEO VINCI Concessions, Louis-Roch Burgard, age 46
Director Corporate Communication, Pierre Duprat, age 51
General Counsel and Secretary, Patrick Richard, age 57
Deputy Managing Director Operations Autoroutes du Sud de la France, Sebastien Fraisse
Chairman and CEO Escota, Philippe E. Daussy
Deputy Managing Director Energy Business Line, Herve Adam
Chairman VINCI Construction France, Gerard Bienfait
Chairman VINCI Construction Grands Projets, Alain Bonnot
Deputy Managing Director Energy Business Line, Michel Cantet
Chairman and CEO Sogea-Satom, Philippe Chavent
President directeur general de VINCI Park, Serge Clemente
CEO Cofiroute, Arnaud Grison
Director Business Development VINCI Concessions, Fadi Selwan
Managing Director, Alain Bellanger
Director, Robert Castaigne, age 66
Director, Patrick Faure, age 68
Director, Michael P. Pragnell, age 67
Director, Francois David
Director, Dominique Ferrero, age 67
Director, Dominique Bazy, age 60
Director, Henri Saint Olive, age 67
Director, Jean-Bernard Levy, age 59
Director, Pascale Sourisse
Chairman Soletanche Freyssinet; Director, Jean-Pierre Lamoure
Director, Yousuf Ahmad Al Hammadi
Director, Elisabeth Boyer
Auditors: SalustroReydel

LOCATIONS

HQ: Vinci SA
1, cours Ferdinand-de-Lesseps, Rueil-Malmaison, Cedex 92851
Phone: (33) 1 47 16 35 00   **Fax:** (33) 1 47 51 91 02
Web: www.vinci.com

Sales

	% of total
France	62

Central and Eastern	6
United	5
Germany	5
Africa	5
Benelux	4
Americas	3
Rest of	3
Asia Middle East and	2
Total	**100**

PRODUCTS/OPERATIONS

Sales

	% of total
Contracting	85
Concessions	15
Total	**100**

Selected Subsidiaries

VINCI Construction
  CFE (46.8%; Benelux)
    DEME (50%; dredging)
  VINCI Construction France
  VINCI PLC (UK)
  VINCI Construction Filiales Internationales (Germany Central Europe overseas France Africa)
  VINCI Construction Grands Projets
  Freyssinet (specialized civil engineering)
VINCI Concessions
VINCI Park
Eurovia
VINCI Energies
  Actemium (industry solutions)
  Axians (voice-data-image communication)
  Citeos (urban lighting)
  Graniou (telecommunications infrastructure)
  Omexom (high-voltage power transmission)
  Opteor (maintenance)

COMPETITORS

Atlantia	HOCHTIEF
Bechtel	Louis Berger
Bilfinger Berger	Parsons Corporation
Bouygues	Schneider Electric
Bovis Lend Lease	Skanska
EIFFAGE	WS Atkins
FCC Barcelona	

HISTORICAL FINANCIALS

Company Type: Public

Income Statement

FYE: December 31

	REVENUE ($ mil.)	NET INCOME ($ mil.)	NET PROFIT MARGIN	EMPLOYEES
12/13	56,568	2,701	4.8%	190,704
12/12	52,062	2,526	4.9%	192,701
12/11	49,023	2,463	5.0%	183,320
12/10	45,821	2,376	5.2%	179,527
12/09	47,089	2,299	4.9%	161,746
Annual Growth	4.7%	4.1%	—	4.2%

2013 Year-End Financials

Debt ratio: 45.4%
Return on equity: 14.2%
Cash ($ mil.): 7,716
Current ratio: 0.83
Long-term debt ($ mil.): 24,164

No. of shares (mil.): 556
Dividends
  Yield: 3.5%
  Payout: 21.4%
Market value ($ mil.): 9,167

	STOCK PRICE ($) FY Close	P/E High/Low		PER SHARE ($) Earnings	Dividends	Book Value
12/13	16.46	9	5	4.87	0.58	34.96
12/12	12.00	6	4	4.67	0.73	32.77
12/11	10.86	9	5	4.50	1.08	30.86
12/10	13.65	9	5	4.42	0.51	30.42
12/09	14.35	10	4	4.62	0.57	28.27
Annual Growth	3.5%	—	—	1.3%	0.3%	5.5%

Vivendi

Vivendi wants to be the life of the party. More than half of the company's business is in telecom services and the rest is in movies TV games and music. Its telecom holdings include SFR (Europe's largest alternative telecom operator) (more than 40% of sales) a controlling stake in Maroc Telecom (the largest telecom company in Morocco) and GVT in Brazil (that country's leading alternative high-speed Internet company). Vivendi's media assets include Universal Music Group (UMG) and the world's #1 independent video game publisher Activision Blizzard. Vivendi also owns CANAL+ the top pay-television provider in France and Europe's largest distributor and producer of films.

Operations

Vivendi's telecom business provides mobile and fixed telecom services including broadband Internet. At less than half of its main telecom company SFR's size is Canal+ Group Vivendi's next largest business. Not much smaller than Canal+ is UMG which gets most of its revenues from recorded music by artists such as Justin Bieber Lady Gaga LMFAO and Rihanna. Activision Blizzard tops rival Electronic Arts and in fact every other video game publisher except Nintendo with game franchises such as Call of Duty (Activision) and World of Warcraft (Blizzard).

Financial Performance

The company's revenue dropped from $38.3 billion in fiscal 2012 down to $30.4 billion in fiscal 2013. However Vivendi's net income spiked from $216 million in fiscal 2012 up to $2.7 billion in fiscal 2013. Even with the increased net income the company's cash flow decreased by more than $2 billion in fiscal 2013 compared to the previous fiscal period.

Strategy

Although Vivendi's strategy concentrates on synergies among its business units and organic innovation acquisitions have also been important.

Mergers and Acquisitions

In 2012 Canal+ agreed to acquire the free-to-air channels and advertising sales operations from Bollore. Vivendi announced in 2011 that it would expand UMG's music library by purchasing London-based music group EMI's recorded music division for Â1.2 billion ($1.9 billion) from Citigroup. Already the global leader in recorded music with the largest catalog of musical works the deal would bring UMG more big names including Pink Floyd Miles Davis and arguably the biggest one in pop music ever The Beatles.

Also that year Vivendi funded an even more significant acquisition by selling its 20% stake in NBCUniversal to NBCUniversal's majority owner General Electric for $5.8 billion. General Electric pushed for the acquisition to facilitate the proposed sale of a controlling 51% interest in NBCUniversal to Philadelphia-based cable operator Comcast. The deal gave Vivendi the funds it needed to take full ownership and total control of its SFR telecom division and thereby bolster its position at home against industry leader France Telecom (later renamed Orange) and other rivals. The company bought out UK-based Vodafone's stake (44%) in SFR for nearly $11.5 billion. SFR and Vodafone are set to extend their commercial partnership for three more years as part of the deal.

HISTORY

Early History

Authorized by an imperial decree Compagnie Generale des Eaux was founded in 1853 by investors such as the Rothschild family and Napoleon III's half-brother to irrigate French farmland and supply water to towns. It won contracts to serve Lyons (1853) Nantes (1854) Paris (1860) and Venice (1880).

After WWI Generale des Eaux created water engineering firm Societe Auxiliaire de Distribution d'Eau (Sade 1918) and extended its water distribution network to several areas of France. By 1953 the company had added trash collection to its services. In the 1960s it began managing district heating networks and waste incineration/composting plants. The company moved into construction in 1972. By the time Guy Dujouany became chairman in 1976 water distribution accounted for less than half of the company's sales.

Dujouany began an expansion drive. In 1980 Generale des Eaux became France's #1 private energy management firm when it bought Generale de Chauffe. Also that year it expanded its wastewater and waste management businesses and moved into transportation buying Compagnie Generale d'Entreprises Automobiles (CGEA). The company also entered communications in the 1980s: it took a 15% stake in pay-TV provider CANAL+ (1983) and it created mobile phone unit Societe Francaise de Radiotelephonie (SFR 1987).

Generale des Eaux took its water services global in the 1990s. Dujouany stepped down in 1996 and was succeeded by Jean-Marie Messier who immediately dumped some businesses. In 1997 the company launched telecom provider Cegetel and increased its stake in publisher Havas to 30%. In 1998 the firm bought the rest of Havas increased its ownership in CANAL+ and took the name Vivendi to represent "vivacity" and "mobility."

Its purchase of USFilter in 1999 made Vivendi the world's largest water company; it also bought US waste management company Superior Services.

Bulking up its media holdings it acquired US educational software and games firm Cendant Software and bought French film producer Pathe. Vivendi sold most of Pathe's assets but kept stakes in Sky plc and CANAL+'s CanalSatellite digital-TV unit. The company sold $985 million worth of real estate to Unibail and it sold its hotel and restaurant businesses to Accor the French hotels group.

In 2000 Vivendi and Vodafone launched an Internet portal Vizzavi. Vivendi brought its environmental services businesses together under the Vivendi Environnement umbrella and sold a minority stake in the company to the public.

Later that year in a $34 billion deal that set the stage for Vivendi's transformation into a global conglomerate the company bought Seagram and the portion of CANAL+ that it didn't already own. The combined company became Vivendi Universal (VU).

EXECUTIVES

Chairman Supervisory Board, Jean-Rene Fourtou, age 75

SEVP Telecoms Activity, Jean-Yves Charlier, age 50

Chairman Management Board, Jean-Francois Dubos, age 69

Chairman Executive Board CANAL+ Group, Bertrand Meheut, age 62

Senior Executive Vice President Communications and Public Affairs, Simon Gillham, age 57

Executive Vice President - Innovation; Deputy Financial Director, Sandrine Dufour, age 43

Senior Executive Vice President Mergers & Acquisitions, Regis Turrini, age 55

IR Contact Officer, Jean-Michel Bonamy, age 43

Senior Vice President Audit and Special Projects, Vincent Vallejo, age 49

Chairman and CEO Universal Music Group, Lucian Grainge, age 53

Chairman Management Board Maroc Telecom, Abdeslam Ahizoune, age 59

SEVP Human Resources, Stephane Roussel, age 52

CFO and Member Management Board, Philippe G. H. Capron, age 56

V.P. Investor Relations, Eileen McLAUGHLIN

Chief Executive Officer, Jean-Bernard Levy

Vice President Corporate Communications, Adam White

Senior Vice President Corporate Communications, Peter Lofrumento

Senior Vice President; Development in the Strategy and Development Department, Arnaud Arnaud Castille Castille

Independent Member of the Supervisory Board, Christophe Christophe de Margerie Margerie

Independent Member of the Supervisory Board, Claude Claude Bebear Bebear

Independent Member of the Supervisory Board, Dominique Dominique Heriard Dubreuil Dubreuil

Vice President; Management and Business Plan Control/Holding Company Accounts, Florent Florent de Cournuaud Cournuaud

Senior Vice President; Head of the Legal Department; Secretary of the Supervisory and Management Boards, Frederic Frederic Crepin Crepin

Independent Member of the Supervisory Board, Jacqueline Jacqueline Tammenoms Bakker Bakker

Member of the Management Board; Chairman and Chief Executive Officer of GVT, Amos Amos Genish Genish

Executive Vice President Human Resources, Mathieu Peycere

Member Supervisory Board, Christophe de Margerie, age 62

Member Supervisory Board, Jean-Yves Charlier, age 49

Member Supervisory Board, Daniel Camus, age 62

Member Supervisory Board, Claude Bebear, age 78

Vice Chairman Supervisory Board, Dominique Heriard Dubreuil, age 67

Member Supervisory Board, Maureen Chiquet, age 51

Member Supervisory Board, Philippe Donnet, age 53

Member Supervisory Board, Pierre Rodocanachi, age 75

Member Supervisory Board, Aliza Jabes, age 51

Member Supervisory Board, Jacqualine Tammenoms Bakker, age 60

Auditors: KPMGAudit

LOCATIONS

HQ: Vivendi
42, avenue de Friedland, Paris, Cedex 08 75380
Phone: (33) 1 71 71 10 00   **Fax:** (33) 1 71 71 10 01
Web: www.vivendi.com

Sales

	% of total
Europe	
France	58
Rest of	11
USA	11
Morocco	8
Brazil	5
Rest of the	7
Total	**100**

PRODUCTS/OPERATIONS

Sales

	% of total
Telecommunication services	
SFR	42
Maroc Telecom	9
GVT	5
Canal+	17
Universal Music	15
Activision	12
Total	**100**

COMPETITORS

Al Jazeera	Net Servicos de
BMG Rights Management	Comunicac?o
Bouygues	Nintendo
Brasil Telecom	Orange
CKX	Orange
Capcom	Sony
Cherry Lane Music	Sony Music
Publishing	THQ
Chrysalis	Take-Two
EMI Group	Tele2
Eidos	Telefonica Brasil
Electronic Arts	Telemar Norte Leste
ITV	Tiscali
Iliad S.A.	Ubisoft
Konami	Virgin Group
Lucasfilm	Warner Music
Entertainment	Warner/Chappell
Microsoft Game Studios	ZeniMax Media
NCsoft	

HISTORICAL FINANCIALS

Company Type: Public

Income Statement

FYE: December 31

	REVENUE ($ mil.)	NET INCOME ($ mil.)	NET PROFIT MARGIN	EMPLOYEES
12/13	30,474	2,708	8.9%	41,439
12/12	38,215	216	0.6%	38,859
12/11	37,268	3,467	9.3%	58,400
12/10	38,649	2,941	7.6%	51,272
12/09	39,085	1,195	3.1%	49,004
Annual Growth	(6.0%)	22.7%	—	(4.1%)

2013 Year-End Financials

Debt ratio: 34.3%
Return on equity: 10.9%
Cash ($ mil.): 1,433
Current ratio: 0.92
Long-term debt ($ mil.): 12,028

No. of shares (mil.): 1,339
Dividends
Yield: 4.8%
Payout: 114.7%
Market value ($ mil.): 35,324

	STOCK PRICE ($) FY Close	P/E High/Low	PER SHARE ($) Earnings	Dividends	Book Value
12/13	26.37	34 23	2.02	1.28	17.94
12/12	22.81	309 199	0.16	1.25	18.40
12/11	21.74	29 16	2.70	3.64	19.54
Annual Growth	10.1% (2.1%)	— —	(7.0%)	(22.9%)	

Vodafone Group Plc

Customers have voted with their phones to make Vodafone one of the world's top wireless phone carriers with more than 430 million customers in nearly 30 countries. (It has partnerships with other mobile networks in another 50 countries.) In terms of subscribers Vodafone trails only China Mobile. The company does around 65% of its business in Europe where it is a leader in the wireless markets in the UK and Germany. It also provides data broadband Internet and fixed-line phone services; in Germany its largest market those services are overseen by subsidiary Arcor. Vodafone increasingly serves callers in Africa the Middle East and Asia through subsidiaries and joint ventures.

Geographic Reach

Altogether Vodafone has direct operations in 27 countries: Albania Australia Congo the Czech Republic Egypt Fiji Germany Ghana Greece Hungary India Ireland Italy Kenya Lesotho Malta Mozambique the Netherlands New Zealand Portugal Qatar Romania South Africa Spain Tanzania Turkey and the UK.

Germany is its largest single market accounting for 22% of overall revenues followed by the UK with 16%. Its Vodacom brand in southern Africa makes up another 12% of sales.

The company has retail stores in all of its markets as well as offshore operations in finance administration IT customer service and human resources across Egypt India and Europe.

Sales and Marketing

Vodafone counts 434 million customers. More than 90% of its mobile customers are individuals and the rest are enterprise customers ranging from large multinational firms to small- and mid-sized businesses. It also has 9.3 million fixed broadband customers mainly in Germany Italy and Spain making it the fourth-largest provider of fixed broadband services in Western Europe.

Financial Performance

Revenue for 2014 fell 5% in US dollars and grew 1% in British pounds. In both currencies profits shot up due to the sale of its stake in US-based Verizon Wireless. Vodafone took in almost $60 billion in cash for that deal.

Strategy

In a major move Vodafone disposed of its 45% stake in US-based Verizon Wireless in early 2014 for $130 billion. Under the deal Vodafone received $58.9 billion in cash $60.2 billion in Verizon stock and an additional $11 billion from smaller transactions. The split was part of Vodafone's strategy to exit joint ventures and partnerships that it doesn't control in order to expand in other areas (Verizon Communications held the majority 55% stake).

At the same time Vodafone agreed to enter the Canadian market through a partnership with that country's #1 mobile service provider Rogers Communications. Under the agreement Rogers became Vodafone's exclusive partner in Canada and the two companies will leverage each other's networks and technologies including 4G roaming services.

One of the biggest hurdles Vodafone faces is customer acquisition and retention costs which are the largest single cost its business faces. The company also wants to improve growth in its average revenue per user which it will try to do through improvements to its network to customer service and by introducing new and differentiated handset services.

Geographically emerging markets such as India and Africa continue to be a big area of focus for Vodafone. The company introduced a money transfer service M-Pesa in a handful of countries there after having success with it in India.

Mergers and Acquisitions

Vodafone has become a global telecom primarily through partnerships and acquisitions. In 2014 it moved to buy Spanish wireless carrier Ono for almost $10 billion. Ono serves almost 2 million customers and is the market leader in high-speed broadband services. Vodafone sees a significant opportunity to accelerate growth in the mature Spanish market by leveraging its distribution and marketing capabilities and through cross-selling to each company's customer base.

In 2012 Vodafone acquired fellow country mate Cable & Wireless Worldwide (CWW) in a deal valued at about $1.6 billion. The purchase had obvious benefits for Vodafone. Because CWW has more than 12000 miles of optical fiber —the largest fiber optic network in the UK —Vodafone will not need to rent as much landline from its competition primarily BT.

Supporting its strategy to grow in emerging markets the company paid $5 billion in 2011 to buy out partner Essar Group in wireless joint venture Vodafone Essar in a bid to bolster its position in India. The deal gave Vodafone a 75% stake in the business with the remaining shares controlled by the company's Indian partners in which Vodafone also holds minority interests. To comply with Indian foreign ownership rules Vodafone subsequently sold about 5% of Vodafone Essar (renamed Vodafone India) to Piramal Healthcare for $640 million.

Vodafone also moved to strengthen its fixed communications portfolio in 2012 when it bought TelstraClear the New Zealand operations of Telstra Corporation for $670 million. As that country's #2 fixed infrastructure operator —behind Telecom New Zealand (TCNZ) —TelstraClear gives Vodafone a more level playing field against regional rival TCNZ in capitalizing on a government-backed infrastructure expansion planned for the next several years.

Divestments have helped the company stay focused. The company sold back its stake in Tokyo-based technology investment firm SOFTBANK for $5 billion in 2010 and sold its 3% stake in China Mobile for about $6.7 billion earlier that year. The following year closer to home Vodafone sold its stake in French wireless provider SFR to Vivendi for about $11.4 billion. SFR and Vodafone are set to extend their commercial partnership for three more years as part of the deal.

HISTORY

Vodafone was formed in 1983 as a joint venture between Racal Electronics (a UK electronics firm) and Millicom (a US telecom company) and was granted one of two mobile phone licenses in the UK. It launched service in 1985 as a Racal subsidiary. Vodafone and Cellnet the other licensee were swamped with demand. In 1988 Racal offered 20% of Vodafone to the public; three years later the rest of the firm was spun off to become Vodafone Group.

Vodafone moved beyond the UK in the 1990s. By 1993 it had interests in mobile phone networks in Australia Greece Hong Kong Malta and Scandinavia.

For a time Vodafone and Cellnet a joint venture of British Telecom (now BT Group) and Securicor enjoyed a duopoly in the UK. Regulators elected not to impose price controls and the pounds rolled in. But in 1993 a new wireless provider One 2 One (now T-Mobile UK) launched a digital network in London. Vodafone countered that year with its own GSM (global system for mobile communications) digital network.

With increasing competition at home Vodafone continued to expand in 1994. It launched or bought stakes in operations in Fiji Germany South Africa and Uganda.

Digital service took on a larger role in Vodafone's UK business and by 1997 some 85% of new subscribers were opting for digital GSM. In 1998 Vodafone sold its French service provider Vodafone SA and bought digital cellular carrier BellSouth New Zealand. It also expanded into Egypt by buying a minority stake in Misrfone marking the largest British investment in Egypt since the Suez Canal.

In 1999 Vodafone prevailed in a brief bidding war with Bell Atlantic (now Verizon) to buy AirTouch Communications for about $60 billion. Vodafone's Chris Gent took over as CEO of the new company Vodafone AirTouch. The prize for Vodafone: entry into the lucrative US market plus the opportunity to consolidate minority interests in European wireless carriers.

Vodafone AirTouch moved to significantly boost its European footprint in 1999 by launching a $131 billion hostile takeover bid for Germany's Mannesmann. The company acquired Mannesmann for about $180 billion in stock in 2000 and agreed to sell the conglomerate's engineering operations and its UK mobile phone unit Orange. (France Telecom —later itself renamed Orange — bought the Orange unit for $37.5 billion later that year.)

In 2000 Vodafone AirTouch expanded its presence in the US by combining its US wireless operations with those of Bell Atlantic and GTE to form Verizon Wireless. The company failed to strengthen its presence in that market two years previously when it lost a bidding war with Cingular Wireless (now AT&T Mobility) over the acquisition of AT&T Wireless.

That year the company dropped AirTouch from its name and became Vodafone Group once again. It also continued its expansion push investing in China Mobile and buying Irish mobile phone operator Eircell (now Vodafone Ireland) in a deal that was completed in 2001. That year Vodafone bought BT's remaining interest in Spain's Airtel (now Vodafone Espana). In 2003 Vodafone sold its stake in Mexico's Grupo Iusacell to Movil@ccess.

Vodafone sold its 98%-owned Vodafone Japan unit in 2006 to SOFTBANK in a deal valued at nearly $16 billion. The group's acquisitions in regions outside of Europe included the 2006 purchase of Telsim (formerly the number two mobile service operator in Turkey) for about $4.6 billion. The next year Vodafone outbid several rivals to win control of one of India's largest telecom companies Hutchison Essar in a deal valued at about $9 billion. Also in 2007 the group bought fixed-line broadband Internet businesses in Italy and Spain from Sweden-based Tele2 for more than $1 billion.

Arun Sarin resigned as Vodafone's CEO in 2008. He was replaced by deputy CEO Vittorio Colao. During his five year tenure Sarin spearheaded the company's push into emerging markets in Eastern Europe as well as India and Turkey. He came under fire from shareholders at times for his aggressive expansion strategy but Sarin succeeded in more than doubling Vodafone's subscriber base and boosted the company's share price by more than 30%.

Also in 2008 Vodafone bought the remaining one-quarter of German fixed-line operator Arcor's shares that it did not already own from Deutsche Post and Deutsche Bahn for about Å474 million. The transaction was part of the company's plan to focus on providing a more extensive range of bundled services to German subscribers.

Vittorio Colao stated that the company's plans included a continued expansion into Africa Asia and the Middle East through acquisitions and partnerships while exiting non-core markets. Its key areas for growth in terms of service segments were mobile data broadband and corporate accounts. To this end Vodafone in 2008 raised its stake in South Africa's largest wireless operator Vodacom from 50% to 65% and took a controlling stake in Ghana's third-largest mobile carrier. The company in 2009 combined its mobile operations in Australia with those of Hong Kong-based Hutchison Telecommunications. As part of the deal Hutchison Telecommunications Australia paid $500 million to acquire Vodafone Hutchison Australia.

EXECUTIVES

Regional President Americas, Terry D. Kramer, age 55

Deputy Chairman, Sir John G. S. Buchanan, age 70, $269,901 total compensation

Chief Executive; Executive Director, Vittorio A. Colao, age 52, $1,944,247 total compensation

Group General Counsel and Company Secretary, Rosemary Martin, age 54

Group Chief Commercial Officer, Morten Lundal, age 49

Managing Director and CEO Vodafone Essar Ltd India, Marten Pieters, age 61

CEO Czech Republic, Muriel Anton

CEO Asia Pacific and Middle East, Nicholas J. (Nick) Read, age 49

CEO Germany, Friedrich P. (Fritz) Joussen, age 51

CTO and Director, Stephen C. (Steve) Pusey, age 53, $491,000 total compensation

Chief Financial Officer; Executive Director, Andrew N. (Andy) Halford, age 56, $1,273,523 total compensation

Director; CEO Europe Region, Michel Combes, age 52

CEO Ireland, Charles Butterworth

Chief Executive; Southern Europe, Paolo Bertoluzzo, age 48

Group Financial Controller, Margherita Della Valle

CFO Europe, John Townsend, age 51

CEO Qatar, Grahame Maher

CEO Australia, Nigel Dews

Chairman, Gerard J. Kleisterlee, age 69

CEO UK, Guy Laurence, age 52

CEO Albania, Haris Broumidis

Director Group External Affairs, Matthew Kirk, age 53

Director Mobile Payments, Cenk Serdar, age 45

Director Group Strategy and Business Development, Warren Finegold, age 58

Director Group Investor Relations, Richard C. Snow, age 46

CEO Partner Markets, Richard Daly

CEO Hungary, Gyorgy Beck, age 59

CEO Malta, I?aki Berroeta

CEO New Zealand, Russell Stanners

CEO Spain, Francisco (Paco) Roman

Group Chief Marketing Officer, Wendy Becker, age 46

Global Director Terminals, Patrick Chomet

CEO Egypt, Hatem Dowidar

Director Human Resources, Ronald Schellekens, age 50

CEO Netherlands, Jens Schulte-Bockum

CEO Turkey, Serpil Timuray

Chief Executive; Northern & Central Europe, Philipp Humm

President Americas, Chuck Pol

President Asia Pacific & Sub-Saharan Africa, Stevan Hoyle

Executive Vice President Managed Network & Services, Nick Lambert

Director, Alan W. Jebson, age 65

Director, Philip E. (Phil) Yea, age 60

Director, Samuel E. (Sam) Jonah, age 64

Director, Anne Lauvergeon, age 55

Deputy Chairman, Sir John G. S. Buchanan, age 70

Director, Luc Vandevelde, age 63

CTO and Director, Stephen C. (Steve) Pusey, age 53

CFO and Director, Andrew N. (Andy) Halford, age 55

Director; CEO Europe Region, Michel Combes, age 52

Director, Renee J. James, age 49

Director, Nick Land, age 67

Director, Anthony (Tony) Watson, age 70

Auditors: DeloitteLLP

LOCATIONS

HQ: Vodafone Group Plc
Vodafone House, The Connection, Newbury, Berkshire RG14 2FN
Phone: (44) 1635 33251   **Fax:** (44) 1635 238080
Web: www.vodafone.com

Sales

	% of total
Europe	
Germany	18
Italy	12
UK	11
Spain	10
Other	18
Africa Middle East Asia/Pacif	

Vodacom (Southern	12
India	9
Other	9
Non-controlled interests & common	1
Total	**100**

PRODUCTS/OPERATIONS

Sales

	% of total
Voice	60
Data	15
Messaging	12
Fixed	8
Other	5
Total	**100**

Countries of Operation interests)
Africa/the East/Asia-
Australia
Congo
Egypt
Fiji
Ghana
India
Lesotho
Mozambique
New Zealand
Qatar
South Africa
Tanzania
Europe
Albania
Czech Republic
Germany
Greece
Hungary
Ireland
Italy
Malta
The Netherland
Portugal
Romania
Spain
Turkey
UK

COMPETITORS

AT&T Mobility	NTT DoCoMo
BT	Orange
Belgacom	Orange
China Mobile	Swisscom
Deutsche Telekom	Telefonica Europe
Hutchison Whampoa	Telekom Austria
KPN	Telstra
M1	Virgin Mobile Telecoms

HISTORICAL FINANCIALS

Company Type: Public

Income Statement

	REVENUE ($ mil.)	NET INCOME ($ mil.)	NET PROFIT MARGIN	EMPLOYEES
03/14	63,838	98,646	154.5%	89,146
03/13	67,539	651	1.0%	91,272
03/12	74,379	11,148	15.0%	86,373
03/11	73,826	12,820	17.4%	83,862
03/10	67,444	13,110	19.4%	84,990
Annual Growth	(1.4%)	65.6%	—	1.2%

FYE: March 31

2014 Year-End Financials

Debt ratio: 39.9%	No. of shares (mil.): —
Return on equity: 83.2%	Dividends
Cash ($ mil.): 16,871	Yield: —
Current ratio: 0.99	Payout: —
Long-term debt ($ mil.): 35,716	Market value ($ mil.): —

STOCK PRICE ($) FY Close	P/E High/Low	PER SHARE ($) Earnings	Dividends	Book Value
03/14	36.81	52 31	3.70	0.00	4.46
03/13	28.40	45083553	0.02	0.00	4.07
03/12	27.67	309241	0.40	0.00	4.55
03/11	28.75	278154	0.45	0.00	5.01
03/10	23.31	202126	0.46	0.00	4.77
Annual Growth	12.1%	— —	68.7%	—	(1.7%)

Volkswagen A.G. (Germany, Fed. Rep.)

With cars named for climate patterns insects and small mammals Volkswagen (VW) leads the Continent as Europe's #1 carmaker. Along with Golf (Gulf Stream reference) and the New Beetle VW's annual production of more than 7 million cars trucks and vans includes such models as Passat (trade wind) Jetta (jet stream) Rabbit and Fox. VW also owns a garage full of luxury carmakers — AUDI Lamborghini Bentley and Bugatti. Other brands include SEAT (family cars Spain) and Skoda (family cars the Czech Republic). Late in 2009 VW acquired a 49.9% stake in Porsche for about E4 billion (almost $6 billion) as the first step in combining the two into an integrated car company.

Geographic Reach

VW sells its cars worldwide with operations in Europe North America South America Africa and Asia. The company holds a global market share of more than 11%.

Sales outside of Germany account for almost 65% of the company's revenue although the rest of Europe accounted for more than 40% of revenue in 2011.

Operations

VW's makes more than 7 million cars trucks and vans annually.

VW AG is the holding company for VW Group that comprises segments including Automotive and Financial Services which provides customer financing leasing banking insurance and fleet management.

VW manufactures its nine brands (10 including Porsche) and almost 200 models in its more than 60 production plants. In mid-2011 VW announced plans for two additional manufacturing plants in China with an expected annual production of 300000 automobiles by 2013.

For its commercial vehicles segment VW holds 68% of the voting rights in Swedish truck maker Scania. It holds more than 30% of MAN which is considered a majority stake.

Financial Performance

The company's revenue has been trending upward and steadily increasing over the course of recent fiscal years. Revenue increased about 17% in fiscal 2011 compared to fiscal 2010.

Strategy

VW has preserved Porsche's brand autonomy. VW sees the combined group —which includes 10 distinct and separate brands along with the Porsche Holding auto trading business currently held by the Porsche and Piech families —as a way to become an industry leader in terms of global market presence innovation purchasing and manufacturing.

Though sales are recovering in North America and Europe the company hopes to continue expanding in Brazil India and Russia —where sales continue to be strong —to offset difficult conditions in North America and Western Europe.

VW's environmentally-friendly orientation and focus on innovation is part of its plan to be the largest car company in the world by 2018. The goal is to increase unit sales to more than 10 million vehicles a year. As part of its quest the company will invest a reported E51.6 billion ($70.6 billion) between 2011 and 2015 to update its manufacturing plants and equipment.

Mergers and Acquisitions

VW has added companies that allow it to expand internationally as well as to develop its products. In early 2010 VW completed a $2.5 billion deal for a 20% stake in Suzuki Motor Corp.

The deal gave VW greater access to markets in India and Southeast Asia where Suzuki is established. Suzuki gained from VW's presence in China which is experiencing sustained growth. VW particularly likes Suzuki's savvy in manufacturing cars inexpensively and profitably and plans to learn from the process.

HISTORY

Since the early 1920s auto engineer Ferdinand Porsche (whose son later founded the Porsche car company) had wanted to make a small car for the masses. He found no backers until he met Adolf Hitler in 1934. Hitler formed the Gesellschaft zur Vorbereitung des deutschen Volkswagen (Company for the Development of the German People's Car) in 1937 and built a factory in Wolfsburg Germany. No cars were delivered during WWII as the company produced military vehicles using the slave labor of Jews and Russian prisoners of war.

Following WWII British occupation forces oversaw the rebuilding of the bomb-damaged plant and initial production of the odd-looking 'people's car' (1945). The British appointed Heinz Nordhoff to manage Volkswagen (1948) and then turned the company over to the German government (1949).

In the 1950s VW launched the Microbus and built foreign plants. Although US sales began slowly by the end of the decade acceptance of the little car had increased. Advertising that coined the name "Beetle" helped carve VW's niche in the US.

VW sold stock to the German public in 1960. In 1966 it purchased Auto Union (AUDI) from Daimler-Benz. The Beetle became a counterculture symbol in the 1960s and US sales took off. By the time of Nordhoff's death in 1968 the Beetle had become the best-selling car in history.

In the 1970s the Beetle was discontinued in every country except Mexico. VW lost heavily during the model-changeover period.

VW agreed to several deals in the 1980s including a car venture in China (1984) the purchase of 75% of SEAT (1986; it bought the rest in 1990) and the merger of its suddenly faltering Brazilian unit with Ford's ailing Argentine operations to form Autolatina (1987). In 1990 the company began building China's largest auto plant and acquired a 70% stake in Czech auto company Skoda. After suffering a loss in excess of $1 billion the company put Ferdinand Piech in the driver's seat in 1993. Under his leadership the company cut costs and boosted sales by resuscitating the SEAT and Skoda brands and launching a bigger more luxurious Passat sedan in 1997.

VW acquired Rolls-Royce Motor Cars Vickers' Cosworth auto engines subsidiary Italian sportscar maker Bugatti and Italy's Automobili Lamborghini —all in 1998. Although less luxurious than VW's other pursuits the New Beetle helped boost US sales that year. Also in 1998 VW established a $12 million fund to compensate the surviving 2000 concentration-camp inmates forced to work as slave labor during WWII. However the company was hit with a class-action lawsuit filed on behalf of Holocaust survivors anyway.

In 1999 Piech announced an end to VW's acquisition binge saying that growth would be driven from within; the company announced it would pour more than $31 billion into modernizing its factories through 2004. VW hoped to tap the market in China after getting approval in 1999 to sell a newly developed minicar there. That year it announced plans to invest $1 billion in its Mexico plant over the next five years.

VW expanded into heavy commercial vehicles in 2000 by purchasing a 34% stake in Swedish truck maker Scania (from holding company Investor). That year it also bought the 30% of Skoda that it didn't already own. Anticipating China's entry into the World Trade Organization VW announced in 2001 that it would invest $1.7 billion in China and the Asia/Pacific region over the next five years. Later in the year —and half a world away —12500 workers at the company's Mexico plant went on strike for 19 days over a pay dispute.

In April 2002 former BMW head Bernd Pischetsrieder succeeded Piech as CEO. In July 2003 the final classic Beetle rolled off the VW assembly line in Mexico concluding a 70-year run of constant production. That year BMW took control of the Rolls-Royce brand from Volkswagen.

After a pretty terrible 2005 VW took steps to turn things around. The company sold its car rental company Europcar to European investment firm Eurazeo in early 2006 and it reorganized its Financial Services division of which Europcar had been a part.

As 2006 wound to a close then VW boss Bernd Pischetsrieder stepped down and was replaced by AUDI chief Martin Winterkorn. The management shake-up was attributed to an internal power struggle between Pischetsrieder and supervisory board chairman Ferdinand Piech a grandson of Porsche founder Ferdinand Porsche. Despite the internal struggle total sales for 2006 had increased by nearly 12% and operating profit jumped by a whopping 51%.

VW acquired a stake in Porsche just shy of 50% for about E3.9 billion (about $5.79 billion) in late 2009. It was the first step in combining the two car companies. That same year VW sold VW Truck & Bus to MAN for nearly E1.2 billion in cash.

In mid-2010 VW acquired a stake in excess of 90% in Italdesign-Giugiaro (IDG) an automobile design and engineering company based in Turin Italy. IDG was the design force behind the Golf I Passat Scirocco and the Audi 80.

Also in 2010 VW completed a $2.5 billion deal for a 20% stake in Suzuki Motor Corp. Domestically in 2010 VW acquired Raffay's 10-car dealer network with almost 80 offices and integrated it into its sales network.

EXECUTIVES

Chairman Supervisory Board, Ferdinand K. Piech, age 77

Member Management Board Group Production, Michael Macht, age 53

Member Management Board Procurement, Francisco Javier Garcia Sanz, age 57

Chairman Management Board; Manager R&D; Chairman Audi; Chairman Management Board Porsche Automobil Holdings, Martin Winterkorn, age 67

Member Management Board China, Jochem Heizmann, age 63

Member Management Board; Chairman Board of Management Audi AG, Rupert Stadler, age 51

Member Management Board Finance and Controlling; CFO Porsche Automobil, Hans D. Potsch, age 63

Member Management Board Human Resources and Organization, Horst G. Neumann, age 65

Member Management Board Sales and Marketing, Christian Klingler, age 46

Member Management Board Group Commercial Vehicles, Leif Ostling

Member Supervisory Board, Michael Frenzel, age 67

Deputy Chairman Supervisory Board, Berthold Huber, age 64

Member Supervisory Board, Hans Michel Piech, age 71

Member Supervisory Board, Wolfgang Porsche

Member Supervisory Board, Hartmut Meine

Member Supervisory Board, Peter Mosch, age 43

Member Supervisory Board, Bernd Osterloh, age 58

Member Supervisory Board, Jurgen Stumpf, age 60

Member Supervisory Board, Bernd Wehlauer, age 60

Member Supervisory Board, Babette Frohlich, age 49

Member Supervisory Board, Peter Jacobs, age 58

Member Supervisory Board, Wolfgang Ritmeier, age 67

Member Supervisory Board, Thomas Zwiebler

Member Supervisory Board, Jorg Bode

Member Supervisory Board, Hussain Ali Al-Abdulla

Member of the Supervisory Board, Annika Falkengren

Member of the Supervisory Board; Employee Representative, Babette Froehlich

Member of the Supervisory Board, David McAllister

Member of the Supervisory Board, Hans Piech

Member of the Supervisory Board, Jassim Kuwari

Member of the Supervisory Board, Ursula Piech

Auditors: PricewaterhouseCoopersAGWirtschaftsprufungsgesellschaft

LOCATIONS

HQ: Volkswagen A.G. (Germany, Fed. Rep.)
Brieffach 1848-2, Wolfsburg D-38436
Phone: (49) 5361 9 0 **Fax:** (49) 5361 928282
Web: www.volkswagen.com

Sales

	% of total
Europe	80
Asia/Pacific	11
Africa	2
Total	**100**

PRODUCTS/OPERATIONS

Selected Brands

Audi
Bentley
Bugatti
Lamborghini
Scania
SEAT
Skoda
Volkswagen
Volkswagen Commercial Vehicles

Selected Makes and Models

AUDI
A1
A3
A3 Cabriolet
A3 Sportback
A4
A4 allroad quattro
A4 Avant
A5 Cabriolet
A5 Coupe
A5 Sportback
A6
A6 allroad quattro
A6 Avant
A7 Sportback
A8
A8L
A8L W12
Q5
Q7
Q7 V12 TDI
R8
R8 Spyder
R8 Spyder FSI quattro
RS5 Coupe
RS6
S3
S3 Sportback
S4
S4 Avant
S5 Cabriolet
S5 Coupe
S5 Sportback
TT Coupe
TT Roadster
TT RS Coupe
TT RS Roadster
TTS Coupe
TTS Roadster
Bentley
Continental Flying Spur
Continental Flying Spur Speed
Continental GT
Continental GTC
Continental GTC Speed
Continental SuperSports
Continental SuperSports Convertible
Mulsanne
Bugatti
Veyron
Veyron Grand Sport
Veyron Super Sport
Lamborghini
Gallardo LP
Gallardo LP Spyder
Gallardo LP Spyder Performante
Gallardo LP Superleggera
Murcielago LP Coupe
Murcielago LP Roadster
Scania
Buses
Engines
Trucks
SEAT
Alhambra
Alhambra ECOMOTIVE
Altea
Altea ECOMOTIVE
Altea Freetrack
Altea XL
Altea XL ECOMOTIVE
Cordoba
Exeo
Exeo ST
Ibiza
Ibiza Cupra
Ibiza ECOMOTIVE
Ibiza FR
Ibiza SC
Ibiza SC Bocanegra
Ibiza ST
Leon
Leon Cupra
Leon ECOMOTIVE
Leon FR
Skoda
Fabia
Fabia Combi
Fabia Combi GreenLine
Fabia Combi RS
Fabia Combi Scout
Fabia GreenLine
Fabia RS
Fabia Scout
Octavia
Octavia Combi
Octavia Combi GreenLine
Octavia Combi GreenLine
Octavia Combi LPG
Octavia GreenLine
Octavia LPG
Octavia RS
Octavia Scout
Octavia Tour
Octavia Tour Combi
Roomster
Roomster GreenLine
Roomster Scout
Praktik
Superb
Superb Combi
Superb Combi GreenLine
Superb GreenLine
Yeti
Yeti GreenLine
Volkswagen Commercial Vehicles
Caddy
California
Caravelle
Crafter
Multivan
Saveiro
Transporter shuttle
Volkswagen Passenger Vehicles
CrossPolo
CrossTouran
Eos
Fox
Golf
Golf Estate
New Beetle
New Beetle Cabriolet
Jetta
Passat
Phaeton
Polo
Routan
Scirocco
Sharan
Tiguan
Touareg
Touran
Voyage

COMPETITORS

BMW	Mazda
Chrysler	Nissan
Daimler	Peugeot
Ford Motor	Renault
Fuji Heavy Industries	Saab Automobile
General Motors	Suzuki Motor
Honda	Toyota
Isuzu	

HISTORICAL FINANCIALS

Company Type: Public

Income Statement   FYE: December 31

	REVENUE ($ mil.)	NET INCOME ($ mil.)	NET PROFIT MARGIN	EMPLOYEES
12/13	271,226	12,481	4.6%	572,800
12/12	253,956	28,624	11.3%	549,763
12/11	206,094	19,930	9.7%	501,956
12/10	169,805	9,147	5.4%	399,381
12/09	151,529	1,382	0.9%	368,500
Annual Growth	15.7%	73.3%	—	11.7%

2013 Year-End Financials

Debt ratio: 51.5%
Return on equity: 10.9%
Cash ($ mil.): 31,909
Current ratio: 1.03
Long-term debt ($ mil.): 84,692

No. of shares (mil.): 295
Dividends
Yield: 1.2%
Payout: 4.6%
Market value ($ mil.): 16,141

	STOCK PRICE ($) FY Close	P/E High/Low		PER SHARE ($) Earnings	Dividends	Book Value
12/13	54.70	6	3	25.65	0.67	409.31
12/12	43.47	2	1	61.18	0.58	346.23
12/11	26.69	2	1	42.81	0.93	252.20
12/10	28.55	4	2	20.30	0.53	208.56
12/09	22.35	67	19	3.43	0.38	172.28
Annual Growth	25.1%	—	—	65.4%	15.5%	24.2%

Volvo AB

Despite the fact that the name "Volvo" still conjures up visions of soccer moms Volvo should really only inspire images of burly truck drivers. The company is one of the world's largest makers of trucks buses and construction equipment. In North America the company makes big rigs through its Volvo Trucks North America unit; Volvo also owns controlling interests in the well-known Mack Trucks brand in North America and Renault Trucks in Europe. Other products include marine (Volvo Penta) and industrial engines. Volvo's most widely known business –auto making –belongs to Geely Automobile of China.

Geographic Reach

Volvo's main business segments (Trucks Construction Equipment Buses Financial Services [financing and insurance] and Penta) sell their products and services in 190 markets worldwide. Overall it has production facilities in nearly 20 countries.

Financial Analysis

As the global economy starts to recover then retreats again the company saw slight decreases in revenue across the board. Operating income dipped 34% but was helped by strong results in the consumer finance division. Volvo blamed decreased sales and restructuring charges for the drop.

Strategy

Part of the company's response to continued economic uncertainty is building smaller less expensive trucks particularly under its Renault label. It positions them for developing markets but lower price appeals to all. Volvo is also working to meet strict EU environmental requirements for trucks buses construction equipment and its Penta vehicles.

Speaking of developing markets Volvo positioned itself to take part in the world's largest economy when in 2013 it signed an agreement with China's Dongfeng Motor Group to produce heavy-duty trucks. The Swedish company will take a 45% stake in Dongfeng Commercial Vehicles a subsidiary of the Chinese firm that will make big trucks for China and other countries.

As it continues to strengthen its core truck construction equipment and other products in its target markets Volvo has been looking into divesting non-core businesses. In late 2012 it sold its Volvo Aero business to GKN for about SEK 6.9 billion (about $1 billion); Volvo already sold Aero's US subsidiary Volvo Aero Services in 2010. Aero accounted for about 3% of the company's total revenue in 2010.

Ownership

Nordic holding company owns about 6% of Volvo.

HISTORY

Swedish ball bearing maker SKF formed Volvo (Latin for "I roll") as a subsidiary in 1915. Volvo began building cars in 1926 trucks in 1928 and bus chassis in 1932 in Gothenburg. Sweden's winters and icy roads made the company keenly attentive to engineering and safety. Volvo bought an engine maker in 1931. In 1935 Volvo became an independent company led by Assar Gabrielsson and Gustaf Larson.

Sweden's neutrality during WWII allowed Volvo to grow and move into component manufacturing and tractor production. Output in 1949 exceeded 100000 units 80% of which were sold in Sweden. The purchase of Bolinder-Munktell (farm machinery diesel engines; Sweden; 1950) enhanced

Volvo's position in the Swedish tractor market. Volvo introduced turbocharged diesel truck engines and windshield defrosters and washers in the 1950s. By 1956 car production had outstripped truck and bus output.

Aware that it was too small to compete in global markets Volvo diversified (energy industrial products food finance and trading). Volvo increased its market share by purchasing several trucking and construction equipment companies that included White Motors' truck unit (US 1981) and Leyland Bus (UK 1986). In the 1980s Volvo acquired drug and biotechnology concern Pharmacia (now Pfizer) and Custos (investments Sweden). The company consolidated its food and drug units with state-controlled holding company Procordia in 1990.

At that time however Volvo was facing stagnant sales. It embarked on the largest industrial undertaking in Swedish history spending more than $2 billion to modernize plants and develop a series of high-performance family sedans which it introduced in 1991. Still high costs and persistent recession in Europe kept the company in the red during the early 1990s.

Adding to its troubles there was public outcry against a planned merger with French automaker Renault. The plan was abandoned in 1993 and the company sold its drug and consumer product interests (which had landed back in Volvo's lap when the government divested Procordia in 1993). These sales brought Volvo back into the black.

In 1997 Volvo sold its 11% stake in Renault left over from the abandoned merger. The next year the company strengthened its line of excavators and its Far Eastern presence by buying Samsung Heavy Industries' construction equipment unit. Volvo also bought Mexico's bus maker Mexicana de Autobuses and GM's share in Volvo GM Heavy Truck (now Volvo Trucks North America).

Anticipating a lower demand for cars Volvo closed an assembly plant in Canada in 1998 and in 1999 Volvo acquired a 13% stake (later upped to 25%) in rival truck maker Scania. To pay for its new focus on making heavy trucks Volvo sold its auto brand and manufacturing operations in Sweden Belgium and the Netherlands to Ford Motor Company for $6.45 billion in 1999. Volvo then agreed to take a 20% stake in the truck and construction equipment operations of Japan's Mitsubishi Motors.

In 2000 Volvo boosted its stake in Scania to 46% but its hope of acquiring a majority interest died when the EU rejected the $7.53 billion deal. Volvo then turned to France's Renault and bought the company's Mack truck unit in exchange for a 15% stake in Volvo.

Volvo's Renault Trucks subsidiary inked a technology transfer deal in 2002 with Chinese truckmaker Dongfeng Motors. The agreement cleared the road for Dongfeng to equip its heavy- and medium-duty trucks with Renault engines. In 2003 Volvo became the first Western truck manufacturer to produce vehicles under its own name in Russia. The following year Volvo opened a new truck factory in China with its partner China National Heavy Truck Corporation. Also in 2004 Volvo Construction Equipment (Volvo CE) sold its line of compact motor graders to Champion LLC a company headed up by Gary Abernathy a former manager at Volvo CE. Volvo acquired the remaining 50% of bus manufacturer Prevost Car from Henlys Group in late 2004.

To boost its presence in Asia in early 2006 Volvo acquired a 13% stake in Nissan Diesel Motor (now named UD Trucks Corporation) for a reported $195 million. Later that year Volvo bought another 6% of Nissan Diesel Motor from Nissan Motor with the intention of acquiring the remaining outstanding shares (which it did in 2007). Also

in 2006 the company negotiated with Nissan and the Chinese government to purchase Nissan's 50% stake in Dongfeng Motor Co. Ltd. –China's largest maker of commercial trucks.

In response to new emissions standards that went into effect in late 2006 in Europe and the beginning of 2007 in North America Volvo has been sprucing up the operations of its Mack and Renault brands. The move is in step with Volvo's other truck operations which also have been revamped to comply with the new standards.

Asia has also been the focus of group's development efforts. The 2007 acquisitions of Japanese truck manufacturer Nissan Diesel and Chinese wheel loader maker Lingong gave Volvo increased manufacturing capacity in the region. Part of its Asian expansion included buying for $1.3 billion. Though its manufacturing facilities are based in the US the target of the acquisition was the heavy compactors pavers and asphalt millers demanded by the growing number of infrastructure projects in China and India.

Scaling back on other operations the company sold its Volvo Material Handling Equipment business in mid-2008 to Linamar's Skyjack division. Volvo's Material Handling unit which had been part of Volvo's acquisition of Ingersoll Rand's road construction equipment business was considered to be peripheral to Volvo's operations.

Beginning in fall 2008 the company responded to the difficult business environment by scaling back production to reduce costs and match demand. Volvo also edged up new product pricing to offset lower sales volumes. Its simultaneous effort to slash inventories resulted in a robust rise cash flow in 2009 that has helped to sustain operations. A 20% reduction in headcount in 2008 through 2009 accompanied the resizing. Nonetheless Volvo suffered more than a SEK 14 million ($2 billion) loss in 2009.

EXECUTIVES

President Volvo Trucks, Staffan Jufors, age 62
Chairman, Louis Schweitzer, age 72
EVP Corporate Legal and Compliance and General Counsel, Eva Persson, age 61
SVP, Stefan Johnsson, age 55
Chairman, Carl-Henric Svanberg
EVP Corporate Strategy, Karin Falk
Chief Technology Officer; EVP Group Trucks Technology, Torbjorn Holmstrom
EVP Group Trucks Sales and Marketing EMEA, Peter Karlsten, age 57
EVP Trucks Sales & Marketing Americas, Dennis R. (Denny) Slagle, age 61
Head Investor Relations, Christer Johansson
Director Investor Relations, Patrik Stenberg
VP Investor Relations North America, John Hartwell
EVP Corporate Communications, M?rten Wikforss
EVP Business Areas, H?kan Karlsson, age 53
President Renault Trucks, Stefano Chmielewski, age 61
President CEO and Director, Olof Persson, age 49
President UD Trucks, Satoru Takeuchi, age 67
President Volvo Trucks Europe, Claes Nilsson
EVP Public and Environmental Affairs, Jan-Eric Sundgren, age 63
EVP Volvo Construction Equipment, Patrick (Pat) Olney
SVP Corporate Communications Volvo Trucks Global, Tommy Kohle
EVP Group Trucks Operations, Mikael Bratt, age 46
President Aero, Staffan Zackrisson, age 61
Director Investor Relations, Anders Christensson
CFO and EVP Finance and Control, Anders Osberg
President Volvo Business Services, Elisabeth Rocke, age 54
President Volvo Penta of the Americas, Clint Moore

EVP Corporate Human Resources, Kerstin Renard, age 54
CIO; EVP Corporate Process and IT, Magnus Carlander, age 60
EVP Group Truck Sales and Marketing and JVs APAC, Joachim Rosenberg
EVP Financial Services, Martin Weissburg
EVP Legal and Compliance; General Counsel, Sofia Frandberg
EVP Public and Environmental Affairs, Niklas Gustavsson
Director, Lars Westerberg, age 66
Director, Peter I. Bijur, age 72
Director, Jean-Baptiste Duzan, age 68
Director, Berth Thulin, age 63
Director, Ravi Venkatesan, age 52
Director, Anders Nyren, age 59
Director, Ying Yeh, age 66
President CEO and Director, Olof Persson, age 49
Director, Hanne de Mora, age 54
Director, Lars Ask, age 54
Director, Peteris Lauberts, age 67
Director, Mikael Sallstrom, age 54
Auditors: PricewaterhouseCoopersAB

LOCATIONS

HQ: Volvo AB
Volvo Bergegaards v., Goeteborg SE-405 08
Phone: (46) 31 66 00 00   **Fax:** (46) 31 53 72 96
Web: www.volvogroup.com

Sales

	% of total
Western	30
Asia	23
North	23
South	10
Eastern	7
Other	7
Total	**100**

PRODUCTS/OPERATIONS

Sales

	% of total
Trucks	64
Construction	21
Buses	7
Financial	3
Volvo	3
Volvo	2
Total	**100**

Selected Products & Brand Names

Buses
  Chassis
  City & intercity buses
  Coaches
Construction equipment
  Articulated haulers
  Asphalt milling machines
  Backhoe loaders
  Compaction equipment
  Crawler excavators
  Motor graders
  Pavers
  Skid steer loaders
  Wheel loaders
  Wheeled excavators
Financial services
  Customer & dealer financing
Trucks
  Mack
  Renault
  UD Trucks
  VE Commercial Vehicles (46% India)
  Volvo
Volvo Penta
  Industrial engines & drive systems (gensets & materials handling)
  Marine engines & drive systems (leisure & commercial boats)

COMPETITORS

Cummins Westport	Mitsubishi Motors
Daimler	Navistar
Daimler Trucks North America	Navistar International
	Nissan
Deere	Oshkosh Truck
Fiat	PACCAR
Fiat Industrial	Penske
Fuji Heavy Industries	Rolls-Royce
General Motors	Scania
Hino Motors	Suzuki Motor
Honda	Terex
Isuzu	Toyota
MAN	

HISTORICAL FINANCIALS

Company Type: Public

Income Statement

FYE: December 31

	REVENUE ($ mil.)	NET INCOME ($ mil.)	NET PROFIT MARGIN	EMPLOYEES
12/13	42,522	558	1.3%	95,533
12/12	46,610	1,694	3.6%	98,717
12/11	45,000	2,573	5.7%	98,162
12/10	39,481	1,620	4.1%	90,409
12/09	30,659	(2,066)	—	90,208
Annual Growth	**8.5%**	**—**		**1.4%**

2013 Year-End Financials

Debt ratio: 6.1%	No. of shares (mil.): 2,028
Return on equity: 4.4%	Dividends
Cash ($ mil.): 4,206	Yield: 3.5%
Current ratio: 1.17	Payout: 4.1%
Long-term debt ($ mil.): 13,016	Market value ($ mil.): 26,643

	STOCK PRICE ($) FY Close	P/E High/Low		PER SHARE ($) Earnings	Dividends	Book Value
12/13	13.14	0	0	0.27	0.47	5.85
12/12	13.67	0	0	0.84	0.44	6.48
12/11	10.84	0	0	1.27	0.01	6.05
12/10	17.61	0	0	0.80	0.00	5.38
12/09	8.46	—	—	(1.02)	0.24	4.60
Annual Growth	**11.6%**	**—**	**—**	**—**	**18.2%**	**6.2%**

Wal-Mart de Mexico S.A.B. de C.V.

Wal-Mart de Mexico y CentroAmerica is the numero uno retailer in Mexico Costa Rica El Salvador Guatemala Honduras and Nicaragua with nearly 2900 stores. These include Bodega food and general merchandise stores and Superama supermarkets Suburbia apparel shops as well as half a dozen Ragazzi Italian restaurants. It also runs Wal-Mart Supercenters SAM'S CLUB and ClubCo warehouse stores and Banco Wal-Mart. Its stores are located in 555 cities throughout the region. Wal-Mart Stores formed a joint venture with Mexico's Cifra in 1991 and in 2000 acquired it and renamed the business Wal-Mart de Mexico. Wal-Mex then added Wal-Mart's operations in Central America and the business became Wal-Mart de Mexico y CentroAmerica.

Financial Performance
Wal-Mart de Mexico y CentroAmerica reported 432.9 billion pesos ($32.8 billion) in sales for the the 12 months ended June 2014.

Strategy

Walmex discontinued its Vips restaurant business in early 2014 with an agreement to sell the 360 restaurants to Alsea S.A.B. de C.V. for about $625 million. The Vips sale is subject to approval by Mexican regulatory authorities and is expected to close in 2014. The move leaves Walmex with just six Italian eateries under the Ragazzi name.

Banco Wal-Mart (launched in 2007) operates more than 260 branches located inside Bodega Aurrera Wal-Mart and SAM'S CLUB stores in some 30 cities and cater to a clientele that for the most part is new to banking. The bank has been losing money for its parent though. To cut its losses in late 2014 Wal-Mart de Mexico y CentroAmerica agreed to sell the banking unit to a group of buyers that includes Grupo Financiero Inbursa the financial services operations of billionaire Carlos Slim Helu. The deal is valued at MXN 3.6 billion ($247 million).

HISTORY

Spanish-born Jeronimo Arango Arias studied art and literature at several American universities without graduating. In his twenties he wandered around Spain Mexico and the US. He struck upon an idea after seeing a crowd waiting in line at the E. J. Korvette discount department store in New York City. Jeronimo called his two brothers Placido and Manuel and convinced them to join him in a new business venture.

Borrowing about $250000 from their father a Spanish immigrant to Mexico successful in textiles the three brothers opened their first Aurrera Bolivar discount store in downtown Mexico City in 1958. Offering goods and clothing well below manufacturers' list prices the store was an immediate hit with consumers but encountered hostility from competing Mexico City retailers. When local retailers threatened to boycott the Arangos' suppliers the company turned to suppliers in Guadalajara and Monterrey.

In 1965 the Arango brothers formed a joint venture with Jewel Cos. of Chicago to open new Aurrera stores. Jewel bought a 49% interest in the business a year later. Placido and Manuel left the business with their portion of the money but Jeronimo stayed as head of the company taking it public in 1976.

By 1981 almost a third of Jewel's earnings came from its operations in Mexico. But the next year the peso crashed obliterating its earnings there. American Stores took over Jewel in 1984 and Jeronimo bought back Jewel's stake in the company (which was renamed Cifra that year).

With the Mexican economy staggering from the peso devaluation weak oil markets and a huge debt crisis Jeronimo was taking a major risk. Although no new stores were opened none were closed. Employees were expected to work longer and those who left were not replaced. With Mexico's middle class hit hard Jeronimo emphasized the Bodega Aurrera no-frills warehouses which discounted all kinds of nonperishable merchandise from canned chili to VCRs.

Cifra and Wal-Mart Stores formed a joint venture in 1991 to open Club Aurrera membership clubs similar to Sam's Club outlets. The two companies expanded the venture the next year to include the development of Sam's Club and Wal-Mart Supercenters in Mexico.

Remodeling began on Cifra's stores in 1992. The work was completed two years later and the company was poised to take advantage of Mexico's much-improved economy.

However devaluation struck again late in 1994. The resulting contraction of credit and rise in prices hit Mexican consumers hard and Cifra's 1995 sales declined 15%. But again it kept on as many employees as possible transferring them to new stores that had been in development. Despite the hard times Cifra opened 27 new stores (including 15 restaurants). The company was able to withstand the difficulties in part because it stayed debt-free.

Wal-Mart consolidated its joint venture into Cifra in 1997 in exchange for about 34% of that company; Wal-Mart later raised its stake to 51%. The cost-conscious companies combined the joint venture stores and Cifra's separate stores under one umbrella. Cifra opened 11 stores and eight restaurants that year.

Cifra opened nine stores and 17 restaurants in 1998; the next year it opened about 20 stores and nearly 25 restaurants. In early 2000 Cifra was renamed Wal-Mart de Mexico. Shortly thereafter Wal-Mart upped its stake in Wal-Mart de Mexico to about 61%.

In 2001 all the Aurrera stores were converted to either Wal-Mart Supercenters or Bodega stores. Eduardo Castro-Wright was promoted in 2002 from COO to CEO of Wal-Mart de Mexico succeeding Cesareo Fernandez who retained the chairman's title. The retailer opened 50 new outlets that year.

In March 2003 Mexico's Federal Competition Commission closed an investigation of Wal-Mex's purchasing practices citing a lack of evidence that the retailer violated competition laws. Overall that year Wal-Mex entered nine new cities in Mexico and added 46 new outlets. In 2004 Mexico's largest retailer grew bigger adding 17 restaurants 23 Aurrera stores eight SAM'S CLUBS six supercenters and four Superama stores.

In January 2005 Fernandez stepped down as chairman and was succeeded by Ernesto Vega. A month later Castro-Wright left Wal-Mex to become EVP and COO of the Wal-Mart Stores Division in the US. He was succeeded by Eduardo Solorzano formerly COO of Wal-Mex. Also that year Wal-Mex acquired the Mexican assets of French retailer Carrefour. Carrefour which operated 29 hypermarkets in Mexico restructured its operations and left the Mexican market.

In November 2006 Wal-Mex received a license from Mexico's Finance Ministry to organize and operate a bank there. Overall in 2006 the retailer opened 120 new locations including stores in Monterrey the country's most affluent city and throughout northern Mexico where its Texas rival H. E. Butt Grocery is well established. In November 2007 Wal-Mart Bank began operations with 16 branches in five Mexican states.

Wal-Mex inked a deal with Tobacco One in August 2008 to distribute the tobacco firm's Rojo cigarette line in about 140 supercenters and some 60 Superarma stores throughout Mexico.

In December 2009 Wal-Mex announced the acquisition of Walmart's operations in Central America from Walmart Stores and two minority partners. The transaction was completed in early 2010 and Wal-Mex became Walmart Mexico and Central America. In January 2010 Eduardo Solorzano Morales resigned as CEO of the company but became chairman. He was succeeded by Scot Rank Crawford.

LOCATIONS

HQ: Wal-Mart de Mexico S.A.B. de C.V.
Blvd. Manuel Avila Camacho # 647, Delegacion Miguel Hidalgo, Mexico, Distrito Federal 11220
Phone: (52) 55 5283 0100   **Fax:** (52) 55 5328 3557
Web: www.walmartmexico.com.mx

2010 Stores

	No.
Mexico	1,730
Central	549
Total	**2,279**

PRODUCTS/OPERATIONS

Sales

	% of total
Bodegas & discount	38
Hypermarkets	27
Warehouse	23
Supermarkets	7
Apparel	3
Restaurants	2
Total	**100**

2010 Stores

	% of total
Bodegas & discount	1,300
Hypermarkets	286
Warehouse	144
Supermarkets	91
Apparel	92
Restaurants	366
Total	**2,279**

Selected Operations

Bodegas & discount stores
  Bodega Aurrera
  Dispensa Familiar
  MAXI Bodega
  PALI
Hypermarkets
  Hiper Paiz
  Hiper Mas
  Walmart
Warehouse clubs
  Sam's Club
  ClubCo
Supermarkets
  La Union
  Mas por Menos
  Paiz
  Superama
Apparel Stores
  Suburbia
Restaurants
  El Porton
  VIPS

HISTORICAL FINANCIALS

Company Type: Public

Income Statement

FYE: December 31

	REVENUE ($ mil.)	NET INCOME ($ mil.)	NET PROFIT MARGIN	EMPLOYEES
12/13	32,467	1,734	5.3%	226,289
12/12	32,172	1,791	5.6%	248,246
12/11	27,120	1,580	5.8%	238,128
12/10	27,091	1,577	5.8%	219,767
12/09	20,658	1,283	6.2%	176,463
Annual Growth	**12.0%**	**7.8%**	**—**	**6.4%**

2013 Year-End Financials

Debt ratio: 1.5%
Return on equity: 16.0%
Cash ($ mil.): 1,613
Current ratio: 1.26
Long-term debt ($ mil.): —

No. of shares (mil.): —
Dividends
Yield: 2.8%
Payout: 4.7%
Market value ($ mil.): —

	STOCK PRICE ($) FY Close	P/E High/Low		PER SHARE ($) Earnings	Dividends	Book Value
12/13	26.12	0	0	0.10	0.75	0.62
12/12	32.78	0	0	0.10	0.40	0.61
12/11	27.39	0	0	0.09	0.00	0.52
12/10	28.58	—	—	0.09	0.57	0.55
12/09	44.95	—	—	0.08	0.44	0.38
Annual Growth	**(12.7%)**	**—**	**—**	**6.5%**	**14.3%**	**13.0%**

Wesfarmers Ltd.

Wesfarmers got its start as a farmers' cooperative in Western Australia a century ago. Today it's one of the country's most diverse companies and largest retailers following its acquisition of food and liquor retailer Coles Group. Wesfarmers has interests in far-ranging businesses including general merchandise (Kmart and Target) home-improvement (Bunnings) and office products retailing; coal mining; gas processing and distribution; chemical and fertilizer production; building materials sales; distribution of maintenance repair and operating products and industrial and safety products; and insurance. True to its heritage Wesfarmers still provides agricultural merchandise and services.

Geographic Reach

Perth-based Wesfarmers rings up 98% of its sales in Australia. New Zealand accounts for the rest. The company also has operations in Bangladesh and the UK.

Operations

The Coles division (formed in 2007) is Wesfarmers' largest business (accounting for 60% of the group's sales and 41% of its EBIT). It is one of Australia's leading food liquor and convenience retailers with a national presence. Wesfarmers has more than 2200 outlets under the Coles and BiLO supermarkets banners First Choice Liquor Liquorland and Vintage Cellars names and Coles Express banner. Other retail operations include Kmart and Target stores home improvement and office supplies stores. Wesfarmers is also engaged in coal production and export insurance (commercial and consumer) chemicals energy and fertilizers as well as industrial and safety products.

Financial Performance

Since buying Australian supermarket and liquor store operator Coles (in 2007) Wesfarmers has seen its sales increase more than 500%. In fiscal 2013 (ended June) Wesfarmers' sales grew 3% (before the impact of currency translation) versus the prior year. Operating income rose 3% over the same period. Driving the annual sales increase was improved performance of Coles and Wesfarmers' other retail operations (with the exception of Target) as well as the insurance and chemicals energy and fertilizers divisions. The company's Resources and Industrial and Safety businesses posted declines.

Strategy

The $18-billion purchase of Cole Group was transformational for Wesfarmers. Indeed the acquisition —at the time ranked as the largest takeover in Australia's history —gave Wesfarmers the designation as the country's top retailer. A five-year turnaround focused on the Coles supermarket chain began soon after the acquisition. As part of the reorganization Coles Group sold its online pharmacy business —Pharmacy Direct —and also shed some supermarket and liquor stores in an effort to improve its overall store network. The grocer also improved its fresh food and produce offerings and remodeled stores. While Coles has made progress and is beginning to regain market share (after years of losses) the 740-store chain continues to trail archrival Woolworths. Together Woolworths and Coles account for almost 80% of supermarket sales in Australia.

Beyond the retail arena recent acquisitions include the purchase of the New Zealand-based packaging firm Expresspak. To strengthen its position in the food service industry Wesfarmers Industrial acquired Expresspak which specializes in paper and plastic food and beverage packaging to add to its Packaging House business. As part of the deal the firm operates independently under the Expresspak name but shares its resources with Wesfarmers' subsidiary Packaging House whose offerings are largely of the industrial sort (steel strapping tape film). The acquisition put Packaging House which provides hygiene food service cleaning and chemicals and industrial packaging in a market-leading position in the food service packaging sector.

In April 2010 the company merged its Wesfarmers Chemicals & Fertilizers and Wesfarmers Energy divisions to form Wesfarmers Chemicals Energy & Fertilisers and also made other organizational and management changes in the industrial divisions. More recently Westfarmers began mulling a bid for ammonia producer Burrup Fertilisers but is meeting resistance from Australia's competition regulator. As part of its reorganization the company in late 2011 sold its Premier Coal (exploration production and processing) businesses to China-based Yanzhou Coal Mining for roughly $296 million.

A series of recent catastrophic events including the 2010 Christchurch New Zealand earthquake brushfires in Western Australia and serewe weather events have led to higher reinsurance costs and claims activity for Wesfarmers' insurance division a tiny part of its overall business.

EXECUTIVES

Executive General Manager Corporate Affairs, Alan Carpenter
Managing Director Target, Dene L. Rogers, age 52
Managing Director Coles, Ian McLeod, age 56
Chief Human Resources Officer, Ben Lawrence
Managing Director, Richard J. Barr Goyder, age 52, $431,009 total compensation
Managing Director Home Improvement and Office Supplies, John Gillam
Managing Director Kmart, Guy Russo
Finance Director, Terry Bowen
Managing Director Wesfarmers Resources, Stewart Butel
Executive General Manager Business Development, Tim Bult
Managing Director Wesfarmers Insurance, Robert Scott
Chairman, Robert (Bob) Every, age 69
Chief Executive Chemicals, Ian Hansen
Managing Director Wesfarmers Industrial and Safety, Olivier Chretien
Managing Director Wesfarmers Chemicals Energy & Fertilizers, Tom O'Leary
Group General Counsel, Paul Meadows
Managing Director, Tom OLeary
Managing Director Wesfarmers Insurance, Anthony Gianotti
Non-Executive Director, Colin B. Carter, age 71
Non-Executive Director, Charles Macek, age 67
Non-Executive Director, James Graham
Auditors: Ernst&Young

LOCATIONS

HQ: Wesfarmers Ltd.
Level 11, Wesfarmers House, 40 The Esplanade, Perth, Western Australia 6000
Phone: (61) 8 9327 4211   **Fax:** (61) 8 9327 4216
Web: www.wesfarmers.com.au

Sales

	% of total
Australia	98
New	2
Total	**100**

PRODUCTS/OPERATIONS

Sales

	% of total
Coles	60
Home improvement & office	15
Kmart	7
Target	6
Chemicals energy &	3
Industrial &	3
Insurance	3
Resources	3
Total	**100**

Selected Retail Operations

Convenience
  Coles Express
General Merchandise
  Kmart
  Target
Home Improvement
  Bunnings
  Bunnings Trade
  Bunnings Warehouse
Liquor Stores
  First Choice Liquor
  Liquorland
  Vintage Cellars
Supermarkets
  BiLo
  Coles
  Coles Online
Office Supply
  Officeworks

COMPETITORS

ALDI	Harvey Norman Holdings
Australia and New	Insurance Australia
Zealand Banking	Metcash
Caltex Australia	Woolworths Limited
Commonwealth Bank of	
Australia	

HISTORICAL FINANCIALS

Company Type: Public

Income Statement

FYE: June 30

	REVENUE ($ mil.)	NET INCOME ($ mil.)	NET PROFIT MARGIN	EMPLOYEES
06/14	56,547	2,526	4.5%	99,000
06/13	55,187	2,085	3.8%	200,000
06/12	59,148	2,165	3.7%	0
06/11	58,821	2,060	3.5%	200,000
06/10	44,176	1,333	3.0%	200,000
Annual Growth	**6.4%**	**17.3%**	**—**	**(16.1%)**

2014 Year-End Financials

Debt ratio: 11.9%
Return on equity: 10.3%
Cash ($ mil.): 1,942
Current ratio: 1.13
Long-term debt ($ mil.): 4,059
No. of shares (mil.): 1,143
Dividends
  Yield: 0.0%
  Payout: 13.7%
Market value ($ mil.): 22,505

	STOCK PRICE ($) FY Close	P/E High/Low		PER SHARE ($) Earnings	Dividends	Book Value
06/14	19.69	8	6	2.20	0.30	21.36
06/13	18.16	11	7	1.80	0.00	20.74
06/12	15.30	10	7	1.87	0.00	22.56
06/11	17.17	13	6	1.78	0.00	23.46
06/10	12.24	9	6	1.15	1.07	18.19
Annual Growth	**12.6%**	**—**	**—**	**17.5%**	**(27.0%)**	**4.1%**

Westdeutsche Genossenschafts-Zentralbank EG (Germany, Fed. Rep.)

WGZ BANK is one of Germany's largest banking institutions and the central bank for more than 220 Volksbanken and Raiffeisenbanken member banks in the state of North Rhine-Westphalia. Supported by branches in Dosseldorf Koblenz and Monster its banks primarily offer refinancing investment and payment transaction products and services in local markets. WGZ BANK's largest subsidiary WL BANK is a mortgage bank that engages in public-sector real estate lending. WGZ BANK also functions as a commercial bank that provides lending to small and midsized businesses. As a wholesale bank it acts as a trading partner in the currency foreign exchange and capital markets as well as in bond issuing and syndications.

Although WGZ BANK is dealing with a difficult market environment it is moving forward with plans to expand outsourcing services advisory services for overall bank management and cooperation models among member banks.

The company is owned by its member banks with about 92% of those shares pooled into WGZ Beteiligungs GmbH & Co. KG.
Auditors: Deloitte&ToucheGmbH

LOCATIONS

HQ: Westdeutsche Genossenschafts- Zentralbank EG (Germany, Fed. Rep.)
Ludwig-Erhard-Allee 20, Duesseldorf 40227
Phone: (49) 211 778 00   **Fax:** (49) 211 778 1277
Web: www.wgz-bank.de

Sales

	% of total
Germany	92
Other European	8
Total	**100**

PRODUCTS/OPERATIONS

Sales

	% of total
Other	48
Capital market	22
Member	15
Real	10
Corporate	5
Total	**100**

Selected Subsidiaries

Domestic
  WGZ Corporate Finance Beratung GmbH (investment banking advisory services)
  WGZ Immobilien + Treuhand GmbH (real estate services)
  WGZ Initiativkapital GmbH (equity business)
  WL BANK (mortgage bank)
Foreign
  WGZ BANK Ireland plc (international credit business)
  WGZ BANK Luxembourg S.A. (secondary services in foreign currency investment and financing)

COMPETITORS

BayernLB	Deutsche Bank
Commerzbank	UniCredit Bank AG
DZ BANK	WestLB

Company Type: Public

Income Statement

FYE: December 31

	ASSETS ($ mil.)	NET INCOME ($ mil.)	INCOME AS % OF ASSETS	EMPLOYEES
12/13	125,180	299	0.2%	1,268
12/12	126,640	493	0.4%	1,263
12/11	121,513	(270)	—	1,239
12/10	125,915	199	0.2%	1,192
12/09	137,780	410	0.3%	1,159
Annual Growth	(2.4%)	(7.6%)	—	2.3%

2013 Year-End Financials

Return on assets: 0.2%
Return on equity: 6.8%
Long-term debt ($ mil.): —
No. of shares (mil.): 6
Sales ($ mil): 3,652

Dividends
Yield: —
Payout: —
Market value ($ mil.): —

Weston (George) Limited

George Weston Limited fuels Canadians through those long winters. About 95% of the company's sales come from its 63%-owned Loblaw Companies Limited Canada's largest supermarket operator (with more than 1000 stores under some 20 banners including Loblaws Extra Foods T&T and Zehrs Markets) and the country's largest wholesale food distributor. The rest comes from Weston Foods with operations in Canada and the US that focus on freshly baked goods frozen dough biscuits and other bakery products. (Its Interbake Foods division is a major supplier of Girl Scout cookies in the US.) Chairman Galen Weston owns about 63% of the company which was founded by his grandfather in 1882.

Both Loblaw and Weston Foods are facing challenges resulting from changing consumer preferences concerning what to eat and where to shop. In response George Weston has been restructuring both businesses to better match changing tastes. The weak economy on both sides of the US and Canadian border have put a damper on sales. Total sales rose less than 1% in 2010 vs. 2009 and were slightly below 2008 levels. The Loblaw segment outperformed Weston Foods with sales up about 1% vs. a nearly 4% decline for Weston Foods. Loblaw's 2010 sales got a boost from the acquisition of T&T Supermarket in late 2009. (T&T is Canada's largest retailer of Asian foods.)

Looking to position itself on a more profitable path to growth George Weston purged a couple of its businesses. In early 2009 the company sold its US-based fresh baked and baked goods business Dunedin Holdings to Mexico's Grupo Bimbo for about $2.5 billion. The sale included the Arnold Brownberry Entenmann's Freihofer Stroehmann and Thomas' brand names. (The company's Interbake Foods and Maplehurst Bakeries businesses in the US were not included in the transaction.) Previously George Weston had sold its Neilson Dairy business to Saputo.

Cash from the divestitures was used to introduce new higher-margin products that customers want to eat and to fund acquisitions. To this end George Weston acquired Keystone Bakery Holdings a US provider of frozen cupcakes doughnuts and cookies for in-store bakeries and foodservice firms. The $185-million deal expanded the frozen baked goods division of its Maplehurst Bakeries unit. Aside from sweet treats George Weston is looking to shift its product mix to include more whole grains as an increased focus on healthier breads has hurt sales of white-flour-based products. In late 2010 the company acquired artisan and European-style bread manufacturer ACE Bakery for C$110 million (US$108 million). Based in Toronto ACE was made a subsidiary of Weston Foods (Canada). Its breads are distributed in Canada and the US.

Loblaw which is in the last year of a five-year restructuring plan is facing increased competition from non-traditional rivals such as Wal-Mart Canada and Costco Wholesale Canada which are claiming a growing share of the retail grocery market. In response the company is cutting prices and sprucing up its retail stores. It's also aggressively expanding its low-price Real Canadian Superstore format which numbers more than 100 stores and its No Frill chain of discount supermarkets to better compete with foreign superstore operators. In recent years Loblaw has been shuttering struggling Provigo stores.

HISTORY

A baker's apprentice George Weston began delivering bread in Toronto with a single horse in 1882. He added the Model Bakery in 1896 and began making cookies and biscuits in 1908.

Upon George's death in 1924 his son Garfield gained control of the company and took it public as George Weston Limited in 1928. Having popularized the premium English biscuit in Canada Garfield acquired bakeries in the UK to make cheap biscuits (uncommon at the time). He grouped the bakeries as a separate public company called Allied Bakeries in 1935 (it later became Associated British Foods and is still controlled by the Weston family).

Expansion-minded Garfield led the company into the US with the purchase of Associated Biscuit in 1939. By the late 1930s George Weston was making cakes breads and almost 500 kinds of candy and biscuits.

During the 1940s the company made a number of acquisitions including papermaker E.B. Eddy (1943; sold 1998 to papermaker Domtar giving it a 20% stake in Domtar) Southern Biscuit (1944) Western Grocers (1944 its first distribution company) and William Neilson (1948 chocolate and dairy products).

In 1953 it acquired a controlling interest in Loblaw Groceterias Canada's largest grocery chain. George Weston continued its acquisitions during the 1950s and 1960s adding grocer National Tea and diversifying into packaging (Somerville Industries 1957) and fisheries (British Columbia Packers 1962; Conners Bros. 1967).

By 1970 when Garfield's son Galen became president the company's holdings were in disarray. Galen brought in new managers consolidated the food distribution and sales operations under Loblaw Companies Limited and cut back on National Tea (which shrank from over 900 stores in 1972 to 82 in 1993). When Garfield died in 1978 Galen became chairman.

Ever since Galen a polo-playing chum of Prince Charles was the target of a failed kidnapping attempt by the Irish Republican Army in 1983 the family has kept a low public profile.

George Weston became the #1 chocolate maker in Canada with its purchase of Cadbury Schweppes' Canadian assets in 1987. The 1980s concluded with a five-year price war in St. Louis among its National Tea stores Kroger and a local grocer. This ultimately proved fruitless and Loblaw sold its US supermarkets in 1995 ending its US retail presence. As part of its divestiture of under-achieving subsidiaries the company sold its Neilson confectionery business back to Cadbury Schweppes in 1996 and sold its chocolate products company in 1998.

In early 1998 Loblaw set its sights on Quebec buying Montreal-based Provigo. Other George Weston acquisitions in the late 1990s included Oshawa Foods' 80-store Agora Foods franchise supermarket unit in eastern Canada and its Fieldfresh Farms dairy business the frozen-bagel business of Quaker Oats Pennsylvania-based Maier's Bakery and Bunge International's Australian meat processor Don Smallgoods. It also sold its British Columbia Packers fisheries unit.

Early in 2001 George Weston surprised analysts when it won Unilever's Bestfoods Baking Company (Entenmann's Oroweat) with a bid of $1.8 billion. The company reduced its stake in Loblaw by 2% and sold its Connors canned seafood business to fund the purchase which was completed in July 2001. To help pay down debt in early 2002 the company sold its Orowheat business in the western US to Mexican bread giant Grupo Bimbo for $610 million.

In 2003 Weston's food distribution business introduced about 1500 private label products. It sold its fisheries operations in Chile at a loss in 2004 for about $20 million. That September the company purchased Quebec-based Boulangerie Gadoua Ltee a family-owned baking business.

In 2005 the company sold its Heritage Salmon subsidiary thus exiting the unprofitable fisheries business entirely. The company also restructured its US biscuit operations and opened a new fresh bakery plant in Orlando Florida in 2005 as part of its push to increase its business in the southeastern US. A new bakery in the midwestern US began production of bread and English muffins in late 2006.

In early 2007 Weston's Loblaw subsidiary announced it was writing down its operations in Quebec to the tune of $768 million tied to its struggling Provigo grocery stores.

In December 2008 the company sold the Neilson dairy division of Weston Foods Canada to Saputo for some C$465 million in cash (about $373 million). It will use the money to pay down debt. In January 2009 it completed the sale of its fresh bread and baked goods business in the US. Later in the year Loblaw acquired T&T Supermarket Canada's largest retailer of Asian food.

In September 2010 George Weston through its Maplehurst Bakeries subsidiary acquired Keystone Bakery Holdings for approximately $185 million. Keystone is comprised of three operating companies: Freed's Bakery of Manchester New Hampshire a leading supplier of frozen thaw and sell iced cupcakes; Granny's Kitchens of Frankfort New York a leading supplier of both frozen pre-fried and frozen thaw and sell donuts; and Heartland Baking of DuQuoin Illinois a specialty supplier of frozen thaw and sell cookies. In November Weston Foods acquired artisan and European-style bread manufacturer ACE Bakery for C$110 million (US$108 million). Based in Toronto ACE was made a subsidiary of Weston Foods (Canada). Its breads are distributed in Canada and the US.

Chairman and president Galen Weston stepped down as the company's president in late 2011 but remained chairman.

EXECUTIVES

SVP Taxation, J. Bradley Holland, age 50
Executive Vice President Corporate Development, Robert G. (Bob) Vaux, age 66
SVP Financial Control and Investor Relations, Geoffrey H. (Geoff) Wilson, age 58

Chairman, W. Galen Weston, age 73, $1,018,300 total compensation
SVP General Counsel Canada and Secretary, Robert A. Balcom, age 52
SVP Finance; SVP Finance Loblaw Companies, Jeremy Roberts, age 50
President, Paviter S. (Pavi) Binning, age 54
Chairman, W. Galen G. Weston, age 41
EVP and CFO, Richard Dufresne
EVP and Chief Legal Officer, Gordon A. M. Currie, age 55
EVP and Chief Legal Officer, Gordon A.M. Currie
VP Commodities, David Farnfield, age 50
VP and Controller, Lina Taglieri, age 45
VP and Legal Counsel, Adam Walsh, age 37
Senior Vice President - Corporate Development, Khush Khush Dadyburjor Dadyburjor
Senior Vice President - Taxation, Bradley Holland
Director, Warren F. Bryant, age 68
Director, John S. Lacey, age 70
Director, A. Charles (Charlie) Baillie, age 74
Director, Isabelle Marcoux, age 44
Deputy Chairman, Allan L. Leighton, age 60
Director, J. Robert S. Prichard, age 65
Director, Robert J. Dart, age 74
Director, Anne L. Fraser, age 72
Director, Anthony R. Graham, age 57
Director, Peter B.M. Eby, age 75
Director, Thomas F. (Tom) Rahilly, age 70
Independent Director, Barbara Barbara Stymiest Stymiest
Independent Director, Darren Darren Entwistle Entwistle
Auditors: KPMGLLP

LOCATIONS

HQ: Weston (George) Limited
22 St. Clair Avenue East, Toronto, Ontario M4T 2S7
Phone: 416 922-2500   **Fax:** 416 922-4395
Web: www.weston.ca

Sales

	% of total
Canada	98
US	2
Total	**100**

PRODUCTS/OPERATIONS

Sales

	% of total
Loblaw	95
Weston	5
Total	**100**

Selected Operating Divisions

Food Distribution (selected Loblaw banners)
  Atlantic SaveEasy
  Dominion
  Extra Foods
  Fortinos
  Loblaws
  Maxi
  Maxi & Co.
  No frills
  The Real Canadian Superstore
  The Real Canadian Wholesale Club
  SuperValu
  T&T Supermarkets
  Your Independent Grocer
  Zehrs Markets
Food Processing (selected units)
  ACE Bakery (artisan breads)
  Interbake Foods Inc. (cookies and crackers US)
  Maplehurst Bakeries Inc. (frozen bakery products US)
  Weston Bakeries Limited (fresh baked goods)

COMPETITORS

7-Eleven	Jean Coutu
Bridgford Foods	Jim Pattison Group
Campbell Canada	Katz Group
Canada Safeway	Kellogg U.S. Snacks
Canadian Tire	METRO
Costco Wholesale Canada	Maple Leaf Foods
Couche-Tard	Otis Spunkmeyer
Flowers Foods	Shoppers Drug Mart
Grupo Bimbo	Sobeys
H&M Company	Urban Outfitters
Hostess Brands	Wal-Mart Canada
IGA	Zara

HISTORICAL FINANCIALS

Company Type: Public

Income Statement

FYE: December 31

	REVENUE ($ mil.)	NET INCOME ($ mil.)	NET PROFIT MARGIN	EMPLOYEES
12/13	31,581	852	2.7%	138,000
12/12	32,920	488	1.5%	140,000
12/11	31,738	622	2.0%	142,000
12/10	31,914	452	1.4%	142,000
12/09	30,351	987	3.3%	143,000
Annual Growth	**1.0%**	**(3.6%)**	**—**	**(0.9%)**

2013 Year-End Financials

Debt ratio: 38.2%
Return on equity: 15.1%
Cash ($ mil.): 2,698
Current ratio: 1.56
Long-term debt ($ mil.): 7,275

No. of shares (mil.): 127
Dividends
  Yield: 0.0%
  Payout: 33.1%
Market value ($ mil.): 9,346

	STOCK PRICE ($) FY Close	P/E High/Low	PER SHARE ($) Earnings	Dividends	Book Value
12/13	73.07	16 13	4.62	1.53	46.51
12/12	71.20	21 15	3.40	1.47	44.63
12/11	65.49	19 13	4.46	9.01	41.75
12/10	83.08	27 19	2.93	1.44	40.56
12/09	62.70	7 5	7.32	1.37	51.30
Annual Growth	**3.9%**	**— —**	**(10.9%)**	**2.7%**	**(2.4%)**

Westpac Banking Corp

Westpac Banking keeps its pact to serve customers in Australia New Zealand and the neighboring Pacific Islands. The company serves some 12 million customers through about 1400 branches and is one of the largest banks in Australia. Retail banking division Australian Financial Services (AFS) group includes Westpac St. George Bank of Melbourne and BankSA branded banking locations. AFS also offers wealth management insurance and consulting through BT Financial Group. Meanwhile Westpac Institutional Bank offers corporate financial services and Westpac New Zealand provides retail wealth and institutional services.

Geographic Reach

Australia accounts for 90% of Westpac's annual revenues. In addition to branches and subsidiaries located across Australia New Zealand and neighboring islands Westpac's institutional division has offices in London New York City Hong Kong and Singapore.

Operations

Through its operating divisions Westpac has a total of some $675 billion in assets. The company's AFS division includes the Westpac Retail and Business Banking unit (consumer and small to mid-sized banking customers) the St. George Banking group and the BT Financial Group as well as the banking products and risk management segments. BT Financial operates under brands including

Ascalon Asgard Advance Asset Management Magnitude and Securitor.

Westpac Institutional Bank serves corporations institutions and government entities across Australia and New Zealand as well as overseas. New Zealand banking primarily serves small to mid-sized businesses and consumers in New Zealand.

Sales and Marketing

Westpac's retail services are promoted through its retail banking locations as well as through relationship managers wealth specialists business banking centers customer service channels and online. The institutional segment conducts sales through dedicated industry relationship and specialist product teams.

Financial Performance

Westpac reported a 2% decrease in revenues to some A$42 billion ($44 billion) in 2012 due to lower sales and services in the Australian retail banking market (offset by growth in the institutional banking segment). Net income also fell by 15% to A$6.0 billion ($6.2 billion) due to higher tax impairment and operating expenses.

Strategy

Westpac's primary operating vision is to become the largest financial services firm in Australia. The company also aims to build strong customer relationships and provide superior shareholder returns. Though it occasionally makes acquisitions Westpac is currently focused on organic growth measures to increase customer numbers. The firm is also working to increase products-per-customer numbers through deposit wealth and insurance cross-selling programs. In addition Westpac is expanding its operations in Asia.

In response to challenging financial service markets Westpac is also reducing costs through streamlining and simplification programs.

HISTORY

Westpac proudly calls itself Australia's "First Bank." But when predecessor Bank of New South Wales was founded in 1817 some 90% of the eponymous colony's inhabitants were convicts or their relatives. (The penal colony was established just 30 years before the bank.) The British challenged the bank's charter forcing it to become a joint-stock company.

New South Wales' parliament rechartered the company as a bank in 1850 amidst the country's first gold rushes. (Some bank branches consisted of tents in mining camps.) Heavy British investment and an influx of colonists kept the country growing. The bank's future partner Commercial Bank of Australia was founded in 1866 in Melbourne in the neighboring colony of Victoria. More than half of the country's banks disappeared in a panic at the end of the century when land speculation and a collapse in wool prices caused a depression.

Australia became a country with the onset of the 20th century and its government formed Commonwealth Bank a central bank. The Bank of New South Wales now known as "The Wales" helped finance Australia's WWI efforts. Along with the rest of the world the country and the bank rode up the Roaring '20s and down the Great Depression.

About 65% of the bank's male staff enlisted during WWII. Its New Guinea branches closed; others were hit by air raids. In 1947 the government moved to nationalize the prospering country's banks within the Commonwealth Bank but the courts helped the banks fend off the attack on their independence.

The Bank of New South Wales moved into the newly opened savings banking market in 1956. The next year it bought into Australian Guarantee Corporation (it bought the rest in 1988).

The bank expanded abroad and diversified operations in the 1970s. Battered by a lagging protectionist economy Australia moved to deregulate banking in the 1980s. As foreign banks hustled in Bank of New South Wales and Commercial Bank of Australia in 1982 made what was then the largest merger in Australia's history.

The new bank known as Westpac (for its Western Pacific market area) began building its non-teller-based banking networks in the early 1980s. The company developed an extensive ATM network and established telephone and computerized banking. Later that decade it bought a stake in London gold dealer Johnson Matthey (1986) and all of William E. Pollock Government Securities (1987).

In 1992 Australia's wealthiest man Kerry Packer took a 10% share in troubled Westpac gaining board seats for himself and friend "Chainsaw" Al Dunlap. Packer's power grab failed and he sold the stake in 1993.

After buying itself into the equities market in the mid-1980s Westpac sold its Ord Minnett brokerage division in 1993. The bank withdrew from Asia and expanded closer to home in the mid 1990s buying Western Australia's Challenge Bank in 1995 Trust Bank of New Zealand in 1996 and Victoria's Bank of Melbourne in 1997.

In 1998 the bank agreed to merge its back-office operations with those of ANZ Banking Group providing economies of scale while avoiding antitrust issues. The next year Westpac announced 3000 job cuts mainly through attrition to ready itself for increased competition from changes in Australian law. Pacific operations caused waves in 2000: Westpac said it would pull out of Kiribati in response to government action and a coup in Fiji prompted the bank to reduce employees' hours (a move that was criticized by the Fiji government). The next year however Westpac was strengthening ties to the Pacific market. It doubled its holdings in the Bank of Tonga (on the island of Tonga) and its share of Pacific Commercial Bank (on the island of Samoa).

In 2007 subsidiary Westpac Essential Services Trust formed a joint venture with another Australian firm to operate the Airport Link Company a rail-to-airport passenger service in Sydney. The trust was established so investors could invest in public-private partnership (PPP) assets.

Westpac's acquisition of St.George Bank in 2008 catapulted Westpac from fourth to second among Australia's leading banks. The combination set Westpac and its St.George subsidiary behind only the National Australia Bank in terms of assets.

EXECUTIVES

Group Executive People and Performance, Ilana Atlas, age 59, $428,502 total compensation
Managing Director and CEO, Gail P. Kelly, age 57
Chief Executive Australian Financial Services, Brian C. Hartzer, age 46
Chief Operating Officer; Senior Company Secretary, John Arthur
Chief Financial Officer, Philip (Phil) Coffey, age 56, $571,692 total compensation
CEO St.George Bank, Rob Chapman
COO Australian Financial Services, Peter Clare, age 51
Group Executive Human Resources and Corporate Affairs, Christine Parker
CEO Westpac New Zealand, George Frazis, age 49
Group Executive Westpac Institutional Bank, Rob Whitfield, age 46, $383,333 total compensation
Senior Media Relations Manager, Jane Counsel
Deputy Chairman, John S. Curtis, age 64
Chairman, Lindsay P. Maxsted
Chief Executive Officer of BT Financial Group, Brad Cooper, age 51, $331,252 total compensation

Group Executive Transformation and Productivity, Peter Hanlon, age 59, $444,805 total compensation
General Manager Consumer Banking New Zealand, Bruce McLachlan
Head Investor Relations, Andrew Bowden
CIO, Clive Whincup
Group Executive Westpac Retail and Business, Jason Yetton
Senior Manager Investor Relations, Hugh Devine
Finance Manager, Linda Schubert
Director, Gordon M. Cairns, age 60
Director, Peter Wilson, age 69
Managing Director and CEO, Gail P. Kelly, age 57
Director, Carolyn Hewson, age 58
Director, Graham J. Reaney, age 71
Director, Elizabeth B. Bryan, age 64
Director, Robert G. Elstone, age 59
Deputy Chairman, John S. Curtis, age 64
Director, Peter J. O. Hawkins, age 60
Auditors: PricewaterhouseCoopers

LOCATIONS

HQ: Westpac Banking Corp
275 Kent Street, Sydney, New South Wales 2000
Phone: (61) 2 9293 9270   **Fax:** (61) 2 8253 4128
Web: www.westpac.com.au

Sales

Australia	90
Other countries	1

PRODUCTS/OPERATIONS

Sales by Segment

	% of total
Westpac Retail and Business	36
St.George	19
Westpac Institutional	18
BT Financial Group	11
Westpac New	9
Other	7
Total	**100**

COMPETITORS

Australia and New Zealand Banking	HSBC
Barclays	Hang Seng Bank
Commonwealth Bank of Australia	Macquarie Group
HBOS Australia	National Australia Bank

HISTORICAL FINANCIALS

Company Type: Public

Income Statement

FYE: September 30

	ASSETS ($ mil.)	NET INCOME ($ mil.)	INCOME AS % OF ASSETS	EMPLOYEES
09/14	671,697	6,588	1.0%	36,373
09/13	648,927	6,349	1.0%	35,597
09/12	704,404	6,230	0.9%	35,675
09/11	651,105	6,791	1.0%	37,806
09/10	598,553	6,143	1.0%	38,962
Annual Growth	**2.9%**	**1.8%**	**—**	**(1.7%)**

2014 Year-End Financials

Return on assets: 1.0%
Return on equity: 15.9%
Long-term debt ($ mil.): —
No. of shares (mil.): —
Sales ($ mil): 33,672

Dividends
Yield: 6.0%
Payout: 66.8%
Market value ($ mil.): —

	STOCK PRICE ($) FY Close	P/E High/Low		PER SHARE ($) Earnings	Dividends	Book Value
09/14	28.11	12	8	2.08	1.71	13.63
09/13	30.67	77	11	2.01	8.75	14.03
09/12	128.33	73	47	1.99	1.72	15.06
09/11	96.06	63	37	2.17	7.73	13.47
09/10	112.30	56	33	2.00	5.38	12.37
Annual Growth	**(29.3%)**	**—**			**0.9%(24.9%)**	**2.5%**

Wilmar International Ltd

Founded in 1991 Wilmar International is among Asia's largest agribusiness groups. The company grows refines and sells palm soy and other edible oils and grains. It is divided into three units: plantations for growing palm and rubber trees; processing plants for refining the oil and grains; and a consumer division which sells the oils in China India and Indonesia. Wilmar International also makes and sells fertilizer and palm-based biodiesel sold in Europe and the US. The company has operations in 15-plus countries on four continents and owns more than 450 processing plants across Southeast Asia. It sells its products in 50-plus countries worldwide. Beyond agribusiness it is acquiring property in China.

EXECUTIVES

Executive Director Chief Operating Officer, Martua Sitorus, age 54
Executive Director Commercial and Board Member, Teo Kim Yong, age 60
Head Operations Indonesia, Hendri Saksti
Head Operations Malaysia, Yee Chek Toong
Head Technical, Matthew J. Morgenroth
Head Plantations Division, Goh Ing Sing
Financial Controller, Sng Ching
Vice Chairman, Mu Kui
Chief Executive Officer, Ian Glasson
Chief Scientific Advisor, Chua Nam-Hai
Executive Director Chief Operating Officer, Martua Sitorus, age 54
Executive Director Commercial and Board Member, Teo Kim Yong, age 60
Auditors: Ernst&YoungLLP

LOCATIONS

HQ: Wilmar International Ltd
56 Neil Road, 088830
Phone: (65) 6216 0244   **Fax:** (65) 6836 1709
Web: www.wilmar-international.com

Sales

	% of total
China	52
Southeast	25
Europe	7
India	4
Others	12
Total	**100**

PRODUCTS/OPERATIONS

Sales

	% of total
Palm &	53
Oilseeds &	28

Consumer	15
Plantation & palm oil	1
Others	3
Total	**100**

COMPETITORS

Amsteel	Hong Leong Malaysia
Anglo-Eastern	IOI Corporation
Plantations	Inch Kenneth Kajang
Asia Food &	Rubber
Properties	Kuala Lumpur Kepong
Bunge Limited	Narborough Plantations
Genting Malaysia	New Britain Palm
Golden Agri-Resources	Sime Darby

HISTORICAL FINANCIALS

Company Type: Public

Income Statement

FYE: December 31

	REVENUE ($ mil.)	NET INCOME ($ mil.)	NET PROFIT MARGIN	EMPLOYEES
12/13	44,085	1,318	3.0%	90,000
12/12	45,463	1,255	2.8%	93,000
12/11	44,710	1,600	3.6%	90,000
12/10	30,377	1,323	4.4%	88,000
12/09	23,885	1,882	7.9%	80,000
Annual Growth	16.6%	(8.5%)	—	3.0%

2013 Year-End Financials

Debt ratio: 56.1%
Return on equity: 8.9%
Cash ($ mil.): 2,400
Current ratio: 1.20
Long-term debt ($ mil.): 6,803

No. of shares (mil.): —
Dividends
  Yield: 1.4%
  Payout: 191.8%
Market value ($ mil.): —

	STOCK PRICE ($) FY Close	P/E High/Low	PER SHARE ($) Earnings	Dividends	Book Value
12/13	26.84	152 116	0.21	0.40	2.34
12/12	27.35	240 126	0.20	0.37	2.24
12/11	38.48	197 138	0.25	0.38	2.09
12/10	43.94	257 188	0.21	0.55	1.85
12/09	45.60	168 59	0.27	0.48	1.71
Annual Growth	(12.4%)	— —	(6.9%)	(4.9%)	8.2%

Woolworths Ltd.

Chow Down Under with Australia's #1 food retailer (ahead of Coles) — Woolworths (aka "Woolies"). The diversified retailer operates about 3200 stores in Australia and New Zealand including more than 1000 supermarkets under the Woolworths Foodtown Countdown and Thomas Dux banners. It also operates BWS and Dan Murphy's liquor stores. In addition Woolworths sells gasoline and leverages its distribution network to provide wholesale merchandise for third-party supermarkets. Woolworths' 165-odd general merchandise discount stores operate under the Big W name. It also runs about 395 consumer electronics shops under the Dick Smith and Tandy brand names. Woolworths also operates nearly 300 hotels.

Woolworths' total fiscal 2011 (ends June) sales rose nearly 5% vs. the previous year. The retailer's supermarket Australian supermarkets outperformed their counterparts in New Zealand. Indeed sales at the New Zealand markets declined slightly in 2011 vs. 2010 while the Australian markets rose more than 4%. Sales at the company's Big W general merchandise stores dipped while the consumer electronics category rose 4%. Online sales increased 63% with Woolworths onlne now available to 85% of Australia's population.

Woolworths along with other Australian retailers has been hit by weak consumer demand and competition from online retailers. Looking to streamline its operations the company in early 2012 announced plans to sell its Dick Smith consumer electronics business but will continue to participate in the category through its Big W stores and an expanded online offering. Stung by competition from Internet retailers the company is focused on expanding its online operations. (The company's pending exit from the Dick Smith business will not impact the its partnership with India's Tata Group for a chain of consumer electronics stores in India. Woolworths is supplying Tata's chain of 50 Croma stores there.)

The decision to sell Dick Smith followed the purchase by the firm's Australian Leisure and Hospitality Group (ALH) of about 30 hotels in New South Wales in late 2011. ALH operates sports bars and pubs restaurants retail liquor stores gaming outlets and nightclubs and hotels across Australia. To stock its liquor cabinet Woolworths in 2011 acquired The Cellarmasters Group from Archer Capital for A$340 million ($346 million). Cellarmasters is a leading direct-to-home wine retailer with operations in Australia and New Zealand. It also has a winemaking operation. The purchase complemented the company's existing liquor brands which include Dan Murphy's BWS Woolworth's Liquor and Langton's.

On the home front Woolworths is taking on the big-box home improvement market in partnership with the #2 home improvement chain in the US — Lowe's Companies. The Danks joint venture which is two-thirds owned by Woolworths has begun opening Lowe's-style home improvement stores in Australia under the Danks and Masters banners. Plans are for more than 150 such sites over the next five years. The stores will compete with market leader Bunnings owned by rival Wesfarmers which also owns Coles.

HISTORY

Harold Percival Christmas first tried a mail-order dress business before opening the popular Frock Salon retail store. Christmas and his partners opened a branch store in the Imperial Arcade in Sydney in 1924 renaming it "Woolworths Stupendous Bargain Basement" and luring customers with advertisements calling it "a handy place where good things are cheap ... you'll want to live at Woolworths." The company borrowed the name from Frank Woolworth's successful US chain after determining that chain had no plans to open stores in Australia. Woolworths was listed on the Australian stock exchange in 1924.

Food sales came more than 30 years later. Woolworths opened its first freestanding full-line supermarket in 1960 then diversified into specialty retail buying the Rockmans women's clothing store chain the next year (sold in 2000). It expanded into discounting with the Big W chain in 1976 and further diversified when it bought 60% of the Dick Smith Electronics store chain in 1981 (buying the remainder in 1983).

The purchase of the Safeway grocery chain (the Australian operations of the US-based chain) put Woolworths on the top of the supermarket heap in 1985. But the company was hurting (it lost $13 million in 1985-86) because of a restructuring in the early 1980s that had weakened management by bulking up the front offices and dividing responsibilities. Woolworths got a shot in the arm from Paul Simons who returned to the company in 1987 after running competitor Franklins. Simons cleaned house in the front offices closed unprof-itable stores and began the successful "Fresh Food People" marketing strategy.

Industrial Equity Limited (IEL) bought the company in 1989; IEL then became part of the Adelaide Steamship group which spun off Woolworths as a public company in 1993. Career Woolworths manager Reg Clairs took over as CEO the following year following the untimely death (on a golf course) in 1993 of Harry Watts who was being groomed for the job. As a result the company has an unwritten rule of avoiding CEOs older than 60.

Clairs took the company in a variety of new directions. Woolworths began supplying fresh food to neighbor Asia in 1995. The company added Plus Petrol outlets adjacent to Woolworths Supermarkets in 1996. It also started a superstore concept for its Dick Smith Electronics chain (Power House) that year. In 1997 the company launched its Woolworths Metro store chain which targets commuters and other on-the-run shoppers in urban areas and it aggressively jumped into wholesaling to independent grocers.

Clairs (who was turning 60 in 1999) stepped down in late 1998 and Roger Corbett took over as CEO. Woolworths also began offering banking services to its customers and bought Dan Murphy a Victoria-based liquor chain in 1998. It divested its Chisholm Manufacturing meat plants in 2000.

In 2001 Woolworths acquired two liquor store chains (Liberty Liquor Booze Bros) more than 200 Tandy Electronics stores and 72 Franklins supermarkets from Hong Kong-based Dairy Farm International Holdings (most of which were later converted to the Woolworths and Food for Less banners). It sold its Crazy Prices general merchandise stores and began restructuring its liquor operations into four distinctive formats.

Woolworths exited the New Zealand market in 2002 when it sold its supermarkets group there to Foodland Associated for $690 million.

Supermarket division chief Bill Wavish resigned in May 2003 and was replaced by former chief general manager of supermarket operations Tom Flood. Wavish was considered one of the top candidates to replace CEO Corbett. Also in 2003 the company discontinued its Australian Independent Wholesalers (AIW) operations. Flood who like Wavish was considered a likely successor to Corbett resigned abruptly in August 2004.

The company acquired Australia's biggest pub owner Australian Leisure & Hospitality (ALH) in 2005. Woolworths operates ALH's retailing activities leaving the pubs and gaming operations to its partner in the purchase The Bruce Mathieson Group. (Previously the duo had acquired a 16% stake in ALH.) In mid-2005 the company acquired the New Zealand supermarkets of Foodland Associated and 22 Action stores in Western Australia Queensland and New South Wales for about $1.8 billion.

In September 2006 the company announced it had purchased a 10% stake in New Zealand's The Warehouse retail chain. Corbett retired as CEO in October. He was succeeded by Michael Luscombe the company's long-serving director of supermarkets.

Woolworths offered about $1.7 billion in 2008 to buy all of New Zealand's leading general merchandise retailer Warehouse Group. The purchase however which would have allowed Woolworths to expand from food into general merchandise in New Zealand was blocked by that country's competition regulator in mid-2008. An attempt to take over Australia's JB Hi-Fi an independent chain of home entertainment products also failed.

In February 2011 Woolworths acquired The Cellarmasters Group from Archer Capital for A$340 million ($346 million). In October Grant O'Brien was named CEO of the company.

EXECUTIVES

Group General Counsel and Company Secretary, Peter Horton

Finance Director, Thomas (Tom) Pockett, $773,894 total compensation

Director of BIG W, Julie Coates, $563,221 total compensation

Director Corporate and Public Affairs, Andrew Hall

General Manager Liquor, Steve Greentree

General Manager Logistics, Geoff Thomas

Director of Supermarkets, Tjeerd Jegen

Acting Director of Human Resources, Catherine Catherine Flynn Flynn

Chief Executive Officer; Managing Director; Executive Director, Grant Grant OBrien OBrien

Director - Multi Channel and Supply Chain, Penelope Penelope Winn Winn

Chairman of the Board, Ralph Ralph Waters Waters

Chief Operating Officer - Australian Supermarkets and Petrol, Steven Greentree

Director, Roderick S. Deane, age 72

Director, Ian J. Macfarlane, age 68

Director, Alison M. Watkins, age 50

Director, Diane J. Grady, age 65

Director, John Astbury, age 69

Managing Director and CEO, Grant O'Brien, age 51

Director, Leon M. L. Huillier, age 70

Non-Executive Director, Allan Allan Douglas Mackay Mackay

Non-Executive Independent Director, Carla Carla Hrdlicka Hrdlicka

Non-Executive Director, Christine Christine Cross Cross

Non-Executive Independent Director, Jillian Jillian Broadbent Broadbent

Non-Executive Director, Michael Michael Ullmer Ullmer

Auditors: DeloitteToucheTohmatsu

LOCATIONS

HQ: Woolworths Ltd.
1 Woolworths Way, Bella Vista, Sydney, New South Wales 2153
Phone: (61) 2 8885 1066   **Fax:** (61) 2 8888 1066
Web: www.woolworthslimited.com.au

2011 Supermarkets

	No.
Australia	840
New	156
Total	**996**

Sales

	% of total
Australia	92
New	8
Total	**100**

PRODUCTS/OPERATIONS

Sales

	% of total
Supermarkets	86
General	11
Hotels &	3
Total	**100**

COMPETITORS

ALDI	Metcash
BP	Royal Dutch Shell
Harvey Norman Holdings	Wesfarmers

HISTORICAL FINANCIALS

Company Type: Public

Income Statement

FYE: June 30

	REVENUE ($ mil.)	NET INCOME ($ mil.)	NET PROFIT MARGIN	EMPLOYEES
06/14	57,272	2,303	4.0%	198,000
06/13	54,119	2,084	3.9%	197,637
06/12	55,514	1,824	3.3%	0
06/11	57,313	2,242	3.9%	190,000
06/10	45,275	1,766	3.9%	188,000
Annual Growth	**6.1%**	**6.9%**	**—**	**1.3%**

2014 Year-End Financials

Debt ratio: 16.9%
Return on equity: 25.4%
Cash ($ mil.): 866
Current ratio: 0.95
Long-term debt ($ mil.): 3,886

No. of shares (mil.): 1,259
Dividends
 Yield: —
 Payout: —
Market value ($ mil.): 42,078

	STOCK PRICE ($) FY Close	P/E High/Low		PER SHARE ($) Earnings	Dividends	Book Value
06/14	33.40	16	12	1.84	0.00	7.65
06/13	30.65	20	14	1.68	0.00	6.66
06/12	27.05	23	14	1.49	0.00	6.68
06/11	28.40	19	12	1.83	0.00	6.59
06/10	24.25	14	9	1.43	0.00	5.38
Annual Growth	**8.3%**	**—**	**—**	**6.5%**	**—**	**9.2%**

Yapi Ve Kredi Bankasi A.S.

Yapi ve Kredi Bankasi (Yapi Kredi for short) provides financial services —including retail and corporate banking —in Turkey through more than 660 branches and about 1875 ATMs. It also has an offshore banking branch in Bahrain and subsidiary banks in Azerbaijan Germany the Netherlands and Russia. Yapi Kredi which launched the first credit card in Turkey in 1988 now has 5.4 million cardholders. The company also provides leasing factoring mutual funds insurance investment banking and brokerage services. Koc Financial Services (KFS) which is jointly owned by UniCredit and Koc Holding owns 82% of Yapi Kredi which was founded in 1944.

Yapi Kredi was previously controlled by Cukurova one of Turkey's largest business congomerates. Cukurova fell to near-collapse in the aftermath of Turkey's economic crisis in 2001 and the group sold Yapi Kredi to Kocbank owner Koc Financial Services (KFS) in 2005. The following year KFS merged Yapi Kredi and Kocbank in what was the largest bank merger Turkey had seen. The combined group took the Yapi Kredi name.

Yapi Kredi has an aggressive growth plan in which it hopes to open 350 new branches in a two-year period. The goal is to have some 974 locations by the end of 2009 as well as to grow its credit card and business banking operations.

LOCATIONS

HQ: Yapi Ve Kredi Bankasi A.S.
Yapi Kredi Plaza D Blok, Istanbul, Levent 34330
Phone: (90) 212 339 70 00   **Fax:** (90) 212 339 60 00
Web: www.yapikredi.com.tr

PRODUCTS/OPERATIONS

HISTORICAL FINANCIALS

Company Type: Public

Income Statement

FYE: December 31

	ASSETS ($ mil.)	NET INCOME ($ mil.)	INCOME AS % OF ASSETS	EMPLOYEES
12/13	74,944	1,710	2.3%	16,680
12/12	73,418	1,165	1.6%	17,459
12/11	62,224	1,210	1.9%	17,350
12/10	59,478	1,444	2.4%	16,780
12/09	47,418	1,056	2.2%	16,713
Annual Growth	**12.1%**	**12.8%**	**—**	**(0.0%)**

2013 Year-End Financials

Return on assets: 2.5%
Return on equity: 21.3%
Long-term debt ($ mil.): —
No. of shares (mil.): —
Sales ($ mil): 6,244

Dividends
 Yield: —
 Payout: 190.6%
Market value ($ mil.): —

Yorkshire Building Society

Yorkshire Building Society (YBS) provides mortgages savings personal loans and brokerage services. One of the UK's largest mutually owned financial institutions the group also offers insurance coverage including mortgage-payment policies and home and auto insurance. The society merged with Chelsea Building Society in 2010 and with Norwich & Peterborough Building Society the following year; the two institutions continue to operate under their own brands along with another YBS nameplate Barnsley Building Society. All together YBS operates more than 300 branches and agency offices in the UK and Northern Ireland. It was established in 1864 as the Huddersfield Equitable Permanent Benefit Building Society.

EXECUTIVES

General Manager, Mark Jenkins

CEO, Iain C. A. Cornish, age 53, $499,590 total compensation

Director Corporate Development, Andy M. Caton, age 50, $373,683 total compensation

Manager Corporate Affairs, Tanya Jackson

Director Sales and Marketing, Ian Bullock, age 53

General Manager Human Resources and Customer Service, Rachel Court, age 46

Director Finance, Robin Churchouse, age 48

General Manager Group Services and CIO, David Henderson, age 53

General Manager, Richard Wells

Auditors: KPMGAuditPlc

LOCATIONS

HQ: Yorkshire Building Society
Yorkshire House, Yorkshire Drive, Bradford BD5 8LJ
Phone:
Web: www.ybs.co.uk

COMPETITORS

The Newcastle	West Bromwich Building
The Principality	Society

HISTORICAL FINANCIALS

Company Type: Public

Income Statement

FYE: December 31

	ASSETS ($ mil.)	NET INCOME ($ mil.)	INCOME AS % OF ASSETS	EMPLOYEES
12/13	56,936	244	0.4%	4,218
12/12	53,992	198	0.4%	4,088
12/11	50,434	164	0.3%	3,266
12/10	46,713	142	0.3%	2,922
12/09	36,800	(5)	—	2,379
Annual Growth	**11.5%**	**—**	**—**	**15.4%**

2013 Year-End Financials

Return on assets: 0.4%
Return on equity: 0.5%
Long-term debt ($ mil.): —
No. of shares (mil.): —
Sales ($ mil): 2,356

Dividends
Yield: —
Payout: —
Market value ($ mil.): —

Zurich Insurance Group Ltd

The operations of Zurich Insurance Group (formerly Zurich Financial Services) have crossed over the Alps and spread around the globe. Serving approximately 170 countries worldwide the company is a major global provider of property/casualty and life insurance. Focused on markets in Europe and North America the company's general insurance segment offers commercial and personal property/casualty and specialty coverage while its global life segment offers life insurance annuities and other investment policies. Zurich's Farmers Group division offers personal property/casualty insurance policies in the US. The company was founded in 1872.

Geographic Reach

With operations spread around the globe Zurich's general insurance division's core markets include Germany Italy Spain Switzerland the UK and the US in addition to the domestic Swiss market. Other international business units are focused in Latin America the Asia/Pacific region China South Africa and other emerging markets.

Operations

Zurich's general insurance segment which accounts for about half of the company's annual premiums and fees provides property/casualty and specialty insurance to a variety of clients. Its global corporate unit focuses on risk management for large international and domestic clients while the Europe general insurance division provides property/casualty and specialty lines for businesses and individuals. In the US Zurich provides commercial and specialty property/casualty policies for small to midsized business customers through its North America commercial unit which includes Zurich American Insurance Company and its subsidiaries.

Zurich's global life segment (40% of premiums and fees) offers life investment pension and savings plans for individuals and groups. Global life operates through regional subsidiaries to provide localized services to its clients. Its businesses include Farmers New World Life in the US Openwork in the UK and other subsidiaries and partnerships in Europe. The division is growing in emerging markets as well.

The company's third major division Farmers Group provides personal auto and homeowners' coverage in the US as well as small business life and specialty insurance policies. Its operating divisions include 21st Century Insurance and Bristol West Holdings.

Marketing and Sales

All of the Zurich operating segments use a mixture of distribution channels to promote their products. The company has affiliated agents and it also uses independent brokers financial advisors and bank representatives to promote its policies.

During 2012 Zurich strengthened its distribution network in emerging markets by expanding agreements to sell through bank representatives in Indonesia Italy Spain and the Middle East; the firm made similar banking arrangements in Latin America during 2011. In addition the Farmers network in the US expanded its network of exclusive agents during 2012.

Financial Performance

Zurich reported a 33% revenue increase to some $70 billion in 2012 as well as 5% profit growth to nearly $4 billion. The company attributed its success to portfolio management and pricing discipline measures especially during challenging market conditions including weather events in the US and disappointing results in the German general insurance market. Overall the US market showed solid returns and Zurich also highlighted successful integration of acquired businesses in Latin America and Malaysia.

The company which has undertaken extensive restructuring efforts in recent years has steadily increased profits over the last four years. However sales growth in 2012 followed a decrease in revenues in both 2010 and 2011.

Strategy

In 2012 the company changed its name from Zurich Financial Services to Zurich Insurance Group to reflect its concentration on the insurance business. The company has undergone nearly ten years of strategic reorganization efforts to refocus its operations around its principal lines of business. The company's reorganization programs have aimed to help Zurich achieve its financial efficiency and expansion goals as well as to increase profitability.

Divestitures of noncore businesses continued into 2012 including the transfer of the UK general insurance portfolio of Eagle Star Insurance Group —a run-off business that does not actively market policies —through a reinsurance agreement with the RiverStone Insurance.

At the same time as it is focused on tightening its organization and improving returns in existing markets Zurich is also looking to expand in high-growth emerging markets such as Brazil China Russia Spain Turkey and Taiwan. Zurich has also benefited from its efforts to expand into markets deemed "under-represented." One strategy is to provide niche product offerings to reach targeted customer segments such as expatriates and minority groups. In the US market the Farmers division is working to expand its operations in the eastern states.

Mergers and Acquisitions

To further expansion efforts in the growing Latin American markets in 2011 Zurich acquired a 51% stake in general and life insurance divisions of Banco Santander in Argentina Brazil Chile Mexico and Uruguay; those divisions now operate as Zurich Santander. Also that year Zurich expanded in the Asia/Pacific region through the purchase of composite insurer Malaysian Assurance Alliance Berhad.

In 2010 it purchased Lebanese general insurance firm Compagnie Libanaise D'Assurances to accelerate its expansion measures in the Middle East.

HISTORY

The roots of Zurich Financial Services stretch back to the 1872 founding of a reinsurer for Switzerland Transport Insurance. The company soon branched out into accident travel and workers' compensation insurance and in 1875 it changed its name to Transport and Accident Insurance plc Zurich to reflect the changes. It then expanded into Berlin (the jumping-off point for its expansion into Scandinavia and Russia) and Stuttgart Germany. The company exited marine lines in 1880; it later left the reinsurance business and expanded into liability insurance; in 1894 it changed its name to Zurich General Accident and Liability Insurance.

In 1912 Zurich crossed the Atlantic expanding operations into the US. It agreed in 1925 to provide insurance for Ford cars at favorable terms. Zurich's business was hard hit during the war years of the late 1930s and 1940s. In 1955 the company changed its name to Zurich Insurance.

Starting in the 1960s Zurich began buying other insurers including Alpina (1965 Switzerland) Agrippina (1969 Germany) and Maryland Casualty Group (1989 US). It also bought the property liability operations of American General.

The company shifted its strategy in the early 1990s expanding into what it deemed underrepresented markets in the UK and the US. Being big wasn't enough; Zurich needed to find a focus. It also jettisoned such marginal or unprofitable business lines as commercial fire insurance in Germany.

In 1995 Zurich bought struggling Chicago-based asset manager Kemper and in 1997 bought lackluster mutual fund manager Scudder Stevens & Clark forming Scudder Kemper. That year it also bought failed Hong Kong investment bank Peregrine Investment Holdings.

Zurich merged in 1998 with the financial services businesses of B.A.T Industries formerly known as the British-American Tobacco Co. created in 1902 as a joint venture between UK-based Imperial Tobacco and American Tobacco. As public disapproval of smoking grew in the 1970s British-American Tobacco began diversifying; it changed its name to B.A.T Industries in 1976 and moved into insurance. In 1984 it rescued UK insurer Eagle Star from a hostile offer by German insurance giant Allianz. The next year it bought Hambro Life Assurance renaming it Allied Dunbar. Moving into the large US market in 1988 B.A.T bought Farmers Insurance Group.

While B.A.T battled the antismoking army of the 1990s the insurance industry struggled with stagnant growth. In 1997 Europe's largest insurance firms were named as defendants in class action lawsuits that sought recovery for unpaid claims on Holocaust-era insurance policies. In 1998 Zurich became a founding member of the International Commission on Holocaust Era Insurance Claims (ICHEIC).

Also in 1998 Zurich and B.A.T's insurance units merged to create Zurich Financial Services. The firm reshuffled some of its holdings and sold Eagle Star Reinsurance. In 1999 Zurich spun off its real estate holdings into PSP Swiss Property and at the turn of the century it focused on expansion buying the new business of insurer Abbey Life which it merged into Allied Dunbar. In 2000 the holding companies formed to own Zurich (Zurich Allied and Allied Zurich) were merged into the firm.

In 2002 Zurich completed the spinoff of reinsurance unit Zurich Re which became Converium. It also sold troubled asset manager Zurich Scudder to Deutsche Bank and acquired the bank's life insurance operations in Italy Spain and Portugal. It also acquired life insurance firm Deutsche Herold as well as German financial services provider Bonnfinanz and mutual fund distributor DGV. Zurich also sold a large holding in its US-based Zurich Life to BANK ONE and sold its operations in Hungary Poland and Slovakia to Italian insurer Generali. Zurich paid out some $900 million in claims related to the September 11 2001 terrorist attacks in the US.

The write-off of assets and strengthening of non-life reserves resulted in Zurich posting a $3.4 billion loss for 2002. Rolf Hoppi Zurich's legendary chairman and CEO stepped down while the company's asset management unit tumbled and investors pulled out. James Schiro previously with PricewaterhouseCoopers was named as the new chief executive and began guiding a turnaround at the company.

Schiro launched a restructuring initiative in 2004. The company began its "The Zurich Way" rebranding efforts the following year which began a financial turnaround for the company. The reorganization program sought to refocus the company's operations around its principal lines of business (including insurance underwriting and reserving risk management and investment management) and consolidate Zurich's General Insurance and Global Life businesses under the Zurich brand.

To enhance efficiencies the firm streamlined its distribution cross-selling customer service and claims management processes. The company estimated that achievements from The Zurich Way program would help save some $2.7 billion annually.

In 2009 after five years of successful restructuring efforts Schiro retired and chief investment officer Martin Senn took over the CEO role.

Continuing with its strategy to grow in emerging markets Zurich Financial entered the Turkish market through the acquisition of TEB Sigorta in 2008. It also acquired a majority stake in Russian insurance provider NASTA for $260 million. In 2009 the company purchased two Brazilian insurers.

To build up Farmers Group Zurich Financial spent $1.9 billion to acquire 21st Century Insurance the personal auto insurance arm of AIG in 2009. The addition of 21st Century's online products and geographic spread secured Farmers Group into the top tier of US auto insurers.

EXECUTIVES

Acting Chairman, Tom de Swaan, age 68
Head Mergers and Acquisition and Strategy, Christian Carl, age 42
Vice Chairman, Josef Ackermann, age 66
Regional Chairman Americas; Chairman Farmers Group, Paul N. Hopkins, age 58
CEO General Insurance, Mario Greco, age 55
Acting CFO, Vibhu R. Sharma, age 48
Chief Executive Officer Global Life, Kevin Hogan, age 52
CEO Global Corporate, Mario P. Vitale, age 59
Senior Advisor, John Amore, age 66
Chief Risk Officer and Regional Chairman Europe, Axel P. Lehmann, age 55
CEO Europe General Insurance, Annette Court, age 52
Regional Chairman Asia Pacific and Middle East, Geoffrey (Geoff) Riddell, age 58
CEO, Martin Senn, age 57
Chief Financial Officer CFO, Pierre Wauthier, age 53
CEO Farmer's Group, Jeffrey J. (Jeff) Dailey, age 56
Chief Underwriting Officer Europe General Insurance and Zurich Insurance plc, Alan Fairhead, age 50
Regional Chairman Europe, Dieter Wemmer, age 57
Group Chief Economist, Daniel M. Hofmann

Chairman, Manfred Gentz, age 72, $56,992 total compensation
CEO General Insurance, Michael G. (Mike) Kerner, age 48
CEO Western Europe, Markus Hongler, age 57
Global Chief Underwriting Officer and Head Organizational Transformation Management, Inga K. Beale, age 51
CEO North American Commercial; Regional Chairman Americas, Mike Foley, age 52
CEO Global Life, Kristof Terryn, age 46
CEO North America Shared Services Platform (ZFUS), Claudia Dill, age 48
CEO Support Office, Malcolm Gilbert
Director Media Relations Farmers, Jerry Davies
Global Head Corporate Communications, Angel Serna
Head Global Corporate Communications and Climate Office, Francis Bouchard, age 48
Head Investor Relations and Rating Agencies, Debra Broek, age 52
CEO Middle East and Africa, Saad Mered, age 46
CFO Australia, Iain C. Howie, age 50
Global Head Mergers and Acquisitions and Chief Underwriting Officer of Directors and Officers liability and Employment Practices Liability Insurance. Global Corporate, Paul Schiavone
Chief Integration Officer Personal Lines Auto US, Keitha Schofield
CEO General Insurance UK, Stephen Lewis
Chief Underwriting Officer, Lee Meyrick
Controller, Scott Egan, age 42
CEO Latin America, Peter Rebrin, age 51
Dipl. Event Manager (incl. Sponsoring) Investor Relations, Patricia Heina
Head Group Media Relations North America, Sean Kevelighan
Manager Media Relations Germany, Bernd O. Engelien
CFO Asia Pacific and Middle East, Pascal Perritaz, age 41
CFO Global Life, Joachim Masur, age 48
Chief Investment Officer, Cecilia Reyes, age 56
Head Investment Strategy Implementation, Urban Angehrn, age 50
Chief Information Technology Officer, Markus Nordlin, age 51
Head Alternative Investments; CEO Zurich Alternative Asset Management, Bernard Joei, age 57
Group General Counsel, Yannick Hausmann
Chief Administrative Officer, Christian Orator, age 51
Manager European Communications Italy, Riccardo Moretto
CEO Europe, Patrick Manley, age 53
CEO Asia/Pacific, Johnny Chen, age 53
Group Head Human Resources, Peter J. Wright, age 59
Chief Marketing Officer, Isabelle M. Conner
Regional Chairman of Asia-Pacific & Middle East, Geoffrey Geoff
Honorary Chairman of the Board, Fritz Fritz Gerber Gerber
President of Programs & Direct Markets, Kathleen Savio
Director, Tom de Swaan, age 68
Director, Susan S. Bies, age 66
Vice Chairman, Josef Ackermann, age 66
Director, Thomas K. Escher, age 65
Director, Armin Meyer, age 65
Director, Fred Kindle, age 55
Director, Rolf Urs Watter, age 56
Director, Vernon L. Sankey
Director, Donald T. (Don) Nicolaisen, age 68
Director, Victor L.L. Chu, age 57
Non-Executive Director, Tom Tom de Swaan Swaan
Auditors: PricewaterhouseCoopersAG

LOCATIONS

HQ: Zurich Insurance Group Ltd
Mythenquai 2, Zurich CH-8002
Phone: (41) 1 625 25 25   **Fax:** (41) 1 625 35 55
Web: www.zurich.com

PRODUCTS/OPERATIONS

2012 Premiums and Fees

	% of total
General	49
Global	41
Farmers	10
Total	**100**

Selected Subsidiaries

Farmers Group Inc. (property/casualty US)
  21st Century Insurance Company (property/casualty US)
  Farmers New World Life Insurance Company (life insurance US)
  Foremost Insurance Company (specialty insurance US)
  Bristol West Holdings Inc. (specialty insurance US)
  Zurich American Insurance Company (general insurance US)
Zurich Insurance plc (general insurance UK)
Zurich International Life Limited (life insurance UK)

Selected Acquisitions

2011
Malaysian Assurance Alliance Berhad (Malaysia composite insurer)
Zurich Santander (51% Latin America general and life insurance divisions of Banco Santander)
2010
Compagnie Libanaise D'Assurances (Lebanon general insurance)

COMPETITORS

AEGON	MetLife
AIG	Mitsui Sumitomo
AXA	Insurance
Allianz	Prudential
Aviva	Prudential plc
CNA Financial	State Farm
GEICO	The Hartford
Generali	Travelers Companies
ING	

HISTORICAL FINANCIALS

Company Type: Public

Income Statement

FYE: December 31

	ASSETS ($ mil.)	NET INCOME ($ mil.)	INCOME AS % OF ASSETS	EMPLOYEES
12/13	415,053	4,028	1.0%	55,102
12/12	409,267	3,878	0.9%	52,722
12/11	385,869	3,766	1.0%	52,648
12/10	375,661	3,434	0.9%	54,934
12/09	368,914	3,215	0.9%	56,668
Annual Growth	3.0%	5.8%	—	(0.7%)

2013 Year-End Financials

Return on assets: 0.9%	Dividends
Return on equity: 12.0%	Yield: 6.1%
Long-term debt ($ mil.): —	Payout: 6.6%
No. of shares (mil.): 147	Market value ($ mil.): 4,305
Sales ($ mil): 72,045	

	STOCK PRICE ($) FY Close	P/E High	P/E Low	PER SHARE ($) Earnings	PER SHARE ($) Dividends	PER SHARE ($) Book Value
12/13	29.17	1	1	27.22	1.80	220.24
12/12	26.80	1	1	26.31	1.82	234.73
12/11	22.68	1	1	25.61	1.83	216.67
12/10	25.89	1	1	23.44	1.47	220.29
12/09	21.74	1	0	22.35	0.96	205.81
Annual Growth	7.6%	—	—	5.1%	17.1%	1.7%

Hoover's Handbook of

World
Business

Executive index

Index of Executives

A

A-nanthothai, Thongchai 47
Aagaard-Svendsen, Birgit 122
Aaker, Tom 332
Aanestad, Ola M. 334
Aasnaes, Hans 335
AbaalKhail, Faris Abdullah 295
Abad, Alfredo Saenz 46
Abadie, Laurent 273
Abanumay, Mohammed S. 310
Abate, Rene 87
Abbasi, Osama 116
Abbott, John 302
Abe, Takashi 232
Abe, Takashi 233
Abe, Ken 236
Abe, Ken 236
Abe, Yasushi 247
Abe, Yasuyuki 336
Abe, Yasuyuki 337
Abe, Kensuke 354
Abe, Ken 373
Abello, Vincent 87
Able, Michael 240
Abols, Tate A. M. 268
Aboulafia, Itzhak 49
Aboumrad, Daniel Hajj 24
Abraham, Leopold 267
Abrahamsson, Jonas 134
Aburatani, Yoshihiro Yoshihiro
  Aburatani 360
Accum, Claude A. 339
Achatz, Reinhold 320
Achleitner, Paul 63
Achleitner, Paul 119
Achleitner, Paul 305
Achurra, Emiliano 152
Acker, Laurens G. van den 289
Ackermann, Josef 303
Ackermann, Josef 320
Ackermann, Josef 320
Ackermann, Josef 392
Ackermann, Josef 392
Acranis, Tina 221
Adachi, Yoroku (Joe) 85
Adachi, Yoroku (Joe) 85
Adachi, Michio 124
Adachi, Toshio 315
Adachi, Takemi Takemi Adachi 360
Adachi, Seiichiro 364
Adachi, Seiichiro 364
Adali, Erhan 365
Adam, Herve 376
Addison, Niall 238
Adeson, Kevin 175
Adeva, Angel Durandez 290
Adler, Reuven 49
Adler, Lothar 320
Adrian, Ken 258
Advani, Deepak 212
Afonso, Horacio Lisboa 145
Agar, James 69
Agarwal, Bhikam C. 29
Agata, Atsunobu 12

Agata, Atsunobu 12
Agata, Shintaro 270
Agata, Tetsuo 363
Agius, Marcus 58
Agnelli, Roger 4
Agnelli, Roger 373
Agnon, Udi 175
Agrawal, S. K. 68
Agreda, Ignacio 30
Agrusti, Raffaele 31
Aguignier, Philippe 316
Aguire, Jose M. Lucia 44
Ahizoune, Abdeslam 377
Ahmad, Kamaludin 220
Ahmadjian, Christina 233
Ahmed, Riaz E. 358
Ahmed, Raiz 358
Ahn, Byung Mo 200
Ahn, Skott 213
Ahn, Charles 281
Aiba, Koji 250
Aich, Andre 64
Aida, Masakazu 101
Aigrain, Jacques 127
Aiguo, Lin 275
Aihua, Pei 99
Aikyo, Katsunori 236
Aili, Liu 96
Aili, Liu 96
Aima, Abhay 164
Ainley, John 34
Airaghi, Enrico 40
Aizawa, Shinichi 117
Aizawa, Naoki 342
Aizawa, Zengo 356
Akamatsu, Yoshio 192
Akikawa, Tadashi 151
Akikawa, Tadashi 151
Akimoto, Nobuyuki 117
Akiyama, Tomofumi 151
Akiyoshi, Mitsuru 223
Aksyutin, Oleg E. 154
Al-Abdrabbuh, Samir A. 310
Al-Abdulla, Hussain Ali 381
Al-Afaleq, Mohammed Abdulaziz 295
Al-Amoudi, Omar A. 310
Al-Ayadhi, Abdullah Ibrahim 295
Al-Benyan, Yousef A. 310
Al-Furaih, Abdulaziz S. 295
Al-Gwaiz, Suliman A. 295
Al-Gwaiz, Majid A. 295
Al-Humaid, Abdulaziz S. 310
Al-Issa, Abdullah M. 295
Al-Issa, Abdullah M. 310
Al-Jarbou, Abdulaziz Saleh 295
Al-Joyan, Adnan S. 295
Al-Mady, Mohamed H. 310
Al-Mady, Mohamed H. 310
Al-Mahasher, Nasser 305
Al-Maker, Awadh 310
Al-Malki, Abdulaziz S. 295
Al-Mana, Khaled 310
Al-Morished, Mutlaq 310
Al-Mubarak, Abdul Majeed A. 295
Al-Odan, Abdulrahman M. 295
Al-Ohali, Mosaed 310

Al-Qudaibi, Talal I. 295
Al-Rabeah, Mohamad A. 295
Al-Rabeeah, Abdullah S. 310
Al-Rashed, Rashed Abdulaziz 295
Al-Saud, Prince Saud bin Abdullah bin
  Thenayan 310
Al-Shamrani, Thalib A. 295
Al-Sheaibi, Fahad 310
Al-Sheikh, Adel A. 295
Al-Siairri, Saeed S. 295
Al-Subaie, Abdulla Abdulla Al-Subaie
  168
Al-Tayeb, Ahmed Y. 295
Al-Tuwaijri, Homood A. 310
Al-Zahrani, Riyadh O. 295
Al-Zahrani, Aiedh M. 295
Al-Zamel, Yousef 310
Aladro, Manuel 41
Albanel, Christine 269
Albanese, Tom 294
Albanese, Tom 294
Albanese, Tom 295
Albertani, Battista 371
Albrecht, Christoph 40
Albrecht, D. Michael 149
Albuquerque, Francisco Roberto de 276
Alciturri, Jose Luis Gomez 46
Alekperov, Vagit Y. 264
Alekperov, Vagit Y. 264
Alemany, Ellen 300
Alessandro, Dominic 340
Alexander, Deborah M. 54
Alexander, Matthew 268
Alexander, Gregor 329
Alexander, Gregor 329
Alexandre, Patrick 13
Alexandridis, Georgios P. 279
Alfonsi, Davide 189
Alhamadi, Mohd 374
Alias, Abdul Farid 220
Alierta, Cesar 349
Alimhamzah, Bapak Bapak Alimhamzah
  220
Allen, Nicholas C. 212
Allen, Stephen 218
Allert, Richard H. (Rick) 25
Almeida, Augusto Augusto Espeschit de
  Almeida 30
Almeida, Manuel Antonio Ribeiro
  Serzedelo de 145
Almeida, Ann 175
Almeida, Marcos Henrique 373
Alonso, Juan 43
Alonso, Emilson 175
Alphandery, Edmond 156
Alsowaidi, Nasser A. 113
Altenschmidt, Hans-Hermann 105
Althoff, Eric 261
Altman, Gideon 49
Alton, Steve 80
Altozano, Angel Manuel Garcia 9
Altozano, Angel Garcia 168
Alvarado, Cristobal Valderas 9
Alvarez, Fernando de Asua 46
Alvarez, Jose Antonio Alvarez 46
Alvarez, Fernando de Asua 46

Alvarez, Luis 81
Alvarez, Manuel 152
Alvera, Marco 141
Alvera, Marco 153
Amado, Nuno 46
Amano, Tsugunobu 354
Amaral, Mario Mosqueira do 145
Ambani, Mukesh D. 287
Ambani, Ramniklal H. 287
Ambe, Shintaro 236
Ambrose, Kathleen A. 320
Amemiya, Hiroshi 355
Amine, Ali Al 212
Amino, Yutaka 337
Ammar, Tarak Ben 225
Ammar, Tarak Ben 349
Ammar, Tarak Tarak Ben Ammar 349
Amore, John 392
Amorim, Americo Ferreira de 45
Amoroso, Greg 146
Amos, Louise 106
Amyot, Lise-Anne 243
Anand, V. 67
Ananenkov, Alexander G. 154
Ancelin, Bruno 289
Andersen, Tonny Thierry 122
Andersen, Ole Gjesso 122
Andersen, Thomas Thune 329
Anderson, Paul 39
Anderson, Paul M. 76
Anderson, John 80
Anderson, Sir John A. 106
Anderson, Sir Roy 158
Anderson, Roy 221
Anderson, William D. (Bill) 339
Andersson, Johan Johan Andersson 323
Ando, Ichiro 230
Ando, Kenji 232
Andrade, Juan C. 8
Andreasen, Lars 122
Andres, Esteban Morras 139
Andres, Juan 261
Andresen, Johan Johan Andresen 323
Andreu, Joan 43
Andrew, Jim 205
Andrews, Nigel D. T. 266
Andrews, Timothy L. 367
Ang, Eric T. L. 123
Angehrn, Urban 392
Angeli, Caroline 269
Angelo, Steve St. 363
Angerbauer, Friedrich 112
Angulo, Gonzalo Hinojosa Fernandez de
  350
Anjolras, Pierre 376
Annaka, Masahiro 247
Annunziato, Franco 78
Annunziato, Paolo 348
Annuscheit, Frank 105
Anthoine, Jean 87
Antinori, Thierry 127
Anto?anzas, Miguel 134
Anton, Muriel 379
Antoniadis, Christodoulos G. 279
Antoniadis, Christodoulos G. 280
Antonietti, Robert 40

Anuchitworawong, Shairit 47
Anwar, A. S. El 175
Anzai, Takashi 313
Anzai, Takashi 313
Anzai, Yuichiro 328
Aoki, Yoshihisa 192
Aoki, Yoshihisa 192
Aoyama, Hajime 101
Aoyama, Shinji 172
Aoyama, Yasushi 356
Apalagaki, Chariklia A. 279
Aparicio, Francisco 45
Apenbrink, Rudolf 175
Apfalter, Guenther 219
Apitzsch, Wolfgang 133
Apitzsch, Hannes 320
Apotheker, Leo 312
Apotheker, Leo 312
Appel, Frank 129
Arai, Masuji 17
Arai, Jun 318
Arai, Jun 318
Arai, Shunichi 336
Araki, Makoto 85
Araki, Makoto 86
Araki, Saburo 234
Araki, Ryuji 234
Araki, Yuji 262
Araki, Yoshifumi 364
Aranha, Brian 30
Arbide, Juan Mata 9
Arboe, Susanne Susanne Arboe 122
Arculus, Sir David G. 350
Arena, Mark 367
Arenal, Pablo Garcia 9
Ariano, Lucia 189
Arias, Sebastian Battaner 180
Ariffin Johan bin Ariffin 220
Arihara, Masahiko 232
Aristizabal, Hector Castano 135
Arledge, David A. 137
Armada, Jose Sainz 180
Armato, Francesco 348
Armengol, Domingo 41
Armstrong, Danny 106
Armstrong, Anthony 116
Armstrong, Danny 242
Armstrong, David 268
Armstrong, Philip 339
Arnault, Bernard 87
Arnault, Bernard 100
Arnault, Bernard 216
Arnault, Antoine 216
Arnault, Delphine 216
Arndt, Frank-Peter 66
Arnet, S.K. 357
Arnold, Michael (Mike) 266
Arnoldussen, Ludger 240
Arnstad, Marit 334
Arnstad, Marit 334
Arora, Rajiv 181
Arora, Ankush 347
Arrago, Andre 163
Arribas, Fernando Garcia 9
Arseneault, Tom 38
Arthur, John 388
Artus, Maj. Patrick 362
Asada, Teruo 223
Asada, Teruo 223
Asai, Shigeo 196
Asama, Yoshimasa 101
Asami, Takao 255
Asami, Hiroyasu 263
Asano, Haruhiko 101
Asano, Haruhiko 101
Asano, Tomoyasu 117
Asano, Tomoyasu 117
Asano, Mikio 364
Asano, Mikio 364
Ashby, Ian R. 69
Asher-Topilsky, Lilach 48
Ashley, Steven 257
Asimopoulos, Spyros 244
Ask, Lars 383
Asmussen, Jorg 130

Aspar, Gerard 107
Assaf, Samir 174
Assaf, S. 175
Assakul, Kirati 117
Asshoff, Gregor 168
Assis, Franciso de 195
Astbury, John 390
Atan, Dato' Tajuddin 292
Atarashi, Akira 315
Athanassopoulos, Antreas 244
Atieh, Michael G. (Mike) 8
Atkins, Chris 80
Atkinson, Kent 52
Atkinson, Kent 53
Atkinson, Stephen 332
Atkinson, Kent 333
Atkinson, Matt 352
Atlas, Ilana 388
Atsumi, Masanori 342
Attal, Alexandre 150
Attinger, Per-Olof 297
Au, Paul 106
Audvard, Yves 289
Audvard, Yves 289
Auer, Werner 320
Auld, Robert (Rob) 268
Aune, J. Brian 283
Auque, Francois 15
Austin, Roxanne S. 143
Austin, Neal 238
Averbeck, Richard 119
Avila, Jose A. 112
Avner, David 49
Awori, Jeremy 332
Axford, Eric 340
Axmann, Michael 320
Aydinli, Ibrahim 365
Aynat, Julio de Miguel 180
Ayukawa, Masaaki 357
Ayyoubi, Silvia 297
Azema, Jean 225
Azema, Jean 324
Aziz, Zafrul Zafrul Abd Aziz 220
Aznar, Vitalino M. Nafria 350
Azuhata, Shigeru 166
Azumi, Tooru 263

B

Ba, Shusong 186
Babani, Susie 33
Babe, Gregory S. (Greg) 63
Babeau, Emmanuel 312
Babeau, Emmauel 312
Babin, Jean-Christophe 216
Babrowski, Claire H. 146
Babu, Amar 212
Bach, Herbert 240
Bacher, Lars C. 334
Bachrach, Ernest G. 82
Back, Jan Erik 323
Backer, Christophe de 174
Backteman, Thomas 344
Bacon, Andrew 80
Bada, Hajime 196
Badrinath, Vivek 269
Bae, Charlie 307
Baete, Oliver 20
Bague, Hugo 295
Bahlmann, Tineke J.P. 188
Bailey, Irving W. 11
Bailey, George 328
Baillie, Douglas A. (Doug) 369
Baillie, Douglas A. (Doug) 370
Baillie, A. Charles (Charlie) 387
Bailly, Jean-Paul 156
Bain, George S. 160
Bain, Peter 266
Bakhshi, Sandeep 181
Bakhshi, Nandita 358
Bakker, Jacqueline Tammenoms 352
Bakker, Jacqueline Jacqueline
   Tammenoms Bakker 377
Bakker, Jacqualine Tammenoms 377

Bakkerud, Lill-Heidi 334
Baksaas, Jon F. 343
Baladron, Daniel Vega 9
Balasubramanian, P. 68
Balbinot, Sergio 31
Balbinot, Sergio 31
Balbinot, Sergio 105
Balcom, Robert A. 387
Baldauf, Sari M. 119
Baldwin, Nick 329
Balko, Jody L. 137
Ball, Tony 81
Balsells, Jaume 43
Balthazard, Michel 289
Balyan, A. K. 264
Balyan, A. K. 264
Balz, Manfred 130
Bamba, Ryoichi 85

Bammann, Linda B. 221
Bancroft, Philip V. 7
Banerjee, Prith 4
Bang, Lars 258
Bank, Ondra 70
Bank, Danske 122
Bansal, A.K. 67
Bansal, Arun 143
Bao-Lang, Chen 148
Baomin, Li 197
Baptista, Benjamin 30
Barahona, Pedro 41
Baraibar, Gonzalo Gomez-Zamalloa 9
Baratta, Paolo 349
Barbassa, Almir G. 276
Barber, Ralph G. 174
Barber, Samantha 180
Barberis, Pierre 75
Barbier, Denis 289
Barbizet, Patricia 75
Barbizet, Patricia 362
Barbosa, Nelson 373
Baril, Thierry Thierry Baril 15
Barker, Glyn 35
Barkov, Anatoly A. 264
Barnes, Peter 81
Barnett, Lee 25
Barollier, Pascal 309
Baron, Mali 48
Barr, G. 238
Barral, David 35
Barreto, Pedro 42
Barrio, Miguel 290
Barros, Patrick Monteiro de 145
Barrow, Mark 81
Barrows, Charles 34
Bartels, Andreas 127
Barten, Heiko 209
Barteselli, Raffaele 40
Bartke, Rolf 16
Bartolomeo, Bill 18
Bartolomeo, Eduardo de Salles 373
Bartolotta, Peter 212
Bartoschek, Werner 135
Baschera, Pius 297
Basecqz, Bernard 145
Baser, Didem Dincer 365
Bashada, Stephen M. 320
Basham-Pyke, Sharanne 81
Bass, Jim 328
Bassermann, Rolf 119
Bassil, Alain 13
Bastian, Ralf-Gerd 62
Bastug, Recep 365
Batchelor, Lance 352
Bates, M. 238
Batista, Joesley Mendonca 195
Batista, Wesley Mendonca 195
Batista, Wesley Mendonca 195
Batista, Jose 195
Batista, Luis Carlos Croissier 290
Batra, Sandeep 181
Battiferri, Simone Simone Battiferri
   349
Bauer, Manuel 20
Bauer, Werner J. 249

Bauert, Ian 294
Baule, Rainer 149
Baumann, Werner 63
Baumann, Wolfgang 267
Baumgartl, Wolf-Dieter 163
Baumgartl, Wolf-Dieter 346
Baumgartner, Fred 62
Baxter, Peter 266
Baxter, Tim 332
Bayle, Pierre 15
Bayswater, Lord Powell of 216
Bazid, Abdullah 310
Bazin, Sebastien 87
Bazin, Sebastien 87
Bazin, Benoit 107
Bazire, Nicolas 87
Bazire, Nicolas 216
Bazoli, Giovanni 189
Bazoli, Giovanni 371
Bazy, Dominique 376
Beale, Inga K. 392
Beamish, Brian 26
Beato, Manuel Perez 9
Beattie, W. Geoffrey (Geoff) 299
Beauchamp, Joan 243
Beaudoin, Pierre 282
Beaulieu, Martin E. (Marty) 339
Beaumont, Glenn 137
Beauregard, Olivier Olivier Costa de
   Beauregard 37
Beauregard, Olivier Costa de 374
Beaven, Peter 70
BeavenBAcc, Peter 69
Bebear, Claude 72
Bebear, Claude 313
Bebear, Claude Claude Bebear 377
Bebear, Claude 377
Bech-Hansen, Henrik 122
Bechat, Jean-Paul 23
Beck, Richard S. 174
Beck, Gyorgy 379
Becke, Wolf 163
Becker, Michael 40
Becker, Hermann-Josef 130
Becker, Michael 320
Becker, Wendy 379
Beckers, Pierre-Olivier 146
Beckmann, Christoph 127
Beerli, Andreas 40
Beeton, Jeremy 329
Beeuwsaert, Dirk 156
Beffa, Jean-Louis 107
Beffa, Jean-Louis 156
Beffa, Jean-Louis 320
Beinecke, Candace K. 23
Beitz, Wolfgang 320
Beitz, Berthold 354
Belair, Douglas E. (Doug) 38
Belchior, Miriam Aparecida 276
Belda, Alain J. P. 289
Belikov, Igor 264
Bell, Sir John Irving 297
Bellanger, Alain 376
Bellini, Luigi 371
Bellodi, Leonardo 141
Belloni, Antonio (Toni) 216
Belloni, Antonio (Toni) 216
Bellozi, Renata 373
Belluzzi, Giovanni 368
Belot, Stanislas 34
Belsham, David 284
Belzberg, Brent S. 84
Belzer, Joan Joan Belzer 116
Ben-Zeev, Itai 49
Bendavid, Laurent 87
Benetton, Gilberto 224
Beng, Na Wu 271
Bengdara, Farhat O. 368
Bengdara, Farhat O. 368
Bengoa, Angel Jado Becerro de 46
Benitez, Jorge L. 6
Benjelloun, Othman 145
Benmosche, Robert H. (Bob) 116
Bennett, Brad 8
Bennett, D. Michael 39

Frere, Baron Albert 216
Frere, Gerald 283
Frere, Gerald 283
Frerichs, Robert N. (Bob) 6
Frerot, Antoine Antoine Frerot 374
Fresco, Louise O. 369
Fresco, Louise O. 370
Frese, Mark 227
Frew, Anita M. 214
Frey, Rainer-Marc 367
Freyne, Colm J. 339
Frial, Pedro Fernandez 290
Frial, Pedro 290
Friberg, Lars 344
Frick, David P. 249
Fried, D. L. 175
Friedberg, Daniel 282
Friedman, Alexander S. 367
Frieling, Hubert 227
Friese, Lard 188
Friis, Morten N 299
Froehlich, Babette 381
Frohlich, Babette 381
Froud, Samantha 8
Fryar, Bob 76
Frykhammar, Jan 143
Fu, Junyuan 94
Fu, Yuning 95
Fu, Chengyu 102
Fucheng, Wang 275
Fudge, Ann M. 261
Fudge, Ann M. 369
Fudge, Ann M. 370
Fueangfu, Charnsak 47
Fuerst, Tracy 219
Fuhrmann, Christian 240
Fuji, Yosaku 337
Fujie, Naofumi 16
Fujie, Naofumi 17
Fujii, Natsuki 78
Fujii, Takashi 117
Fujii, Junsuke 338
Fujimori, Fumio 16
Fujimori, Fumio 17
Fujimoto, Noboru 315
Fujimoto, Toshihiko 315
Fujimura, Kiyoshi 230
Fujino, Michimasa 171
Fujinuma, Tsuguoki 257
Fujinuma, Tsuguoki 337
Fujita, Masami 150
Fujita, Masami 151
Fujita, Masaaki 236
Fujita, Kunitaka 328
Fujita, Hirokazu 355
Fujiwara, Akihiko 232
Fujiwara, Makio 356
Fujiyoshi, Yukihiro 247
Fujiyoshi, Yukihiro 247
Fukakusa, Janice R. 299
Fukakushi, Masahiko (Masa) 360
Fukuda, Yuji 192
Fukui, Takeo 172
Fukui, Masaki 247
Fukunaga, Seiji 182
Fukunaga, Seiji 182
Fukunaga, Takashi 236
Fukuo, Koichi 171
Fukushima, Sakie Tachibana 78
Funabashi, Haruo 117
Funato, Takashi 232
Funayama, Norio 317
Fung, Andrew H. C. 162
Fung, Anita Y. M. 175
Funo, Yukitoshi (Yuki) 363
Funo, Yukitoshi (Yuki) 363
Furihata, Toru 336
Furlan, Luiz Fernando 350
Furong, Zhang 186
Furong, Zhang 186
Furse, Dame Clara H. F. 210
Furubayashi, Kiyoshi 364
Furuhashi, Mamoru 363
Furuhashi, Mamoru 363
Furuichi, Takeshi 250

Furuichi, Takeshi 251
Furukawa, Toshimasa 236
Furusawa, Kiichiro 360
Furuta, Takanobu 192
Furuya, Katsumasa 151
Furuya, Katsumasa 151
Fuseya, Noriaki 232
Fushen, Li 99
Fusilli, Roberto 40
Fuyao, Tong 212
Fyodorov, Igor Y. 154

G

Gabas, Antonio 152
Gabel, Yadl 37
Gabriel, Yves 74
Gabriel, Yves 75
Gachora, John 57
Gadney, Oliver (Ollie) 367
Gaehwiler, Lukas 367
Gaemperle, Chantal 216
Gajecka, Marta 147
Gal, Shimon 48
Galateri, Gabriele 31
Galateri, Gabriele 32
Galbraith, Colin R. 106
Galhau, Francois Villeroy de 72
Galifi, Vincent J. 219
Gallagher, Gerry 185
Gallagher, John 303
Gallia, Fabio 72
Gallia, Franco 189
Gallienne, Segolene 100
Gallo, Juan 290
Gallo, Juan Abello 290
Gallois, Louis 15
Gallois, Louis 15
Gallois, Louis 109
Gallot, Jerome 312
Gallot, Jerome 374
Galloway, Jil 230
Galvin, Mike 80
Galvin, Mike 80
Ganaye, Patrick 87
Gancedo, Eric 45
Gancia, Alessandro Vallarino 100
Gang, Xiao 72
Ganong, David A. 339
Gans, Prof Arieh 49
Gao, Yingxin 72
Gao, Renjie 116
Garanderie, Dominique de La 289
Garavaglia, Carlo 371
Garcia, Victor Revuelta 9
Garcia, Jose Alfonso Nebrera 9
Garcia, Jose Alvaro Cuervo 9
Garcia, Claudio 28
Garcia, Ricardo de Ramon 107
Garcia, Ricardo 108
Garcia, Felix Martin 121
Garcia, Felix 121
Garcia, Bego?a Elices 290
Garcia, Begona 290
Garcia-Ovies, Ramiro Sanchez de Lerin 350
Garcia-Suelto, Jose 42
Garcia-Tu?on, Antonio Basagoiti 46
Gardner, Sir Roy A. 110
Gardner, David 238
Gardner, Paul 340
Garfield, Gary 78
Garibaldi, Pietro 190
Garnadt, Karl U. 127
Garner, Joe D. 175
Garnier, Thierry 87
Garnier, Jean-Pierre (JP) 289
Garrett, Sophie 35
Garrett, Michael W.O. 284
Garwood, Alan 39
Garzon, Sabine 209
Gasquet, Denis 374
Gathoo, S. P. 67
Gatto, Carlo Carlo Gatto 141
Gaul, Hans Michael 320

Gaulin, Jean R. 243
Gaulle, Yves de 156
Gaus, Norbert 320
Gautam, Manica 268
Gauthier, Paule 299
Gautier, Bernard 108
Gavin, Mike 80
Gawaxab, Johannes 266
Gazizullin, Farit R. 154
Ge, Chen 97
Geddes, Paul 300
Geeber, Magnus 344
Gehl, Walter N. 127
Gehrig, Prof Bruno 297
Gehrig, Prof Bruno 297
Gehrig, Prof Bruno 367
Gei?inger, Jurgen 112
Geissler, Nicole 112
Gelblat, Michael J. 268
Gelmon, Mark 26
Gelsomino, Cosma 62
Gemkow, Stephan 127
Genc, Onur 365
Genc, Onur 365
Genish, Amos Amos Genish 377
Genola, Gabriele Galateri di 348
Genola, Gabriele Galateri di 349
Genola, Gabriele Gabriele Galateri di Genola 349
Genova, Juan Maria Nin 144
Genova, Juan Maria Nin 290
Gent, Sir Christopher Charles (Chris) 158
Gentz, Manfred 392
Geoff, Geoffrey 392
Georganas, Iakovos G. 279
George, Jeffrey (Jeff) 261
George, Richard L. (Rick) 299
George, Richard L. (Rick) 340
George, Richard L. (Rick) 340
Gerber, Michel 4
Gerber, Charles 84
Gerber, Fritz Fritz Gerber 392
Gerhards, Tilmann 133
Germiniani, Paolo 348
Gerth, Erich 34
Gerwert, Bernhard Bernhard Gerwert 15
Geschwind, Ben J. 6
Ghazali, Mohd Mohd Nazlan bin Mohd Ghazali 220
Ghizzoni, Federico 368
Ghosh, Pallav 68
Ghosn, Carlos 255
Ghosn, Carlos 289
Giacomin, Francesco 368
Giancarlo, Charles H. 7
Giannidis, Ioannis C. 244
Gianno, Jean-Marie 72
Gianotti, Anthony 385
Giard, Diane 243
Giarda, Piero 40
Gibson, Sir Ian 238
Gibson, Linda T. 266
Giesinger, Jim 339
Giffin, Gordon D. 84
Gilbert, Jackson B. 145
Gilbert, Daniel T. (Danny) 242
Gilbert, Steffen 265
Gilbert, Malcolm 392
Gilchrist, Sean 60
Gilead, Prof Israel 49
Gilibert, Pierluigi 147
Gilis, Kosty 268
Gillam, John 385
Gillard, Ian Guy 47
Gillespie, Alan R. 266
Gillham, Simon 377
Gillies, Crawford 333
Gillingwater, Richard D. 329
Gilstrap, Douglas L. 143
Gilvary, Brian 76
Gilvary, Brian 76
Gina, Jian 212
Giovanni, Gianni Di 141

Girard, Elie 269
Girard, Elie 269
Girardot, Paul-Louis 374
Giroday, Eric Boyer de la 188
Gittler, Juliana 221
Giusto, Mauro 31
Gj?stein, Ann-Mari 335
Gjostein, Ann-Mari 335
Gjurovski, Stojko 344
Gkolemis, Stylianos 280
Gladman, Ian 266
Gladstone, Mira 175
Glaser, William A. (Bill) 328
Glass, Kevin 84
Glasson, Ian 388
Glazer, Rose 320
Gledhill, David 123
Glynn, Martin J. G. 339
Gnudi, Piero 368
Gobeil, Paul 243
Goda, Hirofumi Hirofumi Goda 150
Godal, Bjorn T. 334
Godbehere, Ann F. 284
Godbehere, Ann F. 294
Godbehere, Ann F. 367
Gode, Pierre 100
Gode, Pierre 216
Godsoe, Peter C. 268
Goeltz, Richard K. 35
Goeschel, Burkhard 219
Goetz, Juergen 149
Goetzeler, Martin 320
Goggins, Colleen A. 358
Goh, Euleen Y. K. 35
Goh, Euleen Y. K. 123
Goh, Linus T. L. 271
Golden, Charles E. 369
Golden, Charles E. 370
Goldenstein, Ihno 90
Goldenstein, Ihno 90
Goldfarb, Shlomo 49
Goldman, Yaacov 49
Golemis, Stilianos D. 279
Golko, Yaroslav Y. 154
Golubev, Valery 153
Golubev, Valery A. 154
Gomersall, Sir Stephen 167
Gomes, Sergio 4
Gomes, Renato 373
Gomes, Renato da Cruz 373
Gomez, Eugenio Llorente 9
Gomez, Jose Ramon Arce 56
Gomez, Hernando J. 135
Gomez-Lavin, Javier Polanco 9
Gomi, Kazuhiro 253
Gomwe, Godfrey G. 26
Gonda, Toshihiro 17
Gonensin, Turgay 365
Gong, Huazhou 98
Gongsheng, Pan 186
Gonzales, Miguel 146
Gonzales-Hurtado, Jose C. 87
Gonzalez, Juan Enrique Ruiz 9
Gonzalez, Jose Maria Aguirre 9
Gonzalez-Albo, Jose Romero de Avila 9
Gooding, Valerie F. (Val) 194
Gooding, Valerie F. (Val) 332
Goodmanson, Richard R. 294
Goodmanson, Richard R. 295
Gordillo, Rodrigo Echenique 46
Gordo, Juan Ignacio Apoita 41
Gordo, Juan 41
Gordon, Ray 274
Gordon, Helen 300
Gorman, Raymond (Ray) 212
Goschl, Peter 240
Goss, Andreas J. 320
Goto, Katsuhiro 313
Goto, Katsuhiro 313
Goto, Kazutoshi 315
Goto, Masahiro 317
Goto, Masahiro 317
Gottlob, Martin 122
Gottschalk, Helmut 133
Gottschalk, Helmut 133

Sturm, Stephan 149
Stymiest, Barbara G. 299
Stymiest, Barbara Barbara Stymiest 387
Su, Guoxin 93
Su, C. Y. 148
Su?elbeck, Roswitha 64
Subbotin, Valery 264
Subrahmanyam, Prof Marti G. 181
Subramanian, G. 164
Sucharitkun, Piyada 47
Suckale, Margret 62
Sud, Ashok 332
Suda, Zenichi 182
Sudhakar, S 287
Sudo, Fumio 196
Sudo, Fumio 196
Sudo, Akira 360
Sudo, Seiichi 363
Sudo, Seiichi 363
Sueki, Takayuki 231
Suematsu, Hiroyuki 85
Suess, Michael 320
Sueyoshi, Takejiro 12
Sueyoshi, Takejiro 12
Suffel, Holger 119
Sufrategui, Jose 43
Sugano, Nobuyuki 315
Sugano, Nobuyuki 315
Sugi, Hikaru 124
Sugi, Hikaru 124
Sugihara, Koichi 363
Sugimori, Masato 336
Sugimoto, Toyokazu 342
Sugiura, Masayasu 17
Sugiura, Yasuyuki 230
Sugiyama, Toshiaki 317
Sugizaki, Tomoki 117
Suh, Jin Won 316
Suh, Jin Won 316
Suita, Kiyotsugu 182
Sukthankar, Paresh 164
Sukthankar, Paresh 164
Sulaiman, Norazzah 292
Sulaiman, Puan 292
Sullivan, Damien 8
Sullivan, Brian 76
Sullivan, Chris 300
Sumi, Shuzo 355
Sumihiro, Isao 165
Summerer, Gerhard 133
Sun, Changji 72
Sun, Changji 72
Sun, David P. 90
Sun, David P. 90
Sun, Bo 275
Sun, Jianyi 279
Sun, Jianyi 279
Sunaoshi, Hisashi 224
Sunderland, Sir John M. 58
Sunderland, Sir John M. 60
Sundgren, Jan-Eric 382
Sundstrom, Anders 344
Sundstrom, Anders Anders Sundstrom 344
Sundstrom, Karl-Henrik Karl-Henrik Sundstrom 344
Suning, Tian 212
Sunmonu, Mutiu 303
Suo, Masahiro 17
Surinach, Ignacio Segura 9
Surjaudaja, Pramukti 271
Susan, Hwee 371
Sutanthawibun, Wirasak 47
Sutcliffe, James H. (Jim) 339
Suter, Ursula 367
Sutherland, Peter D. 20
Sutherland, Graham 80
Sutherland, David 183
Suttle, John 39
Sutton, Neil 80
Suzaki, Koichi 337
Suzaki, Koichi 337
Suzuki, Hideo 113
Suzuki, Makoto 236
Suzuki, Masatoshi 262

Suzuki, Tetsuya 263
Suzuki, Masatoshi 263
Suzuki, Toshifumi 313
Suzuki, Tomoyuki 328
Suzuki, Kunimasa 328
Suzuki, Osamu 342
Suzuki, Toshihiro 342
Suzuki, Toshihiro 342
Suzuki, Kazuo 357
Suzuki, Shigeki 363
Svaan, Morten 334
Svanberg, Carl-Henric 76
Svanberg, Carl-Henric 143
Svanberg, Carl-Henric 382
Svanholm, Poul J. 2
Svensson, Siv Siv Svensson 344
Swaan, Tom de 158
Swaan, Tom de 203
Swaan, Tom de 203
Swaan, Tom de 392
Swaan, Tom de 392
Swaan, Tom Tom de Swaan 392
Swaroop, Neeraj 331
Sweeney, Mike 39
Sweeney, Mick 53
Sweet, Julie S. 6
Switzer, Frank T. 339
Symon, Carl G. 39
Symonds, Jonathan R. (Jon) 261
Syriani, Aziz R.D. 116
Syz, David W. 116
Szathmary, Emoke J. E. 160
Szathmary, Emoke 160
Szathmary, Emoke J. E. 282
Szathmary, Emoke 282
Szathmary, Emoke J. E. 283
Szathmary, Emoke 283
Szmurlo, Chuck J. 137

T

T?pholm, Jan 2
Tabacco, Marina 189
Tabernero, Jordi 152
Tachibana-Fukushima, Sakie 78
Tadaki, Keiichi 12
Tadaki, Keiichi 12
Tadeu, Ricardo 28
Taeuber, Annette 127
Tagami, Minoru 255
Tagawa, Joji 255
Taglieri, Lina 387
Tagomori, Satoshi 78
Taguchi, Yasuhiro 263
Tai, Jackson P. 205
Tai, Ichiro 360
Tait, Duncan 150
Taittinger, Anne-Claire 87
Tajima, Akio 124
Takaara, Toshikatsu 354
Takada, Katsumi Katsumi Takada 150
Takagi, Shigeo 169
Takagi, Shigeru 171
Takagi, Shigeru 172
Takaha, Yasuo 313
Takahara, Hirokazu 247
Takahashi, Seiichi 17
Takahashi, Atsushi 117
Takahashi, George 230
Takahashi, Hideaki 247
Takahashi, Yusuke 255
Takahashi, Kunio 313
Takahashi, Kunio 313
Takahashi, Kozo 315
Takahashi, Hiroyuki 317
Takahashi, Katsunori 364
Takahata, Koichi 336
Takamatsu, Norio 337
Takami, Kazunori 273
Takami, Kazunori 273
Takanashi, Kenji 364
Takano, Kengo 55
Takano, Kengo 55
Takano, Hiroshi 364

Takao, Kazushi 225
Takao, Kazushi 225
Takasaki, Hideo 53
Takasaki, Hideo 53
Takase, Susumu 17
Takase, Kenichi 225
Takasugi, Tadashi 230
Takata, Kiyota 254
Takata, Kiyota 254
Takayanagi, Koji 192
Takayanagi, Koji 192
Takeda, Kunitoshi 78
Takeda, Yoshiyuki 263
Takedagawa, Masahiro 171
Takeishi, Hiroaki 85
Takemura, Hideaki 225
Takenaka, Naoki Naoki Takenaka 360
Takenami, Yuichiro 78
Taketomi, Masao 117
Takeuchi, Hirotaka 270
Takeuchi, Kazuhiro 336
Takeuchi, Akira 336
Takeuchi, Satoru 382
Takeyama, Yoshio 117
Takeyama, Yoshio 117
Takizawa, Soichiro 172
Talbot, Graham 303
Talles, Steven E. 268
Talotta, Alessandro 348
Tamagnini, Andrea 189
Tamai, Hiroto 318
Tamai, Takaaki 355
Tamba, Toshihiro 192
Tamburini, Jean-Jacques 40
Tamura, Atsuto 113
Tamura, Atsuto 113
Tamura, Minoru 342
Tamura, Minoru 342
Tamvakakis, Apostolos S. 244
Tamvakakis, Apostolos S. 244
Tan, Man-kou 52
Tan, Bernard 123
Tan, Tat Tat Wai Tan 220
Tan, Cynthia G. H. 271
Tanabe, Yasuo 166
Tanabe, Eiichi 230
Tanabe, Kazuo 338
Tanai, Tsuneo 171
Tanai, Tsuneo 172
Tanaka, Toshizo 85
Tanaka, Toshizo 85
Tanaka, Akio 117
Tanaka, Koji 166
Tanaka, Kazuaki 223
Tanaka, Masaaki (Masa) 234
Tanaka, Tatsuo 234
Tanaka, Tatsuo 234
Tanaka, Seiichi 236
Tanaka, Seiichi 236
Tanaka, Hiroshi 257
Tanaka, Takashi 262
Tanaka, Takashi 263
Tanaka, Yoshihiro 313
Tanaka, Hisao 360
Tanaka, Takaaki 360
Tanbourgi, Gabriel 62
Taneya, Mototaka Mototaka Taneya 315
Tang, Yat Sun (Richard) 162
Tang, Bin 186
Tangtatswas, Singh 47
Tani, Yasuhiro 85
Tani, Yasuhiro 86
Tani, Kenji 230
Tanigaki, Masahide 166
Tanigawa, Hiromichi 254
Tanigawa, Hiromichi 254
Tanigawa, Kazuo 360
Taniguchi, Norihiko 150
Taniguchi, Yuji 225
Taniguchi, Shinichi 252
Taniguchi, Shinichi 252
Taniguchi, Nobuyuki 315
Taniguchi, Nobuyuki 315
Tanimoto, Michihisa 337
Tanizawa, Fumihiko 338

Tanner, Ernst 116
Taohai, Xue 96
Taohai, Xue 96
Tapias, Alcides Lopes 191
Tapling, Mark 262
Tarantini, Graziano 40
Taranto, Francesco 141
Tardio, Vicente 45
Targetti, Ferdinando 190
Tasaka, Hitoshi 124
Tassan, Franck 87
Tat, Lim Hong 220
Tat, Wai Tan 220
Tata, Jimmy 164
Tauby, Anne 15
Tavares, Carlos 255
Tavares, Carlos 289
Tavernier, Jacques 376
Tavolini, Giorgio 348
Tavormina, Valerio 40
Tay, Tong Poh 371
Tayanukorn, Kajornvut 47
Taylor, Roxanne 6
Taylor, Kevin 38
Taylor, C. 238
Taylor, Richard 238
Taylor, Joseph M. (Joe) 273
Taylor, Kathleen P. (Katie) 299
Taylor, Aileen 300
Taylor, Alison 320
Taylor, Carole S. 358
Tchuruk, Serge 362
Teare, David 323
Teck, Lim Cheng 332
Tedesi, Luca 189
Teerlink, Ron 300
Teirlynck, Yves 261
Teixeira, Vicente C. 82
Teixeira, Mario da Silveira 373
Teixeira, Mario 373
Teixeira, Mario da Silveira 373
Tejada, Vicente Prados 9
Tejada, Jaime de Marichalar Y Saenz De 100
Tejera, Pablo Isla Alvarez de 350
Tejima, Shunichiro 247
Telang, Prakash M. 347
Telles, Marcel H. 28
Tellier, Marc P. 243
Tellier, Paul M. 294
Tembo, Akihiko 182
Temel, Ali 365
Tena, Antonio 152
Tena, Nemesio Fernandez-Cuesta Luca de 290
Tena, Nemesio 290
Teo, Lay Lim 6
Teo, Melvin T. W. 123
Teragawa, Masatsugu 315
Terajima, Yoshinori 251
Terakado, Kazuyoshi 197
Teramoto, Hideo 117
Terashi, Shigeki 363
Terazawa, Tatsumaro 55
Terazawa, Tatsumaro 55
Terisse, Pierre-Andre 121
Terium, Peter 305
Terner, Franck 13
Terradas, Salvador 43
Terre, Jaon-David Grima i 9
Terry, James 339
Terryn, Kristof 392
Tessmann, Patrick 209
Tessmar-Pfohl, Werner 144
Testi, Paolo 40
Teulie, Pierre Alexandre 87
Teuwsen, Bjorn 204
Tewell, Dennis 18
Teyssen, Johannes 134
Thabet, Pierre 243
Thaensathit, Suwan 47
Tham, Ming Soong 371
Thananithi, Piyaphan 47
Thanatsrang, Thawisak 47
Thani, Jassim Jassim Al Thani 116